Lecture Notes in Computer Science 5193

Commenced Publication in 1973
Founding and Former Series Editors:
Gerhard Goos, Juris Hartmanis, and Jan van Leeuwen

Dan Halperin   Kurt Mehlhorn (Eds.)

Algorithms – ESA 2008

16th Annual European Symposium
Karlsruhe, Germany, September 15-17, 2008
Proceedings

 Springer

Volume Editors

Dan Halperin
Tel-Aviv University
School of Computer Science
Tel Aviv 69978, Israel
E-mail: danha@tau.ac.il

Kurt Mehlhorn
Max-Planck-Institut für Informatik
66123 Saarbrücken, Germany
E-mail: mehlhorn@mpi-inf.mpg.de

Library of Congress Control Number: 2008934902

CR Subject Classification (1998): F.2, G.1-2, E.1, F.1.3, I.3.5, C.2.4, E.5

LNCS Sublibrary: SL 1 – Theoretical Computer Science and General Issues

ISSN   0302-9743
ISBN-10   3-540-87743-6 Springer Berlin Heidelberg New York
ISBN-13   978-3-540-87743-1 Springer Berlin Heidelberg New York

Springer is a part of Springer Science+Business Media

springer.com

© Springer-Verlag Berlin Heidelberg 2008
Printed in Germany

Typesetting: Camera-ready by author, data conversion by Scientific Publishing Services, Chennai, India
Printed on acid-free paper   SPIN: 12532902   06/3180   5 4 3 2 1 0

Preface

This volume contains the 69 papers presented at the 16th Annual European Symposium on Algorithms (ESA 2008), held in Karlsruhe during September 15–17, 2008, including two papers by the distinguished invited speakers Mark Overmars and Leslie Valiant.

Since 2002, ESA has consisted of two tracks, with separate program committees, dealing with design and mathematical analysis of algorithms, the "Design and Analysis" track, and real-world applications, engineering, and experimental analysis of algorithms, the "Engineering and Applications" track. Previous ESAs in the two-track format were held in Rome, Italy (2002); Budapest, Hungary (2003); Bergen, Norway (2004); Palma de Mallorca, Spain (2005); Zurich, Switzerland (2006); and Eilat, Israel (2007). The proceedings of these symposia were published as Springer's LNCS volumes 2461, 2832, 3221, 3669, 4168, and 4698 respectively.

Papers were solicited in all areas of algorithmic research, including algorithmic aspects of networks, approximation and on-line algorithms, computational biology, computational finance and algorithmic game theory, computational geometry, data structures, databases and information retrieval, external-memory algorithms, streaming algorithms, graph and network algorithms, graph drawing, machine learning, mobile and distributed computing, pattern matching and data compression, quantum computing, randomized algorithms, and algorithm libraries. Submissions were especially encouraged in mathematical programming and operations research, including Combinatorial Optimization, Integer Programming, Polyhedral Combinatorics and Network Optimization.

Each extended abstract was submitted to one of the two tracks. The extended abstracts were typically read by three or four referees each, and evaluated on their quality, originality, and relevance to the symposium. The Program Committees of both tracks met in Karlsruhe on May 24–25, 2008. The design and analysis track selected 51 papers out of 147 submissions. The engineering and applications track selected 16 out of 53 submissions.

ESA 2008 was sponsored by EATCS (the European Association for Theoretical Computer Science). We appreciate the critical financial support of ALGO 2008 by the DFG (Deutsche Forschungsgemeinschaft), the KIT (Karlsruhe Institute of Technology), and the Computer Science Department of the University of Karlsruhe. The EATCS sponsorship included an award for the author of the best paper "Better and Simpler Approximation for the Stable Marriage Problem," by Zoltán Király and for the two best student papers, one from the design and analysis track: "Deterministic Sampling Algorithms for Network Design," by Anke van Zuylen, and one from the engineering and applications track: "Time-Dependent SHARC-Routing," by Daniel Delling, as selected by the Program Committees.

ESA 2008 was held along with the Workshop on Algorithms in Bioinformatics (WABI), the Workshop on Approximation and Online Algorithms (WAOA), and the Workshop on Algorithmic Approaches for Transportation Modeling, Optimization, and Systems (ATMOS), in the context of the combined conference ALGO 2008.

Throughout the entire process of submission, selection, and compilation of the papers into these proceedings, we used the EasyChair system, which was very convenient and freed us from a lot of the technical chores of Program Chairs. We are grateful to the EasyChair people for letting us use the system and for their responsiveness to our queries. We also thank Guy Zucker for his assistance in compiling the proceedings.

July 2008

Dan Halperin
Kurt Mehlhorn

Organization

Program Committee

Design and Analysis Track

Yossi Azar	Tel Aviv University
Xioatie Deng	City University of Hong Kong
Lisa Fleischer	Dartmouth
Gianni Franceschini	University of Pisa
Naveen Garg	IIT, Dehli
Johan Haastad	KTH, Stockholm
Stephen Kobourov	University of Arizona
Christian Knauer	FU Berlin
Kazuhiso Makino	University of Tokyo
Kurt Mehlhorn	MPII Saarbrücken (Chair)
Rasmus Pagh	IT University of Copenhagen
Katarzyna Paluch	University of Wrocław
Mike Paterson	University of Warwick
Nicole Schweikardt	HU Berlin

Engineering and Applications Track

David Applegate	AT&T Labs – Research
Esther M. Arkin	SUNY, Stony Brook
Hagit Attiya	Technion, Haifa
David Coudert	INRIA, Sophia-Antipolis
Camil Demetrescu	University of Rome "La Sapienza"
Rolf Fagerberg	University of Southern Denmark
Joachim Gudmundsson	NICTA, Sydney
Dan Halperin	Tel Aviv University (Chair)
Michael Hoffmann	ETH, Zurich
Marco Lübbecke	TU Berlin
Renato Werneck	Microsoft Research, Silicon Valley

Organizing Committee

Dorothea Wagner (Co-chair)	University of Karlsruhe
Peter Sanders (Co-chair)	University of Karlsruhe
Veit Batz	University of Karlsruhe
Reinhard Bauer	University of Karlsruhe
Michael Baur	University of Karlsruhe
Lilian Beckert	University of Karlsruhe

Anja Blancani	University of Karlsruhe
Daniel Delling	University of Karlsruhe
Dennis Luxen	University of Karlsruhe
Sascha Meinert	University of Karlsruhe
Vitaly Osipov	University of Karlsruhe
Elke Sauer	University of Karlsruhe
Dominik Schultes	University of Karlsruhe

External Reviewers

Mohammad Ali Abam
Manuel Abellanas
Isolde Adler
Hee-Kap Ahn
Nir Ailon
Ernst Althaus
Alexandr Andoni
Diogo Andrade
Spyros Angelopoulos
Michael Anshel
François Anton
Stefan Arnborg
Tetsuo Asano
Mike Atkinson
Per Austrin
Sang Won Bae
Amitabha Bagchi
Sebastian Bala
Nikhil Bansal
Yair Bartal
Cristina Bazgan
Luca Becchetti
Fredrik Bengtsson
Andre Berger
Jerome Besombes
Marcin Bienkowski
Philip Bille
Benjamin Birnbaum
Johannes Blömer
Liad Blumrosen
Manuel Bodirsky
Endre Boros
Glencora Borradaile
Prosenjit Bose
Florent Bouchez

Joan Boyar
Peter Brass
Patrick Briest
Yves Brise
Tianming Bu
Christoph Buchheim
Kevin Buchin
Maike Buchin
Luciana Buriol
Sergio Cabello
LeiZhen Cai
Huiping Cao
Alberto Caprara
Erin Chambers
Timothy M. Chan
Timoth Chan
Kun-Mao Chao
Ioannis Chatzigiannakis
Amitabh Chaudhary
Shuchi Chawla
Chandra Chekuri
Danny Chen
Ke Chen
Ning Chen
Yijia Chen
Siu-Wing Cheng
Benny Chor
Tobias Christ
George Christodoulou
Tomasz Cichocki
Ken Clarkson
Graham Cormode
Jose Correa
Artur Czumaj
Bhaskar DasGupta

Marcelo Dias de Amorim
Colin de la Higuera
Arjen De Vries
Pedro J. de Rezende
Brian Dean
Julius Degesys
Britta Denner-Broser
Martin Dietzfelbinger
Darko Dimitrov
Bojan Djordjevic
Shahar Dobzinski
Ye Du
Vida Dujmovic
Alon Efrat
Friedrich Eisenbrand
Khaled Elbassioni
Matthias Englert
Amir Epstein
Leah Epstein
Thomas Erlebach
Bruno Escoffier
Alejandro Estrella-Balderrama
Eyal Even-Dar
Esther Ezra
Alex Fabrikant
Rolf Fagerberg
Mikael Fallgren
Michalis Faloutsos
Arash Farzan
Lene Favrholdt
Henning Fernau
Paolo Ferragina
Irene Finocchi
Rudolf Fleischer
Fedor Fomin
Dimitris Fotakis
Joe Fowler
Pierre Fraigniaud
Antonio Frangioni
W. Randolph Franklin
Leonor Frias
Bernhard Fuchs
Toshihiro Fujito
Hiroshi Fujiwara
Takuro Fukunaga

Armin Fügenschuh
Bernd Gärtner
Jerome Galtier
Iftah Gamzu
Daya Gaur
Cyril Gavoille
Pawel Gawrychowski
Heidi Gebauer
Loukas Georgiadis
Panos Giannopoulos
Anders Gidenstam
Francesco Giordano
Frederic Giroire
Xavier Goaoc
Andrew Goldberg
Alfredo Goldman
Vineet Goyal
Szymon Grabowski
Fabrizio Grandoni
David Gregg
Ilan Gronau
Roberto Grossi
Romain Grunert
Anupam Gupta
Neelima Gupta
Gregory Gutin
Shai Gutner
Carsten Gutwenger
Takashi Horiyama
Sebastian Hack
Marios Hadjieleftheriou
Magnus M. Halldorsson
Xin Han
Sariel Har-Peled
Tobias Harks
Rolf Harren
Jan-Henrik Haunert
Herman Haverkort
David Hay
Michael Hemmer
Gregorio Hernandez
André Hernich
Marijn Heule
Moritz Hilger
Frank Hoffmann

Jiaqiao Hu
Thore Husfeldt
Robert Irving
Mashhood Ishaque
Toshimasa Ishii
Takehiro Ito
Riko Jacob
Martin Jaggi
Artur Jez
Łukasz Jeż
Li Jian
Öjvind Johansson
David Johnson
Peter Jonsson
Tomasz Jurdzinski
Yoshiyuki Karuno
Naonori Kakimura
Kanela Kaligosi
Frank Kammer
Tom Kamphans
Takafumi Kanamori
Przemka Kanarek
Mihyun Kang
Ming-Yang Kao
Andreas Karrenbauer
Jyrki Katajainen
Michael Kaufmann
Dimitris Kavvadias
Akinori Kawachi
Ken-ichi Kawarabayashi
Balazs Keszegh
Rohit Khandekar
Samir Khuller
Shuji Kijima
David Kirkpatrick
Masashi Kiyomi
Rolf Klein
Tomi Klein
Robert Kleinberg
Jon Kleinberg
Stefan Koerkel
Alex Kogan
Stavros Kolliopoulos
Vladimir Kolmogorov
Rachel Kolodny

Jochen Konemann
Guy Kortsarz
Miroslaw Korzeniowski
Arie Koster
Lukasz Kowalik
Darek Kowalski
Richard Kralovic
Stephan Kreutzer
Klaus Kriegel
Shankar Krishnan
Danny Krizanc
Sven Krumke
Amit Kumar
Maciej Kurowski
Ekkehard Köhler
Arnaud Labourel
Oded Lachish
Jens Lagergren
Soeren Laue
Ron Lavi
Emmanuelle Lebhar
Jonathan Lenchner
Stefano Leonardi
Moshe Lewenstein
Xiangyang Li
Bengu Li
Leo Liberti
Christian Liebchen
Jeff Linderoth
Andrzej Lingas
Giuseppe Liotta
Haowen Liu
Andrea Lodi
Jakub Lopuszanski
Krzysztof Lorys
Tzvi Lotker
Vadim Lozin
Eyal Lubetzky
Fabrizio Luccio
Rune Lyngsoe
Eiji Miyano
Anil Maheshwari
Veli Mäkinen
Daniel Marx
Domagoj Matijevic

Jochen Maydt
Colin McDiarmid
Frank McSherry
Nicole Megow
Julian Mestre
Peter Bro Miltersen
Joe Mitchell
Michael Mitzenmacher
Shuichi Miyazaki
Sonoko Moriyama
Gabriel Moruz
Robin Moser
Matthias Müller-Hannemann
Ian Munro
Nabil Mustafa
Petra Mutzel
Kiyohito Nagano
Rouven Naujoks
Gonzalo Navarro
Yakov Nekrich
C. Thach Nguyen
Rolf Niedermeier
Bengt Nilsson
Stefan Nilsson
Marc Nunkesser
Yoshio Okamoto
Hirotaka Ono
Rotem Oshman
Patric Ostergard
Sang-il Oum
John Owens
Gyula Pap
Maurizio Patrignani
David Peleg
Ulrich Pferschy
Marc E. Pfetsch
Andrea Pietracaprina
Michal Pioro
Marek Piotrow
Marcus Poggi
C.K. Poon
Ely Porat
Andreas Profous
Guido Proietti
Kirk Pruhs

Geppino Pucci
Simon Puglisi
Evangelia Pyrga
Qi Qi
Tomasz Radzik
Prasad Raghavendra
Rajmohan Rajaraman
Rajeev Raman
Rajiv Raman
R. Ravi
Andreas Razen
Joachim Reichel
Mauricio Resende
Dana Ron
Stefan Ropke
Peter Rossmanith
Günter Rote
Jonathan E. Rowe
Shai Rubin
Daniel Russel
Kunihiko Sadakane
Carlos Sanches
Pedro Sander
Peter Sanders
Srinivasa Rao Satti
Rahul Savani
Gilles Savard
Ludmila Scharf
Dominik Scheder
Marc Scherfenberg
Heiko Schilling
Florian Schoppmann
Oded Schwartz
Daria Schymura
Yoav Seginer
Raimund Seidel
Meinolf Sellmann
Jose M. Sempere
Jiri Sgall
Nira Shafrir
Akiyoshi Shioura
Mark Silberstein
Laurent Simon
Jadranka Skorin-Kapov
Martin Skutella

Michiel Smid
Shakhar Smorodinsky
Christian Sohler
Olivier Spanjaard
Bettina Speckmann
Aravind Srinivasan
Grzegorz Stachowiak
Fabian Stehn
Cliff Stein
Rainer Steinwandt
Marek Sulovsky
Zoya Svitkina
Suguru Tamaki
Chuan Yi Tang
Till Tantau
Kavitha Telikepalli
Mitchell Thornton
Mikkel Thorup
Srikanta Tirthapura
Alexander Tiskin
Patrick Traxler
Dekel Tsur
Ryuhei Uehara
Takeaki Uno
Gregory Valiant
Marc van Kreveld
Rob van Stee
George Frederick Viamontes
Anastasios Viglas

Antoine Vigneron
Berthold Voecking
Imrich Vrt'o
Uli Wagner
Magnus Wahlström
Feng Wang
Lusheng Wang
Ron Wein
Carola Wenk
Juergen Werber
Douglas Wikström
Paul Wollan
Bangye Wu
Xiaodong Wu
Avi Yadgar
Masaki Yamamoto
Tommy Yang
Takuya Yoshihiro
Ryo Yoshinaka
Hai Yu
Li Zhang
Xun Zhang
Junqiang Zhou
Binhai Zhu
Roie Zivan
Philipp Zumstein
Uri Zwick
Grazyna Zwozniak

Table of Contents

Flexible Path Planning Using Corridor Maps

Mark Overmars, Ioannis Karamouzas, and Roland Geraerts

Department of Information and Computing Sciences, Utrecht University
3508 TA Utrecht, the Netherlands
markov@cs.uu.nl

Abstract. Path planning is a central problem in virtual environments
and games. When computer-controlled characters move around in virtual worlds they have to plan their paths to desired locations. These
paths must avoid collisions with the environment and with other moving
characters. Also a chosen path must be natural, meaning that it is the
kind of path a real human being could take. The algorithms for planning
such paths must be able to handle hundreds of characters in real-time
and must be flexible.

The Corridor Map Method (CMM) was recently introduced as a flexible
path planning method in interactive virtual environments and games.
The method is fast and flexible and the resulting paths are reasonable.
However, the paths tend to take unnatural turns when characters get
close to other characters or small obstacles. In this paper we will improve
on the CMM by decoupling collision avoidance with the environment and
local steering behavior. The result is a method that keeps the advantages
of the CMM but has much more natural steering. Also the method allows
for more flexibility in the desired routes of the characters.

1 Introduction

Virtual worlds are nowadays commonly used in computer games, simulations,
city models, and on-line communities like Second Life. Such worlds are often
populated by computer-controlled characters. The characters must move around
in the environment and need to plan their paths to desired locations. These paths
must avoid collisions with the environment and with other moving characters.
Also a chosen path must be natural, meaning that it is the kind of path a real
human being could take. The algorithms for planning such paths must be able
to handle hundreds of characters in real-time and must be flexible to e.g. avoid
local hazards or incorporate animation constraints.

The path planning or motion planning problem had received considerable attention over the past twenty years and many algorithms have been devised to
tackle it. (See [1, 2] for an overview.) These algorithms were mainly developed
in the field of robotics, aiming at creating a path for one or a few robots having many degrees of freedom. In virtual worlds the requirements though are
completely different. The environment is very complex and even though path
planning normally can be performed in the 2-dimensional footprint of the environment, we still need to deal with thousands of polygons. We need to plan the

D. Halperin and K. Mehlhorn (Eds.): ESA 2008, LNCS 5193, pp. 1–12, 2008.

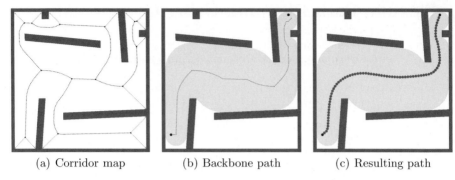

(a) Corridor map   (b) Backbone path   (c) Resulting path

Fig. 1. The Corridor Map Method in action

motion of hundreds of characters in real-time using only a small percentage of the CPU time. Per character only a (fraction of a) millisecond per second CPU time may be spent on path planning. Also paths need not only be collision-free but they must also be natural. On the positive side, we can represent the character as a disk, and, hence, have to deal with only two degrees of freedom of movement.

In conclusion, virtual world applications require algorithms for path planning that are fast, flexible, and generate natural paths. In practice, currently two approaches are common. The first is to let designers script most of the motion, for example using waypoints, and then using potential field approaches (see e.g. [3]) to avoid obstacles and other characters. Such an approach is only possible when the virtual world is predefined by designers. It is also expensive because of the manual work involved. In addition, the method is not very flexible. The potential field approach has the risk of characters getting stuck in local minima and not reaching their goals. Also, as can be seen from many (recent) games, it leads to rather unnatural paths, in particular when waypoints get blocked.

The second common approach is the put a grid on the world and using searches based on A* to create a path through the empty cells. See for example [4, 5]. This method is guaranteed to find a path if one exists. However, it lacks flexibility because a single fixed path is returned. In addition, the paths tend to be unnatural. Also, even though some optimization algorithms exist, when the grids get large and the motion of many characters must be planned, the approach can become too slow to be applied in real-time [6].

Recently, the Corridor Map Method (CMM) has been proposed as a new path planning method in interactive virtual environments and games [7]. The method is fast and flexible and the quality of resulting paths is reasonable. Globally speaking the CMM works as follows (see Fig. 1 for an example). In a preprocessing phase a roadmap of paths is computed for the static part of the environment. Often the medial axis is used for this. With the roadmap, clearance information is stored, defining collision-free corridors around the roadmap edges. This data structure is called the *corridor map*. When a path planning query must be solved a *backbone path* is extracted from the roadmap together with a collision-free *corridor* around it. We move an *attraction point* along the backbone path which attracts the character in such a way that no collisions occur with the environment. This leads the character toward the goal. Local motions are controlled by potential fields inside a corridor, providing the desired flexibility.

Although the CMM is fast and flexible, the paths tend to take unnatural turns when characters get close to other characters or small obstacles. In this paper we will extend the CMM as follows. We separate the *corridor map* from the so-called *control network*. The corridor map is defined as above. The control network provides a roadmap of paths that can be used to lead the characters to their goals. When a query must be solved a *control path* is extracted from the control network. With the control path we find a corresponding *corridor* in the corridor map. We again move an *attraction point* along the control path but this is only used to lead the character to the goal. Separate forces are used to keep the character inside the corridor. Again we use additional forces to steer the character away from other characters, small obstacles and other hazards. As we will show, separating the collision-avoiding forces in the corridor from the attraction forces along the control path, leads to much more natural paths while hardly increasing the computation time. We initially still use the medial axis for the control network but we will also show how even more flexibility can be obtained by using other control networks and paths.

This paper is organized as follows. In Section 2 we provide definitions of corridors and corridor maps and show how such maps can be computed efficiently. In Section 3 we briefly review the original approach for using corridors for path planning. In Section 4 we present our improved approach in which we use the medial axis as a control network to obtain more natural paths. In section 5 we provide results from experiments that show that the resulting paths are considerably better than those produced by the original CMM. In Section 6 we will indicate how the approach can be extended using other control networks and control paths. Finally, in Section 7 we provide some conclusions and plans for further research.

2   The Corridor Map

The *corridor map* is an efficient data structure representing the (walkable) free space in the environment. It was introduced by Geraerts and Overmars [7] and we will outline the most important aspects here. As the walkable space is normally 2-dimensional we will define the corridor map in the plane. The obstacles are the footprints of the original 3-dimensional obstacles in the environment.

The corridor map is a graph whose edges represent collision-free *corridors*. Such a corridor consists of a *backbone path* and a set of disks centered around this path. More formally, a corridor $\mathcal{B} = (B[t], R[t])$ is defined as a sequence of maximum clearance disks with radii $R[t]$ whose center points lie along its backbone path $B[t]$. The parameter t is an index ranging between 0 and 1, and $B[t]$ denotes the coordinates of the center of the disk corresponding to index t. Together, the backbone paths form the *skeleton* of the corridor map. See Fig. 2 for an example of a virtual city, its footprint, and the skeleton defining the corridor map.

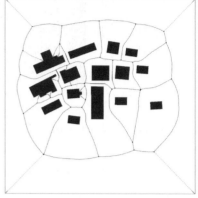

(a) 3D model   (b) Footprint and skeleton

Fig. 2. The McKenna MOUT training site at Fort Benning, Georgia, USA

We will use the corridors to provide the flexibility to handle a broad range of path planning issues, such as avoiding other characters and computing natural paths. To approach these issues, we set the following requirements for the corridor map. First, if a path exists in the free space then a corridor must exist in the map that leads the character from its start to goal position. Second, the map includes all cycles that are present in the environment. These cycles provide short global paths and alternative routes which allow for variation in the characters' routes. Third, corridors extracted from the map have a maximum clearance. Such a corridor provides maximum local flexibility.

These requirements are met by using the Generalized Voronoi Diagram (GVD) as skeleton for the corridor map [8]. A GVD is a decomposition of the free space into regions such that all points p in a region $R(p)$ are closer to a particular obstacle than to any other obstacle in the environment. Such a region is called a *Voronoi region*. The boundaries of the Voronoi regions form the skeleton (i.e. the underlying graph) of the corridor map. We refer the reader to Fig. 2(b) for an example. The boundaries are densely sampled and with each such sampled point, we store the radius of the maximum clearance disk centered at this point. A sequence of these disks forms the corridor.

A GVD can be computed efficiently by exploiting graphics hardware. Like in [9], we compute a 3D distance mesh, consisting of polygons, for each geometric obstacle present in the footprint of the environment. Each of the meshes is rendered on the graphics card in a different color. A parallel projection of the upper envelope of the arrangement of these meshes gives the GVD. The diagram can be retrieved from the graphics card's frame buffer and the clearance values (i.e. distance values) can be found in the Z-buffer. These steps are visualized in Fig. 3. The approach is very fast. For example, the corridor map in Fig. 2(b) was computed in 0.05 seconds on a modern PC with a NVIDIA GeForce 8800 GTX graphics card. Note that the computation of the corridor map happens only once during preprocessing.

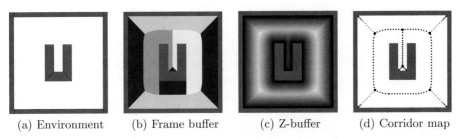

| (a) Environment | (b) Frame buffer | (c) Z-buffer | (d) Corridor map |

Fig. 3. Construction of the Corridor map using graphics hardware

3 The Original Corridor Map Method

In our original description [7], the corridor map is used as follows to answer path planning queries. To plan a path for a character, which is modeled by a disk with radius r, we first compute the shortest backbone path connecting the start to the goal. After connecting the start and goal positions to the roadmap, this backbone path is obtained by applying the A* shortest path algorithm on the skeleton graph. The corresponding corridor is formed by concatenating the corridors of the edges of the backbone path. See Fig. 1(b) for an example of a backbone path.

The backbone path guides the global motions of the character. Its local motions are controlled by continuously applying one or more forces to the character. The basic force steers the character toward the goal and keeps the character inside the corridor. For this purpose, we create an *attraction point* $\alpha(x)$ that runs along the backbone path and attracts the character.

Definition 1 (Attraction point). *Let x be the current position of the character with radius r. The attraction point $\alpha(x)$ is the point $B[t]$ on the backbone path B having the largest time index $t : t \in [0 : 1]$ such that Euclidean distance $(x, B[t]) < R[t] - r$.*

The character is attracted to the attraction point with force $\mathbf{F}_a$. Let d be the Euclidean distance between the character's position x and the attraction point $\alpha(x)$. Then

$$\mathbf{F}_a(x) = f \frac{\alpha(x) - x}{||\alpha(x) - x||}, \text{ where } f = \frac{1}{R[t] - r - d} - \frac{1}{R[t] - r}.$$

The scalar f is chosen such that the force will be 0 when the character is positioned on the attraction point. In addition, f will be ∞ when the character touches the boundary of the clearance disk. (However, f will never reach ∞ since we require that the radii of the disks are strictly larger than r.)

Additional behavior can be incorporated by adding extra forces to $\mathbf{F}_a$, resulting in a force $\mathbf{F}$. The final path is obtained by iteratively integrating $\mathbf{F}$ over time while updating the velocity, position and attraction point of the character. In [7], it is proved that the resulting path is smooth (i.e. C^1-continuous). An example of such a path is displayed in Fig. 1(c).

4   The Improved Approach

In the previous section, we used a force function $\mathbf{F}_a$ which simultaneously steers the character toward the goal and keeps it inside the corridor. This sometimes results in rather unnatural motions, in particular when characters also have to avoid each other. The cause for this is that due to the choice of the attraction point, the position of the character lies close to the boundary of the clearance disk, and, hence, the force $\mathbf{F}_a$ gets very large.

In this section we will show how to avoid this by decoupling $\mathbf{F}_a$ into two forces. The boundary force $\mathbf{F}_b$ will push the character away from the boundary of the corridor. The steering force $\mathbf{F}_s$ will guide the character toward the goal. For the latter we again use an attraction point on a path to the goal. However this path no longer needs to be the same as the backbone path of the corridor. Hence, from now on we refer to this path as the *control path*.

To be able to compute the boundary force we need an explicit representation of the boundary of the corridor.

4.1   Computing an Explicit Corridor Boundary Representation

Up to now we used an *implicit* description of a corridor, i.e. the corridor is retrieved from the map as a sequence of disks. However, such a sequential representation does not allow for easy/efficient computation of a closest point on the boundary which is required for computing the boundary force. Hence, we need an *explicit* description of the corridor's boundary (see Fig. 4(c)).

We can obtain this description by adding information to the corridor map in the preprocessing phase. For each sampled point on the skeleton we compute the set of closest points to the obstacles. By exploiting graphics hardware, we can efficiently compute these closest points. Let B be a sample point on the skeleton. We determine the position of B in the frame buffer. Next we consider the colors

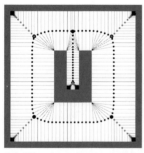 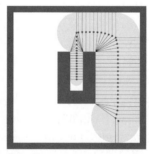 

(a) Closest points stored in the corridor map

(b) Closest points corresponding to a corridor

(c) Explicit representation of the corridor's boundary

Fig. 4. Closest points to the obstacles. By concatenating the points with line segments and circular arcs, we obtain an explicit representation of the corridor's boundary.

of the pixels neighboring B. These colors correspond to unique obstacles and the closest points must lie on these obstacles. Computing these points can then be achieved by simple geometric calculations.

Fig. 4(a) shows the corridor map and corresponding closest points of our running example. Each sample point is linked to exactly two closest points, except for the vertices of an edge because they have at least two (and at most four) closest points.

To obtain an explicit description of a corridor's boundary, we need to know for each point B which closest point is on the left side and which one is on the right side with respect to the *local orientation* of the edge at B. This information can easily be obtained by inspecting the location of the pixels in the frame buffer relative to this orientation. An example of a corridor, together with its left and right closest points, is displayed in Fig. 4(b).

From this information we can efficiently compute the closest boundary point $cp(x)$ to any point x in the corridor. First, the sample point B is retrieved whose corresponding left (or right) boundary point is closest to point x. Then the previous and next sample point are extracted along with their corresponding boundary points. In case the three boundary points define a line segment on the outline of the corridor, the closest boundary point $cp(x)$ is computed using simple linear algebra. Otherwise, $cp(x)$ lies on an arc. Let a and b denote the start and the end of the arc, respectively, and $\theta = \arccos(a - B, x - B)$. Then $cp(x) = \mathcal{R}(\theta)\,(a - B)$ where $\mathcal{R}(\theta)$ represents the 2D rotation matrix.

4.2   The Boundary Force

To ensure that the character remains inside the corridor, a repulsive force $\mathbf{F}_b$ from the boundary of the corridor toward the character is applied. Since people prefer to keep a safe distance from walls, streets, buildings, etc. [10, 11], such a force is only exerted if the distance between the character and its corresponding boundary point is below a threshold value. Let d_b be the Euclidean distance between the character's position x and its corresponding closest point $cp(x)$ on the boundary of the corridor. Let r be the radius of the character and let d_{safe} denote the preferred safe distance. Then the force is defined as follows:

$$
\mathbf{F}_b = \begin{cases} c_b \dfrac{x - cp(x)}{||x - cp(x)||}, & \text{if } d_b - r < d_{\text{safe}} \\ \\ 0 & \text{otherwise.} \end{cases}
$$

The scalar $c_b = \dfrac{d_{\text{safe}} + r - d_b}{d_b}$ is chosen such that the force will become ∞ when the character and the boundary point touch. By modifying the safe distance d_{safe} a wide variety of behaviors can be achieved. A typical value that is also used in our experiments is to set $d_{\text{safe}} = r$.[1]

---

[1] Note that the safe distance should be taken into account upon the extraction of a corridor. i.e. $R[t] > r + d_{\text{safe}}$. Otherwise, the character will be continuously pushed from the left to the right side of the corridor and vice versa (d_b will always be less than $r + d_{\text{safe}}$ and hence, a $\mathbf{F}_b$ will be exerted on the character at every time step).

4.3   The Steering Force

The character should also feel the urge to move forward toward its goal position. Thus, at every time step a steering force F_s is needed to guide the character at position x toward an attraction point $\alpha(x)$. The force is defined as

$$\mathbf{F}_s = c_s \, \frac{\alpha(x) - x}{||\alpha(x) - x||},$$

where c_s specifies the relative strength of the force. This scalar can remain fixed, or it can vary depending on the distance between the character and the attraction point, making the character speed up or slow down. In our experimental setting we used $c_s = 1$.

Having defined the forces that acted upon the character, we calculate its new position by numerically integrating its acceleration and velocity. We use an integration scheme that is quite stable and can deal with stiff differential equations. In our simulations we used Verlet integration with step size $\Delta t = 0.05$ and set the maximum acceleration to $5m/s^2$ in order to keep the error minimal.

5   Experiments

We have implemented the new method to experimentally validate whether it can generate paths that are smoother than the ones computed by the original CMM. All the simulations were performed on a Pentium IV 2.4 GHz computer with 1GB memory.

The experiments were conducted for the environment depicted in Fig. 2. This is a model of the McKenna MOUT (military operations in urban terrain) training center, hosted at Fort Benning, Georgia, USA. Its corridor map, displayed in Fig. 2(b), was computed in 0.3 seconds (0.05s for the GVD and clearance, and 0.25s for the closest points).

In all of the experiments we used the medial axis as the control network of the new method and defined the attraction points as in the original CMM. Therefore, the two approaches were only differentiated by the forces used to generate the character's motion inside the corridor. In the original CMM the attraction force $\mathbf{F}_a$ makes the character both move forward and stay inside the corridor, whereas in the new approach the two forces $(\mathbf{F}_s + \mathbf{F}_b)$ are used to guide the character through the corridor.

To evaluate the quality of the paths when avoiding other characters we populated the environment with a number of static characters (obstacles). We chose static characters because this makes it easier to compare the results. To avoid the static characters, an additional collision response force has to be applied on the character. Thus, both of the methods were enhanced with a simple obstacle avoidance model [7]. At every iteration a repulsive force is exerted from each obstacle $O_i : i \in [1 : n]$ that lies inside the clearance disk corresponding to the attraction point $\alpha(x)$ of the character. This force is monotonically decreasing

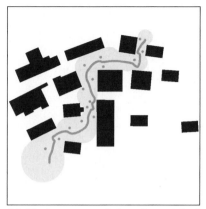
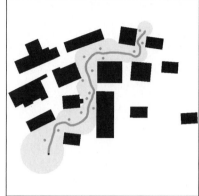

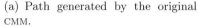

(a) Path generated by the original CMM.

(b) Path generated by the revised method.

Fig. 5. Comparing the paths generated by the original and the revised CMM

with the Euclidean distance d_i between the obstacle O_i and the character's position x. Given the radius r of the character and the radius r_i of each obstacle, the total repulsive force $\mathbf{F}_{\text{obs}}$ can be computed as

$$\mathbf{F}_{\text{obs}} = \sum_{i=1}^{n} c_{\text{obs}} \frac{x - O_i}{||x - O_i||}, \text{ where } c_{\text{obs}} = \frac{1}{d_i - r_i - r}.$$

5.1 Results

Fig. 5 shows the paths created by the two methods for an example query ($r = 0.75$, $r_i = 1$). It must be pointed out that some of the artifacts in the resulting paths are due to the simple obstacle avoidance method that was used. A more sophisticated approach would have improved the quality of the paths. However, our goal was to evaluate the two methods regardless of any specific details.

To quantitatively describe the quality of the resulting motions we measured the length as well as the average curvature of the paths. Given any three successive points on a path we approximated the curvature at the middle point as $\kappa = 1/\rho$, where ρ is the radius of the circumscribing circle that passes through each of these three points. By taking the average over all points we were able to detect poor and irregular paths.

Table 1 shows the corresponding statistics for the two paths. As it can be inferred both by the table and Fig. 5(a), the original CMM generates a longer and more erratic path (high-curvature). Due to the way the attraction point is defined (furthest advanced point for which the character is still enclosed by the clearance disk), at every integration step the character lies very close to the boundary of the disk. Thus, an almost infinite attraction force steers the character, rendering impossible to exhibit smooth motions when other obstacles and/or entities are present in the environment. The character has to be very

Table 1. Curvature and path length statistics for the example query, shown in Fig. 5

	Compared Methods	
	Original CMM	**Improved Method**
Path Length	155.12	150.61
Avg. Curvature	0.27	0.13

close to an obstacle to avoid it, and only at the very last moment, it changes its direction (i.e. when the repulsive force from the obstacle becomes very strong). Hence, the resulting motion is far from realistic.

The revised method handles the obstacles more naturally, generating a smoother path (i.e. the path is shorter with less curvature). As it can be observed in Fig. 5(b) the oscillations noted in the original method are reduced. The character is more "relaxed", in the sense that it is not pulled toward the attraction point with an infinite force. Therefore, if an obstacle is encountered the character will start evading soon enough, ensuring a more realistic behavior.

Other queries in the same and other scenes led to similar results. The performance of the two methods was similar (i.e. computing the closest boundary points and decoupling the attraction force into two separate forces influenced the running time marginally). Hence, we can conclude that the revised approach has clear advantages over the original CMM. It is more flexible, it provides better control over the character's motion and consequently leads to more believable paths.

Clearly, the quality of the resulting paths can be further improved by varying the parameters of the revised model and by using a more elaborate approach for collisions avoidance, like Helbing's social force model [12]. For example, more convincing paths can be obtained, as displayed in Fig. 6, as follows. We can increase the safe distance that the character keeps from the boundary of the corridor ($d_{\text{safe}} = 2r$). In addition, we can apply a repulsive force only for obstacles that are perceived within the character's desired direction of motion.

6   Using Alternative Control Paths

Up to now we have used the medial axis as the control network. This works fine in environments in which there are no wide open spaces. However, it will encourage the characters to stay in the middle of the corridors which can be unnatural. So in practice one might want to use alternative control networks and control paths. Such control networks could be indicated manually by a designer to encourage certain character behavior. Also they could be computed automatically based on required behavior. For example we could use the Voronoi-Visibility diagram as introduced in [13] that allows for shortcuts when there is enough clearance. Alternatively we can determine control paths during queries based on perceived danger or interesting places that characters like to visit.

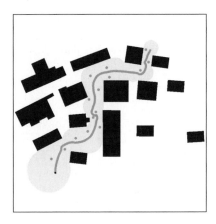

Fig. 6. An alternative path is obtained by increasing the safe distance from the boundary of the corridor

Using alternative control paths is possible but leads to a number of complications. First of all, given such a control path we need to compute the corresponding corridor. The easiest way to achieve this is to retract the control path onto the medial axis [14]. Using the boundary representation described in Section 4 this can be done efficiently.

Secondly, we need a method to choose the location of the attraction point on the control path. The method described above, in which we pick the furthest point along the control path for which the character still lies within the clearance disk, will not be suited anymore when the control path passes close to obstacles. Different options are possible here. We can use an attraction point that moves with constant speed (as long as the character does not lag too far behind). We can also use an attraction point at a particular distance from the character (that can vary over the control path and will determine how closely the control path must be followed). Or we can pick the attraction point based on visibility, although such calculations are relatively expensive. In a future paper we will explore these possibilities further.

7   Conclusions

In this paper we have presented an improved version of the Corridor Map Method. The method can be used to plan in real time natural paths for a large number of characters in complicated environments. It is relatively easy to implement and is flexible enough to incorporate many additional constraints on the resulting paths.

We are currently investigating the effect of using alternative control paths on the behavior of the characters. Also we are studying improved local force models that create even better paths in environments with many moving characters. We also want to incorporate the notions of dangerous and interesting regions and we want to incorporate small groups of moving characters that stick together. This all should lead to very efficient and high-quality path planning for individuals, groups and whole crowds of computer-controlled characters.

Acknowledgments

This research has been supported by the GATE project, funded by the Netherlands Organization for Scientific Research (NWO) and the Netherlands ICT Research and Innovation Authority (ICT Regie). In addition, part of this research has been funded by the Dutch BSIK/BRICKS project.

References

1. Latombe, J.C.: Robot Motion Planning. Kluwer, Dordrecht (1991)
2. LaValle, S.: Planning Algorithms (2006), `http://planning.cs.uiuc.edu`
3. Rimon, E., Koditschek, D.: Exact robot navigation using artificial potential fields. IEEE Transactions on Robotics and Automation 8, 501–518 (1992)
4. DeLoura, M.: Game Programming Gems 1. Charles River Media, Inc. (2000)
5. Russell, S., Norvig, P.: Artificial Intelligence: A Modern Approach. Prentice-Hall, Englewood Cliffs (1994)
6. Geraerts, R., Overmars, M.: Creating high-quality paths for motion planning. International Journal of Robotics Research 26, 845–863 (2007)
7. Geraerts, R., Overmars, M.: The corridor map method: A general framework for real-time high-quality path planning. Computer Animation and Virtual Worlds 18, 107–119 (2007)
8. Geraerts, R., Overmars, M.: Enhancing corridor maps for real-time path planning in virtual environments. In: Computer Animation and Social Agents (2008)
9. Hoff, K., Culver, T., Keyser, J., Lin, M., Manocha, D.: Fast computation of generalized voronoi diagrams using graphics hardware. In: International Conference on Computer Graphics and Interactive Techniques, pp. 277–286 (1999)
10. Stucki, P.: Obstacles in pedestrian simulations. Master's thesis, Swiss Federal Institute of Technology ETH (September 2003)
11. Transportation Research Board, National Research Council Washington, D.C: Highway Capacity Manual (2000)
12. Helbing, D., Molnár, P.: Social force model for pedestrian dynamics. Physical Review 51, 4282–4287 (1995)
13. Wein, R., Berg, J., Halperin, D.: The Visibility-Voronoi complex and its applications. In: Annual Symposium on Computational Geometry, pp. 63–72 (2005)
14. Ó'Dúnlaing, C., Sharir, M., Yap, C.: Retraction: A new approach to motion planning. In: ACM Symposium on Theory of Computing, pp. 207–220 (1983)

A Bridging Model for Multi-core Computing*

Leslie G. Valiant

School of Engineering and Applied Sciences
Harvard University
valiant@seas.harvard.edu

Abstract. We propose a bridging model aimed at capturing the most basic resource parameters of multi-core architectures. We suggest that the considerable intellectual effort needed for designing efficient algorithms for such architectures may be most fruitfully pursued as an effort in designing portable algorithms for such a bridging model. Portable algorithms would contain efficient designs for all reasonable ranges of the basic resource parameters and input sizes, and would form the basis for implementation or compilation for particular machines.

1 Introduction

The designer of parallel algorithms for multi-core computers has to face at least four sources of considerable challenge. First, the underlying computational substrate is much more intricate than it is for conventional sequential computing and hence the design effort is much more onerous. Second, the resulting algorithms have to compete with and outperform existing sequential algorithms that are often much better understood and highly optimized. Third, the ultimate reward of all this effort is limited, at best a speedup of a constant factor, the number of processors. Fourth, machines differ, and speedups obtained for one machine may not translate to speedups on others, so that all the design effort may be substantially wasted. For all these reasons it is problematic how or whether efficient parallel algorithms will be created and exploited in the foreseeable future, in spite of the many relevant algorithmic discoveries that have been made by researchers over the last several decades.

We have argued previously that the general problem of parallel computing should be approached via two notions [13, 28]. First, it needs to be recognized as a primary goal to write *portable parallel algorithms* those that are parameter-aware and designed to run efficiently on machines with the widest range of performance parameters. Second, such portable algorithms have to be supported by a *bridging model*, one that bridges in a performance-faithful manner what the hardware executes and what is in the minds of the software writer. It is this bridging model that defines the necessary performance parameters for the parameter-aware software.

The originally proposed bridging model was the BSP model [28]. Its main features are that: (i) it *is* a computational model, (ii) it incorporates numerical

---

* This work was supported in part by NSF-CCF-04-27129.

D. Halperin and K. Mehlhorn (Eds.): ESA 2008, LNCS 5193, pp. 13–28, 2008.

parameters that reflect ultimate physical constraints, and (iii) it has as its non-local primitive barrier synchronization which is powerful and relatively easy to realize.

In this paper we introduce the Multi-BSP model which extends BSP in two ways. First, it is a hierarchical model with an arbitrary number of levels that recognizes the physical realities of multiple memory and cache levels in single chips, as well as in multi-chip architectures constructed from these. The aim is to model *all* levels of an architecture together. An algorithm that is aware of the relevant parameters at only some of the levels will not be portable in any useful sense. Second, at each level, Multi-BSP incorporates memory size as a further parameter. After all, it is the physical limitation on the amount of memory that can be accessed in a fixed amount of time that creates the need for multiple levels.

The Multi-BSP model for depth d will be specified by $4d$ numerical parameters $(p_1, g_1, L_1, m_1)(p_2, g_2, L_2, m_2)(p_3, g_3, L_3, m_3) \cdots (p_d, g_d, L_d, m_d)$. It is a depth d tree with memories/caches at the internal nodes and processors at the leaves. At each level the four parameters quantify, respectively, the number of subcomponents, the bandwidth, the synchronization cost, and the memory/cache size.

It may be thought that proliferating numerical parameters only further exponentiates the difficulty of designing parallel algorithms. The main observation of this paper is that this is not necessarily the case. In particular we show, by means mostly of well-known ideas, that for problems such as matrix multiplication, fast Fourier transform and sorting, for which optimal algorithms can be written with the few parameters of the standard BSP model, the same holds also for an arbitrary number of levels. Our purpose is to persuade that it is feasible and beneficial to write down the best algorithmic ideas we have in a standardized form that will be compilable to run efficiently on arbitrary machines and guaranteed to be optimal in a specifiable sense .

In order to elucidate this striking phenomenon, we shall define a *parameter-free* notion of an *optimal Multi-BSP algorithm with respect to a given algorithm A* to mean the following: (i) It is optimal in computation steps to within additive lower order terms, (ii) it is optimal in total communication costs to constant multiplicative factors among distributed (even non-Multi-BSP) algorithms, and (iii) it is optimal in synchronization costs to within constant multiplicative factors among Multi-BSP algorithms. Insisting on optimality to a factor of 1 in one of the measures is significant and distinguishes this work from much of the parallel algorithms literature. We also note that the multiplicative factors in the other two measures will be independent of the p, g, L and m parameters, but may depend on d. Of course, specifying particular constant multipliers for all three measures would give even stricter notions of optimality, and would be needed when designing actual portable algorithms.

There have existed several previous models that have substantial commonality with Multi-BSP. Using memory size as a fourth BSP parameter was proposed and investigated by Tiskin [27] and by McColl and Tiskin [22]. In a different direction a variety of hierarchical versions of BSP have been proposed such as the D-BSP of de la Torre and Kruskal [9], which has been further investigated by Bilardi *et al.* [5, 6]. The D-BSP captures hierarchies in communication while Multi-BSP seeks also to capture hierarchies in the cache/memory system. In [6] a cache-oblivious [10] result is proved in this network hierarchical context that, like our analyses, allows for arbitrary parameters at each level.

In a different direction, numerous models have been proposed for studying varieties of memory or cache hierarchies both in the sequential [1] and in the parallel [30] contexts. In Alpern *et al.* [3] a tree structure of memories akin to ours is defined. For such hierarchical models in both the sequential and parallel contexts authors have generally taken some uniform cost view of the various levels, rather than analyzing the effect of arbitrary parameters at each level. Savage [24] has analyzed the communication requirements of a hierarchical memory model, with arbitrary parameters at each level, using a generalization of the Hong-Kung [17] pebble model. Very recently, also motivated by multi-core machines, multi-level cache models have been proposed and analyzed by Blelloch *et al.* [7], Chowdhury and Ramachandran [8], and Arge *et al.*, [4]. The analyses published for these have been for two levels with arbitrary parameters.

In comparison with the previous literature we emphasize that our goal is that of finding a bridging model that isolates the most fundamental and unevadable issues of multi-core computing and allows them to be usefully studied in some detail. The Multi-BSP model reflects the view that fundamentally there are just two unevadable sources of increasing cost that the physical world imposes at increasing distances: (i) a cost g for bandwidth, and (ii) a cost L related to latency that must be charged for synchronization and for messages that are too short. The model is a comprehensive model of computation in that it has mechanisms for synchronization as well as for computation and communication. The suggestion is that these unevadable costs already capture enough complications that we would be best advised to understand algorithmic issues in this *bridging* framework first. Designing algorithms for more detailed *performance* models that reflect further details of particular architectures may be regarded as further refinements.

There are of course several issues relevant to multi-core computing that we do not explore here. One is the use of multi-core for executing independent tasks, or code automatically compiled from sequential code, or code compiled from languages in which parallelism is expressed but not scheduled. This paper is predicated on the idea that there will be a demand for exploiting multi-core architectures beyond what is possible by these means. Another issue not discussed here is the role of non-homogeneous cores [16, 21].

The main commonality between the previous literature and our algorithmic results is the observation that certain recursive algorithms are well suited to models with multiple parameters. We push this observation further by allowing an arbitrary number of arbitrary parameter. One can paraphrase our main point as one that asserts that for computational problems for which parallelism is understandable, it is sometimes the case that it is embarrassingly understandable. However, even for these, programming them to be efficient for all input sizes for even one machine is an onerous task. Our suggestion is that with the use of a bridging model it may be possible for these and other problems to make one big effort once and for all to write a program that is efficient for all inputs and all machines.

2   The Multi-BSP Model

To define an instance of Multi-BSP we fix d the *depth* or number of levels, and $4d$ further parameters $(p_1, g_1, L_1, m_1)(p_2, g_2, L_2, m_2)(p_3, g_3, L_3, m_3) \cdots , (p_d, g_d, L_d, m_d)$. At the ith level there are a number of *components* specified by the parameters (p_i, g_i, L_i, m_i) and each containing a number of $i-1^{st}$ level components, where:

(i) p_i is the number of $i-1^{st}$ level components inside an ith level component. If $i = 1$ then p_1 is the number of raw processors in this lowest level component. One computational step of a raw processor on data in level 1 memory is taken as one *basic unit* of time.

(ii) g_i, the communication bandwidth parameter, is the ratio of the number of operations that a raw processor can do in a second, to the number of words that can be transmitted in a second between an ith level component and the memory of the $i + 1^{st}$ level component of which it is a part. A word here is the amount of data on which a raw processor operation is performed. Note that we shall assume here that the level 1 memories can keep up with the raw processors, or in other words that g_0 if it were defined would have value 1.

(iii) A level i superstep is a construct within a level i component that allows each of its p_i level $i - 1$ components to execute independently until they reach a barrier. When all p_i of them have reached the barrier all its p_i level $i - 1$ components can exchange information with the m_i memory of the level i component. The next level i superstep can then start. L_i is the cost charged for this barrier synchronization for a level i superstep. (In this paper we use $L_1 = 0$, since the subcomponents of a level 1 component have no memories and directly read from and write to the level 1 memory.)

(iv) m_i is the number of words of memory and caches inside an ith level component that is not inside any $i - 1^{st}$ level component.

Finally we have to specify the nature of the communication between a level i and the level $i + 1$ component of which it is a part. The question is whether concurrent reading or writing (or some other combining operation) is allowed in either direction. The algorithms in this paper are all exclusive read and exclusive write (EREW), while the lower bounds hold for the strongest concurrent (CRCW) version.

We note that the parameters of the model imply values for certain other useful measures. The number of raw processors in a level i component will be $P_i = p_1 \cdots p_i$. The number of level i components in a level j component will be $Q_{i,j} = p_{i+1} \cdots p_j$, and the number in the whole system will be $Q_{i,d} = Q_i = p_{i+1} \cdots p_d$. The total memory in a level i component will be $M_i = m_i + p_i m_{i-1} + p_{i-1} p_i m_{i-2} + \cdots + p_2 \cdots p_{i-1} p_i m_1$. The gap or bandwith parameter that characterizes the cost of communication from level 1 to outside level i is $G_i = g_i + g_{i-1} + g_{i-2} + \cdots + g_1$.

Since the intention is to model the entire system, defining as many levels as necessary, we assume by convention that $Q_d = 1$ and that g_d is infinite. The latter condition reflects the fact that there is no communication analysed off the level d components. For the same reason it is assumed that for any problem instance of size n and an algorithm for it, the level d memory is sufficient to support the computation, and certainly $m_d \geq n$. In the applications in this paper $m_d = O(n)$ is sufficient.

We make the assumption that for all i

$$m_i \geq m_{i-1} \tag{1}$$

in order to simplify certain analyses. Also, we sometimes invoke the assumption that for for some constant $c > 0$

$$m_i \geq cM_i \tag{2}$$

which is true with $c = 1/d$ for conventional caches where any word at one level has copies at every higher level. We note that in the treatment here we do not otherwise distinguish between memory and caches.

As far as relationships to other models we note that the depth $d = 1$ Multi-BSP with $(p_1 \geq 1, g_1 = 1, L_1 = 0, m_1)$ is the PRAM [11, 20] model. Of course, $(p_1 = 1, g_1 = 1, L_1 = 0, m_1)$ is the von Neumann model. The BSP model [26] with parameters (p, g, L) where the basic unit has memory m corresponds to $d = 2$ with $(p_1 = 1, g_1 = g, L_1 = 0, m_1 = m)(p_2 = p, g_2 = \infty, L_2 = L, m_2)$. The difference is that in the basic BSP model communication is allowed horizontally between units at the same level, while in Multi-BSP such communication would need to be simulated via memory at a higher level. This $(p_1 = 1, g_1 = g, L_1 = 0, m_1 = m)(p_2 = p, g_2 = \infty, L_2 = L, m_2)$ corresponds precisely to the BSPRAM model of Tiskin [27].

In general, in expressing resource bounds F_1, F_2 in terms of the parameters $\{p_i, g_i, L_i, m_i | 1 \leq i \leq d\}$ and the input size n, we shall define $F_1 \precsim F_2$ to mean that for all $\varepsilon > 0, F_1 < (1 + \varepsilon)F_2$ for all sufficiently large values of n and of $m = \min\{m_i | 1 \leq i \leq d\}$. This enables expressions such as $(1 + 1/m_i), (1 + 1/m_i^{1/2})$ or $(1 + 1/\log m_i)$ to be approximately upper bounded by 1.

Also, we define $F_1 \precsim_d F_2$ to mean that for some constant c_d depending possibly on d but on none of the parameters $\{p_i, g_i, L_i, m_i | 1 \leq i \leq d\}$ or $n, F_1 < c_d F_2$ for all sufficiently large values of n and m.

Because we can suppress constant multipliers with these notations, in the discussion where appropriate we shall assume that the various parameters are appropriate multiples of each other, and sometimes write m_j, for example, for some fixed multiple of itself.

For a Multi-BSP algorithm A^* we shall define $\text{Comp}(A^*)$, $\text{Comm}(A^*)$, and $\text{Synch}(A^*)$ to be the *parallel* costs of computation, computation, and synchronization respectively on a Multi-BSP machine H in the sense that for any computation of A^* on H and along any single critical path in it, at most $\text{Comp}(A^*)$ raw processor steps have been executed and at most $\text{Comm}(A^*)$ communication charge and at most $\text{Synch}(A^*)$ synchronization charge has been incurred. (For randomized algorithms the same claim holds with high probability.) Note that all three charges are expressed in terms of the basic unit of time taken by a raw processor to perform one operation.

To quantify the efficiency of A^* we specify a baseline algorithm A of which A^* is the Multi-BSP implementation and for that:

(i) Comp(A) is the total number of computational operations of A divided by P_d the total number of raw processors in H.

(ii) Comm(A) is the minimal communication cost on any distributed implementation of A with the M_i and p_i parameters of H. Thus it certainly lower bounds the best Multi-BSP algorithm on H.

(iii) Synch(A) is the minimal synchronization cost of any Multi-BSP implementation of A on H.

A Multi-BSP algorithm A^* is *optimal with respect to algorithm A* if

(i) Comp(A^*) $\precsim$ Comp(A),

(ii) Comm(A^*) $\precsim_d$ Comm(A), and

(iii) Synch(A^*) $\precsim_d$ Synch(A).

Allowing at each level some efficiency loss in communication and synchronization is tolerable for problems for which computational costs dominate asymptotically. It frees the analysis of several concerns, such as whether the input size is exactly of the right form, such as being an exact multiple of the memory sizes. Analogous to the role of the polynomial time criterion in sequential computing, we believe that freeing the algorithm designer from the tedium of certain well-chosen optimality criteria will encourage the development of practical algorithms. In this instance we permit a constant factor inefficiency at each level in the communication and synchronization, but not in computation. In all three measures additive lower order terms that have a vanishing relative contribution as the input size n and $m = \min\{m_i | 1 \leq i \leq d\}$ grow, are also allowed.

It has been amply demonstrated that the performance of one level parallel machines can be well modeled by appropriate BSP parameters [14, 15]. The architecture of multi-core machines is still evolving. The most appropriate way of modeling them by Multi-BSP parameters is yet to be determined. Of course, we can read off some approximations to these parameters from technical specifications of existing architectures. For example, consider a parallel machine consisting of p Sun Niagara UltraSparc T1 multi-core chips connected to an external storage device that is large enough to store the input to the problem at hand. Then the parameters of the chip according to one interpretation of the specifications and modulo the serious qualifications listed below, would be the following:

Level 1: 1 core has 1 processor with 4 threads plus L1 cache: ($p_1 = 4, g_1 = 1, L_1^* = 3, m_1 = 8$kB).

Level 2: 1 chip has 8 cores plus L2 cache: ($p_2 = 8, g_2 = 3, L_2^* = 23, m_2 = 3$MB).

Level 3: p multi-core chips with external memory m_3 accessible via a network accessible at rate g_2 : ($p_3 = p, g_3 = \infty, L_3^* = 108, m_3 \leq 128$GB).

Now the qualifications include the following: First, the L^*-parameters listed are certain latency parameters given in the chip specifications, rather than the cost of a synchronization which is needed in the BSP interpretation. Second, the caches on the chip are caches with certain cache protocols, rather than memories where addressing is fully controlled. Third, in the actual chip the lowest level processors run four threads sharing a processor, and groups of processors share a common arithmetic unit. Hence, while the relative values shown of the various g values and the various L^* values are meaningful, their absolute values are harder to pin down.

We note, however, that while we advocate that the proposed bridging model be faithful to physical realities in terms of numerical parameters, we also believe that there is room for architects to design systems that are faithful to the bridging model. For example, if it turns out that the Multi-BSP model is a good vehicle for the design of parallel algorithms then it would seem reasonable that architectures should reflect it, by efficiently supporting the associated synchronization operation as well as by allowing more explicit control of the caches.

3   Work-Limited Algorithms

Our proofs of optimality for communication and synchronization all derive from lower bounds on the number of communication steps required in distributed algorithms and are direct applications of previous work, particularly of Hong and Kung [17], Aggarwal and Vitter [2], and Irony, Toledo and Tiskin [18].

Defn. An algorithm A is $w(m)$-*limited* if when the algorithm execution is partitioned into disjoint sequences $S_1, ..., S_t$ of operations each sequence S_i using at most m words of memory for reading and writing, each sequence S_i consists of no more than $w(m)$ operations.

Note that such a memory limitation to m words imposes the twin constraints that at most m words can be used as data by the algorithm fragment, and at most m words can be used to pass values computed in this fragment to later computation steps.

We first consider *associative composition* AC(n): Here, given a linear array A of n elements, an associative binary operation $\otimes$ on these elements, and disjoint contiguous sublists of A, the object is to compute the composition of each sublist under $\otimes$ in some order.

Proposition 1. *For any n and m, any algorithm with minimum total operations for associative composition $AC(n)$ is $(m-1)$-limited.*

Proof. On sublists of total length m at most $m-1$ operations can be performed.□

Next we consider the problem MM($n \times n$) of multiplying two $n \times n$ matrices by the standard algorithm, where the additions can be performed in any order.

Proposition 2. *For any n and m, the standard matrix multiplication algorithm $MM(n \times n)$ is $O(m^{3/2})$-limited.*

Proof. This is proved by Irony, Toledo and Tiskin[18] and follows a closely related result of Hong and Kung [17].   □

Next we consider $FFT(n)$ the standard algorithm for computing the one-dimensional Fast Fourier transform on n points.

Proposition 3. *For any n and m, the standard fast Fourier transform algorithm $FFT(n)$ is $O(m \log m)$-limited.*

Proof. This has been shown by Hong and Kung [17] and by Aggarwal and Vitter[2].   □

Finally we shall consider $Sort(n)$ the problem of sorting where the only operation allowed that is dependent on the elements to be sorted is pairwise comparison, and these are the only operations counted.

4   General Lower Bounds

Our lower bound results we derive using the approach of Irony, Toledo and Tiskin [18]. The communication bounds will be stated for Multi-BSP but, except for sorting, the lower bound arguments hold more generally for all distributed algorithms with the same hierarchy of memory sizes and costs of communication. In other words, they hold even if communication happens at arbitrary times.

Lemma 1. *Suppose W computational steps are to be performed of a $w(m)$-limited algorithm on a Multi-BSP machine. Then the total number of words transmitted between level j components and the level $j + 1$ components to which they belong is at least*

$$M_j(W/w(2M_j) - Q_j),\tag{3}$$

and the total number of component supersteps at least

$$W/w(M_j).\tag{4}$$

Proof. The lower bound we argue for any distributed algorithm, even if the data exchanges are regarded as going at arbitrary times rather than bulk synchronized. For each level j component divide the computation into phases, where each phase ends when the total number of messages sent to or received from level $j + 1$ reaches M_j. In each phase therefore at most $2M_j$ words are available, including those residing in memory before the start of the phase. Then at most $w(2M_j)$ operations can be performed by each phase. It follows that the total number of such component phases is at least $W/w(2M_j)$. Further, each of these phases must complete and involve a movement of M_j data except possibly the last phase for each component. Hence the total amount of data movement between level j and level $j + 1$ is at least as claimed in (3).

By the same argument, since in component supersteps at most $w(M_j)$ steps can be performed, at least $W/w(M_j)$ component supersteps are needed, which gives (4). □

Theorem 1. *Suppose $W(n)$ operations are to be performed of a $w(m)$-limited algorithm A on input size n on a depth d Multi-BSP machine. Then the bandwidth cost over the whole machine is at least*

$$Comm(n,d) \gtrsim_d \sum_{i=1\cdots d-1} (W(n)/(Q_i w(2M_i)) - 1)M_i g_i \tag{5}$$

and the synchronization cost at least

$$Synch(n,d) \gtrsim_d \sum_{i=1\cdots d-1} W(n)L_{i+1}/(Q_i w(M_i)) \tag{6}$$

Proof. This follows from Lemma 1 by adding the costs over all the levels. Consider the Q_1 paths from the level 1 components to the level d component in the tree hierarchy as potential critical paths of the executions. The average load on these, and hence the worst case also, is as claimed in (5) and (6). □

Corollary 1

$$\text{AC-Comm}(n,d) \gtrsim_d \sum_{i=1\cdots d-1} (n/(M_i Q_i) - 1)M_i g_i \tag{7}$$

$$\text{AC-Synch}(n,d) \gtrsim_d \sum_{i=1\cdots d-1} nL_{i+1}/(Q_i M_i) \tag{8}$$

$$\text{MM-Comm}(n \times n, d) \gtrsim_d \sum_{i=1\cdots d-1} (n^3/(Q_i M_i^{3/2}) - 1)M_i g_i \tag{9}$$

$$\text{MM-Synch}(n \times n, d) \gtrsim_d \sum_{i=1\cdots d-1} n^3 L_{i+1}/(Q_i M_i^{3/2}) \tag{10}$$

$$\text{FFT-Comm}(n,d) \gtrsim_d \sum_{i=1\cdots d-1} (n\log(n)/(Q_i M_i \log M_i) - 1)M_i g_i \tag{11}$$

$$\text{FFT-Synch}(n,d) \gtrsim_d \sum_{i=1\cdots d-1} n\log(n)L_{i+1}/(Q_i M_i \log M_i) \tag{12}$$

$$\text{Sort-Comm}(n,d) \gtrsim_d \sum_{i=1\cdots d-1} (n\log(n)/(Q_i M_i \log M_i) - 1)M_i g_i \tag{13}$$

$$\text{Sort-Synch}(n,d) \gtrsim_d \sum_{i=1\cdots d-1} n\log(n)L_{i+1}/(Q_i M_i \log M_i) \tag{14}$$

Proof. Applying Theorem 1 directly gives the first six inequalities. The bounds for sorting follow from an adversarial argument in the style of [2]. □

5   Optimal Algorithms

We shall describe algorithms that at *every* level j component will execute supersteps that perform $\Omega_d(w(m_j))$ computational operations on the average, where Ω_d denotes that the multiplicative constant in the lower bound can depend on d but on none of the other parameters. This is optimal up to constant factors for communication, even over algorithms that are not constrained to be Multi-BSP, under assumption (2) which allows us to replace M_j by m_j in lower bounds. They will also be optimal up to constant factors for synchronization among Multi-BSP algorithms, since they communicate as infrequently as possible, only when communication is unavoidable.

In describing algorithms we shall use the term *level j (global) superstep* to refer to all the Q_j level j components executing a superstep in parallel (but not necessarily simultaneously.) A *level j component superstep* will refer to what a single level j component performs in a level j superstep.

For each of the algorithms described below it is easy to verify that the condition $\mathrm{Comp}(A^*) \precsim \mathrm{Comp}(A)$ of optimality is satisfied, and we shall not comment on this further.

5.1   Associative Composition

For $\mathrm{AC}(n)$ consider the recursive process where each level j component contains contiguous sequences of total length m_j, distributes the task of performing the required compositions of subsequences of length m_{j-1} of those sequences to its p_j subcomponents, and when it receives the results back it performs up to m_j/m_{j-1} further pairwise $\otimes$ operations recursively.

The costs of the recursion at *one* level j component can be divided into (i) the data movement steps between the level j component and its level $j-1$ components, and (ii) the recursive computation of the m_j/m_{j-1} further pairwise $\otimes$ operations. For (i) since at most m_j/m_{j-1} times in the overall computation a level $j-1$ memory has to be filled with information from level j (and one word returned), the cost of communication at this level is at most

$$(m_j/(p_j m_{j-1}))(m_{j-1}+1)g_{j-1} \precsim m_j g_{j-1}/p_j$$

and the total cost of synchronization at most

$$\precsim m_j L_j/(p_j m_{j-1})$$

For (ii) we observe that the cost corresponds to the original problem for a level j superstep component, but for input length m_j/m_{j-1} rather than m_j. In other words its costs are $\mathrm{AC\text{-}Comp}(m_j/m_{j-1}, j)$, $\mathrm{AC\text{-}Comm}(m_j/m_{j-1}, j)$ and $\mathrm{AC\text{-}Synch}(m_j/m_{j-1}, j)$. Hence,

$\mathrm{AC\text{-}Comm}(m_j, j)$
$\precsim m_j g_{j-1}/p_j + (m_j/(p_j m_{j-1}))\mathrm{AC\text{-}Comm}(m_{j-1}, j-1) + \mathrm{AC\text{-}Comm}(m_j/m_{j-1}, j)$

and

AC-Synch$(m_j, j) \precsim m_j L_j/(p_j m_{j-1}) + (m_j/(p_j m_{j-1}))$AC-Synch$(m_{j-1}, j-1) +$ AC-Synch$(m_j/m_{j-1}, j)$

Expanding the first gives

AC-Comm(m_j, j)
$\precsim (m_j g_{j-1}/p_j + (m_j/(p_j m_{j-1}))$AC-Comm$(m_{j-1}, j-1))(1+1/m_{j-1}+1/m_{j-1}^2 \cdots)$
$\precsim_d (m_j g_{j-1}/p_j + (m_j/(p_j m_{j-1}))$AC-Comm$(m_{j-1}, j-1))$.

Since we can equate the input size n with m_d, it follows by induction on j that

$$\text{AC-Comm}(n, d) \precsim_d \sum_{i=1 \cdots d-1} n g_i/Q_i. \tag{15}$$

Expanding the second recurrence gives in exactly the same way

$$\text{AC-Synch}(n, d) \precsim_d \sum_{i=1 \cdots d-1} n L_{i+1}/(Q_i m_i). \tag{16}$$

5.2   Matrix Multiplication

For matrix multiplication $w(m) = O(m^{3/2})$ and in a level j superstep it is optimal to within constant factors to do $w(3m)$ operations per component having total memory $3m$, by inputting an $m^{1/2} \times m^{1/2}$ submatrix of each of A and B, computing the products of these submatrices, and outputting the m sums as contributions to each of m entries in the appropriate $m^{1/2} \times m^{1/2}$ submatrix of $C = AB$.

Hence at level 1 a component superstep consists of an $m_1^{1/2} \times m_1^{1/2}$ matrix multiplication. Overall one will need $n^3/m_1^{3/2}$ such executions, and hence $n^3/(Q_1 m_1^{3/2})$ level 1 component supersteps where Q_1 is the total number of level 1 processors.

In general, a level j component superstep consists (within multiplicative constant factors) of an $m_j^{1/2} \times m_j^{1/2}$ matrix multiplication. Overall one will need $n^3/m_j^{3/2}$ such component supersteps, and hence $n^3/(Q_j m_j^{3/2})$ global supersteps.

In a level j local superstep there will be $m_j^{3/2}/(m_{j-1}^{3/2})$ level j-1 local supersteps of $m_{j-1}^{1/2} \times m_{j-1}^{1/2}$ matrix multiplications. In addition we will charge to this level the further $m_j(m_j^{1/2}/m_{j-1}^{1/2}) = m_j^{3/2}/m_{j-1}^{1/2}$ additions needed to combine the results from the level $j-1$ local supersteps. For the latter operations we will use $m_j^{1/2}/m_{j-1}^{1/2}$ successive Associative Composition operations AC$(m_j, j))$ we analyzed earlier, each such operation performing compositions on various sets of size $m_j^{1/2}/m_{j-1}^{1/2}$. Hence using (15) and $Q_i \geq 1$, the total communication cost we charge at level j is

$$(n^3/(m_j^{3/2} Q_j))(g_j m_j + (m_j^{1/2}/m_{j-1}^{1/2})\text{AC-Comm}(m_j, j))$$
$$\precsim_d (n^3/(m_j^{3/2} Q_j))(g_j m_j + (m_j^{3/2}/m_{j-1}^{1/2}) \sum_{i=1 \cdots j-1} g_i/Q_i)$$
$$\precsim_d n^3 g_j/(m_j^{1/2} Q_j) + (n^3/m_{j-1}^{1/2}) \sum_{i=1 \cdots j-1} g_i/Q_i.$$

Hence adding over all levels gives

$$\text{MM-Comm}(n \times n, d) \precsim_d \sum_{i=1\cdots d-1} (n^3 g_i/Q_i) \sum_{k=i\cdots d-1} (1/m_k^{1/2})$$

$$\precsim_d n^3 \sum_{j=1\cdots d-1} g_j m_j^{-1/2}/Q_j \tag{17}$$

since by (1) the m_j are nondecreasing in j. Assuming (2) this meets the lower bound (9).

Similarly, the total charge for synchronization at level j is

$$(n^3/(Q_j m_j^{3/2}))(L_{j+1} + (m_j^{1/2}/m_{j-1}^{1/2})\text{AC-Synch}(m_j, j))$$
$$\precsim_d (n^3/(m_j^{3/2}Q_j))(L_{j+1} + (m_j^{3/2}/m_{j-1}^{1/2})\sum_{i=1\cdots j-1} L_{i+1}/(Q_i m_i))$$
$$\precsim_d n^3 L_{j+1}/(m_j^{3/2}Q_j) + (n^3/m_{j-1}^{3/2})\sum_{i=1\cdots j-1} L_{i+1}/Q_i.$$

Hence adding over all levels gives

$$\text{MM-Synch}(n \times n, d) \precsim_d \sum_{i=1\cdots d-1} (n^3 L_{i+1}/Q_i) \sum_{k=i\cdots d-1} (1/m_k^{3/2})$$

$$\precsim_d n^3 \sum_{j=1\cdots d-1} L_{j+1} m_j^{-3/2}/Q_j. \tag{18}$$

since by (1) the m_j are nondecreasing in j. Assuming (2) this meets the lower bound (10).

5.3   Fast Fourier Transform

We consider the FFT problem for input size $N = 2^u$ as a straight line program where each operation corresponds to a node, and an operation at layer k is a linear combination of the values produced at its two antecedent nodes at level $k - 1$. The operation sequence can be represented as a directed acyclic graph with nodes $(i_1 i_2 \cdots i_u, k)$ where $i_j \in \{0, 1\}$ and $k \in \{0, 1, \cdots, u\}$, and edges $((i_1 i_2 \cdots i_u, k), (i_1 i_2 \cdots i_u, k+1))$ and $((i_1 i_2 \cdots i_u, k), (i_1 i_2 \cdots i_{k+1}^* \cdots i_u, k+1))$ where for $i \in \{0, 1\}, i^* \in \{0, 1\}$ is the complement, namely $i + i^* = 1 \bmod 2$.

Our basic algorithm $\text{FFT}(m_j, x, j)$ for x FFTs on disjoint sets of m_j/x points all initially held in the level j memory with the output to be held also at that level will be performed by doing

  (i) m_j/m_{j-1} problems of type $\text{FFT}(m_{j-1}, 1, j-1)$, and
  (ii) on the m_j values so obtained doing $\text{FFT}(m_j, x m_{j-1}, j)$.

In other words (i) will solve each disjoint set of m_j/x points by doing $m_j/(x m_{j-1})$ FFT's on m_{j-1} points each, and (ii) states that the effect of this is to increase the number (and hence reduce the size) of the resulting FFT problems remaining by a factor of m_{j-1}. Note that after $r = \log m_j / \log m_{j-1}$ iterations of steps (i) and (ii) together, FFT(m_j, x, j) will be called with $m_j = x$, which requires no operations. Hence if we denote by FFT-Comm(m_j, x, j) and FFT-Synch(m_j, x, j) the communication and synchronization costs of this task then

$$\text{FFT-Comm}(m_j, x, j) = (m_j/(m_{j-1}p_j))[m_{j-1}g_{j-1} + \text{FFT-Comm}(m_{j-1}, 1, j-1)]$$
$$+ \text{FFT-Comm}(m_j, xm_{j-1}, j)$$

and

$$\text{FFT-Synch}(m_j, x, j) = (m_j/(m_{j-1}p_j))[L_j + \text{FFT-Synch}(m_{j-1}, 1, j-1)]$$
$$+ \text{FFT-Synch}(m_j, xm_{j-1}, j).$$

Expanding the first gives for $r = \log m_j / \log m_{j-1}$ that

$$\text{FFT-Comm}(m_j, x, j)$$
$$= (m_j/(m_{j-1}p_j))[m_{j-1}g_{j-1} + \text{FFT-Comm}(m_{j-1}, 1, j-1)]$$

.

.

.

$$+ (m_j/(m_{j-1}p_j))[m_{j-1}g_{j-1} + \text{FFT-Comm}(m_{j-1}, 1, j-1)]$$
$$+ \text{FFT-Comm}(m_j, x(m_{j-1})^r, j),$$

$$= r(m_j/(m_{j-1}p_j))[m_{j-1}g_{j-1} + \text{FFT-Comm}(m_{j-1}, 1, j-1)]$$

$$= (\log m_j / \log m_{j-1})g_{j-1}m_j/p_j$$
$$+ (m_j \log m_j / (p_j m_{j-1} \log m_{j-1})) \text{FFT-Comm}(m_{j-1}, 1, j-1)]$$

Now assuming by induction that

$$\text{FFT-Comm}(m_{j-1}, 1, j-1) \leq \sum_{i=1..j-2}(\log m_{j-1}/\log m_i)g_i m_{j-1}/Q_{i,j-1}$$

and substituting in the above using $Q_{i,j-1}p_j = Q_{i,j}$ gives

$$(\log m_j / \log m_{j-1})g_{j-1}m_j/p_j$$
$$+ (m_j \log m_j / (p_j m_{j-1} \log m_{j-1})) \sum_{i=1..j-2}(\log m_{j-1}/\log m_i)g_i m_{j-1}/Q_{i,j-1}$$

$$= (\log m_j / \log m_{j-1})g_{j-1}m_j/p_j$$
$$+ (m_j \log m_j \sum_{i=1..j-2}(1/\log m_i)g_i/Q_{i,j}$$

$$= m_j \log m_j \sum_{i=1..j-1}(1/\log m_i)g_i/Q_{i,j}.$$

Then for $n \leq m_d$

$$\text{FFT-Comm}(n, 1, d) \precsim_d \sum_{i=1\cdots d-1} n \log(n) g_i/(Q_i \log m_i) \tag{19}$$

Now for synchronization the second recurrence gives by an identical argument

$$\text{FFT-Synch}(n, 1, d) \precsim_d \sum_{i=1\cdots d-1} n \log(n) L_{i+1}/(Q_i m_i \log m_i). \tag{20}$$

5.4 Sorting

Sorting by deterministic oversampling and splitting into smaller subsets of about equal size is known to be achievable using the following idea [12, 23, 26]:

Lemma 2. *For numbers N, S, G and t one can find a set of S splitters in any ordered set X of N elements such that in the ordering on X the number of elements between two successive splitters is $N/S \pm 2tG$ by using the following procedure: Partition X into G sets of N/G elements each, sort each such set, pick out every t^{th} element from each such sorted list, sort the resulting N/t elements, and finally pick every $N/(tS)^{th}$ element of that.*

Let $\text{Sort}(n, x, j)$ be a procedure for sorting a set Y of size $n \leq m_j$ residing in level j memory that includes a set of x splitters that already split Y into sets of about equal size. Our recursive step will divide the set into xm_{j-1}/t^2 sorted sublists of about equal size at the next stage for $t = e^{\sqrt{(\log m)}}$ where $m = \min\{m_i | 1 \leq i \leq d\}$. This is achieved for every sorted sublist of Y by the method of the above paragraph with $N = (m_j/x)$, $S = m_{j-1}/t^2$, $G = N/m_{j-1}$. On the assumption that the sublists are of exactly the same length we get the recurrence

$$\begin{aligned}
\text{Sort-Comm}&(m_j, x, j) \\
&\precsim (m_j/(m_{j-1}p_j))(g_{i-1}m_{j-1} + \text{Sort-Comm}(m_{j-1}, 0, j-1)) \\
&+ \text{Sort-Comm}(m_j, xm_{j-1}/t^2, j) + \text{Sort-Comm}(m_j/t, 0, j).
\end{aligned}$$

Since $m_j/t = o(m_j/\log m_j)$ the last term will contribute a lower order term even if implemented by a sorting algorithm in which the communication cost is proportional to the computation cost (rather than a logarithmic factor cheaper) and can be ignored, leaving the same recurrence as for FFT-Comm but with the multiplier m_{j-1}/t^2 rather than m_{j-1} in the second term. This will therefore yield the following solutions analogous to (19) and (20):

$$\text{Sort-Comm}(n, d) \precsim_d \sum_{i=1\cdots d-1} n \log(n) g_i/(Q_i \log m_i) \tag{21}$$

$$\text{Sort-Synch}(n, d) \precsim_d \sum_{i=1\cdots d-1} n \log(n) L_{i+1}/(Q_i m_i \log m_i). \tag{22}$$

The approach can make it significantly simpler to implement kinetic algorithms for a number of reasons: only the static algorithms need to be implemented[2]; algorithms are trivial to compose as static algorithms compose in the normal way; and simultaneous update of multiple certificates are possible because the change propagation algorithm can handle any number of changes. Acar et al. [ABTV06] used the ability to process multiple updates to help deal with numerical inaccuracy. The observation was that if the roots can be limited to an interval in time (e.g. using interval arithmetic), then one need only identify a position in time not covered by any root. It is then safe to move the simulation forward to that position and simultaneously process all certificates before it. Although the approach using floating-point number arithmetic worked for 2D examples in that paper, it has proved to be more difficult to find such positions in time for problems in three dimensions.

In this paper, we propose another approach to advancing time for robust motion simulation and apply it to a 3D convex hull algorithm. We then evaluate the approach experimentally. The approach is a hybrid between kinetic event-based scheduling and classic fixed-time sampling. The idea is to partition time into a lattice of intervals of fixed size δ, and only identify events to the resolution of an interval. If many roots fall within an interval, they are processed as a batch without regard to their ordering. As with kinetic event-based scheduling, we maintain a priority queue, but in our approach, the queue maintains non-empty intervals each possibly with multiple events. To separate roots to the resolution of intervals, we use Sturm sequences in a similar way as used for exact separation of roots [GK99], but the fixed resolution allows us to stop the process early. More specifically, in exact separation, one finds smaller and smaller intervals (e.g. using binary search) until all roots fall into separate intervals. In our case, once we reach the lattice interval, we can stop without further separation. This means that if events are degenerate and happen at the same time, for example, we need not determine this potentially expensive fact.

For kinetic 3D convex hulls, we use a static randomized incremental convex hull algorithm [CS89, BDH96, MR95] and kinetize it using self-adjusting computation. To ensure that the algorithm responds to kinetic events efficiently, we make some small changes to the standard incremental 3D convex-hull algorithm. This makes progress on the problem of kinetic 3D convex hulls, which was identified in late 1990s [Gui98]. To the best of our knowledge, currently the best way to compute the 3D kinetic convex hulls is to use the kinetic Delaunay algorithm of the CGAL package [Boa07], which computes the convex hull as a byproduct of the 3D Delaunay triangulation (of which the convex hull would be a subset). As shown in our experiment, this existing solution generally requires processing many more events than necessary for computing convex hulls.

We present experimental results for the the proposed kinetic 3D convex hull algorithm with the robust motion simulator. Using our implementation, we can run simulations with tens of thousands of moving points in 3D and test their accuracy. We can perform robust motion simulation by processing an average

---

[2] In the current system, some annotations are needed to mark changeable values.

of about two certificate failures per step. The 3D hull algorithm seems to take (poly) logarithmic time on average to respond to a certificate failure as well as an integrated event—an insertion or deletion that occurs during a motion simulation.

2   Robust Motion Simulation on a Lattice

We propose an approach to robust motion simulation that combines event-based kinetic simulation and the classic idea of fixed-time sampling. The motivation behind the approach is to avoid ordering the roots of polynomials, because it requires high-precision exact arithmetic when the roots are close. To achieve this, we discretize the time axis to form a lattice $\{k \cdot \delta \mid k \in \mathbb{Z}_+\}$ defined by the *precision* parameter δ. We then perform motion simulations at the resolution of the lattice by processing the certificates that fail within an interval of the lattice simultaneously. This approach requires that the update mechanism used for revising the computed property be able to handle multiple certificate failures at once. In this paper, we use self-adjusting computation, where computations can respond to any change in their data correctly by means of a generic change propagation algorithm. The correctness of change propagation has been proven elsewhere, sometimes by providing machine-checked proofs [ABD07, AAB08].

For robust motion simulations, we will need to perform the following operations:

- Compute the signs of a polynomial and its derivatives at a given lattice point.
- Compute the intervals of the lattice that contain the roots of a polynomial.

In our approach, we assume that the coefficients of the polynomials are integers (up to a scaling factor) and use exact integer arithmetic to compute the signs of the polynomial and its derivatives. For finding the roots, we use a root solver described below.

The Root Solver. Our root solver relies on a procedure, which we call a *Sturm query*, that returns the number of roots of a square-free polynomial that are smaller than a given lattice point. To answer such a query, we compute the Sturm sequence (a.k.a. standard sequence) of the polynomial, which consists of the intermediary polynomials generated by the Euclid's algorithm for finding the greatest common divisor (GCD) of the polynomial and its derivative. The answer to the query is the difference in the number of alternations in the signs of the sequence at $-\infty$ and at the query point. Using the Sturm query, we can find the roots of a square-free polynomial by performing a variant of a binary search.[3] We can eliminate the square-free assumption by a known technique that factors the polynomial into square and square-free polynomials.

Motion Simulation. We maintain a priority queue of events (initially empty), and a global simulation time (initially 0). We start by running the static

---

[3] In practice, we start with an approximation computed by floating-point arithmetic.

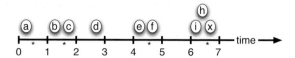

Fig. 1. The lattice ($\delta = 1$) and the events (certificate failures)

algorithm in the self-adjusting framework. This computes a certificate polynomial for each comparison. For each certificate, we find the lattice intervals at which the sign of the corresponding polynomial changes, and for each such interval, we insert an event into the priority queue. After the initialization, we simulate motion by advancing the time to the smallest lattice point t such that the lattice interval $[t - \delta, t)$ contains an event. To find the new time t we remove from the priority queue all the events contained in the earliest nonempty interval. We then change the outcome of the removed certificates and perform a change-propagation at time t. Change propagation updates the output and the queue by inserting new events and removing invalidated ones. We repeat this process until there is no more certificate failure. Figure 1 shows a hypothetical example with $\delta = 1$. We perform change propagation at times $1, 2, 3, 5, 7$. Note that multiple events are propagated simultaneously at time 2 (events b and c), time 5 (events e and f), and time 7 (events h, i and, x).

When performing change propagation at a given time t, we may encounter a polynomial that is zero at t representing a degeneracy. In this case, we use the derivatives of the polynomial to determine the sign immediately before t. Using this approach, we are able to avoid degeneracies throughout the simulation, as long as the certificate polynomials are not identically zero.

We note that the approach described here is quite different from the approach suggested by Ali Abam et al. [AAdBY06]. In that approach, root isolation is avoided by allowing certificate failures to be processed out of order. This can lead to incorrect transient results and requires care in the design of the kinetic structures. We do not process certificates out of order but rather as a batch.

3   Algorithm

In the kinetic framework based on self-adjusting computation [ABTV06], we can use any static algorithm directly. The performance of the approach, however, depends critically on the cost of the change propagation algorithm when applied after changes are made to input or predicate values. In particular, when invoked, the change-propagation algorithm updates the current trace (sequence of operations together with their data) by removing outdated operations and re-executing parts of the algorithm that cannot be reused from the current trace. The performance of change propagation therefore depends on some form of the edit distance between the execution trace before and after the changes. This edit distance has been formalized in the definition of *trace stability* [ABH+04]. In this section, we describe a variant of the randomized incremental convex-hull algorithm [CS89, BDH96, MR95], and remark on some of its features that are crucial for stability—i.e., that minimize the number of operations that need to be updated when a certificate fails.

Given $S \subseteq \mathbb{R}^3$, the convex hull of S, denoted by $conv(S)$, is the smallest convex polyhedron enclosing all points in S. During the execution of the algorithm on input S, each face f of the convex hull will be associated with a set $\Sigma(f) \subset S$ of points (possibly empty). Each input point p will be given a real number $\pi(p) \in [0,1]$, called its *priority*. Each face f will have the priority $\pi(f) := \min\{\pi(p) : p \in \Sigma(f)\}$. We say that a face of the hull is *visible* from a point if the point is outside the plane defined by the face.

The algorithm takes as input a set of points $S = \{p_1, p_2, \ldots, p_n\}$, and performs the following steps:

1. Assign to each p_i a random *priority* $\pi(p_i) \in [0,1]$.
2. Initialize $H := conv(A_4)$, where A_4 is the set of four highest-priority points.
3. Pick a *center* point c inside the convex body H.
4. For each $f \in H$, set $\Sigma(f) := \{p \in S \setminus H : \text{the ray } \overrightarrow{cp} \text{ penetrates } f\}$.
5. While $\exists f \in H$ such that $\Sigma(f) \neq \emptyset$:
   (a) Choose the face f^* with the highest priority, and let $p^* \in \Sigma(f)$ be the point with the highest priority.
   (b) Delete all faces on H visible from p^*. This creates a cavity in the convex hull whose boundary is defined by *horizon edges* that are incident to both deleted and live faces.
   (c) Update H by creating new faces each of which consists of p^* and a horizon edge to fill up the cavity. Set $\Sigma(f) := \{p^* \in S \setminus H : \text{the ray } \overrightarrow{cp^*} \text{ penetrates } f\}$ for each new faces f.

In our implementation, we maintain a priority queue of faces ordered by priorities of the faces. We also store at each face the point in $\Sigma(f)$ with priority $\pi(f)$. This allows us to perform step 5(a) efficiently.

Even though the algorithm presented above is fairly standard, certain key elements of this implementation appear to be crucial for stability—without them, the algorithm would be unstable. For stability, we want the edit distance between the traces to be small. Towards this goal, the algorithm should always insert points in the same order—even when new points are added or old points deleted. We ensure this by assigning a random priority to every input point. The use of random priorities makes it easy to handle new points, and obviates the need to explicitly remember the insertion order.

For better stability, we also want the insertion of a point p to visit faces of the convex hull in the same order every time. While the presented algorithm cannot guarantee this, we use the following heuristic to enhance stability. The point-to-face assignment with respect to a center point c ensures that the insertion of p^* always starts excavating at the same face, increasing the likelihood that the faces are visited in the same order. Note that the choice of the center point is arbitrary, with the only requirement that the center point has to lie in the convex hull. Our implementation takes c to be the centroid of the tetrahedron formed by A_4.

4   Implementation

Our implementation consists of three main components: 1) the self-adjusting-computation library, 2) the incremental 3D convex-hull algorithm, and 3) the motion simulator. Previous work [ABBT06] provided an implementation of the self-adjusting computation library. The library requires that the user adds some notations to their static algorithms to mark what values can change and what needs to be memoized. These notations are used by the system to track the dependences and know when to reuse subcomputations.

In our experiments, we use both the original static 3D convex-hull algorithm and the self-adjusting version with the annotations added. The static version uses exact arithmetic predicates to determine the outcomes of comparisons precisely (we use the static version for checking the robustness of the simulation). The self-adjusting version uses the root solver to find the roots of the polynomial certificates, and inserts them into the event queue of the motion simulator. We implement a motion simulator as described in Section 2. Given a precision parameter δ and a bound M_t on the simulation time, the simulator uses an event scheduler to perform a motion simulation on the lattice with precision δ until M_t is reached. We model the points with an initial location traveling at constant speed in a fixed direction. For each coordinate, we use B_ℓ and B_v bits to represent the initial location and the velocity respectively; B_ℓ and B_v can be assigned to arbitrary positive natural numbers.

5   Experiments

We describe an experimental evaluation of our kinetic 3D convex-hull algorithm. The evaluation investigates the effectiveness of our approach according to a number of metrics proposed in the previous work [BGH99], i.e., responsiveness, efficiency, locality, and compactness. Following that, we report timing results for the integrated dynamic and kinetic experiments.

Experimental Setup. All of the experiments were performed on a 2.66Ghz dual-core Xeon machine, with 8 GB of memory, running Ubuntu Linux 7.10. We compiled the applications with the MLton compiler [MLt, Wee06] with the option "-runtime ram-slop 0.75," directing the run-time system to allocate at most 75% of system memory. Our timings measure the wall-clock time (in seconds).

Input Generation. In our experiments, we pick the initial positions of the points on each axis to fit into 20 bits, i.e., $B_\ell = 20$, and the velocity along each axis to fit into 8 bits, i.e, $B_v = 8$. We pick both the initial locations and the velocities uniformly randomly from the cube $[-1.0, 1.0]^3$. We perform motion simulations on lattice defined by $\delta = 2^{-10}$, with a maximum time of $M_t = 2^{27}$. With this setting, we process an average of about two certificates simultaneously.

Checking for robustness. We check that our algorithm simulates motion robustly by comparing it to our exact static algorithm after each event in the

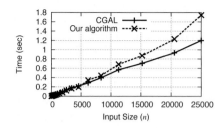

Fig. 2. Static algorithms compared

	CGAL		Our Algorithm	
Input	#	Total	#	Total
Size	Events	Time (s)	Events	Time (s)
22	357	13.42	71	2.66
49	1501	152.41	151	11.80
73	2374	391.31	218	23.42
109	4662	1270.24	316	40.37
163	7842	3552.48	380	70.74
244	15309	12170.08	513	125.16

Fig. 3. Simulations compared

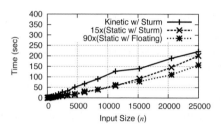

Fig. 4. Kinetic and static runs

kinetic simulation. When the inputs are large (more than 1000 points), we check the output at randomly selected events (with varying probabilities between 1 and 20%) to save time.

Baseline Comparison. To assess the efficiency of the static version of our algorithm, we compare it to CGAL 3.3's implementation of the incremental convex-hull algorithm. Figure 2 shows the timings for our static algorithm and for the CGAL implementation with the `Homogeneous<double>` kernel. Inputs to the algorithms are generated by sampling from the same distribution; the reported numbers averaged over three runs. Our implementation is about 30% slower than CGAL's. Implementation details or our use of a high-level, garbage-collected language may be causing this difference.

We also want to compare our kinetic implementation with an existing kinetic implementation capable of computing 3D convex hulls. Since there is no direct implementation for kinetic 3D convex hulls, we compare our implementation with CGAL's kinetic 3D Delaunay-triangulation implementation, which computes the convex hull as part of the triangulation. Figure 3 shows the timings for our algorithm and for CGAL's implementation of kinetic 3D Delaunay (using the `Exact_simulation_traits` traits).These experiments are run until the event queue is empty. As expected, the experiments show that kinetic Delaunay processes many more events than necessary for computing convex hulls.

Kinetic motion simulation. To perform a motion simulation, we first run our kinetic algorithm on the given input at time $t = 0$, which we refer to as the *initial run*. This computes the certificates and inserts them into the priority queue of the motion scheduler. Figure 4 illustrates the running time for the initial run of the kinetic algorithm compared to that of our static algorithm which does not create certificates. Timings show a factor of about 15 gap between the kinetic algorithm (using Sturm sequences) and the static algorithm that uses exact arithmetic. The static algorithm runs by a factor of 6 slower when it uses exact arithmetic compared to using floating-point arithmetic. These experiments indicate that the overheads of initializing the kinetic simulations is moderately high: more than an order of magnitude over the static algorithm with exact arithmetic and almost two orders of magnitude over the the static algorithm with floating-point arithmetic. This is due to both the cost of creating certificates and to the overhead of maintaining the dependence structures used by the change propagation algorithm.

After completing the initial run, we are ready to perform the motion simulation. One measure of the effectiveness of the motion simulation is the average time for a kinetic event, calculated as the total time for the simulation divided by the number of events. Figure 5 shows the average times for a kinetic event when we use our δ-precision root solver. These averages are for the first $5 \cdot n$ events on an input size of n. The average time per kinetic event appears asymptotically bounded by the logarithm of the input size. A kinetic structure is said to be *responsive* if the cost per kinetic event is small, usually in the worst case. Although our experiments do not indicate responsiveness in the worst case, they do indicate responsiveness in the average case.

One concern with motion simulation with kinetic data structures is that the overhead of computing the roots can exceed the speedup that we may hope to obtain by performing efficient updates. This does *not* appear to be the case in our system. Figure 6 shows the speedup for a kinetic event, computed as the time for change propagation divided by the time for a from-scratch execution of the static algorithm using our solver.

In many cases, we also want to be able to insert and remove points or change the motion parameters during the motion simulation. This is naturally supported in our system, because self-adjusting computations can respond to any combination of changes to their data. We perform the following experiment to study the effectiveness of our approach at supporting these *integrated changes*. During the motion simulation, at every event, the motion function of an input point is updated from $r(t)$ to $\frac{3}{4}r(t)$. We update these points in the order they appear in the input, ensuring that every point is updated at least once. From this

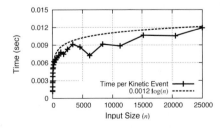

Fig. 5. Time per kinetic event

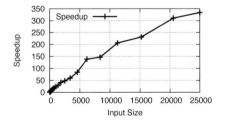

Fig. 6. Speedup for a kinetic event

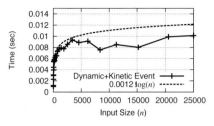
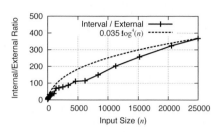

Fig. 7. Time per integrated event   **Fig. 8.** Interval/external events

experiment, we report the average time per integrated event, calculated by dividing the total time to the number of events. Figure 7 shows the average time per integrated event for different input sizes. The time per integrated event appears asymptotically bounded by the logarithm of the input size and are similar to those for kinetic events only. A kinetic structure is said to have good *locality* if the number of certificates a point is involved in is small. We note that the time for a dynamic change is directly affected by the number of certificates it is involved in. Again, although our experiments do not indicate good locality in the worst case, they do indicate good locality averaged across points.

In a kinetic simulation, we say that an event is *internal* if it does not cause the output to change. Similarly, we say that an event is *external* if it causes the output to change. A kinetic algorithm is said to be *efficient* if the ratio of interval events to external events is small. Figure 8 shows this ratio in complete simulations with out algorithm. The ratio can be reasonably large but appears to grow sublinearly.

Another measure of the effectiveness of a kinetic motion simulation is *compactness*, which is a measure of the total number of certificates that are live at any time. Since our implementation uses change-propagation to update the computation when a certificate fails, it guarantees that the total number of certificates is equal to the number of certifi-

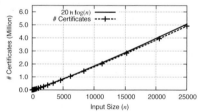

Fig. 9. Number of certificates

cates created by a from-scratch execution at the current position of the points. Figure 9 shows the total number of certificates created by a from-scratch run of the algorithm with the initial positions. The number of certificates appears to be bounded by $O(n \log n)$.

6   Conclusion

We present a technique for robust motion simulation based on a hybrid of kinetic event scheduling and fixed-time sampling. The idea behind the approach is to partition the time line into a lattice of intervals and perform motion simulation at the resolution of an interval by processing the events in the same interval

altogether, regardless of their relative order. To separate roots to the resolution
of intervals, we use Sturm sequences in a similar way as used for exact separation
of roots in previous work, but the fixed resolution allows us to stop the process
early. The approach critically relies on self-adjusting computation, which enables
processing multiple events simultaneously. Although the hybrid technique using
kinetic-event-scheduling and fixed-time sampling was primarily motivated by
robustness issues, it may also be helpful in situations where explicit motion
prediction is difficult [AGE+02].

We apply the approach to the problem of kinetic convex hulls in 3D by kine-
tizing a version of the incremental convex-hull algorithm via self-adjusting computation. We implement the motion simulator and the algorithm and perform an
experimental evaluation. Our experiments show that our algorithm is effective
in practice: we are able to run efficient robust simulations involving thousands
of points. Our experiments also indicate that the data structure can respond to
a kinetic event, as well as an integrated dynamic change (an insertion/deletion
during motion simulation) in logarithmic time in the size of the input. To the
best of our knowledge, this is the first implementation of kinetic 3D convex hulls
that can guarantee robustness and efficiency for reasonably large input sizes.

References

[AAB08]   Acar, U.A., Ahmed, A., Blume, M.: Imperative self-adjusting computation.
             In: Proceedings of the 25th Annual ACM Symposium on Principles of
             Programming Languages (POPL) (2008)
[AAdBY06]   Abam, M.A., Agarwal, P.K., de Berg, M., Yu, H.: Out-of-order event
             processing in kinetic data structures. In: Azar, Y., Erlebach, T. (eds.) ESA
             2006. LNCS, vol. 4168, pp. 624–635. Springer, Heidelberg (2006)
[ABBT06]   Acar, U.A., Blelloch, G.E., Blume, M., Tangwongsan, K.: An experimental
             analysis of self-adjusting computation. In: Proceedings of the ACM SIG-
             PLAN Conference on Programming Language Design and Implementation
             (2006)
[ABD07]   Acar, U.A., Blume, M., Donham, J.: A consistent semantics of self-
             adjusting computation. In: De Nicola, R. (ed.) ESOP 2007. LNCS,
             vol. 4421, pp. 458–474. Springer, Heidelberg (2007)
[ABH+04]   Acar, U.A., Blelloch, G.E., Harper, R., Vittes, J.L., Woo, M.: Dynamizing
             static algorithms with applications to dynamic trees and history indepen-
             dence. In: ACM-SIAM Symposium on Discrete Algorithms (SODA) (2004)
[ABTV06]   Acar, U.A., Blelloch, G.E., Tangwongsan, K., Vittes, J.L.: Kinetic algo-
             rithms via self-adjusting computation. In: Azar, Y., Erlebach, T. (eds.)
             ESA 2006. LNCS, vol. 4168, pp. 636–647. Springer, Heidelberg (2006)
[Aca05]   Acar, U.A.: Self-Adjusting Computation. PhD thesis, Department of Com-
             puter Science, Carnegie Mellon University (May 2005)
[AGE+02]   Agarwal, P.K., Guibas, L.J., Edelsbrunner, H., Erickson, J., Isard, M.,
             Har-Peled, S., Hershberger, J., Jensen, C., Kavraki, L., Koehl, P., Lin, M.,
             Manocha, D., Metaxas, D., Mirtich, B., Mount, D., Muthukrishnan, S.,
             Pai, D., Sacks, E., Snoeyink, J., Suri, S., Wolefson, O.: Algorithmic issues
             in modeling motion. ACM Comput. Surv. 34(4), 550–572 (2002)

[AH06]   Acar, U.A., Hudson, B.: Optimal-time dynamic mesh refinement: prelimi-
          nary results. In: Proceedings of the 16th Annual Fall Workshop on Com-
          putational Geometry (2006)
[BDH96]   Barber, C.B., Dobkin, D.P., Huhdanpaa, H.: The quickhull algorithm for
          convex hulls. ACM Trans. Math. Softw. 22(4), 469–483 (1996)
[BGH99]   Basch, J., Guibas, L.J., Hershberger, J.: Data structures for mobile data.
          Journal of Algorithms 31(1), 1–28 (1999)
[Boa07]   CGAL Editorial Board. CGAL User and Reference Manual, 3.3 edn. (2007)
[CS89]   Clarkson, K.L., Shor, P.W.: Applications of random sampling in computa-
          tional geometry, II. Discrete and Computational Geometry 4(1), 387–421
          (1989)
[GK99]   Guibas, L.J., Karavelas, M.I.: Interval methods for kinetic simulations. In:
          SCG 1999: Proceedings of the fifteenth annual symposium on Computa-
          tional geometry, pp. 255–264. ACM Press, New York (1999)
[GR04]   Guibas, L., Russel, D.: An empirical comparison of techniques for updating
          delaunay triangulations. In: SCG 2004: Proceedings of the twentieth annual
          symposium on Computational geometry, pp. 170–179. ACM Press, New
          York (2004)
[Gui98]   Guibas, L.J.: Kinetic data structures: a state of the art report. In: WAFR
          1998: Proceedings of the third workshop on the algorithmic foundations of
          robotics on Robotics: the algorithmic perspective, Natick, MA, USA, pp.
          191–209. A. K. Peters, Ltd (1998)
[Gui04]   Guibas, L.: Modeling motion. In: Goodman, J., O'Rourke, J. (eds.) Hand-
          book of Discrete and Computational Geometry, 2nd edn., pp. 1117–1134.
          Chapman and Hall/CRC (2004)
[MLt]   MLton
[MR95]   Motwani, R., Raghavan, P.: Randomized Algorithms. Cambridge Univer-
          sity Press, Cambridge (1995)
[RKG07]   Russel, D., Karavelas, M.I., Guibas, L.J.: A package for exact kinetic data
          structures and sweepline algorithms. Comput. Geom. Theory Appl. 38(1-
          2), 111–127 (2007)
[Rus07]   Ruseel, D.: Kinetic Data Structures in Practice. PhD thesis, Department
          of Computer Science, Stanford University (March 2007)
[Wee06]   Weeks, S.: Whole-Program Compilation in Mlton. In: ML 2006: Proceed-
          ings of the 2006 workshop on ML, p. 1. ACM, New York (2006)

On Dominance Reporting in 3D

Peyman Afshani

School of Computer Science
University of Waterloo
Waterloo, Ontario, N2L 3G1, Canada
pafshani@uwaterloo.ca

Abstract. In this paper, we study the 3D dominance reporting problem in different models of computations and offer optimal results in the pointer machine and the external memory models and a near optimal result in the RAM model; all our results consume linear space. We can answer queries in $O(\log n + k)$ time on a pointer machine, with $O(\log_B n + k/B)$ I/Os in the external memory model and in $O((\log \log n)^2 + \log \log U + k)$ time in the RAM model and in a $U \times U \times U$ integer grid. These improve the results of various papers, such as Makris and Tsakalidis (IPL'98), Vengroff and Vitter (STOC'96) and Nekrich (SOCG'07). Here, n, k and B are the input, output and block size respectively. With a $\log^3 n$ fold increase in the space complexity these can be turned into orthogonal range reporting algorithms with matching query times, improving the previous orthogonal range searching results in the pointer machine and RAM models. Using our 3D results as base cases, we can provide improved orthogonal range reporting algorithms in $\mathbb{R}^d$, $d \geq 4$. We use randomization only in the pre-processing part and our query bounds are all worst case.

1 Introduction

Let P be a set of n points in $\mathbb{R}^d$. In the dominance reporting problem we are given a query point $q = (q_1, \ldots, q_d)$ and we are asked to find all the points $p = (x_1, \ldots, x_d) \in P$ such that $x_i < q_i$, $1 \leq i \leq d$. Dominance reporting is one of the important problems in the orthogonal range searching area; it emerges naturally when studying various problems regarding orthogonal objects [1], it is an important special case of orthogonal range searching (which has been studied extensively, see [2,3,4,5]) and many times it is used as a basis of various orthogonal range searching algorithms [6,7,8].

Previous results. Previously, in the pointer machine model, we were quite close to the optimal answer. Makris and Tsakalidis [9] had shown it is possible to achieve the query time of $O(\log n \log \log n + k)$ with linear space, improving an old result from 1987 [10] (here, n and k are the input size and output size respectively). Also in the same paper [9], they achieve the query time of $O((\log \log U)^2 \log \log \log U + k \log \log U)$ in the RAM model and with linear space (for points in a $U \times U \times U$ integer grid). Further results in the RAM model include an algorithm with linear space and query time of $O(\frac{\log n}{\log \log n} + k)$ [11] assuming integer inputs. However,

D. Halperin and K. Mehlhorn (Eds.): ESA 2008, LNCS 5193, pp. 41–51, 2008.

Table 1. Results on 3D dominance reporting problem. Here, n, k, B are input, output and block size respectively. The results in RAM assume the input is from a $U \times U \times U$ integer grid. Optimal query complexities are marked with a star. The last two rows assume an external memory model of computation in the RAM model where the input is on a $U \times U \times U$ integer grid.

Model	Space	Query complexity	Source
pointer machine	$O(n)$	$O(\log n \log \log n + k)$	[9]
pointer machine	$O(n \log n)$	$O(\log n + k)^*$	[10]
pointer machine	$O(n)$	$O(\log n + k)^*$	this paper
RAM	$O(n)$	$O((\log \log U)^2 \log \log \log U + k \log \log U)$	[9]
RAM	$O(n)$	$O(\frac{\log n}{\log \log n} + k)$	[11]
RAM	$O(n \log n)$	$O((\log \log n)^2 + \log \log U + k)$	[6]
RAM	$O(n)$	$O((\log \log n)^2 + \log \log U + k)$	this paper
external memory	$O(n \log n)$	$O(\log_B n + k/B)^*$	[8]
external memory	$O(n)$	$O(\log_B n + k/B)^*$	this paper
EM & integer grid	$O(n \log n)$	$O(\log \log_B U + (\log \log n)^2 + k/B)$	[13]
EM & integer grid	$O(n \log_B n)$	$O(\log \log_B U + (\log \log n)^2 + k/B)$	this paper

these are not the fastest data structures, since if we allow $O(n \log n)$ space we can achieve the query time of $O((\log \log n)^2 + \log \log U + k)$ [6]. In the external memory model, there are much fewer results and it is believed that solving such orthogonal range reporting problems in this model is more difficult than the main memory model [7]. Currently, the best algorithm in the traditional external memory model uses $O(n \log n)$ space and can answer queries with optimal $O(\log_B n + k/B)$ I/Os [8,12] (here B is the block size). Very recently, Nekrich has proposed another algorithm using $O(n \log_B n)$ space which can answer rectangular point location queries in a $U \times U$ grid with $O(\log \log_B U + (\log \log n)^2)$ I/Os [13]. Using this, he provides another dominance reporting algorithm with $O(n \log n)$ space and $O(\log \log_B U + (\log \log n)^2 + k/B)$ query I/Os.

Our results. In this paper we solve the 3D dominance reporting problem in pointer machine and external memory models and match the fast $O((\log \log n)^2 + \log \log U + k)$ query time of Nekrich [6] with a linear space algorithm. In essence, our techniques allow us to reduce the dominance reporting problem to point location in planar rectilinear arrangements. For instance, this enables us to use the new point location data structure of Nekrich [13] as black box and obtain another algorithm using $O(n \log_B n)$ space and with $O(\log \log_B U + (\log \log n)^2 + k/B)$ query I/Os, assuming the input is a subset of $U \times U \times U$ integer grid.

A summary of our results in comparison with the previous work is shown in Table 1. Using our efficient dominance reporting algorithms as base cases we can obtain new algorithms for orthogonal range reporting in the RAM model. These improvements have been listed in Table 2.

Unlike some previous algorithms, our methods use many common ideas and techniques with the other important cases of range searching, namely halfspace

Table 2. The fastest known orthogonal range reporting algorithms for $d \geq 3$. Here, n, k, B are input, output and block size respectively.

Model	Dimension	Space	Query complexity	Source
RAM	$d = 3$	$O(n \log^4 n)$	$O((\log \log n)^2 + \log \log U + k)$	[6]
RAM	$d = 3$	$O(n \log^3 n)$	$O((\log \log n)^2 + \log \log U + k)$	this paper
RAM	$d > 3$	$O(n \log^{d+1+\varepsilon} n)$	$O(\log^{d-3} n/(\log \log n)^{d-5} + k)$	[6]
RAM	$d > 3$	$O(n \log^{d-2+\varepsilon} n)$	$O(\log^{d-2} n/(\log \log n)^{d-2} + k)$	[4]
RAM	$d > 3$	$O(n \log^{d+\varepsilon} n)$	$O(\log^{d-3} n/(\log \log n)^{d-5} + k)$	this paper
external memory	$d = 3$	$O(n \log^4 n)$	$O(\log_B n + k/B)$	[8]
external memory	$d = 3$	$O(n \log^3 n)$	$O(\log_B n + k/B)$	this paper

and simplicial range searching. In fact, an underlying implication of our techniques is that both halfspace range reporting and dominance reporting in 3D can be attacked within the same framework and using the same array of techniques and tools. We believe this is one of the important contributions of our paper since apparently this had eluded the previous researchers. For instance, we use the shallow cutting lemma provided by Agarwal et al. [14] for a general class of surfaces (which is inspired by Matoušek's shallow cutting lemma for halfspaces [15]) and observe that it leads to approximate levels of optimal size. A concept similar to approximate levels was previously employed by Vengroff and Vitter [8] and later by Nekrich [6] but only under the name of B-approximate boundaries and with non-optimal and complicated constructions.

Given this, one might wonder whether other fundamental theorems of halfspace or simplicial range searching such as the shallow partition theorem can also be proven in this context. We do not investigate these questions and for two reasons (aside from being outside the scope of this paper). First, as we noted, the latter challenge has already been undertaken by Agarwal et al. [14] and second, we show the existence of a novel partition type theorem (it is not a partition per se and only resembles the partition theorem in "spirit") for the dominance reporting problem; unfortunately (or fortunately) our proof technique neither is inspired nor resembles the original shallow partition theorem. Nonetheless, this theorem seems to be stronger than an analogous of the shallow partition theorem for the dominance reporting problem since it leads to an optimal external memory data structure (fortunately). A similar result for the halfspace range reporting problem has not been obtained yet [16].

As a consequence of our results, we can obtain two orthogonal range reporting algorithms consuming $O(n \log^3 n)$ space; one with $O((\log \log n)^2 + \log \log U + k)$ query time in the RAM model and another with $O(\log_B n + k/B)$ I/Os in the external memory model. Previously, best results consumed $O(n \log^4 n)$ space in both cases. We only use randomization in the preprocessing part and our query bounds are all worst case.

2 Preliminaries

For two points A and B in $\mathbb{R}^d$, we say A *dominates* B if and only if all the coordinates of A are greater than those of B. In this paper, we shall deal with a special form of geometric ranges that we call a *downward corner*, which is uniquely determined by a point $A \in \mathbb{R}^d$ (called *apex*) and contains all the points of $\mathbb{R}^d$ which are dominated by A. Let P be a set of n points in $\mathbb{R}^d$. To make the notation consistent, we will reserve $\mathbf{r}$ for downward corners and with an abuse of notation, sometimes we will use $\mathbf{r}$ to refer both to the geometric object and the subset of P inside the geometric object. We define an *approximate k-level* $\mathcal{L}_k$ as a set of downward corners with the following two properties: (i) any downward corner $\mathbf{r} \in \mathcal{L}_k$ must contain at most $c_1 k$ points of P and (ii) any downward corner $\mathbf{r}'$ which contains at most k points of P must be contained in a downward corner $\mathbf{r} \in \mathcal{L}_k$. Here, c_1 can be chosen to be an arbitrary constant (by our algorithms). The size of an approximate level is the number of its downward corners. For a set S of geometric objects, we will use the shorthand notation of S_x to refer to the subset of S intersecting another geometric object x. Finally, for the sake of simplicity of description, we assume the input point set and the query points are in general position; a restriction that can be overcome using standard tricks.

3 Optimal Approximate Levels

We define the level of a point $p \in \mathbb{R}^3$ to be the number of downward corners of S which contain p. As with the case of halfspaces, we define the $(\leq k)$-level to be the set of all the vertices the arrangement $\mathscr{A}$ formed by S with level at most k. Thus, the (≤ 0)-level of $\mathscr{A}$ contains all the vertices of the arrangement that are not inside any downward corner of S.

One crucial requirement of any optimal lemma on approximate levels is a linear bound on the size of the (≤ 0)-level of the arrangement formed by the set of geometric objects.

Lemma 1. *For a set S of n downward corners the size of the (≤ 0)-level is $O(n)$.*

Proof. Sweep a plane h parallel to the xy plane from $z = +\infty$ to $z = -\infty$. We will count the vertices of the (≤ 0)-level of the arrangement as they appear on this sweep plane.

The apex A of an element $\mathbf{r} \in S$ will appear on h when the z-coordinate of h becomes equal to the z-coordinate of A and it will disappear as soon as another point q' on h dominates A (in 2D sense). The crucial observation is that if a point disappears from h it no longer can contribute any new vertices to the (≤ 0)-level (Fig. 1(a,b,c)). So, at any moment we have an active set of downward corners on this plane with none dominating another; these points form a chain on this plane (Fig. 1(d)). Assume a new point c_{t+1} appears on this plane. If c_{t+1} creates j new vertices then it will have to dominate and remove $\Omega(j-4)$ active points from h (Fig. 1(c,e)). A simple charging argument implies that number of vertices of the (≤ 0)-level is $O(n)$. $\square$

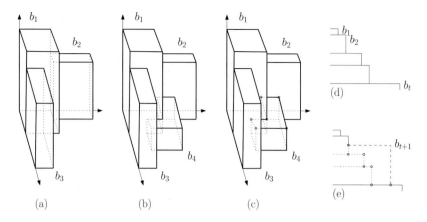

Fig. 1. (a) Boxes b_1, b_2 and b_3 already swept (b) Sweep plane discovers b_4 and from this point b_1 can be ignored. (c) Marks denote the new vertices on the 0-level. (d,e) View on plane h.

The shallow cutting lemma of Agarwal et al. [14] operates on a general class of surfaces and thus accepts a parameter $\phi(r)$ which is the worst case size of the (≤ 0)-level of any collection of r surfaces. The above lemma implies in our problem we have $\phi(r) = O(r)$. Combining this with the theorem of Agarwal et al. [14] we obtain the following lemma.

Lemma 2. *Given a set S of n downward corners in 3D and a parameter k, one can build a set $\mathcal{B}$ of $O\left(\frac{n}{k}\right)$ boxes which cover the ($\leq k$)-level of the arrangement formed by S where each box is intersected by $O(k)$ downward corners.*

Proof. With slight perturbations we can turn a downward corner into a continuous surface which fits the framework of Agarwal et al. [14] and use their shallow cutting lemma with $r = \frac{n}{k}$. The fact that the set $\mathcal{B}$ can be taken as a set of boxes follows from the vertical decomposition used by Agarwal et al. [14]. The source of randomness is the sampling technique used in the same paper.   □

The above shallow cutting result can be used to construct approximate levels.

Lemma 3. *There exists approximate k-levels of size $O(\frac{n}{k})$, $1 \leq k \leq n$, for the dominance reporting problem.*

Proof. Let P be an input set of size n. For a point $p \in \mathbb{R}^3$, define an *upward corner with apex p* to be the subset of $\mathbb{R}^3$ which dominates p. Let S be the set of n upward corners determined by points of P as apexes and let $\mathscr{A}$ be the arrangement formed by S. A point reflection with origin can transform $\mathscr{A}$ into an arrangement of n downward corners, A', and thus we can use Lemma 2 and build a collection $\mathcal{B}'$ of $O(\frac{n}{k})$ boxes which cover the ($\leq k$)-level of $\mathscr{A}'$. Perform the point reflection on elements of $\mathcal{B}'$ and let $\mathcal{B}$ be the resulting set of boxes. For every box in $b \in \mathcal{B}$, place the vertex with the maximum coordinates, denoted with $m(b)$, in a set C. We claim the set of downward corners defined by apexes in C is an approximate level.

Consider a downward corner r with apex A which contains less than k points of P. This means that there are less than k upward corners of S which contain A. The reflection A' of A by the origin lies in the $(\leq k)$-level of $\mathscr{A}'$ and thus there is a box $b \in \mathcal{B}$ which contains A. The downward corner defined by $m(b) \in C$ contains r.

On the other hand, Lemma 2 implies every box $b' \in \mathcal{B}'$ lies in the $(\leq O(k))$-level of $\mathscr{A}'$. Thus, every vertex of $b \in \mathcal{B}$ can dominate at most $O(k)$ vertices of P.   □

Remarks. Agarwal et al. [14] do not discuss the construction time of their general shallow cutting theorem. Unfortunately, to achieve a decent bound on the construction time we will need to deal with the details of their construction which we feel would be distracting, despite the fact that for our set of ranges it is possible to simplify their argument. We postpone the details for the full version of the paper (simply claim a polynomial bound here) but it can be seen that we can employ the techniques used by Ramos [17] and build the cutting in a gradual fashion (similar to the case for halfspaces) in $O(n \log n)$ expected time.

4   Solving the Dominance Reporting Problem

To solve the dominance reporting in the RAM and pointer machine we simply need a linear size data structure with polylogarithmic query time to combine it with our lemma on approximate levels. For instance, we can either use the data structure of Makris and Tsakalidis [9] or Eledsbrunner and Chazelle [10]. For the moment assume that we have access to a linear size data structure with $O(\log^2 n + k)$ query time.

Theorem 1. *Given a set of n points P in $\mathbb{R}^3$, dominance reporting queries can be answered in $O(\log n + k)$ worst case time in a pointer machine and using linear space.*

Proof. Let $\mathcal{A}$ be a data structure consuming linear space which can answer dominance reporting queries in $O(\log^2 n + k)$ time. Build an approximate $\log^2 n$-level C. For every downward corner $r \in C$ implement the data structure $\mathcal{A}$ on the points contained in r and at the end build on extra copy for the whole point set P.

If $k = \Omega(\log^2 n)$ then we can use the data structure on P to answer the query in $O(\log^2 n + k) = O(k)$ time. Otherwise, one downward corner r in C will contain q. Finding q is known to be equivalent to a point location query in a 2D orthogonal arrangement [9,6] and thus can be solved in $O(\log n)$ time. Since r will contain at most $\log^2 n$ points, the query can be answered in $O((\log \log^2 n)^2 + k) = O((\log \log n)^2 + k)$ time using the data structure implemented on r. Combining all these results in a query time of $O(\log n + k)$.   □

The exact same idea can be applied in the RAM model, by employing the point location data structure of [18] which offers the query time of $O((\log \log U)^2)$ in a $U \times U \times U$ integer grid.

Theorem 2. *Given n points in $U \times U \times U$ integer grid, dominance reporting queries can be answered in $O((\log \log U)^2 + k)$ worst case time in the RAM model using linear space.*

Reduction to the rank space and predecessor search are common techniques and tools which have appeared in many places (e.g., see [4] for more references and details) and they allow us obtain the following results.

Corollary 1. *For n points in $\mathbb{R}^3$, dominance reporting queries can be answered in $O((\log \log n)^2 + \log \log U + k)$ time using only linear space.*

Also, by using standard techniques to reduce orthogonal range reporting queries to dominance reporting queries (e.g., see [6,8]) we can have the following.

Corollary 2. *There exists a data structure capable of answering 3D orthogonal range reporting queries on a $U \times U \times U$ grid in $O((\log \log n)^2 + \log \log U + k)$ time, using $O(n \log^3 n)$ space.*

The above can be extended to higher dimensions [4].

Corollary 3. *There exists a data structure capable of answering orthogonal range reporting queries in $\mathbb{R}^d$ using $O(n \log^{d+\varepsilon} n)$ space and with $O(\log^{d-3} n/ (\log \log n)^{d-5} + k)$ query time.*

We also note that any improvements to the data structure for point location in a planar rectangular subdivision [18] can be carried over automatically to the dominance reporting problem and thus all the above corollaries.

Unfortunately, we cannot do the same trick to obtain an optimal algorithm in the external memory model, since in this model, up to our knowledge, there is no linear space algorithm with reasonable query time to combine with our approximate levels. Thus, to get an optimal algorithm in the external memory model, we need to develop additional tools and ideas. This is done in the next section.

5   The External Memory Model

We use B to denote the block size in the external memory model. As we claimed in the introduction, our result on approximate levels can simplify the data structure of Vengroff and Vitter [12] by building a hierarchy of approximate levels. Of course, the space consumption would still be more than linear. To reduce the space complexity, we will need the following lemma.

Lemma 4. *Let $P \subset \mathbb{R}^3$ be a set of n points such that the level of each point is at most m for a parameter m. We can find $t = O(\frac{n}{m})$ sets, $V_1, \ldots, V_t \subset P$, $|V_i| = O(m)$ such that for any downward corner $\mathbf{r}$ containing k points there exist $s = O(\frac{k}{m})$ sets $V_{t_1}, \ldots, V_{t_s}$ with $|P_\mathbf{r} \setminus (\bigcup_{i=1}^s V_{t_i})| = O(m)$ in which $P_\mathbf{r} = P \cap \mathbf{r}$.*

Proof. Let $\mathcal{C} = \{\mathbf{r}_1, \ldots, \mathbf{r}_t\}$ be an approximate Cm-level for a constant C to be determined later. With a slight abuse of the notation, we will use $\mathbf{r}_i$ to refer to both the downward corner $\mathbf{r}_i$ and the subset of P contained in $\mathbf{r}_i$. We claim $\mathbf{r}_1, \ldots, \mathbf{r}_t$ are the sets claimed in the lemma. By Lemma 3 we know $t = O(\frac{n}{m})$.

Consider a downward corner $\mathbf{r}$ containing k points. According to Lemma 3, we can find an approximate m-level, $\mathcal{C}' = \{\mathbf{r}'_1, \ldots, \mathbf{r}'_t\}$, of size $t' = O(\frac{k}{m})$ for the points inside $\mathbf{r}$. By definition, $\mathcal{C}'$ covers the $(\leq m)$-level of $P_\mathbf{r}$ and so every point of $P_\mathbf{r}$ is contained in at least one downward corner of $\mathcal{C}'$. Thus, $P_\mathbf{r} = \bigcup_{i=1}^{t'} \mathbf{r}'_i$. If we could show that for every $\mathbf{r}'_i \in \mathcal{C}'$ there is another downward corner $\mathbf{r}_j \in \mathcal{C}$ which contains $\mathbf{r}'_i$, then our lemma could be easily solved. Unfortunately this is not true and in fact, $\mathbf{r}'_i$ may contain $\Omega(n)$ points of P (although it can only contain $O(m)$ points of $P_\mathbf{r}$). Because of this we aim for a slightly weaker claim.

Let (x, y, z) be the coordinates of the apex A of $\mathbf{r}$ and (x', y', z') be the coordinates of the apex A'_i of $\mathbf{r}'_i$. By Lemma 3 we know each $\mathbf{r}'_i$ contains $O(m)$ points; assume the constant in the O notation is c. Pick $C > c$. We have four important cases:

1. A dominates A'_i (Fig. 2(a)): In this case $\mathbf{r}'_i$ contains at most Cm points of P and is contained in at least one downward corner $\mathbf{r}_i \in \mathcal{C}$. Thus, in this case $\mathbf{r}'_i \subset \mathbf{r}_i$.
2. Only one coordinate of A'_i is not dominated by that of A (Fig. 2(b)): Without loss of generality assume it is the x-coordinate (i.e., $x < x', y > y'$ and $z > z'$). In this case, the point $Q = (x, y', z')$ is contained in $\mathbf{r}$ and thus dominates at most Cm points of P which means Q is contained in at least one downward corner $\mathbf{r}_i \in \mathcal{C}$. Thus, in this case $\mathbf{r}'_i \cap \mathbf{r} \subset \mathbf{r}_i$.
3. Only one coordinate of A dominates that of A'_i (Fig. 2(c)): This case can only happen for three elements of $\mathcal{C}'$, once for each coordinate; for instance, if $x' > x$ and $z' > z$, then $\mathbf{r}'_i$ contains at most Cm points with minimum y-coordinates in $P_\mathbf{r}$.
4. A'_i dominates A. This case can only happen if $P_\mathbf{r}$ contains less than Cm points.

For every downward corner $\mathbf{r}'_i \in \mathcal{C}'$, the first two cases provide us with another downward corner $\mathbf{r}_i \in \mathcal{C}$ such that $\mathbf{r}'_i \cap \mathbf{r} \subset \mathbf{r}_i$. The other two cases only cover

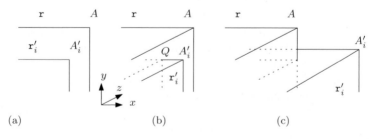

(a)　　　　　　　　　(b)　　　　　　　　　(c)

Fig. 2. (a) $\mathbf{r}'_i$ is contained inside $\mathbf{r}$. (b) Only the x-coordinate of A'_i is greater than that of A. (c) Two coordinates of A'_i are greater than those of A.

$O(m)$ points. Thus, we can find at most t' downward corners $\mathbf{r}_1, \ldots \mathbf{r}_{t''}, \in \mathcal{C}$ such that $|P_{\mathbf{r}} \setminus (\cup_{i=1}^{t''} \mathbf{r}_{t_i})| = O(m)$ with $t'' = O(k/m)$.   □

Remarks. The closest theorem in the context of the halfspace range searching to the above lemma is the shallow partition theorem by Matoušek [15]; however, the above lemma does not partition the point set and does not cover all the points inside the downward corner $\mathbf{r}$. Also, it can be viewed as "output sensitive" in the sense that the number of sets contained or intersected by $\mathbf{r}$ depends on the number of points, k, contained in $\mathbf{r}$. It has been observed that such dependence on k is a desirable property [19]. Thus, an interesting question is whether it is possible to obtain a similar result for halfspace range searching; if so, we can also obtain an optimal halfspace range searching data structure in the external memory model.

Lemma 5. *There is a data structure for a set P of n points in $\mathbb{R}^3$ which can answer dominance reporting queries with $O(\log_B n + k/B)$ I/Os using $O(n)$ space.*

Proof. Partition P into subsets $P_1, \ldots, P_r$ in the following way: define P_1 to be the set of points $p \in P$ with level at most $B \log_B n$, remove P_1 and repeat and continue this operation until P is partitioned. This construction ensures that every point $p \in P_i$ has level at most $O(B \log_B n)$ in P_i.

Assume for every P_i we have a data structure which uses $O(|P_i|)$ space and can answer queries with $O(\log_B |P_i| + k/B)$ I/Os. Given a query $\mathbf{r}$, we start from P_1 and using the data structure implemented on P_1 we return all the points of P_1 inside $\mathbf{r}$ and then move on to the next set P_2 and continue this until we reach a point set P_i which does not contain any point in $\mathbf{r}$; at this point we terminate the search. The crucial observation is that if $\mathbf{r}$ contains at least one point from P_{i+1} then it must contain at least $B \log_B n$ points from P_{i-1}. This implies $k = \Omega(iB \log_B n)$ and thus the total query complexity will add up to $O((i+1) \log_B n + k/B) = O(\log_B n + k/B)$. In short, this means that it suffices to solve the problem for point sets P in which the level of every point is at most $B \log_B n$. This will be our assumption in the rest of the proof.

Let $m = B \log_B n$. Using Lemma 4, compute $t = O(\frac{n}{m})$ sets, $V_1, \ldots, V_t$, $|V_i| = O(m)$ and store the points of each set V_i sequentially. Consider a downward corner $\mathbf{r}$ containing k points. According to Lemma 4 there are $s = O(\frac{k}{m})$ sets $V_{t_1}, \ldots, V_{t_s}$ such that $|P_{\mathbf{r}} \setminus (\cup_{i=1}^{s} V_{t_i})| = O(m)$. We can represent the points inside $\mathbf{r}$ using $O(\frac{k}{m})$ pointers to sets V_{t_i} and an additional list of $O(m)$ points. This is our storage scheme for the list of points inside a downward corner $\mathbf{r}$.

To make the data structure, we build a hierarchy of approximate k_i-levels for $k_i = 2^i m, 0 \leq i \leq O(\log(n/B))$ and we store the list of points in every downward corner of the approximate levels using our storage scheme. Every downward corner in an approximate $2^i m$-level has $O(2^i m)$ points and thus will be stored using $O(2^i)$ pointers and a list of $O(m)$ points. Since this approximate level contains $O(\frac{n}{2^i m})$ ranges, the total space consumption for this level will be $O(\frac{n}{m} + m)$. Summing this up over all the approximate levels and including the space needed to store the sets $V_1, \ldots, V_t$ yields the space complexity of

$$O\left(n + \frac{n \log(n/B)}{m} + m \log(n/B)\right).$$

A simple calculation reveals this is always $O(n)$ for all values of B.

To answer the query, we find the smallest i that a downward corner $\mathbf{r}_j$ of an approximate $2^i m$-level contains $\mathbf{r}$. This can be done with $O(i+1)$ steps of point location, once for every approximate level up to the i-th one. This will also ensure that $\mathbf{r}_j$ contains $\Theta(m2^i) = \Theta(k)$ points. The output can be determined by a linear scan of all the points in $\mathbf{r}_j$; however, we have not stored the list of points of $\mathbf{r}_j$ directly and thus we must perform $O(\frac{k}{m})$ I/Os to just access the pointers, $O(\frac{k}{B})$ I/Os to access the list of points referenced by these pointers and finally an additional $O(\frac{m}{B})$ I/Os to access the list of points stored at $\mathbf{r}_j$. This amounts to $O\left((i+1)\log_B n + \frac{k+m}{B}\right) = O(\log_B n + k/B)$ I/Os.   □

Combined with the standard reductions (e.g., see [6]), we can obtain the following corollary.

Corollary 4. *There is a data structure for a set of n points in $\mathbb{R}^3$ which that can answer orthogonal range reporting queries using $O(n \log^3 n)$ space and $O(\log_B n + k/B)$ I/Os.*

Using new point location data structure of Nekrich [13] we can also have the following result.

Corollary 5. *There is a data structure for a set of n points in $\mathbb{R}^3$ which that can answer dominance reporting queries using $O(n \log_B n)$ space and $O(\log\log_B U + (\log\log n)^2 + k/B)$ I/Os.*

The super-linear space complexity of the above corollary stems from the super-linear requirement of the point location data structure.

Acknowledgements. The author is in debt to Timothy Chan for many great suggestions, ideas and references which significantly improved the presentation of this article.

References

1. Edelsbrunner, H., Overmars, M.H.: On the equivalence of some rectangle problems. Information Processing Letters 14 (May 1982)
2. Agarwal, P.K.: Range searching. In: Goodman, J.E., O'Rourke, J. (eds.) CPC Handbook of Discrete and Computational Geometry (2004)
3. Agarwal, P.K., Erickson, J.: Geometric range searching and its relatives. In: Chazelle, B., Goodman, J.E., Pollack, R. (eds.) Advances in Discrete and Computational Geometry. AMS Press, Providence (1999)
4. Alstrup, S., Brodal, G.S., Rauhe, T.: New data structures for orthogonal range searching. In: FOCS 2000: Proceedings of the 41st annual symposium on foundations of computer science, Washington, DC, USA, p. 198. IEEE Computer Society, Los Alamitos (2000)
5. Chazelle, B.: Functional approach to data structures and its use in multidimensional searching. SIAM J. Comput. 17(3), 427–462 (1988)

6. Nekrich, Y.: A data structure for multi-dimensional range reporting. In: SCG 2007: Proceedings of the 23rd annual symposium on computational geometry, pp. 344–353. ACM, New York (2007)

7. Subramanian, S., Ramaswamy, S.: The P-range tree: a new data structure for range searching in secondary memory. In: SODA '95: Proceedings of the 6th annual ACM-SIAM symposium on Discrete algorithms, Philadelphia, PA, USA, pp. 378–387 (1995)

8. Vengroff, D.E., Vitter, J.S.: Efficient 3-D range searching in external memory. In: STOC 1996: Proceedings of the 28th annual ACM symposium on theory of computing, pp. 192–201. ACM, New York (1996)

9. Makris, C., Tsakalidis, A.: Algorithms for three-dimensional dominance searching in linear space. Inf. Process. Lett. 66(6), 277–283 (1998)

10. Chazelle, B., Edelsbrunner, H.: Linear space data structures for two types of range search. Discrete and Computational Geometry 2(1), 113, 126 (1987)

11. JaJa, J., Mortensen, C.W., Shi, Q.: Space-efficient and fast algorithms for multidimensional dominance reporting and counting. In: Fleischer, R., Trippen, G. (eds.) ISAAC 2004. LNCS, vol. 3341, pp. 558–568. Springer, Heidelberg (2004)

12. Vitter, J.S.: External memory algorithms and data structures: dealing with massive data. ACM Comput. Surv. 33(2), 209–271 (2001) (updated, 2007),
http://www.cs.duke.edu/~jsv/Papers/catalog/

13. Nekrich, Y.: I/O-efficient point location in a set of rectangles. In: Laber, E.S., Bornstein, C., Nogueira, L.T., Faria, L. (eds.) LATIN 2008. LNCS, vol. 4957, pp. 687–698. Springer, Heidelberg (2008)

14. Agarwal, P.K., Efrat, A., Sharir, M.: Vertical decomposition of shallow levels in 3-dimensional arrangements and its applications. SIAM J. Comput. 29(3), 912–953 (2000)

15. Matoušek, J.: Reporting points in halfspaces. Computational Geometry: Theory and Applications 2(3), 169–186 (1992)

16. Agarwal, P.K., Arge, L., Erickson, J., Franciosa, P.G., Vitter, J.S.: Efficient searching with linear constraints. J. Comput. Syst. Sci. 61(2), 194–216 (2000)

17. Ramos, E.A.: On range reporting, ray shooting and k-level construction. In: SCG 1999:Proceedings of the 14th Annual Symposium on Computational Geometry, pp. 390–399 (1999)

18. de Berg, M., van Kreveld, M., Snoeyink, J.: Two- and three-dimensional point location in rectangular subdivisions. J. Algorithms 18(2), 256–277 (1995)

19. Aronov, B., Har-Peled, S., Sharir, M.: On approximate halfspace range counting and relative epsilon-approximations. In: SCG 2007: Proceedings of the 23rd annual symposium on Computational geometry, pp. 327–336. ACM, New York (2007)

Stabbing Convex Polygons with a Segment or a Polygon[*]

Pankaj K. Agarwal[1], Danny Z. Chen[2], Shashidhara K. Ganjugunte[1], Ewa Misiołek[3], Micha Sharir[4], and Kai Tang[5]

[1] Dept. of Comp. Sci., Duke University, Durham, NC 27708-0129
[2] Dept. of Comp. Sci. and Engg., University of Notre Dame, Notre Dame, IN 46556
[3] Mathematics Dept., Saint Mary's College, Notre Dame, IN 46556
[4] School of Comp. Sci., Tel Aviv University, Tel Aviv 69978, and Courant Inst. of Math. Sci., NYC, NY 10012
[5] Dept. of Mech. Engg., HKUST, Hong Kong, China

Abstract. Let $\mathcal{O} = \{O_1, \ldots, O_m\}$ be a set of m convex polygons in $\mathbb{R}^2$ with a total of n vertices, and let B be another convex k-gon. A *placement* of B, any congruent copy of B (without reflection), is called *free* if B does not intersect the interior of any polygon in $\mathcal{O}$ at this placement. A placement z of B is called *critical* if B forms three "distinct" contacts with $\mathcal{O}$ at z. Let $\varphi(B, \mathcal{O})$ be the number of free critical placements. A set of placements of B is called a *stabbing set* of $\mathcal{O}$ if each polygon in $\mathcal{O}$ intersects at least one placement of B in this set.

We develop efficient Monte Carlo algorithms that compute a stabbing set of size $h = O(h^* \log m)$, with high probability, where h^* is the size of the optimal stabbing set of $\mathcal{O}$. We also improve bounds on $\varphi(B, \mathcal{O})$ for the following three cases, namely, (i) B is a line segment and the obstacles in $\mathcal{O}$ are pairwise-disjoint, (ii) B is a line segment and the obstacles in $\mathcal{O}$ may intersect (iii) B is a convex k-gon and the obstacles in $\mathcal{O}$ are disjoint, and use these improved bounds to analyze the running time of our stabbing-set algorithm.

1 Introduction

Problem statement. Let $\mathcal{O} = \{O_1, \ldots, O_m\}$ be a set of m convex polygons in $\mathbb{R}^2$ with a total of n vertices, and let B be another convex polygon. A *placement* of B is any congruent copy of B (without reflection). A set of placements of B is

---

[*] Work by P.A, S.G, and M.S, was supported by a grant from the U.S.-Israel Binational Science Foundation. Work by P.A. and S.G. was also supported by NSF under grants CNS-05-40347, CFF-06-35000, and DEB-04-25465, by ARO grants W911NF-04-1-0278 and W911NF-07-1-0376, and by an NIH grant 1P50-GM-08183-01 and by a DOE grant OEGP200A070505. Work by M.S. was partially supported by NSF Grant CCF-05-14079, by grant 155/05 from the Israel Science Fund, by a grant from the AFIRST joint French-Israeli program, and by the Hermann Minkowski–MINERVA Center for Geometry at Tel Aviv University. Work of D.C. was supported in part by the NSF under Grant CCF-0515203.

D. Halperin and K. Mehlhorn (Eds.): ESA 2008, LNCS 5193, pp. 52–63, 2008.
© Springer-Verlag Berlin Heidelberg 2008

called a *stabbing set* of $\mathcal{O}$ if each polygon in $\mathcal{O}$ intersects at least one copy of B in this set. In this paper we study the problem of computing a small-size stabbing set of $\mathcal{O}$.

Terminology. A placement of B can be represented by three real parameters $(x, y, \tan(\theta/2))$ where (x, y) is the position of a reference point o in B, and θ is the counterclockwise angle by which B is rotated from some fixed orientation. The space of all placements of B, known as the *configuration space* of B, can thus be identified with $\mathbb{R}^3$ (a more precise identification would be with $\mathbb{R}^2 \times \mathbb{S}^1$; we use the simpler, albeit topologically less accurate identification with $\mathbb{R}^3$).

For a given point $z \in \mathbb{R}^3$, we use $B[z]$ to denote the corresponding placement (congruent copy) of B. Similarly, for a point $p \in B$ or a subset $X \subseteq B$, we use $p[z]$ and $X[z]$ to denote the corresponding point and subset, respectively, in $B[z]$. A placement z of B is called *free* if $B[z]$ does not intersect the interior of any polygon in $\mathcal{O}$, and *semifree* if $B[z]$ touches the boundary of some polygon(s) in $\mathcal{O}$ but does not intersect the interior of any polygon. Let $\mathbb{F}(B, \mathcal{O}) \subseteq \mathbb{R}^3$ denote the set of all free placements of B. For $1 \leq i \leq m$, let $K_i \subseteq \mathbb{R}^3$ denote the set of placements of B at which it intersects O_i. We refer to K_i as a *c-polygon*. Set $\mathcal{K}(B, \mathcal{O}) = \{K_1, \ldots, K_m\}$. If B and the set $\mathcal{O}$ are obvious from the context, we use $\mathbb{F}$ and $\mathcal{K}$ to denote $\mathbb{F}(B, \mathcal{O})$ and $\mathcal{K}(B, \mathcal{O})$, respectively. Note that $\mathbb{F}(B, \mathcal{O}) = \mathrm{cl}(\mathbb{R}^3 \setminus \bigcup \mathcal{K}(B, \mathcal{O}))$, where cl is the closure operator. If $\{B[z_1], \ldots, B[z_h]\}$ is a stabbing set for $\mathcal{O}$, then each K_i contains at least one point in the set $\mathcal{Z} = \{z_1, \ldots, z_h\}$, i.e., $\mathcal{Z}$ is a *hitting-set* for $\mathcal{K}$. Hence, the problem of computing a small-size stabbing set of $\mathcal{O}$ reduces to computing a small-size hitting set of $\mathcal{K}$.

We use a standard greedy algorithm (see, e.g., [6]) to compute a hitting set of $\mathcal{K}$. The efficiency of our algorithm depends on the combinatorial complexity of $\mathbb{F}$, defined below. We consider the following three cases:

(C1) B is a line segment and the polygons in $\mathcal{O}$ may intersect.
(C2) B is a line segment and the polygons in $\mathcal{O}$ are pairwise disjoint.
(C3) B is a convex k-gon and the polygons in $\mathcal{O}$ are pairwise disjoint.

A *contact* C is defined to be a pair (s, w) where s is a vertex of B and w is an edge of $O \in \mathcal{O}$, or w is a vertex of O and s is an edge of B. A *double contact* is a pair of contacts, and a *triple contact* is a triple of contacts. A placement z *forms* a contact $C = (s, w)$ if $s[z]$ touches w and $B[z]$ does not intersect the interior of the polygon $O \in \mathcal{O}$ containing w. A placement z *forms* a double contact $\{C_1, C_2\}$ if it forms both the contacts C_1 and C_2, and similarly it forms a triple contact $\{C_1, C_2, C_3\}$ if it forms all three of them; we also refer to triple-contact placements as *critical*. A double (or triple) contact is *realizable* if there is a placement of B at which this contact is formed. We call a double contact $\{C_1, C_2\}$ *degenerate* if both the contacts C_1 and C_2 involve the same polygon of $\mathcal{O}$. If z forms a degenerate double contact then either a vertex of $B[z]$ touches a vertex of $\mathcal{O}$ or an edge of $B[z]$ is flush with an edge of $\mathcal{O}$. A triple contact is called *degenerate* if its three contacts involve at most two polygons of $\mathcal{O}$, i.e., if it involves a degenerate double contact. If we decompose ∂K_i into maximal connected components so that all placements within a component form the same contact(s), then the edges and vertices on ∂K_i correspond to degenerate double and triple contacts, respectively (more precisely, the vertices are those triple contacts that involve at most two polygons). A *non-degenerate* triple contact (or *critical*) placement is formed by the intersection of the boundaries of three distinct c-polygons. Using the fact that each O_i is a convex polygon and B is also a convex polygon, it can be shown (see, e.g., [11]) that the complexity of $\mathbb{F}$ is proportional to the number of semifree critical placements, which we denote by $\varphi(B, \mathcal{O})$. We use $\varphi^*(B, \mathcal{O})$ to denote the number of semifree non-degenerate critical placements. In many cases $\varphi(B, \mathcal{O})$ is proportional to $\varphi^*(B, \mathcal{O})$ but in some cases $\varphi^*(B, \mathcal{O})$ can be much smaller. We improve the bounds on $\varphi(B, \mathcal{O})$ for all three cases (C1)–(C3), and on $\varphi^*(B, \mathcal{O})$ for (C2).

Related work. The general hitting-set problem is NP-hard, and it is believed to be intractable to obtain an $o(\log n)$-approximation [7]. An $O(\log n)$-approximation can be achieved by a simple greedy algorithm [16]. The hitting-set problem remains NP-hard even in a geometric setting [12,13], and in some instances also hard to approximate [4]. However, in many cases polynomial-time algorithms with approximation factors better than $O(\log n)$ are known. For example, Hochbaum and Maass [9] devise $(1 + \varepsilon)$-approximation algorithms (for any $\varepsilon > 0$), for the problem of hitting a set of unit disks by a set of points. For set systems that typically arise in geometric problems, the approximation factor can be improved to $O(\log c^*)$, where c^* is the size of the optimal solution, and in some settings a constant factor approximation is also possible; see, e.g., [5].

Motivated by motion-planning and related problems in robotics, there is a rich body of literature on analyzing the complexity of the free space of a variety of moving systems B ("robots"), and a considerable amount of the earlier work has focussed on the cases where B is a line segment or a convex polygon translating and rotating in a planar polygonal workspace. Cases (C2) and (C3) correspond to these scenarios. It is beyond the scope of this paper to review all of this work. We refer the reader to the surveys [8,14,15]. We briefly mention the results that are directly related to our study. Leven and Sharir [10] proved that $\varphi(B, \mathcal{O}) = O(n^2)$ if B is a line segment and $\mathcal{O}$ is a set of pairwise-disjoint polygons with a total of n vertices. They also give a near-quadratic algorithm to compute $\mathbb{F}(B, O)$. For the case where B is a convex k-gon, Leven and Sharir [11] proved that $\varphi(B, \mathcal{O}) = O(k^2 n^2 \beta_6(kn))$, where $\beta_s(t) = \lambda_s(t)/t$, and $\lambda_s(t)$ is the maximum length of an (t, s)-Davenport-Schinzel sequence [15]; $\beta_s(t)$ is an extremely slowly growing function of t.

Our results. There are two main contributions of this paper. First, we refine the earlier bounds on $\varphi(B, \mathcal{O})$ so that they also depend on the number m of polygons in $\mathcal{O}$, and not just on their total number of vertices, since $m \ll n$ in many cases. Second, we present a general approach for computing a hitting set, which leads to faster algorithms for computing stabbing sets.

Specifically, we first prove (in Section 2), for the case where B is a line segment, that the complexity of $\mathbb{F}(B, \mathcal{O})$ is $O(mn\alpha(n))$, and that $\mathbb{F}(B, \mathcal{O})$ can be computed in $O(mn\alpha(n) \log^2 n)$ randomized expected time. If the polygons in $\mathcal{O}$ are pairwise disjoint, then $\varphi(B, \mathcal{O}) = \Theta(mn)$, but $\varphi^*(B, \mathcal{O}) = O(m^2 + n)$. We then show that we can compute, in $O((m^2 + n) \log m \log^2 n)$ randomized expected time, an implicit representation of $\mathbb{F}$ of size $O(m^2 + n)$, which is sufficient for many applications (including ours). We then consider case (C3) (Section 3). We show that $\varphi(B, \mathcal{O}) = O(k^2 mn\beta_6(kn))$ in this case, and that $\mathbb{F}$ can be computed in expected time $O(k^2 mn\beta_6(kn) \log(kn) \log n)$.

The subsequent results in this paper depend on the complexity of $\mathbb{F}$. Since we are mainly interested in bounds that are functions of the number of polygons and of their total size, we abuse the notation a little, and write $\varphi(m, n)$ to denote the maximum complexity of $\mathbb{F}$ for each of the three cases; the maximum is taken over all m convex polygons with a total of n vertices, and these polygons are disjoint for cases (C2) and (C3). Similarly we define $\varphi^*(m, n)$ for the maximum number of nondegenerate critical placements (in case (C3), the bounds also depend on k).

For a point $z \in \mathbb{R}^3$, we define its *depth* to be the number of c-polygons K_i that contain z. We present a randomized algorithm DEPTH_THRESHOLD, which, given an integer $l \leq m$, determines whether the maximum depth of a placement (with respect to $\mathcal{O}$) is at most l. If not, it returns all critical placements (of depth at most l). The expected running time of this algorithm is $O(l^3 \varphi(m/l, n/l) \log n)$. For (C2), the procedure runs in expected time $O(l^3 \varphi^*(m/l, n/l) \log^2 n)$ time.

Finally, we describe algorithms for computing a hitting set of $\mathcal{K}$ of size $O(h^* \log m)$ where h^* is the size of the smallest hitting set of $\mathcal{K}$. Basically, we use the standard greedy approach, mentioned above, to compute such a hitting set, but we use more efficient implementations, which exploit the geometric structure of the problems at hand. The first implementation runs in $O(\Delta^3 \varphi(m/\Delta, n/\Delta) \log n)$ time, where Δ is the maximum depth of a placement. The second implementation is a Monte Carlo algorithm, based on a technique of Aronov and Har-Peled [3] for approximating the depth in an arrangement. The expected running time of the second implementation is $O(\varphi(m, n)h \log m \log n + mn^{1+\varepsilon})$ time, where h is the size of the hitting set computed by the algorithm, which is $O(h^* \log m)$, with high probability. Finally, we combine the two approaches and obtain a Monte Carlo algorithm whose running time is $O(\varphi(m, n) \cdot n^\varepsilon + \eta^3 \varphi(m/\eta, n/\eta) \log n \log^3 m)$, for any $\varepsilon > 0$, where $\eta = \min\{h^{1/3}, m^{1/4}\}$ and $h = O(h^* \log m)$, with high probability. For case (C2), the expected running time can be improved to $O(\varphi^*(m, n) \cdot n^\varepsilon + \eta^3 \varphi^*(m/\eta, n/\eta) \log^c n))$, for some constant $c > 1$. We believe that one should be able to improve the expected running time to $O(\varphi(m, n) \log^{O(1)} n)$, but such a bound remains elusive for now. Because of lack of space many algorithms and proofs are omitted from this abstract, which can be found in the full version of this paper [1].

2   Complexity of $\mathbb{F}$ for a Segment

Let B be a line segment of length d, and let $\mathcal{O}$ be a set of m convex polygons in $\mathbb{R}^2$ with a total of n vertices. We first bound the number of critical placements when the polygons in $\mathcal{O}$ may intersect, and then prove a refined bound when the polygons are pairwise disjoint. We omit the algorithms for computing these placements from this abstract.

The case of intersecting polygons. There are several types of critical placements of B (see Figure 1(a)):

(i) A placement where one endpoint of B touches a vertex of one polygon and the other endpoint touches an edge of another polygon.
(ii) A placement where one endpoint of B touches a vertex of one polygon and the relative interior of B touches a vertex of another polygon.
(iii) The relative interior of B touches two vertices (of the same or of distinct polygons) and one endpoint of B touches a polygon edge.
(iv) The relative interior of B touches a vertex of a polygon, and one of its endpoints touches an intersection point of two edges (of distinct polygons).
(v) One endpoint of B touches an intersection point of two edges (of distinct polygons), and the other endpoint touches a third edge.
(vi) The relative interior of B touches a vertex of a polygon, and its two endpoints touch two respective edges (of distinct polygons).

There are $O(mn)$ placements of types (i) and (ii), and $O(m^2 + n)$ placements of type (iii).

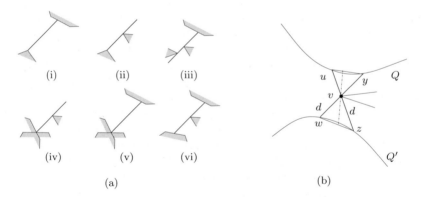

(i)   (ii)   (iii)

(iv)   (v)   (vi)

(a)

(b)

Fig. 1. (a) Critical free placements of B; (b) F_Q and $G_{Q'}$ intersect at most twice

Consider the placements of types (iv) and (v). Let u be an intersection point of two polygon boundaries (which lies on the boundary of their union), and let H denote the *hole* (i.e., connected component of the complement) of the union of $\mathcal{O}$ which contains u on its boundary. Again, placing an endpoint of B at u leaves B with one degree of freedom of rotation about u. However, at any such free placement, B must be fully contained in (the closure of) H. For any polygon $O \in \mathcal{O}$ whose boundary contributes to ∂H, there are at most two critical free placements of types (iv) and (v) where B swings around u and touches O, and no other polygon (namely, those which do not show up on ∂H) can generate such a placement. It follows that, for any polygon $O \in \mathcal{O}$, the intersection points u that can form with O critical free placements of type (iv) or (v) are vertices of the *zone* of ∂O in the arrangement $\mathcal{A}(\mathcal{O} \setminus \{O\})$. Since ∂O is convex, the complexity of the zone is $O(n\alpha(n))$ [2]. Hence the overall number of such placements is $O(mn\alpha(n))$.

Finally, consider critical free placements of type (vi). Let v be a fixed vertex of some polygon (not lying inside any other polygon). The placements of B at which its relative interior touches v can be parametrized in a polar coordinate system (r, θ), where r is the distance of one endpoint a of B from v, and θ is the orientation of B, oriented towards a, so that O lies to the right of (the line supporting) B. The admissible values of (r, θ) can be restricted to the rectangle $[0, d] \times I$, where I is the range of orientations of tangent lines to O at v, for which O lies to their right. For any polygon $Q \in \mathcal{O} \setminus \{O\}$, we define a *forward function* $r = F_Q(\theta)$ and a *backward function* $r = G_Q(\theta)$, where $F_Q(\theta)$ (resp., $G_Q(\theta)$) is the distance from v to $\ell_\theta \cap Q$ (resp., d minus that distance), where ℓ_θ is the line at orientation θ that passes through v. $F_Q(\theta)$ (resp., $G_Q(\theta)$) is defined only when $\ell_\theta \cap Q$ is nonempty, lies ahead (resp., behind) v along ℓ_θ, and its distance from v is at most d; in all other cases, we set $F_Q(\theta) := d$ (resp., $G_Q(\theta) := 0$). It is clear that the set $\mathbb{F}_v$ of free placements of B when its relative interior hinges over v, is given in parametric form by

$$\{(r, \theta) \mid \max_Q G_Q(\theta) \leq r \leq \min_Q F_Q(\theta)\}.$$

That is, $\mathbb{F}_v$, in parametric form, is the *sandwich region* between the lower envelope of the functions F_Q and the upper envelope of the functions G_Q. It follows that the combinatorial complexity of $\mathbb{F}_v$ is proportional to the sum of the complexities of the two individual envelopes. A placement of B, where one endpoint lies either at a vertex of some polygon (including v itself), or at the intersection point between two edges of distinct polygons, its relative interior touches v, and the portion of B between these two contacts is free, corresponds to a *breakpoint* in one of the envelopes. Arguing as in the analysis of the preceding types of critical placements, the overall number of such placements, summed over all vertices v, is $O(mn\alpha(n))$. It follows that the overall number of critical placements of type (vi) is also $O(mn\alpha(n))$. Putting everything together, we obtain:

Theorem 1. *Let B be a line segment and let $\mathcal{O}$ be a set of m (possibly intersecting) convex polygons in $\mathbb{R}^2$ with n vertices in total. The number of free critical placements of B is $O(mn\alpha(n))$.*

The case of pairwise-disjoint polygons. We now prove a refined bound on the number of free critical placements if the polygons in $\mathcal{O}$ are pairwise disjoint. A trivial construction shows that, even in this case, there can be $\Omega(mn)$ free critical placements of types (i) and (ii). However, most of these placements involve contacts with only two distinct polygons, so they are degenerate critical contacts. As we next show, the number of nondegenerate critical contacts is smaller. Specifically, we argue that there are only $O(m^2 + n)$ free nondegenerate critical placements.

We have already ruled out critical placements of types (i) and (ii) because they are degenerate, and we rule out placements of type (iv) and (v) because they involve intersecting polygons. It thus remains to bound the number of free critical placements of types (iii) and (vi). There are only $O(m^2 + n)$ critical placements of type (iii), as argued above. For placements of type (vi), we use the same scheme as above, fixing the pivot vertex v and considering the system of functions $F_Q(\theta)$, $G_Q(\theta)$ in polar coordinates about v. Let $\mathcal{L}_v(\theta) = \min_Q F_Q(\theta)$ and $\mathcal{U}_v(\theta) = \max_Q G_Q(\theta)$; Let μ_v (resp. ν_v) be the number of breakpoints in $\mathcal{L}_v$ (resp. $\mathcal{U}_v$). Using the fact that the functions F_Q (and G_Q) are pairwise disjoint, we claim the following:

Lemma 1. $\sum_v (\mu_v + \nu_v) = O(m^2 + n)$.

If we mark the θ-values at which a breakpoint of $\mathcal{L}_v$ or $\mathcal{U}_v$ occurs, we partition the θ-range into intervals so that each of $\mathcal{L}_v$ and $\mathcal{U}_v$ is attained by (a connected portion of the graph of) a single function, say F_Q and $G_{Q'}$, respectively. We claim that F_Q and $G_{Q'}$ intersect in at most two points in this interval, i.e., there are two semifree placements of B such that v lies in the interior of B and the endpoints of B lie on ∂Q and $\partial Q'$; see Figure 1(b). Hence, the number of vertices in the sandwich region between $\mathcal{L}_v$ and $\mathcal{U}_v$ is $O(\mu_v + \nu_v)$. Putting everything together, we obtain:

Theorem 2. *Let B be a line segment, and let $\mathcal{O}$ be a set of pairwise-disjoint convex polygons with n vertices in total. The number of nondegenerate free critical placements of B is $O(m^2 + n)$.*

3   Complexity of $\mathbb{F}$ for a Convex k-gon

In this section we derive an improved bound on $\varphi(B, \mathcal{O})$ for the case where B is a convex k-gon and $\mathcal{O}$ is a set of m pairwise-disjoint convex polygons in $\mathbb{R}^2$ with n vertices in total. We assume that the polygons in $\mathcal{O}$ are in general position, as in [11]. We first prove that the number of degenerate free critical placements is $O(k^2 mn)$, and then show that the total number of realizable double contacts is $O(k^2 mn)$. By adapting the argument of Leven and Sharir [11], we then prove that $\varphi(B, \mathcal{O}) = O(k^2 mn\beta_6(kn))$. We begin by stating a lemma, which establishes an upper bound on the number of realizable double contacts when there are only two obstacles.

Lemma 2. *Let B be a convex k-gon, and let O_1 and O_2 be two disjoint convex polygons with n_1 and n_2 vertices, respectively, then the number of semifree degenerate critical placements in $\mathbb{F}(B, \{O_1, O_2\})$ is $O(k^2(n_1 + n_2))$.*

The following corollary follows immediately from Lemma 2.

Corollary 1. *Let B be a convex k-gon and let $\mathcal{O}$ be a set of m pairwise-disjoint convex polygons with n vertices in total. The number of degenerate critical placements in $\mathbb{F}(B, \mathcal{O})$ is $O(k^2 mn)$.*

Next, we bound the number of realizable double contacts. It is tempting to prove that a fixed contact C can realize only $O(km)$ double contacts, but, as shown in the full version, a contact may be involved in $\Omega(kn)$ realizable double contacts, so we have to rely on a more global counting argument. Note first that the preceding argument shows that the number of degenerate double contacts is $O(k^2mn)$, so it suffices to consider only nondegenerate double contacts. Since we assume that the polygons are in general position, the locus of placements forming a fixed non-degenerate double contact $\{C_1, C_2\}$ is a curve in $\mathbb{R}^3$. Let O_1 and O_2 be the two (distinct) polygons involved in $\{C_1, C_2\}$. Adapting the argument in [15, Lemma 8.55], one can show that at least one endpoint of this curve is a degenerate triple contact, which we denote by $z(C_1, C_2)$, which is semifree with respect to O_1 and O_2. We thus charge $\{C_1, C_2\}$ to $z(C_1, C_2)$, and argue that each nondegenerate triple contact in $\mathbb{F}(B, \{O_1, O_2\})$ is charged at most $O(1)$ times. Omitting all further details, we obtain:

Lemma 3. *Let B be a convex k-gon and let $\mathcal{O}$ be a set of m pairwise-disjoint convex polygons with n vertices in total. The number of realizable double contacts is $O(k^2mn)$.*

Plugging Corollary 1 and Lemma 3 into the proof of Leven and Sharir [11], we obtain the main result of this section.

Theorem 3. *Let B be a convex k-gon, and let $\mathcal{O}$ be a set of m pairwise-disjoint convex polygons with n vertices in total. Then $\varphi(B, \mathcal{O}) = O(k^2mn\beta_6(kn))$.*

4 Computing Critical Placements

So far, we have only considered *semifree* critical placements, but, since we want to construct a set of stabbing placements of B, we need to consider (and compute) the set of all (nonfree) critical placements.

Bounding the number of critical placements. Let $\mathcal{K} = \{K_1, \ldots, K_m\}$ be the set of c-polygons yielded by B and $\mathcal{O}$, as defined in the Introduction, and let $\mathcal{A}(\mathcal{K})$ denote the 3-dimensional arrangement of $\mathcal{K}$. For a point $z \in \mathbb{R}^3$ and a subset $\mathcal{G} \subseteq \mathcal{K}$, let $\Delta(z, \mathcal{G})$ denote the *depth* of z with respect to $\mathcal{G}$, i.e., the number of c-polygons in $\mathcal{G}$ containing z in their interior; we use $\Delta(z)$ to denote $\Delta(z, \mathcal{K})$. Let $\Phi_l(\mathcal{K})$ denote the set of vertices of $\mathcal{A}(\mathcal{K})$, whose depth is l, and put $\Phi_{\leq l}(\mathcal{K}) = \bigcup_{h \leq l} \Phi_h(\mathcal{K})$. Set $\varphi_l(\mathcal{K}) = |\Phi_l(\mathcal{K})|$ and $\varphi_{\leq l}(\mathcal{K}) = |\Phi_{\leq l}(\mathcal{K})|$. We now state a theorem, whose proof is deferred to the full version of this paper.

Theorem 4. *(i) Let B be a line segment, let $\mathcal{O}$ be a set of m convex polygons in $\mathbb{R}^2$ with a total of n vertices, and let $\mathcal{K} = \mathcal{K}(B, \mathcal{O})$. Then, for any $1 \leq l \leq m$, we have $\varphi_{\leq l}(\mathcal{K}) = O(mnl\alpha(n))$. If the polygons in $\mathcal{O}$ are pairwise disjoint, then the number of non-degenerate critical placements in $\Phi_{\leq l}(\mathcal{K})$ is $O(m^2l + nl^2)$.*

(ii) Let B be a convex k-gon, let $\mathcal{O}$ be a set of m pairwise-disjoint polygons in $\mathbb{R}^2$ with a total of n vertices, and let $\mathcal{K} = \mathcal{K}(B, \mathcal{O})$. Then, for any $1 \leq l \leq m$, we have $\varphi_{\leq l}(\mathcal{K}) = O(k^2mnl\beta_6(kn))$.

The DEPTH_THRESHOLD *procedure.* One of the strategies that we will use for computing a stabbing set is based on determining whether the maximal depth in $\mathcal{A}(\mathcal{K})$ exceeds a given threshold l. For this we use the DEPTH_THRESHOLD procedure, which, given an integer $l \geq 1$, determines whether DEPTH $(\mathcal{K}) \leq l$. If not, it returns a critical placement whose depth is greater than l. Otherwise, it returns all critical placements of B (which are all the vertices of $\mathcal{A}(\mathcal{K})$). Without describing the details of this procedure, we claim the following.

Theorem 5. *(i) Let B be a line segment, and let $\mathcal{O}$ be a set of m convex polygons in $\mathbb{R}^2$ with a total of n vertices. For a given integer $1 \leq l \leq m$, the* DEPTH_THRESHOLD *(l) procedure takes $O(mn(\log n + l\alpha(n)))$ expected time. If the polygons in $\mathcal{O}$ are pairwise disjoint, the expected running time is $O((m^2 l + nl^2)\log^2 n)$.*

(ii) Let B be a convex k-gon and $\mathcal{O}$ be a set of m pairwise-disjoint convex polygons in $\mathbb{R}^2$ with a total of n vertices. For a given integer $1 \leq l \leq m$, the DEPTH_THRESHOLD *(l) procedure takes $O(k^2 mn(\log n + l\beta_6(kn)))$ expected time.*

5   Computing a Hitting Set

Let $\mathcal{K} = \{K_1, \ldots, K_m\}$ be the set of c-polygons, for an input collection $\mathcal{O}$ of convex polygons and a line segment or convex polygon B, as above. Our goal is to compute a small-size hitting set for $\mathcal{K}$, and we do it by applying a standard greedy technique which proceeds as follows. In the beginning of the ith step we have a subset $\mathcal{K}_i \subseteq \mathcal{K}$; initially $\mathcal{K}_1 = \mathcal{K}$. We compute a placement $z_i \in \mathbb{R}^3$ such that $\Delta(z_i, \mathcal{K}_i) = $ DEPTH $(\mathcal{K}_i)$, and we also compute the set $\mathcal{K}_{z_i} \subseteq \mathcal{K}_i$ of the c-polygons that contain z_i. We add z_i to H, and set $\mathcal{K}_{i+1} = \mathcal{K}_i \setminus \mathcal{K}_{z_i}$. The algorithm stops when $\mathcal{K}_i$ becomes empty. The standard analysis of the greedy algorithm [6] shows that $|H| = O(h^* \log m)$, where h^* is the size of the smallest hitting set for $\mathcal{K}$. In fact, the size of H remains $O(h^* \log m)$, even if at each step we choose a point z_i such that $\Delta(z_i, \mathcal{K}_i) \geq $ DEPTH $(\mathcal{K}_i)/2$. We describe three different procedures to implement this greedy algorithm. The first one, a Las Vegas algorithm, works well when DEPTH $(\mathcal{K})$ is small. The second one, a Monte Carlo algorithm, works well when h^* is small. Finally, we combine the two approaches to obtain an improved Monte Carlo algorithm. For simplicity, and due to lack of space, we focus on case (C1): B is a segment and the polygons in $\mathcal{O}$ may intersect.

The Las Vegas algorithm. It suffices to find a deepest point in $\mathcal{A}(\mathcal{K})$ that lies on ∂K_i for some i, and that (assuming general position), we may assume it to lie in the relative interior of some 2-face (the depth of all the points within the same 2-face is the same). Thus, for each 2-face f of $\mathcal{A}(\mathcal{K})$ we choose a sample point z_f. Let $\mathcal{Z} \subseteq \mathbb{R}^3$ be the set of these points. We maintain $\Delta(z, \mathcal{K}_i)$ for each $z \in \mathcal{Z}$, as we run the greedy algorithm, and return $z_i = \arg\max_{z \in \mathcal{Z}} \Delta(z, \mathcal{K}_i)$ at each step, and delete the c-polygons containing z_i from $\mathcal{K}$. It will be expensive to maintain the depth of each point in $\mathcal{Z}$ explicitly. We describe a data structure that maintains the depth of each placement z_i in $\mathcal{Z}$ implicitly, supports deletion of c-polygons and returns a placement of maximum depth. For each c-polygon K_j, let $\Gamma_j = \{\gamma_{ji} = \partial K_j \cap K_i \mid i \neq j\}$ be a set of regions on ∂K_j. We compute $\mathcal{A}(\Gamma_j)$ using Theorem 5. Let $\mathcal{D}(\Gamma_j)$ be the planar graph that is dual to $\mathcal{A}(\Gamma_j)$. We choose a representative point z_f from each face f of $\mathcal{A}(\Gamma_j)$, and use z_f to denote the node of $\mathcal{D}(\Gamma_j)$ dual to f. If an edge e of $\mathcal{A}(\Gamma_j)$ lies on ∂K_a, for some $K_a \in \mathcal{K}$, we label the edge e of $\mathcal{D}(\Gamma_j)$ with K_a and denote this label by $\chi(e)$. We compute a spanning tree T of $\mathcal{D}(\Gamma_j)$, and then convert T into a path Π by performing a traversal of T, starting from some leaf v; each edge of T appears twice in Π. The sequence of vertices in Π can be decomposed into intervals, such that all vertices in each interval either lie in a c-polygon K_a or none of them lie inside K_a. Let J_a be the subset of those intervals whose vertices lie inside K_a. We represent an interval $v_x, \ldots, v_y$ by the pair $[x, y]$. Set $J = \bigcup_{a \neq j} J_a$. For any vertex $v_s \in \Pi$, we define the weight $w(v_s)$ to be the number of intervals $[x, y]$ in J that contain v_s, i.e., intervals satisfying $x \leq s \leq y$. For a subset $\mathcal{G} \subseteq \mathcal{K}$, $\Delta(v_s, \mathcal{G})$ is the number of intervals in $\bigcup_{K_a \in \mathcal{G}} J_a$ that contain v_s. We store J in a segment tree, Σ, built on the sequence of edges in Π. Each node σ of Σ corresponds to a subpath Π_σ of Π. For each σ, we maintain the vertex of Π_σ of the maximum weight. The root of Σ stores a vertex of Π of the maximum weight. Once we have computed $\mathcal{A}(\Gamma_j)$, J and Σ can be constructed in $O(\kappa_j \log \kappa_j)$ time, where κ_j is the complexity of $\mathcal{A}(\Gamma_j)$. We have $\sum_j \kappa_j = O(mn\Delta\alpha(n))$, where $\Delta = \textsc{Depth} (\mathcal{K})$. The information in Σ can be updated in $O(\log n)$ time when an interval is deleted from J. When the greedy algorithm deletes a c-polygon K_a, we delete all intervals in J_a from J and update Σ. The total time spent in updating Σ is $O(\kappa_j \log n)$. Maintaining this structure for each c-polygon K_j, the greedy algorithm can be implemented in $O(mn\Delta\alpha(n) \log n)$ expected time.

Lemma 4. *A hitting set of $\mathcal{K}$ of size $O(h^* \log m)$ can be computed in expected time $O(mn\Delta\alpha(n) \log n)$, where $\Delta = \textsc{Depth} (\mathcal{K})$ and where h^* is the size of a smallest hitting set of $\mathcal{K}$.*

A simple Monte Carlo algorithm. Let $\Delta = \textsc{Depth} (\mathcal{K})$. If $\Delta = O(\log m)$, we use the above algorithm and compute a hitting set in time $O(mn\alpha(n) \log m \log n)$. So assume that $\Delta \geq c \log m$ for some constant $c \geq 1$. We use a procedure by Aronov and Har-Peled [3], which computes a placement whose depth is at least $\Delta/2$. Their main algorithm is based on the following observation. Fix an integer $l \geq \Delta/4$. Let $\mathcal{G} \subseteq \mathcal{K}$ be a random subset obtained by choosing each c-polygon of $\mathcal{K}$ with probability $\rho = (c_1 \ln m)/l$, where c_1 is an appropriate constant. Then the following two conditions hold with high probability, (i) if $\Delta \geq l$ then $\textsc{Depth} (\mathcal{G}) \geq 3l\rho/2 = (3c_1/2) \ln m$, and, ii) if $\Delta \leq l$ then $\textsc{Depth} (\mathcal{G}) \leq 5l\rho/4 = (5c_1/4) \ln m$.

   This observation immediately leads to a binary-search procedure for approximating $\textsc{Depth} (\mathcal{K})$. Let $\tau = (5c_1/4) \ln m$. In the ith step, for $i \leq \lceil \log_2(m/\log_2 m) \rceil$, we set $l_i = m/2^i$. We choose a random subset $\mathcal{G}_i \subseteq \mathcal{K}$ using the parameter $l = l_i$, and then run the procedure $\textsc{Depth\_Threshold}$ on $\mathcal{G}_i$ with parameter τ. If the procedure determines that $\textsc{Depth} (\mathcal{G}_i) \leq \tau$, then we conclude that $\textsc{Depth} (\mathcal{K}) \leq l_i$, and we continue with the next iteration. Otherwise, the algorithm returns a point $z \in \mathbb{R}^3$ such that $\Delta(z, \mathcal{G}_i) \geq \tau$. We need a data structure for reporting the set of polygons in $\mathcal{O}$ intersected by $B[z]$ for a placement $z \in \mathbb{R}^3$. As we show in the full version, we can preprocess $\mathcal{O}$ into a data structure of size $O(mn^{1+\varepsilon})$, for any $\varepsilon > 0$, so that a convex polygon O_i of $\mathcal{O}$ can be deleted in time $O(|O_i| \cdot n^\varepsilon)$, where $|O_i|$ is the number of vertices of O_i, and so that the set of all κ polygons intersecting a query placement $B[z]$ of B can be reported in time $O((1 + \kappa) \log n)$.

Set $m_i = |\mathcal{G}_i|$, and let n_i be the number of vertices in the original polygons corresponding to the c-polygons in $\mathcal{G}_i$. Then the expected running time of the ith iteration is $O(m_i n_i \tau \alpha(n) \log n)$. Since $E[m_i n_i] = O(mn\rho^2 + n\rho)$, the expected running time of the ith iteration is $O((mn/l_i^2)\alpha(n) \log^3 m \log n)$.

Since the algorithm always stops after at most $\lceil \log_2(m/\log_2 m) \rceil$ iterations, the overall expected running time is $O(mn\alpha(n) \log m \log n)$. Note that if the algorithm stops after i steps, then, with high probability, $\Delta \in [l_i, 2l_i]$. Hence, the expected running time of the algorithm is $O((mn/\Delta^2)\alpha(n) \log^3 m \log n)$. Plugging this procedure into the greedy algorithm described above, and accounting for $O(mn^{1+\varepsilon})$ time for preprocessing and reporting the polygons intersecting a placement z, we get the following lemma.

Lemma 5. *There is a Monte Carlo algorithm for computing a hitting set of $\mathcal{K}$ whose size is $h = O(h^* \log m)$ with probability at least $1 - 1/m^{O(1)}$, and whose expected running time is $O(mnh\alpha(n) \log m \log n + mn^{1+\varepsilon})$.*

An improved Monte Carlo algorithm. We now combine the two algorithms given above, to obtain a faster algorithm for computing a small-size hitting set of $\mathcal{K}$. For this we use the data structure mentioned above, which preprocesses $\mathcal{O}$ in $O(mn^{1+\varepsilon})$ time to support deletion.

We now run the greedy algorithm as follows. We begin by running the Monte Carlo algorithm described above. In the ith iteration, it returns a point z_i such that $\Delta(z_i, \mathcal{K}_i) \geq \text{DEPTH}(\mathcal{K}_i)/2$, with high probability. We use the above data structure to report the set $\mathcal{O}_{z_i}$ of all polygons that intersect the query placement $B[z_i]$, or, equivalently, the set $\mathcal{K}_{z_i}$ of the c-polygons that contain z_i. We delete these polygons from the data structure. If $|\mathcal{O}_{z_i}| < i^{1/3}$ then we switch to the Las Vegas algorithm described earlier, to compute a hitting set of $\mathcal{K}_{i+1}$.

We now analyze the expected running time of the algorithm. The total time spent in reporting the polygons intersected by the placements $B[z_1], \ldots, B[z_h]$, is $O(mn^{1+\varepsilon})$, so it suffices to bound the time spent in computing $z_1, \ldots, z_h$. Suppose that the algorithm switches to the second stage after $\xi + 1$ steps. Then $\text{DEPTH}(\mathcal{K}_i) \geq \xi^{1/3}$, for $1 \leq i \leq \xi$, and, the expected running time of each of the iterations of the first stage is $O((mn/\xi^{2/3})\alpha(n) \log n \log^3 m)$. Hence, the expected running time of the first stage is $O(mn\xi^{1/3}\alpha(n) \log n \log^3 m)$. The expected running time of the second stage is $O(mn\xi^{1/3}\alpha(n) \log n)$ because $\text{DEPTH}(\mathcal{K}_{\xi+2}) \leq 2\xi^{1/3}$. Suppose h is the size of the hitting set computed by the algorithm. Then $\xi \leq h$. Moreover, for $1 \leq i \leq \xi$, each z_i lies inside at least $(\xi^{1/3})/2$ c-polygons of $\mathcal{K}_i$, and all these polygons are distinct. Therefore, $\xi^{4/3} \leq 2m$. The expected running time of the overall algorithm is $O(mn\eta\alpha(n) \log n \log^3 m + mn^{1+\varepsilon})$, where $\eta = \min\{m^{1/4}, h^{1/3}\}$. We thus obtain the following.

Theorem 6. *Let B be a line segment, and let $\mathcal{O}$ be a set of m (possibly intersecting) convex polygons in $\mathbb{R}^2$, with a total of n vertices. A stabbing set of $\mathcal{O}$ of $h = O(h^* \log m)$ placements of B can be computed, with probability at least $1 - 1/m^{O(1)}$, in expected time $O(mn(n^\varepsilon + \eta\alpha(n) \log n \log^3 m))$, where $\eta = \min\{m^{1/4}, h^{1/3}\}$, h^* is the smallest size of a hitting set, and $\varepsilon > 0$ is an arbitrarily small constant.*

Remark: The expected running time of the above approach is $O((m^2 + n)n^\varepsilon + (m^2\eta + n\eta^2)\log^c(n))$ for case (C2) and $O(k^2mn(n^\varepsilon + \eta\beta_6(kn) \log n \log^3 m))$ for case (C3).

References

1. Agarwal, P.K., Chen, D.Z., Ganjugunte, S.K., Misołek, E., Sharir, M., Tang, K.: Stabbing convex polygons with a segment or a polygon (2008),
   http://www.cs.duke.edu/~shashigk/sstab/shortstab.pdf
2. Agarwal, P.K., Sharir, M.: Arrangements and their applications. In: Sack, J.-R., Urrutia, J. (eds.) Handbook of Computational Geometry, pp. 49–119. Elsevier, Amsterdam (2000)
3. Aronov, B., Har-Peled, S.: On approximating the depth and related problems. In: Proc. of the 16th Annu. ACM-SIAM Sympos. Discrete Algorithms, pp. 886–894 (2005)
4. Berman, P., DasGupta, B.: Complexities of efficient solutions of rectilinear polygon cover problems. Algorithmica 17, 331–356 (1997)
5. Clarkson, K.L., Varadarajan, K.: Improved approximation algorithms for geometric set cover. Discrete Comput. Geom. 37, 43–58 (2007)
6. Cormen, T.H., Leiserson, C.E., Rivest, R.L., Stein, C.: Introduction to Algorithms. MIT Press, Cambridge (2001)
7. Feige, U.: A threshold of $\ln n$ for approximating set cover. J. ACM 45, 634–652 (1998)
8. Halperin, D., Kavraki, L., Latombe, J.-C.: Robotics. In: Goodman, J.E., O'Rourke, J. (eds.) Handbook of Discrete and Computational Geometry, pp. 755–778. CRC Press, Boca Raton (1997)
9. Hochbaum, D.S., Maass, W.: Approximation schemes for covering and packing problems in image processing and VLSI. J. ACM 32, 130–136 (1985)
10. Leven, D., Sharir, M.: An efficient and simple motion planning algorithm for a ladder moving in two-dimensional space amidst polygonal barriers. In: Proc. 1st Annu. Sympos. on Comput. Geom., pp. 221–227. ACM, New York (1985)
11. Leven, D., Sharir, M.: On the number of critical free contacts of a convex polygonal object moving in two-dimensional polygonal space. Discrete Comput. Geom. 2, 255–270 (1987)
12. Megiddo, N., Supowit, K.J.: On the complexity of some common geometric location problems. SIAM J. Comput. 13, 182–196 (1984)
13. Megiddo, N., Tamir, A.: On the complexity of locating linear facilities in the plane. Operations Research Letters 1, 194–197 (1982)
14. Sharir, M.: Algorithmic motion planning in robotics. IEEE Computer 22, 9–20 (1989)
15. Sharir, M., Agarwal, P.K.: Davenport-Schinzel Sequences and their Geometric Applications. Cambridge University Press, New York (1995)
16. Vazirani, V.: Approximation Algorithms. Springer, Heidelberg (2004)

An Efficient Algorithm for 2D Euclidean 2-Center with Outliers[*]

Pankaj K. Agarwal and Jeff M. Phillips

Department of Computer Science, Duke University, Durham, NC 27708

Abstract. For a set P of n points in $\mathbb{R}^2$, the Euclidean 2-center problem computes a pair of congruent disks of the minimal radius that cover P. We extend this to the $(2, k)$-center problem where we compute the minimal radius pair of congruent disks to cover $n - k$ points of P. We present a randomized algorithm with $O(nk^7 \log^3 n)$ expected running time for the $(2, k)$-center problem. We also study the (p, k)-center problem in $\mathbb{R}^2$ under the ℓ_∞-metric. We give solutions for $p = 4$ in $O(k^{O(1)} n \log n)$ time and for $p = 5$ in $O(k^{O(1)} n \log^5 n)$ time.

1 Introduction

Let P be a set of n points in $\mathbb{R}^2$. For a pair of integers $0 \le k \le n$ and $p \ge 1$, a family of p congruent disks is called a (p, k)-*center* if the disks cover at least $n - k$ points of P; $(p, 0)$-center is the standard p-center. The Euclidean (p, k)-center problems asks for computing a (p, k)-center of P of the smallest radius. In this paper we study the $(2, k)$-center problem. We also study the (p, k)-center problem under the ℓ_∞-metric for small values of p and k. Here we wish to cover all but k points of P by p congruent axis-aligned squares of the smallest side length. Our goal is to develop algorithms whose running time is $n(k \log n)^{O(1)}$.

Related work. There has been extensive work on the p-center problem in algorithms and operations research communities [4,14,18,9]. If p is part of the input, the problem is NP-hard [22] even for the Euclidean case in $\mathbb{R}^2$. The Euclidean 1-center problem is known to be LP-type [20], and therefore can be solved in linear time for any fixed dimension. The Euclidean 2-center problem is not LP-type. Agarwal and Sharir [3] proposed an $O(n^2 \log^3 n)$ time algorithm for the 2-center problem. The running time was improved to $O(n \log^{O(1)} n)$ by Sharir [24]. The exponent of the $\log n$ factor was subsequently improved in [15,6]. The best known deterministic algorithm takes $O(n \log^2 n \log^2 \log n)$ time in the worst case, and the best known randomized algorithm takes $O(n \log^2 n)$ expected time.

There is little work on the (p, k)-center problem. Using a framework described by Matoušek [19], the $(1, k)$-center problem can be solved in $O(n \log k + k^3 n^\varepsilon)$

---

[*] This work is supported by NSF under grants CNS-05-40347, CFF-06-35000, and DEB-04-25465, by ARO grants W911NF-04-1-0278 and W911NF-07-1-0376, by an NIH grant 1P50-GM-08183-01, by a DOE grant OEGP200A070505, and by a grant from the U.S. Israel Binational Science Foundation.

D. Halperin and K. Mehlhorn (Eds.): ESA 2008, LNCS 5193, pp. 64–75, 2008.

time for any $\varepsilon > 0$. In general, Matoušek shows how to solve this problem with k outliers in $O(nk^d)$ time where d is the inherent number of constraints in the solution. The bound for the $(1, k)$-center problem is improved by Chan [7] to $O(n\beta(n)\log n + k^2 n^\varepsilon)$ expected time, where $\beta(\cdot)$ is a slow-growing inverse-Ackermann-like function and $\varepsilon > 0$.

The p-center problem under ℓ_∞-metric is dramatically simpler. Sharir and Welzl [25] show how to compute the ℓ_∞ p-center in near-linear time for $p \leq 5$. In fact, they show that the rectilinear 2- and 3-center problems are LP-type problems and can be solved in $O(n)$ time. Also, they show the 1-dimensional version of the problem is an LP-type problem for any p, with combinatorial dimension $O(p)$. Thus applying Matoušek's framework [19], the ℓ_∞ (p, k)-center in $\mathbb{R}^2$ for $p \leq 3$, can be found in $O(k^{O(1)}n)$ time and in $O(k^{O(p)}n)$, for any p, if the points lie in $\mathbb{R}^1$.

Our results. Our main result is a randomized algorithm for the Euclidean $(2, k)$-center problem in $\mathbb{R}^2$ whose expected running time is $O(nk^7 \log^3 n)$. We follow the general framework of Sharir and subsequent improvements by Eppstein. To handle outliers we first prove, in Section 2, a few structural properties of levels in an arrangement of unit disks, which are of independent interest.

As in [24,15], our solution breaks the $(2, k)$-center problem into two cases depending on the distance between the centers of the optimal disks; (i) the centers are further apart than the optimal radius, and (ii) they are closer than their radius. The first subproblem, which we refer to as the *well-separated case* and describe in Section 3, takes $O(k^6 n \log^3 n)$ time in the worst case and uses parametric search [21]. The second subproblem, which we refer to as the *nearly concentric case* and describe in Section 4, takes $O(k^7 n \log^3 n)$ expected time. Thus we solve the $(2, k)$-center problem in $O(k^7 n \log^3 n)$ expected time. We can solve the nearly concentric case and hence the $(2, k)$-center problem in $O(k^7 n^{1+\delta})$ deterministic time, for any $\delta > 0$. We present near-linear algorithms for the ℓ_∞ (p, k)-center in $\mathbb{R}^2$ for $p = 4, 5$. The ℓ_∞ $(4, k)$-center problem takes $O(k^{O(1)}n \log n)$ time, and the ℓ_∞ $(5, k)$-center problem takes $O(k^{O(1)}n \log^5 n)$ time. See the full version [2] for the description of these results. We have not made an attempt to minimize the exponent of k. We believe that it can be improved by a more careful analysis.

2   Arrangement of Unit Disks

Let $\mathcal{D} = \{D_1, \ldots, D_n\}$ be a set of n unit disks in $\mathbb{R}^2$. Let $\mathcal{A}(\mathcal{D})$ be the arrangement of $\mathcal{D}$.[1] $\mathcal{A}(\mathcal{D})$ consists of $O(n^2)$ vertices, edges, and faces. For a subset $\mathcal{R} \subseteq \mathcal{D}$, let $\mathfrak{I}(\mathcal{R}) = \bigcap_{D \in \mathcal{R}} D$ denote the intersection of disks in $\mathcal{R}$. Each disk in $\mathcal{R}$ contributes at most one edge in $\mathfrak{I}(\mathcal{R})$. We refer to $\mathfrak{I}(\mathcal{R})$ as a *unit-disk polygon* and a connected portion of $\partial \mathfrak{I}(\mathcal{R})$ as a *unit-disk curve*. We introduce the notion

---

[1] The *arrangement* of $\mathcal{D}$ is the planar decomposition induced by $\mathcal{D}$; its vertices are the intersection points of boundaries of two disks, its edges are the maximal portions of disk boundaries that do not contain a vertex, and its faces are the maximal connected regions of the plane that do not intersect the boundary of any disk.

of level in $\mathcal{A}(\mathcal{D})$, prove a few structural properties of levels, and describe an algorithm that will be useful for our overall algorithm.

Levels and their structural properties. For a point $x \in \mathbb{R}^2$, the *level* of x with respect to $\mathcal{D}$, denoted by $\lambda(x, \mathcal{D})$, is the number of disks in $\mathcal{D}$ that *do not* contain x. (Our definition of level is different from the more common definition in which it is defined as the number of disks whose interiors contain x.) All points lying on an edge or face ϕ of $\mathcal{A}(\mathcal{D})$ have the same level, which we denote by $\lambda(\phi)$. For $k \leq n$, let $\mathcal{A}_k(\mathcal{D})$ (resp. $\mathcal{A}_{\leq k}(\mathcal{D})$) denote the set of points in $\mathbb{R}^2$ whose level is k (resp. at most k); see Fig. 1. By definition, $\mathcal{A}_0(\mathcal{D}) = \mathcal{A}_{\leq 0}(\mathcal{D}) = \mathcal{I}(\mathcal{D})$.

The boundary of $\mathcal{A}_{\leq k}(\mathcal{D})$ is composed of the edges of $\mathcal{A}(\mathcal{D})$. Let $v \in \partial D_1 \cap \partial D_2$, for $D_1, D_2 \in \mathcal{D}$, be a vertex of $\partial \mathcal{A}_{\leq k}(\mathcal{D})$. We call v *convex* (resp. *concave*) if $\mathcal{A}_{\leq k}(\mathcal{D})$ lies in $D_1 \cap D_2$ (resp. $D_1 \cup D_2$) in a sufficiently small neighborhood of v. $\partial \bar{\mathcal{A}}_{\leq 0}(\mathcal{D})$ is composed of convex vertices; see Fig. 1(a). We define the complexity of $\mathcal{A}_{\leq k}(\mathcal{D})$ to be the number of edges of $\mathcal{A}(\mathcal{D})$ whose levels are at most k. Since the complexity of $\mathcal{A}_{\leq 0}(\mathcal{D})$ is n, the following lemma follows from the result by Clarkson and Shor [11] (see also Sharir [23] and Chan [8]).

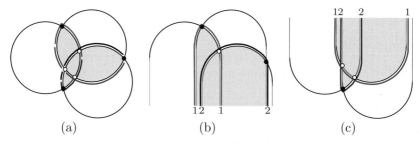

Fig. 1. (a) $\mathcal{A}(\mathcal{D})$, shaded region is $\mathcal{A}_{\leq 1}(\mathcal{D})$, filled (resp. hollow) vertices are convex (resp. concave) vertices of $\mathcal{A}_{\leq 1}(\mathcal{D})$, covering of $\mathcal{A}_{\leq 1}(\mathcal{D})$ edges by six unit-disk curves. (b) $\mathcal{A}(\Gamma^+)$, shaded region is $\mathcal{A}_{\leq 1}(\Gamma^+)$, and the covering of $\mathcal{A}_{\leq 1}(\Gamma^+)$ edges by two concave chains. (c) $\mathcal{A}(\Gamma^-)$, shaded region is $\mathcal{A}_{\leq 1}(\Gamma^-)$, and the covering of $\mathcal{A}_{\leq 1}(\Gamma^-)$ edges by two convex chains.

Lemma 1. [11] *For $k \geq 0$, the complexity of $\mathcal{A}_{\leq k}(\mathcal{D})$ is $O(nk)$.*

Remark 1. The argument by Clarkson and Shor can also be used to prove that $\mathcal{A}_{\leq k}(\mathcal{D})$ has $O(k^2)$ connected components and that it has $O(k^2)$ local minima in $(+y)$-direction. See also [19,10]. These bounds are tight in the worst case; see Fig. 2.

It is well known that the edges in the $\leq k$-level of a line arrangement can be covered by $k + 1$ concave chains [17], as used in [13,7]. We prove a similar result for $\mathcal{A}_{\leq k}(\mathcal{D})$; it can be covered by $O(k)$ unit-disk curves.

For a disk D_i, let γ_i^+ (resp. γ_i^-) denote the set of points that lie in or below (resp. above) D_i; $\partial \gamma_i^+$ consists of the upper semicircle of ∂D_i plus two vertical downward rays emanating from the left and right endpoints of the semicircle

— we refer to these rays as left and right rays. The curve $\partial\gamma_i^-$ has a similar structure. See Fig. 1(b). Set $\Gamma^+ = \{\gamma_i^+ \mid 1 \leq i \leq n\}$ and $\Gamma^- = \{\gamma_i^- \mid 1 \leq i \leq n\}$. Each pair of curves $\partial\gamma_i^+, \partial\gamma_j^+$ intersect in at most one point. (If we assume that the left and right rays are not vertical but have very large positive and negative slopes, respectively, then each pair of boundary curves intersects in exactly one point.) We define the level of a point with respect to Γ^+, Γ^-, or $\Gamma^+ \cup \Gamma^-$ in the same way as with respect to $\mathcal{D}$. A point lies in a disk D_i if and only if it lies in both γ_i^+ and γ_i^-, so we obtain the following inequalities:

$$\max\{\lambda(x, \Gamma^+), \lambda(x, \Gamma^-)\} \leq \lambda(x, \mathcal{D}). \tag{1}$$

$$\lambda(x, \mathcal{D}) \leq \lambda(x, \Gamma^+ \cup \Gamma^-) \leq 2\lambda(x, \mathcal{D}). \tag{2}$$

We cover the edges of $\mathcal{A}_{\leq k}(\Gamma^+)$ by $k + 1$ concave chains as follows. The level of the $(k + 1)$st rightmost left ray is at most k at $y = -\infty$. Let ρ_i be such a ray, belonging to γ_i^+. We trace $\partial\gamma_i^+$, beginning from the point at $y = -\infty$ on ρ_i, as long as $\partial\gamma_i^+$ remains in $\mathcal{A}_{\leq k}(\Gamma^+)$. We stop when we have reached a vertex $v \in \mathcal{A}_{\leq k}(\Gamma^+)$ at which it leaves $\mathcal{A}_{\leq k}(\Gamma^+)$; v is a convex vertex on $\mathcal{A}_{\leq k}(\Gamma^+)$. Suppose $v = \partial\gamma_i^+ \cap \partial\gamma_j^+$. Then $\partial\mathcal{A}_{\leq k}(\Gamma^+)$ follows $\partial\gamma_j^+$ immediately to the right of v, so we switch to $\partial\gamma_j^+$ and repeat the same process. It can be checked that we finally reach $y = -\infty$ on a right ray. Since we switch the curve on a convex vertex, the chain Λ_i^+ we trace is a concave chain composed of a left ray, followed by a unit-disk curve ξ_i^+, and then followed by a right ray. Let $\Lambda_0^+, \Lambda_1^+, \dots, \Lambda_k^+$ be the $k+1$ chains traversed by this procedure. These chains cover all edges of $\mathcal{A}_{\leq k}(\Gamma^+)$, and each edge lies exactly on one chain. Similarly we cover the edges of $\mathcal{A}_{\leq k}(\Gamma^-)$ by $k + 1$ convex curves $\Lambda_0^-, \Lambda_1^-, \dots, \Lambda_k^-$. Let $\Xi = \{\xi_0^+, \dots, \xi_k^+, \xi_0^-, \dots, \xi_k^-\}$ be the family of unit-disk curves induced by these convex and concave chains. By (1), Ξ covers all edges of $\mathcal{A}_{\leq k}(\mathcal{D})$. Since a unit circle intersects a unit-disk curve in at most two points, we conclude the following.

Lemma 2. *The edges of $\mathcal{A}_{\leq k}(\mathcal{D})$ can be covered by at most $2k + 2$ unit-disk curves, and a unit circle intersects $O(k)$ edges of $\mathcal{A}_{\leq k}(\mathcal{D})$.*

The curves in Ξ may contain edges of $\mathcal{A}(\mathcal{D})$ whose levels are greater that k. If we wish to find a family of unit-disk curves whose union is the set of edges in $\mathcal{A}_{\leq k}(\mathcal{D})$, we proceed as follows. We add the x-extremal points of each disk as vertices of $\mathcal{A}(\mathcal{D})$, so each edge is now x-monotone and lies in a lower or an upper semicircle. By (1), only $O(k)$ such vertices lie in $\mathcal{A}_{\leq k}(\mathcal{D})$. We call a vertex of $\mathcal{A}_{\leq k}(\mathcal{D})$ *extremal* if it is an x-extremal point on a disk or an intersection point of a lower and an upper semicircle. Lemma 2 implies that there are $O(k^2)$ extremal vertices. For each extremal vertex v we do the following. If there is an edge e of $\mathcal{A}_{\leq k}(\mathcal{D})$ lying to the right of v, we follow the arc containing e until we reach an extremal vertex or we leave $\mathcal{A}_{\leq k}(\mathcal{D})$. In the former case we stop. In the latter case we are at a convex vertex v' of $\partial\mathcal{A}_{\leq k}(\mathcal{D})$, and we switch to the other arc incident on v' and continue. These curves have been drawn in Fig. 1(a). This procedure returns an x-monotone unit-disk curve that lies in $\mathcal{A}_{\leq k}(\mathcal{D})$. It can be shown that this procedure covers all edges of $\mathcal{A}_{\leq k}(\mathcal{D})$. We thus obtain the following:

Lemma 3. *Let $\mathcal{D}$ be a set of n unit disks in $\mathbb{R}^2$. Given $\mathcal{A}_{\leq k}(\mathcal{D})$, we can compute, in time $O(nk)$, a family of $O(k^2)$ x-monotone unit-disk curves whose union is the set of edges of $\mathcal{A}_{\leq k}(\mathcal{D})$.*

Remark 2. Since $\mathcal{A}_{\leq k}(\mathcal{D})$ can consist of $\Omega(k^2)$ connected components, the $O(k^2)$ bound is tight in the worst case; see Fig. 2.

Emptiness detection of $\mathcal{A}_{\leq k}(\mathcal{D})$. We need a dynamic data structure for storing a set $\mathcal{D}$ of unit disks that supports the following two operations:

- (O1) Insert a disk into $\mathcal{D}$ or delete a disk from $\mathcal{D}$;
- (O2) For a given k, determine whether $\mathcal{A}_{\leq k}(\mathcal{D}) \neq \emptyset$.

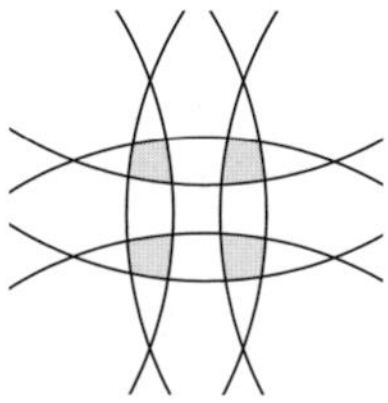

As described by Sharir [24], $\mathcal{I}(\mathcal{D})$ can be maintained under insertion/deletion in $O(\log^2 n)$ time per update. Matoušek [19] has described a data structure for solving LP-type problems with violations. Finding the lowest point in $\mathcal{I}(\mathcal{D})$ can be formulated as an LP-type problem. Therefore using the dynamic data structure with Matoušek's algorithm, we can obtain the following result.

Fig. 2. Lower bound. $\mathcal{A}_{\leq 2}(\mathcal{D})$ (shaded region) has 4 connected components

Lemma 4. *There exists a dynamic data structure for storing a set of n unit disks so that (O1) can be performed in $O(\log^2 n)$ time, and (O2) takes $O(k^3 \log^2 n)$ time.*

3   Well-Separated Disks

In this section we describe an algorithm for the case in which the two disks D_1, D_2 of the optimal solution are well separated. That is, let c_1 and c_2 be the centers of D_1 and D_2, and let r^* be their radius. Then $\|c_1 c_2\| \geq r^*$; see Fig. 3(a). Without loss of generality, let us assume that c_1 lies to the left of c_2. Let D_1^- be the semidisk lying to the left of the line passing through c_1 in direction normal to $c_1 c_2$. A line ℓ is called a separator line if $D_1 \cap D_2 = \emptyset$ and ℓ separates D_1^- from D_2, or $D_1 \cap D_2 \neq \emptyset$ and ℓ separates D_1^- from the intersection points $\partial D_1 \cap \partial D_2$. We first show that we can quickly compute a set of $O(k^2)$ lines that contains a separator line. Next, we describe a decision algorithm, and then we describe the algorithm for computing D_1 and D_2 provided they are well separated.

Computing separator lines. We fix a sufficiently large constant h and choose a set $U = \{u_1, \ldots, u_h\} \subseteq \mathbb{S}^1$ of directions, where $u_i = (\cos(2\pi i/h), \sin(2\pi i/h))$.

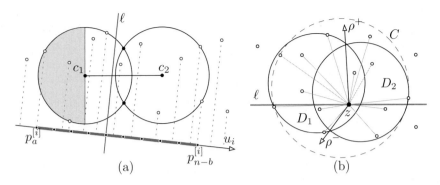

Fig. 3. (a) Let ℓ is a separator line for disks D_1 and D_2. (b) Two unit disks D_1 and D_2 or radius r^* with centers closer than a distance r^*.

For a point $p \in \mathbb{R}^2$ and a direction u_i, let $p^{[i]}$ be the projection of p in the direction normal to u_i. Let $P^{[i]} = \langle p_1^{[i]}, \ldots, p_n^{[i]} \rangle$ be the sorted sequence of projections of points in the direction normal to u_i. For each pair a, b such that $a + b \leq k$, we choose the interval $\delta_{a,b}^{[i]} = [p_a^{[i]}, p_{n-b}^{[i]}]$ and we place $O(1)$ equidistant points in this interval. See Fig. 3(a). Let $L_{a,b}^{[i]}$ be the set of (oriented) lines in the direction normal to u_i and passing though these points. Set

$$L = \bigcup_{\substack{1 \leq i \leq h \\ a+b \leq k}} L_{a,b}^{[i]}.$$

We claim that L contains at least one separator line. Intuitively, let $u_i \in U$ be the direction closest to $\overrightarrow{c_1 c_2}$. Suppose p_a and p_{n-b} are the first and the last points of P in the direction u_i that lie inside $D_1 \cup D_2$. Since $|P \setminus (D_1 \cup D_2)| \leq k$, $a + b \leq k$. If $D_1 \cap D_2 = \emptyset$, then let q be the extreme points of D_1 in direction $\overrightarrow{c_1 c_2}$. Otherwise, let q be the first intersection point of $\partial D_1 \cap \partial D_2$ in direction u_i. Following the same argument as Sharir [24], one can argue that

$$\langle c_1 - q, u_i \rangle \geq \alpha \langle p_{n-b} - p_a, u_i \rangle,$$

where $\alpha \leq 1$ is a constant. Hence if at least 2α points are chosen in the interval $\delta_{a,b}^{[i]}$, then one of the lines in $L_{a,b}^{[i]}$ is a separator line. Omitting all the details, which are similar to the one in [24], we conclude the following.

Lemma 5. *We can compute in $O(k^2 n \log n)$ time a set L of $O(k^2)$ lines that contains a separator line.*

Let D_1, D_2 be a $(2, k)$-center of P, let $\ell \in L$ be a line, and let $P^- \subseteq P$ be the set of points that lie in the left halfspace bounded by ℓ. We call D_1, D_2 a $(2, k)$-center *consistent with* ℓ if $P^- \cap (D_1 \cup D_2) \subseteq D_1$, the center of D_1 lies to the left of ℓ, and ∂D_1 contains at least one point of P^-. We describe a decision algorithm that determines whether there is a $(2, k)$-center of unit radius that is consistent with ℓ. Next, we describe an algorithm for computing a $(2, k)$-center consistent with ℓ, which will lead to computing an optimal $(2, k)$-center of P, provided there is a well-separated optimal $(2, k)$-center of P.

Decision algorithm. Let $\ell \in L$ be a line. We describe an algorithm for determining whether there is a unit radius $(2, k)$-center of P that is consistent with ℓ. Let P^- (resp. P^+) be the subset of points in P that lie in the left (resp. right) halfspace bounded by ℓ; set $n^- = |P^-|$, $n^+ = |P^+|$. Suppose D_1, D_2 is a unit-radius $(2, k)$-center of P consistent with ℓ, and let c_1, c_2 be their centers. Then $P^- \cap (D_1 \cup D_2) \subseteq D_1$ and $|P^- \cap D_1| \geq n^- - k$. For a subset $Q \subset P$, let $\mathcal{D}(Q) = \{D(q) \mid q \in Q\}$ where $D(q)$ is the unit disk centered at q. Let $\mathcal{D}^- = \mathcal{D}(P^-)$ and $\mathcal{D}^+ = \mathcal{D}(P^+)$. For a point $x \in \mathbb{R}^2$, let $\mathcal{D}_x^+ = \{D \in \mathcal{D}^+ \mid x \in D\}$. Since ∂D_1 contains a point of P^- and at most k points of P^- do not lie in D_1, c_1 lies on an edge of $\mathcal{A}_{\leq k}(\mathcal{D}^-)$.

We first compute $\mathcal{A}_{\leq k}(\mathcal{D}^-)$ in $O(nk \log n)$ time. For each disk $D \in \mathcal{D}^+$, we compute the intersection points of ∂D with the edges of $\mathcal{A}_{\leq k}(\mathcal{D}^-)$. By Lemma 2, there are $O(nk)$ such intersection points, and these intersection points split each edge into *edgelets*. The total number of edgelets is also $O(nk)$. Using Lemma 2, we can compute all edgelets in time $O(nk \log n)$. All points on an edgelet γ lie in the same subset of disks of $\mathcal{D}^+$, which we denote by $\mathcal{D}_\gamma^+$. Let $P_\gamma^+ \subseteq P^+$ be the set of centers of disks in $\mathcal{D}_\gamma^+$, and let $\kappa_\gamma = \lambda(\gamma, \mathcal{D}^-)$. A unit disk centered at a point on γ contains P_γ^+ and all but κ_γ points of P^-. If at least $k' = k - \kappa_\gamma$ points of $P^+ \setminus P_\gamma^+$ can be covered by a unit disk, which is equivalent to $\mathcal{A}_{\leq k'}(\mathcal{D}^+ \setminus \mathcal{D}_\gamma)$ being nonempty, then all but k points of P can be covered by two unit disks.

When we move from one edgelet γ of $\mathcal{A}_{\leq k}(\mathcal{D}^-)$ to an adjacent one γ' with σ as their common endpoint, then $\mathcal{D}_\gamma^+ = \mathcal{D}_{\gamma'}^+$ (if σ is a vertex of $\mathcal{A}_{\leq k}(\mathcal{D}^-)$), $\mathcal{D}_{\gamma'}^+ = \mathcal{D}_\gamma^+ \cup \{D\}$ (if $\sigma \in \partial D$ and $\gamma' \subset \{D\}$), or $\mathcal{D}_{\gamma'}^+ = \mathcal{D}_\gamma^+ \setminus \{D\}$ (if $\sigma \in \partial D$ and $\gamma \subset D$). We therefore traverse the graph induced by the edgelets of $\mathcal{A}_{\leq k}(\mathcal{D})$ and maintain $\mathcal{D}_\gamma^+$ in the dynamic data structure described in Section 2 as we visit the edgelets γ of $\mathcal{A}_{\leq k}(\mathcal{D}^-)$. At each step we process an edgelet γ, insert or delete a disk into $\mathcal{D}_\gamma^+$, and test whether $\mathcal{A}_{\leq j}(\mathcal{D}_\gamma^+) = \emptyset$ where $j = k - \lambda(\gamma, \mathcal{D}^-)$. If the answer is yes at any step, we stop. We spend $O(k^3 \log^2 n)$ time at each step, by Lemma 4. Since the number of edgelets is $O(nk)$, we obtain the following.

Lemma 6. *Let P be a set of n points in $\mathbb{R}^2$, ℓ a line in L, and $0 \leq k \leq n$ an integer. We can determine in $O(nk^4 \log^2 n)$ time whether there is a unit-radius $(2, k)$-center of P that is consistent with ℓ.*

Optimization algorithm. Let ℓ be a line in L. Let r^* be the smallest radius of a $(2, k)$-center of P that is consistent with ℓ. Our goal is to compute a $(2, k)$-center of P of radius r^* that is consistent with ℓ. We use the parametric search technique [21] — we simulate the decision algorithm generically at r^* and use the decision algorithm to resolve each comparison, which will be of the form: given $r_0 \in \mathbb{R}^+$, is $r_0 \leq r^*$? We simulate a parallel version of the decision procedure to reduce the number of times the decision algorithm is invoked to resolve a comparison. Note that we need to parallelize only those steps of the simulation that depend on r^*, i.e., that require comparing a value with r^*. Instead of simulating the entire decision algorithm, as in [15], we stop the simulation after computing the edgelets and return the smallest $(2, k)$-center found so far, i.e., the smallest radius for which the decision algorithm returned "yes." Since we stop the simulation earlier, we do not guarantee that we find the a $(2, k)$-center of P of radius r^* that is consistent with ℓ. However, as argued by Eppstein [15], this is sufficient for our purpose.

Let P^-, P^+ be the same as in the decision algorithm. Let $\mathcal{D}^-$, $\mathcal{D}^+$ etc. be the same as above except that each disk is of radius r^* (recall that we do not know the value of r^*). We simulate the algorithm to compute the edgelets of $\mathcal{A}_{\leq k}(\mathcal{D}^-)$ as follows. First, we compute the $\leq k^{th}$ order farthest point Voronoi diagram of P^- in time $O(n \log n + nk^2)$ [5]. Let e be an edge of the diagram with points p and q of P^- as its neighbors, i.e., e is a portion of the bisector of p and q. Then for each point $x \in e$, the disk of radius $||xp||$ centered at x contains at least $n^- - k$ points of P^-. We associate an interval $\delta_e = \{||xp|| \mid x \in e\}$. By definition, e corresponds to a vertex of $\mathcal{A}_{\leq k}(\mathcal{D}^-)$ if and only if $r^* \in \delta_e$; namely, if $||xp|| = r^*$, for some $x \in e$, then x is a vertex of $\mathcal{A}_{\leq k}(\mathcal{D}^-)$, incident upon the edges that are portions of $\partial D(p)$ and $\partial D(q)$. Let X be the sorted sequence of the endpoints of the intervals. By doing a binary search on X and using the decision procedure at each step, we can find two consecutive endpoints between which r^* lies. We can now compute all edges e of the Voronoi diagram such that $r^* \in \delta_e$. We thus compute all vertices of $\mathcal{A}_{\leq k}(\mathcal{D}^-)$. Since we do not know r^*, we do not have actual coordinates of the vertices. We represent each vertex as a pair of points. Similarly, each edge is represented as a point $p \in P^-$, indiciating that e lies in $\partial D(p)$. Once we have all the edges of $\mathcal{A}_{\leq k}(P^-)$, we can construct the graph induced by them and compute $O(k^2)$ x-monotone unit-disk curves whose union is the set of edges in $\mathcal{A}_{\leq k}(P^-)$, using Lemma 3. Since this step does not depend on the value of r^*, we need not parallelize it. Let $\Xi = \{\xi_i, \ldots, \xi_u\}$, $u = O(k^2)$, be the set of these curves.

Next, for each disk $D \in \mathcal{D}^+$ and for each $\xi_i \in \Xi$, we compute the edges of ξ_i that ∂D intersects, using a binary search. We perform these $O(nk^2)$ binary searches in parallel and use the decision algorithm at each step. Incorporating Cole's technique [12] in the binary search we need to invoke the decision procedure only $O(\log n)$ times. For an edge $e \in \mathcal{A}_{\leq k}(\mathcal{D})$, let $\mathcal{D}_e^+ \in \mathcal{D}$ be the set of disks whose boundaries intersect e. We sort the disks in $\mathcal{D}_e^+$ by the order in which their boundaries intersect e. By doing this in parallel for all edges and using a parallel sorting algorithm for each edge, we can perform this step by invoking the decision algorithm $O(\log n)$ times. The total time spent is $O(nk^4 \log^3 n)$.

Putting pieces together. We repeat the optimization algorithm for all lines in L and return the smallest $(2, k)$-center that is consistent with a line in L. The argument of Eppstein [15] implies that if an optimal $(2, k)$-center of P is well-separated, then the above algorithm returns an optimal $(2, k)$-center of P. Hence, we conclude the following:

Lemma 7. *Let P be a set of n points in $\mathbb{R}^2$ and $0 \leq k \leq n$ an integer. If an optimal $(2, k)$-center of P is well separated, then the $(2, k)$-center problem for P can be solved in $O(nk^6 \log^3 n)$ time.*

4   Nearly Concentric Disks

In this section we describe an algorithm for when the two disks D_1 and D_2 of the optimal solution are not well separated. More specifically, let c_1 and c_2 be the centers of D_1 and D_2 and let r^* be their radius. Then this section handles the case where $||c_1 c_2|| \leq r^*$.

First, we find an *intersector point* z of D_1 and D_2 — a point that lies in $D_1 \cap D_2$. We show how z defines a set $\mathcal{P}$ of $O(n^2)$ possible partitions of P into two subsets, such that for one partition $P_{i,j}$, $P \setminus P_{i,j}$ the following holds: $(D_1 \cup D_2) \cap P = (D_1 \cap P_{i,j}) \cup (D_2 \cap (P \setminus P_{i,j}))$. Finally, we show how to search through the set $\mathcal{P}$ in $O(k^7 n^{1+\delta})$ time, deterministically, for any $\delta > 0$, or in $O(k^7 n \log^3 n)$ expected time.

Finding an intersector point. Let C be the circumcircle of $P \cap (D_1 \cup D_2)$. Eppstein [15] shows that we can select $O(1)$ points inside C such that at least one, z, lies in $D_1 \cap D_2$. We can hence prove the following.

Lemma 8. *Let P be a set of n points in $\mathbb{R}^2$. We can generate in $O(nk^3)$ time a set $\mathcal{Z}$ of $O(k^3)$ points such that for any nearly concentric $(2, k)$-center D_1, D_2, one of the points in $\mathcal{Z}$ is their intersector point.*

Proof. If the circumcircle of P is not C, then at least one point of $P \cap \partial C$ must not be in $D_1 \cup D_2$. We remove each point and recurse until we have removed k points. Matoušek [19] shows that we can keep track of which subsets have already been evaluated and bounds the size of the recursion tree to $O(k^3)$. Building the entire recursion tree takes $O(nk^3)$ time. Since $|P \setminus C| \leq k$, at least one node in the recursion tree describes $P \cup C$. Generating $O(1)$ possible intersector points for each node completes the proof. □

Let z be an intersector point of D_1 and D_2, and let ρ^+, ρ^- be the two rays from z to the points of $\partial D_1 \cap \partial D_2$. Since D_1 and D_2 are nearly concentric, the angle between them is at least some constant θ. We choose a set $U \subseteq S^1$ of $h = \lceil 2\pi/\theta \rceil$ uniformly distributed directions. For at least one $u \in U$, the line ℓ in direction u and passing through z separates ρ^+ and ρ^-, see Fig. 3(b). We fix a pair z, u in $\mathcal{Z} \times U$ and compute a $(2, k)$-center of P, as described below. We repeat this algorithm for every pair. If D_1 and D_2 are nearly concentric, then our algorithm returns an optimal $(2, k)$-center.

Fixing z and u. For a subset $X \subset P$ and for an integer $t \geq 0$, let $r^t(X)$ denote the minimum radius of a $(1, t)$-center of X. Let P^+ (resp. P^-) be the subset of P lying above (resp. below) the x-axis; set $n^+ = |P^+|$ and $n^- = |P^-|$. Sort $P^+ = \langle p_1^+, \ldots, p_{n^+}^+ \rangle$ in clockwise order and $P^- = \langle p_1^-, \ldots, p_{n^-}^- \rangle$ in counterclockwise order. For $0 \leq i \leq n^+$, $0 \leq j \leq n^-$, let $P_{i,j} = \{p_1^+, \ldots, p_i^+, p_1^-, \ldots, p_j^-\}$ and $Q_{i,j} = P \setminus P_{i,j}$. For $0 \leq t \leq k$, let

$$m_{i,j}^t = \max\{r^t(P_{i,j}), r^{k-t}(Q_{i,j})\}.$$

For $0 \leq t \leq k$, we define an $n^+ \times n^-$ matrix M^t such that $M^t(i,j) = m_{i,j}^t$.

Suppose z is an intersector point of D_1 and D_2, ℓ separates ρ^+ and ρ^-, and ρ^+ (resp. ρ^-) lies between p_a^+, p_{a+1}^+ (resp. p_b^-, p_{b+1}^-). Then $P \cap (D_1 \cup D_2) = (P_{a,b} \cap D_1) \cup (Q_{a,b} \cup D_2)$; see Fig 3(b). If $|P_{a,b} \setminus D_1| = t$, then $r^* = m_{a,b}^t$. The problem thus reduces to computing

$$\mu(z, u) = \min_{i,j,t} m_{i,j}^t$$

where the minimum is taken over $0 \leq i \leq n^+$, $0 \leq j \leq n^-$, and $0 \leq t \leq k$. For each t, we compute $\mu^t(z, u) = \min_{i,j} m_{i,j}^t$ and choose the smallest among them.

Computing $\mu^t(z, u)$. We note two properties of the matrix M^t that will help search for $\mu^t(z, u)$:

- (P1) If $r^t(P_{i,j}) > r^{k-t}(Q_{i,j})$ then $m_{i,j}^t \leq m_{i',j'}^t$ for $i' \geq i$ and $j' \geq j$. These partitions only add points to $P_{i,j}$ and thus cannot decrease $r^t(P_{i,j})$. Similarly, if $r^{k-t}(Q_{i,j}) > r^t(P_{i,j})$, then $m_{i,j}^t < m_{i',j'}^t$ for $i' \leq i$ and $j' \leq j$.
- (P2) Given a value r, if $r^t(P_{i,j}) > r$, then $m_{i',j'}^t > r$ for $i' \geq i$ and $j' \geq j$, and if $r^t(Q_{i,j}) > r$, then $m_{i',j'}^t > r$ for $i' \leq i$ and $j' \leq j$.

Deterministic solution. We now have the machinery to use a technique of Frederickson and Johnson [16]. For simplicity, let us assume that $n^+ = n^- = 2^{\tau+1}$ where $\tau = \lceil \log_2 n \rceil + O(1)$. The algorithm works in τ phases. In the beginning of the hth phase we have a collection $\mathcal{M}_h$ of $O(2^h)$ submatrices of M^t, each of size $(2^{\tau-h+1}+1) \times (2^{\tau-h+1}+1)$. Initially $\mathcal{M}_1 = \{M^t\}$. In the hth phase we divide each matrix $N \in \mathcal{M}_h$ into four submatrices each of size $(2^{\tau-h}+1) \times (2^{\tau-h}+1)$ that overlap along one row and one column. We call the cell common to all four submatrices the center cell of N. Let $\mathcal{M}_h'$ be the resulting set of matrices. Let $\mathcal{C} = \{(i_1, j_1), \ldots, (i_s, j_s)\}$ be the set of center cells of matrices in $\mathcal{M}_h$. We compute m_{i_l,j_l}^t for each $1 \leq l \leq s$. We use (P1) to remove the matrices of $\mathcal{M}_h$ that are guaranteed not to contain the value $\mu^t(z, u)$. In particular, if $m_{i_l,j_l}^t = r^t(P_{i_l,j_l})$ and there is a matrix $N \in \mathcal{M}_h'$ with the upper-left corner cell (i', j') such that $i' \geq i_l$ and $j' \geq j_l$, then we can remove N. Similarly if $m_{i_l,j_l}^t = r^{k-t}(Q_{i,j})$ and there is a matrix $N \in \mathcal{M}_h'$ with the lower-right corner cell (i', j') such that $i' \leq i_l$ and $j' \leq j_l$, we can delete N. It can be proved that after the pruning step if we have a matrix N in $\mathcal{M}_h'$ such that it spans $[a_1, a_2]$ rows and $[b_1, b_2]$ columns of M^t, then $m_{a_1,b_1}^t = r^t(P_{a_1,b_1})$ and $m_{a_2,b_2}^t = r^{k-t}(Q_{a_2,b_2})$. This implies that $O(n)$ cells remain in $\mathcal{M}_h'$ after the pruning step. We set $\mathcal{M}_h'$ to $\mathcal{M}_{h+1}$.

Finally, it is shown in [15] that the center cells in $\mathcal{C}$ can be connected by a monotone path in M^t, which consists of $O(n)$ cells. Since $P_{i,j}$ differs from $P_{i-1,j}$ and $P_{i,j-1}$ by one point, we can compute m_{i_l,j_l}^t for all $(i_l, j_l) \in \mathcal{C}$ using an algorithm of Agarwal and Matoušek [1] in total time $O(k^3 n^{1+\delta})$ for any $\delta > 0$. Agarwal and Matoušek's data structure can maintain the value of the radius of the smallest enclosing disk under insertions and deletions in $O(n^\delta)$ time per update. Each step in the path is one update, and then searching through the $O(k^3)$ nodes of the recursion tree of all possible outliers — each requires $O(1)$ updates — takes $O(k^3 n^\delta)$ time per cell. Hence, each phase of the algorithm takes $O(k^3 n^{1+\delta})$ time.

Lemma 9. *Given $z \in Z$, $u \in U$, and $0 \le t \le k$, $\mu^t(z, u)$ can be computed in time $O(k^3 n^{1+\delta})$, for any $\delta > 0$.*

Randomized solution. We can slightly improve the dependence on n by using the dynamic data structure in Section 2 and (P2). As before, in the hth phase, for some constant $c > 1$, we maintain a set $\mathcal{M}_h$ of at most $c2^h$ submatrices of M^t, each of side length $2^{\tau-h+1}+1$, and their center cells $\mathcal{C}$. Each submatrix is divided into four submatrices of side length $2^{\tau-h}+1$, forming a set $\mathcal{M}'_h$. To reduce the size of $\mathcal{M}'_h$, we choose a random center cell (i, j) from $\mathcal{C}$ and evaluate $r = m^t_{i,j}$ in $O(k^3 n)$ time. For each other center cell $(i', j') \in \mathcal{C}$, $m^t_{i',j'} > r$ with probability $1/2$, and using (P2), we can remove a submatrix from $\mathcal{M}'_h$. Eppstein [15] shows that by repeating this process a constant number of times, we expect to reduce the size of $\mathcal{M}'_h$ to $c2^{h+1}$.

On each iteration we use the dynamic data structure described in Section 2. For $O(n)$ insertions and deletions, it can compare each center cell from $\mathcal{C}$ to r in $O(k^3 n \log^2 n)$ time. Thus, finding $\mu^t(z, u)$ takes expected $O(nk^3 \log^3 n)$ time.

Lemma 10. *Given $z \in Z$, $u \in U$, and $0 \le t \le k$, $\mu^t(z, u)$ can be computed in expected time $O(k^3 \log^3 n)$.*

Putting pieces together. By repeating either above algorithm for all $0 \le t \le k$ and for all pair $(z, u) \in Z \times U$, we can compute a $(2, k)$-center of P that is optimal if D_1 and D_2 are nearly concentric. Combining this with Lemma 7, we obtain the main result of the paper.

Theorem 1. *Given a set P of n points in $\mathbb{R}^2$ and an integer $k \ge 0$, an optimal $(2, k)$-center of P can be computed in $O(k^7 n^{1+\delta})$ (deterministic) time, for any $\delta > 0$ or in $O(k^7 n \log^3 n)$ expected time.*

Acknowledgements. We thank Sariel Har-Peled for posing the problem and for several helpful discussions.

References

1. Agarwal, P.K., Matoušek, J.: Dynamic half-space range reporting and its applications. Algorithmica 13, 325–345 (1995)
2. Agarwal, P.K., Phillips, J.M.: An efficient algorithm for 2D Euclidean 2-center with outliers (2008) arXiV:0806.4326

3. Agarwal, P.K., Sharir, M.: Planar geometric locations problems. Algorithmica 11, 185–195 (1994)
4. Agarwal, P.K., Sharir, M.: Efficient algorithms for geometric optimization. ACM Computing Surveys 30, 412–458 (1998)
5. Aggarwal, A., Guibas, L.J., Saxe, J., Shor, P.W.: A linear-time algorithm for computing the voronoi diagram of a convex polygon. Discrete Comput. Geom. 4, 591–604 (1989)
6. Chan, T.: More planar two-center algorithms. Comput. Geom.: Theory Apps. 13, 189–198 (1999)
7. Chan, T.: Low-dimensional linear programming with violations. SIAM J. Comput. 34, 879–893 (2005)
8. Chan, T.: On the bichromatic k-set problem. In: Proc. 19th Annu. ACM-SIAM Sympos. Discrete Algs., pp. 561–570 (2007)
9. Charikar, M., Khuller, S., Mount, D.M., Narasimhan, G.: Algorithms for faciity location problems with outliers. In: 12th Annu. ACM-SIAM Sympos. on Discrete Algs., pp. 642–651 (2001)
10. Clarkson, K.L.: A bound on local minima of arrangements that implies the upper bound theorem. Discrete Comput. Geom. 10, 427–433 (1993)
11. Clarkson, K.L., Shor, P.W.: Applications of random sampling in geometry, II. Discrete Comput. Geom. 4, 387–421 (1989)
12. Cole, R.: Slowing down sorting networks to obtain faster sorting algorithms. Journal of ACM 34, 200–208 (1987)
13. Dey, T.K.: Improved bounds for planar k-sets and related problems. Discrete Comput. Geom. 19, 373–382 (1998)
14. Drezner, Z., Hamacher, H.: Facility Location: Applications and Theory. Springer, Heidelberg (2002)
15. Eppstein, D.: Faster construction of planar two-centers. In: Proc. 8th Annu. ACM-SIAM Sympos. on Discrete Algs., pp. 131–138 (1997)
16. Frederickson, G.N., Johnson, D.B.: The complexity of selection and ranking in $x+y$ and matrices with sorted columns. J. Comput. Syst. Sci. 24, 197–208 (1982)
17. Gusfield, D.: Bounds for the parametric minimum spanning tree problem. In: Humboldt Conf. on Graph Theory, Combinatorics Comput., pp. 173–183. Utilitas Mathematica (1979)
18. Hochbaum, D.S. (ed.): Approximation Algorithms for NP-hard Problems. PWS Publishing Company (1995)
19. Matoušek, J.: On geometric optimization with few violated constraints. Discrete Comput. Geom. 14, 365–384 (1995)
20. Matoušek, J., Welzl, E., Sharir, M.: A subexponential bound for linear programming and related problems. Algorithmica 16, 498–516 (1996)
21. Megiddo, N.: Linear-time algorithms for linear programming in $\mathbb{R}^3$ and related problems. SIAM J. Comput. 12, 759–776 (1983)
22. Megiddo, N., Supowit, K.J.: On the complexity of some common geometric location problems. SIAM J. Comput. 12, 759–776 (1983)
23. Sharir, M.: On k-sets in arrangement of curves and surfaces. Discrete Comput. Geom. 6, 593–613 (1991)
24. Sharir, M.: A near-linear time algorithm for the planar 2-center problem. Discrete Comput. Geom. 18, 125–134 (1997)
25. Sharir, M., Welzl, E.: Rectilinear and polygonal p-piercing and p-center problems. In: Proc. 12th Annu. Sympos. Comput. Geom., pp. 122–132 (1996)

A Near-Tight Bound for the Online Steiner Tree Problem in Graphs of Bounded Asymmetry

Spyros Angelopoulos

Max-Planck-Institut für Informatik
Campus E1 4, Saarbrücken 66123, Germany
sangelop@mpi-inf.mpg.de

Abstract. The edge asymmetry of a directed, edge-weighted graph is defined as the maximum ratio of the weight of antiparallel edges in the graph, and can be used as a measure of the heterogeneity of links in a data communication network. In this paper we provide a near-tight upper bound on the competitive ratio of the Online Steiner Tree problem in graphs of bounded edge asymmetry α. This problem has applications in efficient multicasting over networks with non-symmetric links. We show an improved upper bound of $O\left(\min\left\{\max\left\{\alpha\frac{\log k}{\log \alpha}, \alpha\frac{\log k}{\log\log k}\right\}, k\right\}\right)$ on the competitive ratio of a simple greedy algorithm, for any request sequence of k terminals. The result almost matches the lower bound of $\Omega\left(\min\left\{\max\left\{\alpha\frac{\log k}{\log \alpha}, \alpha\frac{\log k}{\log\log k}\right\}, k^{1-\epsilon}\right\}\right)$ (where ϵ is an arbitrarily small constant) due to Faloutsos *et al.* [8] and Angelopoulos [2].

1 Introduction

The *Steiner Tree* problem occupies a central place in the area of approximation and online algorithms. In its standard version, the problem is defined as follows. Given an undirected graph $G = (V, E)$ with a weight (cost) function $c : E \to \mathbb{R}^+$ on the edges, and a subset of vertices $K \subseteq V$ with $|K| = k$ (also called *terminals*), the goal is to find a minimum-cost tree which spans all vertices in K. When the input graph is *directed*, the input to the problem must specify, in addition to G and K, a vertex $r \in V$ called the *root*. The problem is then to find a minimum cost *arborescence* rooted at r which spans all vertices in K.

In the *online* version of the problem, the terminals in K are revealed to the algorithm as a sequence of requests. When a request for terminal $u \in V$ is issued, and assuming a directed graph, the algorithm must guarantee a directed path from r to u. The input graph G is assumed to be known to the algorithm. Using the standard framework of competitive analysis (see, e.g., [6]), the objective is then to design online algorithms of small *competitive ratio*.

Apart from its theoretical importance, the Steiner tree problem is useful in modeling efficient multicast communication over a network. The reader is referred to [10] for an in-depth study of the relation between Steiner tree problems and network multicasting.

D. Halperin and K. Mehlhorn (Eds.): ESA 2008, LNCS 5193, pp. 76–87, 2008.

The majority of existing research in Steiner trees and its generalizations applies to undirected graphs. In contrast, actual communication networks contain, in their majority, links asymmetric in the quality of service they offer; this situation is even mored prevalent in satellite and radio networks [7]. Motivated by this observation, Ramanathan [11] introduced the problem of multicast-tree generation in the presence of asymmetric links. To this end, he considered several metrics of network asymmetry, among which the *maximum edge asymmetry* is the most intuitive and easiest to measure in a real network. Formally, the measure is defined as the maximum ratio of the weights of antiparallel links. More precisely, let A denote the set of pairs of vertices in V such that if the pair u, v is in A, then either $(v, u) \in E$ or $(u, v) \in E$ (i.e, there is an edge from u to v or an edge from v to u or both). Then the edge asymmetry is defined as

$$\alpha = \max_{\{v,u\} \in A} \frac{c(v, u)}{c(u, v)}$$

According to this measure, undirected graphs are the class of graphs of asymmetry $\alpha = 1$, whereas directed graphs in which there is at least one pair of vertices v, u such that $(v, u) \in E$, but $(u, v) \notin E$ are graphs with unbounded asymmetry ($\alpha = \infty$). Between these extreme cases, graphs of bounded asymmetry can be useful in modeling networks with a certain degree of link heterogeneity.

The competitive ratio of the online Steiner tree problem in graphs of either constant, or unbounded asymmetry is tightly bound. For the former class, Imase and Waxman [9] showed a bound of $\Theta(\log k)$, achieved by a simple greedy algorithm, (a result which was extended by Berman and Coulston [5] to the Generalized Steiner Problem). The performance of the greedy algorithm for online Steiner Trees and its genereralizations has also been studied by Awerbuch *et al.* [3] and Westbrook and Yan [13]. For the online Steiner Tree in the Euclidean plane, the best known lower bound on the competitive ratio is $\Omega(\log k / \log \log k)$ due to Alon and Azar [4]. On the other hand, Westbrook and Yan [12] showed that in directed graphs (of unbounded asymmetry), the competitive ratio can be bad as $\Omega(k)$.

Faloutsos *et al.* [8] were the first to study the online Steiner tree problem in graphs of bounded asymmetry. They showed that a simple greedy algorithm (to which we refer to as GREEDY) has competitive ratio $O(\min\{\alpha \log k, k\})$. The algorithm works by connecting each requested terminal u to the current arborescence by buying the edges in a least-cost directed path from the current arborescence to u. On the negative side, they showed a lower bound of $\Omega\left(\min\left\{\frac{\alpha \log k}{\log \alpha}, k\right\}\right)$ on the competitive ratio of every deterministic algorithm. Angelopoulos [2] (see also [1] for the full version) improved the upper bound on the competitiveness of GREEDY to $O\left(\min\left\{\alpha \frac{\log k}{\log \log \alpha}, k\right\}\right)$, and showed a corresponding lower bound of $\Omega\left(\min\left\{\frac{\alpha \log k}{\log \log k}, k^{1-\epsilon}\right\}\right)$ for every constant $0 < \epsilon < 1$.

It is important to note that when $\alpha \in \Omega(k)$ the lower bound on the competitive ratio due to [8] is $\Omega(k)$, which is obviously tight (using the trivial upper bound of $O(k)$ for GREEDY). Thus the problem is interesting only when $\alpha \in o(k)$.

In this paper we show[1] the following near-tight upper bound:

Theorem 1. *The competitive ratio of* GREEDY *for an input graph of asymmetry* α *and a request sequence of k terminals is* $O\left(\min\left\{\max\left\{\alpha\frac{\log k}{\log\alpha}, \alpha\frac{\log k}{\log\log k}\right\}, k\right\}\right)$.

The result almost matches the lower bound due to [8] and [2], namely $\Omega\left(\min\left\{\max\left\{\alpha\frac{\log k}{\log\alpha}, \alpha\frac{\log k}{\log\log k}\right\}, k^{1-\epsilon}\right\}\right)$ (where ϵ is any arbitrarily small constant) In particular it provides a tight bound on the competitive ratio of the problem for the case where either $\alpha \in O(k^{1-\epsilon})$ (for some constant $\epsilon \in (0,1)$) or $\alpha \in \Omega(k)$. In contrast, [2] is not tight when α is relatively small, e.g., when α is polylogarithmic in k. Note that a gap still remains for a narrow interval of values for α, namely when $\alpha \in \omega(k^{1-\epsilon})$ for all ϵ, and also $\alpha \in O(k)$ (for instance when $\alpha = k/f(k)$, with $f(k)$ polylogarithmic in k). In such a case, the best upper bound we can guarantee is $O(k)$, whereas the best lower bound is $\Omega(\alpha)$.

1.1   Preliminaries and Notation

We denote by $e = (v, u)$ and $\bar{e} = (u, v)$ a pair of antiparallel directed edges. Let $T = (r', V', E')$ be an arborescence rooted at r', we denote by $\hat{T}$ the graph (V', E''), with $E'' = E' \cup \{\bar{e} : e \in E'\}$. In words, $\hat{T}$ induces all edges in T as well as all their antiparallel edges. We denote by $p_T(u, v)$ (resp. $p_{\hat{T}(u,v)}$) the simple directed path from u to v using exclusively edges in T (resp. $\hat{T}$). Note that such paths are uniquely defined (provided that $p_T(u, v)$ exists in T).

The cost of a directed path p will be denoted by $c(p)$. We denote by $c(T)$ the cost of arborescence T, namely the sum of the cost of the directed edges in T. We emphasize that only edges in T and none of their antiparallel edges contribute to $c(T)$. We will always use T^* to denote the optimal arborescence on input (G, K), with $|K| = k$, and $OPT = c(T^*)$. For any $K' \subseteq K$, we let $c_{GR}(K')$ denote the cost that GREEDY pays on the subset K' of the input (in other words, the contribution of terminals in K' towards the total cost of GREEDY). For convenience, we will be using the term "tree" to refer to a (rooted) arborescence.

2   Outline of the Proof of Theorem 1 and Intuition

In order to prove Theorem 1, we first show that it applies to situations in which the spanning arborescence has a fairly simple structure: in particular, to instances called *comb instances* in [2] (see Figure 1 for an illustration).

Definition 1. *Let T' denote a tree rooted at vertex $r' \in V$ and let $K' \subseteq K$, with $|K'| = k'$. We call the triplet $C = (T', K', r')$ a comb instance, or simply comb if the following hold: T' consists of a directed path P from r' to a certain vertex v_1, which visits vertices $v_{k'}, \ldots, v_1$ in this order (but possibly other vertices too);*

---

[1] Due to space constraints, several technical proofs are either omitted or only sketched in this paper.

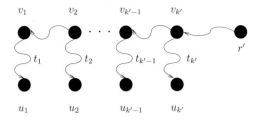

Fig. 1. The structure of a comb instance

there are also disjoint directed paths t_i from v_i to u_i. No other edges are in T'. Finally the set K' is precisely the set $\{u_1, \ldots, u_{k'}\}$. We call P the backbone of $\mathcal{C}$, and the paths t_i the terminal paths of the comb. The vertex set of $\mathcal{C}$ is the set of vertices in T'.

The following is a key theorem in the analysis of GREEDY.

Theorem 2. *Given the comb* $\mathcal{C} = (T', K', r')$, *let* $z \in K'$ *denote the terminal requested the earliest among all terminals in* K'. *Then* $c_{GR}(K') = c_{GR}(z) + O\left(\max\left\{\alpha\frac{\log k'}{\log \alpha}, \alpha\frac{\log k'}{\log \log k'}\right\}\right)c(T')$.

Given Theorem 2, the main result (Theorem 1) follows by partitioning the set of all requests K into a collection of near-disjoint comb-instances, along the lines of Lemma 3.1 in [2] (we omit the proof). Here, by near-disjoint we require that every edge in T^* appears in at most two comb instances.

In order to prove Theorem 2, let π denote a permutation of $\{1, \ldots, k'\}$ such that $\sigma = u_{\pi_1}, \ldots, u_{\pi_{k'}}$ is the sequence of the requests in K' in the order in which they are requested (hence $z = u_{\pi_1}$). Note that we aim towards bounding $c_{GR}(K' \setminus u_{\pi_1})$. To this end, we will determine an assignment for every terminal u_{π_i} with $2 \leq i \leq k'$ to a *specific* terminal $\bar{u}_{\pi_i} \in \{u_{\pi_1}, \ldots u_{\pi_{i-1}}\}$. We call terminal $\bar{u}_{\pi_i}$ the *mate* of u_{π_i}. Let q_i denote the directed path in $\hat{T}$ from $\bar{u}_{\pi_i}$ to u_{π_i}, also called the *connection path* for u_{π_i}. It suffices to show that

$$C \overset{\text{def}}{=} \sum_{i=2}^{k'} c(q_i) = O\left(\max\left\{\alpha\frac{\log k'}{\log \alpha}, \alpha\frac{\log k'}{\log \log k'}\right\}\right)c(T'). \tag{1}$$

Comb instances were identified in [2] as the hard instances for the problem, and for such instances, a weaker version of Theorem 2 was proved (c.f. Lemma 3.2 in [2]). More precisely, the definition of the comb in [2] requires a strict upper bound of $O(\alpha)$ on the number of terminals in the comb: this leads to an upper bound for $c_{GR}(K' \setminus u_{\pi_1})$ equal to $O\left(\alpha\frac{\log \alpha}{\log \log \alpha}\right)c(T')$. The proof of the main result in [2] proceeds then by first extending the result to all subtrees of T^* of $O(\alpha)$ terminals (not necessarily combs), and then by applying it, in a recursive manner, in a hierarchical partition of T^* in trees of $O(\alpha)$ terminals each. This process yields an additional multiplicative overhead of $\log k / \log \alpha$ compared to the cost incurred by a comb instance of size $O(\alpha)$.

In this paper we follow a different approach. We allow the combs to contain an arbitrarily large number of terminals, which may very well be in $\Omega(\alpha)$. This allows us to bypass the need for recursion, and thus to save the factor $\log k / \log \alpha$. Instead, as already mentioned, suffices to decompose T^* (and K) into a collection of near-disjoint comb instances. In this more general setting, some of the high-level proof ideas remain as in [2]: we will still partition the terminals in a comb in appropriately defined subsets called *runs* which dictate how to select the proper mate for each terminal. However, the definition of runs and the assignment of mates in [2] is not applicable anymore when $k' \in \Omega(\alpha)$: In [2] a connection path can be as costly as the cost of the backbone (which becomes far too expensive if the number of terminals in the comb is in $\Omega(k)$). Instead, a substantially more involved assignment is required.

Definition 2. *Let $\mathcal{C} = (T', K', r')$ be a comb instance. For a terminal u_i in the comb we say that its* index *is i. For two terminals u_i, u_j in the comb with $i < j$ we say that u_i precedes u_j in $\mathcal{C}$ (denoted by $u_i \prec u_j$). We say that u_j is* between *u_i and $u_{i'}$ iff $u_i \prec u_j \prec u_{i'}$. For $u_i \prec u_j$ we call the path $p_{T'}(v_j, v_i)$ the segment of u_i, u_j and we denote it by $s(u_i, u_j)$. The* interval *(u_i, u_j) is simply the pair of indices of u_i, u_j , namely the pair (i, j). A terminal u_l is in the interval (i, j) if $u_i \preceq u_l \preceq u_j$ (here $u_i \preceq u_l$ means either $u_i \prec u_l$ or u_i is identical to u_l).*

With a slight abuse of notation, we use the term "segment" to refer to both a path and its cost, when this is clear from context.

3   Proof of Theorem 2

3.1   Assignment of Terminals to Their Mates

The first step towards bounding the cost of the connection paths for terminals in the comb is to assign each terminal to a unique mate. This assignment is determined by Algorithm 1. We also seek a partition of terminals as they are being requested, in particular, every terminal becomes the member of a unique *run* (we can think of each run as being assigned a unique integer id, starting with 0 and increasing by 1 every time a new run is initiated). For a terminal u we denote by $run(u)$ the run to which u is assigned. Define $w = \min\{\alpha, x\}$, where x is the solution to $x^x = k'$, hence $x = \Theta(\frac{\log k'}{\log \log k'})$. Without loss of generality we will assume that x is integral.

Let $u = u_{\pi_{i+1}}$ denote the current request and U_i denote the set of the i previously requested terminals. Every terminal u (with the exception of terminals in run 0) is characterized by two unique terminals in the set U_i, say terminals $u_l, u_h \in U_i$ such that $u_l \prec u \prec u_h$, and no other terminal in U_i is in the interval (u_l, u_h). We call u_l and u_h the *immediate successor and predecessor of* u, respectively, *at the time of the request to* u. After u is revealed, the algorithm assigns a *label* to each of the resulting intervals (u_l, u) and (u, u_h). There are four types of labels an interval can be assigned, and their semantics is related to the action at the time u is requested:

- If the interval (u_l, u_h) has been labeled `free`, then u will initiate a new run, say r. We call u the *initiator* of r (denoted by $in(r) = u$).
- If the interval (u_l, u_h) has been labeled `left` then u will be assigned u_l as its mate (i.e its immediate predecessor at the time of request).
- If the interval (u_l, u_h) has been labeled `right` then u will be assigned u_h as its mate (i.e. its immediate successor at the time of request).
- A `blank` label is the default labeling for an interval, if the assignment algorithm does not explicitly assign a label in the set {`free`, `left`, `right`}.

At a high-level, the assignment algorithm works as follows: In the event u is not between two terminals in U_i (i.e., it does not have either a successor or a predecessor in U_i) it will become part of run 0 (lines 1-9): this is a set-up phase for all remaining runs. Otherwise, let u_l and u_h denote the immediate predecessor/successor of u among terminals in U_i, at the time u is requested. (Note that u_{max} is defined as the terminal of highest index in the comb, among terminals in U_i, whereas u_{min} is the terminal of smallest such index).

If the interval (u_l, u_h) is free, then the assignment algorithm invokes algorithm `Free` which initiates a new run, say r: the run is associated with a *representative*, defined as $rep(r) \equiv u_h$, the *left-end of the run*, defined as $l(r) = u_l$ and a *segment*, defined by $seg(r) = s(u_l, u_h) = s(l(r), rep(r))$. The representative of the run is assigned to be the mate of u. Last, we set the parameter $R(u')$ to be equal to r, for all u' between u_l and u_h in the comb. The meaning of this assignment is that future requests for terminals within (u_l, u_h) should become members of the run r (unless their $R()$ value changes, in the meantime, due to subsequent requests).

In any other case the assignment algorithm invokes algorithm `NonFree` which assigns u to the run $r = R(u)$, and follows a more complicated rule for assigning a mate and labels: More specifically, if the interval (u_l, u_h) is left (resp right) then the assignment and labeling is performed in lines 2–6 (resp 7–11), and u is assigned its immediate predecessor (resp. successor) as its mate. The only remaining possibility is for (u_l, u_h) to be a blank interval (lines 13–23). In this case, if u is "close" to u_l (resp. u_h) wrt the cost $s(u_l, u)$ (resp. $s(u, u_h)$), then u is assigned u_l as its mate in lines 13–16 (resp. u is assigned u_h as its mate in lines 17–20). If u is not close to either terminal then it is assigned the representative of the run it belongs to as its mate (line 22).

In order to bound the total connection cost C, we will express C as the sum of six partial costs, denoted by $C_1, \ldots C_6$ ($C_1, \ldots, C_5$ apply to terminals in runs other than run 0). In particular:

- C_1 is defined as the cost of connection paths due to edges e such that $\bar{e}$ belongs in some terminal path t_i in the comb (i.e., the cost of edges antiparallel to edges of a terminal path).
- C_2 is defined as the cost of connection paths due to edges e such that $\bar{e}$ belongs in the backbone P (i.e., the cost of edges antiparallel to edges in the backbone) and which are bought by connection paths established in either line 3 or line 14 of `NonFree` (i.e., when the current request is assigned its immediate predecessor as its mate).

Input : Request u and the existing assignment of terminals in U_i
Output: Assignment of u to an appropriate run and an appropriate mate
1 **if** $u \succ u_{max}$ **then**
2   assign u to run 0
3      $mate(u) \leftarrow u_{max}$
4   label interval (u_{max}, u) free
5 **end**
6 **if** $u \prec u_{min}$ **then**
7   assign u to run 0
8      $mate(u) \leftarrow u_{min}$
9   label interval (u, u_{min}) free
10 **end**
11 **else**
12   Let u_l and u_h be the immediate successor and predecessor of u, among terminals in U_i
13   **if** $interval$ (u_l, u_h) is free **then**
14   Free(u,u_l,u_h)
15   **end**
16   **else**
17   Non-free(u,u_l,u_h)
18   **end**
19 **end**

Algorithm 1. Assignment of terminals to runs and mates

---

1 Initiate a run r with $seg(r) = s(u_l, u_h)$; set $rep(r) \leftarrow u_h$ and $l(r) \leftarrow u_l$
2 label (u_l, u) and (u, u_h) blank
3 Set $mate(u) \leftarrow u_h$
4 **if** $s(u, u_h) \leq seg(r)/w$ **then**
5   label (u, u_h) left
6 **end**
7 **if** $s(u_l, u) \leq seg(r)/w$ **then**
8   label (u_l, u) right
9 **end**
10 For all $u' \in C$, with $u_l \prec u' \prec u_h$ set $R(u') \leftarrow r$

Algorithm 2. Algorithm Free(u, u_l, u_h)

- C_3 is defined as the cost of connection paths due to edges e such that e belongs in the backbone P, and which are bought by connection paths established in either line 8 or line 18 of NonFree (i.e., when the current request is assigned its immediate successor as its mate).
- C_4 is defined as the cost of connection paths due to edges e such that e belongs in the backbone P, and which are bought by connection paths established in either line 3 of Free or line 22 of NonFree.

```
 1  Assign u to run r = R(u). Label (u_l, u), (u, u_h) blank
 2  if (u_l, u_h) is left then
 3      set mate(u) ← u_l
 4      label (u_l, u) free
 5      label (u, u_h) left
 6  end
 7  if (u_l, u_h) is right then
 8      set mate(u) ← u_h
 9      label (u, u_h) free
10      label (u_l, u) right
11  end
12  else
13      if s(u_l, u) ≤ seg(r)/w then
14          set mate(u) ← u_l
15          label (u_l, u) right
16      end
17      else if s(u, u_h) ≤ seg(r)/w then
18          set mate(u) ← u_h
19          label (u, u_h) left
20      end
21      else
22          set mate(u) ← rep(r)
23      end
24  end
```

Algorithm 3. Algorithm NonFree(u, u_l, u_h)

- C_5 is defined as the cost due to edges e such that e belongs in some terminal path t_i in the comb.
- C_6 is defined as the cost of connection paths for terminals in run 0.

It can be shown easily that C_6 is bounded by $O(\alpha) \cdot c(T')$, hence we will focus only on terminals in runs> 0 from this point on. Also, since the terminal paths t_i are edge-disjoint, it follows that $C_5 \leq c(T')$. Thus, it remains to bound C_j, $j \in [1, 4]$. We will denote by $C_{j,i}$ the contribution of the connection path q_i for terminal u_{π_i} to the cost $C_{j,i}$, which means that $C_j = \sum_{i=1}^{k'} C_{j,i}$.

3.2 Properties of Runs and Labellings

Property 1. Every terminal u can be the representative and/or the left-end of at most one run. In addition, for every terminal u, $l(run(u)) \prec u \prec rep(run(u))$.

We say that an interval (u, u') is *contained within* interval (v, v') $(u, u', v, v'$ denote terminals in the comb) if each of u, u' is contained within interval (v, v'). We say that a run r is contained within interval (u, u') if $(l(r), rep(r))$ is contained within (u, u') (and hence from Property 1 the same holds for all terminals in r).

Last, r is contained within r' if $(l(r), rep(r))$ is contained within $(l(r'), rep(r'))$. Note that this implies that $seg(r) \leq seg(r')$.

Property 2. Let (u, v) be an interval labeled `free` at some point in the execution of the assignment algorithm. Then for every future request u' with $u \prec u' \prec v$, u' will become member of a run r which is contained within the interval (u, v).

Property 3. Let terminal u be requested, with immediate predecessor and successor at the time of its request u_l, u_h, respectively, and suppose that the interval (u, u_h) becomes `left` as a result of line 5 of `NonFree`. Suppose also that there exists a pair of terminals u_1, u_2, in immediate successor/predecessor relation at the time of one of their requests such that $u_1 \prec u_l \prec u_h \preceq u_2$, and (u_1, u_2) was labeled `free`. Then there exists a terminal v with the following properties:

- $u_1 \prec v \preceq u_l$;
- At the time v is requested no terminal other than u_h has been requested in the interval (v, u_h);
- Interval (v, u_h) becomes `left` as a result of the execution of either line 5 in algorithm `Free` or line 19 in algorithm `NonFree`.

Lemma 1. *For any given run r, at most w terminals in K' are assigned $rep(r)$ as their mate in line 22 of algorithm* `NonFree`.

3.3   Bounding the Cost $C_{1,i}$

Lemma 2. $C_{1,i} \leq \alpha(w + 5) \cdot c(t_i)$, *where t_i is the terminal path for u_{π_i}.*

Proof sketch. Fix a terminal $v = u_{\pi_i}$: we will bound the number of terminals in K' which are assigned v as their mate. There are six possible cases for which a requested terminal u is assigned v as its mate, in particular during executions of the following lines: line 3 for $Free(*, *, v)$; line 8 or line 18 for $NonFree(*, *, v)$; line 3 or line 14 for $NonFree(*, v, *)$; and last, line 22 of `NonFree`, more specifically during the call $NonFree(u, u_l, u_h)$ for some terminals u, u_h, u_l, with $rep(r) \equiv v$. Here, "*" denotes any arbitrary terminal. One can show that, for fixed v, all invocations will occur at most once, with the exception of line 22 which will be invoked at most w times (due to Lemma 1). The lemma then follows.   □

3.4   Bounding $C_{2,i}$ and $C_{3,i}$

We first show how to bound $C_{2,i}$, then the bound for $C_{3,i}$ will follow an almost identical proof. We say that u_{π_i} *contributes* the directed edge e, with $\bar{e} \in P$ when the connection path q_i for u_{π_i} includes e. For the remainder of the proof for $C_{2,i}$ we will call such edges *expensive*. Also, let q'_i denote the subpath of q_i which consists of expensive edges only (i.e., the subpath of q_i which consists of edges antiparallel to edges in the backbone of the comb), then clearly $C_{2,i} = c(q'_i)$. Let X denote the subset of the set of comb terminals K' which consists of terminals with non-zero contribution to C_2. Consider the sequence of connection paths for terminals in X, as such terminals are requested over time. More precisely, we can think of all edges in q_i' being "bought", as the connection path between the terminal and its mate is *established*, at the precise moment $u_{\pi_i} \in X$ is requested. In this view, every time an expensive edge is contributed due to such an assignment, we say that the *depth* of the edge increases by 1 (initially, i.e., before any terminals have been requested, all expensive edges have depth zero).

Lemma 3. *For $u_{\pi_i} \in X$, all expensive edges in q_i' have the same depth.*

Lemma 3 asserts that it is meaningful to say that terminal $u_{\pi_i} \in X$ is of depth δ if right after it is assigned to its mate, and the connection path q_i is established, the depth of all expensive edges at the connection path becomes equal to δ. Thus we can partition X into sets $X_1, X_2 \ldots$ such that X_i consists of all terminals of depth i. Note that for all i with $u_{\pi_i} \in X_j$, the paths q_i' are edge-disjoint.

The following is the main technical lemma of this section. The lemma shows that the contribution of a terminal to C_2 decreases exponentially with its depth (recall that $c(P)$ denotes the cost of the backbone P of the comb).

Lemma 4. *For a terminal $u_{\pi_i} \in X_j$, with $j \geq 1$, $C_{2,i} \leq \frac{\alpha c(P)}{w^{j-1}}$.*

A similar upper bound can be shown for $C_{3,i}$, since terminals which contribute to $C_{3,i}$ follow assignments to mates which are symmetric to the assignments for terminals with contribution to $C_{2,i}$ (even strongly, the α factor does not appear in the upper bound since connection paths which contribute to $C_{3,i}$ follow edges in the backbone, and not their antiparallel edges).

3.5   Towards Bounding Cost $C_{4,i}$

In this section we establish a lemma which is instrumental in bounding $C_{4,i}$. For a given $e \in P$ define the *r-depth* (or for simplicity *depth* for the remainder of this section) of e as the total number of runs $r \neq 0$, (i.e., excluding run 0) whose segment $seg(r)$ includes edge e. Let R denote the set of all runs (again, excluding run 0) established by the assignment algorithm. We say that every time a new run r is initiated (line 1 of `Free`), the depth of every edge in $seg(r)$ increases by 1 (before any terminal is requested, all edges in P have zero depth).

Lemma 5. *All edges in $seg(r)$ have the same depth after r is established.*

Lemma 5 asserts that we can partition R into sets $R_1, R_2, \ldots$ such that R_i consists of all runs of depth i. Note that for every two runs r and r' with $r, r' \in R_j$, the segments of r and r' are disjoint.

Lemma 6. *For a run $r \in R_j$, $seg(r) \leq \frac{c(P)}{w^{j-1}}$.*

Proof sketch. By induction on j. The lemma is trivially true for $j = 1$. Suppose the lemma holds for j, we will show that it holds for $j + 1$. Let r be a run in R_{j+1}. We will show that r is contained within a run r' of depth j for which it holds that $seg(r) \leq seg(r')/w$: by induction hypothesis, we will then have that $seg(r) \leq \frac{c(P)}{w^j}$, and the lemma is proved.

It is easy to see first that there exists a run r' of depth j such that r is contained within r' (similar to the proof of Lemma 5); more precisely, $l(r') \prec l(r) \prec rep(r) \prec rep(r')$. Recall that at the time right before $in(r')$ is requested, the interval $(l(r'), rep(r'))$ is a free interval. Likewise, at the time right before $in(r)$ is requested, the interval $((l(r), rep(r))$ is a free interval. We thus consider cases, depending on how the interval $(l(r), rep(r))$ became free:

Case 1. $(l(r), rep(r))$ became free as a result of line 4 of NonFree. Then there exists a terminal u with $rep(r) \prec u \preceq rep(r')$ such that when $rep(r)$ was requested, the interval $(l(r), u)$ was a left interval. From Property 3 there must exist a terminal v such that $l(r') \prec v \preceq l(r)$ and the interval (v, u) became left as a result of either line 19 of NonFree or line 5 of Free. Let r'' denote the run that v joins, then from the two cases above, we have that the if-condition of line 17 of NonFree, or line 4 of Free, respectively, holds, hence $s(v, u) \leq seg(r'')/w$. Note that $(l(r), rep(r))$ is contained within the interval (v, u), thus $seg(r) \leq s(v, u)$; in addition from Property 2 r'' is contained within run r', hence $seg(r'') \leq seg(r')$. Combining the above inequalities we deduce that $seg(r) \leq seg(r')/w$.

Case 2. $((l(r), rep(r))$ became free as a result of line 9 of NonFree. This case is very similar to Case 1, in the sense that left intervals are now "replaced" by right intervals. We also require a property symmetric to Property 3.   □

3.6   Adding Up the Individual Contributions

Recall from the discussion in section 3.2 that the total connection cost C for terminals in the comb is expressed as the sum of the partial costs $C_1, \ldots C_6$, and that C_5 and C_6 have only a small asymptotic contribution to C. Also, using Lemma 2, and given the disjointness of terminal paths, it is easy to show that $C_1 \leq \alpha(x + 5) \cdot c(T')$. We thus need to focus on costs $C_2, \ldots C_4$. Recall also that w is defined as $\min\{\alpha, x\}$, x is such that $x^x = k'$ and that y is such that $\alpha^y = k'$.

We first show how to bound C_4. Let $Z \subseteq K'$ be the set of terminals contributing to C_4. Recall that a terminal $u \in Z$ which belongs to a run r is assigned as a mate the representative of the run r. Moreover, the contribution of u to C_4 is at most the segment of the run r, $seg(r)$. Using the notation introduced in section 3.5, we say that a terminal $u \in Z$ belongs in class $Z_j \subseteq Z$ if and only if its corresponding run belongs in the class R_j. Denote by $c_4(Z_j)$ the contribution of terminals in Z_j to Z.

From Lemma 1 we know that for any fixed run r there are at most w terminals in Z which contribute to C_4 due to line 22 of NonFree, and their total contribution is bounded by $w \cdot seg(r)$. On the other had, since r has a unique initiator for a fixed r at most one terminal in Z contributes to cost C_4 due to line 3 of Free. In total, for a given run r at most $w + 1$ terminals in run r contribute to C_4, and their total contribution is bounded by $(w + 1) \cdot seg(r)$. For fixed j the segments of all runs in R_j are edge-disjoint, which yields $c_4(Z_j) \leq (w + 1) \cdot c(P)$. Combining this fact with Lemma 6 we have $c_4(Z_j) \leq \min\{(w + 1) \cdot c(P), (w + 1)\frac{c(P)}{w^{j-1}}|Z_j|\}$

Since $C_4 = \sum_j c_4(Z_j)$, and there are at most as many runs as terminals in the comb, it follows that C_4 is maximized if $|Z_j| = w^{j-1}$, for all $j \geq 2$, which yields $C_4 \in O(w \max\{x, y\} \cdot c(P)) = O(\alpha \max\{x, y\} \cdot c(P))$.

For costs C_2 and C_3 one can show the following bounds, using a similar argument based on the lemmas of section 3.4:

$$C_2 = O(\max\{\alpha x \cdot c(P), \alpha y \cdot c(P)\}) \qquad and \qquad C_3 = O(\max\{x \cdot c(P), y \cdot c(P)\}).$$

Theorem 2 follows by adding $C_1, \ldots C_6$ and the fact $c(P) \leq c(T')$.   □

References

1. Angelopoulos, S.: Improved Bounds for the Online Steiner Tree Problem in Graphs of Bounded Edge-Asymmetry. Technical Report CS-2006-36, David R. Cheriton School of Computer Science, University of Waterloo (2006)
2. Angelopoulos, S.: Improved Bounds for the Online Steiner Tree Problem in Graphs of Bounded Edge-Asymmetry. In: Bansal, N., Pruhs, K., Stein, C. (eds.) Proceedings of the Eighteenth Annual ACM-SIAM Symposium on Discrete Algorithms, pp. 248–257. ACM Press, New York (2007)
3. Awerbuch, B., Azar, Y., Bartal, B.: On-line Generalized Steiner Problem. Theor. Comp. Sci. 324(2–3), 313–324 (2004)
4. Azar, Y., Alon, N.: On-line Steiner Trees in the Euclidean Plane. Discrete and Computational Geometry 10, 113–121 (1993)
5. Berman, P., Coulston, C.: Online Algorithms for Steiner Tree Problems. In: Proceedings of the Twenty-Ninth Annual ACM Symposium on the Theory of Computing, pp. 344–353 (1997)
6. Borodin, A., El-Yaniv, R.: Online Computation and Competitive Analysis. Cambridge University Press, Cambridge (1998)
7. Claffy, K.G., Polyzos, B.H.W.: Traffic Characteristics of the T1 NSFnet Backbone. In: IEEE-Infocom, pp. 885–892 (1993)
8. Faloutsos, M., Pankaj, R., Sevcik, K.C.: The Effect of Asymmetry on the On-line Multicast Routing Problem. Int. J. Found. Comput. Sci. 13(6), 889–910 (2002)
9. Imase, M., Waxman, B.: The Dynamic Steiner Tree Problem. SIAM Journal on Discrte Mathematics 4(3), 369–384 (1991)
10. Oliveira, C.A.S., Pardalos, P.M.: A Survey of Combinatorial Optimization Problems in Multicast Routing. Comput. Oper. Res. 32(8), 1953–1981 (2005)
11. Ramanathan, S.: Multicast Tree Generation in Networks with Asymmetric Links. IEEE/ACM Trans. Netw. 4(4), 558–568 (1996)
12. Westbrook, J., Yam, D.C.K.: Linear Bounds for On-line Steiner Problems. Inf. Proc. Ltrs. 55(2), 59–63 (1995)
13. Westbrook, J., Yan, D.C.K.: The Performance of Greedy Algorithms for the On-line Steiner Tree and Related Problems. Math. Syst. Theory 28(5), 451–468 (1995)

Cache-Oblivious Red-Blue
Line Segment Intersection

Lars Arge[1,*], Thomas Mølhave[1,**], and Norbert Zeh[2,***]

[1] MADALGO[†], Department of Computer Science, University of Aarhus, Denmark
{large,thomasm}@madalgo.au.dk
[2] Faculty of Computer Science, Dalhousie University, Halifax, Nova Scotia, Canada
nzeh@cs.dal.ca

Abstract. We present an optimal cache-oblivious algorithm for finding
all intersections between a set of non-intersecting red segments and a
set of non-intersecting blue segments in the plane. Our algorithm uses
$O(\frac{N}{B} \log_{M/B} \frac{N}{B} + T/B)$ memory transfers, where N is the total number
of segments, M and B are the memory and block transfer sizes of any
two consecutive levels of any multilevel memory hierarchy, and T is the
number of intersections.

1 Introduction

The memory systems of modern computers are becoming increasingly complex;
they consist of a hierarchy of several levels of cache, main memory, and disk. The
access times of different levels of memory often vary by orders of magnitude and,
to amortize the large access times of memory levels far away from the processor,
data is normally transferred between levels in large blocks. Thus, it is important
to design algorithms that are sensitive to the architecture of the memory system
and have a high degree of locality in their memory access patterns.

Building on the two-level *external-memory* model [1] introduced to model the
large difference between the access times of main memory and disk, the *cache-oblivious* model [8] was introduced as a way of obtaining algorithms that are
efficient on *all* levels of arbitrary memory hierarchies. In this paper, we develop
a cache-oblivious algorithm for the *red-blue line segment intersection problem*,

* Supported in part by the US Army Research Office through grant W911NF-04-01-0278, by an Ole Roemer Scholarship from the Danish National Science Research
  Council, a NABIIT grant from the Danish Strategic Research Council, and by the
  Danish National Research Foundation.
** Supported in part by an Ole Roemer Scholarship from the Danish National Science
  Research Council, a NABIIT grant from the Danish Strategic Research Council,
  and by the Danish National Research Foundation.
*** Supported by the Canada Research Chairs program, the Natural Sciences and
  Engineering Research Council of Canada, and the Canadian Foundation for Inno-
  vation.
† Center for Massive Data Algorithmics, a Center of the Danish National Research
  Foundation.

D. Halperin and K. Mehlhorn (Eds.): ESA 2008, LNCS 5193, pp. 88–99, 2008.

that is, for finding all intersections between a set of non-intersecting red segments and a set of non-intersecting blue segments in the plane. Our algorithm is optimal and, to the best of our knowledge, the first efficient cache-oblivious algorithm for any intersection problem involving non-axis-parallel objects.

External-memory model. In the two-level *external-memory model* [1], the memory hierarchy consists of an *internal memory* big enough to hold M elements and an arbitrarily large *external memory* partitioned into blocks of B consecutive elements. A *memory transfer* moves one block between internal and external memory. Computation can occur only on data in internal memory. The complexity of an algorithm in this model (an *external-memory algorithm*) is measured in terms of the number of memory transfers it performs. Aggarwal and Vitter proved that the number of memory transfers needed to sort N data items in the external-memory model is $\mathrm{Sort}(N) = \Theta(\frac{N}{B} \log_{M/B} \frac{N}{B})$ [1]. Subsequently, a large number of algorithms have been developed in this model; see [10, 2] for an overview. Below we briefly review results directly related to our work.

In the first paper to consider computational geometry problems in external memory [9], Goodrich et al. introduced the *distribution sweeping* technique (a combination of M/B-way distribution sort and plane sweeping) and showed how it can be used to solve a large number of geometric problems in the plane using $O(\mathrm{Sort}(N) + T/B)$ memory transfers, where T is the output size of the problem (eg., number of intersections). The problems they considered include the orthogonal line segment intersection problem and other problems involving axis-parallel objects. Arge et al. developed an algorithm that solves the red-blue line segment intersection problem using $O(\mathrm{Sort}(N)+T/B)$ memory transfers [4], which is optimal. The algorithm uses the distribution sweeping technique [9] and introduces the notion of *multi-slabs*; if the plane is divided into vertical slabs, a multi-slab is defined as the union of any number of consecutive slabs. Multi-slabs are used to efficiently deal with segments spanning a range of consecutive slabs. The key is that, if there are only $\sqrt{M/B}$ slabs, there are less than M/B multi-slabs, which allows the distribution of segments into multi-slabs during a plane sweep using standard M/B-way distribution. Arge et al. also extended their algorithm to obtain a solution to the general line segment intersection problem using $O(\mathrm{Sort}(N + T))$ memory transfers [4].

Cache-oblivious model. In the *cache-oblivious model* [8], the idea is to design a standard RAM-model algorithm that has not knowledge of the parameters of the memory hierarchy but analyze it in the external-memory model assuming that an offline optimal paging strategy performs the memory transfers necessary to bring accessed elements into memory. Often it is also assumed that $M \geq B^2$ (the *tall-cache assumption*). The main advantage of the cache-oblivious model is that it allows us to reason about a simple two-level memory model but prove results about an unknown, multi-level memory hierarchy [8].

Frigo et al. [8] developed optimal cache-oblivious sorting algorithms, as well as algorithms for a number of other fundamental problems. Subsequently, algorithms and data structures for a range of problems have been developed [3].

Relevant to this paper, Bender et al. [5] developed a cache-oblivious algorithm that solves the offline planar point location problem using $O(\text{Sort}(N))$ memory transfers; Brodal and Fagerberg [6] developed a cache-oblivious version of distribution sweeping and showed how to use it to solve the orthogonal line segment intersection problem, as well as several other problems involving axis-parallel objects, cache-obliviously using $O(\text{Sort}(N) + T/B)$ memory transfers. To the best of our knowledge, no cache-oblivious algorithm was previously known for any intersection problem involving *non-axis-parallel* objects.

Our results. We present a cache-oblivious algorithm for the red-blue line segment intersection problem that uses $O(\text{Sort}(N) + T/B)$ memory transfer. This matches the bound of the external-memory algorithm of [4] and is optimal.

As discussed, the external-memory algorithm for this problem [4] is based on an extended version of distribution sweeping utilizing multi-slabs. Our new algorithm borrows ideas from both the external-memory algorithm for the red-blue line segment intersection problem [4] and the cache-oblivious algorithm for the orthogonal line-segment intersection problem [6]. In order to obtain a useful notion of sweeping the plane top-down or bottom-up, we utilize the same total ordering as in [4] on a set of non-intersecting segments, which arranges the segments intersected by any vertical line in the same order as the y-coordinates of their intersections with the line. In the case of axis-parallel objects, such an ordering is equivalent to the y-ordering of the vertices of the objects; in the non-axis-parallel case, this ordering is more difficult to obtain [4]. Similar to the cache-oblivious orthogonal line-segment intersection algorithm [6], we employ the cache-oblivious distribution sweeping paradigm, which uses two-way merging rather than $\sqrt{M/B}$-way distribution. While this eliminates the need for multi-slabs, which do not seem to have an efficient cache-oblivious counterpart, it also results in a recursion depth of $\Theta(\log_2 N)$ rather than $\Theta(\log_{M/B} N)$. This implies that one cannot afford to spend even $1/B$ memory transfers per line segment at each level of the recursion. For axis-parallel objects, Brodal and Fagerberg [6] addressed this problem using the so-called k-merger technique, which was introduced as the central idea in Funnel Sort (ie., cache-oblivious Merge Sort) [8]. This technique allows N elements to be passed through a $\log_2 N$-level merge process using only $O(\text{Sort}(N))$ memory transfers, but generates the output of each merge process in bursts, each of which has to be consumed by the next merge process before the next burst is produced. This creates a new challenge, as a segment may have intersections with all segments in the output stream of a given merge process and, thus, needs access to the entire output stream to report these intersections. To overcome this problem, Brodal and Fagerberg [6] provided a technique to detect, count, and collect intersected segments at each level of recursion that ensures that the number of additional accesses needed to report intersections is proportional to the output size.

Our main contribution is the development of non-trivial new methods to extend the counting technique of Brodal and Fagerberg [6] to the case of non-axis-parallel line segments. These ideas include a *look-ahead* method for identifying certain critical segments ahead of the time they are accessed during a merge, as well as an *approximate counting* method needed because exact counting of intersected segments (as utilized in the case of axis-parallel objects) seems to be no easier than actually reporting intersections.

2   Vertically Sorting Non-intersecting Segments

In this section, we briefly sketch a cache-oblivious algorithm to vertically sort a set S of N non-intersecting segments in the plane. Let s_1 and s_2 be segments in S. We say that s_2 is *above* s_1, denoted $s_1 <_A s_2$, if there exists a vertical line intersecting s_1 and s_2 in points (x, y_1) and (x, y_2), respectively, and $y_1 < y_2$. Some segments in S may be incomparable under $<_A$, and the problem of vertically sorting S is to extend the partial order $<_A$ to a total order $<_t$ such that $s_1 <_A s_2$ implies $s_1 <_t s_2$ [4]. We call $<_t$ a *vertical ordering* of the segments.

Our cache-oblivious algorithm for vertically sorting S is an adaptation of the corresponding external-memory algorithm [4]. The main ingredients are an algorithm for finding the segments immediately above and below every segment endpoint and an algorithm for topologically sorting the resulting planar *st*-graph. The former can be solved using an offline cache-oblivious point location algorithm [5]; for the latter we use a cache-oblivious adaptation of the external-memory algorithm [7]. Details will appear in the full paper.

Theorem 1. *A vertical ordering of N non-intersecting line segments in the plane can be computed cache-obliviously using $O(\text{Sort}(N))$ memory transfers and linear space.*

3   Red-Blue Line Segment Intersection

In this section, we give an overview of our algorithm for finding all intersections between a set R of non-intersecting red segments and a set B of non-intersecting blue segments. For simplicity we assume that the x- and y-coordinates of all endpoints are distinct. Sections 4 and 5 present the details of our algorithm.

The $\sqrt{N}$-merger. Our algorithm uses the $\sqrt{N}$-merger technique [6, 8] extensively. A $\sqrt{N}$-merger merges $\sqrt{N}$ sorted input streams of length $\sqrt{N}$ into one sorted output stream. It is defined recursively in terms of smaller k-mergers. A k-merger takes k sorted input streams of total length at least k^2 and produces a sorted output stream by merging the input streams. The cost of merging k^2 elements using a k-merger is $O(\text{Sort}(k^2))$, which is $O(\text{Sort}(N))$ for $k = \sqrt{N}$ [6,8].

A k-merger is a complete binary tree over $k/2$ leaves with a buffer associated with each edge. If $k = 2$, the merger consists of a single node with two input streams and one output stream; see Fig. 1(a). Otherwise, it consists of $\sqrt{k}+1$ $\sqrt{k}$-mergers as shown in Fig. 1(b); the buffers associated with the edges between the top merger and the bottom mergers have size k. The merge process is performed by invoking a FILL operation on the root of the merger. A FILL operation on a node u fills the output buffer $S(u)$ of u (the buffer between u and its parent) by

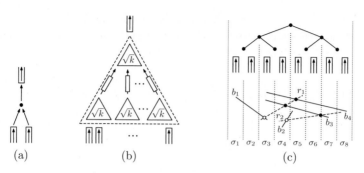

Fig. 1. (a) A 2-merger. (b) A k-merger for $k > 2$. (c) Slabs and intersection types.

repeatedly removing the minimum element from $S(l(u))$ or $S(r(u))$ and placing it into $S(u)$, where $l(u)$ and $r(u)$ denote the left and right children of u. When $S(l(u))$ or $S(r(u))$ becomes empty, a FILL operation is invoked recursively on the corresponding child before continuing to fill $S(u)$. The FILL operation returns when $S(u)$ is full or there are no elements left any buffer below u. Since the root's output buffer has size N, only one FILL operation on the root is required to place all elements in the input streams into a sorted output stream.

The basic concept in the analysis of a $\sqrt{N}$-merger is that of a *base tree*, which is the largest subtree in the recursive definition of a $\sqrt{N}$-merger such that the entire tree plus one block for each of its input and output buffers fit in memory. The central observation is that, in order to achieve the $O(\mathrm{Sort}(k^2))$ merge bound, a FILL operation on a base tree root can afford to load the whole base tree into memory and perform $O(1)$ memory transfers per node in the base tree; note that this means that FILL operations on other nodes of the base tree are free. It also means that we can associate $O(1)$ auxiliary buffers with each merger node u and that we can assume that a FILL operation at node u can access the first $O(1)$ blocks of each auxiliary buffer without any memory transfers. See [6] for details.

Distribution sweeping. To find all intersections between red and blue segments, we start by dividing the plane into $q = \sqrt{N}$ vertical slabs $\sigma_1, \ldots, \sigma_q$ containing $2\sqrt{N}$ segment endpoints each, where $N = |R| + |B|$ is the total number of segments. We recurse on each slab σ_i to find the intersections in σ_i between segments with at least one endpoint in this slab; these intersections are shown using white dots in Fig. 1(c). Each of the remaining intersections, shown as black dots in Fig. 1(c), involves at least one segment that completely spans the slab containing the intersection. To find these intersections, we use a $\sqrt{N}$-merger whose input streams are sorted lists of segments and/or segment endpoints associated with slabs $\sigma_1, \ldots, \sigma_q$. We also associate slabs with the nodes of the merger. The slab σ_u associated with a node u is the union of the slabs corresponding to the input streams of u's subtree. We use $l(\sigma_u)$ and $r(\sigma_u)$ to denote its left and right boundaries, respectively. We call a segment with an endpoint in σ_u *long* wrt. slab $\sigma_{l(u)}$ if it spans $\sigma_{l(u)}$ (segment b_3 in Fig. 2(a)), and *short* otherwise (segments b_1, b_2, b_4 in Fig. 2(a)). We call an intersection in $\sigma_{l(u)}$ *long-long* if it involves two long segments wrt. slab $\sigma_{l(u)}$ (point p_3 in Fig. 2(a)), and *short-long* if it involves a short and a long segment (points p_1 and p_2 in Fig. 2(a)). Short and long segments and short-long and long-long intersections in slab $\sigma_{r(u)}$ are defined analogously. It is easy to see that every intersection in a slab σ_i that involves a segment spanning σ_i is long-long or short-long at exactly one merger node. Hence, our goal in merging the streams corresponding to slabs $\sigma_1, \ldots, \sigma_q$ is to report all long-long and short-long intersections at each merger node.

Throughout this paper, we only discuss finding, at every merger node u, short-long and long-long intersections inside $\sigma_{l(u)}$. The intersections in $\sigma_{r(u)}$ can be found analogously. Our algorithm finds short-long and long-long intersections separately and finds each intersection type using several applications of the $\sqrt{N}$-merger to appropriate input streams associated with slabs $\sigma_1, \ldots, \sigma_q$. We call one such application a *pass* through the merger. In the process of merging the input streams of the merger, each pass either reports intersections or performs some preprocessing to allow a subsequent pass to report intersections. As we show in Sect. 4 and 5, $O(1)$ passes are sufficient to report all short-long and long-long intersections, and each pass uses $O(\mathrm{Sort}(N) + T_s/B)$ memory transfers and linear space, where T_s is the number of reported intersections. Let N_i denote the number of short segments in slab σ_i, T_i the number of intersections between these segments, and $C(N, T)$ the complexity of our algorithm on N segments that have T intersections. Then the complexity of our algorithm is given by the recurrence $C(N, T) = \sum_{i=1}^{\sqrt{N}} C(N_i, T_i) + O(\mathrm{Sort}(N) + T_s/B)$, which solves to $C(N, T) = O(\mathrm{Sort}(N) + T/B)$ because each original segment participates as a non-spanning segment in at most two slabs on each level of the recursion.

Theorem 2. *The red-blue line segment intersection problem can be solved cache-obliviously using $O(\mathrm{Sort}(N) + T/B)$ memory transfers and linear space, where N is the total number of line segments and T is the number of intersections.*

4   Short-Long Intersections

In this section, we discuss how to find all short-long intersections at all merger nodes using $O(1)$ passes through the merger. Recall that we focus only on intersections inside $\sigma_{l(u)}$. We call such an intersection between a long red segment r and a short blue segment b *upward* if b has at least one endpoint in $\sigma_{l(u)}$ that is below r (points p_2, p_3, p_5 in Fig. 2(b)); otherwise, the intersection is *downward* (points p_1 and p_4 in Fig. 2(b)). We focus on finding upward short-long intersections between long red and short blue segments in the remainder of this section. The other types of short-long intersections can be found analogously. We discuss first how to find these intersections in the desired number of memory transfers using linear extra space per merger node. Then we discusses how to reduce the space bound to $O(N)$ in total.

Our algorithm uses two passes through the $\sqrt{N}$-merger. The first pass associates a *red list* $R(u)$ of size N (big enough to hold all segments in the input

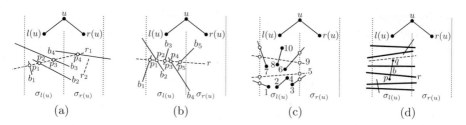

Fig. 2. (a) Short-long and long-long intersections. (b) Upward and downward intersections. (c) Detecting long segments involved in upward short-long intersections. (d) Reporting upward short-long intersections. Dashed segments are not in $R(u)$.

if necessary) with every merger node u and populates it with all red segments that are long wrt. $\sigma_{l(u)}$ and are involved in upward short-long intersections at node u. The second pass uses these red lists to report all upward short-long intersections. Both passes merge segment streams sorted by the vertical segment ordering from Sect. 2. More precisely, we construct a set R' containing all red segments and one zero-length segment per blue segment endpoint and use the vertical ordering on R' as a total ordering of red segments and blue segment endpoints, bottom-up. The *rank* of a red segment or blue segment endpoint is its position in this ordering.

Populating red lists. To populate all red lists, we initialize the input streams of the merger so that the stream corresponding to slab σ_i stores all red segments whose right endpoints are in σ_i, as well as all blue segment endpoints in σ_i. The entries of the stream are sorted bottom-up (by increasing rank). Now we merge these streams to produce one sorted output stream, where the output stream of each merger node u contains all red segments with right endpoints in σ_u and all blue segment endpoints in σ_u, again sorted bottom-up. The FILL operation at a node u is the standard FILL operation of a $\sqrt{N}$-merger, except that, when placing a red segment r into u's output stream $S(u)$, we check whether r is involved in an upward short-long intersection at node u. If it is, we also append segment r to u's red list $R(u)$.

To see how this test is performed, consider an upward short-long intersection between a short blue segment b and a long red segment r. Segment b must have at least one endpoint in $\sigma_{l(u)}$ that is below r (has lower rank than r). Since b and r intersect in $\sigma_{l(u)}$, either b's other endpoint q also lies in $\sigma_{l(u)}$ and is above r (has higher rank than r), or b intersects one of the slab boundaries of $\sigma_{l(u)}$ above r; see Fig. 2(c). Since we merge segments and segment endpoints at each node u bottom-up, we process (ie., place into $S(u)$) all short blue segment endpoints below r before we process r. We call a blue segment *processed* if we have processed at least one of its endpoints. A segment b with one endpoint in $\sigma_{l(u)}$ is *internal*, *left-intersecting*, or *right-intersecting* depending on whether both its endpoints are in $\sigma_{l(u)}$, b intersects $l(\sigma_{l(u)})$ or b intersects $r(\sigma_{l(u)})$. Let $\rho(u)$ be the highest rank of all endpoints of processed internal blue segments, and $y_l(u)$ the y-coordinate of the highest intersection between $l(\sigma_{l(u)})$ and processed left-intersecting blue segments; $y_r(u)$ is defined analogously for processed right-intersecting blue segments. By our previous discussion, r has an upward short-long intersection at u if and only if r has rank less than $\rho(u)$, intersects $l(\sigma_{l(u)})$ below y-coordinate $y_l(u)$ or intersects $r(\sigma_{l(u)})$ below $y_r(u)$; see Fig. 2(c).

Values $\rho(u)$, $y_l(u)$, and $y_r(u)$ are easily maintained as the FILL operation at node u processes blue segment endpoints. When processing a red segment r, it is easy to test whether it is long wrt. $\sigma_{l(u)}$ and its rank is less than $\rho(u)$, its intersection with $l(\sigma_{l(u)})$ has y-coordinate less than $y_l(u)$ or its intersection with $r(\sigma_{l(u)})$ has y-coordinate less than $y_r(u)$. If this is the case, r has at least one upward short-long intersection at u, and we append it to u's red list $R(u)$.

Reporting short-long intersections. Given the populated red lists, the second pass starts out with the input stream of each slab σ_i containing all blue segment endpoints in σ_i, sorted top-down (ie., by decreasing ranks). We merge these points so that every node u outputs a stream of blue segment endpoints in σ_u, sorted top-down. To report all short-long intersections at a node u, the FILL operation at node u keeps track of the *current position* in $R(u)$, which is the segment with minimum rank in $R(u)$ we have inspected during the current pass. Initially, this is the last segment in $R(u)$. Now when processing an endpoint $p \in \sigma_{l(u)}$ of a blue segment b, we first scan backwards in $R(u)$ from the current position to find the segment r with minimum rank in $R(u)$ whose rank is greater than that of p. Segment r becomes the new current position in $R(u)$. Segment r is the lowest segment in $R(u)$ that can have an upward intersection with b, and all segments having such intersections with b form a contiguous sequence in $R(u)$ starting with r. Therefore, we scan forward from r, reporting intersections between scanned segments and b until we find the first segment in $R(u)$ that does not have an upward short-long intersection with b; see Fig. 2(d).

Since every segment placed into $R(u)$ is involved in at least one intersection and all but $O(1)$ accesses to a segment in $R(u)$ can be charged to reported intersections, the scanning of red lists adds only $O(T_s/B)$ to the $O(\text{Sort}(N))$ cost of the merger. The space usage of the algorithm can be reduced to $O(N + T_s)$ by running the pass populating red lists twice. The first time, we only count segments that would be placed into each list and then allocate a list of the appropriate size to each node. The second time, we place segments into the allocated lists. Using the same technique as in [6], the space can then be reduced further to $O(N)$. Details will appear in the full paper.

Lemma 1. *Short-long intersections can be reported using* $O(\text{Sort}(N) + T_s/B)$ *memory transfers and linear space.*

5   Long-Long Intersections

In this section, we discuss how to find the long-long intersections at all merger nodes. Again, we focus on finding, at every node u, only long-long intersections inside slab $\sigma_{l(u)}$. Similar to the short-long case, we first describe our procedure assuming we can allocate *two* lists of size N to each node. Later we discuss how to reduce the space usage to $O(N)$.

A simple solution using superlinear space. After some preprocessing discussed later in this section, long-long intersections can be found using one pass through the $\sqrt{N}$-merger. This time, the input stream corresponding to slab σ_i contains all segments whose right endpoints are inside σ_i and which intersect $l(\sigma_i)$. The segments are sorted by decreasing y-coordinates of their intersections with $l(\sigma_i)$. The goal of the merge process at a merger node u is to produce an output stream of all segments with right endpoints in σ_u and which intersect $l(\sigma_u)$. Again, these segments are to be output sorted by decreasing y-coordinates of their intersections with $l(\sigma_u)$. In the process of producing its output stream, each merger node u reports all long-long intersections inside $\sigma_{l(u)}$.

This merge process in itself poses a challenge compared to the short-long case, as segments in $S(r(u))$ that intersect both $r(\sigma_{l(u)})$ and $l(\sigma_{l(u)})$ may have to be placed into $S(u)$ in a different order from the one in which they arrive in $S(r(u))$; see Fig. 3(a). Thus, we need to allow segments to "pass each other", which we accomplish using two buffers $B(u)$ and $R(u)$ of size N associated with each node u in the merger. Buffer $B(u)$ is used to temporarily hold blue segments that need to be overtaken by red segments at u; these segments are sorted by the y-coordinates of their intersections with $l(\sigma_u)$. Buffer $R(u)$ serves the same purpose for red segments. Initially, $B(u)$ and $R(u)$ are empty.

To implement the merge process, we also need a "look-ahead" mechanism that allows each node u to identify the next long segment of each color to be retrieved from $S(r(u))$ without actually retrieving it. We discuss below how to provide such a mechanism. Again, the need for such a mechanism arises because long red and blue segments may change their order between $S(r(u))$ and $S(u)$. If the topmost segment b in $S(r(u))$ is long and blue, we can decide whether it is the next segment to be placed into $S(u)$ only if we know whether the next long red segment r intersects $l(\sigma_u)$ above b; but there may be an arbitrary number of blue and short red segments between b and r in $S(r(u))$, and we cannot afford to scan ahead until we find r in $S(r(u))$. Look-ahead provides us with r without the need to scan through $S(r(u))$.

A FILL operation at node u now reduces to repeatedly identifying the next segment s to be placed into $S(u)$. This segment is currently in $S(l(u))$, $S(r(u))$, $R(u)$ or $B(u)$ and is the one with the highest intersection with $l(\sigma_u)$ among the segments remaining in these streams. Thus, if s belongs to $S(l(u))$, it must be the next segment s' in $S(l(u))$ because the segments in $S(l(u))$ are sorted by their intersections with $l(\sigma_{l(u)}) = l(\sigma_u)$. If s belongs to $S(r(u))$, $R(u)$ or $B(u)$, it must be the next long red segment r or the next long blue segment b to be placed into $S(u)$. Note that our look-ahead mechanism provides us with r and b. To decide which of s', r, and b is the next segment s to be placed into $S(u)$, it suffices to compare their intersections with $l(\sigma_u)$.

In order to place s into $S(u)$, we need to locate it in $S(l(u))$, $S(r(u))$, $B(u)$ or $R(u)$, remove it, and output it into $S(u)$. If $s \in S(l(u))$, $B(u)$ or $R(u)$, this is easy because s is the next segment in $S(l(u))$ or the first segment in $B(u)$ or $R(u)$. So assume that s is long, wlog. red, and stored in $S(r(u))$. Then we retrieve segments from $S(r(u))$ until we retrieve s. Since the segments in $S(r(u))$

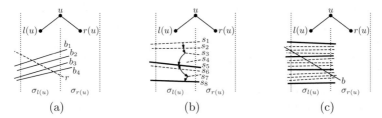

Fig. 3. (a) Segments b_1, b_2, b_3, b_4 arrive before r in $S(r(u))$ but need to be placed into $S(u)$ after r. Thus, r must be able to overtake them at u. (b) Implementation of look-ahead. Bold solid segments are in $R_t(u)$, dashed ones are not. Arrows indicate how every long segment finds the next long segment. (c) Approximate counting using sampling. The bold segments are in the sample, the dashed ones are not.

are sorted by their intersections with $l(\sigma_{r(u)})$ and red segments do not intersect, there cannot be any long red segment in $S(r(u))$ that is retrieved before s. Thus, all segments retrieved from $S(r(u))$ before s are blue or short. Short segments can be discarded because they cannot be involved in any long-long intersections at u or any of its ancestors. Long blue segments are appended to $B(u)$ in the order they are retrieved, which is easily seen to maintain the segments in $B(u)$ sorted by their intersections with $l(\sigma_{l(u)})$.

So far we have talked only about outputting the segments at each node u in the correct order. To discuss how to report intersections, we say that a segment is placed into $S(u)$ *directly* if it is never placed into $R(u)$ or $B(u)$; otherwise, we say that it is *overtaken* by at least one segment. It is not hard to see that every long-long intersection at a node u involves a segment s placed directly into $S(u)$ and a segment that is overtaken by s; a segment s placed directly into $S(u)$ has long-long intersections with exactly those segments of the other color that are in $B(u)$ or $R(u)$ at the time when s is placed into $S(u)$. Thus, we can augment the merge process at u to report long-long intersections as follows. Immediately before placing a long red segment r directly into $S(u)$, we scan $B(u)$ to report all intersections between r and the segments in $B(u)$. When a long blue segment b is placed directly into $S(u)$, we scan $R(u)$ instead. Since only segments that are overtaken (and thus involved in at least one intersection) are placed into $R(u)$ and $B(u)$ and every scan of $R(u)$ and $B(u)$ reports one intersection per scanned segment, the manipulation of these buffers at all merger nodes adds only $O(T_s/B)$ memory transfers to the $O(\text{Sort}(N))$ cost of the merger. Next we discuss how to implement the look-ahead mechanism using only $O(\text{Sort}(N))$ additional memory transfers, which leads to an $O(\text{Sort}(N) + T_s/B)$ cost for finding all long-long intersections.

Look-ahead. Consider the merge process reporting long-long intersections at a node u. Given look-ahead at u's children, it is easy to ensure that every segment in $S(l(u))$ or $S(r(u))$ knows the next segment s' of the same color in $S(l(u))$ or $S(r(u))$, respectively. When placing a long segment s from $S(r(u))$ into $S(u)$, however, we need to identify not the next segment of the same color as s in

$S(r(u))$ but the next *long* such segment s''. If s' is long, then $s'' = s'$. Otherwise, we say that s' *terminates* at node u, as it is not placed into $S(u)$. In this case, s' comes between s and s'' in $S(r(u))$. Note also that every segment terminates at exactly one node in the merger.

To allow us to identify segment s'', we preprocess the merger and associate two lists $R_t(u)$ and $B_t(u)$ with every node u. List $R_t(u)$ (resp., $B_t(u)$) contains all those long red (resp., blue) segments in $S(r(u))$ that are immediately preceded by red (resp., blue) segments that terminate at u. Given these lists, a long segment s in $S(r(u))$ that is succeeded by a terminating segment of the same color in $S(r(u))$ can identify the next long segment of the same color by retrieving the next segment from $R_t(u)$ or $B_t(u)$, depending on its color; see Fig. 3(b). These lists are easily constructed in $O(\mathrm{Sort}(N))$ memory transfers by merging the blue and red segments independently; details will appear in the full paper. In order to ensure that each list uses only as much space as it needs—and, thus, that all look-ahead lists use only $O(N)$ space—we run each merge twice. The first pass counts the number of segments to be placed into each list, the second one populates the lists after allocating the required space to each list.

During the merge that reports long-long intersections, each list $R_t(u)$ or $B_t(u)$ is scanned exactly once, as the segments in these lists are retrieved in the order they are stored. Thus, scanning these lists uses $O(N/B)$ memory transfers.

Linear space via approximate counting of intersected segments. Finally, we discuss how to reduce the space usage of the merge that finds long-long intersections to $O(N + T_s)$. Using the same technique as in [6] again, the space usage can then be reduced further to $O(N)$. Details appear in the full paper.

To achieve this space reduction, we need to reduce the total size of the red and blue buffers $R(u)$ and $B(u)$ to $O(N + T_s)$. We observe that $R(u)$ and $B(u)$ never contain more than $c_b(u)$ and $c_r(u)$ segments, respectively, where $c_b(u)$ and $c_r(u)$ denote the maximum number of red (resp., blue) segments intersected by any long blue (resp., red) segment at u. Hence, it suffices to determine these values and allocate $c_b(u)$ space for $R(u)$ and $c_r(u)$ space for $B(u)$. Since these values summed over all nodes of the merger do not sum to more than T_s, this would ensure that the total space usage of all buffers $R(u)$ and $B(u)$ is at most T_s. However, it seems difficult to determine $c_b(u)$ and $c_r(u)$ exactly without already using buffers $R(u)$ and $B(u)$. Instead, we compute upper bounds $c_b'(u)$ and $c_r'(u)$ such that $c_b(u) \leq c_b'(u) \leq c_b(u) + \sqrt{N}$ and $c_r(u) \leq c_r'(u) \leq c_r(u) + \sqrt{N}$, which can be done in linear space. By allocating $c_b'(u)$ space for buffer $R(u)$ and $c_r'(u)$ space for buffer $B(u)$, each buffer is big enough and we waste only $O(\sqrt{N})$ space per merger node. Since there are $O(\sqrt{N})$ merger nodes, the total space used by all buffers is therefore $O(N + T_s)$.

We discuss how to compute values $c_b'(u)$, as values $c_r'(u)$ can be computed similarly. To compute values $c_b'(u)$, we compute a $\sqrt{N}/2$-sample of the long red segments passing through each node u and determine for every long blue segment b how many segments in the sample it intersects. If this number is $h(b)$, then b intersects between $\sqrt{N}(h(b) - 1)/2$ and $\sqrt{N}(h(b) + 1)/2$ long red segments at node u. See Fig. 3(c). We choose $c'_b(u)$ to be the maximum of $\sqrt{N}(h(b)+1)/2$ taken over all long blue segments b at node u.

More precisely, we use two passes through the $\sqrt{N}$-merger after allocating a sample buffer $R_s(u)$ of size $2\sqrt{N}$ to each node. The first pass merges red segments by their intersections with left slab boundaries. At a node u, every $\sqrt{N}/2$'th long segment is placed into $R_s(u)$. The second pass merges blue segments by their intersections with left slab boundaries. Before this pass, we set $c'_b(u) = 0$ for every node u. During the merge, when we process a long blue segment b, we determine the number $h_l(b)$ of segments in $R_s(u)$ that intersect $l(\sigma_{l(u)})$ below b, as well as the number $h_r(b)$ of segments in $R_s(u)$ that intersect $r(\sigma_{l(u)})$ below r. Let $h(b) = |h_r(b) - h_l(b)|$. If $\sqrt{N}(h(b)+1)/2 > c'_b(u)$, we set $c'_b(u) = \sqrt{N}(h(b)+1)/2$.

Since we allocate only $O(\sqrt{N})$ space to each merger node during the approximate counting of intersections, the space usage of this step is linear. Moreover, we merge red and blue segments once, and it can be shown that the computation of values $h_r(b)$ and $h_l(b)$ for all blue segments b passing through node u requires two scans of list $R_s(u)$ in total. Hence, this adds $O(N/B)$ to the merge cost, and we obtain the following lemma, which completes the proof of Theorem 2.

Lemma 2. *Long-long intersections can be reported using $O(\mathrm{Sort}(N) + T_s/B)$ memory transfers and linear space.*

References

1. Aggarwal, A., Vitter, J.S.: The Input/Output complexity of sorting and related problems. Comm. ACM 31(9), 1116–1127 (1988)
2. Arge, L.: External memory data structures. In: Abello, J., Pardalos, P.M., Resende, M.G.C. (eds.) Handbook of Massive Data Sets. Kluwer Academic Publishers, Dordrecht (2002)
3. Arge, L., Brodal, G.S., Fagerberg, R.: Cache-oblivious data structures. In: Mehta, D., Sahni, S. (eds.) Handbook on Data Structures and Applications. CRC Press, Boca Raton (2005)
4. Arge, L., Vengroff, D.E., Vitter, J.S.: External-memory algorithms for processing line segments in geographic information systems. Algorithmica 47, 1–25 (2007)
5. Bender, M.A., Cole, R., Raman, R.: Exponential structures for cache-oblivious algorithms. In: Widmayer, P., Triguero, F., Morales, R., Hennessy, M., Eidenbenz, S., Conejo, R. (eds.) ICALP 2002. LNCS, vol. 2380, pp. 195–207. Springer, Heidelberg (2002)
6. Brodal, G.S., Fagerberg, R.: Cache oblivious distribution sweeping. In: Widmayer, P., Triguero, F., Morales, R., Hennessy, M., Eidenbenz, S., Conejo, R. (eds.) ICALP 2002. LNCS, vol. 2380, pp. 426–438. Springer, Heidelberg (2002)
7. Chiang, Y.-J., Goodrich, M.T., Grove, E.F., Tamassia, R., Vengroff, D.E., Vitter, J.S.: External-memory graph algorithms. In: Proc. SODA, pp. 139–149 (1995)
8. Frigo, M., Leiserson, C.E., Prokop, H., Ramachandran, S.: Cache-oblivious algorithms. In: Proc. FOCS, pp. 285–298 (1999)
9. Goodrich, M.T., Tsay, J.-J., Vengroff, D.E., Vitter, J.S.: External-memory computational geometry. In: Proc. FOCS, pp. 714–723 (1993)
10. Vitter, J.S.: External memory algorithms and data structures: Dealing with MASSIVE data. ACM Comp. Surveys 33(2), 209–271 (2001)

The Complexity of Bisectors and Voronoi Diagrams on Realistic Terrains

Boris Aronov[1], Mark de Berg[2], and Shripad Thite[3]

[1] Department of Computer and Information Science, Polytechnic University, USA
`aronov@poly.edu`
[2] Department of Computing Science, TU-Eindhoven, the Netherlands
`mdberg@win.tue.nl`
[3] California Institute of Technology, Center for the Mathematics of Information, USA
`shripad@caltech.edu`

Abstract. We prove tight bounds on the complexity of bisectors and Voronoi diagrams on so-called realistic terrains, under the geodesic distance. In particular, if n denotes the number of triangles in the terrain, we show the following two results.

(i) If the triangles of the terrain have bounded slope and the projection of the set of triangles onto the xy-plane has low density, then the worst-case complexity of a bisector is $\Theta(n)$.

(ii) If, in addition, the triangles have similar sizes and the domain of the terrain is a rectangle of bounded aspect ratio, then the worst-case complexity of the Voronoi diagram of m point sites is $\Theta(n + m\sqrt{n})$.

1 Introduction

Motivation. The *Voronoi diagram* of a set S of m sites in a metric space is the decomposition of the space into m cells, one per site, such that the cell corresponding to a site $p \in S$ contains exactly those points for which p is the closest site. Often the sites are points and the ambient space is a Euclidean space, but there are many other interesting settings. Voronoi diagrams play a role in numerous applications and they have been studied extensively—see for example the book by Okabe *et al.* [9] or one of the several surveys [1, 2, 6] dedicated to Voronoi diagrams. One of the areas where Voronoi diagrams are frequently used is geographic information systems. A natural setting in this application is where the sites are points in a mountainous terrain, and the distance between any two points on the terrain is the geodesic distance. (The *geodesic distance* between two points is the length of a shortest path on the terrain connecting them.) This is the setting of our paper.

A standard way to model a terrain is using a *triangulated irregular network*, or *TIN* for short: a triangulation of a convex polygonal domain in the xy-plane— usually the domain is simply a rectangle—where each vertex is given an elevation. In computational geometry, a TIN is called a *polyhedral terrain*. Hereafter, the term *terrain* refers to a polyhedral terrain.

D. Halperin and K. Mehlhorn (Eds.): ESA 2008, LNCS 5193, pp. 100–111, 2008.

A fundamental issue in the study of Voronoi diagrams is their combinatorial complexity. It is well known that the complexity—that is, the number of vertices, edges, and cells—of the Voronoi diagram of m sites in the plane under the Euclidean distance is $\Theta(m)$. This follows easily from the fact that the Voronoi diagram is a planar subdivision with m faces, whose vertices have degree at least three and whose edges are line segments or half lines. For Voronoi diagrams on a terrain, things are more complicated. Here, the complexity depends not only on the number of sites but also on the number of triangles in the terrain. Indeed, a single bisector—the *bisector* of two sites is the set of points equidistant from both sites—on a terrain consisting of n triangles can already have complexity $\Omega(n^2)$ [8] and the Voronoi diagram of m sites can have complexity $\Omega((n+m)n)$. Fortunately, these high-complexity bisectors and Voronoi diagrams seem to arise only on carefully constructed, artificial terrains—terrains in practical applications probably behave much better. Thus the question arises: how can we formalize the notion of a "well-behaved terrain" and what is the worst-case complexity of bisectors and Voronoi diagrams on such terrains?

Previous results. These considerations lead Moet *et al.* [8] to study terrains with the following properties: (i) the triangles in the terrain have bounded slope; (ii) the set of terrain triangles has low density; (iii) the domain of the terrain has bounded aspect ratio; (iv) all terrain triangles have roughly the same size. (A more formal definition of these properties is given in Section 2.) They call a terrain with these four properties a *realistic terrain*. Moet investigates [7] whether the assumption of bounded slope, density etc. is pragmatic by measuring these parameters of terrain models of various mountainous regions in the US, which she concludes indeed have the properties listed above.

Moet *et al.* prove that the complexity of a single bisector on a realistic terrain with n triangles is $O(n\sqrt{n})$ and can sometimes be $\Omega(n)$. Moreover, they show that the complexity of the Voronoi diagram on a realistic terrain is $O((n+m)\sqrt{n})$, and can sometimes be $\Omega(n + m\sqrt{n})$.

Recently, Schreiber [11] studied the computation of shortest paths on realistic terrains (or, more generally, realistic polyhedra). Schreiber computes an *implicit* representation of the Voronoi diagram on a realistic terrain in $O((n + m)\log(n + m))$ time, so that the site closest to a query point can be reported in $O(\log(n + m))$ time. For some applications it will be sufficient to have such an implicit representation; for others one needs an explicit representation. The explicit Voronoi diagram can be constructed in $O((n+m)\log(n+m)+k)$ time, where k is the combinatorial complexity of the Voronoi diagram, by an extension of Schreiber's algorithm [12]. The question now arises: what is the maximum combinatorial complexity of the Voronoi diagram on a realistic terrain? This is the question studied by Moet *et al.* [8,7] and explored further in this paper.

Our results. We improve on the results by Moet *et al.* [8] and give tight bounds on the complexity of bisectors and Voronoi diagrams on realistic terrains.

First, we prove that the worst-case complexity of a single bisector on a realistic terrain is $\Theta(n)$. We obtain our improved bound by studying the global shape of the bisector and showing essentially that it cannot "wiggle" too wildly. More precisely, we prove that the set of pieces forming the bisector has low density. We believe that this result is of independent interest. Interestingly, our proof only requires the terrain to have properties (i) and (ii) listed above; thus it yields not only a significantly better bound than what was known, but it also applies to a wider class of terrains.

Second, we show that the worst-case complexity of the Voronoi diagram on a realistic terrain is $\Theta(n + m\sqrt{n})$. This result is based partially on our improved bound on the complexity of a bisector and partially on a careful investigation of the structure of the Voronoi diagram.

2   Preliminaries

Let $\mathcal{T}$ be a terrain with n triangles. In this section, we denote the vertical projection of any subset $o \subset \mathcal{T}$ to the xy-plane by $\bar{o}$. We will use D to denote the domain of $\mathcal{T}$, which is a subset of the xy-plane. For simplicity, and because this is mostly the case in practice, we assume that D is a rectangle; our results can easily be extended to the case where D is an arbitrary convex region. Notice that $\overline{\mathcal{T}}$ is a triangulation of D.

Next we formally define the parameters that measure how well-behaved a terrain is.

- The *slope* of a triangle Δ in $\mathbb{R}^3$ is the maximum slope of any line segment contained in Δ. For example, a triangle parallel to the xy-plane has slope 0, while a vertical triangle—a triangle parallel to the z-axis—has infinite slope. The slope ξ of the terrain $\mathcal{T}$ is the maximum slope of any of its triangles. Note that a terrain does not contain vertical triangles by definition, so it has finite slope.
- The *density* [4] of a set S of objects in the plane is defined as the smallest number λ such that any disk B intersects at most λ objects $o \in S$ such that $\mathrm{diam}(o) \geqslant \mathrm{diam}(B)$, where $\mathrm{diam}(\cdot)$ denotes the diameter. The density λ of the terrain $\mathcal{T}$ is the density of the set of edges of $\overline{\mathcal{T}}$. In other words, the density refers to the edges of the triangulation of the domain D that corresponds to $\mathcal{T}$.
- The *aspect ratio* of a rectangle with width w and height h is defined as $\max(w/h, h/w)$. The aspect ratio ρ of $\mathcal{T}$ is the aspect ratio of its domain D.
- The *scale factor* σ of $\mathcal{T}$ is the ratio between the maximum and the minimum length of any edge of $\overline{\mathcal{T}}$.

Moet *et al.* [8] define a realistic terrain as a terrain whose slope ξ, density λ, aspect ratio ρ, and scale factor σ are constants independent of n, and then prove bounds on the complexity of bisectors and Voronoi diagrams as a function of n only, with the dependence on ξ, λ, ρ, and σ hidden in the asymptotic notation. We make this dependence explicit in all our bounds.

For two points $p, q \in \mathcal{T}$, we use $\mathrm{dist}(p, q)$ to denote the geodesic distance between p and q. In other words, $\mathrm{dist}(p, q)$ is the length of a shortest path from

p to q on $\mathcal{T}$. Furthermore, we use $|\overline{pq}|$ to denote the Euclidean distance between $\overline{p}$ and $\overline{q}$. As already observed by Moet *et al.* [8], the geodesic distance between two points on a terrain with bounded slope is closely related to the Euclidean distance between their projections:

Lemma 1. [8] *For any two points p, q on a terrain $\mathcal{T}$ with slope ξ, we have* $\text{dist}(p, q) \leqslant \sqrt{\xi^2 + 1} \cdot |\overline{pq}|.$

A second basic fact that we will use is that shortest paths on a realistic terrain cross $O(\sqrt{n})$ triangles.

Lemma 2. [8] *Let $\mathcal{T}$ be a terrain with slope ξ, density λ, aspect ratio ρ, and scale factor σ. Then any shortest path on $\mathcal{T}$ crosses $O(c\sqrt{n})$ terrain edges, where* $c = \xi \lambda \sigma \sqrt{\rho}.$

Finally, we will use the following result, which follows easily from the definition of density (just charge every intersecting pair (o_1, o_2) to the object with smaller diameter). Similar results have been used in previous papers [3, 13] dealing with low-density scenes.

Lemma 3. *Let S_1 be a set of n_1 objects and density λ_1, and let S_2 be a set of n_2 objects and density λ_2. Then the number of pairs $(o_1, o_2) \in S_1 \times S_2$ such that o_1 intersects o_2 is $O(\lambda_2 n_1 + \lambda_1 n_2)$.*

There is a natural one-to-one correspondence (obtained by vertical projection) between points on the terrain $\mathcal{T}$ and points in the domain D. Hence, we can view Voronoi diagrams and bisectors as subsets of $\mathcal{T}$, or as subsets of D. From now on, we will take the latter view and consider these structures to be subsets of D. It is then also convenient to no longer make an explicit distinction between geometric entities—points, shortest paths, bisectors, etc.—on the terrain $\mathcal{T}$ and their projections to the domain D, and drop the notation $\overline{o}$ for the projection of an object o. Thus, for example, when we speak of a shortest path π between two points s and t on the terrain, we actually refer to the path $\overline{\pi}$ that connects $\overline{s}$ to $\overline{t}$. (When it is important to make the distinction between an object and its projection, we will explicitly do so.) Moreover, $|xy|$ refers to the Euclidean distance between points x and y on D, while $\text{dist}(x, y)$ refers to the length of a shortest path between the corresponding points on $\mathcal{T}$.

The structure of shortest paths on a terrain. A shortest path $\pi(x, y)$ between $x, y \in \mathcal{T}$ is a polygonal path that stays straight within individual terrain triangles and unfolds to a straight line segment whenever it crosses a terrain edge away from a vertex. A shortest path may pass through a terrain vertex (the vertex has to be non-convex in a technical sense that is not important in this paper). Two shortest paths $\pi(x, y)$ and $\pi(x, z)$ emanating from the same point x do not properly cross, nor overlap and then diverge, except possibly at (non-convex) vertices of $\mathcal{T}$.

If two sites are equidistant from a terrain vertex, their bisector need not be a curve; it may contain entire two-dimensional regions. So, in order for bisectors and Voronoi diagrams to be properly defined, following previous work [8], we therefore make the *general position assumption* that no two sites are equidistant from a terrain vertex. This assumption guarantees that bisectors are 1-dimensional and that Voronoi cells are regions that cover $\mathcal{T}$ without overlap, except at their common boundaries.

Moreover, in this version of the paper, we also add another *non-degeneracy assumption* that is not needed for the results presented to hold but that simplifies the presentation; the assumption is removed in the full version of the paper. Namely, we assume that each site s is connected to every vertex v of the terrain by a *unique* shortest path. Non-degeneracy implies that, for every point $x \in \mathcal{T}$, all shortest paths between s and x are pairwise non-crossing; they may overlap but they cannot cross. Now, for any two shortest paths $\pi(s,x)$ and $\pi(s,y)$, for $x \neq y$, there must exist a point z (which might coincide with s) so that $\pi(s,x) \cap \pi(s,y) = \pi(s,z)$. Moreover, for any two distinct shortest paths $\pi_1(s,x)$ and $\pi_2(s,x)$ from s to the same point x there must exist a point $z \neq x$ with a unique shortest path $\pi(s,z)$ from s so that $\pi_1(s,x) \cap \pi_2(s,x) = \pi(s,z) \cup \{x\}$.

3   The Bisector

Let s and t be two point sites (not necessarily vertices) on a terrain $\mathcal{T}$. In this section we study the complexity of the bisector $b = b(s,t)$ of s and t on $\mathcal{T}$. We will do the analysis in terms of n, the number of triangles of the terrain, and its slope ξ and density λ.

The bisector b, by definition, consists of all points $p \in \mathcal{T}$ such that $\text{dist}(p,s) = \text{dist}(p,t)$. It partitions $\mathcal{T}$ into two regions: $\mathcal{V}(s)$, the *Voronoi cell* of s, which contains the points closer to s, and $\mathcal{V}(t)$, the *Voronoi cell* of t, which contains the points closer to t. Since Voronoi cells are connected, b is a simple curve that is either closed—this can happen, for instance, when s is the peak of a mountain and t is at the foot of the mountain—or connects two points on the boundary of the terrain.

For most points on b, there is a unique shortest path to s and a unique shortest path to t. For some points, however, there are multiple shortest paths to s and/or to t. We call such points *breakpoints*. The number of breakpoints on b is at most n, because each of them can be attributed to a terrain vertex [10]. The breakpoints partition b into *pieces*; the intersection of a piece with a terrain triangle is a line segment or hyperbolic arc [10]. The *complexity* of b is now defined as the number of breakpoints plus the number of times that b crosses a terrain edge.

We denote the set of all bisector pieces by Γ. Moet *et al.* [8] prove that on a realistic terrain any piece $\gamma \in \Gamma$ can cross only $O(\sqrt{n})$ triangles. Since $|\Gamma| \leqslant n+1$, this implies that the total complexity of the bisector is $O(n\sqrt{n})$. To improve upon this, we take a more global look at the bisector and show that the set Γ has low density. (Here it is important to recall that we view Γ as a set of curves in the xy-plane, that is, as a collection of subsets of D.) The result will then readily follow from Lemma 3 and the fact that $\mathcal{T}$ has low density.

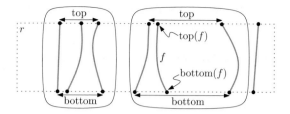

Fig. 1. Seven fragments and the two blocks defined by them. The rightmost fragment does not belong to any block.

Let r be a rectangle in the xy-plane, and assume without loss of generality that r is axis-parallel. We say that a piece γ *crosses* r if $\gamma \cap r$ has a connected component with one endpoint on the top edge of r and one endpoint on the bottom edge of r. We call such a component a *fragment* of γ. To bound the density of Γ, we first show that r cannot be crossed too many times.

We denote the top endpoint of a fragment f by top(f) and its bottom endpoint by bottom(f). For each piece γ that crosses r, we pick one of its fragments, and we let F denote the set of all such fragments. Since each fragment $f \in F$ connects the top edge of r to the bottom edge of r, we can order the fragments from left to right. We group the fragments from left to right in triples, and we call such an (ordered) triple a *block*—see Fig. 1. We start by proving a lemma on the structure of the shortest paths from the endpoints of the fragments in a block to s and t.

Define the *top* of a block to be the line segment connecting the top of the leftmost fragment of the triple to that of its rightmost fragment. Define the *bottom* of a block analogously.

Lemma 4. *Let (f_1, f_2, f_3) be a block. Then at least one of the three top endpoints has a shortest path to s or t that intersects the bottom of the block. Similarly, at least one of the three bottom endpoints has a shortest path to s or t that intersects the top of the block.*

Proof. We will prove the lemma for the top endpoints; the proof for the bottom endpoints is symmetric.

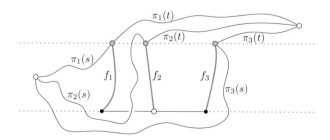

Fig. 2. One of the paths from the top endpoints must intersect the bottom of the block

For $i \in \{1, 2, 3\}$ and $q \in \{s, t\}$, let $\pi_i(q)$ denote the shortest path from $\text{top}(f_i)$ to q. Let $V_1 := \{\text{top}(f_1), \text{top}(f_2), \text{top}(f_3)\}$ and $V_2 := \{s, t, \text{bottom}(f_2)\}$.

Consider a geometric realization of the graph $K_{3,3}$, where $V_1 \cup V_2$ is the set of nodes and the arcs are realized as follows—see also Fig. 2. The arcs from nodes in V_1 to s and t are given by the shortest paths $\pi_i(s)$ and $\pi_i(t)$; the arc from $\text{top}(f_2)$ to $\text{bottom}(f_2)$ is given by f_2; and for $i = 1, 3$ the arc from $\text{top}(f_i)$ to $\text{bottom}(f_2)$ is given by the concatenation of f_i and the segment connecting $\text{bottom}(f_i)$ to $\text{bottom}(f_2)$.

Since $K_{3,3}$ is non-planar, there must be an intersection between some pair of arcs. Recall that the fragments f_i are all part of the bisector b, which also means that the points $\text{top}(f_i)$ lie on b. Hence, the paths $\pi_i(s)$ and $\pi_i(t)$ lie inside $\mathcal{V}(s)$ and $\mathcal{V}(t)$, respectively. This implies that the paths $\pi_i(s)$ and $\pi_i(t)$ do not intersect any of the fragments f_j, and also that a path $\pi_i(s)$ does not intersect any path $\pi_j(t)$ (except possibly at common endpoints). Furthermore, after two shortest paths $\pi_i(s)$ and $\pi_j(s)$ meet for the first time, they follow the same subpath, by our non-degeneracy assumption. Hence, a small perturbation yields paths that are disjoint (except at s). Similarly, we can enforce that the paths $\pi_i(t)$ and $\pi_j(t)$ are disjoint except at t. Finally, two fragments f_i, f_j do not intersect each other, by construction. The only remaining possibility is that one of the paths $\pi_i(s)$ or $\pi_i(t)$ intersects one of the segments connecting $\text{bottom}(f_i)$ to $\text{bottom}(f_2)$ for $i = 1, 3$. In other words, one of these paths intersects the bottom of the block.   □

Now define the *top width* of a block (f_1, f_2, f_3) as the length of the top of the block, define its *bottom width* analogously, and define the *width* of a block as the maximum of its top and bottom widths. The previous lemma allows us to prove a lower bound on the width of a block.

Lemma 5. *The width of any block (f_1, f_2, f_3) is at least $h/\sqrt{\xi^2 + 1}$, where h is the height of the rectangle r.*

Proof. By Lemma 4 one of the top endpoints, say $\text{top}(f_i)$, has a shortest path to s or t that intersects the bottom of the block. Similarly, one of the bottom endpoints, say $\text{bottom}(f_j)$, has a shortest path to s or t that intersects the top of the block. We can assume, without loss of generality, that $\text{dist}(\text{top}(f_i), s) \leqslant \text{dist}(\text{bottom}(f_j), s)$. Since $\text{top}(f_i)$ and $\text{bottom}(f_j)$ lie on the bisector b, we get

$$\text{dist}(\text{top}(f_i), t) = \text{dist}(\text{top}(f_i), s) \leqslant \text{dist}(\text{bottom}(f_j), s) = \text{dist}(\text{bottom}(f_j), t).$$

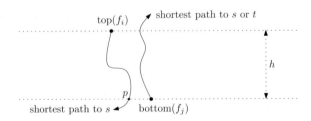

Fig. 3. The width of a block cannot be too small

Now assume, also without loss of generality, that the shortest path from $\text{top}(f_i)$ that crosses the bottom of the block is the shortest path to s, and let the point where it crosses the bottom be denoted by p—see Fig. 3. Then we have

$$
\begin{aligned}
\text{dist}(\text{top}(f_i), s) &\leqslant \text{dist}(\text{bottom}(f_j), s) \\
&\leqslant \text{dist}(\text{bottom}(f_j), p) + \text{dist}(p, s) \\
&\leqslant \sqrt{\xi^2 + 1} \cdot |\text{bottom}(f_j)p| + \text{dist}(p, s) \qquad \text{by Lemma 1} \\
&\leqslant \sqrt{\xi^2 + 1} \cdot |\text{bottom}(f_j)p| + \text{dist}(\text{top}(f_i), s) - h
\end{aligned}
$$

It follows that $|\text{bottom}(f_j)p| \geqslant h/\sqrt{\xi^2 + 1}$. □

The previous lemma implies that a rectangle r of small aspect ratio cannot be crossed by too many bisector pieces.

Lemma 6. *The rectangle r is crossed by at most $2 + 6w\sqrt{\xi^2 + 1}/h$ bisector pieces, where h is the height of the rectangle r and w is its width.*

Proof. Consider the set of fragments induced by the bisector pieces crossing r, as defined above. These fragments are grouped into blocks of three, with at most two fragments not belonging to any block. Hence, we must show that the number of blocks is at most $2w\sqrt{\xi^2 + 1}/h$. By Lemma 5, either the top width or the bottom width of any block is at least $h/\sqrt{\xi^2 + 1}$. Since the width of r is w, there can be at most $w/\sqrt{\xi^2 + 1}/h$ blocks whose top width is at least at least $h/\sqrt{\xi^2 + 1}$. Similarly, there can be at most $w\sqrt{\xi^2 + 1}/h$ blocks whose bottom width is at least $h/\sqrt{\xi^2 + 1}$, and so the total number of blocks is as claimed. □

Using Lemma 6 we obtain the following theorem. Its proof is very similar to a low-density proof by De Berg [3], and therefore omitted.

Theorem 1. *Let s and t be any two points on a terrain $\mathcal{T}$, let $b(s,t)$ be their bisector, and let Γ be the collection of (projected) bisector pieces obtained by splitting $b(s,t)$ at breakpoints as defined above. Then Γ has density $O(\xi)$, where ξ is the slope of $\mathcal{T}$.*

Combining Theorem 1 with Lemma 3 immediately leads to the following result.

Corollary 1. *The bisector of two points on a terrain $\mathcal{T}$ with n triangles has complexity $O((\xi + \lambda)n)$, where ξ is the slope of $\mathcal{T}$ and λ is its density.*

4   The Voronoi Diagram

Let $S := \{s_1, \ldots, s_m\}$ be a set of m point sites on a terrain $\mathcal{T}$ with n triangles, and let $\mathcal{VD}(S)$ denote the Voronoi diagram of S. Each Voronoi edge is a portion of some bisector $b(s_i, s_j)$, and the number of Voronoi edges is $O(m)$. (Note that a Voronoi edge is not necessarily incident to two Voronoi vertices; it can also be a closed curve or have one or both endpoints on the boundary of D.) Bounding the complexity of the Voronoi diagram amounts to bounding the total complexity of all Voronoi edges. In the previous section we bounded the complexity of a single bisector as a function of n, and the slope ξ and density λ of $\mathcal{T}$. The bound on the complexity of the Voronoi diagram that we will prove in this section also depends on the aspect ratio ρ and the scale factor σ of $\mathcal{T}$.

Recall that a bisector $b(s_i, s_j)$ is partitioned into pieces at breakpoints—points where the shortest path to s_i and/or to s_j is not unique—and that the intersection of such a piece with a terrain triangle is a hyperbolic arc or line segment. Because a breakpoint on a Voronoi edge that is part of $b(s_i, s_j)$ can be uniquely attributed to a vertex lying inside one of the Voronoi cells $\mathcal{V}(s_i)$ or $\mathcal{V}(s_j)$, the total number of breakpoints over all Voronoi edges is $O(n)$ [8]. Hence, the total complexity of the Voronoi edges is proportional to $m + n$ plus the total number of intersections between Voronoi edges and terrain edges. The rest of this section is devoted to bounding the number of intersections between Voronoi edges and terrain edges.

Consider a breakpoint p on the Voronoi edge generated by $b(s_i, s_j)$. We call p a *special breakpoint* if it has two shortest paths to s_i that enclose at least one hole in $\mathcal{V}(s_i)$, or two shortest paths to s_j that enclose at least one hole in $\mathcal{V}(s_j)$. (A *hole* in $\mathcal{V}(s_i)$ is formed by one or more other Voronoi cells $\mathcal{V}(s_k)$ enclosed by $\mathcal{V}(s_i)$. As remarked earlier, this can happen for instance if s_i is at the foot of a steep mountain and s_k is at the peak.) Let B be the set of all special breakpoints. The special breakpoints subdivide the Voronoi edges into *subedges*. To simplify the presentation, we augment B with $O(m)$ additional points to ensure that B contains, for each site s_i, at least two points on every component of $\partial \mathcal{V}(s_i)$.

Lemma 7. *Let p and q be the endpoints of a subedge γ on $\partial \mathcal{V}(s_i)$. Then there exists a shortest path $\pi(p)$ from p to s_i and a shortest path $\pi(q)$ from q to s_i, such that the region $\mathcal{V}(\gamma, s_i) \subset \mathcal{V}(s_i)$ enclosed by γ, $\pi(p)$ and $\pi(q)$ is simply connected. Moreover, there is a choice of shortest paths $\pi(p), \pi(q)$ for all subedges γ that guarantees that $\mathcal{V}(\gamma, s_i)$ and $\mathcal{V}(\gamma', s_j)$ do not overlap for $(\gamma, s_i) \neq (\gamma', s_j)$.*

Proof. Since we augmented B with extra points, p and q cannot coincide. Take any point r in the interior of γ, and draw a shortest path $\pi(r)$ from r to s_i. Imagine moving r towards p. As we move r continuously, we can also transform $\pi(r)$ continuously such that it stays shortest, except when r moves over a breakpoint: at that point $\pi(r)$ jumps. (More precisely, when r reaches a breakpoint which, by definition, has more than one shortest path to s_i, $\pi(r)$ coincides with one of these paths. To be able to continuously deform the path further while remaining shortest, we have to switch $\pi(r)$ to one of the other shortest paths. This is what we refer to as "jumping" of a shortest path.) Since γ is a subedge, however, a breakpoint in its interior cannot be a special breakpoint. Hence, $\pi(r)$ does not jump over a hole of $\mathcal{V}(s_i)$, i.e., the region bounded by the two shortest paths to the breakpoint is fully contained in $\mathcal{V}(s_i)$ and is simply connected. The same argument shows that $\pi(r)$ will not jump over a hole when we move r to q. Hence, we can find shortest paths from p and q to s_i such that the region $\mathcal{V}(\gamma, s_i)$ enclosed by them and γ is simply connected.

Since $\mathcal{V}(\gamma, s_i) \subset \mathcal{V}(s_i)$, regions belonging to different sites cannot overlap. We claim that $\mathcal{V}(\gamma, s_i)$ and $\mathcal{V}(\gamma', s_i)$, for different subedges γ, γ', do not overlap either. Recall from Section 2 that the non-degeneracy assumption implies that shortest paths from s_i to points x, y, after diverging for the first time (as seen from s_i), do not meet again (except at x when $x = y$). Hence, the shortest paths that bound the regions $\mathcal{V}(\gamma, s_i)$ form a tree-like structure, which implies the regions $\mathcal{V}(\gamma, s_i)$ and $\mathcal{V}(\gamma', s_i)$ for different subedges do not overlap.   □

Next we bound the total number of subedges.

Lemma 8. *The total number of subedges is $O(m)$.*

Proof. The number of edges of the Voronoi diagram is $O(m)$, so to prove the lemma we must show that the total number of special breakpoints is $O(m)$. For each special breakpoint p, there is a Voronoi cell $\mathcal{V}(s_i)$ such that p has two shortest paths α, β to s_i so that the loop $\alpha \cup \beta$ encloses a hole of $\mathcal{V}(s_i)$. Because shortest paths do not cross (by the non-degeneracy assumption), two such cycles can never cross, though they may partially overlap. Thus we obtain a collection of non-crossing loops, each containing one or more holes (and thus sites) in its interior. These loops may nest, but each loop contains a different subset of sites. We can conclude that the overall number of loops—and, hence, the overall number of special breakpoints—is $O(m)$.   □

We are now ready to prove a bound on the number of intersections between Voronoi edges and terrain edges and, hence, obtain our main result.

Theorem 2. *The complexity of the Voronoi diagram of m point sites on a terrain $\mathcal{T}$ with n triangles is $O(c_1 n + c_2 m \sqrt{n})$, where $c_1 = \xi + \lambda$ and $c_2 = \xi^2 \lambda \sigma \sqrt{\rho}$. Here ξ, λ, ρ, and σ denote the slope, density, aspect ratio, and scale factor of $\mathcal{T}$, respectively.*

Proof. We already observed that, up to an additive $O(n + m)$ term, the complexity of the Voronoi diagram is bounded by the total number of intersections between Voronoi edges and terrain edges.

Let Γ denote the set of subedges as defined above. Let $\gamma \in \Gamma$ be a subedge lying on the common boundary of Voronoi cells $\mathcal{V}(s_i)$ and $\mathcal{V}(s_j)$. For any terrain edge intersecting γ, at least one of the following two conditions holds: (i) it has an endpoint inside $\mathcal{V}(\gamma, s_i)$ or $\mathcal{V}(\gamma, s_j)$, or (ii) it intersects a shortest path from an endpoint of γ to s_i or s_j, i.e., the boundary of $\mathcal{V}(\gamma, s_i) \cup \mathcal{V}(\gamma, s_j)$. In Fig. 4, the edge e illustrates case (i) and e' case (ii). Let $E_{\mathcal{T}}(\gamma)$ denote the set of all terrain edges for which one of the two cases (i) and (ii) hold. From Lemmas 8 and 2 we can conclude that

$$\sum_{\gamma \in \Gamma} |E_{\mathcal{T}}(\gamma)| = O(n + cm\sqrt{n}),$$

where $c = \xi \lambda \sigma \sqrt{\rho}$, because every edge of $\mathcal{T}$ can contribute at most two to the count in case (i) and each shortest path contributes at most $O(c\sqrt{n})$ edges in case (ii). Now partition each subedge γ into pieces, by adding all the breakpoints on γ; let $E_{\mathcal{VD}}(\gamma)$ denote the set of these pieces. Since the overall number of

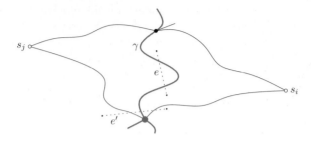

Fig. 4. Two terrain edges, e and e', intersecting a subedge γ

breakpoints is $O(n)$, we have $\sum_{\gamma \in \Gamma} |E_{\mathcal{VD}}(\gamma)| = O(n + m)$. Trivially, the total number of intersections between Voronoi edges and terrain edges is equal to the sum, over all $\gamma \in \Gamma$, of the number of intersections between pieces in $E_{\mathcal{VD}}(\gamma)$ and terrain edges in $E_{\mathcal{T}}(\gamma)$. Moreover, $E_{\mathcal{VD}}(\gamma)$ has density $O(\xi)$ by Theorem 1, and $E_{\mathcal{T}}(\gamma)$ has density λ by definition. Hence, by Lemma 3, the number of intersections between pieces in $E_{\mathcal{VD}}(\gamma)$ and terrain edges in $E_{\mathcal{T}}(\gamma)$ is

$$O(\xi \cdot |E_{\mathcal{T}}(\gamma)| + \lambda \cdot |E_{\mathcal{VD}}(\gamma)|).$$

It follows that the total number of intersections is bounded by

$$\sum_{\gamma \in \Gamma} O(\xi \cdot |E_{\mathcal{T}}(\gamma)| + \lambda \cdot |E_{\mathcal{VD}}(\gamma)|) = O(\xi(n + cm\sqrt{n}) + \lambda(n + m)),$$

which gives the claimed bound.   □

5   Conclusion

We proved tight bounds on the complexity of bisectors and Voronoi diagrams on the *realistic terrains* introduced by Moet et al. [8]. Even though our bounds are tight, there are still some interesting open questions. In particular, we have shown that the total number of intersections between bisector pieces and terrain edges is $O(n)$, but we suspect that this bound is not tight. Improving this bound will not lead to a better bound on the complexity of the bisector, since the number of bisector pieces can already be $\Omega(n)$. Nevertheless, a tight bound on the number of intersections between a bisector and terrain edges would give more insight into the global shape of bisectors. Moreover, an $O(\sqrt{n})$ bound on the number of triangle edges crossed by a bisector would immediately imply an $O(n + m\sqrt{n})$ bound on the complexity of the Voronoi diagram—something that requires a more involved argument in our current paper.

   Another direction for further research is to see under what conditions one can prove an $O(n+m)$ bound on the complexity of the Voronoi diagram. For this one would probably also need to make assumptions on how the sites are distributed, and not only on the properties of the terrain.

As remarked in the introduction, Moet [7] studied some terrain models for mountainous regions in the US and found that the values of the four parameters defined in Section 2 are indeed bounded by a constant independent of the terrain size. Some of these values, however, are still fairly high. Usually this is caused by only a few triangles in the terrain. Hence, it would be interesting to obtain bounds that depend on the average slope of the triangles rather than the maximum slope.

Acknowledgments. Work by Boris Aronov has been partially supported by a grant from the U.S.-Israel Binational Science Foundation and by NSA MSP Grant H98230-06-1-0016. Research by Mark de Berg has been supported by the Netherlands' Organisation for Scientific Research (NWO) under project no. 639.023.301. Part of the research was carried out by Shripad Thite at TU/e, supported by NWO project no. 639.023.301, and by Boris Aronov while visiting TU/e in January 2007 and January 2008.

References

1. Aurenhammer, F.: Voronoi diagrams: A survey of a fundamental geometric data structure. ACM Comput. Surv. 23, 345–405 (1991)
2. Aurenhammer, F., Klein, R.: Voronoi diagrams. In: Sack, J.-R., Urrutia, J. (eds.) Handbook of Computational Geometry, ch. 5. Elsevier, Amsterdam (1999)
3. de Berg, M.: Improved bounds for the union complexity of fat objects. Discr. Comput. Geom. (in print, 2008)
4. de Berg, M., van der Stappen, A.F., Vleugels, J., Katz, M.J.: Realistic input models for geometric algorithms. Algorithmica 34, 81–97 (2002)
5. Chen, J., Han, Y.: Shortest paths on a polyhedron. Int. J. Comput. Geom. Appl. 6, 127–144 (1996)
6. Fortune, S.: Voronoi diagrams and Delaunay triangulations. In: Goodman, J.E., O'Rourke, J. (eds.) Handbook of Discrete and Computational Geometry, ch. 23. CRC Press, Boca Raton (2004)
7. Moet, E.: Computation and complexity of visibility in geometric environments. PhD thesis, Utrecht University (2008)
8. Moet, E., van Kreveld, M., van der Stappen, A.F.: On realistic terrains. In: Proc. 22nd ACM Sympos. Comput. Geom., pp. 177–186 (2006)
9. Okabe, A., Boots, B., Sugihara, K.: Spatial tesselations: Concepts and applications of Voronoi diagrams. John Wiley & Sons, Chichester (1992)
10. Mitchell, J.S.B., Mount, D.M., Papadimitriou, C.H.: The discrete geodesic problem. SIAM J. Comput. 16, 647–668 (1987)
11. Schreiber, Y.: Shortest paths on realistic polyhedra. In: Proc. 23rd ACM Sympos. Comput. Geom., pp. 74–83 (2007)
12. Schreiber, Y.: Personal communication (April 2008)
13. van der Stappen, A.F.: Motion planning amidst fat obstacles. Ph.D. thesis, Utrecht University (1994)

Space-Time Tradeoffs for Proximity Searching in Doubling Spaces

Sunil Arya[1,*], David M. Mount[2,**], Antoine Vigneron[3,***], and Jian Xia[1,†]

[1] Department of Computer Science and Engineering,
The Hong Kong University of Science and Technology,
Clear Water Bay, Kowloon, Hong Kong
{arya,piper}@cse.ust.hk
[2] Department of Computer Science and Institute for Advanced Computer Studies,
University of Maryland, College Park, Maryland 20742
mount@cs.umd.edu
[3] INRA, UR341 Mathématiques et Informatique Appliquées,
78352 Jouy-en-Josas, France
antoine.vigneron@jouy.inra.fr

Abstract. We consider approximate nearest neighbor searching in metric spaces of constant doubling dimension. More formally, we are given a set S of n points and an error bound $\varepsilon > 0$. The objective is to build a data structure so that given any query point q in the space, it is possible to efficiently determine a point of S whose distance from q is within a factor of $(1 + \varepsilon)$ of the distance between q and its nearest neighbor in S. In this paper we obtain the following space-time tradeoffs. Given a parameter $\gamma \in [2, 1/\varepsilon]$, we show how to construct a data structure of space $n\gamma^{O(\dim)} \log(1/\varepsilon)$ space that can answer queries in time $O(\log(n\gamma)) + (1/(\varepsilon\gamma))^{O(\dim)}$. This is the first result that offers space-time tradeoffs for approximate nearest neighbor queries in doubling spaces. At one extreme it nearly matches the best result currently known for doubling spaces, and at the other extreme it results in a data structure that can answer queries in time $O(\log(n/\varepsilon))$, which matches the best query times in Euclidean space. Our approach involves a novel generalization of the AVD data structure from Euclidean space to doubling space.

1 Introduction

Nearest neighbor searching is a fundamental problem in computational geometry with numerous applications in areas such as pattern recognition, information retrieval, machine learning, and robotics. The goal is to store a set S of n points so that, for any query point q, we can quickly return its nearest neighbor in S. As the problem is computationally difficult in most settings, researchers have

---

* Research supported by RGC Grant HKUST6184/04E.
** Research supported in part by NSF grant CCF–0635099.
*** Research partially supported by a Marie Curie international reintegration grant.
† Research supported by RGC Grant HKUST6184/04E.

D. Halperin and K. Mehlhorn (Eds.): ESA 2008, LNCS 5193, pp. 112–123, 2008.
© Springer-Verlag Berlin Heidelberg 2008

considered a variant in which it suffices to return an approximate answer. Given an error bound $\varepsilon > 0$, a point $p \in S$ is said to be an ε-*approximate nearest neighbor* (denoted ε-*NN*) of q if its distance from q is at most $(1 + \varepsilon)$ times the distance between q and its nearest neighbor in S.

Approximate nearest neighbor searching has been studied extensively in Euclidean spaces. Recently there has been considerable interest in metric spaces as well. Data structures for proximity searching in metric spaces have been known for some time (see, e.g., [6, 10, 18]). Clarkson [8] and later Karger and Ruhl [14] introduced models designed to capture the sphere packing and local growth properties of low-dimensional Euclidean spaces. Much of the recent work has focused on metric spaces of low doubling dimension [4, 11]. The *doubling dimension* of a metric space is the minimum value ρ such that every ball in the space can be covered by 2^ρ balls of half the radius. This model was applied to various proximity problems by Krauthgamer, Lee, and co-authors [11, 15, 16, 17]. The results have been extended by Har-Peled and Mendel [13] and others [5, 9].

The results described in these papers on doubling spaces apply in the so called *black-box model*, in which points of the space can only be accessed through a black box that computes the distance between any two points in constant time. One of the advantages of this approach is that it relies on the barest set of assumptions, and so it is possible to obtain the conceptually simplest and most general algorithms. In this model, it is known that given a set of n points in a metric space of doubling dimension dim, ε-approximate nearest neighbor queries can be answered in time $O(\log n) + (1/\varepsilon)^{O(\dim)}$ using a data structure of linear space [9, 13]. It is also observed in [13] that this result is optimal in the black-box model, as there is a lower bound of $\Omega(\log n) + (1/\varepsilon)^{\Omega(\dim)}$ on the query time in this model irrespective of the space used. (These asymptotic bounds, like ours, hide multiplicative factors that depend on the doubling dimension, except for the space bounds of Cole and Gottlieb [9], which are truly $O(n)$, irrespective of the dimension.)

Unfortunately, this query time compares unfavorably to the fastest query times known for Euclidean spaces. In Euclidean d-space, it is possible to answer ε-approximate nearest neighbor queries in time $O(\log(n/\varepsilon))$ and space roughly $O(n/\varepsilon^d)$ through the use of a data structure called an *approximate Voronoi diagram* (or *AVD*) [1, 2, 12]. The difference in query time is quite significant, since in practice factors of the form $(1/\varepsilon)^d$ dominate the query time. It is also shown in [2] that space-time tradeoffs can be achieved. Thus, by limiting consideration to the purely implicit black-box model, simplicity and generality are achieved at the expense of efficiency and flexibility.

This raises the important question of whether it is possible to achieve results for approximate nearest neighbor searching that are comparable to the best results for Euclidean space in efficiency and flexibility, but in a model that provides the generality of metric spaces of low doubling dimension. The aforementioned lower bound indicates that this is not possible within the black-box model. In this paper we provide an affirmative answer to this question by strengthening the model slightly, which we call the *weakly explicit model*. In particular, we assume the doubling space is endowed with a *doubling oracle*, which, given any ball in the metric space returns in constant time a covering with a constant number of balls of half the radius (see Section 2).

Our approach is based on generalizing the AVD data structure to metric spaces in the weakly explicit model. We obtain the following space-time trade-offs for approximate nearest neighbor searching in metric spaces of doubling dimension dim. Given a parameter $\gamma \in [2, 1/\varepsilon]$, we show how to construct AVDs of $n\gamma^{O(\dim)} \log(1/\varepsilon)$ space that can answer ε-NN queries in time $O(\log(n\gamma)) + (1/(\varepsilon\gamma))^{O(\dim)}$. This is the first result that offers space-time tradeoffs for approximate nearest neighbor queries in doubling spaces. At one extreme ($\gamma = 2$), we obtain an AVD of $O(n \log(1/\varepsilon))$ space that answers queries in time $O(\log n) + (1/\varepsilon)^{O(\dim)}$. This result nearly matches the best result currently known for doubling spaces [9, 13], albeit in our stronger model. At the other extreme ($\gamma = 1/\varepsilon$), we obtain an AVD of $n(1/\varepsilon)^{O(\dim)}$ space that can answer queries in time $O(\log(n/\varepsilon))$. This matches the query times for AVDs in Euclidean spaces, and overcomes the restrictive lower bound imposed by the black-box model for doubling spaces.

1.1 Overview of Techniques

In Euclidean space, the AVD is a quadtree-based partitioning of space into constant complexity cells, where each cell stores one or more representatives such that, given a query point q that lies within a cell, one of the associated representatives is an ε-NN of q. Queries are answered by first locating the cell that contains the query point and then scanning the list of stored representatives to find the closest one. The key idea underlying the construction of AVDs in Euclidean space is to partition space into cells, such that each cell enjoys certain *separation properties* with respect to the point set S. These separation properties assert that the region surrounding each cell is simple enough that we can answer ε-NN queries with the help of a small set of representatives. The construction is based on the *box-decomposition tree* (or the *compressed quadtree*), which yields a hierarchical partitioning of space into *fat* cells. The construction is bottom-up, first generating quadtree boxes and then building a tree structure over them.

In metric spaces we do not have the same explicit access to the ambient space's structure, and so we need a different approach. While similar in spirit, our generalization of AVDs to doubling metric spaces differs in the types of cells generated, the method used to generate these cells, and the separation properties they satisfy. It will be necessary to relax the AVD's partitioning of space to allow for a covering instead. We know of no analogous decomposition structure to the box-decomposition tree in doubling spaces, and so we have developed a hybrid construction, which is neither purely top-down nor bottom-up. Roughly speaking, the cells corresponding to all the nodes in the hierarchy that are in the vicinity of the point set S are generated right in the beginning. Next, for each such cell, we identify its children independently. We determine both the cells and the child-parent relationships between them on the basis of the well-separated pair decomposition [7, 13] of the point set. The resulting data structure is not a tree, but a rooted directed acyclic graph, which we call a *region-DAG*. The cells associated with the leaves of the region-DAG cover all of space and satisfy certain separation properties with respect to the point set S. This feature enables us to use region-DAGs for constructing AVDs in doubling spaces.

2   Preliminaries

We begin with some definitions. Let (M, d) be a metric space. We let $B(x, r)$ denote the closed ball of radius r centered at x, i.e., $B(x, r) = \{y \in M : d(x, y) \leqslant r\}$. For a ball b and any positive real η, we use ηb to denote the ball with the same center as b and whose radius is η times the radius of b, and $\bar{b}$ to denote the set of points that are not in b.

The *doubling dimension* of M, denoted $\dim(M)$, is the minimum value ρ such that every ball in M can be covered by 2^ρ balls of half the radius. When there is no ambiguity, we will write dim instead of $\dim(M)$. We say that M is a *doubling space* if it has constant doubling dimension.

Throughout this paper, we will assume that the metric space M is doubling. As mentioned earlier, our constructions will assume the existence of a *doubling oracle*, which given any ball b of radius r in M, returns in $2^{O(\dim(M))}$ time a set of $2^{O(\dim(M))}$ balls of radius $r/2$ covering b. Note that the centers of these balls are not necessarily in the input point set. We view the points (data, query, and covering-ball centers) as being drawn from some ambient metric space to which this oracle has access. This motivates our use of the term *weakly explicit* to describe this model.

A subset $S \subseteq M$ is defined to be an *r-net* of M if (i) every point of M is covered by a ball of radius r centered at some point of S and (ii) the pairwise distance between any two points of S is $\Omega(r)$. It is well-known that such nets always exist for any $r > 0$.

Throughout, we treat n, ε and γ as asymptotic quantities. The constant factors hidden by the $O(\cdot)$ notation are independent of n, ε and γ, but may depend on the doubling dimension.

2.1   The Well-Separated Pair Decomposition

We briefly review the notion of well-separated pair decomposition, as our constructions rely on it. Let S be a set of n points in the doubling space M. We say that two sets of points $X \subseteq S$ and $Y \subseteq S$ are *well-separated* if there exist two disjoint balls of radius r covering X and Y respectively, such that the distance between the centers of these balls is at least σr, where $\sigma \geqslant 2$ is a real parameter called the *separation factor*. We refer to (X, Y) as a *well-separated pair*. In Euclidean space, if we imagine joining the centers of these two balls by a line segment, the resulting geometric shape resembles a *dumbbell*. The balls are the heads of the dumbbell. The *length* of a dumbbell is defined as the distance between the centers of the balls.

Let x and y be two points in S. We say that a well-separated pair (X, Y) *contains* x if $x \in X \cup Y$, and we say that it *separates* x and y if (x, y)

$\in (X \times Y) \cup (Y \times X)$. These notions can also be applied in a natural way to the dumbbell associated with a well-separated pair.

A *well-separated pair decomposition* (WSPD) of S is a set $\mathcal{P}_{S,\sigma} = \{\{X_1, Y_1\}, \dots, \{X_m, Y_m\}\}$ of pairs of subsets of S such that (i) for $1 \leqslant i \leqslant m$, X_i and Y_i are well-separated, and (ii) for any distinct points $x, y \in S$, there exists a unique pair (X_i, Y_i) that separates x and y. Given any n-point set in constant-dimensional Euclidean space, Callahan and Kosaraju [7] showed that there exists a WSPD of linear size. This result was generalized to doubling spaces by Har-Peled and Mendel [13], who showed that the number of pairs in the WSPD of S is $\sigma^{O(\dim)} n$ and it can be constructed in $2^{O(\dim)} n \log n + \sigma^{O(\dim)} n$ time. For each pair, their construction also provides the corresponding dumbbell satisfying the separation criteria mentioned above. Furthermore, the centers of both the dumbbell heads are points of S.

The following preliminary lemma will be useful for us. It follows from the definition of well-separatedness and the triangle inequality.

Lemma 1. *Consider the WSPD of S with separation factor $\sigma \geqslant 16$. Consider the dumbbell for a pair $P = (X, Y)$ in this WSPD. Let x and y denote the centers of the dumbbell heads, and let $\ell = d(x, y)$ be the length of the dumbbell. Then for any $x' \in X$ and $y' \in Y$ we have $d(x, x') \leqslant \ell/16$ and $7\ell/8 \leqslant d(x', y') \leqslant 9\ell/8$.*

3   The Region-DAG

In this section, we describe our construction of the *region-DAG*, which can be viewed as a generalization of the box-decomposition tree [3] to doubling spaces. Our AVD construction in doubling spaces described in Section 4 will rely crucially on this data structure.

Let S be a set of n points in a doubling space (M, d). The *region-DAG* for S is a directed acyclic graph in which each node is associated with a region of space called a *cell*, which is the difference of two concentric balls, an *outer ball* and an (optional) *inner ball*. If the inner ball exists, its radius is at most half the radius of the outer ball. If a cell has no inner ball, we call it a *simple cell* (the corresponding node is called a *simple node*), otherwise we call it a *doughnut cell* (the corresponding node is called a *doughnut node*). Throughout this paper, for a simple node u, we let b_u denote the associated cell. The *size* of a cell (and the corresponding node) is defined to be the radius of its outer ball. If a cell contains no points of S, we say that it is *empty*, otherwise it is *nonempty*. If there is an edge from node u to node v, we say that v is a *child* of u. If a node has no children, it is called a *leaf*, otherwise it is an *internal node*.

Our construction of the region-DAG involves two parameters $\gamma \geqslant 2$ and $\beta \geqslant \gamma$. These parameters help to control the degree of separation enjoyed by the leaf cells with respect to the points of S. As we will see later, varying these parameters enables us to achieve space-time tradeoffs in our AVD constructions. The key properties satisfied by the region-DAG are given below. We provide some intuition on how these properties aid in constructing AVDs in doubling spaces. Property (i) says that there is a node whose associated ball, which is called the *root ball*, contains the point set S close to its center. This property is useful for answering queries when the query point q lies outside the root ball. If, however, q lies inside the root ball, then we first find a leaf cell containing q. Such a leaf cell must exist because, by property (iii), the cell associated with any internal node is covered by the cells associated with its children. Property (iv) guarantees that we can find this leaf cell quickly (even though the depth of the region-DAG can be large). Property (ii) describes the separation properties satisfied by the leaves, which help in answering queries efficiently.

(i) There exists a node whose associated cell is a ball b, which is centered at a point of S and which satisfies $S \subseteq \frac{1}{\beta}b$. (We maintain a pointer to one node satisfying this property, which is called the *root* of the region-DAG. The cell associated with the root is called the *root ball*.)

(ii) There are two kinds of leaves, simple leaves and doughnut leaves, with the following separation properties. (See Figure 1.)

    (a) Let ball b denote the cell associated with a simple leaf. Then either the ball γb is empty, or it contains one point of S, which is the center of b.

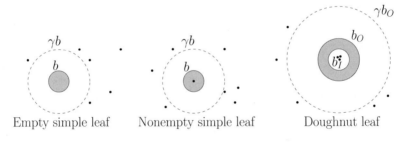

Fig. 1. Separation properties of leaf cells

    (b) Let b_O and b_I denote the outer and inner ball, respectively, of the cell associated with a doughnut leaf. Then $S \cap \gamma b_O \subseteq \left(\frac{1}{\beta}\right) b_I$. (Note that the doughnut cell $b_O \setminus b_I$ is empty.)

(iii) The cell associated with an internal node is always simple, and is covered by the cells associated with its children. More precisely, there are two kinds of internal nodes, *splitting nodes* and *shrinking nodes*, with the following properties. Let the cell associated with an internal node u be a ball b of radius r.

    (a) If u is a splitting node, then it has a constant number of children (depending on the doubling dimension). Moreover, each child is simple, and its size is in $[r/64, r/2]$.

    (b) If u is a shrinking node, then it has two children. One of these children is a doughnut leaf. The outer ball associated with this leaf is b, and the inner ball associated with it is a ball b', whose radius is at most $r/2$. (That is, the doughnut leaf cell is $b \setminus b'$.) The cell associated with the other child is a ball covering b', having radius at most $r/2$. We refer to the child that is a doughnut leaf as the *outer child* of u and refer to the other child as the *inner child* of u.

(iv) Let b denote the root ball defined in property (i). Given a point $q \in b$, we can find a leaf cell containing q in $O(\log(n\gamma))$ time.

It is clear from property (iii) that the size of a node is always smaller than that of its parent by a factor of at least two, except for a doughnut leaf, whose size is the same as that of its parent. It follows that the region-DAG has no cycle.

In Section 3.1, we will establish the following theorem, which shows that any set S in doubling space admits a region-DAG of size linear in n, and it can be constructed efficiently.

Theorem 1. *Let $\gamma \geq 2$ and $\beta \geq \gamma$ be two real parameters. Given a set S of n points in doubling space M, there exists a region-DAG of size $n\gamma^{O(\dim)} \log \beta$ satisfying all of the above properties. Furthermore, this structure can be constructed in time $O(n \log n) + n\gamma^{O(\dim)} \log^2 \beta$.*

3.1   Construction

Recall that our construction uses two parameters $\gamma \geq 2$ and $\beta \geq \gamma$ that determine the separation properties of the leaves with respect to the points of S. Before constructing the region-DAG, we first construct a WSPD for S using $\sigma = 16$. The number of pairs in the WSPD is $O(n)$ and the time to construct it is $O(n \log n)$. We associate each pair in this WSPD with several balls as follows. Let $x, y \in S$ denote the points at the centers of the heads of the dumbbell corresponding to a pair, and let $\ell = d(x, y)$ denote the length of this dumbbell. Then the associated balls are the balls of radius $2^i \ell$ centered at x and y, for all integers i such that $\left\lfloor \log \left(\frac{1}{c_1 \beta} \right) \right\rfloor \leq i \leq \lceil \log(c_2 \beta) \rceil$, where $c_1, c_2 \geq 1$ are suitable large positive constants. We will refer to these balls as *type-1* balls. We associate a unique node in the DAG with each distinct type-1 ball. Note that for this purpose, we treat any two type-1 balls as distinct if they have different centers or radii or are generated by different pairs in the WSPD. We will refer to these nodes as *type-1* nodes. Since there are $O(n)$ pairs in the WSPD and we generate $O(\log \beta)$ balls for each pair, the total number of type-1 nodes is $O(n \log \beta)$. Since there is a point of S at the center of each type-1 ball, these nodes are always nonempty. Besides the type-1 nodes, we will also create some new nodes in the DAG during the construction, which will always be empty (but not necessarily leaves). We will call them *type-2* nodes.

We process each type-1 node u as follows. Recall that b_u denotes the cell associated with u. We assume that b_u is a ball of radius r centered at a point $p \in S$. Roughly speaking, if all the points of $S \setminus \{p\}$ are very far from p, we will make u a leaf, and if all the points of $S \cap \gamma b_u$ are very close to p, we will make it a shrinking node. Otherwise, if there are points of S at intermediate distances (i.e., neither too far nor too close), then we will make u a splitting node. Since it is too time consuming to examine the points of S for the purpose of these tests,

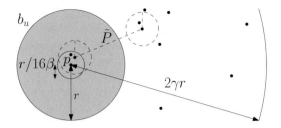

Fig. 2. Case where u is a splitting node

we will instead examine certain well-separated pairs containing p, which yield sufficient information on the position of the points.

We begin by finding the shortest dumbbell $\tilde{P}$ in the WSPD that contains p and has length at least $r/(16\beta)$. If $\tilde{P}$ has length at most $2\gamma r$, then u is made into a splitting node. (See Figure 2.) Otherwise, it is clear that there are no dumbbells containing p of length between $r/(16\beta)$ and $2\gamma r$. We then look for the longest dumbbell $\hat{P}$ containing p that has length at most $r/(16\beta)$. If we find such a dumbbell, then u is made into a shrinking node (See Figure 3), otherwise it is made into a simple leaf. We will establish property (ii.a) for the case when u is made into a simple leaf. After that we will describe how children are assigned when u is a shrinking and splitting node, respectively, and establish properties (ii) and (iii) for these cases.

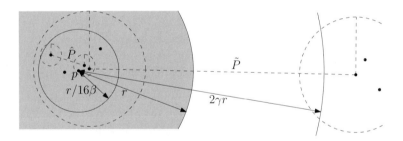

Fig. 3. Case where u is a shrinking node

u is a leaf. We first consider the case when u is made into a leaf. Recall that in this case there are no dumbbells containing p of length at most $2\gamma r$. By Lemma 1, it follows that the distance between p and any other point of S is at least $(7/8)2\gamma r$. Thus, all the points of $S \setminus \{p\}$ lie outside the ball γb_u, which proves that u satisfies property (ii.a).

u is a shrinking node. We next consider the case when u is made into a shrinking node. Recall that in this case there are no dumbbells containing p that have length between $r/(16\beta)$ and $2\gamma r$. Recall also that we have already found the longest dumbbell $\hat{P}$ containing p that has length at most $r/(16\beta)$. We will assign two children to node u. Before describing these children, we first show that all the points of S in γb_u are very close to p. Let $\hat{\ell}$ denote the length of $\hat{P}$ and let $\hat{b}$ denote the ball $B(p, 2\hat{\ell})$. We claim that $S \cap \gamma b_u \subseteq \hat{b}$. To prove this claim, let x be any point of $S \cap \gamma b_u$. Since $d(p, x) \leqslant \gamma r$, it follows from Lemma 1 that the length ℓ of the dumbbell separating p and x is at most $8\gamma r/7 < 2\gamma r$. By our earlier remarks, there are no dumbbells containing p that have length between $r/(16\beta)$ and $2\gamma r$. Therefore, $\ell < r/(16\beta)$. Since $\hat{P}$ is the longest dumbbell containing p that has length at most $r/(16\beta)$, it follows that $\ell \leqslant \hat{\ell}$. Again, applying Lemma 1, it follows that $d(p, x) \leqslant 9\ell/8 \leqslant 9\hat{\ell}/8 \leqslant 2\hat{\ell}$. Thus, $x \in \hat{b}$, which proves the claim.

We can now describe the two children of u. For one of these children, we create a new node in the region-DAG whose associated cell is $b_u \setminus b'$, where b' is the ball $\beta\hat{b}$. We make this child a doughnut leaf whose only parent is u. By the claim above, $S \cap \gamma b_u \subseteq \left(\frac{1}{\beta}\right) b'$, and so (ii.b) holds. Further, since the radius of b' is $2\beta\hat{\ell}$ and $\hat{\ell} \leqslant r/(16\beta)$, it follows that the radius of b' does not exceed $r/8 < r/2$. Thus the condition given in (iii.b) for this child is satisfied.

We now describe the other child of u. Let p' denote the point of S at the center of that head of dumbbell $\hat{P}$ that contains p, and let b'' denote the ball $B(p', 2^{\lceil \log 3\beta \rceil}\hat{\ell})$. Assuming that $c_2 \geqslant 3$, it is easy to see that b'' is one of the type-1 balls associated with dumbbell $\hat{P}$ and so must have a unique corresponding node in the region-DAG. We make this type-1 node the second child of u. To establish property (iii.b), we need to show that b'' covers b' and has radius at most $r/2$. Clearly, the radius of b'' is at most $6\beta\hat{\ell}$. Since $\hat{\ell} \leqslant r/(16\beta)$, it follows that the radius of b'' is at most $3r/8 < r/2$. By Lemma 1 we have $d(p, p') \leqslant \hat{\ell}/16$. Using this fact and the triangle inequality, it follows that

$$b' = B(p, 2\beta\hat{\ell}) \subseteq B\left(p', \frac{\hat{\ell}}{16} + 2\beta\hat{\ell}\right) \subseteq B(p', 3\beta\hat{\ell}) \subseteq b''.$$

This establishes property (iii.b) and completes the description of the processing required for a shrinking node.

u is a splitting node. Finally, we consider the case when u is made into a splitting node. Recall that in this case there exists a dumbbell containing p that has length between $r/(16\beta)$ and $2\gamma r$. In the full version, we show that this fact implies that node u can be assigned $O(1)$ children, whose associated cells together cover the ball b_u and satisfy certain properties. Some of these children are of type-1 while the rest are newly created type-2 nodes associated with empty balls. Roughly speaking, the role of the type-1 children is to cover the parts of b_u that lie close to the points of S and the role of the type-2 children is to cover the parts of b_u that remain uncovered. More precisely, we have the following lemma.

Lemma 2. *There exists a set $\mathcal{B}_1$ of type-1 balls and a set $\mathcal{B}_2$ of type-2 balls such that (i) the total number of balls of $\mathcal{B}_1$ and $\mathcal{B}_2$ is $2^{O(\dim)}$, (ii) any ball of $\mathcal{B}_1 \cup \mathcal{B}_2$ has radius between $r/64$ and $r/2$, (iii) the balls of $\mathcal{B}_1$ and $\mathcal{B}_2$ together cover b_u, and (iv) for any ball $b \in \mathcal{B}_2$, there are no points of S in the ball $4b$.*

The nodes corresponding to the balls of $\mathcal{B}_1$ and $\mathcal{B}_2$ are made children of u. From the above lemma, it is easy to see that property (iii) holds for u.

It remains to discuss the processing for the type-2 children of u. Observe that we cannot make these nodes into leaves because their γ-expansion may contain points of S and so they do not necessarily satisfy property (ii.a). However, by Lemma 2(iv), we do know that a 4-expansion of any ball in $\mathcal{B}_2$ is free of points of S. To increase this expansion factor to γ, we proceed as follows for each type-2 child v of u. Let b_v denote the ball associated with v, and let r' denote its radius. Using the doubling oracle, in $2^{O(\mathrm{dim})}$ time we can find $2^{O(\mathrm{dim})}$ balls of radius $r'/2$ which overlap b_v. We create type-2 nodes for these balls and make them all children of v. We apply this procedure recursively to the children of v, terminating when we finally reach nodes of size $r'/2^{\lceil \log \gamma \rceil}$, which are made leaves of the region-DAG. It is easy to see that v is the root of a subtree with $\gamma^{O(\mathrm{dim})}$ nodes and $\lceil \log \gamma \rceil + 1$ levels. All nodes in this subtree, except at the bottom level, are splitting nodes, and clearly satisfy property (iii). Applying Lemma 2(iv) and noting that the radii of the associated balls decrease by at least a factor of 2 as we descend this subtree, it is easy to show that the leaves satisfy property (ii.a).

Next we bound the size of the region-DAG.

Lemma 3. *The size of the region-DAG for an n-point set is $n\gamma^{O(\mathrm{dim})} \log \beta$.*

Proof: Recall that the region-DAG has $O(n \log \beta)$ type-1 nodes. It is clear from our discussion above that a shrinking node acquires one child that is not of type-1 (this child is a doughnut leaf), and a type-1 splitting node acquires $\gamma^{O(\mathrm{dim})}$ descendants that are not of type-1. Therefore, the size of the region-DAG is $n\gamma^{O(\mathrm{dim})} \log \beta$. $\qquad\square$

In the full version, we show that the region-DAG for an n-point set can be constructed in time $O(n \log n) + n\gamma^{O(\mathrm{dim})} \log^2 \beta$, and also satisfies properties (i) and (iv). This completes the proof of Theorem 1.

4 Approximate Voronoi Diagrams

In this section we show how to construct approximate Voronoi diagrams in doubling spaces. Let (M, d) be a metric space with constant doubling dimension. Our main result is as follows.

Theorem 2. *Let S be a set of n points in M, and let $0 < \varepsilon \leqslant 1/2$ and $2 \leqslant \gamma \leqslant 1/\varepsilon$ be two real parameters. We can construct an AVD of $n\gamma^{O(\mathrm{dim})} \log(1/\varepsilon)$ space that allows us to answer ε-approximate nearest neighbor queries in time $O(\log(n\gamma)) + (1/(\varepsilon\gamma))^{O(\mathrm{dim})}$. The time to construct the AVD is $n(1/\varepsilon)^{O(\mathrm{dim})} \log n$.*

Given the region-DAG, the proof of this theorem is straightforward by adapting the ideas used previously for Euclidean AVDs [1, 2]. We sketch the main ideas briefly. Given the point set S and parameters $0 < \varepsilon \leqslant 1/2$ and $2 \leqslant \gamma \leqslant 1/\varepsilon$, we construct the region-DAG described in Theorem 1 for $\beta = 1/\varepsilon$. The number of nodes in the region-DAG is $n\gamma^{O(\mathrm{dim})} \log(1/\varepsilon)$. Recall that the leaves of this structure satisfy certain separation properties with respect to S (region-DAG property (ii)). These properties enable us to answer queries efficiently with the help of a sparse set of representatives stored with each leaf. The following lemma provides a bound on the number of representatives we need to store with each cell. Given a set X of points and a point q, let $\mathrm{NN}_q(X)$ be the distance from q to its nearest neighbor in X. We say that a subset $R \subseteq S$ is an ε-representative set for a region w (with respect to S) if for any query point $q \in w$, we have $\mathrm{NN}_q(R) \leqslant (1 + \varepsilon)\mathrm{NN}_q(S)$.

Lemma 4 (Concentric Ball Lemma). *Let $0 < \varepsilon \leqslant 1/2$ and $\gamma \geqslant 2$ be two real parameters. Let S be a set of points in M. Let b_1 and b_2 be two concentric balls of radius r and γr, respectively. Then there exist subsets $R_1, R_2 \subseteq S$ each consisting of at most $(1 + 1/(\varepsilon\gamma))^{O(\mathrm{dim})}$ points such that (i) R_1 is an ε-representative set for b_1 with respect to $S \cap \overline{b_2}$, and (ii) R_2 is an ε-representative set for $\overline{b_2}$ with respect to $S \cap b_1$.*

In part (i), the set R_1 is formed by choosing an $(\varepsilon/2)$-NN of each point in an $(\varepsilon\gamma r/c)$-net for b_1, where c is a suitable constant. Applying the triangle inequality, it is easy to prove part (i). The proof of part (ii) is analogous. For each leaf cell u, we can use the above lemma to find an ε-representative set R for u with respect to S. We illustrate this for the case of a doughnut leaf cell u (the case where u is a simple leaf is easier and is omitted). Let b_O and b_I denote the outer and inner ball, respectively, for u. Recall that $u = b_O \setminus b_I$. It follows from region-DAG property (ii.b) that all the points of S are either outside γb_O or inside εb_I. By Lemma 4(i), there exists an ε-representative set R_1 of size $(1/(\varepsilon\gamma))^{O(\mathrm{dim})}$ for u with respect to $S \cap \overline{\gamma b_O}$, and by Lemma 4(ii), there exists an ε-representative set R_2 of size $O(1)$ for u with respect to $S \cap \varepsilon b_I$. Clearly, the set $R = R_1 \cup R_2$ is an ε-representative set of size $(1/(\varepsilon\gamma))^{O(\mathrm{dim})}$ for u with respect to S. We store the set R with u. The resulting AVD can be used for answering ε-NN queries as follows. Suppose that the query point q lies inside the root ball. By region-DAG property (iv), we can find a leaf that contains q in $O(\log(n\gamma))$ time. Then we return the closest representative stored with this leaf cell as the answer. The total query time is $O(\log(n\gamma)) + (1/(\varepsilon\gamma))^{O(\mathrm{dim})}$. If q lies outside the root ball, a similar approach works using region-DAG property (i).

Consider next the space used by this AVD. A naive analysis of the space bound is provided by the product of the number of nodes in the region-DAG and the maximum number of representatives per cell, which yields a total of $n/\varepsilon^{O(\mathrm{dim})}$. We can improve this bound significantly by applying a charging technique similar to that employed earlier in the Euclidean context [2]. This technique shows that although for a given cell, $(1/(\varepsilon\gamma))^{\Omega(\mathrm{dim})}$ representatives may be needed, this cannot be the case for most of the cells. We omit the details due to lack of space. Applying this technique we can show that the total number of representatives summed over all the cells is $n\gamma^{O(\mathrm{dim})}\log(1/\varepsilon)$, and they can be computed in time $n(1/\varepsilon)^{O(\mathrm{dim})}\log n$. This completes the proof of Theorem 2.

References

1. Arya, S., Malamatos, T.: Linear-size approximate Voronoi diagrams. In: Proc. 13th ACM-SIAM Sympos. Discrete Algorithms, pp. 147–155 (2002)
2. Arya, S., Malamatos, T., Mount, D.M.: Space-efficient approximate Voronoi diagrams. In: Proc. 34th Annu. ACM Sympos. Theory Comput., pp. 721–730 (2002)
3. Arya, S., Mount, D.M., Netanyahu, N., Silverman, R., Wu, A.Y.: An optimal algorithm for approximate nearest neighbor searching in fixed dimensions. In: Proc. 5th ACM-SIAM Sympos. Discrete Algorithms, pp. 573–582 (1994)
4. Assouad, P.: Plongements lipschitziens dans $\mathbb{R}^n$. Bull. Soc. Math. France 111(4), 429–448 (1983)
5. Beygelzimer, A., Kakade, S., Langford, J.: Cover trees for nearest neighbor. In: Proceedings of the 23rd International Conference on Machine Learning, pp. 97–104 (2006)
6. Brin, S.: Near neighbor search in large metric spaces. In: Proc. 21st International Conf. on Very Large Data Bases, pp. 574–584 (1995)
7. Callahan, P.B., Kosaraju, S.R.: A decomposition of multidimensional point sets with applications to k-nearest-neighbors and n-body potential fields. J. Assoc. Comput. Mach. 42, 67–90 (1995)
8. Clarkson, K.L.: Nearest neighbor queries in metric spaces. Discrete Comput. Geom. 22(1), 63–93 (1999)
9. Cole, R., Gottlieb, L.: Searching dynamic point sets in spaces with bounded doubling dimension. In: Proc. 38th Annu. ACM Sympos. Theory Comput., pp. 574–583 (2006)
10. Feustel, C.D., Shapiro, L.G.: The nearest neighbor problem in an abstract metric space. Pattern Recognition Letters 1(2), 125–128 (1982)
11. Gupta, A., Krauthgamer, R., Lee, J.R.: Bounded geometries, fractals, and low-distortion embeddings. In: Proc. 44th Annu. IEEE Sympos. Found. Comput. Sci., pp. 534–543 (2003)
12. Har-Peled, S.: A replacement for Voronoi diagrams of near linear size. In: Proc. 42nd Annu. IEEE Sympos. Found. Comput. Sci., pp. 94–103 (2001)
13. Har-Peled, S., Mendel, M.: Fast construction of nets in low dimensional metrics, and their applications. SIAM J. Comput. 35(5), 1148–1184 (2006)
14. Karger, D.R., Ruhl, M.: Finding nearest neighbors in growth-restricted metrics. In: Proc. 34th Annu. ACM Sympos. Theory Comput., pp. 741–750 (2002)
15. Krauthgamer, R., Lee, J.R.: Navigating nets: simple algorithms for proximity search. In: Proc. 15th ACM-SIAM Sympos. Discrete Algorithms, pp. 798–807 (2004)
16. Krauthgamer, R., Lee, J.R.: The black-box complexity of nearest-neighbor search. Theoretical Computer Science 348(2-3), 262–276 (2005)
17. Krauthgamer, R., Lee, J.R.: Algorithms on negatively curved spaces. In: Proc. 47th Annu. IEEE Sympos. Found. Comput. Sci., pp. 119–132 (2006)
18. Yianilos, P.N.: Data structures and algorithms for nearest neighbor search in general metric spaces. In: Proc. 4th ACM-SIAM Sympos. Discrete Algorithms, pp. 311–321 (1993)

A Scaling Algorithm for the Maximum Node-Capacitated Multiflow Problem

Maxim A. Babenko[1],[*] and Alexander V. Karzanov[2],[**]

[1] Dept. of Mechanics and Mathematics, Moscow State University;
Leninskie Gory, 119991 Moscow, Russia
max@adde.math.msu.su
[2] Institute for System Analysis;
9, Prospect 60 Let Oktyabrya, 117312 Moscow, Russia
sasha@cs.isa.ru

Abstract. We study the problem of finding a fractional node-capacitated multiflow of maximum value in an undirected network. Previously known methods for this problem are based on linear programming and the ellipsoid method. In this paper we apply a capacity scaling approach and develop a purely combinatorial weakly polynomial algorithm of time complexity $O(\Lambda(n, m, U)\, n^2 \log^2 n \, \log U)$, where n, m, U are the number of nodes, the number of edges, and the maximum node capacity, respectively, and $\Lambda(n, m, U)$ denotes the complexity of finding a maximum integer flow in a digraph with n nodes, m edges, and integer arc capacities not exceeding $U \in \mathbb{Z}_+$.

1 Introduction

In an undirected graph G, the sets of nodes and edges are denoted by VG and EG, respectively. When G is a directed graph, we speak of arcs rather than edges and write AG instead of EG. A similar notation is used for paths, cycles, and etc.

We consider an undirected graph G and a distinguished subset $T \subseteq VG$ of nodes, called *terminals*. Nodes in $VG - T$ are called *inner*. A T-*path* is a path in G that connects a pair of distinct terminals and has all other (intermediate) nodes in $VG - T$. The set of T-paths is denoted by $\mathcal{P}(G, T)$. A *multiflow* is a function $F \colon \mathcal{P}(G, T) \to \mathbb{R}_+$. Equivalently, one may think of F as a collection

$$\{(\alpha_1, P_1), \ldots, (\alpha_q, P_q)\}, \tag{1.1}$$

where the P_i are T-paths and the α_i are non-negative reals, called *weights* of paths. Sometimes (e.g., in [IKN98]) such a multiflow F is called *free* to emphasize that all pairs of distinct terminals are allowed to be connected by flows. The *value* $\mathrm{val}\,(F)$ of F is the sum $\sum_P F(P)$.

[*] Supported by RFBR grants 03-01-00475, 05-01-02803, and 06-01-00122.
[**] Supported by NWO–RFBR grant 047.011.2004.017 and by RFBR grant 05-01-02805 CNRSL_a.

D. Halperin and K. Mehlhorn (Eds.): ESA 2008, LNCS 5193, pp. 124–135, 2008.

For a subset A of a set X, the *incidence vector* of A in $\mathbb{R}^X$ is denoted by χ^A, i.e., $\chi^A(e)$ is 1 for $e \in A$ and 0 for $e \in X - A$ (usually X is clear from the context).

Let $c \colon VG \to \mathbb{Z}_+$ be a nonnegative integer function of *node capacities*. For a multiflow F, define the function ζ^F on VG by

$$\zeta^F := \sum \left(F(P) \cdot \chi^{VP} \colon P \in \mathcal{P}(G,T) \right).$$

We say that F is *c-feasible* if $\zeta^F \leq c$.

This paper deals with the following problem:

(P) *Given G, T, c as above, find a c-feasible multiflow F whose value* $\mathrm{val}(F)$ *is maximum.*

It is known that this problem has a half-integer optimal primal [Pap07] and dual solutions [Vaz01]. Also (P) is solvable in polynomial time by use of the ellipsoid method [Pap07]. However, no efficient combinatorial algorithm for (P) has been known so far.

We present a combinatorial algorithm that solves (P) via capacity scaling. Our approach relies on earlier results of Ibaraki, Karzanov, and Nagamochi [IKN98] concerning an edge-capacitated analog of (P). As a result, the time complexity of our algorithm for (P) is $O(\Lambda(n, m, U)\, n^2 \log^2 n \, \log U)$. Hereinafter n, m, U denote the number of nodes, the number of edges, and the maximum capacity, respectively, and $\Lambda(n, m, U)$ stands for the complexity of finding a maximum integer flow in a digraph with n nodes, m edges, and integer arc capacities not exceeding $U \in \mathbb{Z}_+$. In particular, applying the algorithm of Goldberg and Rao [GR98], problem (P) can be solved in $O(n^2 m \min(n^{2/3}, m^{1/2}) \log(n^2/m) \log^2 n \log^2 U)$ time.

The paper is organized as follows. Section 2 contains backgrounds. An outline of the algorithm and a sketch of a proof of its correctness are given in Section 3. Section 4 estimates the time complexity of the algorithm.

2   Preliminaries

Let A be a subset of nodes of a graph (or a digraph). We denote by $\gamma(A)$ the set of edges of the graph (or arcs of the digraph) with both endpoints in A, and by $\delta(A)$ the set of edges (or arcs) with exactly one endpoint in A. Also in case of a digraph, $\delta^{\mathrm{in}}(A)$ (resp. $\delta^{\mathrm{out}}(A)$) denotes the set of arcs that enter A (resp. leave A). When A is a singleton $\{v\}$, we use the abbreviated notation $\delta(v)$, $\delta^{\mathrm{in}}(v)$, and $\delta^{\mathrm{out}}(v)$.

Clearly (P) is a linear program, with variables $F(P)$ associated to T-paths P. To state its dual program, we call a function $\pi \colon VG \to \mathbb{R}_+$ a *(fractional) cover* if $\pi(VP) \geq 1$ holds for each T-path P. (As usual, for a function f on a set X and a subset $X' \subseteq X$, $f(X')$ denotes $\sum_{x \in X'} f(x)$; so $\pi(VP)$ means $\sum_{v \in VP} \pi(v)$.) By the *c-value* of a cover π we mean the inner product $c\pi := \sum_{v \in VG} c(v)\pi(v)$.

Then the program dual of (P) is:

(C) *Find a cover π whose c-value $c\pi$ is minimum.*

We will use standard definitions and some facts about flows and multiflows (for details, see, e.g., [Schr03]). Let G be a digraph with distinguished subsets $S, T \subset VG$, $S \cap T = \emptyset$. The nodes in S (resp. T) are regarded as *sources* (resp. *sinks*), and the other nodes are called *inner*. A function $f \colon AG \to \mathbb{R}_+$ is an *S–T flow* if (i) $f(\delta^{\mathrm{in}}(s)) = 0$ for any source s; (ii) $f(\delta^{\mathrm{out}}(t)) = 0$ for any sink t; (iii) $f(\delta^{\mathrm{in}}(v)) = f(\delta^{\mathrm{out}}(v))$ for any inner node v. The *value* of f is $\mathrm{val}\,(f) := \sum (f(\delta^{\mathrm{out}}(s)) : s \in S)$.

Given *arc capacities* $c \colon AG \to \mathbb{R}_+$, a flow f is *c-feasible* if $f \leq c$. The *max-flow problem* is:

(MF) *Given G, S, T, c as above, find a c-feasible flow f of maximum value* $\mathrm{val}\,(f)$.

Theorem 1 (Goldberg, Rao [GR98]). *For arbitrary integer arc capacities not exceeding $U \in \mathbb{Z}_+$, an integer maximum flow can be found in $O(m \min(m^{1/2}, n^{2/3}) \log(n^2/m) \log U)$ time.*

Next, we will also deal with an analog of (MF) for *node capacitated* networks. For a flow f and a node $v \in VG$, define the *value of flow through v* as

$$f[v] := \max \left(f(\delta^{\mathrm{in}}(v)), f(\delta^{\mathrm{out}}(v)) \right).$$

Then for *node capacities* $c : VG \to \mathbb{R}_+$, function f is said to be *c-feasible* if $f[v] \leq c(v)$ for all $v \in VG$.

There are well-known facts about the node-capacitated max-flow problem. A set $A \subseteq VG$ is called an *S–T separator* if each (directed) S–T path meets A.

Fact 1 (a version of Menger theorem). *For $c : VG \to \mathbb{Z}_+$, one has*

$$\max \mathrm{val}\,(f) = \min c(A),$$

where the maximum is taken over all integer c-feasible (node-capacitated) S–T flows f, and the minimum over all S–T separators A.

Suppose that a *c*-feasible *S–T* flow f is not maximum. Then one can increase $\mathrm{val}\,(f)$ by use of a standard construction. More precisely, consider a sequence

$$R = (v_0, a_1, v_1, a_2, \ldots, a_l, v_l), \tag{2.1}$$

where $v_0 \in S$, $v_l \in T$, $v_i \in VG$ $(1 \leq i < l)$, $a_i \in AG$ $(1 \leq i \leq l)$. Also, for each $1 \leq i \leq l$ either $a_i = (v_{i-1}, v_i)$ (then a_i is said to be *forward*) or $a_i = (v_i, v_{i-1})$ (then a_i is said to be *backward*). An occurrence of node v_i in R is called *increasing* if either $i = 0$, or $i = l$, or $0 < i < l$ and both a_i and a_{i+1} are forward.

Then R is called *f-augmenting* if the following conditions hold:

1. if v_i is increasing then $f[v_i] < c(v_i)$,
2. if a_i is backward then $f(a_i) > 0$,
3. all arcs in R are distinct,
4. each node occurs in R at most twice, moreover, if $v_i = v_j$ for $0 \leq i < j \leq l$ then neither v_i nor v_j is increasing.

Note that since no arc with positive flow enters a source and no arc with positive flow leaves a sink, the arcs a_1 and a_l are forward.

Fact 2. *For $c: VG \to \mathbb{Z}_+$, let f be an integer c-feasible node-capacitated flow and R an f-augmenting sequence. Define*

$$
f'(a) := \begin{cases} f(a) + 1 & \text{if } a \text{ is a forward arc,} \\ f(a) - 1 & \text{if } a \text{ is a backward arc,} \\ f(a) & \text{otherwise.} \end{cases}
$$

Then f' is an integer c-feasible flow of value $\mathrm{val}\,(f) + 1$.

Fact 3. *A c-feasible node-capacitated flow f admits an f-augmenting sequence R if and only if $\mathrm{val}(f)$ is not maximum. Moreover, in $O(m)$ time, one can find either an f-augmenting sequence or an S–T separator A such that $c(A) = \mathrm{val}\,(f)$.*

Finally, some important facts and tools that will be extensively used throughout the paper are borrowed from the theory of edge- and arc-capacitated multiflows. Typically problems on such multiflows are somewhat "simpler" than their node-capacitated counterparts.

Let G be a graph (or a digraph), and $T = \{t_1, \ldots, t_k\} \subseteq VG$ be a set of terminals. For a multiflow $F: \mathcal{P}(G, T) \to \mathbb{R}_+$, define the function ξ^F on EG by

$$
\xi^F := \sum \left(F(P) \cdot \chi^{EP} : P \in \mathcal{P}(G, T) \right).
$$

In case of a digraph G, the term EP in this definition is replaced by AP.

Let, in addition, G be endowed with edge (resp. arc) capacities c. A multiflow F is c-feasible if $\xi^F \le c$. The problem is:

(MMF) *Given G, T, c as above, find a c-feasible (edge- or arc-capacitated) multiflow F whose value $\mathrm{val}\,(F)$ is maximum.*

The function c is said to be *inner Eulerian* if c is integer-valued and $c(\delta(v))$ is even, in the undirected case (resp. $c(\delta^{\mathrm{in}}(v)) = c(\delta^{\mathrm{out}}(v))$, in the directed case) for each inner node $v \in VG - T$.

Consider a collection $\mathcal{Q} = \{Q_1, \ldots, Q_k\}$ of pairwise disjoint subsets of VG such that $t_i \in Q_i$ for $i = 1, \ldots, k$. Following terminology in [Bab07], the sets Q_i are called *islands*, and $\mathcal{Q}$ an *island collection*.

Theorem 2 (Lovász [Lov76], Cherkassky [Che77]). *In the undirected case of (MMF) with inner Eulerian capacities, one has*

$$
\max \mathrm{val}\,(F) = \frac{1}{2} \min \sum_{t \in T} c(\delta(Q_t)),
$$

where the maximum is taken over all integer c-feasible multiflows F, and the minimum over all island collections $\mathcal{Q} = \{Q_t \mid t \in T\}$.

Remark 1. *When G is a digraph and c is inner Eulerian, a similar max-min relation also takes place. This is due to Lomonosov (unpublished manuscript, 1978); see also [Kar79, Fr89].*

In the undirected case of (MMF), given a multiflow F, an island collection $\{Q_t \mid t \in T\}$ is called F-*tight* if $\xi^F(\delta(t)) = c(\delta(Q_t))$ holds for all $t \in T$. The following is immediate from Theorem 2.

Corollary 1. *A multiflow F is maximum if and only if there exists an F-tight island collection.*

Theorem 3 (Ibaraki, Karzanov, Nagamochi [IKN98]). *In the undirected case of (MMF) with inner Eulerian capacities, a maximum integer multiflow can be found in $O(\Lambda(n, m, U) \log |T|)$ time. In the directed case of (MMF) with inner Eulerian capacities a maximum integer multiflow can be found in $O(\Lambda(n, m, U) \log |T| + n^2 m)$ time. In both cases, the maximum value of a multiflow and an optimal island collection can be found in $O(\Lambda(n, m, U) \log |T|)$ time.*

We will also use the following corollary of that result.

Corollary 2. *In the undirected case of (MMF) with inner Eulerian edge capacities, the function ξ^F for some maximum integer multiflow F can be constructed in $O(\Lambda(n, m, U) \log |T|)$ time. Also, by spending additional $O(mn \log |T|)$ time, one can turn F into a path packing (of the form (1.1)).*

Remark 2. *Strictly speaking, the time bounds figured in Theorem 3 are valid under some assumption concerning $\Lambda(n, m, U)$; see [IKN98] for details. Fortunately, this assumption is satisfied for reasonable max-flow algorithms, in particular, for the algorithm of Goldberg and Rao [GR98].*

3 Algorithm Outline

3.1 Scaling Step

The general scheme of our approach for solving (P) resembles that of Ford and Fulkerson's capacity scaling algorithm [FF62]. Namely, let $c_0 \colon VG \to Z_+$ be the original node capacities. We assume that c_0 is even for all nodes and construct an integer-valued maximum c_0-feasible multiflow. Clearly, this is equivalent to constructing a half-integral multiflow for arbitrary integer capacities.

The algorithm performs $O(\log U)$ *scaling steps*. Each such step takes the previous even-valued capacity function c and the corresponding maximum c-feasible integer multiflow F. Initially $c := 0$ and $F := 0$. On each scaling step unit is added to capacities of some nodes (namely, to those having 1 at the corresponding position in the binary representation of c_0) and then all capacities are multiplied by 2, thus producing an even-valued function $c' \colon VG \to \mathbb{Z}_+$. Then a maximum c'-feasible integer multiflow F' is computed. To this aim, the current function F is replaced by $2F$ and a certain augmenting path approach is applied.

The process stops when $c = c_0$, and the last c-feasible multiflow F is the answer. So $O(\log U)$ scaling steps are needed to compute this F.

Our algorithm does not store F explicitly as a path packing. Instead, it maintains certain edge capacities $w \colon EG \to \mathbb{Z}_+$. For $v \in VG - T$, put $w[v] := \frac{1}{2} w(\delta(v))$, and for $v \in T$, put $w[v] := w(\delta(v))$. Define $w[T] := \frac{1}{2} \sum_{t \in T} w[t]$. The function w obeys the following conditions:

(3.1) w is inner Eulerian,

(3.2) $w[v] \leq c(v)$ for all $v \in VG$,

(3.3) there exists an integer edge-capacitated w-feasible multiflow in G of value $w[T]$.

Note that (3.2) implies that any multiflow constructed from w by (3.3) is c-feasible.

Scaling step first puts $w := 2w$ and then applies a number of augmentation steps that increase $w[T]$. When augmentation steps are complete, $w[T]$ is equal to the value of a maximum c'-feasible node-capacitated multiflow. The following lemma bounds the number of augmentation steps that are needed to turn $2F$ into a maximum c'-feasible multiflow (call the latter F').

Lemma 1. $\mathrm{val}\,(F') - \mathrm{val}\,(2F) \leq 2n$.

When the scaling steps are complete, the final function w is converted (with the help of Theorem 2) into the desired multiflow in the path-packing form, in $O(\Lambda(n, m, U) \log n + mn \log n)$ time.

3.2   Augmentation Step

Consider the current node capacities c and edge capacities w (obeying (3.1)–(3.3)). The core of the algorithm is an augmentation procedure that either updates w to increase $w[T]$ by 1 (while maintaining (3.1)–(3.3)) or detects that $w[T]$ is equal to the value of a maximum c-feasible multiflow.

In our approach we are forced to strengthen problem (P) by imposing certain conditions on T-paths. For an island collection $\mathcal{Q} = \{Q_1, \ldots, Q_k\}$, a T-path P is called $\mathcal{Q}$-feasible if $|EP \cap \delta(Q_i)| \leq 1$ for $i = 1, \ldots, k$ (in particular, P meets exactly two islands). Accordingly, we say that a c-feasible multiflow F is $(\mathcal{Q}, c)$-feasible if each path P in the support $\mathrm{supp}\,(F) := \{P \mid F(P) \neq 0\}$ of F is $\mathcal{Q}$-feasible.

The needed strengthening of (P) is the following problem (which turns into (P) when the island collection is formed by single terminals):

(QP) *Given $\mathcal{Q}$ as above, find a $(\mathcal{Q}, c)$-feasible multiflow F whose value $\mathrm{val}\,(F)$ is maximum.*

Let us say that a function $\pi \colon VG \to \mathbb{R}_+$ is a $\mathcal{Q}$-*cover* if $\pi(VP) \geq 1$ holds for any $\mathcal{Q}$-feasible T-path P. Then, similar to the duality of (P) and (C), the program dual of (QP) is:

(QC) *Find a $\mathcal{Q}$-cover π whose c-value $c\pi$ is minimum.*

The augmentation step grows an island collection $\mathcal{Q}$ in G and consists of a sequence of *extension steps*. These steps deal with the refined problem (QP) rather than (P). The process starts with the *trivial* collection: $Q_i := \{t_i\}$ for $i = 1, \ldots, k$. Also two additional invariants concerning w are maintained.

Firstly, the algorithm handles w-feasible multiflows F of value $w[T]$ that consist of $\mathcal{Q}$-feasible paths, and the collection $\mathcal{Q}$ is required to be F-tight. In terms of w, this turns into the following condition:

(3.4) $w[t_i] = w(\delta(Q_i))$ for all $1 \leq i \leq k$.

Secondly, let $\nu(c)$ (resp. $\nu(\mathcal{Q}, c)$) denote the value of a maximum c-feasible (resp. $(\mathcal{Q}, c)$-feasible) multiflow in G. The algorithm ensures that problem (QP) remains equivalent, in a sense, to (P):

(3.5) if $w[T] = \nu(\mathcal{Q}, c)$ and if, moreover, there exists a half-integral $\mathcal{Q}$-cover π obeying $\nu(\mathcal{Q}, c) = \pi c$, then $w[T] = \nu(c)$.

Each extension step either (i) updates the current function w so as to increase $w[T]$ by 1 while maintaining (3.1)–(3.3), or (ii) updates both w and $\mathcal{Q}$ while preserving $w[T]$, increasing some island and non-decreasing the other ones, and maintaining (3.1)–(3.3), (3.4), (3.5). In case (i), the current augmentation step completes, and in case (ii), the algorithm proceeds with a next extension step.

3.3   Extension Step

A sketch of performing an extension step is as follows. In order to increase $w[T]$, the algorithm tries to find a sort of "augmenting path" P for w. This path connects a pair of (possibly coinciding) terminals. Also P may contain terminals as intermediate nodes and need not be node- or edge-simple. Each edge of P is marked as either "positive" or "negative". The first and the last edges of P are always positive. (The function w will be updated by increasing by 1 on the positive edges and decreasing by 1 on the negative ones.)

Unfortunately some additional constraints that we have to impose on P do not seem to be easily expressible in terms of graph G. For this reason, P will be obtained as a *projection* of an augmenting sequence (as in (2.1)) in a specially designed *partially doubly covering digraph* $\widehat{G}$ (constructed from G and $\mathcal{Q}$). This digraph was introduced in [Bab07] for solving the uncapacitated version of (P) and is close to the notion of *doubly covering digraph* that was used in [Kar94] to study the edge-capacitated min-cost multiflow problem. The precise definition of $\widehat{G}$ will be given later.

The following three cases can occur:

- **Case (A):** no augmenting sequence in $\widehat{G}$ exists; then the current scaling step completes;
- **Case (B):** an augmenting sequence exists and, in a sense, can be "fully applied" to w; then the current function w updates with increasing $w[T]$, and the current augmentation step completes;

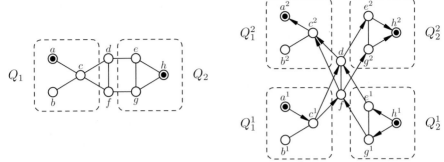

(a) Graph G and an island collection $\mathcal{Q} = \{Q_1, Q_2\}$.

(b) Graph $\widehat{G}$ (undirected edges denote pairs of oppositely directed arcs).

Fig. 1. Constructing the partially doubly covering digraph $\widehat{G}$

- **Case (C):** an augmenting sequence exists but cannot be "fully applied" to ω; then the function ω updates with preserving $\omega[T]$, some island in $\mathcal{Q}$ increases, and the current extension step completes.

Now we define the partially doubly covering digraph $\widehat{G}$ formally. Put $Q = Q(\mathcal{Q}) := Q_1 \cup \ldots \cup Q_k$ and $Z = Z(\mathcal{Q}) := VG - Q$; the elements of Q and Z are referred to as *island* and *central* nodes, respectively. Each node $v \in Q$ is split into a pair v^1, v^2 of nodes in $\widehat{G}$. Each node $v \in Z$ corresponds to a unique node in $\widehat{G}$; we identify the latter node in $\widehat{G}$ with v. Each edge $\{u, v\} \in \gamma(Z)$ generates a pair of arcs $(u, v), (v, u)$ in $\widehat{G}$. Each edge $\{u, v\} \in \gamma(Q_i)$, $1 \leq i \leq k$, generates four arcs $(u^j, v^j), (v^j, u^j)$ in $\widehat{G}$, $j = 1, 2$. Each edge $\{u, v\} \in EG$ with $u \in Q$ and $v \in Z$ generates arcs (u^1, v) and (v, u^2) in $\widehat{G}$. Each edge $\{u, v\} \in EG$ with $u \in Q_i$ and $v \in Q_j$, $i \neq j$, generates arcs $(u^1, v^2), (v^1, u^2)$ in $\widehat{G}$. Finally, $\widehat{G}$ is trimmed: all arcs entering nodes in T^1 and all arcs leaving nodes in T^2 are deleted. (We define $A^i := \{v^i \mid v \in A\}$ for any set $A \subseteq Q$.) An example is depicted in Fig. 1.

We assign capacities $\widehat{c}$ to the nodes of $\widehat{G}$ by

(3.6) $\widehat{c}(v) := c(v)$ for all $v \in Z$, and $\widehat{c}(v^1) := \widehat{c}(v^2) := \frac{1}{2}c(v)$ for all $v \in Q$.

Since the capacities c are even, $\widehat{c}$ is integer-valued.

We need some notation that relates objects in graphs $\widehat{G}$ and G. Each arc a in $\widehat{G}$ corresponds to the uniquely defined edge $\Omega(a)$ in G. Next, let $\widehat{\varphi}$ be an arbitrary integer T^1–T^2 flow in $\widehat{G}$. Then, $\widehat{\varphi}$ generates an inner Eulerian function $\varphi := \Omega(\widehat{\varphi})$ on EG by $\varphi(e) := \sum(\widehat{\varphi}(a) : \Omega(a) = e)$.

As mentioned earlier, the algorithm deals with augmenting sequences in $\widehat{G}$ rather than G. More precisely, the function ω is lifted to an integer $\widehat{c}$-feasible T^1–T^2 flow $\widehat{\omega}$ in $\widehat{G}$ of value $\omega[T]$ that obeys $\omega = \Omega(\widehat{\omega})$. This transformation is not straightforward and will be described in the full version of the paper. The algorithm seeks for an $\widehat{\omega}$-augmenting sequence in $\widehat{G}$. If the latter does not exist, then Case (A) applies, the scaling step completes.

Lemma 2. *If $\widehat{\omega}$ admits no augmenting sequence then $\omega[T] = \nu(c)$.*

Proof. According to Fact 3 there exists a T^1–T^2 separator A of $\widehat{c}$-capacity equal to $\mathrm{val}\,(\widehat{\omega}) = \omega[T]$. Construct the function $\pi \colon VG \to \{0, \frac{1}{2}, 1\}$ as follows:

$$\pi(v) := \begin{cases} |A \cap \{v\}| & \text{if } v \in Z, \\ \frac{1}{2} \cdot |A \cap \{v^1, v^2\}| & \text{if } v \in Q. \end{cases}$$

We claim that π is a Q-cover. Suppose, for a contradiction, that there is a Q-admissible T-path P in G such that $\pi(VP) \leq \frac{1}{2}$. Lift P to a directed T^1–T^2 path $\widehat{P}$ in $\widehat{G}$. Since $\widehat{P}$ meets A, it follows that $\pi(VP) \geq \frac{1}{2}$, therefore $\pi(VP) = \frac{1}{2}$. Hence, all central nodes of $\widehat{P}$ do not belong to A and there is a unique island node of $\widehat{P}$ belonging to A. Consider the reversed path P^{-1}. Its image $\widehat{P}^{-1}$ in $\widehat{G}$ does not contain nodes from A, which is a contradiction.

From $\pi c = \widehat{c}(A) = \omega[T]$ and (3.5) it follows that $\omega[T] = \nu(c)$, as needed.

Now let $\widehat{R}$ be an $\widehat{\omega}$-augmenting sequence in $\widehat{G}$. We introduce the notion of "partial application" of $\widehat{R}$ as follows. First of all we construct another digraph $\overline{G}$ from $\widehat{G}$ by merging, for each $i = 1, \ldots, k$, nodes t_i^1 and t_i^2 back into node t_i. Also we add an auxiliary terminal t_0 with no incident arcs. Note that the above contractions do not remove any arcs since there are no arcs between nodes t_i^1 and t_i^2. Nodes $\overline{T} := T \cup \{t_0\}$ are regarded as terminals in $\overline{G}$. The arcs of $\overline{G}$ are identified with the corresponding arcs of $\widehat{G}$ and we regard $\widehat{\omega}$ as a capacity function in $\overline{G}$. For each $1 \leq i \leq k$ and $j = 1, 2$ put $\overline{Q}_i^j$ to be the image of Q_i^j in $\overline{G}$, that is, $Q_i^j - \{t_i^j\} \cup \{t_i\}$. Also put $\overline{Q}_i := \overline{Q}_i^1 \cup \overline{Q}_i^2$.

The sequence $\widehat{R}$ in $\widehat{G}$ induces a sequence $\overline{R} = (v_0, a_1, v_1, a_2, \ldots, a_l, v_l)$ of nodes and arcs in $\overline{G}$. For $i = 1, \ldots, l$, consider the first i arcs $A\overline{R}_i := \{a_1, \ldots, a_i\}$ of $\overline{R}$. Suppose we are going to increase $\widehat{\omega}$ by 1 on the forward arcs in $A\overline{R}_i$ and simultaneously decrease by 1 on the backward arcs. This may result in arc capacities that are not inner Eulerian. To overcome this difficulty, we add an auxiliary arc (v_i, t_0) of capacity 1 unless $i > 0$ and $v_i \in T$. The resulting digraph (resp. capacities function) obtained from $\overline{G}$ (resp. from $\widehat{\omega}$) is denoted by $\overline{G}_i$ (resp. $\overline{\omega}_i$). It is easy to check that $\overline{\omega}_i$ is inner Eulerian (w.r.t. $\overline{T}$).

By taking trivial islands $\{t_j\}$, $j = 0, \ldots, k$, one can see that the maximum value of an $\overline{\omega}_i$-feasible integer multiflow in $\overline{G}_i$ does not exceed $\omega[T] + 1$. If the latter is exactly $\omega[T] + 1$, we call index i *good*; otherwise i is called *bad*. One can prove the following:

Lemma 3. *Index 0 is good.*

The algorithm examines index l by applying the algorithm of Ibaraki, Karzanov, and Nagamochi, see Theorem 3. First suppose that l is good; this corresponds to Case (B). There exists an integer $\overline{\omega}_l$-feasible multiflow $\overline{F}$ in $\overline{G}_l = \overline{G}$ of value $\omega[T] + 1$. The algorithm applies Theorem 2 to construct $\xi^{\overline{F}}$ and updates ω by taking the projection $\omega := \Omega(\xi^{\overline{F}})$. Thus, $\omega[T]$ increases by 1. Invariants (3.1) and (3.2) follow from the construction of $\widehat{G}$, $\widehat{c}$ and Fact 2. Invariant (3.3) follows from the existence of $\overline{F}$.

Finally, suppose that l is bad; this corresponds to Case (C). Consider the sequence of graphs $\overline{G}_0, \ldots, \overline{G}_l$ and the corresponding sequence of capacity functions $\overline{\omega}_0, \ldots, \overline{\omega}_l$. Our aim is to find an index j such that j is good whereas $j+1$ is bad. To make this quickly, the algorithm performs a binary search over the range $\{0, \ldots, l\}$. At each step it maintains a pair of indices (j^-, j^+), $j^- < j^+$ such that j^- is good while j^+ is bad (initially $j^- := 0$, $j^+ := l$). Put $i := \lfloor \frac{1}{2}(j^- + j^+) \rfloor$, consider graph $\overline{G}_i$, capacities $\overline{\omega}_i$, and solve (MMF) for this pair. If i is good, put $j^- := i$; otherwise put $j^+ := i$. This process converges to a required pair $(j, j+1)$ after $O(\log n)$ maximum multiflow computations.

Then, function ω and collection $\mathcal{Q}$ are updated as follows. Let $\overline{F}_j$ denote an integer $\overline{\omega}_j$-feasible multiflow in $\overline{G}_j$ of value $\omega[T] + 1$. One can easily see that val $(\overline{F}_j) = \omega[T] + 1$ implies that $\overline{F}_j$ saturates all terminals $\overline{T}$, i.e. $\xi^{\overline{F}_j}(\delta(t_i)) = \overline{\omega}_j(\delta(t_i))$ for all $0 \leq i \leq k$.

We shall use the following statement:

Lemma 4. There exist, and can be found in $O(\Lambda(n, m, U) \log n)$ time, a terminal $t_\alpha \in T$ and a set $\overline{A}_\alpha \subseteq V\overline{G}$ obeying the following properties (in $\overline{G}_j$):

1. $\overline{A}_\alpha \cap \overline{T} = \{t_\alpha\}$,
2. $\overline{Q}_\alpha \subseteq \overline{A}_\alpha$,
3. $\overline{Q}_\beta \cap \overline{A}_\alpha = \emptyset$ for all $\beta \neq \alpha$,
4. $v_j \in \overline{A}_\alpha - \overline{Q}_\alpha^1$,
5. $\xi^{\overline{F}_j}(\delta^{out}(\overline{A}_\alpha)) = \overline{\omega}_j(\delta^{out}(\overline{A}_\alpha)) = \overline{\omega}_j(\delta^{out}(t_\alpha))$,
6. $\xi^{\overline{F}_j}(\delta^{in}(\overline{A}_\alpha)) = \overline{\omega}_j(\delta^{in}(\overline{A}_\alpha)) = \overline{\omega}_j(\delta^{in}(t_\alpha))$.

Applying Lemma 4 the algorithm finds t_α and set $\overline{A}_\alpha$. Note that from Property (4) in the above Lemma 4 and the construction of $\overline{G}_j$ it follows that $v_j \notin T$, so arc (v_j, t_0) is present in $\overline{G}_j$.

The rest of the extension step consists of two phases. Firstly, one needs to update function ω to make it consistent with the upcoming extension of islands. This is achieved as follows.

Consider graph $\overline{G}_j$ and contract the set $V\overline{G}_j - \overline{A}_\alpha - \{t_0\}$ into a new node w. Denote the resulting graph by $\overline{H}$. It is endowed with inner Eulerian arc capacities $\overline{\omega}_j$. Nodes $\{t_\alpha, t_0, w\}$ are regarded as terminals in $\overline{H}$.

From Lemma 4 it follows that $\xi^{\overline{F}_j}(\delta(\overline{A}_\alpha)) = \overline{\omega}_j(\delta(\overline{A}_\alpha))$ in $\overline{H}$. Hence, graph $\overline{H}$ also admits an integer multiflow that saturates all its terminals. Moreover, the latter multiflow can only contain t_α–w, w–t_α, and t_α–t_0 paths and, hence, may be represented by a collection $\{\overline{g}_1, \overline{g}_2, \overline{g}_3\}$, where $\overline{g}_1$ is an integer t_α–w flow, $\overline{g}_2$ is an integer w–t_α flow, and $\overline{g}_3$ is an integer t_α–t_0 flow. These flows obey $\overline{g}_1 + \overline{g}_2 + \overline{g}_3 \leq \overline{\omega}_j$ and val $(\overline{g}_1) + $ val $(\overline{g}_2) + $ val $(\overline{g}_3) = \overline{\omega}_j(\delta(t_\alpha))$. Moreover, val $(\overline{g}_3) = 1$.

To compute $\overline{g}_1, \overline{g}_2, \overline{g}_3$ as above, the algorithm finds a maximum integer t_α–$\{w, t_0\}$ flow $\overline{g}_1 + \overline{g}_3$ (in $O(\Lambda(n, m, U)$ time) and then decomposes it into $\overline{g}_1$ and $\overline{g}_3$. Since val $(\overline{g}_3) = 1$, the latter decomposition takes $O(m)$ time. Next, the algorithm puts $\overline{g}_2 := \overline{\omega}_j - (\overline{g}_1 + \overline{g}_3)$.

Consider an inner Eulerian function $\overline{\omega}' \colon A\overline{G} \to \mathbb{Z}_+$ defined by

$$
\overline{\omega}'(a) := \begin{cases} \overline{g}_1(a) + \overline{g}_2(a) & \text{if } a \in \gamma(\overline{A}_\alpha), \\ 0 & \text{if } a = (v_j, t_0), \\ \overline{\omega}_j(a) & \text{otherwise.} \end{cases}
$$

Replacing $\overline{\omega}_j$ by $\overline{\omega}'$ eliminates the auxiliary t_α–t_0 component of $\overline{F}_j$, therefore $\overline{\omega}' = \xi^{\overline{F}'}$ for some integer multiflow $\overline{F}'$ in $\overline{G}$ of value $\omega[T]$. Put $\omega' := \Omega(\overline{\omega}')$.

Lemma 5. *Function ω' is inner Eulerian and obeys $\omega'[v] \leq c(v)$ for all $v \in VG$.*

This completes the description of the first phase.

Now let us proceed with the second phase and explain how the island collection $\mathcal{Q}$ is updated. Let A_α be the image of $\overline{A}_\alpha$ in G (i.e. $A_\alpha := \overline{A}_\alpha - \overline{Q}_\alpha \cup Q_\alpha$). Contract the set $VG - A_\alpha$ into a new node z and denote the resulting graph by H. Consider the digraph $\overrightarrow{H}$ obtained by replacing each edge $\{u, v\}$ of H with a pair of oppositely directed arcs (u, v) and (v, u). Function ω' induces arc capacities in $\overrightarrow{H}$ by $\omega'(u, v) = \omega'(v, u) := \omega'(\{u, v\})$.

Existence of the multiflow $\Omega(\overline{F}')$ in G implies that there is an integer ω'-feasible t_α–z flow h in $\overrightarrow{H}$ of value $\omega(\delta(t_\alpha)) = \omega(\delta(z))$. The algorithm constructs h by applying a max-flow algorithm. Additionally, it adjusts h to ensure that $\mathrm{supp}\,(h)$ is acyclic (e.g. with the help of an $O(m \log n)$-time algorithm from [ST83]).

Since $\mathrm{val}\,(\overline{g}_3) = 1$, there exists (and can be found in $O(m)$ time) a t_α–t_0 path $\overline{L}$ in $\overline{H}$ (and, hence, in $\overline{G}_j$) such that $\chi^{A\overline{L}} \leq \overline{g}_3$. By Property (4) from Lemma 4, one has $v_j \notin \overline{Q}_\alpha^1$, hence $\overline{L}$ contains at least one central node. We follow $\overline{L}$ from t_α to t_0 and denote the first central node on this path by q. Put L_1 to be the $\overrightarrow{H}$-image of the t_α–q prefix of $\overline{L}$.

We call a node $x \in A_\alpha - Q_\alpha$ *reachable* if there exists a path in $\overrightarrow{H}$ from x to q consisting of arcs in $\mathrm{supp}\,(h)$. Add all reachable nodes to Q_α and denote the resulting set by Q_α'. Put $\mathcal{Q}' := \mathcal{Q} - \{Q_\alpha\} \cup \{Q_\alpha'\}$.

Lemma 6. *There exists an integer ω'-feasible multiflow F' in G of value $\omega[T]$ such that each path $P \in \mathrm{supp}\,(F')$ is both $\mathcal{Q}$-feasible and $\mathcal{Q}'$-feasible.*

Lemma 7. *Suppose that π is a half-integral $\mathcal{Q}'$-cover obeying $\omega'[T] = \pi c$. Then $\omega'[T] = \nu(c)$.*

The island extension completes by putting $\omega := \omega'$ and $\mathcal{Q} := \mathcal{Q}'$. Lemma 5, Lemma 6, and Lemma 7 imply that the above change of ω and $\mathcal{Q}$ preserves invariants (3.1)–(3.3) and (3.4)–(3.5).

4   Running Time

The algorithm totally performs $O(\log U)$ scaling steps; each of the latter consists of $O(n)$ augmentation steps (by Lemma 1). Each augmentation step is a sequence of at most $O(n)$ extension steps. To bound the complexity of a single extension step note the following. It takes $\Lambda(n, m, U)$ time to construct graph $\widehat{G}$ and flow $\widehat{\omega}$. The existence of an augmenting sequence is checked in $O(m)$ time. Next, $O(\Lambda(n, m, U) \log n)$ time is sufficient to check if the augmenting sequence is fully applicable. If it is not the case, the binary search is performed. The later executes $O(\log n)$ checks, each requires solving (MMF). Next, islands $\mathcal{Q}$ are extended and function ω is updated, this takes $O(\Lambda(n, m, U) \log n)$ time. Finally, transforming ω into the desired multiflow in path packing form takes $O(\Lambda(n, m, U) \log n + mn \log n)$ time.

Summing up the above estimates one concludes as follows:

Theorem 4. *Problem (P) can be solved in $O(\Lambda(n, m, U)\, n^2 \log^2 n \, \log U)$ time.*

References

[Bab07]   Babenko, M.A.: A fast algorithm for path 2-packing problem. In: Diekert, V., Volkov, M.V., Voronkov, A. (eds.) CSR 2007. LNCS, vol. 4649, pp. 70–81. Springer, Heidelberg (2007)

[Che77]   Cherkassky, B.V.: A solution of a problem on multicommodity flows in a network. Ekonomika i Matematicheskie Metody 13(1), 143–151 (1977)

[FF62]   Ford, L., Fulkerson, D.: Flows in Netwerks. Princeton University Press, Princeton (1962)

[Fr89]   Frank, A.: On connectivity properties of Eulerian digraphs. Ann. Discrete Math. 41, 179–194 (1989)

[GR98]   Goldberg, A.V., Rao, S.: Beyond the flow decomposition barrier. J. ACM 45(5), 783–797 (1998)

[IKN98]   Ibaraki, T., Karzanov, A.V., Nagamochi, H.: A fast algorithm for finding a maximum free multiflow in an inner Eulerian network and some generalizations. Combinatorica 18(1), 61–83 (1998)

[Kar79]   Karzanov, A.V.: Combinatorial methods to solve cut-dependent multiflow problems. Combinatorial Methods for Flow Problems (Inst. for System Studies, Moscow (3), 6–69 (1979) (in russian)

[Kar94]   Karzanov, A.V.: Minimum cost multiflows in undirected networks. Math. Program. 66(3), 313–325 (1994)

[Lov76]   Lovász, L.: On some connectivity properties of Eulerian graphs. Acta Math. Akad. Sci. Hung. 28, 129–138 (1976)

[Lov80]   Lovász, L.: Matroid matching and some applications. J. Combinatorial Theory, Ser. B 28, 208–236 (1980)

[Pap07]   Pap, G.: Some new results on node-capacitated packing of a-paths. In: STOC 2007: Proceedings of the thirty-ninth annual ACM symposium on Theory of computing, pp. 599–604. ACM Press, New York (2007)

[Schr03] Schrijver, A.: Combinatorial Optimization, vol. A, C. Springer, Heidelberg (2003)

[ST83]   Sleator, D., Tarjan, R.: A data structure for dynamic trees. J. Comput. Syst. Sci. 26(3), 362–391 (1983)

[Vaz01]   Vazirani, V.: Approximation Algorithms. Springer, Heidelberg (2001)

Linear Time Planarity Testing and Embedding of Strongly Connected Cyclic Level Graphs

Christian Bachmaier and Wolfgang Brunner

University of Passau, Germany
{bachmaier,brunner}@fim.uni-passau.de

Abstract. A level graph is a directed acyclic graph with a level assignment for each node. Such graphs play a prominent role in graph drawing. They express strict dependencies and occur in many areas, e. g., in scheduling problems and program inheritance structures.

In this paper we extend level graphs to cyclic level graphs. Such graphs occur as repeating processes in cyclic scheduling, visual data mining, life sciences, and VLSI. We provide a complete study of strongly connected cyclic level graphs. In particular, we present a linear time algorithm for the planarity testing and embedding problem, and we characterize forbidden subgraphs. Our results generalize earlier work on level graphs.

1 Introduction

Cyclic level planar graphs receive their motivation from two sources: level planar graphs and recurrent hierarchies. A level graph is a directed acyclic graph with a level assignment for each node. Nodes on the same level are placed at different positions on a horizontal line and edges are drawn downwards from the upper to the lower end node. The challenging problems on level graphs are planarity testing and embedding algorithms in linear time and a characterization in terms of forbidden subgraphs. This parallels the situation for planar graphs, where nowadays there are many $\mathcal{O}(|V|)$ testing and embedding algorithms [3,8,12] and the famous Kuratowski graphs [11]: Each graph is planar if it does not contain a subgraph that is homeomorphic to the complete graph with 5 nodes K_5 or the complete bipartite graph $K_{3,3}$ with 3 nodes in each set. Level planarity has been studied intensively in recent years [4,6]. Jünger and Leipert [9] finally established a linear time algorithm for the level planarity testing and embedding problem. Healy et al. [7] gave a complete set of seven level non-planarity patterns for hierarchies. Fowler and Kobourov [5] added two more forbidden graphs for a complete set for arbitrary level graphs. Bachmaier et al. [1] extended level planarity to radial level planarity. There the levels are concentric circles and the edges are directed from inner to outer circles.

Recurrent hierarchies were introduced by Sugiyama et al. [15] more than 25 years ago. A recurrent hierarchy is a level graph with additional edges from the last to the first level. Here two drawings are natural: The first is a 2D drawing, where the levels are rays from a common center, and are sorted counterclockwise by their number, see Fig. 1(a). All nodes of one level are placed at different

D. Halperin and K. Mehlhorn (Eds.): ESA 2008, LNCS 5193, pp. 136–147, 2008.

positions on their ray and an edge $e = (u, v)$ is drawn as a monotone counterclockwise curve from u to v wrapping around the center at most once. The
second is a 3D drawing on a cylinder, see Fig. 1(b). A planar recurrent hierarchy
is shown on the cover of the book by Kaufmann and Wagner [10]. There it is
stated that recurrent hierarchies are "unfortunately [...] still not well studied".

The standard method to visualize directed graphs is the Sugiyama algorithm [15], which eliminates all cycles in the graph. This may be acceptable
in many applications. But there are areas in which it is important that the cycles are preserved and represented as cycles, e. g., visual data mining, or chemical
reactions in the life sciences [14]. Important applications can further be found in
the layout of regular VLSI circuits [13]. Recurrent hierarchies are well suited to
visualize such cyclic or regular structures. To enhance the readability of drawings, edge crossings should be avoided and even excluded.

In this paper we improve our earlier result [2] of an $\mathcal{O}(|V| \log |V|)$ planarity
testing and embedding algorithm on strongly connected cyclic level graphs and
present an optimal linear time algorithm. Moreover, we characterize forbidden
subgraphs for such graphs. This settles the major questions on strongly connected cyclic level graphs.

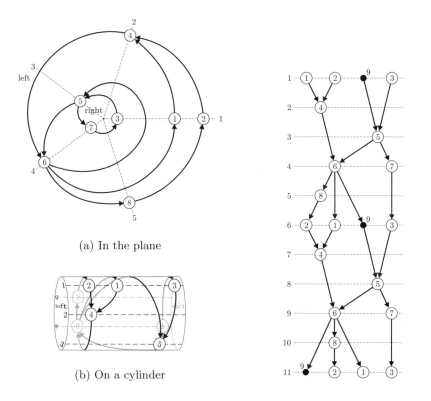

(a) In the plane

(b) On a cylinder

Fig. 1. Drawings of a cyclic 5-level graph G **Fig. 2.** $(2, 1)$-hierarchy of G

2   Preliminaries

A *cyclic k-level graph* $G = (V(G), E(G), \phi_G)$ $(k \geq 2)$ is a directed graph without self-loops with a given surjective level assignment of the nodes $\phi_G \colon V \to \{1, 2, \ldots, k\}$. For two nodes $u_G, v_G \in V(G)$ let $\mathrm{span}(u_G, v_G) := \phi_G(v_G) - \phi_G(u_G)$ if $\phi_G(u_G) < \phi_G(v_G)$, and $\mathrm{span}(u_G, v_G) := \phi_G(v_G) - \phi_G(u_G) + k$ otherwise. For an edge $e = (u_G, v_G) \in E(G)$ we define $\mathrm{span}(e) := \mathrm{span}(u_G, v_G)$. For a simple path or a simple cycle P define $\mathrm{span}(P) := \sum_{e \in E(P)} \mathrm{span}(e)$. All paths and cycles in this paper are directed if not stated otherwise. A graph is strongly connected if for all $u_G, v_G \in V(G)$ a path from u_G to v_G exists. A cyclic k-level graph G is a k-level graph if $\phi_G(u_G) < \phi_G(v_G)$ for each edge $(u_G, v_G) \in E(G)$ holds. A drawing is *(cyclic) level plane* if the edges do not cross except on common endpoints. A (cyclic) k-level graph is *(cyclic) level planar* if such a drawing exists. The *right outer face* is the face of the 2D drawing containing the center and the *left outer face* is the unbounded face (see Fig. 1(a)). A *(cyclic) level planar embedding* $\mathcal{G}$ of G consists of two lists $N_G^-(v_G)$ and $N_G^+(v_G)$ for each node $v_G \in V(G)$ which contain the end nodes of ingoing and outgoing edges, respectively. Both lists are ordered from left to right. A *hierarchy* is a level graph G s.t. each node v_G with $\phi_G(v_G) \neq 1$ has an ingoing edge.

3   Cyclic Level Non-planarity Patterns

In this section we give a characterization of cyclic level non-planarity patterns in strongly connected graphs (SCLNP).

Definition 1. *A (cyclic) level non-planarity pattern P is a set of (cyclic) level non-planar graphs with structural similarities. We call a pattern* minimal *if for each element of P the removal of one edge makes the graph (cyclic) level planar. A (cyclic) level graph G matches a pattern P if there exists $p \in P$ s.t. p is a subgraph of G. A set of patterns S is minimal if each pattern in S is minimal. S is* complete *if each (cyclic) level non-planar graph matches a pattern in S.*

Concerning level non-planarity patterns, Di Battista and Nardelli [4] presented three patterns for hierarchies (HLNP). This set is complete but not minimal. Healy et al. [7] gave seven minimal level non-planarity patterns for hierarchies (MHLNP). This complete set consists of two tree patterns T1 (Fig. 3(a)) and T2 (Fig. 3(b)), a level non-planar cycle C0 (Fig. 3(c)), and four level planar cycles with one (C1, Fig. 3(d)) to four (C4, Fig. 3(h)) paths starting from the cycle (C2 having two subcases). For the formal definition of the patterns see [7]. Note, that contrary to graph planarity, the partition of all minimal (cyclic) non-level planar graphs into patterns is somewhat arbitrary. Thus, nobody has treated the minimal cardinality of a minimal set of patterns.

Fowler and Kobourov [5] showed that the MHLNP set is not complete for general level graphs and added two more tree patterns, which are not needed for hierarchies, however. These nine patterns (MLNP) are minimal and complete for the general case. To formally describe cyclic level non-planarity patterns, we need the following definition.

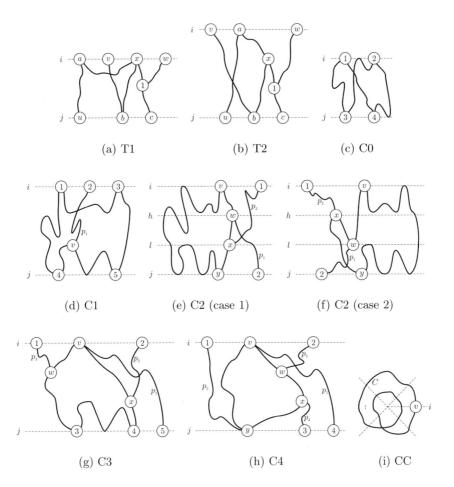

Fig. 3. The cyclic level non-planarity patterns for strongly connected graphs (SCLNP)

Definition 2. *Let G be a cyclic k-level graph. Let $c \in \mathbb{N}$ and $l \in \{1, \ldots, k\}$. Suppose that no edge crosses level l (if such an edge $e = (u_G, v_G)$ exists, add a node d_G to level l, remove the edge e and add the edges (u_G, d_G) and (d_G, v_G) to the graph). The (c, l)-hierarchy H of G is a $(ck + 1)$-level hierarchy. For each node v_G on level l H has $c + 1$ duplicates $v_1, v_{k+1}, \ldots v_{ck+1}$ with v_i on level i. Let w_G be a node with $\phi_G(w_G) \neq l$ and let $l' = \phi_G(w_G) - l + 1$ if $\phi_G(w_G) > l$ and $l' = \phi_G(w_G) - l + k + 1$ otherwise. For each such node w_G, H has c duplicated nodes $w_{l'}, w_{k+l'}, \ldots w_{(c-1)k+l'}$ with w_i on level i. For each edge $e = (u_G, v_G)$ and for each duplicate u_i in H with $i < ck + 1$ H contains the edge $(u_i, v_{i+\text{span}(e)})$.*

Informally speaking, the (c, l)-hierarchy H of G is obtained by splitting G at level l (thus creating a level graph) and duplicating the graph c times one below the other. We will use the notation v_i for a duplicate of $v_G \in V(G)$ on level i in H in the following. Figure 1 shows a cyclic 5-level graph and Fig. 2 a level plane

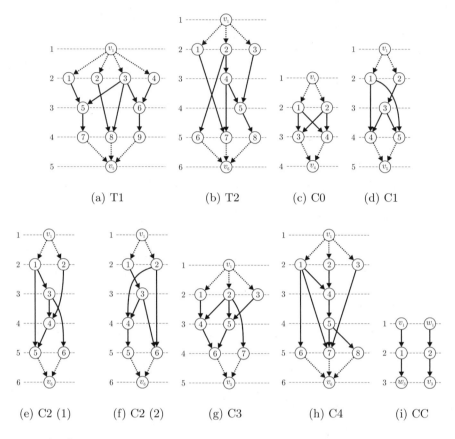

(a) T1   (b) T2   (c) C0   (d) C1

(e) C2 (1)   (f) C2 (2)   (g) C3   (h) C4   (i) CC

Fig. 4. (1, 1)-hierarchies of cyclic graphs matching exactly one of the SCLNP patterns

drawing of the corresponding (2, 1)-hierarchy. Note that a (c, l)-hierarchy does not include an embedding.

In a hierarchy, each node v with $\phi(v) > 1$ has an ingoing edge. In strongly connected cyclic level graphs each node has an ingoing and outgoing edge. Therefore, it is not obvious that each of the seven MHLNP patterns can occur in the cyclic case. But for each of the patterns a strongly connected cyclic level graph can be constructed. Figures 4(a) to (h) show (1, 1)-hierarchies of strongly connected cyclic k-level graphs which match exactly one of the MHLNP patterns. The edges needed for the patterns are drawn as full lines. Obviously each of the MHLNP patterns is a proof of non-planarity in the cyclic case as well. Therefore, we define a cyclic version of each of the seven MHLNP patterns:

Definition 3. *Let G be a cyclic k-level graph. We say that G matches the pattern CT1 if there exists $c \in \mathbb{N}$ s.t. the $(c, 1)$-hierarchy of G matches T1. We define the remaining six patterns in an analog way and set SCLNP' = {CT1, CT2, CC0, CC1, CC2, CC3, CC4}.*

Definition 4. *Let G be a cyclic k-level graph and $c \in \mathbb{N} \setminus \{0\}$. A c-cycle is a simple cycle with span $c \cdot k$.*

Figure 4(i) shows the $(1, 1)$-hierarchy of a strongly connected cyclic 2-level graph which is a 2-cycle. Note that this graph is cyclic level non-planar, but does not match any pattern of SCLNP'. On the other hand none of the graphs in Fig. 4(a) to (h) contains a 2-cycle. Therefore, an eighth cyclic level non-planarity pattern is needed.

Definition 5. *We define CC as the set of all c-cycles in cyclic k-level graphs with $c, k \in \mathbb{N}, c > 1$ (Fig. 3(i)). We set $SCLNP = SCLNP' \cup \{CC\}$.*

Proposition 1. *Let G be a cyclic k-level graph. If G matches CC, then G is cyclic level non-planar.*

Note that CC is a minimal pattern, as removing one edge from the cycle leads to a cyclic level planar graph.

Definition 6. *We call a (c, l)-hierarchy H of a cyclic level graph G strongly level planar if it is level planar and has a level planar embedding s. t. the first and last level have the same permutation. We call such an embedding a strongly level planar embedding.*

Proposition 2. *Let G be a strongly connected cyclic k-level graph and $l \in \{1, \ldots k\}$. G is cyclic level planar if and only if the $(1, l)$-hierarchy of G is strongly level planar. Let $c \in \mathbb{N}$. If the (c, l)-hierarchy of G is (strongly) level non-planar, then G is cyclic level non-planar.*

Definition 7. *Let H be a level graph with a fixed level planar embedding $\mathcal{H}$ and u, v be two nodes on the same level. We say $u < v$ $(u > v)$ if u lies left (right) of v in $\mathcal{H}$.*

Definition 8. *Let U, V, W be three permutations of the same node set. We define the* lexicographical ordering with respect to U *on the set of permutations in the following way: If V and W are the same permutations, then they are equal in the ordering. Otherwise there is a leftmost position on which V and W have different nodes. Let v and w be the nodes on this position in V and W, respectively. We define $V < W$ if $v < w$ in U and $V > W$ if $v > w$ in U.*

Another way to look at this ordering is as follows: The permutation U definies an ordering on an alphabet. A permutation V is then smaller than W if the word it builds is smaller than the word of W in the lexicographical ordering.

Lemma 1. *Let G be a strongly connected cyclic k-level graph s. t. G does not match CC. Let H be the $(2, 1)$-hierarchy of G. Let H be level planar with a fixed level planar embedding $\mathcal{H}$. Then G is cyclic level planar and a cyclic level planar embedding $\mathcal{G}$ of G exists s. t. the permutation of level 1 in $\mathcal{G}$ is the same as the permutation of level $k + 1$ in $\mathcal{H}$.*

Proof. Assume for contradiction that such an embedding $\mathcal{G}$ of G does not exist. Consider all level planar embeddings of H which have the same permutation of

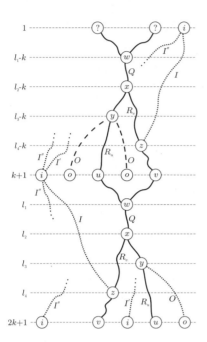

Fig. 5. Sketch for the proof of Lemma 1

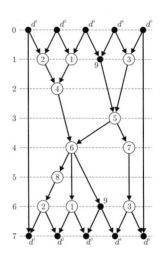

Fig. 6. Rigid $(1, 1)$-hierarchy

level $k+1$ as $\mathcal{H}$. None of these embeddings has this permutation on level $2k+1$, too (otherwise G would be cyclic level planar with the same permutation on level 1). Of all these embeddings choose one which has the minimal permutation on level $2k+1$ in the lexicographical ordering with respect to the ordering of level $k+1$. We consider this embedding from now on. We show that we can construct a new embedding with an even smaller permutation on level $2k+1$, which is a contradiction.

As the permutations of level $k+1$ and $2k+1$ are not the same, there have to exist two nodes u and v s.t. $u_{k+1} < v_{k+1}$ but $u_{2k+1} > v_{2k+1}$. W.l.o.g. let u_{2k+1} and v_{2k+1} be a pair of nodes with the wrong orientation that have the maximal number of nodes between them. See Fig. 5 for a sketch in which we omit the indices indicating the levels.

As G is strongly connected but does not match CC, each node lies on a 1-cycle. Thus, there have to be paths Q_u from u_{k+1} to u_{2k+1} and Q_v from v_{k+1} to v_{2k+1}. As the embedding is level planar, Q_u and Q_v cannot be disjoint. Therefore, we have a path Q_l from u_{k+1} to v_{2k+1} and a path Q_r from v_{k+1} to u_{2k+1}. As G does not match CC, Q_l and Q_r cannot be disjoint. Even more than that, there has to exist a node which lies on all paths from u_{k+1} to v_{2k+1} and on all paths from v_{k+1} to u_{2k+1} (otherwise the leftmost path from u_{k+1} to v_{2k+1} and the rightmost path from v_{k+1} to u_{2k+1} would be disjoint and generate a graph in CC). Let w_{l_1} and x_{l_2} be the uppermost and lowest such nodes, respectively, and Q be one path between them.

Let R_v be the leftmost path from x_{l_2} to v_{2k+1}. Let R_u be the rightmost path from x_{l_2} to u_{2k+1}. We now prove that we can flip all nodes between R_v and R_u, thus creating a smaller permutation on level $2k + 1$ in the lexicographical ordering and thus a contradiction.

Consider the nodes on the path R_u from level $l_2 + 1$ to $2k$. Assume for contradiction that a node y_{l_3} on the path has an outgoing edge right to R_u. We follow this path O downwards. If O ends on R_u, then R_u was not the rightmost path. Therefore, it has to reach a node o_{2k+1} on level $2k + 1$ right of u_{2k+1}. As O is disjoint to R_v, o_{k+1} has to lie left of v_{k+1} (we do not know whether $o_{k+1} < u_{k+1}$ or $o_{k+1} > u_{k+1}$ holds). But then o_{2k+1} and v_{2k+1} have the wrong orientation and have more nodes between them than v_{2k+1} and u_{2k+1}. A contradiction. The same argument can be used for R_v (switching left and right).

Now consider the nodes on the path R_v from level $l_2 + 1$ to $2k + 1$. Assume for contradiction that a node z_{l_4} on the path has an ingoing edge left to R_v. We follow this path I upwards. If I ends on R_v below or on x_{l_2}, then R_v was not the leftmost path. If I ends on $Q \setminus \{x_{l_2}\}$, then x_{l_2} would not lie on each path from u_{k+1} to v_{2k+1}. If it ends on the leftmost connection of u_{k+1} to w_{l_1} above w_{l_1}, then there would be disjoint paths from u_{k+1} to v_{2k+1} and from v_{k+1} to u_{2k+1}. The only remaining possibility is that I reaches the level $k + 1$ on a node i_{k+1} left of u_{k+1}. Due to the path I, i_1 has to lie right of u_1 and v_1. However, we do not know whether $u_1 < v_1$ or $u_1 > v_1$ holds.

We now consider the position of i_{2k+1}. If $i_{2k+1} > u_{2k+1}$ and, therefore, $i_{2k+1} > v_{2k+1}$, then i_{2k+1} and v_{2k+1} have the wrong orientation and more nodes between them than u_{2k+1} and v_{2k+1}. If i_{2k+1} lies between v_{2k+1} and u_{2k+1}, we consider the path I' from i_{2k+1} upwards. If I' reaches R_u, then we have disjoint paths from v_{k+1} to i_{2k+1} and from i_{k+1} to v_{2k+1} and thus G matches CC. If I' reaches R_v first, then I' would cause a crossing from i_{k+1} upwards. The remaining possibility is that $i_{2k+1} < v_{2k+1} < u_{2k+1}$. Now the same path I'' from i_1 to i_{k+1} and from i_{k+1} to i_{2k+1} has to exist. I'' cannot be disjoint with Q_u or Q_v as i_1 is right of u_1 and v_1 but i_{k+1} is left of u_{k+1} and v_{k+1}. Therefore, from i_{2k+1} upwards I'' has to reach I or R_v first to reach Q_u. In both cases a crossing from i_{k+1} upwards occurs, which is a contradiction. The same argument can be used to show that no path from R_u upwards exists.

As a consequence, we do not have any outgoing or ingoing edges on R_v to the left between $l_2 + 1$ and $2k + 1$. Analogously, we do not have outgoing or ingoing edges to the right of R_u between the same levels. So we can flip the subgraph between R_v and R_u and thus create a permutation of level $2k+1$ which is smaller than the given one in the lexicographical ordering with respect to the ordering of level $k + 1$. A contradiction. Thus, G is cyclic level planar with an embedding $\mathcal{G}$ s.t. the permutation of level 1 in $\mathcal{G}$ is the permutation of level $k + 1$ in $\mathcal{H}$.   □

Figure 1 shows a strongly connected cyclic 5-level graph and Fig. 2 an arbitrary level plane drawing of its $(2, 1)$-hierarchy. Note that levels 1, 6, and 11 have three different permutations. According to Lemma 1, we can fix the embedding of level 6 and change the permutation of level 11 to the permutation of level 6. We search for two nodes on level 11 which have the wrong orientation according to level 6 and the maximal number of nodes between them. These nodes are $u = 1$ and $v = 9$. We get $w = x = 6$ and flip the tree below node 6. After that 1 and 2 have the wrong orientation (with $w = 4$ and $x = 6$) and we flip these two nodes. Thereafter, levels 6 and 11 have the same permutation. This permutation is used for the cyclic level plane drawings in Fig. 1.

Theorem 1. *Let G be a strongly connected cyclic k-level graph. G is cyclic level planar if and only if it does not match a pattern in SCLNP.*

Proof. "⇒" We show the contrapositive. If G matches a pattern of SCLNP', then there exists $c \in \mathbb{N}$ s.t. the $(c, 1)$-hierarchy H of G matches an MHLNP pattern. Therefore, H is level non-planar. According to Proposition 2, G is cyclic level non-planar then. If G matches the pattern CC, then G is cyclic level non-planar according to Proposition 1.

"⇐" We show the contrapositive. Let G be cyclic level non-planar and let H be its $(2, 1)$-hierarchy. If H is level non-planar, then H matches a MHLNP pattern and, therefore, G matches a SCLNP' pattern. If H is level planar, then (the contrapositive of) Lemma 1 shows that G matches the pattern CC.   □

Note that according to Lemma 1 for each strongly connected cyclic k-level non-planar graph not matching CC its $(2, 1)$-hierarchy matches an MHLNP pattern. Therefore, patterns in SCLNP' can be limited to $2k + 1$ levels.

4   Cyclic Level Planarity Testing and Embedding

In this section we give a simple linear time level planarity testing and embedding algorithm.

Definition 9. *Let G be a cyclic k-level graph and H the $(2, 1)$-hierarchy of G. Let H be level planar with embedding $\mathcal{H}$. Let $F = (v_{k+1}^1, v_{k+1}^2, \ldots, v_{k+1}^s)$ be the permutation of level $k+1$ in $\mathcal{H}$. The rigid $(1, 1)$-hierarchy H' of $\mathcal{H}$ consists of the $(1, 1)$-hierarchy of G and the additional levels 0 and $k + 2$. Level 0 has the nodes $d_0^1, d_0^2, \ldots d_0^{s+1}$ and level $k + 2$ the nodes $d_{k+2}^1, d_{k+2}^2, \ldots, d_{k+2}^{s+1}$. H' contains the edges (d_0^i, v_1^i), (d_0^{i+1}, v_1^i), (v_{k+1}^i, d_{k+2}^i) and $(v_{k+1}^i, d_{k+2}^{i+1})$ for each $i \in \{1, \ldots, s\}$ as well as the edges (d_0^1, d_{k+2}^1) and $(d_0^{s+1}, d_{k+2}^{s+1})$.*

Note that the rigid $(1, 1)$-hierarchy H' of $\mathcal{H}$ is level planar if and only if it has an embedding s.t. the levels 1 and $k + 1$ have the same permutation F. Then H is strongly level planar and G cyclic level planar. From Theorem 1 we get the following idea for a cyclic level planarity testing and embedding algorithm.

Let $G = (V(G), E(G), \phi_G)$ be a strongly connected cyclic k-level graph. We first test whether $|E(G)| \leq 3|V(G)| - 6$ holds (otherwise G cannot be (cyclic level) planar (Euler)). Construct the $(2, 1)$-hierarchy H of G then. If H is level non-planar, then G is cyclic level non-planar. Otherwise let $\mathcal{H}$ be a level planar embedding of H. We construct the rigid $(1, 1)$-hierarchy H' of $\mathcal{H}$ and test its level planarity. If it fails G is cyclic level non-planar. If it does not fail, we transform the level planar embedding $\mathcal{H}'$ of H' into a cyclic level planar embedding $\mathcal{G}$ of G in a straight forward way: Let $v_G \in V(G)$ with $\phi_G(v_G) \neq 1$. Let v_l be the corresponding node in H'. We set $N_G^-(v_G) = N_{H'}^-(v_l)$ and $N_G^+(v_G) = N_{H'}^+(v_l)$. For a node $v_G \in V(G)$ with $\phi_G(v_G) = 1$ we set $N_G^-(v_G) = N_{H'}^-(v_{k+1})$ and $N_G^+(v_G) = N_{H'}^+(v_1)$. In both cases we identify the nodes in H' with the corresponding nodes in G.

Algorithm 1. cyclicLevelPlanarEmbedding

Input: A strongly connected cyclic k-level graph $G = (V(G), E(G), \phi_G)$
Output: A cyclic level planar embedding $\mathcal{G}$ or $false$

1   **if** $|E(G)| > 3|V(G)| - 6$ **then**
2 | **return** $false$

3   Let H be the $(2,1)$-hierarchy of G
4   **if** $\neg levelPlanar(H)$ **then**
5 | **return** $false$

6   Let $\mathcal{H}$ be a level planar embedding of H
7   Let H' be the rigid $(1,1)$-hierarchy of $\mathcal{H}$
8   **if** $\neg levelPlanar(H')$ **then**
9 | **return** $false$

10   Let $\mathcal{H}'$ be a level planar embedding of H'
11   Construct cyclic level planar embedding $\mathcal{G}$ of G from $\mathcal{H}'$
12   **return** $\mathcal{G}$

Theorem 2. *Cyclic level planarity testing and embedding on strongly connected cyclic level graphs can be achieved by Algorithm 1 in linear time.*

Proof. The correctness of Algorithm 1 follows directly from Theorem 1. To prove its time complexity, we consider the construction of the $(2,1)$-hierarchy H of G first. The addition of dummy nodes on level 1 increases the number of nodes and edges by at most $E(G)$. After that the graph is duplicated: Each node on level 1 has three duplicates, all remaining nodes and all edges have two duplicates. Therefore, the size of H is linear in the size of G. All steps can easily be done in linear time. To test the level planarity of H any linear time level planarity testing and embedding algorithm for hierarchies can be used [4,9]. The construction of the $(1,1)$-hierarchy is possible in linear time as well. Let w be the number of nodes on level 1 in this hierarchy. To build the rigid $(1,1)$-hierarchy, we add $2(w+1)$ nodes and $4w+2$ edges and again use a linear time level planarity testing and embedding algorithm. The construction of $\mathcal{G}$ from $\mathcal{H}'$ can again easily be done in linear time.   □

5   Summary and Open Problems

We have shown that each of the seven MHLNP patterns of Healy et al. [7] are necessary in the strongly connected cyclic level case. To build a complete set, an eighth pattern is needed: a simple cycle wrapping around the center more than once (CC). This leads to a simple linear time level planarity testing and embedding algorithm.

As open problems remain finding a linear time planarity testing and embedding algorithm for arbitrary cyclic level graphs, a stronger characterization of the SCLNP patterns as well as finding patterns for the arbitrary cyclic level case.

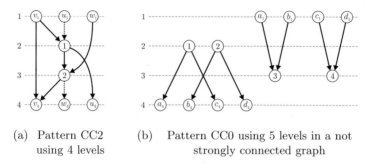

(a) Pattern CC2   (b)   Pattern CC0 using 5 levels in a not
     using 4 levels   strongly connected graph

Fig. 7. $(1, 1)$-hierarchies of cyclic 3-level graphs matching one SCLNP pattern

Conjecture 1. Let G be a strongly connected cyclic k-level graph. G is cyclic level planar if and only if G does not match a pattern in SCLNP with the patterns in SCLNP' using at most $k + 1$ levels.

Figure 7(a) shows a $(1, 1)$-hierarchy of a cyclic 3-level graph which matches the pattern CC2 (case 1) and uses 4 levels. If Conjecture 1 holds, it is not possible to construct a strongly connected cyclic k-level non-planar graph not matching CC s.t. all patterns use more than $k + 1$ levels. Obviously, this is false for not strongly connected graphs, as the cyclic 3-level graph in Fig. 7(b) shows. The only pattern it matches is the pattern CC0 using 5 levels. This example can easily be enlarged s.t. the pattern uses an arbitrary amount of levels.

Conjecture 2. Let G be a (not necessarily strongly connected) cyclic k-level graph. G is cyclic level planar if and only if there does not exist $c \in \mathbb{N}$ s.t. the $(c, 1)$-hierarchy matches one of the nine MLNP patterns and G does not contain an undirected simple cycle wrapping around the center more than once.

Lemma 2 is a strong indication for Conjecture 1:

Lemma 2. *Let G be a strongly connected cyclic k-level graph not matching CC. If G matches an SCLNP' pattern using less than $2k + 1$ and more than $k + 2$ levels, then it matches another instance of an SCLNP' pattern.*

Proof. Let H be the $(2, 1)$-hierarchy of G. W.l.o.g. let 1 be the first level of the pattern in H. Note that H matches the pattern, but the $(2, 2)$-hierarchy H' of G does not match it, as the level 1 of G is missing at the top. As more than $k + 2$

levels are used by the pattern, the pattern is not completely there from level k downwards as well. H' has to match another SCLNP' pattern, as we could use H' instead of H in Lemma 1.   □

Note that Lemma 2 does not make a statement on patterns using $2k+1$ or $k+2$ levels. Nevertheless, we conjecture that the patterns use $k+1$ levels at most, as all strongly connected cyclic level graphs matching a longer pattern seem to match a shorter pattern or a CC pattern as well.

References

1. Bachmaier, C., Brandenburg, F.J., Forster, M.: Radial level planarity testing and embedding in linear time. Journal of Graph Algorithms and Applications 9(1), 53–97 (2005)
2. Bachmaier, C., Brunner, W., König, C.: Cyclic level planarity testing and embedding (extended abstract). In: Hong, S.-H., Nishizeki, T., Quan, W. (eds.) GD 2007. LNCS, vol. 4875, pp. 50–61. Springer, Heidelberg (2008)
3. Boyer, J., Myrvold, W.: On the cutting edge: Simplified $\mathcal{O}(n)$ planarity by edge addition. Journal of Graph Algorithms and Applications 8(3), 241–273 (2004)
4. Di Battista, G., Nardelli, E.: Hierarchies and planarity theory. IEEE Transactions on Systems, Man, and Cybernetics 18(6), 1035–1046 (1988)
5. Fowler, J.J., Kobourov, S.G.: Minimum level nonplanar patterns for trees. In: Hong, S.-H., Nishizeki, T., Quan, W. (eds.) GD 2007. LNCS, vol. 4875, pp. 69–75. Springer, Heidelberg (2008)
6. Healy, P., Kuusik, A.: Algorithms for multi-level graph planarity testing and layout. Theoretical Computer Science 320(2–3), 331–344 (2004)
7. Healy, P., Kuusik, A., Leipert, S.: A characterization of level planar graphs. Discrete Mathematics 280, 51–63 (2004)
8. Hopcroft, J.E., Tarjan, R.E.: Efficient planarity testing. Journal of the ACM 21(4), 549–568 (1974)
9. Jünger, M., Leipert, S.: Level planar embedding in linear time. Journal of Graph Algorithms and Applications 6(1), 67–113 (2002)
10. Kaufmann, M., Wagner, D.: Drawing Graphs. LNCS, vol. 2025. Springer, Heidelberg (2001)
11. Kuratowski, K.: Sur le problème des courbes gauches en topologie. Fundamenta Mathematicae 15, 271–283 (1930)
12. Lempel, A., Even, S., Cederbaum, I.: An algorithm for planarity testing of graphs. In: International Symposium, Rome, pp. 215–232 (1967)
13. Mehlhorn, K., Rülling, W.: Compaction on the torus. IEEE Transactions on Computer-Aided Design 9(4), 389–397 (1990)
14. Michal, G.: Biochemical Pathways: An Atlas of Biochemistry and Molecular Biology. Wiley, Chichester (1999)
15. Sugiyama, K., Tagawa, S., Toda, M.: Methods for visual understanding of hierarchical system structures. IEEE Transactions on Systems, Man, and Cybernetics 11(2), 109–125 (1981)

Straight Skeletons of Three-Dimensional Polyhedra[*]

Gill Barequet[1], David Eppstein[2], Michael T. Goodrich[2], and Amir Vaxman[1]

[1] Dept. of Computer Science
Technion—Israel Institute of Technology
Haifa 32000, Israel
{barequet,avaxman}@cs.technion.ac.il
[2] Computer Science Department
Univ. of California, Irvine
{eppstein,goodrich}@ics.uci.edu

Abstract. We study the straight skeleton of polyhedra in 3D. We first show that the skeleton of voxel-based polyhedra may be constructed by an algorithm taking constant time per voxel. We also describe a more complex algorithm for skeletons of voxel polyhedra, which takes time proportional to the surface-area of the skeleton rather than the volume of the polyhedron. We also show that any n-vertex axis-parallel polyhedron has a straight skeleton with $O(n^2)$ features. We provide algorithms for constructing the skeleton, which run in $O(\min(n^2 \log n, k \log^{O(1)} n))$ time, where k is the output complexity. Next, we show that the straight skeleton of a general nonconvex polyhedron has an ambiguity, suggesting a consistent method to resolve it. We prove that the skeleton of a general polyhedron has a superquadratic complexity in the worst case. Finally, we report on an implementation of an algorithm for the general case.

1 Introduction

The straight skeleton is a geometric construction that reduces two-dimensional shapes—polygons—to one-dimensional sets of segments approximating the same shape. It is defined in terms of an offset process in which edges move inward, remaining straight and meeting at vertices. When a vertex meets an offset edge, the process continues within the two pieces so formed. The straight segments traced out by vertices during this process define the skeleton. Introduced by Aichholzer et al. [1,2], the two-dimensional straight skeleton has since found many applications, e.g., surface folding [9], offset curve construction [13], interpolation of surfaces in three dimensions from cross sections [3], automated interpretation of geographic data [15], polygon decomposition [21], etc. The straight skeleton is more complex to compute than other types of skeleton [6,13], but its piecewise-linear form offers many advantages. The best known alternative, the medial axis [5], consists of both linear and quadratic curve segments.

---

[*] Work on this paper by the first and fourth authors has been supported in part by a French-Israeli Research Cooperation Grant 3-3413.

D. Halperin and K. Mehlhorn (Eds.): ESA 2008, LNCS 5193, pp. 148–160, 2008.

It is natural, then, to try to develop algorithms for skeleton construction of a polyhedron in 3D. The most well-known type of 3D skeleton, the medial axis, has found applications, e.g., in mesh generation [17] and surface reconstruction [4]. Unlike its 2D counterpart, the 3D medial axis can be quite complex, both combinatorially and geometrically. Thus, we would like an alternative way to characterize the shape of 3D polyhedra using a simpler type of 2D skeleton.

1.1   Related Prior Work

We are not aware of any prior work on 3D straight skeletons, other than Demaine et al. [8], who give the basic properties of 3D straight skeletons, but do not study them in detail w.r.t. their algorithmic, combinatorial, or geometric properties.

Held [16] showed that in the worst case, the complexity of the medial axis of a convex polyhedron of complexity n is $\Omega(n^2)$, which implies a similar bound for the 3D straight skeleton. Perhaps the most relevant prior work is on shape characterization using the 3D medial axis, defined from a 3D polyhedron as the Voronoi diagram of the set of faces, edges, and vertices of the polyhedron. The best known upper bound for its combinatorial complexity is $O(n^{3+\varepsilon})$ [18].

Because of these drawbacks, a number of researchers have studied algorithms for approximating 3D medial axes. Sherbrooke et al. [20] give an algorithm that traces out the curved edges of the 3D medial skeleton. Culver et al. [7] use exact arithmetic to compute a representation of a 3D medial axis. In both cases, the running time depends on both the combinatorial and geometric complexity of the medial axis. Foskey et al. [14] construct an approximate medial axis using a voxel-based approach that runs in time $O(nV)$, where n is the number of features of the input polyhedron and V is the volume of the voxel mesh that contains it. Sheehy et al. [19] use instead the 3D Delaunay triangulation of a cloud of points on the surface of the input polyhedron to approximate 3D medial axis. Likewise, Dey and Zhao [10] study the 3D medial axis as a subcomplex of the Voronoi diagram of a sampling of points approximating the input polyhedron.

1.2   Our Results

- We study the straight skeleton of orthogonal polyhedra formed as unions of voxels. We analyze how the skeleton may intersect each voxel, and describe a suitable a simple voxel-sweeping algorithm taking constant time per voxel.
- We give a more complex algorithm for skeletons of voxel polyhedra, which, rather than taking time proportional to the total volume, takes time proportional to the the number of voxels it intersects.
- We show that any n-vertex axis-parallel polyhedron has a skeleton with $O(n^2)$ features. We provide two algorithms for computing it, resulting in a runtime of $O(\min(n^2 \log n, k \log^{O(1)} n))$, where k is the output complexity.
- We discuss the ambiguity in defining skeletons for general polyhedra and suggest a consistent method for resolving it. We show that for a general polyhedron, the straight skeleton can have superquadratic complexity. We also describe an algorithm for computing the skeleton in the general case.

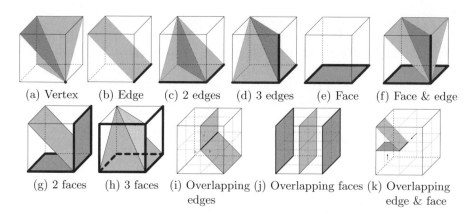

(a) Vertex   (b) Edge   (c) 2 edges   (d) 3 edges   (e) Face   (f) Face & edge

(g) 2 faces   (h) 3 faces   (i) Overlapping   (j) Overlapping faces   (k) Overlapping
                                   edges   edge & face

Fig. 1. Cases of straight skeleton within a subvoxel (a-h) or voxel (i-k)

2   Voxel Polyhedra

In this section we consider the case in which the polyhedron is a polycube, that
is, a rectilinear polyhedron all of whose vertices have integer coordinates. The
"cubes" making up the polyhedron are also called voxels. For voxels, and more
generally for orthogonal polyhedra, the straight skeleton is a superset of the L_∞
Voronoi diagram. Due to this relationship, the straight skeleton is significantly
easier to compute for orthogonal inputs than in the general case.

As in the general case, the straight skeleton of a polycube can be modeled
by offsetting the boundary of the polycube inward, and tracing the movement
of the boundary. During this sweep, the boundary forms a moving front whose
features are faces, edges, and vertices. An edge can be either convex or concave,
while a vertex can be convex, concave, or a saddle. In the course of this process,
features may disappear or appear.

The sweep starts at time 0, when the front is the boundary of the polycube.
In the first time unit we process all the voxels adjacent to the boundary. In the
ith round ($i \geq 1$) we process all the voxels adjacent to voxels processed in the
$(i-1)$st round, that have never been processed before. Processing a voxel means
the computation of the piece of the skeleton lying within the voxel. During this
process, the polycube is shrunk, and may be broken into several components.
The process continues for every piece separately until it vanishes.

2.1   A Volume Proportional-Time Algorithm

Theorem 1. *The combinatorial complexity of the straight skeleton of a polycube
of volume V is $O(V)$. The skeleton can be computed in $O(V)$ time.*

Proof. The claims follow from the fact that the complexity of the skeleton within
every voxel (or, more precisely, within every 1/8-voxel), as well as the time
needed to compute it during the sweep, is $O(1)$. Fig. 1 illustrates the different
cases. The full details are given in the full version of the paper.   □

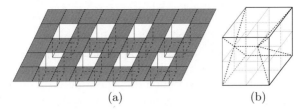

Fig. 2. A polycube of volume V whose skeleton has complexity $\Theta(V)$

This algorithm is worst-case optimal, since in the worst case the complexity of the skeleton of a polycube made of V voxels is $\Theta(V)$. One such example, shown in Fig. 2(a), is made of a flat layer of cubes (not shown), with a grid of supporting "legs," each a single cube. The number of legs is about $1/5$ of the total number of voxels. The skeleton of this object has features within every leg, see Fig. 2(b) (the bottom of a leg corresponds to the right side of the figure).

2.2   Output-Sensitive Voxel Sweep

The straight skeleton of a polycube, as constructed by the previous algorithm, contains features within some voxels, but other voxels may not participate in the skeleton; nevertheless, the algorithm must consider all voxels and pay in its running time for them. In this section we outline a more efficient algorithm that computes the straight skeleton in time proportional only to the number of voxels containing skeleton features, or equivalently, in time proportional to the *surface area* of the straight skeleton rather than its volume. Necessarily, we assume that the input polycube is provided as a space-efficient boundary representation rather than as a set of voxels, for otherwise simply scanning the input would take more time than we wish to spend.

Our algorithm consists of an outer loop, in which we advance the moving front of the polycube boundary one time step at a time, and an inner loop, in which we capture all features of the straight skeleton formed in that time step. During the algorithm, we maintain at each step a representation of the moving front, as a collection of polygons having orthogonal and diagonal edges. As long as each operation performed in the inner and outer loops of the algorithm can be charged against straight skeleton output features, the total time will be proportional to the output size.

In order to avoid the randomization needed for hashing, several steps of our algorithm will use as a data structure a direct-addressed lookup table, which we summarize in the following lemma:

Lemma 1. *In time proportional to the boundary of an input polycube, we may initialize a data structure that can repeatedly process a collection of objects, indexed by integers within the range of coordinates of the polycube vertices, and produce as output a graph, in which the vertices are sets of objects that have equal indices and the edges are pairs of sets with index values that differ by one. The time per operation is proportional to the number of objects given as input.*

In each step of the outer loop of the algorithm, we perform the following:

1. Advance each face of the wavefront one unit inward. In this advancement process, we may detect events in which a wavefront edge shrinks to a point, forming a straight skeleton vertex. However, events involving pairs of features that are near in space but far apart on the wavefront may remain undetected. Thus, after this step, the wavefront may include overlapping pairs of coplanar oppositely-moving faces.
2. For each plane containing faces of the new wavefront boundary, detect pairs of faces that overlap within that plane, and find the features in which two overlapping face edges intersect or in which a vertex of one face lies in the interior of another face. (Details are provided in the full version of the paper.)
3. In the inner loop of the algorithm, propagate straight skeleton features within each face of the wavefront from the points detected in the previous step to the rest of the face. If two faces overlap in a single plane, the previous step will have found some of the points at which they form skeleton vertices, but the entire overlap region will form a face of the skeleton. We propagate outward from the detected intersection points using DFS, voxel by voxel, to determine the skeleton features contained within the overlap region.

In summary, we have:

Theorem 2. *One can compute the straight skeleton of a polycube in time proportional to its surface area.*

3   Orthogonal Polyhedra

3.1   Definition

We consider here the more general *orthogonal polyhedra*, in which all faces are parallel to two of the coordinate axes. As in the 2D case, we define the straight skeleton of an orthogonal polyhedron P by a continuous shrinking process in which a sequence of nested "offset surfaces" are formed, starting from the boundary of the polyhedron, with each face moving inward at a constant speed. At time t in this process, the offset surface P_t for P consists of the set of points at L_∞ distance exactly t from the boundary of P. For almost all values of t, P_t will be a polyhedron, but at some time steps P_t may have a non-manifold topology, possibly including flat sheets of surface that do not bound any interior region. When this happens, the evolution of the surface undergoes sudden discontinuous changes, as these surfaces vanish at time steps after t in a discontinuous way. More precisely, we define a *degenerate point* of P_t to be a point p that is on the boundary of P_t, s.t., for some δ, and all $\varepsilon > 0$, $P_{t+\varepsilon}$ does not contain any point within distance δ of p.

At each step in the shrinking process, we imagine the surface of P_t as *decorated* with *seams* left over when sheets of degenerate points occur. Specifically, suppose that P contains two disjoint xy-parallel faces at the same z-height; then, as we shrink P, the corresponding faces of P_t may grow toward each other. When they meet, they leave a seam between them. Seams can also occur when two parts of the same nonconvex face grow toward and meet each other. After a seam forms, it remains on the face of P_t on which it formed, orthogonal to the position at which it originally formed.

We define the straight skeleton of P as the union of three sets: 1. Points that, for some t, belong to an edge or vertex of P_t; 2. Degenerate points for P_t for some t; and 3. Points that, for some t, belong to a seam of P_t.

3.2   Complexity Bounds

As each face has at least one boundary edge, and each edge has at least one vertex, we may bound the complexity of the straight skeleton by bounding the number of its vertices. Each vertex corresponds to an *event*, that is, a point p (the location of the vertex), the time t for which p belongs to the boundary of P_t, and the set of features of $P_{t-\varepsilon}$ near p for small values of ε that contribute to the event. We may classify events into six types.

Concave-vertex events, in which one of the features of $P_{t-\varepsilon}$ involved in the event is a *concave vertex*: that is, a vertex of $P_{t-\varepsilon}$ s.t. seven of the eight quadrants surrounding that vertex lie within $P_{t-\varepsilon}$. In such an event, this vertex must collide against some oppositely-moving feature of P_t.

Reflex-reflex events are not concave-vertex events, but these events involve the collision between two components of boundary of $P_{t-\varepsilon}$ that prior to the event are far from each other as measured in geodesic distance around the boundary, both of which include a reflex edge. These components may either be a reflex edge, or a vertex that has a reflex edge within its neighborhood.

Reflex-seam events are not either of the above two types, but they involve the collision between two different components of boundary of $P_{t-\varepsilon}$, one of which includes a reflex edge. The other component must be a seam edge or vertex, because it is not possible for a reflex edge to collide with a convex edge of $P_{t-\varepsilon}$ unless both edges are part of a single boundary component.

Seam-seam events in which vertices or edges on two seams, on oppositely oriented parallel faces of $P_{t-\varepsilon}$, collide with each other.

Seam-face events in which a seam vertex on one face of $P_{t-\varepsilon}$ collides with a point on an oppositely oriented face that does not belong to a seam.

Single-component events in which the boundary points near p in $P_{t-\varepsilon}$ form a single connected subset.

Theorem 3. *The straight skeleton of an n-vertex orthogonal polyhedron has complexity $O(n^2)$.*

Proof. (Sketch) We count the events of each different type. There are $O(n)$ concave-vertex and seam-face events, while there are $O(n^2)$ reflex-reflex, reflex-seam, and seam-seam events. Single-component events can be charged against the events of other types. Each event contributes a constant amount of skeletal features. More details are given in the full version of the paper.   □

3.3   Algorithms

Again, we view the skeleton as generated by a moving surface that changes at discrete events. It is easy to fully process an event in constant time, so the problem reduces to determining efficiently the sequence of events, and distinguishing actual events from false events. To this aim we provide two algorithms.

Theorem 4. *There is a constant c, s.t. the skeleton of an n-vertex orthogonal polyhedron with k skeletal features may be constructed in time $O(k \log^c n)$.*

Proof. Each event in our classification (except single-component events, which may be handled by an event queue) is generated by the interaction of two features of the moving surface P_t. To generate these events, ordered by the time at which they occur, we use a data structure of Eppstein [11,12] for maintaining a set of items and finding the pair of items minimizing some binary function $f(x, y)$—the time at which an event is generated by the interaction of items x and y ($+\infty$ if there is no interaction). The data structure reduces this problem (with polylogarithmic overhead) to a simpler problem: maintain a dynamic set X of items, and answer queries asking for the first interaction between an item $x \in X$ and a query item y. We need separate first-interaction data structures of this type for edge-edge, vertex-face, and face-vertex interactions. In the full version of the paper we provide the implementation details of these data structures.   □

A simpler algorithm is worst-case (rather than output-sensitive) optimal.

Theorem 5. *The straight skeleton of an orthogonal polyhedron with n vertices and k straight skeleton features may be constructed in time $O(n^2 \log n)$.*

Proof. For each pair of objects that may interact (features of the input polyhedron P or of the 2D straight skeletons S_Π in each face plane Π), we compute the time of interaction. We process the pairs of objects by the order of these times; whenever we process a pair (x, y), we consult an additional data structure to determine whether the pair causes an event or whether the event that they might have caused has been blocked by some other features of the skeleton.

To test whether an edge-edge pair causes an event, we maintain a binary search tree for each edge, representing the family of segments into which the line containing that edge (translated according to the motion of the surface P_t) has been subdivided in the current state of the surface P_t. An edge-edge pair causes an event if the point at which the event would occur currently belongs to line segments from the lines of both edges, which may be tested in logarithmic time.

To test whether a vertex-face pair causes an event, we check whether the vertex still exists at the time of the event, and then perform a point location query to locate the point in S_Π at which it would collide with a face belonging to Π. The collision occurs if the orthogonal distance within Π from this point to the nearest face is smaller than the time at which the collision would occur. We do not need to check whether other features of the skeleton might have blocked features of S_Π from belonging to the boundary of P_t, for if they did they would also have led to an earlier vertex-face event causing the removal of the vertex.

Thus, each object pair may be tested using either a dynamic binary search tree or a static point location data structure, in logarithmic time per pair.   □

4   General Polyhedra

4.1   Ambiguity

Defining the straight skeleton of a general polyhedron is inherently ambiguous, unlike the cases for convex and orthogonal polyhedra. The ambiguity stems from the fact that, whereas convex polyhedra are defined uniquely by the planes supporting their faces, nonconvex polyhedra are defined by *both* the supporting planes and a given topology, which is not necessarily unique. Thus, while being offset, a polyhedron can propagate from a given state into multiple equally valid topological configurations. (This issue was alluded to in [8].) A simple example is shown in Fig. 3(a). The problem is illustrated w.r.t. two boundary pieces—a wedge, A, and a tabletop, B—that are growing relative to each other. Due to the angle of the two front planes of A, the growing wedge eventually grows past the tabletop. The issue is to determine how the wavefronts continue growing. Possible choices include: (i) The wedge A grows through to the other side of B when A reaches the edge of B and moves past the edge; (ii) The wedge continues growing forward, but is blocked from growing downward by clipping it with the plane defined by the top of the tabletop; (iii) The wedge suddenly projects into the empty space in front of the table and continues growing out from there. In fact, all suggestions above cause a contradiction or a noncontinuous propagation of the wavefront. The actual solution that we chose is to blunt the front end of the wedge A by clipping it with the plane defined by the side of the tabletop.

A more general example of the ambiguity of the propagation of the skeleton is shown in Fig. 3(b). The figure shows a vertex of degree 5, and two possible topologies during the propagation. This is the so-called weighted-rooftop problem: Given a base polygon and slopes of walls, all sharing one vertex, determine the topology of the rooftop of the polygon, which does not always have a unique solution. In our definition of the skeleton, we define a consistent method for the initial topology and for establishing topological changes while processing the algorithm's events, based on the 2D weighted straight skeleton (see Section 4.3).

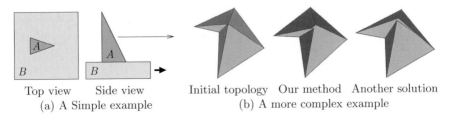

Top view   Side view   Initial topology   Our method   Another solution
(a) A Simple example   (b) A more complex example

Fig. 3. 3D skeleton ambiguity

4.2   A Combinatorial Lower Bound

Theorem 6. *The complexity of a 3D skeleton for a simple polyhedron is $\Omega(n^2\alpha^2(n))$ in the worst case, where $\alpha(n)$ is the inverse of the Ackermann function.*

Proof.   (Sketch) We use an example (see Fig. 4), in which a sequence of triangular prisms result in a growing wavefront whose complexity is that of the upper envelope of n line segments, that is, $\Omega(n\alpha(n))$ [22]. We attach two such sequences of prisms to the "floor" and "ceiling" of the polyhedron, obtaining two growing wavefronts which produce $\Omega(n^2\alpha^2(n))$ skeletal features.   □

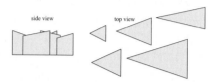

Fig. 4. Illustrating 3D skeleton complexity

4.3   The Algorithm

Our algorithm is an event-based simulation of the propagation of the boundary of the polyhedron. Events occur whenever four planes, supporting faces of the polyhedron, meet at one point. At these points the propagating boundary undergoes topological events. The algorithm consists of the following steps:

1. Collect all possible initial events.
2. While the event queue is not empty:
    (a) Retrieve the next event and check its validity. If not valid, go to Step 2.
    (b) Create a vertex at the location of the event and connect to it the vertices participating in the event.
    (c) Change the topology of the propagating polyhedron according to actions in Step 2(b). Set the location of the event to the newly-created vertices.
    (d) Create new events for newly-created vertices, edges, and faces and their neighbors, if needed.

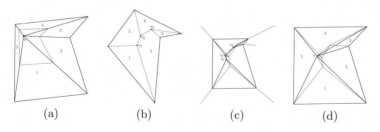

(a)   (b)   (c)   (d)

Fig. 5. Changing the initial topology of a vertex of degree ≥ 4 (skeleton in dashed lines): (a) The original polyhedron. Vertex v has degree 5; (b) The cross-section and its weighted straight skeleton. Vertex v becomes three new vertices v_1, v_2, v_3; (c) The straight skeleton of the polyhedron. Vertex v spawned three skeletal edges; (d) The propagated polyhedron. Vertices v_1, v_2, v_3 trace their skeletal edges.

We next describe the different events and how each type is dealt with. The procedure always terminates since the number of all possible events is bounded from above by the number of combinations of four propagating faces.

Initial Topology. At the start of the propagation, we need to split each vertex of degree greater than 3 into several vertices of degree 3 (see Fig. 5). This is the ambiguous situation discussed earlier; it can have several valid solutions. Our approach is based on cutting the faces surrounding the vertex with one or more planes (any cutting plane intersecting all faces and parallel to none suffices), and finding the weighted straight skeleton of the intersection of these faces with the cutting plane, with the weights determined by the dihedral angles of these faces with the cutting plane, after an infinitesimally-small propagation. The topology of this 2D straight skeleton tells us the connectivity to use subsequently, and always yields a unique valid solution. In the full version of the paper we detail the application of this method for all types of vertices.

Collecting Events. In the full version of the paper we describe how events are collected, classified as valid or invalid, and handled by the algorithm. In a nutshell, each event arises from interactions of features of the wavefront, and gives rise to potential future events. However, a potential event may be found invalid already when it is created, or later when it is fetched for processing. Each valid event results in the creation of features of the skeleton, and in a topological change in the structure of the propagating polyhedron.

Handling Events. Propagating vertices are defined as the intersection of propagating planes. Such a vertex is uniquely defined by exactly three planes, which also define the three propagating edges adjacent to the vertex. (When an event creates a vertex of degree greater than 3, we handle it as as in the initial topology.) The topology of the polyhedron remains unchanged during the propagation between events. The possible events are:

1. **Edge Event.** An edge vanishes as its two endpoints meet, at the meeting point of the four planes around the edge.
2. **Hole Event.** A reflex vertex (adjacent to three reflex edges, called a "spike") runs into a face. The three planes adjacent to this vertex meet the plane of the face. After the event, the spike meets the face in a small triangle.
3. **Split Event.** A ridge vertex (adjacent to one or two reflex edges) runs into an opposite edge. The faces adjacent to the ridge meet the face adjacent to the twin of the split edge. This creates a vertex of degree greater than 3, handled as in the initial topology.
4. **Edge-Split event.** Two reflex edges cross each other. Every edge is adjacent to two planes.
5. **Vertex event.** Two ridges sharing a common reflex edge meet. This is a special case of the edge event, but it has different effects, and so it is considered a different event. Vertex events occur when a reflex edge runs twice into a face, and the two endpoints of this edge meet.

Data Structures. We use an event queue which holds all possible events sorted by time, and a set of propagating polyhedra, initialized to the input polyhedron, after the initialization of topology. The used structure is a generalization of the SLAV structure in 2D. We provide the details in the full version of the paper.

Running Time. Let n be the total complexity of the polyhedron, r be the number of reflex vertices (or edges), and k the number of events. For collecting the initial events, we iterate over all vertices, faces, and edges. Edge events require looking at each edge's neighborhood, which is done in $O(n)$ time. Finding hole events requires considering all pairs of a reflex vertex and a face. This takes $O(rn)$ time. Computing a split event is bounded within the edges of the common face, but this can take $O(rn)$ time, and computing edge-split events takes $O(r^2)$ time.

The algorithm computes and processes events. For a convex polyhedron, only edge events are created, each one computed locally in $O(1)$ time. However, for a general polyhedron, every edge might be split by any ridge and stabbed by any

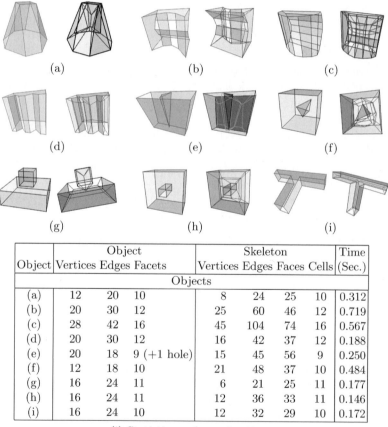

	Object			Skeleton				Time
Object	Vertices	Edges	Facets	Vertices	Edges	Faces	Cells	(Sec.)
Objects								
(a)	12	20	10	8	24	25	10	0.312
(b)	20	30	12	25	60	46	12	0.719
(c)	28	42	16	45	104	74	16	0.567
(d)	20	30	12	16	42	37	12	0.188
(e)	20	18	9 (+1 hole)	15	45	56	9	0.250
(f)	12	18	10	21	48	37	10	0.484
(g)	16	24	11	6	21	25	11	0.177
(h)	16	24	11	12	36	33	11	0.146
(i)	16	24	10	12	32	29	10	0.172

(j) Statistics and running times

Fig. 6. Sample objects

spike. In addition, new spikes and ridges can be created when events are processed, and they have to be tested against all other features of their propagating component. Since $O(1)$ vertices and edges are created in every event, every event can take $O(n)$ time to handle. (The time needed to perform queue operations per a single event, $O(\log n)$, is negligible.) The total time needed for processing the events is, thus, $O(kn)$. This is also the total running time.

We have implemented the algorithm for computing the straight skeleton of a general polyhedron in Visual C++ .NET2005, and experimented with the software on a 3GHz Athlon 64 processor PC with 1GB of RAM. We used the CGAL library to perform basic geometric operations. The source code consists of about 6,500 lines of code. Fig. 6 shows the straight skeletons of a few simple objects, and the performance of our implementation.

References

1. Aichholzer, O., Aurenhammer, F.: Straight skeletons for general polygonal figures in the plane. In: Cai, J.-Y., Wong, C.K. (eds.) COCOON 1996. LNCS, vol. 1090, pp. 117–126. Springer, Heidelberg (1996)
2. Aichholzer, O., Aurenhammer, F., Alberts, D., Gärtner, B.: A novel type of skeleton for polygons. J. of Universal Computer Science 1(12), 752–761 (1995)
3. Barequet, G., Goodrich, M.T., Levi-Steiner, A., Steiner, D.: Contour interpolation by straight skeletons. Graphical Models 66(4), 245–260 (2004)
4. Bittar, E., Tsingos, N., Gascuel, M.-P.: Automatic reconstruction of unstructured 3D data: Combining a medial axis and implicit surfaces. Computer Graphics Forum 14(3), 457–468 (1995)
5. Blum, H.: A transformation for extracting new descriptors of shape. In: Wathen-Dunn, W. (ed.) Models for the Perception of Speech and Visual Form, pp. 362–380. MIT Press, Cambridge (1967)
6. Cheng, S.-W., Vigneron, A.: Motorcycle graphs and straight skeletons. In: Proc. 13th Ann. ACM-SIAM Symp. on Discrete Algorithms, pp. 156–165 (January 2002)
7. Culver, T., Keyser, J., Manocha, D.: Accurate computation of the medial axis of a polyhedron. In: Proc. 5th ACM Symp. on Solid Modeling and Applications, New York, NY, pp. 179–190 (1999)
8. Demaine, E.D., Demaine, M.L., Lindy, J.F., Souvaine, D.L.: Hinged dissection of polypolyhedra. In: Dehne, F., López-Ortiz, A., Sack, J.-R. (eds.) WADS 2005. LNCS, vol. 3608, pp. 205–217. Springer, Heidelberg (2005)
9. Demaine, E.D., Demaine, M.L., Lubiw, A.: Folding and cutting paper. In: Akiyama, J., Kano, M., Urabe, M. (eds.) JCDCG 1998. LNCS, vol. 1763, pp. 104–118. Springer, Heidelberg (2000)
10. Dey, T.K., Zhao, W.: Approximate medial axis as a Voronoi subcomplex. Computer-Aided Design 36, 195–202 (2004)
11. Eppstein, D.: Dynamic Euclidean minimum spanning trees and extrema of binary functions. Discrete & Computational Geometry 13, 111–122 (1995)
12. Eppstein, D.: Fast hierarchical clustering and other applications of dynamic closest pairs. ACM J. Experimental Algorithmics 5(1), 1–23 (2000)
13. Eppstein, D., Erickson, J.: Raising roofs, crashing cycles, and playing pool: Applications of a data structure for finding pairwise interactions. Discrete & Computational Geometry 22(4), 569–592 (1999)

14. Foskey, M., Lin, M.C., Manocha, D.: Efficient computation of a simplified medial axis. J. of Computing and Information Science in Engineering 3(4), 274–284 (2003)
15. Haunert, J.-H., Sester, M.: Using the straight skeleton for generalisation in a multiple representation environment. In: ICA Workshop on Generalisation and Multiple Representation (2004)
16. Held, M.: On computing Voronoi diagrams of convex polyhedra by means of wavefront propagation. In: Proc. 6th Canadian Conf. on Computational Geometry, pp. 128–133 (August 1994)
17. Price, M.A., Armstrong, C.G., Sabin, M.A.: Hexahedral mesh generation by medial surface subdivision: Part I. Solids with convex edges. Int. J. for Numerical Methods in Engineering 38(19), 3335–3359 (1995)
18. Sharir, M.: Almost tight upper bounds for lower envelopes in higher dimensions. Discrete & Computational Geometry 12, 327–345 (1994)
19. Sheehy, D.J., Armstrong, C.G., Robinson, D.J.: Shape description by medial surface construction. IEEE Trans. on Visualization and Computer Graphics 2(1), 62–72 (1996)
20. Sherbrooke, E.C., Patrikalakis, N.M., Brisson, E.: An algorithm for the medial axis transform of 3d polyhedral solids. IEEE Trans. on Visualization and Computer Graphics 2(1), 45–61 (1996)
21. Tănase, M., Veltkamp, R.C.: Polygon decomposition based on the straight line skeleton. In: Proc. 19th Ann. ACM Symp. on Computational Geometry, pp. 58–67 (June 2003)
22. Wiernik, A., Sharir, M.: Planar realizations of nonlinear Davenport-Schinzel sequences by segments. Discrete & Computational Geometry 3, 15–47 (1988)

Randomized Competitive Analysis for Two-Server Problems

Wolfgang Bein[1], Kazuo Iwama[2], and Jun Kawahara[2]

[1] Center for the Advanced Study of Algorithms, School of Computer Science,
University of Nevada, Las Vegas, Nevada 89154, USA[*]
bein@cs.unlv.edu
[2] School of Informatics, Kyoto University,
Kyoto 606-8501, Japan
iwama@kuis.kyoto-u.ac.jp, jkawahara@kuis.kyoto-u.ac.jp

Abstract. We prove that there exits a randomized online algorithm for
the 2-server 3-point problem whose expected competitive ratio is at most
1.5897. This is the first nontrivial upper bound for randomized k-server
algorithms in a general metric space whose competitive ratio is well below
the corresponding deterministic lower bound ($= 2$ in the 2-server case).

1   Introduction

The k-server problem, introduced by Manasse, McGeoch and Sleator [20], is one
of the most fundamental online problems. In this problem the input is given as k
initial server positions and a sequence $p_1, p_2, \cdots$ of requests in the Euclidean space,
or more generally in any metric space. For each request p_i, the online player has to
select, without any knowledge of future requests, one of the k servers and to move
it to p_i. The goal is to minimize the total moving distance of the servers.

The k-server problem is widely considered instructive to the understanding of
online problems in general, yet, there are only scattered results. The most notable
open problem is perhaps the k-server conjecture, which states that the k-server
problem is k-competitive. The conjecture remains open for $k \geq 3$, despite years
of effort by many researchers; it is solved for a very few special cases, and remains
open even for 3 servers when the metric space has more than 6-points.

In the randomized case, even less is known. One of the the most daunting
problems in online algorithms is to determine the exact randomized competitiveness of the k-server problem, that is, the minimum competitiveness of any
randomized online algorithm for the server problem. Even in the case $k = 2$ it is
not known whether its competitiveness is lower than 2, the known value of the
deterministic competitiveness. This is surprising, since it seems intuitive that
randomization should help. It should be noted that generally randomization is
quite powerful for online problems, since it obviously reduces the power of the
adversary (see our paragraph "Related Work" below). Such seems to be the case
for the 2-server problem as well.

---

[*] Research of the first author (Bein) done while visiting Kyoto University as Kyoto
University Visiting Professor.

D. Halperin and K. Mehlhorn (Eds.): ESA 2008, LNCS 5193, pp. 161–172, 2008.

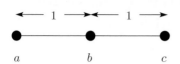

Fig. 1. 3 points on a line

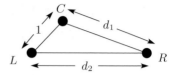

Fig. 2. Triangle CLR

The following example illustrates this intuition. Consider a simple 2-server problem on the three fixed points a, b and c on a line (See Fig. 1). It is easy to prove a lower bound of 2 for the competitive ratio of any deterministic algorithm: The adversary always gives a request on the point the server is missing. Thus for any online algorithm, $\mathcal{A}$, its total cost is at least n – the number of request. But it turns out by a simple case analysis that the offline cost is $n/2$.

Suppose instead that $\mathcal{A}$ is randomized. Now if the request comes on b (with missing server), then $\mathcal{A}$ can decide by a coin flip which server (a or c) to move. An (oblivious) adversary knows $\mathcal{A}$'s algorithm completely but does not know the result of the coin flip and hence cannot determine which point (a or c) has the server missing in the next step. The adversary would make the next request on a but this time a has a server with probability $1/2$ and $\mathcal{A}$ can reduce its cost. Without giving details, it is not hard to show that this algorithm $\mathcal{A}$ – with the randomized action for a request to b and a greedy action one for others – has a competitive ratio of 1.5.

Indeed, one would imagine that it might be quite straightforward to design randomized algorithms which perform significantly better than deterministic ones for the 2-server problem. A bit surprisingly, this has not been the case. Only few special cases have yielded success. Bartal, Chrobak, and Larmore gave a randomized algorithm for the 2-server problem on the line, whose competitive ratio is slightly better than 2 ($\frac{155}{78} \approx 1.987$) [3]. One other result by Bein et. al. [4] uses a novel technique, the knowledge state method, to derive a $\frac{19}{12}$ competitive randomized algorithm for the special case of Cross Polytope Spaces. Using similar techniques a new result for paging (the k-server problem in uniform spaces) was recently obtained. Bein et al. [5] gave an H_k-competitive randomized algorithm which requires only $O(k)$ memory for k-paging. (Though the techniques in this paper are inspired by this work, the knowledge state method is not used here.) Lund and Reingold showed that if specific three positions are given, then an optimal randomized algorithm for the 2-server problem over those three points can be derived in principle by using linear programming [19]. However, they do not give actual values of its competitive ratio and to this date the problem is still open even for the 2-server 3-points case.

Our Contribution. In this paper, we prove that the randomized competitive ratio of the 2-server 3-point problem in a general metric space is at most 1.5897 and also give a strong conjecture that it is at most $e/(e-1) + \varepsilon \approx 1.5819$.

The underlying idea is to find a finite set S of triangles (i.e. three points) such that if the expected competitive ratio (abbreviated by ECR) for each triangle in S is at most c, then the ECR for all triangles in any metric space is at most $c \cdot \delta(S)$ where $\delta(S) \geq 1$ is a value determined by S. To bound the ECR for each triangle in S, we apply linear programming. As we consider larger sets, the value of $\delta(S)$ becomes smaller and approaches 1. Thus the upper bound of the general ECR also approaches the maximum ECR of triangles in S and we can obtain arbitrarily close upper bounds by increasing the size of the computation.

Related Work. As for the (deterministic) k-server conjecture, the current best upper bound is $2k-1$ given by Koutsoupias and Papadimitriou in 1994 [18]. The conjecture is true for $k = 2$, for the line [7], trees [8], and on fixed $k+1$ or $k+2$ points [17]. It is still open for the 3-server problem on more than six points and also on the circle [6]. The lower bound is k which is shown in the original paper [20]. For the randomized case, in addition to the papers mentioned above, Bartal et al. [2] have an asymptotic lower bound, namely that the competitiveness of any randomized online algorithm for an arbitrary metric space is $\Omega(\log k / \log^2 \log k)$. Chrobak et. al. [10] provided a lower bound of $1 + e^{-\frac{1}{2}} \approx 1.6065$ for the ECR of the 2-server problem in general spaces. For special cases, see for example, [15] for ski-rental problems, [21] for list access problems, and [12] for paging.

Our result in this paper strongly depends on computer simulations similar to earlier work based on knowledge states. Indeed, there are several successful examples of such an approach, which usually consists of two stages; (i) reducing infinitely many cases of a mathematical proof to finitely many cases (where this number is still too large for a "standard proof") and (ii) using computer programs to prove the finitely many cases. See [1,11,13,16,23] for design and analysis of such algorithms. In particular, for online competitive analysis, Seiden proved the currently best upper bound, 1.5889, for online bin-packing [22]. Also by this approach, [14] obtained an optimal competitive ratio for the online knapsack problem with resource augmentation by buffer bins.

2   Our Approach

Since we consider only three fixed points, we can assume without loss of generality that they are given in the two-dimensional Euclidean space. The three points are denoted by L, C and R, furthermore let $d(C, L) = 1$, $d(C, R) = d_1$, and $d(L, R) = d_2$ (see Fig. 2). Again without loss of generality, we assume that $1 \leq d_1 \leq d_2 \leq d_1 + 1$. The 2-server problem on L, C and R is denoted by $\Delta(1, d_1, d_2)$, where the two servers are on L and R initially and the input is given as a sequence σ of points $\in \{L, C, R\}$. $\Delta(1, d_1, d_2)$ is also used to denote the triangle itself. The cost of an online algorithm $\mathcal{A}$ for the input sequence σ is denoted by $ALG_{\mathcal{A}}(\sigma)$ and the cost of the offline algorithm by $OPT(\sigma)$. Suppose that for some constant $\alpha \geq 0$, $E[ALG_{\mathcal{A}}(\sigma)] \leq r \cdot OPT(\sigma) + \alpha$, holds for any input sequence σ. Then we say that the ECR of $\mathcal{A}$ is at most r.

We first consider the case that the three points are on a line and both d_1 and d_2 are integers. In this case, we can design a general online algorithm as follows. The proof is given in the next section.

Lemma 1. *Let n be a positive integer. Then there exists an online algorithm for $\Delta(1, n, n+1)$ whose ECR is at most $C_n = \frac{(1+\frac{1}{n})^n - \frac{1}{n+1}}{(1+\frac{1}{n})^n - 1}$.*

Note that if triangles Δ_1 and Δ_2 are different, then "good" algorithms for Δ_1 and Δ_2 are also different. However, the next lemma says that if Δ_1 and Δ_2 do not differ too much, then one can use an algorithm for Δ_1 as an algorithm for Δ_2 with a small sacrifice on the competitive ratio.

Lemma 2. *Suppose that there are two triangles $\Delta_1 = \Delta(1, a_1, b_1)$ and $\Delta_2 = \Delta(1, a_2, b_2)$ such that $a_1 \geq a_2$ and $b_1 \geq b_2$ and that the ECR of algorithm $\mathcal{A}$ for Δ_1 is at most r. Then the ECR of $\mathcal{A}$ for Δ_2 is at most $r \cdot \max(\frac{a_1}{a_2}, \frac{b_1}{b_2})$.*

Proof. Let $\alpha = \max(\frac{a_1}{a_2}, \frac{b_1}{b_2})$ and $\Delta_\alpha = \Delta(1/\alpha, a_1/\alpha, b_1/\alpha)$. Fix an arbitrary input sequence σ and let the optimal offline cost against σ be OPT_1, OPT_2 and OPT_α for Δ_1, Δ_2 and Δ_α, respectively. Since Δ_α is similar to Δ_1 and the length of each side is $1/\alpha$, OPT_α is obviously $(1/\alpha)OPT_1$. Since every side of Δ_2 is at least as long as the corresponding side of Δ_α, $OPT_2 \geq OPT_\alpha = (1/\alpha)OPT_1$.

Let the expected cost of $\mathcal{A}$ against σ for Δ_1 and Δ_2 be ALG_1 and ALG_2, respectively. Note that $\mathcal{A}$ moves the servers exactly in the same (randomized) way for Δ_1 and Δ_2. Since each side of Δ_2 is at most as long as the corresponding side of Δ_1, $ALG_2 \leq ALG_1$.

We have $\frac{ALG_2}{OPT_2} \leq \frac{ALG_1}{(1/\alpha)OPT_1} = \max(\frac{a_1}{a_2}, \frac{b_1}{b_2}) \cdot \frac{ALG_1}{OPT_1}$. $\square$

Thus we can "approximate" all triangles, whose α-value is at most within some constant, by a finite set S of triangles as follows: Suppose that the target competitive ratio, i.e. the competitive ratio one wishes to achieve, is r_0. Then we first calculate the minimum integer n_0 such that $r_0 \geq \frac{n_0+2}{n_0} \cdot C_{n_0+1}$, where C_{n_0+1} is the value given in the statement of Lemma 1. We then construct the set S such that for any two numbers a and b with $1 \leq a \leq n_0$ and $b \leq a + 1$, there exist two triangles $\Delta_1 = \Delta(1, a_1, b_1)$ and $\Delta_2 = \Delta(1, a_2, b_2)$ in S such that the following conditions are met:

(i) $a_2 < a \leq a_1$ and $b_2 < b \leq b_1$,
(ii) there exists an algorithm for Δ_1 whose ECR is r_1, and
(iii) $r_1 \cdot \max(\frac{a_1}{a_2}, \frac{b_1}{b_2}) \leq r_0$.

We call such a set an "approximation set".

Lemma 3. *If one can construct an approximation set S, then there is an online algorithm whose ECR is at most r_0.*

Proof. Consider the following algorithm $\mathcal{A}(a, b)$ which takes the values a and b of the triangle $\Delta(1, a, b)$. Note that $\mathcal{A}(a, b)$ is an infinite set of different algorithms from which we select one due to the values of a and b. If $a \geq n_0$, then we select the maximum integer n such that $a \geq n$. Then $\mathcal{A}(a, b)$ uses the algorithm for $\Delta(1, n+1, n+2)$. Clearly we have $a \leq n+1$ and $b \leq n+2$. Therefore, by Lemma 2, the ECR of this algorithm for $\Delta(1, a, b)$ is at most (recall that C_{n+1} is the ECR of this algorithm for $\Delta(1, n+1, n+2)$ given in Lemma 1)

$$\max(\frac{n+1}{a}, \frac{n+2}{b}) \cdot C_{n+1} \leq \frac{n+2}{n} \cdot C_{n+1} \leq \frac{n_0+2}{n_0} \cdot C_{n_0+1} \leq r_0.$$

By a simple calculation we have that $\frac{n+2}{n} \cdot C_{n+1} = \frac{n+2}{n} \cdot \frac{\left(1+\frac{1}{n}\right)^n - \frac{1}{n+1}}{\left(1+\frac{1}{n}\right)^n - 1}$ monotonically decreases, which implies the inequality second to last.

If $a < n_0$, then we have the two triangles Δ_1 and Δ_2 satisfying the conditions (i) to (iii) above. Then we use the algorithm for Δ_1 guaranteed by condition (ii). Its ECR for $\Delta(1, a, b)$ is obviously at most r_0 by Lemma 2. □

3   Three Points on a Line

In order to prove Lemma 1, we first need a state diagram, called an *offset graph*, which shows the value of the work function $W(s, \sigma)$ [9]. Recall that $W(s, \sigma)$ is an optimal offline cost such that all the requests given by σ are served and the final state after σ must be s, where s is one of (L, C), (L, R) and (C, R) in our case.

Fig. 3 shows the offset graph, G_n^{OPT} for $\Delta(1, n, n + 1)$. Each state includes a triple (x, y, z), further explained next. In the figure, the top middle state, denoted by V_{LR}, is the initial state (recall that our initial server placement is (L, R)). This state includes $(n, 0, 1)$, which means that $W((L, C), \phi) = n$, $W((L, R), \phi) = 0$, and $W((C, R), \phi) = 1$. Those values are correct for the following reason: Since this is the initial state, we do not have any request yet, or the request sequence is empty (denoted by ϕ). Also since our initial server placement is (L, R), in order

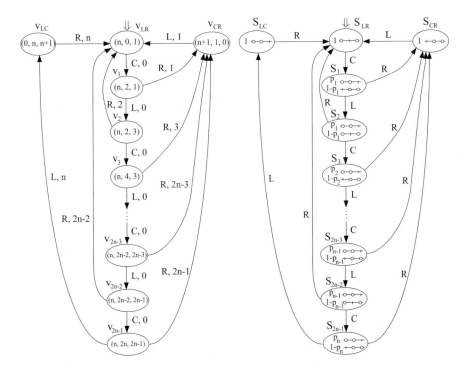

Fig. 3. Offset graph   **Fig. 4.** State diagram of the algorithm

to change this placement into (L, C), we can optimally move a server from R to C, which needs a cost of n. This is why $W((L, C), \phi) = n$. Similarly for the others.

In the figure, V_3 is the forth state from the top. The triple in this state shows the value of the work function for the request sequence CLC, i.e., $W((L, C), CLC)$, $W((L, R), CLC)$ and $W((C, R), CLC)$. Note that this request sequence, CLC, is obtained by concatenating the labels of arrows from the initial state V_{LR} to V_3. For example, Fig. 3 shows that $W((L, R), CLC) = 4$, which is calculated from the previous state, V_2, as follows: Namely, server position (L, R) can be achieved from previous (L, R) $(= 2)$ plus 2 $(=$ the cost of moving a server on L to C and back to L) or from previous (C, R) $(= 3)$ plus 1 $(=$ the cost of moving a server on C to L). Both are 4. From this state V_3, there is an arrow to V_{CR} by request R. Carrying out a similar calculation, one can see that the triple should change from $(n, 4, 3)$ to $(n+4, 4, 3)$ by this transition. However, the triple in V_{CR} is $(n + 1, 1, 0)$. The reason for this is that we have an offset value, 3, on the arrow from V_3 to V_{CR}. Namely, $(n + 1, 1, 0)$ in V_{CR} is obtained from $(n+4, 4, 3)$ by reducing each value by 3. Because of this offset values, we can use such a finite graph to represent the values of the work function the value of which can be infinitely large. Thus one can see that $(n, 0, 1)$ in the initial state V_{LR} also means $(n + 4, 4, 5), (n + 8, 8, 9), \cdots$ by traversing the cycle $V_{LR}V_1V_2V_3V_{CR}$ repeatedly. Although we omit a formal proof, it is not hard to verify that Fig. 3 is a valid offset graph for $\Delta(1, n, n + 1)$.

We next introduce another state graph, called the algorithm graph. Fig. 4 shows the algorithm graph, G_n^{ALG}, for $\Delta(1, n, n+1)$. Notice that G_n^{ALG} is similar to G_n^{OPT}. Each state includes a triple (q_1, q_2, q_3) such that $q_1 \geq 0, q_2 \geq 0, q_3 \geq 0$ and $q_1 + q_2 + q_3 = 1$, which means that the probabilities of placements (C, L), (L, R) and (C, R) are q_1, q_2 and q_3, respectively. (Since the most recent request must be served, one of the three values is zero. In the figure, therefore, only two probabilities are given, for example, in S_1, the probabilities for $(L, C)(= p_1)$ and for $(C, R)(= 1 - p_1)$ are given.) In our specific algorithm G_n^{ALG}, set those values as follows:

$$S_{LC} = (1, 0, 0), \; S_{LR} = (0, 1, 0), \; S_{CR} = (0, 0, 1),$$
$$S_{2i-1} = (p_i, 0, 1 - p_i) \; (i = 1, \ldots, n), \quad S_{2i} = (p_i, 1 - p_i, 0) \; (i = 1, \ldots, n - 1)$$
where p_i is $\frac{n}{n+1} \cdot \frac{(1+\frac{1}{n})^i - 1}{(1+\frac{1}{n})^n - 1}$.

We describe how an algorithm graph is converted to the specific algorithm. Namely we can calculate how to move servers and its average cost as follows: Suppose for example that the request sequence is CL. Then we are now in S_2, and suppose that the next request is C. The state transition from S_2 to S_3 occurs. Suppose that S_2 has placement-probability pairs (C_1, q_1), (C_2, q_2), and (C_3, q_3) $(C_1 = (L, C), C_2 = (L, R)$ and $C_3 = (C, R))$ and S_3 has (D_1, r_1), (D_2, r_2), and (D_3, r_3). We introduce variables x_{ij} $(i, j = 1, 2, 3)$ such that x_{ij} is equal to the probability that the placement before the transition is C_i and the placement after the transition is D_j. By an abuse of notation the x_{ij} values can be considered as the algorithm itself. The x_{ij} values also allow us to calculate the average cost of the algorithm as described next.

The average cost for a transition is given by $cost = \sum_{i=1}^{3} \sum_{j=1}^{3} x_{ij} d(C_i, D_j)$, where $d(C_i, D_j)$ is the cost to change the placement from C_i to D_j. We can select the values of x_{ij} in such a way that they minimize the above cost under the condition that $\sum_{j=1}^{3} x_{ij} = q_i$, $\sum_{i=1}^{3} x_{ij} = r_j$. In the case of three points on the line, it is straightforward to solve this LP in general. If the servers are on L and C and the request is R, then the greedy move $(C \to R)$ is optimal. If the servers are on L and R and the request is C, then the optimal probability is just a proportional distribution due to $d(L, C)$ and $d(C, R)$. These values x_{ij} also show the actual moves of the servers. For example, if the servers are on L and R in S_2, we move a server in L to C with probability x_{23}/q_2 and R to C with probability x_{21}/q_2.

From the values of x_{ij}, one can also obtain the expected cost of an algorithm for each transition, given as follows:

$\text{cost}(S_{LC}, S_{LR}) = n$, $\text{cost}(S_{CR}, S_{LR}) = 1$, $\text{cost}(S_{LR}, S_1) = np_1 + 1 - p_1$,
$\text{cost}(S_{2i-1}, S_{2i}) = 1 - p_i$ $(i = 1, \ldots, n-1)$,
$\text{cost}(S_{2i}, S_{2i+1}) = n(p_{i+1} - p_i) + 1 - p_{i+1}$ $(i = 1, \ldots, n-1)$,
$\text{cost}(S_{2i-1}, S_{CR}) = (n+1)p_i$ $(i = 1, \ldots, n)$,
$\text{cost}(S_{2i}, S_{LR}) = np_i$ $(i = 1, \ldots, n-1)$,
$\text{cost}(S_{2n-1}, S_{LC}) = (n+1)(1 - p_n)$.

We are now ready to prove Lemma 1. Recall that G_n^{OPT} and G_n^{ALG} are the same graph. With a request sequence σ, we can thus associate a same sequence, $\lambda(\sigma)$, of transitions in G_n^{OPT} and G_n^{ALG}. The offline cost for $\lambda(\sigma)$ can be calculated from G_n^{OPT} and the average online cost from G_n^{ALG}. By comparing these two costs, we have the ECR for σ.

Omitting details we can prove that it suffices to consider only the following three sequences (cycles) for this purpose:

(1) $S_1, S_2, \ldots, S_{2h-1}, S_{CR}, S_{LR}$ $(h = 1, \ldots, n-1)$
(2) $S_1, S_2, \ldots, S_{2h}, S_{LR}$ $(h = 1, \ldots, n-1)$
(3) $S_1, S_2, \ldots, S_{2n-1}, S_{LC}, S_{LR}$.

For sequence (1), the OPT cost is $2h$ and ALG cost is $2np_h + 2h - 2\sum_{j=1}^{h-1} p_j = 2hC_n$. Similarly, for sequence (2), $OPT = 2h$ and $ALG < 2hC_n$ and for sequence (3) $OPT = 2n$ and $ALG = 4n - 2\sum_{j=1}^{n} p_j = 2nC_n$. Thus the ECR is at most C_n for any of these sequences, which proves the lemma. $\qquad \square$

4 Construction of the Finite Set of Triangles

For triangle $\Delta_1 = \Delta(1, a, b)$ and $d > 0$, let $\Delta_2 = \Delta(1, a', b')$ be any triangle such that $a - d \le a' \le a$ and $b - d \le b' \le b$. Then as shown in Sec. 2 the ECR for Δ_2, denoted by $f(\Delta_2)$, can be written as

$$f(\Delta_2) \le \max\left(\frac{a}{a'}, \frac{b}{b'}\right) f(\Delta_1) \le \max\left(\frac{a}{a-d}, \frac{b}{b-d}\right) f(\Delta_1) \le \frac{a}{a-d} f(\Delta_1).$$

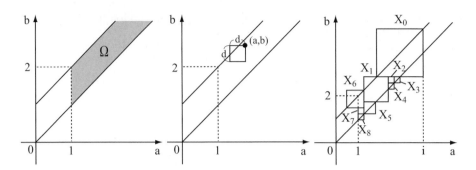

Fig. 5. Area Ω **Fig. 6.** Square $[a, b; d]$ **Fig. 7.** Set of squares

(The last inequality comes the fact that $a \le b$.) Recall that triangle $\Delta(1, a, b)$ always satisfies $1 \le a \le b \le a+1$, which means that (a, b) is in the area Ω shown in Fig. 5. Consider point (a, b) in this area and the square X of size d, whose right upper corner is (a, b) (Fig. 6). Such a square is also denoted by $[a, b; d]$. Then for any triangle whose (a, b)-values are within this square (some portion of it may be outside Ω), its ECR can be bounded by $\frac{a}{a-d} f(\Delta(1, a, b))$, which we call the competitive ratio of the square X and denote by $g(X)$ or $g([a, b; d])$.

Consider a finite set of squares $X_0, X_1, \ldots, X_i = [a_i, b_i; d_i], \ldots, X_m$ with the following properties (see also Fig. 7):

(1) The right-upper corners of all the squares are in Ω.
(2) X_0 is the rightmost square, which must be $[i, i+1, 2]$ for some i.
(3) The area of Ω between $a = 1$ and i must be covered by those squares, or any point (a, b) in Ω such that $1 \le a \le i$ must be in some square.

Suppose that all the values of $g(X_i)$ for $0 \le i \le m$ are at most r_0. Then one can easily see that the set $S = \bigcup_{i=0,m} \{\Delta(1, a_i, b_i), \Delta(1, a_i - d_i, b_i - d_i)\}$ of triangles satisfies conditions (i) to (iii) given in Sec. 2, i.e., we have obtained the algorithm whose competitive ratio is at most r_0.

The issue is how to generate those squares efficiently. Note that $g(X)$ becomes smaller if the size d of the square X becomes smaller. Namely we can subdivide each square into smaller ones to obtain a better competitive ratio. However, it is not clever to subdivide all squares evenly since $g(X)$ for a square X of the same size substantially differs in different positions in Ω. Note the phenomenon especially between positions close to the origin (i.e., both a and b are small) and those far from the origin (the former is larger). Thus our approach is to subdivide squares X dynamically, or to divide the one with the largest $g(X)$ value in each step.

We give an intuitive description of the procedure for generating the squares. We start with a single square $[2, 3; 2]$. Of course, its g-value is poor (indeed becomes infinite) and we divide $[2, 3; 2]$ into four half-sized squares as shown in Fig. 8: $[1, 3; 1], [1, 2; 1], [2, 2; 1]$ and $[2, 3; 1]$ of size one. Simultaneously we introduce square $[3, 4; 2]$ of size 2. In general, if the square $[i, i+1; 2]$ of size 2 is divided

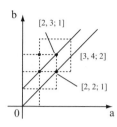

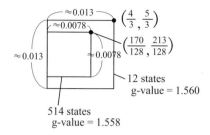

Fig. 8. Division of a square   **Fig. 9.** Approximation of a square

and $[i+1, i+2; 2]$ of size 2 does not exists yet, we introduce $[i+1, i+2; 2]$. By this we can always satisfy the condition (2). Thus we have four squares of size 1 (two of them are indeed outside Ω) and one square of size 2 at this stage. In the next step we divide again one of the three squares (inside Ω) whose g value is the worst. Continue this and take the worst g-value as an upper bound of the competitive ratio.

Thus the squares are becoming progressively smaller (as might the maximum g-value). An issue regarding the efficiency of the procedure is that the number of states of the state diagram used by the algorithm for a (small) square (or for the corresponding triangle) becomes large. This implies a large amount of computation time to solve the LP in order to obtain the algorithm for the square in question and to obtain its competitive ratio. Consider for example the triangle $(1, \frac{170}{128}, \frac{213}{128})$ (or the square $[\frac{170}{128}, \frac{213}{128}; \frac{1}{128}]$). It turns out that we need 514 states for the diagram (and a substantial computation time for LP solving. However, note that we have slightly larger triangle, $(1, \frac{4}{3}, \frac{5}{3})$ (or the square $[\frac{4}{3}, \frac{5}{3}; \frac{5}{384}]$), which only needs 12 states to solve the LP (Fig. 9). Thus we can save computation time by using $[\frac{4}{3}, \frac{5}{3}; \frac{5}{384}]$ instead of $[\frac{170}{128}, \frac{213}{128}; \frac{1}{128}]$ and the g-value of the former $(= 1.5606)$, which is certainly worse than that of the latter $(= 1.5549)$, is not excessively bad. Although we do not have an exact relation between the triangle and the number of states, it is very likely that if the ratio of the three sides of the triangle can be represented by three small integers then the number of states is also small. In our procedure, therefore, we do not simply calculate $g(X)$ for a square X, but we try to find X' which contains X and has such desirable properties.

Procedure 1 gives the formal description of our procedure. Each square $X = [a, b; d]$ is represented by $p = (a, b, d, r)$, where r is an upper bound of $g(X)$. The main procedure SQUAREGENERATION divides the square, whose g value is the worst, into four half-sized squares and, if necessary, also creates a new rightmost square of size 2. Then we calculate the g-values of those new squares by procedure CALCULATECR. However, as described before, we try to find a "better" square. Suppose that the current square is $X = [a, b; d]$. Then we want to find $\tilde{X} = [\tilde{a}, \tilde{b}; \tilde{d}]$ which contains X and $\tilde{a}$ can be represented by $\frac{\beta}{\alpha}$, where both α and β are integers and α is at most 31 (similarly for $\tilde{b}$). (We have confirmed that the number of states and the computation time for the LP are reasonably small if α is at most this large). To do this we use procedure FINDAPPROXPOINT. Note that we scan the value of α only from 17 to 31. This is sufficient; for example, $\alpha = 10$ can be covered by $\alpha = 20$ and $\alpha = 16$ is not needed either since it should have been calculated previously in the course of subdivision. If $g(\tilde{X})$ is smaller than the g-value of the original (double-sized) square, then we use that value as the g-value of X. Otherwise we abandon such an approximation and calculate $g(X)$ directly.

Now suppose that SQUAREGENERATION has terminated. Then for any $p = (a, b, d, r)$ in P, it is guaranteed that $r \leq R_0$. This means that we have created the set of squares which satisfy the conditions (1) to (3) previously given. As mentioned there, we have also created the set of triangles satisfying the conditions of Sec. 2. Thus by Lemma 3, we can conclude:

Theorem 1. *There is an online algorithm for the 2-server 3-point problem whose competitive ratio is at most R_0.*

We now give results of our computer experiments: For the whole area Ω, the current upper bound is 1.5897 (recall that the conjecture is 1.5819). The number N of squares generated is 13285, in which the size m of smallest squares is $1/256$ and the size M of largest squares is 2. We also conducted experiments for small subareas of Ω: (1) For $[5/4, 7/4, 1/16]$: The upper bound is 1.5784 (better than the conjecture but this is not a contradiction since our triangles are restricted). $(N, M, m) = (69, 1/64, 1/128)$. (2) For $[7/4, 9/4, 1/4]$: The upper bound is 1.5825. $(N, M, m) = (555, 1/64, 1/2048)$. (3) For $[10, 11, 1]$: The upper bound is 1.5887. $(N, M, m) = (135, 1/16, 1/32)$.

5   Concluding Remarks

There are at least two directions for the future research: The first one is to prove that the ECR of the 2-server 3-point problem is analytically at most $e/(e-1)+\varepsilon$. The second one is to extend our current approach (i.e., approximation of infinite point locations by finite ones) to four and move points. For the latter, we already have a partial result for the 4-point case where two of the four points are close (obviously it is similar to the 3-point case), but the generalization does not appear easy.

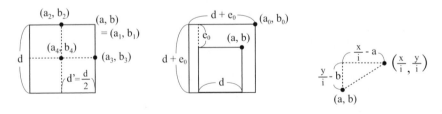

Fig. 10. Lines 9-13   **Fig. 11.** Line 27   **Fig. 12.** Lines 40-47

Procedure 1. SquareGeneration

procedure SquareGeneration(R_0)
  $p \leftarrow (2, 3, 2, C_2 \cdot 2/(2-2) = \infty)$
  Mark p.
  $P \leftarrow \{p\}$
  while $\exists p = (a, b, d, r)$ such that $r > R_0$
    $p \leftarrow$ the point in P whose r is maximum.
    $P \leftarrow P \backslash \{p\}$
    Let $p = (a, b, d, r)$
    $d' \leftarrow d/2$
    $a_1 \leftarrow a,\ b_1 \leftarrow b$
    $a_2 \leftarrow a - d',\ b_2 \leftarrow b$
    $a_3 \leftarrow a,\ b_3 \leftarrow b - d'$
    $a_4 \leftarrow a - d',\ b_4 \leftarrow b - d'$ $\triangleright$ See Fig. 10.
    for $i \leftarrow 1$ **to** 4
      if $(a_i, b_i) \in \Omega$
        $r_i \leftarrow$ CALCULATECR(a_i, b_i, d', r)
        $P \leftarrow P \cup \{(a_i, b_i, d', r_i)\}$
      end if
    end for
    if p is marked
      $p' \leftarrow (a + 1, b + 1, 2, C_{a+1} \cdot a/(a - 2))$.
      Mark p'. Unmark p.
      $P \leftarrow P \cup \{p'\}$
    end if
  end while
end procedure

procedure CalculateCR(a, b, d, r)
  $(a_0, b_0) \leftarrow$ FINDAPPROXPOINT(a, b)
    $\triangleright$ See Fig. 11.
  $r_0 \leftarrow$ GETCR_FROMLP(a_0, b_0)
  $e_0 \leftarrow \max(a - a_0, b - b_0)$
  $\tilde{r}_0 \leftarrow r_0 \cdot a_0/(a_0 - d - e_0)$
  if $\tilde{r}_0 < r_0$
    return $\tilde{r}_0$
  else
    $r_0 \leftarrow$ GETCR_FROMLP(a, b)
    $\tilde{r}_0 \leftarrow r_0 \cdot a_0/(a_0 - d)$
    return $\tilde{r}_0$
  end if
end procedure
procedure FindApproxPoint(a, b)
    $\triangleright$ See Fig. 12.
  $e_{min} \leftarrow \infty$
  for $i \leftarrow 31$ **to** 17
    $x \leftarrow \lceil a \cdot i \rceil,\ y \leftarrow \lceil b \cdot i \rceil$
    $e \leftarrow \max(x/i - a, y/i - b)$
    if $e < e_{min}$
      $e_{min} \leftarrow e,\ i_{min} \leftarrow i$
      $x_{min} \leftarrow x,\ y_{min} \leftarrow y$
    end if
  end for
  return $(x_{min}/i_{min}, y_{min}/i_{min})$
end procedure

References

1. Appel, K., Haken, W.: Every planar map is four colorable. Illinois Journal of Mathematics 21(5), 429–597 (1977)
2. Bartal, Y., Bollobas, B., Mendel, M.: A Ramsey-type theorem for metric spaces and its applications for metrical task systems and related problems. In: Proc. 42nd FOCS, pp. 396–405. IEEE, Los Alamitos (2001)
3. Bartal, Y., Chrobak, M., Larmore, L.L.: A randomized algorithm for two servers on the line. In: Bilardi, G., Pietracaprina, A., Italiano, G.F., Pucci, G. (eds.) ESA 1998. LNCS, vol. 1461, pp. 247–258. Springer, Heidelberg (1998)
4. Bein, W., Iwama, K., Kawahara, J., Larmore, L.L., Oravec, J.A.: A randomized algorithm for two servers in cross polytope spaces. In: Kaklamanis, C., Skutella, M. (eds.) WAOA 2007. LNCS, vol. 4927, pp. 246–259. Springer, Heidelberg (2008)
5. Bein, W., Larmore, L.L., Noga, J.: Equitable revisited. In: Arge, L., Hoffmann, M., Welzl, E. (eds.) ESA 2007. LNCS, vol. 4698, pp. 419–426. Springer, Heidelberg (2007)

6. Bein, W., Chrobak, M., Larmore, L.L.: The 3-server problem in the plane. In: Nešetřil, J. (ed.) ESA 1999. LNCS, vol. 1643, pp. 301–312. Springer, Heidelberg (1999)
7. Chrobak, M., Karloff, H., Payne, T.H., Vishwanathan, S.: New results on server problems. SIAM J. Discrete Math. 4, 172–181 (1991)
8. Chrobak, M., Larmore, L.L.: An optimal online algorithm for k servers on trees. SIAM J. Comput. 20, 144–148 (1991)
9. Chrobak, M., Larmore, L.L.: The server problem and on-line games. In: McGeoch, L.A., Sleator, D.D. (eds.) On-line Algorithms. DIMACS Series in Discrete Mathematics and Theoretical Computer Science, vol. 7, pp. 11–64. AMS/ACM (1992)
10. Chrobak, M., Larmore, L.L., Lund, C., Reingold, N.: A better lower bound on the competitive ratio of the randomized 2-server problem. Inform. Process. Lett. 63, 79–83 (1997)
11. Feige, U., Goemans, M.X.: Approximating the value of two prover proof systems, with applications to max-2sat and max-dicut. In: Proc. 3rd ISTCS, pp. 182–189 (1995)
12. Fiat, A., Karp, R., Luby, M., McGeoch, L.A., Sleator, D., Young, N.E.: Competitive paging algorithms. J. Algorithms 12, 685–699 (1991)
13. Goemans, M.X., Williamson, D.P.: Improved approximation algorithms for maximum cut and satisfiability problems using semidefinite programming. J. ACM 42(6), 1115–1145 (1995)
14. Horiyama, T., Iwama, K., Kawahara, J.: Finite-state online algorithms and their automated competitive analysis. In: Asano, T. (ed.) ISAAC 2006. LNCS, vol. 4288, pp. 71–80. Springer, Heidelberg (2006)
15. Karlin, A.R., Kenyon, C., Randall, D.: Dynamic tcp acknowledgement and other stories about $e/(e-1)$. In: Proc. 33rd STOC, pp. 502–509. ACM, New York (2001)
16. Karloff, H., Zwick, U.: A 7/8-approximation algorithm for max 3sat. In: Proc. 38th FOCS, pp. 406–417. IEEE, Los Alamitos (1997)
17. Koutsoupias, E., Papadimitriou, C.: Beyond competitive analysis. In: Proc. 35th FOCS, pp. 394–400. IEEE, Los Alamitos (1994)
18. Koutsoupias, E., Papadimitriou, C.: On the k-server conjecture. J. ACM 42, 971–983 (1995)
19. Lund, C., Reingold, N.: Linear programs for randomized on-line algorithms. In: Proc. 5th SODA, pp. 382–391. ACM/SIAM (1994)
20. Manasse, M., McGeoch, L.A., Sleator, D.: Competitive algorithms for server problems. J. Algorithms 11, 208–230 (1990)
21. Reingold, N., Westbrook, J., Sleator, D.D.: Randomized competitive algorithms for the list update problem. Algorithmica 11, 15–32 (1994)
22. Seiden, S.S.: On the online bin packing problem. J. ACM 49(5), 640–671 (2002)
23. Trevisan, L., Sorkin, G.B., Sudan, M., Williamson, D.P.: Gadgets, approximation, and linear programming. SIAM J. Comput. 29(6), 2074–2097 (2000)

Decompositions and Boundary Coverings of Non-convex Fat Polyhedra*

Mark de Berg and Chris Gray

Department of Computing Science, TU Eindhoven
{mdberg,cgray}@win.tue.nl

Abstract. We show that any locally-fat (or (α, β)-covered) polyhedron with convex fat faces can be decomposed into $O(n)$ tetrahedra, where n is the number of vertices of the polyhedron. We also show that the restriction that the faces are fat is necessary: there are locally-fat polyhedra with non-fat faces that require $\Omega(n^2)$ pieces in any convex decomposition. Furthermore, we show that if we want the polyhedra in the decomposition to be fat themselves, then the worst-case number of tetrahedra cannot be bounded as a function of n. Finally, we obtain several results on the problem where we want to only cover the boundary of the polyhedron, and not its entire interior.

1 Introduction

Polyhedra and their planar equivalent, polygons, play an important role in many geometric problems. From an algorithmic point of view, however, general polyhedra are unwieldy to handle directly: several algorithms can only handle *convex* polyhedra, preferably of *constant complexity*. Hence, there has been extensive research into decomposing polyhedra (or, more generally, arrangements of triangles) into tetrahedra or other constant-complexity convex pieces. The two main issues in developing decomposition algorithms are (i) to keep the number of pieces in the decomposition small, and (ii) to compute the decomposition quickly.

In the planar setting the number of pieces is, in fact, not an issue if the pieces should be triangles: any polygon admits a triangulation, and any triangulation of a polygon with n vertices has $n - 2$ triangles. Hence, research focused on developing fast triangulation algorithms, culminating in Chazelle's linear-time triangulation algorithm [12]. An extensive survey of algorithms for decomposing polygons and their applications is given by Keil [16].

For 3-dimensional polyhedra, however, the situation is much less rosy. First of all, not every non-convex polyhedron admits a tetrahedralization: there are polyhedra that cannot be decomposed into tetrahedra without using Steiner points. Moreover, deciding whether a polyhedron admits a tetrahedralization without Steiner points is NP-complete [18]. Thus we have to settle for decompositions using Steiner points. Chazelle [11] has shown that any polyhedron with n vertices can be

---

* This research was supported by the Netherlands' Organisation for Scientific Research (NWO) under project no. 639.023.301.

D. Halperin and K. Mehlhorn (Eds.): ESA 2008, LNCS 5193, pp. 173–184, 2008.

decomposed into $O(n^2)$ tetrahedra, and that this is tight in the worst case: there are polyhedra with n vertices for which any decomposition uses $\Omega(n^2)$ tetrahedra. (In fact, the result is even stronger: any *convex decomposition*—a decomposition into convex pieces—uses $\Omega(n^2)$ pieces, even if one allows pieces of non-constant complexity.) Since the complexity of algorithms that need a decomposition depends on the number of pieces in the decomposition, this is rather disappointing. The polyhedron used in Chazelle's lower-bound example is quite special, however, and one may hope that polyhedra arising in practical applications are easier to handle. This is the topic of our paper: are there types of polyhedra that can be decomposed into fewer than a quadratic number of pieces?

Erickson [14] has answered this question affirmatively for so-called *local polyhedra* (see below) by showing that any such 3-dimensional polyhedron P can be decomposed into $O(n \log n)$ tetrahedra and that this bound is tight. We consider a different class of polyhedra, namely *fat polyhedra*.

Types of fatness. Before we can state our results, we first need to give the definition of fatness that we use. In the study of realistic input models [10], many definitions for fatness have been proposed. When the input is convex, most of these definitions are equivalent up to constants. When the input is not convex, however, this is not the case: polyhedra that are fat under one definition may not be fat under a different definition. Therefore we study two different definitions.

The first definition that we use was introduced by De Berg [5]. For an object o and a ball B whose center lies inside o, we define $B \sqcap o$ to be the connected component of $B \cap o$ that contains the center of B. An object o is *locally-γ-fat* if for every ball B that has its center inside o and which does not completely contain o, we have $vol(B \sqcap o) \geq \gamma \cdot vol(B)$, where $vol(\cdot)$ denotes the volume of an object. We call an object *locally fat* if it is locally γ-fat for a fixed constant γ. If we replace $\sqcap$ with $\cap$—that is, we do not restrict the intersection to the component containing the center of B—then we get the definition of fat polyhedra proposed by Van der Stappen [19]. Note that for convex objects the two definitions are equivalent. Hence, for convex objects we can omit the adjective "locally" from the terminology. For non-convex objects the definitions are not equivalent: a polyhedron that is fat under Van der Stappen's definition can have skinny pieces, unlike locally-fat polyhedra.

The second definition is a generalization of the (α, β)-covered objects introduced by Efrat [13] to 3-dimensional objects. A simply-connected object P in $\mathbb{R}^3$ is (α, β)-*covered* if the following condition is satisfied: for each point $p \in \partial P$ there is a tetrahedron $T_p \subset P$ with one vertex at p that is α-fat and has diameter $\beta \cdot diam(P)$, where ∂P denotes the boundary of P and $diam(P)$ denotes the diameter of P. Here a tetrahedron is called α-fat if it is α-fat under the definition of Van der Stappen. (Equivalently, we could define a tetrahedron to be α-fat if all its solid angles are at least α.) The tetrahedron T_p is called a *good tetrahedron* for p.

As observed by De Berg [5] the class of locally-γ-fat objects is strictly more general than the class of (α, β)-covered objects: any object that is (α, β)-covered for some constants α and β is also locally-γ-fat for some constant γ (depending on α and β), but the reverse is not true.

For comparison, let us also give the definition of a local polyhedron P [14]. To this end, define the *scale factor at a vertex* v of P as the ratio between the length of the longest edge incident to v and the minimum distance from v to any other vertex. The *local scale factor* of P is now the maximum scale factor at any vertex. The *global scale factor* of P is the ratio between the longest and shortest edge lengths of the whole polyhedron. Finally, P is called a *local polyhedron* if its local scale factor is a constant, while its global scale factor is polynomial in the number of vertices of P. It is easy to see that local polyhedra need not be fat, while fat polyhedra need not be local.

Our Results. First we study the decomposition of (α, β)-covered polyhedra and locally-γ-fat polyhedra into tetrahedra. By modifying Chazelle's polyhedron so that it becomes (α, β)-covered, we obtain the following negative result.

- There are (α, β)-covered (and, hence, locally-fat) polyhedra with n vertices such that any decomposition into convex pieces uses $\Omega(n^2)$ pieces.

Next we restrict the class of fat polyhedra further by requiring that their faces should be convex and fat, when considered as planar polygons in the plane containing them. For this class of polyhedra we obtain a positive result.

- Any locally-fat polyhedron (and, hence, any (α, β)-covered polyhedron) with n vertices whose faces are convex and fat can be decomposed into $O(n)$ tetrahedra in $O(n \log n)$ time.

Several applications that need a decomposition or covering of a polyhedron into tetrahedra would profit if the tetrahedra were fat. In the plane any fat polygon can be covered by $O(n)$ fat triangles, as shown by Van Kreveld [17] (for a slightly different definition of fatness). We show that a similar result is, unfortunately, not possible in 3-dimensional space.

- There are (α, β)-covered (and, hence, locally-fat) polyhedra with n vertices and convex fat faces such that the number of tetrahedra in any covering that only uses fat tetrahedra cannot be bounded as a function of n.

For some applications—ray shooting is an example—we do not need a decomposition of the full interior of the given polyhedron P; instead it is sufficient to have a *boundary covering*, that is, a set of objects whose union is contained in P and that together cover the boundary of P. Interestingly, when we consider boundary coverings there is a distinction between (α, β)-covered polyhedra and locally-fat polyhedra:

- The boundary of any (α, β)-covered polyhedron P, can be covered by $O(n^2 \log n)$ fat convex constant-complexity polyhedra, and there are (α, β)-covered polyhedra that require $\Omega(n^2)$ convex pieces in any boundary covering. If the faces of the (α, β)-covered polyhedron are fat, convex and of approximately the same size, then the boundary can be covered with only $O(n)$ convex fat polyhedra. Furthermore, the worst-case number of convex pieces needed to cover the boundary of a locally-fat polyhedron cannot be bounded as a function of n.

Finally, we consider boundary coverings using so-called *towers* [1]—a type of decomposition that has previously been used for ray-shooting. Unfortunately, we must relegate most discussion of these results to the full paper for space reasons. Table 1 summarizes our results.

Table 1. Overview of results on decomposing and covering polyhedra. An entry marked × means that the corresponding decomposition or covering is not always possible. (For example, since general polyhedra can have arbitrarily sharp vertices, they cannot always be decomposed into fat tetrahedra.)

	decomposition of interior by		covering of boundary by	
	tetrahedra	fat tetrahedra	fat convex polyhedra	towers
general	$\Theta(n^2)$ [11]	×	×	unbounded
local	$\Theta(n \log n)$ [14]	×	×	unbounded
locally fat	$\Theta(n^2)$	unbounded	unbounded	unbounded
with fat faces	$\Theta(n)$	unbounded	unbounded	unbounded
(α, β)-covered	$\Theta(n^2)$	unbounded	$O(n^2 \log n)$, $\Omega(n^2)$	$\Theta(1)$
with fat faces	$\Theta(n)$	unbounded	$O(n^2 \log n)$	$\Theta(1)$

Applications. As already mentioned, decomposing polyhedra into tetrahedra or other convex pieces is an important preprocessing step in many applications. Below we mention some of these applications, where our results help to get improved performance when the input polyhedra are fat.

Hachenberger [15] studied the computation of Minkowski sums of non-convex polyhedra. To obtain a robust and efficient algorithm for this problem, he first decomposes the polyhedra into convex pieces. Our results imply that this first step can be done such that the resulting number of pieces is $O(n)$ if the input polyhedra are locally fat with fat faces, while in general this number can be quadratic.

Another application is in computing depth orders. The best-known algorithm to compute a depth order for n tetrahedra runs in time $O(n^{4/3+\varepsilon})$ [3]. De Berg and Gray [7] recently showed that for fat convex polyhedra of constant complexity, this can be improved to $O(n \log^3 n)$. Our results imply that any constant-complexity (α, β)-covered polyhedron can be decomposed into constant-complexity fat convex polyhedra. It can be shown that this is sufficient to be able to use the depth-order algorithm of [7]. Similarly, our results imply that the results from De Berg and Gray [7] on vertical ray shooting in convex polyhedra extend to constant-complexity (α, β)-covered polyhedra. Finally, our results on boundary coverings with towers (in the full paper) imply that we can use the method of Aronov *et al.* [1] to answer ray-shooting queries in (α, β)-covered polyhedra in $O((n/\sqrt{m}) \log^2 n)$ time with a structure that uses $O(m^{1+\varepsilon})$ storage, for any $n \le m \le n^2$. This is in contrast to the best-known data structure for arbitrary polyhedra [3], which gives $O(n^{1+\varepsilon}/m^{1/4})$ query time with $O(m^{1+\varepsilon})$ storage for $n \leq m \leq n^4$.

2 Decomposing the Interior

In this section we discuss decomposing the interior of fat non-convex objects into tetrahedra. We start with decompositions into arbitrary tetrahedra, and then we consider decompositions into fat tetrahedra.

2.1 Decompositions into Arbitrary Tetrahedra

The upper bound. Let P be a locally-γ-fat polyhedron in $\mathbb{R}^3$ whose faces, when viewed as polygons in the plane containing the face, are convex and β-fat. We will prove that P can be decomposed into $O(n)$ tetrahedra in $O(n \log n)$ time.

In our proof, we will need the concept of density. The *density* [6] of a set S of objects in $\mathbb{R}^3$ is defined as the smallest number λ such that the following holds: any ball $B \subset \mathbb{R}^3$ is intersected by at most λ objects $o \in S$ such that $diam(o) \geq diam(B)$.

We also need the following technical lemma. Its proof is standard and therefore omitted.

Lemma 1. *Let P be a convex β-fat polygon embedded in $\mathbb{R}^3$ where $diam(P) \geq 1$. Let C and C' be axis-aligned cubes centered at the same point. Let the side length of C be 1 and the side length of C' be $2\sqrt{3}/3$. If P intersects C, then $P' := P \cap C'$ is β'-fat for some $\beta' = \Omega(\beta)$.*

The following lemma shows that the faces of a locally-γ-fat polyhedron have low density if they are fat themselves.

Lemma 2. *Let F_P be the set of faces of a locally-γ-fat polyhedron P. If the faces of P are themselves β-fat and convex, then F_P has density $O(1/\gamma\beta^3)$.*

Proof. Without loss of generality, let S be a sphere with unit radius. We wish to show that the number of faces $f \in F_P$ with $diam(f) \geq 1$ that intersect S is $O(1/\gamma\beta^3)$.

Partition the bounding cube of S into eight equal-sized cubes by bisecting it along each dimension. Consider one of the cubes: call it C. Also construct an axis-aligned cube C' that has side length $2\sqrt{3}/3$ and concentric with C. For all faces f intersecting C that have $diam(f) \geq 1$, we define $f' := f \cap C'$. By Lemma 1, we know that f' is β'-fat for some $\beta' = \Omega(\beta)$.

Since f' is a fat convex polygon with a diameter of at least $2\sqrt{3}/3 - 1$, it must contain a circle c of radius $\rho = \beta'(2\sqrt{3}/3 - 1)/8$ [19]. For any such circle c, there is a face F of C' such that the projection of c onto F is an ellipse which has a minor axis with length at least $\rho/\sqrt{2}$.

We make a grid on each face of C' where every grid cell has side length $\rho/2$. We call the rectangular prism between two grid cells on opposite faces of C' a

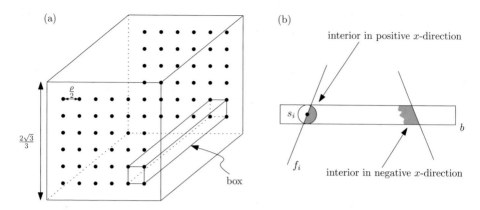

Fig. 1. (a) A box. (b) A box b (side view) and the different types of faces assigned to it.

box—see Figure 1(a). Each face f' has an intersection with some box that is the entire cross-section of the box. We assign each face to such a box.

We now consider the set of faces that can be assigned to any one box b. There are two types of faces in this set—see Figure 1(b). For example, if b has its long edges parallel to the x axis, there are the faces that have the interior of P in the positive x direction and the faces that have the interior in the negative x direction. We consider one type of face at a time. For each face f_i, we place a sphere s_i with radius $\rho/4$ so that its center is on f_i and in the center of b (that is, the center is exactly between the long faces of b). Since P is locally-γ-fat, $vol(P \sqcap s_i) \geq \frac{\gamma 4\pi}{3}\left(\frac{\rho}{4}\right)^3 = \gamma\pi\rho^3/48$. Since we only consider one type of face, $(P \sqcap s_i) \cap (P \sqcap s_j) = \emptyset$ for any $s_j \neq s_i$. Therefore the number of faces of one type that can cross one box is $48/(\sqrt{3}\gamma\pi\rho^2)$. The number of faces that can cross one box is twice that. The number of boxes per direction is $\frac{2\sqrt{3}/3}{\rho/2} = \frac{4}{\rho\sqrt{3}}$ and the number of directions is 3. Hence, the number of faces that can intersect S is at most

$$2 \cdot 3 \cdot \frac{48}{\sqrt{3}\gamma\pi\rho^2} \cdot \frac{4}{\rho\sqrt{3}} = \frac{184}{\pi\gamma\rho^3}.$$

Since $\rho = \Omega(\beta)$, this is $O(1/\gamma\beta^3)$. □

Since the set F_P of faces of the polyhedron P has density $O(1/\gamma\beta^3) = O(1)$, there is a BSP for F_P of size $O(n)$ that can be computed in $O(n\log n)$ time [4]. The cells of the BSP are convex and contain at most one facet, so we can easily decompose all cells further into $O(n)$ tetrahedra in total.

Theorem 1. *Let γ and β be fixed constants. Any locally-γ-fat polyhedron with β-fat convex faces can be partitioned into $O(n)$ tetrahedra in $O(n\log n)$ time, where n is the number of vertices of the polyhedron.*

The lower bound. Next we show that the restriction that the faces of the polyhedron are fat is necessary, because there are fat polyhedra with non-fat faces that need a quadratic number of tetrahedra to be covered.

The polyhedron known as *Chazelle's polyhedron* [11]—see Figure 2(b)—is an important polyhedron used to construct lower-bound examples. We describe a slight modification of that polyhedron which makes it (α, β)-covered and retains the properties needed for the lower bound.

The essential property of Chazelle's polyhedron is that it contains a region sandwiched between a set L of line segments defined as follows. Fix a small positive constant $\varepsilon > 0$. For an integer i with $1 \le i \le n$, define the line segment ℓ_i as $\ell_i := \{(x, y, z) : 0 \le x \le n + 1 \text{ and } y = i \text{ and } z = ix - \varepsilon\}$ and the line segment ℓ_i' as $\ell_i' := \{(x, y, z) : x = i \text{ and } 0 \le y \le n + 1 \text{ and } z = iy\}$. Next define $L := \{\ell_i : 1 \le i \le n\} \cup \{\ell_i' : 1 \le i \le n\}$.

The region $\Sigma := \{(x, y, z) : 1 \le x, y \le n \text{ and } xy - \varepsilon \le z \le xy\}$ between these segments has volume $\Theta(\varepsilon n^2)$. Chazelle showed that for any convex object o that does not intersect any of the segments in L we have $vol(o \cap \Sigma) = O(\varepsilon)$. These two facts are enough to show that $\Omega(n^2)$ convex objects are required to cover any polyhedron that contains Σ but whose interior does not intersect the segments in L.

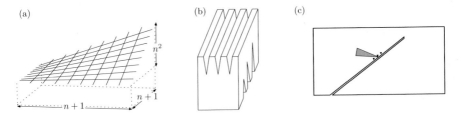

Fig. 2. (a) The line segments used in the lower-bound construction (not to scale). (b) Chazelle's polyhedron before modification (also not to scale). (c) Cross-section of the polyhedron P shown with the cross-section of a good tetrahedron (shaded).

Chazelle turns the set of line segments into a polyhedron by putting a box around L, and making a slit into the box for each segment, as shown in Figure 2(b). The resulting polyhedron has each of the segments in L as one of its edges, and contains the sandwich region Σ. Hence, any convex decomposition or covering of its interior needs $\Omega(n^2)$ pieces.

Chazelle's polyhedron is not (α, β)-covered. We therefore modify it as follows. First of all, we make the outer box from which the polyhedron is formed a cube of size $6n^2 \times 6n^2 \times 3n^2$ centered at the origin. Second, we replace the slits by long triangular prisms—we will call the prisms *needles* from now on—sticking into the cube. Thus, for each segment in L, there is a needle that has an edge containing the segment. We do not completely pierce the cube with the needles, so that the resulting polyhedron, P, remains simple (that is, topologically equivalent to a sphere). Note that Σ is still contained in P, and that for each segment in L there is an edge containing it.

Next we argue that P is (α, β)-covered. First, consider a point $p \in \partial P$ on one of the needles. Assume without loss of generality that the needle is parallel to the xz-plane. If p is near one of the needles going into the other direction, then the situation is as in Figure 2(c).

Note that the distance between consecutive needles of the same orientation—that is, the distance between the small triangles in Figure 2(c)—is at least 1. Moreover, we can choose the distance ε between the needles of opposite orientation—that is, the distance between the small triangles and the long needle in the figure—as small as we like. The same is true for the "width" of the needles—that is, the size of the small triangles in the figure. Hence, we can make the construction such that we can always put a good (that is, large and fat) tetrahedron at p.

Next, consider a point $p \in \partial P$ that is near one of the places where a needle "enters" the cube. Note that the segments in L have slopes ranging from 1 to n, and that any needle passes near the center of the cube—this is true since the cube has size $6n^2 \times 6n^2 \times 3n^2$, while the segments in L all pass at a distance at most n from the cube's center. Hence, the needles will intersect the bottom facet of the cube, and they make an angle of at least $45°$ with the bottom facet. This implies that also for points p near the places where these needles enter the cube, we can place a good tetrahedron.

Finally, it is easy to see that for points p on a cube facet, and for points on a needle that are not close to a needle of opposite orientation, we can also put a good tetrahedron. We can conclude with the following theorem.

Theorem 2. *There are constants $\alpha > 0$ and $\beta > 0$, such that there are (α, β)-covered polyhedra for which any convex decomposition consists of $\Omega(n^2)$ convex pieces, where n is the number of vertices of the polyhedron.*

2.2   Decompositions and Coverings with Fat Tetrahedra

When we attempt to partition non-convex polyhedra into fat tetrahedra, or other fat convex objects, the news is uniformly bad. That is, no matter which of the realistic input models we use (of those we are studying), the number of fat convex objects necessary to cover the polyhedron can be made arbitrarily high. For polyhedra without fatness restrictions, there are many examples which require an arbitrary number of fat convex objects for partitioning. In fact, for any constant $\beta > 0$ we can even construct a polyhedron that cannot be covered at all into β-fat convex objects—simply take a polyhedron that has a vertex whose solid angle is much smaller than β. It is also not hard to construct, for any given $\beta > 0$, a local polyhedron that cannot be covered with β-fat convex objects. For instance, we can take a pyramid whose base is a unit square and whose top vertex is at distance $\varepsilon \ll \beta$ above the center of the base.

Next we show how to construct, for any given k, an (α, β)-covered polyhedron of constant complexity and with convex fat faces, which requires $\Omega(k)$ fat convex objects to cover it. First we observe that a rectangular box of size $1 \times (\beta/k) \times (\beta/k)$ requires $\Omega(k)$ β-fat convex objects to cover it. Now consider the (α, β)-covered polyhedron in Figure 3. The essential feature of the construction in Figure 3 is that from any point p along the long axis of the tube, one cannot see much outside the tube. Thus any convex object inside P that contains p must stay mainly within the tube, and the tube basically acts as a rectangular box of size $1 \times (\beta/k) \times (\beta/k)$. Hence, $\Omega(k)$ β-fat tetrahedra are required in any convex covering of the polyhedron. We obtain the following result.

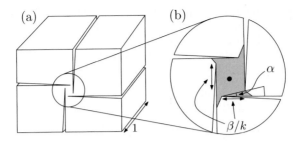

Fig. 3. (a) An (α, β)-covered polyhedron with fat faces whose interior cannot be covered by a bounded number of fat tetrahedra. (b) The part of the polyhedron seen by a point in the center. Note that the polyhedron is constructed so that a good tetrahedron just fits at the points on the boundary inside the central "tube".

Theorem 3. *There are (α, β)-covered (and, hence, locally-fat) polyhedra with n vertices and convex fat faces, such that the number of objects used in any covering by fat convex objects cannot be bounded as a function of n. Furthermore, for any given $\beta > 0$ there are local polyhedra for which no convex covering with β-fat tetrahedra exists.*

3   Covering the Boundary

In the previous section we have seen that the number of fat convex objects needed to cover the interior of a fat non-convex polyhedron P cannot be bounded as a function of n. In this section we show that we can do better if we only wish to cover the boundary of P. Unfortunately, this only holds when P is (α, β)-covered; when P is locally fat, we may still need an arbitrarily large number of fat convex objects to cover its boundary.

Recall that for each point p on the boundary of an (α, β)-covered polyhedron P, there is a good tetrahedron $T_p \subset P$ with one vertex at p, that is, a tetrahedron that is α-fat and has diameter $\beta \cdot diam(P)$. We first observe that we can actually replace T_p by a canonical tetrahedron, as made precise in the following lemma.

Lemma 3. *Let P be an (α, β)-covered polyhedron. There exists a set $\mathcal{C}$ of $O(1/\alpha)$ canonical tetrahedra that are $\Omega(\alpha)$-fat and have diameter $\Omega(\beta \cdot diam(P))$ with the following property: for any point $p \in \partial P$, there is a translated copy T'_p of a canonical tetrahedron that is contained in P and has p as a vertex.*

Proof. Cover the boundary of the unit sphere S in a grid-like fashion by $O(1/\alpha)$ triangular surface patches, each of area roughly $c\alpha$, for a suitably small constant c. For each triangular patch, define a canonical tetrahedron that has the origin as one of its vertices, and that has edges going through the vertices of the patch. Scale the resulting set of tetrahedra appropriately, thus giving the set $\mathcal{C}$. Now consider a good tetrahedron p. Place (a suitably scaled copy) of the sphere S with its center at p. T_p will intersect S in a fat region R of area α. By choosing

c appropriately we can ensure that R contains one of the triangular patches. This implies we can select a tetrahedron T'_p from $\mathcal{C}$ with the required properties.   □

Now we can prove that we can cover the boundary of an (α, β)-covered polyhedron with a bounded number of fat convex objects.

Theorem 4. *The boundary of an (α, β)-covered polyhedron with complexity n can be covered by $O(n^2 \log n)$ convex, fat, constant-complexity polyhedra.*

Proof. Let $\mathcal{C}$ be the set of canonical tetrahedra defined in Lemma 3. Fix a canonical tetrahedron $T \in \mathcal{C}$. Note that when we put a translated copy of T at some point $p \in \partial P$ according to Lemma 3, we always put the same vertex, v, at p. (Namely, the vertex coinciding with the origin before the translation.) For a face f of P, let $f(T) \subset f$ be the subset of points p on f such that we can place T with its designated vertex v at p in such a way that T is contained in P. The region $f(T)$ is polygonal. We triangulate $f(T)$, and for each triangle t in this triangulation, we define a convex polyhedron by taking the union of all the translated copies of T that have $v \in t$. By doing this for all faces f, we get a collection C_T of convex polyhedra that together cover $\bigcup_f f(T)$.

We claim that every convex object $o \in C_T$ is fat. This follows from the fact that T is fat and that T cannot be much smaller than t. Indeed, $diam(T) = \Omega(\beta \cdot diam(P)) = \Omega(\beta \cdot diam(t))$.

Next, we claim that $|C_T| = O(n^2 \log n)$. This follows directly from the fact that the complexity of $\bigcup_f f(T)$ is upper bounded by the complexity of the *free space* of T, when it is translated amidst the faces of P. Aronov and Sharir [2] showed that this free space has complexity $O(n^2 \log n)$.

Finally, we observe that $\bigcup_{T \in \mathcal{C}} \bigcup_f f(T) = \partial P$ by Lemma 3. In other words, the convex objects in the set $\bigcup_{T \in \mathcal{C}} C_T$ together cover the boundary of P.   □

Theorem 4 implies that the boundary of a constant-complexity (α, β)-covered polyhedron P can be covered by a constant number of fat objects. Unfortunately, the number of convex objects used in the boundary covering grows quadratically in the complexity of P. If P has convex fat faces that are roughly the same size, then the number of convex fat objects required to cover the boundary reduces to linear. We summarize this in the following theorem, the proof of which is very similar to the proof of Theorem 4. It uses the observation by Van der Stappen [19] that the free space in such a situation has linear complexity.

Theorem 5. *Let P be an (α, β)-covered polyhedron with convex β'-fat faces. Further, let there be a constant c where, for any two faces f_1 and f_2 of P, $diam(f_1) \le c \cdot diam(f_2)$. Then the boundary of P can be covered by $O(n)$ convex, fat, constant-complexity polyhedra.*

We claim that any covering of the boundary of an (α, β)-covered polyhedron by fat convex objects requires $\Omega(n^2)$ pieces. To show this, we slightly modify our version of Chazelle's polyhedron from the previous section. In particular, we replace the edges of the needles that contain the segments in the set L by long and thin rectangular facets. The resulting polyhedron is still (α, β)-covered, and it requires $\Omega(n^2)$ fat convex polyhedra to cover the newly introduced facets.

Theorem 6. *There are constants $\alpha > 0$ and $\beta > 0$ such that there are (α, β)-covered polyhedra P for which any decomposition of ∂P into fat convex polyhedra requires $\Omega(n^2)$ pieces.*

The number of fat convex polyhedra necessary to cover the boundary of a polyhedron P that is not (α, β)-covered can not be bounded as a function of n. To see this, we make a simple modification to the polyhedron of Figure 3. We reduce the gaps that separate the interior "tube" from the rest of P to some arbitrarily small constant ε. This forces any fat convex polyhedron that covers the part of the boundary of the polyhedron inside the tube to be inside the tube. Now for any k, we can reduce the width and height of the tube until its boundary requires more than k fat convex polyhedra to be covered. This example remains locally fat with fat convex faces and it is a local polyhedron. Note that P is no longer (α, β)-covered: reducing the gaps that separate the tube from the rest of the polyhedron causes the points on the boundary inside the tube to no longer have a good tetrahedron.

Theorem 7. *For any given k, there exist locally-γ-fat polyhedra for some absolute constant γ with faces that are β-fat for some absolute constant β which require at least k fat convex polyhedra to cover their boundaries. These polyhedra are also local polyhedra.*

4   Concluding Remarks

We studied decompositions and boundary coverings of fat polyhedra. Our bounds on the number of objects needed in the decomposition (or covering) are tight, except for the bound on the number of convex fat polyhedra needed to cover the boundary of an (α, β)-covered object. In particular, there is still a large gap for the case that the facets of the polyhedron are also fat. It would be interesting to get tight bounds for this case.

Acknowledgments

The second author thanks Herman Haverkort, Elena Mumford, and Bettina Speckmann for conversations regarding this topic.

References

1. Aronov, B., De Berg, M., Gray, C.: Ray shooting and intersection searching amidst fat convex polyhedra in 3-space. Computational Geometry: Theory and Applications 41, 68–76 (2008)
2. Aronov, B., Sharir, M.: On translational motion planning of a convex polyhedron in 3-space. SIAM J. Comput. 26, 1785–1803 (1997)
3. De Berg, M.: Ray Shooting, Depth Orders and Hidden Surface Removal. LNCS, vol. 703. Springer, New York (1993)
4. De Berg, M.: Linear size binary space partitions for uncluttered scenes. Algorithmica 28, 353–366 (2000)

5. De Berg, M.: Improved bounds on the union complexity of fat objects. Discr. Comput. Geom. (to appear) doi:10.1007/s00454-007-9029-7
6. De Berg, M., Cheong, O., Van Kreveld, M., Overmars, M.: Computational Geometry: Algorithms and Applications, 3rd edn. Springer, Heidelberg (2008)
7. De Berg, M., Gray, C.: Vertical ray shooting and computing depth orders for fat objects. SIAM J. Comput. 38(1), 257–275 (2008)
8. De Berg, M., Gray, C.: Computing the visibility map of fat objects. In: Dehne, F., Sack, J.-R., Zeh, N. (eds.) WADS 2007. LNCS, vol. 4619, pp. 251–262. Springer, Heidelberg (2007)
9. De Berg, M., David, H., Katz, M.J., Overmars, M., Van Der Stappen, A.F., Vleugels, J.: Guarding scenes against invasive hypercubes. Computational Geometry: Theory and Applications 26, 99–117 (2003)
10. De Berg, M., Van Der Stappen, A.F., Vleugels, J., Katz, M.J.: Realistic input models for geometric algorithms. Algorithmica 34, 81–97 (2002)
11. Chazelle, B.: Convex partitions of polyhedra: a lower bound and worst-case optimal algorithm. SIAM J. Comput. 13, 488–507 (1984)
12. Chazelle, B.: Triangulating a simple polygon in linear time. Discr. Comput. Geom. 6, 485–524 (1991)
13. Efrat, A.: The complexity of the union of (α, β)-covered objects. SIAM J. Comput. 34, 775–787 (2005)
14. Erickson, J.: Local polyhedra and geometric graphs. Computational Geometry: Theory and Applications 31, 101–125 (2005)
15. Hachenberger, P.: Exact Minkowski sums of polyhedra and exact and efficient decomposition of polyhedra in convex pieces. In: Arge, L., Hoffmann, M., Welzl, E. (eds.) ESA 2007. LNCS, vol. 4698, pp. 669–680. Springer, Heidelberg (2007)
16. Keil, J.M.: Polygon Decomposition. In: Sack, J.-R., Urrutia, J. (eds.) Handbook of Computational Geometry, pp. 491–518 (2000)
17. Van Kreveld, M.: On fat partitioning, fat covering, and the union size of polygons. Comput. Geom. Theory Appl. 9, 197–210 (1998)
18. Rupert, J., Seidel, R.: On the difficulty of triangulating three-dimensional nonconvex polyhedra. Discr. Comput. Geom. 7, 227–253 (1992)
19. Van Der Stappen, A.F.: Motion planning amidst fat obstacles. Ph.D. thesis, Utrecht University, Utrecht, the Netherlands (1994)

Approximating Multi-criteria Max-TSP

Markus Bläser, Bodo Manthey, and Oliver Putz

Saarland University, Computer Science
Postfach 151150, 66041 Saarbrücken, Germany
blaeser/manthey@cs.uni-sb.de, oli.putz@gmx.de

Abstract. We present randomized approximation algorithms for multi-criteria Max-TSP. For Max-STSP with $k > 1$ objective functions, we obtain an approximation ratio of $\frac{1}{k} - \varepsilon$ for arbitrarily small $\varepsilon > 0$. For Max-ATSP with k objective functions, we obtain a ratio of $\frac{1}{k+1} - \varepsilon$.

1 Multi-criteria Traveling Salesman Problem

1.1 Traveling Salesman Problem

The traveling salesman problem (TSP) is one of the most fundamental problems in combinatorial optimization. Given a graph, the goal is to find a Hamiltonian cycle of minimum or maximum weight. We consider finding Hamiltonian cycles of maximum weight (Max-TSP).

An instance of Max-TSP is a complete graph $G = (V, E)$ with edge weights $w : E \to \mathbb{N}$. The goal is to find a Hamiltonian cycle of maximum weight. The weight of a Hamiltonian cycle (or, more general, of a subset of E) is the sum of the weights of its edges. If G is undirected, we speak of Max-STSP (symmetric TSP). If G is directed, we have Max-ATSP (asymmetric TSP).

Both Max-STSP and Max-ATSP are NP-hard and APX-hard. Thus, we are in need of approximation algorithms. The currently best approximation algorithms for Max-STSP and Max-ATSP achieve approximation ratios of 61/81 and 2/3, respectively [3,5].

Cycle covers are an important tool for designing approximation algorithms for the TSP. A cycle cover of a graph is a set of vertex-disjoint cycles such that every vertex is part of exactly one cycle. Hamiltonian cycles are special cases of cycle covers that consist of just one cycle. Thus, the weight of a maximum-weight cycle cover is an upper bound for the weight of a maximum-weight Hamiltonian cycle. In contrast to Hamiltonian cycles, cycle covers of maximum weight can be computed efficiently using matching algorithms [1].

1.2 Multi-criteria Optimization

In many optimization problems, there is more than one objective function. Consider buying a car: We might want to buy a cheap, fast car with a good gas mileage. How do we decide which car suits us best? With multiple criteria involved, there is no natural notion of a best choice. Instead, we have to be content

D. Halperin and K. Mehlhorn (Eds.): ESA 2008, LNCS 5193, pp. 185–197, 2008.

with a trade-off. The aim of multi-criteria optimization is to cope with this problem. To transfer the concept of an optimal solution to multi-criteria optimization problems, the notion of *Pareto curves* was introduced (cf. Ehrgott [4]). A Pareto curve is a set of solutions that can be considered optimal.

More formally, a k-criteria optimization problem consists of instances I, solutions $\mathrm{sol}(X)$ for every instance $X \in I$, and k objective functions $w_1, \ldots, w_k$ that map $X \in I$ and $Y \in \mathrm{sol}(X)$ to $\mathbb{N}$. Throughout this paper, our aim is to maximize the objective functions. We say that a solution $Y \in \mathrm{sol}(X)$ *dominates* another solution $Z \in \mathrm{sol}(X)$ if $w_i(Y, X) \geq w_i(Z, X)$ for all $i \in [k] = \{1, \ldots, k\}$ and $w_i(Y, X) > w_i(Z, X)$ for at least one i. This means that Y is strictly preferable to Z. A *Pareto curve* contains all solutions that are not dominated by another solution. Unfortunately, Pareto curves cannot be computed efficiently in many cases: They are often of exponential size, and they are often NP-hard to compute even for otherwise easy problems. Thus, we have to be content with approximate Pareto curves.

For simpler notation, let $w(Y, X) = (w_1(Y, X), \ldots, w_k(Y, X))$. We will omit the instance X if it is clear from the context. Inequalities are meant componentwise. A set $\mathcal{P} \subseteq \mathrm{sol}(X)$ of solutions is called an α *approximate Pareto curve* for $X \in I$ if the following holds: For every solution $Z \in \mathrm{sol}(X)$, there exists a $Y \in \mathcal{P}$ with $w(Y) \geq \alpha w(Z)$. We have $\alpha \leq 1$, and a 1 approximate Pareto curve is a Pareto curve. (This is not precisely true if there are several solutions whose objective values agree. However, in our case this is inconsequential, and we will not elaborate on this for the sake of clarity.) An algorithm is called an α *approximation algorithm* if, given the instance X, it computes an α approximate Pareto curve. It is called a randomized α approximation algorithm if its success probability is at least $1/2$. This success probability can be amplified to $1 - 2^{-m}$ by executing the algorithm m times and taking the union of all sets of solutions. (We can remove dominated solutions from this union, but this is not required by the definition of an approximate Pareto curve.)

Papadimitriou and Yannakakis [8] showed that $(1 - \varepsilon)$ approximate Pareto curves of size polynomial in the instance size and $1/\varepsilon$ exist. The technical requirement for the existence is that the objective values of solutions in $\mathrm{sol}(X)$ are bounded from above by $2^{p(N)}$ for some polynomial p, where N is the size of X. This is fulfilled in most optimization problems and in particular in our case.

A *fully polynomial time approximation scheme* (FPTAS) for a multi-criteria optimization problem computes $(1 - \varepsilon)$ approximate Pareto curves in time polynomial in the size of the instance and $1/\varepsilon$ for all $\varepsilon > 0$. Papadimitriou and Yannakakis [8] showed that multi-criteria minimum-weight matching admits a *randomized FPTAS*, i. e., the algorithm succeeds in computing a $(1 - \varepsilon)$ approximate Pareto curve with constant probability. This yields also a randomized FPTAS for the multi-criteria maximum-weight cycle cover problem [7], which we will use in the following.

Manthey and Ram [6,7] designed randomized approximation algorithms for several variants of multi-criteria Min-TSP. However, they leave it as an open problem to design any approximation algorithm for Max-TSP.

1.3   New Results

We devise the first approximation algorithm for multi-criteria Max-TSP. For k-criteria Max-STSP, we achieve an approximation ratio of $\frac{1}{k} - \varepsilon$ for arbitrarily small $\varepsilon > 0$. For k-criteria Max-ATSP, we achieve $\frac{1}{k+1} - \varepsilon$. Our algorithm is randomized. Its running-time is polynomial in the input size and $1/\varepsilon$ and exponential in the number k of criteria. However, the number of different objective functions is usually a small constant. The main ingredient for our algorithm is a decomposition technique for cycle covers and a reduction from k-criteria instances to $(k - 1)$-criteria instances.

Due to lack of space, some proofs are omitted. For complete proofs, we refer to the full version of this paper [2].

2   Outline and Idea

A straight-forward $1/2$ approximation for mono-criterion Max-ATSP is the following: First, we compute a maximum-weight cycle cover C. Then we remove the lightest edge of each cycle, thus losing at most half of C's weight. In this way, we obtain a collection of paths. Finally, we add edges to connect the paths to get a Hamiltonian cycle. For Max-STSP, the same approach yields a $2/3$ approximation since the length of every cycle is at least three.

Unfortunately, this does not generalize to multi-criteria Max-TSP for which "lightest edge" is usually not well defined: If we break an edge that has little weight with respect to one objective, we might lose a lot of weight with respect to another objective. Based on this observation, the basic idea behind our algorithm and its analysis is the following case distinction:

Light-weight edges: If all edges of our cycle cover contribute only little to its weight, then removing one edge does not decrease the overall weight by too much. Now we choose the edges to be removed such that no objective loses too much of its weight.

Heavy-weight edges: If there is one edge that is very heavy with respect to at least one objective, then we take only this edge from the cycle cover. In this way, we have enough weight for one objective, and we proceed recursively on the remaining graph with $k - 1$ objectives.

In this way, the approximation ratio for k-criteria Max-TSP depends on two questions: First, how well can we decompose a cycle cover consisting solely of light-weight edges? Second, how well can $(k - 1)$-criteria Max-TSP be approximated? We deal with the first question in Section 3. In Section 4, we present and analyze our approximation algorithms, which also gives an answer to the second question. Finally, we give evidence that the analysis of the approximation ratios is tight and point out some ideas that might lead to better approximation ratios (Section 5).

3   Decompositions

Let $\alpha \in (0, 1]$, and let C be a cycle cover. We call a collection $P \subseteq C$ of paths an α-*decomposition of* C if $w(P) \geq \alpha w(C)$ (recall that all inequalities are meant component-wise). In the following, our aim is to find α-decompositions of cycle covers consisting solely of light-weight edges, that is, $w(e) \leq \alpha w(C)$ for all $e \in C$.

Of course, not every cycle cover possesses an α-decomposition for every α. For instance, a single directed cycle of length two, where each edge has a weight of 1 shows that $\alpha = 1/2$ is best possible for a single objective function in directed graphs. On the other hand, by removing the lightest edge of every cycle, we obtain a 1/2-decomposition.

For undirected graphs and $k = 1$, $\alpha = 2/3$ is optimal: We can find a 2/3-decomposition by removing the lightest edge of every cycle, and a single cycle of length three, where each edge weight is 1, shows that this is tight.

More general, we define $\alpha_k^d \in (0, 1]$ to be the maximum number such that every directed cycle cover C with $w(e) \leq \alpha_k^d \cdot w(C)$ for all $e \in C$ possesses an α_k^d-decomposition. Analogously, $\alpha_k^u \in (0, 1]$ is the maximum number such that every undirected cycle cover C with $w(e) \leq \alpha_k^u \cdot w(C)$ possesses an α_k^u-decomposition. We have $\alpha_1^d = \frac{1}{2}$ and $\alpha_1^u = \frac{2}{3}$, as we have already argued above. We also have $\alpha_k^u \geq \alpha_k^d$ and $\alpha_k^u \leq \alpha_{k-1}^u$ as well as $\alpha_k^d \leq \alpha_{k-1}^d$.

3.1   Existence of Decompositions

In this section, we investigate for which values of α such α-decompositions exist. In the subsequent section, we show how to actually find good decompositions. We have already dealt with α_1^u and α_1^d. Thus, $k \geq 2$ remains to be considered in the following theorems. In particular, only $k \geq 2$ is needed for the analysis of our algorithms.

Let us first normalize our cycle covers to make the proofs in the following a bit easier. For directed cycle covers C, we can restrict ourselves to cycles of length two: If we have a cycle c of length ℓ with edges $e_1, \ldots, e_\ell$, we replace it by $\lfloor \ell/2 \rfloor$ cycles (e_{2j-1}, e_{2j}) for $j = 1, \ldots, \lfloor \ell/2 \rfloor$. If ℓ is odd, then we add a edge $e_{\ell+1}$ with $w(e_{\ell+1}) = 0$ and add the cycle $(e_\ell, e_{\ell+1})$. (Strictly speaking, edges are 2-tuples of vertices, and we cannot simply reconnect them. What we mean is that we remove the edges of the cycle and create new edges with the same names and weights together with appropriate new vertices.) We do this for all cycles of length at least three and call the resulting cycle cover C'. Now any α-decomposition P' of the new cycle cover C' yields an α-decomposition P of the original cycle cover C by removing the newly added edges $e_{\ell+1}$: In C, we have to remove at least one edge of the cycle c to obtain a decomposition. In C', we have to remove at least $\lfloor \ell/2 \rfloor$ edges of c, thus at least one. Furthermore, if $w(e) \leq \alpha \cdot w(C)$ for every $e \in C$, then also $w(e) \leq \alpha \cdot w(C')$ for every $e \in C'$ since we kept all edge weights. This also shows $w(P) = w(P')$.

We are interested in α-decompositions that work for all cycle covers with k objective functions. Thus in particular, we have to be able to decompose C'.

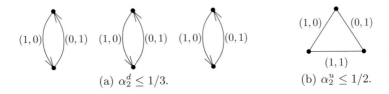

(a) $\alpha_2^d \leq 1/3$.   (b) $\alpha_2^u \leq 1/2$.

Fig. 1. Examples that limit the possibility of decomposition

The consequence is that if every directed cycle cover consisting solely of cycles of length two possesses an α-decomposition, then all directed cycle covers do so.

For undirected cycle covers, we can restrict ourselves to cycles of length three: We replace a cycle $c = (e_1, \ldots, e_\ell)$ by $\lfloor \ell/3 \rfloor$ cycles $(e_{3j-2}, e_{3j-1}, e_{3j})$ for $1 \leq j \leq \lfloor \ell/3 \rfloor$. If ℓ is not divisible by three, then we add one or two edges $e_{\ell+1}, e_{\ell+2}$ to form a cycle of length three with the remaining edge(s). Again, every α-decomposition of the new cycle cover yields an α-decomposition of the original cycle cover.

The following two theorems are proved using the probabilistic method.

Theorem 1. *For all $k \geq 2$, we have $\alpha_k^u \geq 1/k$.*

For undirected graphs and $k = 2$, we do not need the assumption that the weight of each edge is at most α_2^u times the weight of the cycle cover. Lemma 1 below immediately yields a $(1/2 - \varepsilon)$ approximation for bi-criteria Max-STSP: First, we compute a Pareto curve of cycle covers. Second, we decompose each cycle cover to obtain a collection of paths, which we then connect to form Hamiltonian cycles. The following lemma can also be generalized to arbitrary k that do not contain cycles of length at most k.

Lemma 1. *For every undirected cycle cover C with edge weights $w = (w_1, w_2)$, there exists a collection $P \subseteq C$ of paths with $w(P) \geq w(C)/2$.*

For directed cycle covers, our aim is again to show that the probability of having not enough weight in one component is less than $1/k$. Hoeffding's inequality works only for $k \geq 7$. We use a different approach, which immediately gives us the desired result for $k \geq 6$, and which can be tweaked to work also for small k.

Theorem 2. *For all $k \geq 2$, we have $\alpha_k^d \geq 1/(k+1)$.*

Figure 1 shows that Theorems 1 and 2, respectively, are tight for $k = 2$. Due to these limitations for $k = 2$, proving larger values for α_k^u or α_k^d does not immediately yield better approximation ratios (see Section 5). However, for larger values of k, Hoeffding's inequality yields the existence of $\Omega(1/\log k)$-decompositions. Together with a different technique for heavy-weight cycle covers, this might lead to improved approximation algorithms for larger values of k.

Lemma 2. *We have $\alpha_k^u, \alpha_k^d \in \Omega(1/\log k)$.*

3.2   Finding Decompositions

While we know that decompositions exist due to the previous section, we have to find them efficiently in order to use them in our approximation algorithm. We present a deterministic algorithm and a faster randomized algorithm for finding decompositions.

DECOMPOSE (Algorithm 1) is a deterministic algorithm for finding a decomposition. The idea behind this algorithm is as follows: First, we scale the weights such that $w(C) = 1/\alpha$. Then $w(e) \leq 1$ for all edges $e \in C$. Second, we normalize all cycle covers such that they consist solely of cycles of length two (in case of directed graphs) or three (in case of undirected graphs). Third, we combine very light cycles as long as possible. More precisely, if there are two cycles c and c' such that $w'(c) \leq 1/2$ and $w'(c') \leq 1/2$, we combine them to one cycle $\tilde{c}$ with $w'(\tilde{c}) \leq 1$. The requirements for an α-decomposition to exist are still fulfilled. Furthermore, any α-decomposition of C' immediately yields an α-decomposition of C.

$P \leftarrow$ DECOMPOSE(C, w, k, α)

input: cycle cover C, edge weights w, $k \geq 2$, $w(e) \leq \alpha \cdot w(C)$ for all $e \in C$
output: a collection P of paths
 1: obtain w' from w by scaling each component such that $w_i'(C) = 1/\alpha$ for all i
 2: normalize C to C' as described in the text such that C' consists solely of cycles
        of length three (undirected) or two (directed)
 3: **while** there are cycles c and c' in C' with $w'(c) \leq 1/2$ and $w'(c') \leq 1/2$ **do**
 4:      combine c and c' to $\tilde{c}$ with $w'(\tilde{c}) = w'(c) + w'(c')$
 5:      replace c and c' by $\tilde{c}$ in C'
 6: try all possible combinations of decompositions
 7: choose one P' that maximizes $\min_{i \in [k]} w_i'(P)$
 8: translate $P' \subseteq C'$ back to obtain a decomposition $P \subseteq C$
 9: return P

Algorithm 1. A deterministic algorithm for finding a decomposition

Lemma 3. Let $k \geq 2$. Let C be an undirected cycle cover and $w_1, \ldots, w_k$ be edge weights such that $w(e) \leq \alpha_k^u \cdot w(C)$. Then DECOMPOSE$(C, w, k, \alpha_k^u)$ returns a collection P of paths with $w(P) \geq \alpha_k^u \cdot w(C)$.

Let C be a directed cycle cover and $w_1, \ldots, w_k$ be edge weights such that $w(e) \leq \alpha_k^d \cdot w(C)$. Then DECOMPOSE$(C, w, k, \alpha_k^d)$ returns a collection P of paths with $w(P) \geq \alpha_k^d \cdot w(C)$.

Let us also estimate the running-time of DECOMPOSE. The normalization in lines 1 to 5 can be implemented to run in linear time. Due to the normalization, the weight of every cycle is at least $1/2$ with respect to at least one w_i'. Thus, we have at most $2k/\alpha_k^u$ cycles in C' in the undirected case and at most $2k/\alpha_k^d$ cycles in C' in the directed case. In either case, we have $O(k^2)$ cycles. All of these cycles are of length two or of length three. Thus, we find an optimal decomposition, which in particular is an α_k^u or α_k^d-decomposition, in time linear in the input size and exponential in k.

$P \leftarrow \text{RandDecompose}(C, w, k, \alpha)$

input: cycle cover C, edge weights $w = (w_1, \ldots, w_k)$, $k \geq 2$, $w(e) \leq \alpha \cdot w(C)$ for all
    $e \in C$

output: a collection P of paths with $w(P) \geq \alpha \cdot w(C)$

1: **if** $k \geq 6$ **then**
2:     **repeat**
3:         randomly choose one edge of every cycle of C
4:         remove the chosen edges to obtain P
5:     **until** $w(P) \geq \alpha \cdot w(C)$
6: **else**
7:     $P \leftarrow \text{Decompose}(C, w, k, \alpha)$

Algorithm 2. A randomized algorithm for finding a decomposition

By exploiting the probabilistic argument of the previous section, we can find a decomposition much faster with a randomized algorithm. RandDecompose (Algorithm 2) does this: We choose the edges to be deleted uniformly at random for every cycle. The probability that we obtain a decomposition as required is positive and bounded from below by a constant. Furthermore, as the proofs of Theorems 1 and 2 show, this probability tends to one as k increases. For $k \geq 6$, it is at least approximately 0.7 for undirected cycle covers and at least $1/4$ for directed cycle covers. For $k < 6$, we just use our deterministic algorithm, which has linear running-time for constant k. The following lemma follows from the considerations above.

Lemma 4. *Let $k \geq 2$. Let C be an undirected cycle cover and $w_1, \ldots, w_k$ be edge weights such that $w(e) \leq \alpha_k^u \cdot w(C)$. Then $\text{RandDecompose}(C, w, k, \alpha_k^u)$ returns a collection P of paths with $w(P) \geq \alpha_k^u \cdot w(C)$.*

Let C be a directed cycle cover and $w_1, \ldots, w_k$ be edge weights such that $w(e) \leq \alpha_k^d \cdot w(C)$. Then $\text{RandDecompose}(C, w, k, \alpha_k^d)$ returns a collection P of paths with $w(P) \geq \alpha_k^d \cdot w(C)$.

The expected running-time of RandDecompose is $O(|C|)$.

4 Approximation Algorithms

Based on the idea sketched in Section 2, we can now present our approximation algorithms for multi-criteria Max-ATSP and Max-STSP. However, in particular for Max-STSP, some additional work has to be done if heavy edges are present.

4.1 Multi-criteria Max-ATSP

We first present our algorithm for Max-ATSP (Algorithm 3) since it is a bit easier to analyze.

First of all, we compute a $(1 - \varepsilon)$ approximate Pareto curve $\mathcal{C}$ of cycle covers. Then, for every cycle cover $C \in \mathcal{C}$, we decide whether it is a light-weight cycle cover or a heavy-weight cycle cover (line 7). If C has only light-weight edges,

$\mathcal{P}_{\text{TSP}} \leftarrow$ MC-MAXATSP(G, w, k, ε)

input: directed complete graph $G = (V, E)$, $k \geq 1$, edge weights $w : E \to \mathbb{N}^k$, $\varepsilon > 0$

output: approximate Pareto curve $\mathcal{P}_{\text{TSP}}$ for k-criteria Max-TSP

1: **if** $k = 1$ **then**
2:     compute a $2/3$ approximation $\mathcal{P}_{\text{TSP}}$
3: **else**
4:     compute a $(1 - \varepsilon)$ approximate Pareto curve $\mathcal{C}$ of cycle covers
5:     $\mathcal{P}_{\text{TSP}} \leftarrow \emptyset$
6:     **for all** cycle covers $C \in \mathcal{C}$ **do**
7:         **if** $w(e) \leq \alpha_k^d \cdot w(C)$ for all edges $e \in C$ **then**
8:             $P \leftarrow$ DECOMPOSE(C, w, k)
9:             add edges to P to form a Hamiltonian cycle H; add H to $\mathcal{P}_{\text{TSP}}$
10:        **else**
11:            let $e = (u, v) \in C$ be an edge with $w(e) \not\leq \alpha_k^d \cdot w(C)$
12:            **for all** $a, b, c, d \in V$ such that $P_{a,b,c,d}^e$ is legal **do**
13:                **for** $i \leftarrow 1$ **to** k **do**
14:                    obtain G' from G by contracting the paths of $P_{a,b,c,d}^e$
15:                    obtain w' from w by removing the ith objective
16:                    $\mathcal{P}_{\text{TSP}}' \leftarrow$ MC-MAXATSP$(G', w', k - 1, \varepsilon)$
17:                    **for all** $H' \in \mathcal{P}_{\text{TSP}}'$ **do**
18:                        form a Hamilton cycle from H' plus $P_{a,b,c,d}^e$; add it to $\mathcal{P}_{\text{TSP}}$
19:                        form a Hamilton cycle from H' plus (u, v); add it to $\mathcal{P}_{\text{TSP}}$

Algorithm 3. Approximation algorithm for k-criteria Max-ATSP

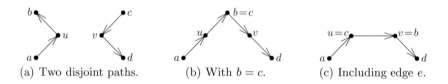

(a) Two disjoint paths.   (b) With $b = c$.   (c) Including edge e.

Fig. 2. The three possibilities of $P_{a,b,c,d}^e$. Symmetrically to (b), we also have $a = d$. Symmetrically to (c), we also have $v = a$ and $u = d$.

we decompose it to obtain a collection P of paths. Then we add edges to P to obtain a Hamiltonian cycle H, which we then add to $\mathcal{P}_{\text{TSP}}$.

If C contains a heavy-weight edge, then there exists an edge $e = (u, v)$ and an i with $w_i(e) > \alpha_k \cdot w_i(C)$. We pick one such edge. Then we iterate over all possible vertices a, b, c, d (including equalities and including u and v). We denote by $P_{a,b,c,d}^e$ the graph with vertices u, v, a, b, c, d and edges (a, u), (u, b), (c, v), and (v, d). We call $P_{a,b,c,d}^e$ *legal* if it can be extended to a Hamiltonian cycle: $P_{a,b,c,d}^e$ is legal if and only if it consists of one or two vertex-disjoint directed paths. Figure 2 shows the different possibilities.

For every legal $P_{a,b,c,d}^e$, we contract the paths as follows: We remove all outgoing edges of a and c, all incoming edges of b and d, and all edges incident to u or v. Then we identify a and b as well as c and d. If $P_{a,b,c,d}^e$ consists of a single path, then we remove all vertices except the two endpoints of this path, and we identify these two endpoints.

In this way, we obtain a slightly smaller instance G'. Then, for every i, we remove the ith objective to obtain w', and recurse on G' with only $k-1$ objectives w'. This yields a approximate Pareto curves $\mathcal{P}'_{\text{TSP}}$ of Hamiltonian cycles of G'. Now consider any $H' \in \mathcal{P}'_{\text{TSP}}$. We expand the contracted paths to obtain H. Then we construct two tours: First, we just add $P^e_{a,b,c,d}$ to H, which yields a Hamiltonian cycle by construction. Second, we observe that no edge in H is incident to u or v. We add the edge (u, v) to H as well as some more edges such that we obtain a Hamiltonian cycle. We put the Hamiltonian cycles thus constructed into $\mathcal{P}_{\text{TSP}}$.

We have not yet discussed the success probability. Randomness is needed for computing the approximate Pareto curves of cycle covers and the recursive calls of MC-MaxATSP with $k - 1$ objectives. Let N be the size of the instance at hand, and let $p_k(N, 1/\varepsilon)$ is a polynomial that bounds the size of a $(1 - \varepsilon)$ approximate Pareto curve from above. Then we need at most $N^4 \cdot p_k(N, 1/\varepsilon)$ recursive calls of MC-MaxATSP. In total, the number of calls of randomized algorithms is bounded by some polynomial $q_k(N, 1/\varepsilon)$. We amplify the success probabilities of these calls such that the probability is at least $1 - \frac{1}{2 \cdot q_k(N, 1/\varepsilon)}$. Thus, the probability that one such call is not successful is at most $q_k(N, 1/\varepsilon) \cdot \frac{1}{2 \cdot q_k(N, 1/\varepsilon)} \leq 1/2$ by a union bound. Hence, the success probability of the algorithm is at least $1/2$.

Instead of Decompose, we can also use RandDecompose. We modify RandDecompose such that the running-time is guaranteed to be polynomial and that there is only a small probability that RandDecompose errs. Furthermore, we have to make the error probabilities of the cycle cover computation as well as the recursive calls of MC-MaxATSP slightly smaller to maintain an overall success probability of at least $1/2$.

The running-time of MC-MaxATSP is polynomial in the input size and $1/\varepsilon$, which can be seen by induction on k: We have a polynomial time approximation algorithm for $k = 1$. For $k > 1$, the approximate Pareto curve of cycle covers can be computed in polynomial time, yielding a polynomial number of cycle covers. All further computations can also be implemented to run in polynomial time since MC-MaxATSP for $k-1$ runs in polynomial time by induction hypothesis.

Theorem 3. MC-MaxATSP *is a randomized* $\frac{1}{k+1} - \varepsilon$ *approximation for multi-criteria Max-ATSP. Its running-time is polynomial in the input size and* $1/\varepsilon$.

Proof. We have already discussed the error probabilities and the running-time. Thus, it remains to consider the approximation ratio, and we can assume in the following, that all randomized computations are successful. We prove the theorem by induction on k. For $k = 1$, this follows since mono-criterion Max-ATSP can be approximated with a factor $2/3 > 1/2$.

Now assume that the theorem holds for $k - 1$. We have to prove that, for every Hamiltonian cycle $\hat{H}$, there exists a Hamiltonian cycle $H \in \mathcal{P}_{\text{TSP}}$ with $w(H) \geq \left(\frac{1}{k+1} - \varepsilon\right) \cdot w(\hat{H})$. Since every Hamiltonian cycle is in particular a cycle cover, there exists a $C \in \mathcal{C}$ with $w(C) \geq (1 - \varepsilon) \cdot w(\hat{H})$. Now we distinguish two cases. The first case is that C consists solely of light-weight edges, i. e., $w(e) \leq \frac{1}{k+1} \cdot w(C)$, then DECOMPOSE returns a collection P of paths with $w(P) \geq \frac{1}{k+1} \cdot w(C) \geq \left(\frac{1}{k+1} - \varepsilon\right) \cdot w(\hat{H})$, which yields a Hamiltonian cycle H with $w(H) \geq w(P) \geq \left(\frac{1}{k+1} - \varepsilon\right) \cdot w(\hat{H})$ as claimed.

The second case is that C contains at least one heavy-weight edge $e = (u, v)$. Let (a, u), (u, b), (c, v), and (v, d) be the edges in $\hat{H}$ that are incident to u or v. (We may have some equalities among the vertices as shown in Figure 2.) Note that $\hat{H}$ does not necessarily contain the edge e. We consider the corresponding $P^e_{a,b,c,d}$ and divide the second case into two subcases.

The first subcase is that there is a $j \in [k]$ with $w_j(P^e_{a,b,c,d}) \geq \frac{1}{k+1} \cdot w_j(\hat{H})$, i. e., at least a $\frac{1}{k+1}$ fraction of the jth objective is concentrated in $P^e_{a,b,c,d}$. (We can have $j = i$ or $j \neq i$.) Let $J \subseteq [k]$ be the set of such j.

We fix one $j \in J$ arbitrarily and consider the graph G' obtained by removing the jth objective and contracting the paths (a, u, b) and (c, v, d). A fraction of $1 - \frac{1}{k+1} = \frac{k}{k+1}$ of the weight of $\hat{H}$ is left in G' with respect to all objectives but those in J. Thus, G' contains a Hamiltonian cycle $\hat{H}'$ with $w_\ell(\hat{H}') \geq \frac{k}{k+1} \cdot w_\ell(\hat{H})$ for all $\ell \in [k] \setminus J$. Since $(k-1)$-criteria Max-ATSP can be approximated with a factor of $\frac{1}{k} - \varepsilon$ by assumption, $\mathcal{P}'_{\text{TSP}}$ contains a Hamiltonian cycle H' with $w_\ell(H') \geq (\frac{1}{k} - \varepsilon) \cdot \frac{k}{k+1} \cdot w_\ell(\hat{H}) \geq \left(\frac{1}{k+1} - \varepsilon\right) \cdot w_\ell(\hat{H})$ for all $\ell \in [k] \setminus J$. Together with $P^e_{a,b,c,d}$, which contributes enough weight to the objectives in J, we obtain a Hamiltonian cycle H with $w(H) \geq \left(\frac{1}{k+1} - \varepsilon\right) \cdot w(\hat{H})$, which is as claimed.

The second subcase is that $w_j(P^e_{a,b,c,d}) \leq \frac{1}{k+1} \cdot w_j(H)$ for all $j \in [k]$. Thus, at least a fraction of $\frac{k}{k+1}$ of the weight of $\hat{H}$ is outside of $P^e_{a,b,c,d}$. We consider the case with the ith objective removed. Then, with the same argument as in the first subcase, we obtain a Hamiltonian cycle H' of G' with $w_\ell(H') \geq \left(\frac{1}{k+1} - \varepsilon\right) \cdot w_\ell(\hat{H})$ for all $\ell \in [k] \setminus \{i\}$. To obtain a Hamiltonian cycle of G, we take the edge $e = (u, v)$ and connect its endpoints appropriately. (For instance, if a, b, c, d are distinct, then we add the path (a, u, v, d) and the edge (c, b).) This yields enough weight for the ith objective in order to obtain a Hamiltonian cycle H with $w(H) \geq \left(\frac{1}{k+1} - \varepsilon\right) \cdot w(\hat{H})$ since $w_i(e) \geq \frac{1}{k+1} \cdot w(C) \geq \left(\frac{1}{k+1} - \varepsilon\right) \cdot w(\hat{H})$.

4.2   Multi-criteria Max-STSP

MC-MAXATSP works of course also for undirected graphs, for which it achieves an approximation ratio of $\frac{1}{k+1} - \varepsilon$. But we can do better for undirected graphs.

Our algorithm MC-MAXSTSP for undirected graphs (Algorithm 4) starts by computing an approximate Pareto curve of cycle covers just as MC-MAXATSP did. Then we consider each cycle cover C separately. If C consists solely of light-weight edges, then we can decompose C using DECOMPOSE. If C contains one or more heavy-weight edges, then some more work has to be done than in the case of directed graphs. The reason is that we cannot simply contract paths – this would make the new graph G' (and the edge weights w') asymmetric.

So assume that a cycle cover $C \in \mathcal{C}$ contains a heavy-weight edge $e = \{u, v\}$. Let $i \in [k]$ be such that $w_i(e) \geq w_i(C)/k$. In a first attempt, we remove the ith

---

$\mathcal{P}_{\text{TSP}} \leftarrow$ MC-MaxSTSP(G, w, k, ε)

input: undirected complete graph $G = (V, E)$, $k \geq 2$, edge weights $w : E \rightarrow \mathbb{N}^k$, $\varepsilon > 0$

output: approximate Pareto curve $\mathcal{P}_{\text{TSP}}$ for k-criteria Max-TSP

1: compute a $(1 - \varepsilon)$ approximate Pareto curve $\mathcal{C}$ of cycle covers
2: $\mathcal{P}_{\text{TSP}} \leftarrow \emptyset$
3: **if** $k = 2$ **then**
4:     **for all** $C \in \mathcal{C}$ **do**
5:         $P \leftarrow$ Decompose(C, w, k)
6:         add edges to P to form a Hamiltonian cycle H; add H to $\mathcal{P}_{\text{TSP}}$
7: **else**
8:     **for all** cycle covers $C \in \mathcal{C}$ **do**
9:         **if** $w(e) \leq w(C)/k$ for edges $e \in C$ **then**
10:           $P \leftarrow$ Decompose(C, w, k)
11:           add edges to P to form a Hamiltonian cycle H; add H to $\mathcal{P}_{\text{TSP}}$
12:         **else**
13:           let $i \in [k]$ and $e = \{u, v\} \in C$ with $w_i(e) > w_i(C)/k$
14:           **for all** $\ell \in \{0, \ldots, 4k\}$, distinct $x_1, \ldots, x_\ell \in V \setminus \{u, v\}$, and $k \in [k]$ **do**
15:             $U \leftarrow \{x_1, \ldots, x_\ell, u, v\}$
16:             obtain w' from w by removing the jth objective
17:             set $w'(f) = 0$ for all edges f incident to U
18:             $\mathcal{P}_{\text{TSP}}^{U,j} \leftarrow$ MC-MaxSTSP$(G, w', k - 1, \varepsilon)$
19:             **for all** $H \in \mathcal{P}_{\text{TSP}}^{U,j}$ **do**
20:                 remove all edges f from H with $f \subseteq U$ to obtain H'
21:                 **for all** H_U such that $H' \cup H_U$ is a Hamiltonian cycle **do**
22:                     add $H' \cup H_U$ to $\mathcal{P}_{\text{TSP}}$

Algorithm 4. Approximation algorithm for k-criteria Max-STSP.

objective to obtain w'. Then we set $w'(f) = 0$ for all edges f incident to u or v. We recurse with $k - 1$ objectives on G with edge weights w'. This yields a tour H' on G. Now we remove all edges incident to u or v of H' and add new edges including e. In this way, we get enough weight with respect to objective i. Unfortunately, there is a problem if there is an objective j and an edge f incident to u or v such that f contains almost all weight with respect to w_j: We cannot guarantee that this edge f is included in H without further modifying H'. To cope with this problem, we do the following: In addition to u and v, we set the weight of all edges incident to the other vertex of f to 0. Then we recurse. Unfortunately, there may be another objective j' that now causes problems. To solve the whole problem, we iterate over all $\ell = 0, \ldots, 4k$ and over all additional vertices $x_1, \ldots, x_\ell \neq u, v$. Let $U = \{x_1, \ldots, x_\ell, u, v\}$. We remove one objective $i \in [k]$ to obtain w', set the weight of all edges incident to U to 0, and recurse with $k - 1$ objectives. Although the time needed to do this is exponential in k, we maintain polynomial running-time for fixed k.

As in the case of directed graphs, we can make the success probability of every randomized computation small enough to maintain a success probability of at least $1/2$.

The base case is now $k = 2$: In this case, every cycle cover possesses a $1/2$ decomposition, and we do not have to care about heavy-weight edges. Overall, we obtain the following result.

Theorem 4. MC-MAXSTSP *is a randomized* $\frac{1}{k} - \varepsilon$ *approximation for multi-criteria Max-STSP. Its running-time is polynomial in the input size and* $1/\varepsilon$.

5 Remarks

The analysis of the approximation ratios of our algorithms is essentially optimal: Our approach can at best lead to approximation ratios of $\frac{1}{k+c}$ for some $c \in \mathbb{Z}$. The reason is as follows: Assume that $(k-1)$-criteria Max-TSP can be approximated with a factor of τ_k. If we have a k-criteria instance, we have to set the threshold for heavy-weight edges somewhere. Assume for the moment that this threshold α_k be arbitrary. Then the ratio for k-criteria Max-TSP is $\min\{\alpha_k, (1 - \alpha_k) \cdot \tau_{k-1}\}$. Choosing $\alpha_k = \frac{\tau_{k-1}}{\tau_{k-1}+1}$ maximizes this ratio. Thus, if $\tau_{k-1} = 1/T$ for some T, then $\tau_k \leq \frac{\tau_{k-1}}{\tau_{k-1}+1} = \frac{1}{T+1}$. We conclude that the denominator of the approximation ratio increases by at least 1 if we go from $k-1$ to k.

For undirected graphs, we have obtained a ratio of roughly $1/k$, which is optimal since $\alpha_2^u = 1/2$ implies $c \geq 0$. Similarly, for directed graphs, we have a ratio of $\frac{1}{k+1}$, which is also optimal since $\alpha_2^d = 1/3$ implies $c \geq 1$.

Due to the existence of $\Omega(1/\log k)$-decompositions, we conjecture that both k-criteria Max-STSP and k-criteria Max-ATSP can in fact be approximated with factors of $\Omega(1/\log k)$. This, however, requires a different approach or at least a new technique for heavy-weight edges.

References

1. Ahuja, R.K., Magnanti, T.L., Orlin, J.B.: Network Flows: Theory, Algorithms, and Applications. Prentice-Hall, Englewood Cliffs (1993)
2. Bläser, M., Manthey, B., Putz, O.: Approximating multi-criteria Max-TSP. Computing Research Repository (2008) arXiv:0806.3668 [cs.DS]
3. Chen, Z.-Z., Okamoto, Y., Wang, L.: Improved deterministic approximation algorithms for Max TSP. Information Processing Letters 95(2), 333–342 (2005)
4. Ehrgott, M.: Multicriteria Optimization. Springer, Heidelberg (2005)
5. Kaplan, H., Lewenstein, M., Shafrir, N., Sviridenko, M.I.: Approximation algorithms for asymmetric TSP by decomposing directed regular multigraphs. Journal of the ACM 52(4), 602–626 (2005)

6. Manthey, B.: Approximate pareto curves for the asymmetric traveling salesman problem. Computing Research Repository (2007) cs.DS/0711.2157, arXiv
7. Manthey, B., Ram, L.S.: Approximation algorithms for multi-criteria traveling salesman problems. Algorithmica (to appear)
8. Papadimitriou, C.H., Yannakakis, M.: On the approximability of trade-offs and optimal access of web sources. In: Proc. of the 41st Ann. IEEE Symp. on Foundations of Computer Science (FOCS), pp. 86–92. IEEE Computer Society, Los Alamitos (2000)

An Integer Programming Algorithm for Routing Optimization in IP Networks

Andreas Bley

Zuse Institute Berlin
Takustr. 7, D-14195 Berlin, Germany
bley@zib.de

Abstract. Most data networks nowadays use shortest path protocols to route the traffic. Given administrative routing lengths for the links of the network, all data packets are sent along shortest paths with respect to these lengths from their source to their destination.

In this paper, we present an integer programming algorithm for the minimum congestion unsplittable shortest path routing problem, which arises in the operational planning of such networks. Given a capacitated directed graph and a set of communication demands, the goal is to find routing lengths that define a unique shortest path for each demand and minimize the maximum congestion over all links in the resulting routing. We illustrate the general decomposition approach our algorithm is based on, present the integer and linear programming models used to solve the master and the client problem, and discuss the most important implementational aspects. Finally, we report computational results for various benchmark problems, which demonstrate the efficiency of our algorithm.

Keywords: Shortest Path Routing, Integer Programming.

1 Introduction

In this paper, we present an integer programming algorithm to optimize the routing in communication networks based on shortest path routing protocols such as OSPF [22] or IS-IS [16], which are widely used in the Internet. With these routing protocols, all end-to-end traffic streams are routed along shortest paths with respect to some administrative link lengths (or routing weights), that form the so-called routing metric. Finding a routing metric that induces a set of globally efficient end-to-end routing paths is a major difficulty in such networks. The shortest path routing paradigm enforces rather complicated and subtle interdependencies among the paths that comprise a valid routing. The routing paths can be controlled only jointly and only indirectly via the link lengths. In this paper, we consider the unsplittable shortest path routing variant, where the lengths must be chosen such that the shortest paths are unique and each traffic stream is sent unsplit via its single shortest path.

One of the most important operational planning tasks in such networks is traffic engineering. Its goal is to improve the service quality in the existing network

D. Halperin and K. Mehlhorn (Eds.): ESA 2008, LNCS 5193, pp. 198–209, 2008.

by (re-)optimizing the routing of the traffic, but leaving the network topology and hardware configuration unchanged. Mathematically, this can be formulated as the minimum congestion unsplittable shortest path routing problem (MIN-CON-USPR). The problem input consists of a digraph $D = (V, A)$ with arc capacities $c_a \in \mathbb{Z}$ for all $a \in A$, and a set of directed commodities $K \subseteq V \times V$ with demand values $d_{st} \in \mathbb{Z}$ for all $(s, t) \in K$. A feasible solution is an unsplittable shortest path routing (USPR) of the commodities, i.e., a metric of link lengths $w_a \in \mathbb{Z}$, $a \in A$, that induce a unique shortest (s, t)-path for each commodity $(s, t) \in K$. Each commodity's demand is sent unsplit along its shortest path. The objective is to minimize the maximum congestion (i.e., the flow to capacity ratio) over all arcs. The maximum congestion is a good measure and typically used as a key indicator for the overall network service quality.

Due to their great practical relevance, shortest path routing problems have been studied quite intensively in the last decade. Ben-Ameur and Gourdin [3], Broström and Holmberg [13,14] studied the combinatorial properties of path sets that correspond to shortest (multi-)path routings and devised linear programming models to find lengths that induce a set of presumed shortest paths (or prove that no such lengths exist). Bley [5,9], on the other hand, showed that finding a smallest shortest-path conflict in a set of presumed shortest paths or the smallest integer lengths inducing these paths is $\mathcal{NP}$-hard. Bley [6,7] also proved that MIN-CON-USPR is inapproximable within a factor of $\Omega(|V|^{1-\epsilon})$ for any $\epsilon > 0$, presented examples where the smallest link congestion that can be obtained with unsplittable shortest path routing exceeds the congestion that can be obtained with multicommodity flow or unsplittable flow routing by a factor of $\Omega(|V|^2)$, and proposed polynomial time approximation algorithms for several special cases of MIN-CON-USPR and related network design problems. The minimum congestion shortest multi-path routing problem has been shown to be inapproximable within a factor less than 3/2 by Fortz and Thorup [18].

Various approaches for the solution of network design and routing problems in shortest path networks have been proposed. Algorithms using local search, simulated annealing, or Lagrangian relaxation techniques with the routing lengths as primary decision variables are presented in [4,10,15,17,18], for example. These length-based methods work well for shortest multi-path routing problems, where traffic may be split among several equally long shortest paths, but they often produce only suboptimal solutions for hard unsplittable shortest path routing problems. As they deliver no or only weak quality guarantees, they cannot guarantee to find provenly optimal solutions.

Using mixed integer programming formulations that contain variables for the routing lengths as well as for the resulting shortest paths and traffic flows, shortest path routing problems can – in principle – be solved to optimality. Formulations of this type are discussed in [10,19,24,26,29], for example. Unfortunately, the relation between the shortest paths and the routing length always leads to quadratic or very large big-M models, which are computationally extremely hard and not suitable for practical problems.

In this paper, we present an integer programming algorithm that decomposes the routing problem into the two tasks of first finding the optimal end-to-end routing paths and then, secondly, finding a routing metric that induce these paths. As we will show, this approach permits the solution of real-world problems. An implementation of this algorithm [11,9] is used successfully in the planning of the German national education and research network for several years. Variants of this decomposition approach for shortest multi-path and shortest path multicast routing problems are discussed in [12,20,27,28,29].

The remainder of this paper is organized as follows. In Section 2, we formally define the problem addressed in this paper and introduce the basic notion and notation. The overall decomposition algorithm, the integer and linear programming models and sub-algorithms used for the solution of the master and the client problem, and the most important aspects of our implementation are described in Section 3. In Section 4, we finally report on numerical results obtained with this algorithm for numerous real-world and benchmark problems and illustrate the relevance of optimizing the routing in practice.

2   Notation and Preliminaries

Let $D = (V, A)$ be a directed graph with arc capacities $c_a \in \mathbb{Z}$ for all $a \in A$ and let $K \subseteq V \times V$ be a set of directed commodities with demand values $d_{st} \in \mathbb{Z}$ for all $(s,t) \in K$. A metric $\mathbf{w} = (w_a) \in \mathbb{Z}^A$ of arc lengths is said to define an *unsplittable shortest path routing (USPR)* for the commodities K, if the shortest (s,t)-path P_{st}^* with respect to $\mathbf{w}$ is uniquely determined for each commodity $(s,t) \in K$. The demand of each commodity is routed unsplit along the respective shortest path. For a metric $\mathbf{w}$ that defines such an USPR, the total flow through an arc $a \in A$ then is

$$f_a(\mathbf{w}) := \sum_{(s,t) \in K : a \in P_{st}^*(\mathbf{w})} d_{st} \, . \tag{1}$$

The task in the minimum congestion unsplittable shortest path routing problem MIN-CON-USPR is to find a metric $\mathbf{w} \in \mathbb{Z}^A$ that defines an USPR for the given commodity set K and minimizes the maximum congestion $L := \max\{f_a(\mathbf{w})/c_a : a \in A\}$.

Before presenting of our algorithm, we need to introduce some further notation. We say that a metric $\mathbf{w}$ is *compatible* with a set $\mathcal{P}$ of end-to-end routing paths, if each path $P \in \mathcal{P}$ is the unique shortest path between its terminals with respect to $\mathbf{w}$. A metric $\mathbf{w}$ is said to be *compatible* with set of node-arc pairs $F \subset V \times A$, if arc a is on a unique shortest path towards t for all $(t,a) \in F$. If there exists such a metric, we say that the set F is a valid *unique shortest path forwarding (USPF)*, otherwise we call it an *(USPF-) conflict*. One easily verifies that a metric is compatible with a path set $\mathcal{P}$ if and only if it is compatible with the set of node-arc pairs $F := \bigcup_{P \in \mathcal{P}} \{(t,a) : t \text{ is destination of } P, a \in P\}$.

Clearly, any subset (including the empty set) of an USPF is an USPF as well. Hence, the family of all USPF in the digraph D forms an independence system (or hereditary family) $\mathcal{I} \subset 2^{V \times A}$. The circuits of this independence system are exactly the irreducible conflicts. The family of all irreducible conflicts is denoted by $\mathcal{C} \subset 2^{V \times A}$.

In general, these set families can be extremely complex and computationally intractable [9]. Given an arbitrary set $F \subset V \times A$, the smallest conflict (with respect to the number of node-arc pairs) in F may be arbitrarily large and even approximating its size within a factor less than $7/6$ is $\mathcal{NP}$-hard. Approximating the size of the largest valid USPF in F within a factor less than $8/7$ is $\mathcal{NP}$-hard as well. However, one can decide in polynomial time whether or not a given set $F \subset V \times A$ is a valid USPF and, depending on that, either find a compatible metric or some (not necessarily minimal) irreducible conflict in F, which is the foundation of the algorithm described in this paper.

3   Integer Programming Algorithm

Similar to Bender's decomposition, our algorithm decomposes the problem of finding an optimal shortest path routing into the master problem of finding the optimal end-to-end paths and the client problem of finding compatible routing lengths for these paths.

The master problem is formulated as an integer linear program and solved with a branch-and-cut algorithm. Instead of using routing weight variables, the underlying formulation contains special inequalities to exclude routing path configurations that are no valid unsplittable shortest path routings. These inequalities are generated dynamically as cutting planes by the client problem during the execution or the branch-and-cut algorithm.

Given a set of routing paths computed by the master problem's branch-and-cut algorithm, the client problem then is to find a metric of routing lengths that induce exactly these paths. As we will see in Section 3.2, this problem can be formulated and solved as a linear program. If the given paths indeed form a valid shortest path routing, the solution of this linear program yields a compatible metric. If the given paths do not form a valid unsplittable shortest path routing, the client linear program is infeasible. In this case, the given routing paths contain a conflict that must not occur in any admissible shortest path routing. This conflict, which can be derived from the dual solution of the infeasible client linear program, then can be turned into an inequality for the master problem, which is valid for all admissible shortest path routings, but violated by the current routing. Adding this inequality to the master problem, we then cut off the current non-admissible routing and proceed with the master branch-and-cut algorithm to compute another candidate routing.

3.1   Master Problem

There are several ways to formulate the master problem of MIN-CON-USPR as a mixed integer program. For notational simplicity, we present a variation of the disaggregated arc-routing formulation used in our algorithm, which contains additional artificial variables that describe the unique shortest path forwarding defined by the routing.

The primary decision variables used in this formulation are the variables $x_a^{st} \in \{0,1\}$ for all $(s,t) \in K$ and $a \in A$. These variables describe which arcs are contained in the routing paths. Variable x_a^{st} is supposed to be 1 if and only if arc a is contained in the routing path for commodity (s,t). A single variable $L \in \mathbb{R}$ represents the maximum congestion that is attained by the routing. The additional artificial variables $y_a^t \in \{0,1\}$ for all $t \in V$ and $a \in A$ describe the forwarding defined by the routing paths. Variable y_a^t is supposed to be 1 if there is a routing path towards t that contains arc a. With these variables the master problem of MIN-CON-USPR can be formulated as follows:

$$\min \quad L \tag{2a}$$

$$\text{s.t.} \quad \sum_{a \in \delta^+(v)} x_a^{st} - \sum_{a \in \delta^-(v)} x_a^{st} = \begin{cases} -1 & \text{if } v = s \\ 1 & \text{if } v = t \\ 0 & \text{else} \end{cases} \quad (s,t) \in K,\, v \in V \tag{2b}$$

$$\sum_{(s,t) \in K} d_{st} x_a^{st} \leq c_a L \qquad a \in A \tag{2c}$$

$$x_a^{st} \leq y_a^t \qquad (s,t) \in K,\, a \in A \tag{2d}$$

$$\sum_{a \in \delta^+(v)} y_a^t \leq 1 \qquad t \in V,\, v \in V \tag{2e}$$

$$\sum_{(a,t) \in C} y_a^t \leq |C| - 1 \qquad C \in \mathcal{C} \tag{2f}$$

$$x_a^{st} \in \{0,1\} \qquad (s,t) \in K,\, a \in A \tag{2g}$$

$$L \geq 0. \tag{2h}$$

Subproblem (2a)–(2c) together with the integrality and non-negativity constraints (2g) and (2h) is a standard arc-routing formulation for the unsplittable multicommodity flow problem, whose objective is to minimize the congestion L.

Inequalities (2d) force the artificial variables y_a^t to be (at least) 1 for all arcs a that are contained in some routing path towards destination t. Together with the out-degree constraints (2e) this ensures that, for each destination $t \in V$, the routing paths towards t form an anti-arborescence (a reversely oriented tree). This is clearly necessary for the paths in any valid unsplittable shortest path routing.

Constraints (2f) finally ensure that no integer solution of (2) contains all node-arc pairs of any (irreducible) USPF-conflict $C \in \mathcal{C}$. As the irreducible conflicts are exactly the circuits of the independence system formed by all valid unique shortest path forwarding, this implies that the artificial variables y_a^t describe a valid USPF. Consequently, the routing given by any integer feasible solution of (2) is a valid unsplittable shortest path routing. In general, the number of these conflict constraints (2f) can be exponentially large. They are separated via the client problem during the branch-and-cut solution process.

Note that the model contains no explicit constraints forcing the artificial variables y_a^t to attain only values 0 or 1. These constrains are not necessary. Any solution $(\mathbf{x}, \mathbf{y}, L)$ with $x_a^{st} \in \{0, 1\}$ for all $(s, t) \in K$ and $a \in A$ can be easily turned into an equivalent solution with $y_t^a \in \{0, 1\}$ for all $t \in V$ and $a \in A$ by setting $y_t^a := \max\{x_a^{st} : s \text{ with } (s, t) \in K\}$ for all t and a.

3.2   Client Problem

Now suppose we are given an integer solution $(\mathbf{x}, \mathbf{y}, L)$ of formulation (2) or, more precisely, of a subsystem of (2) containing only some of the conflict constraints (2f) so far.

Let F be the presumed unique shortest path forwarding given by this solution, i.e., $F = \{(t, a) : y_a^t = 1\}$. Our goal in the client problem is to find a compatible metric $\mathbf{w}$ for F. However, if the given solution $(\mathbf{x}, \mathbf{y}, L)$ violates some of the conflict constraints (2f) that have not yet been added to the master formulation, such a metric does not exist. In this case, the task is to generate one of these violated inequalities.

The first part of this problem can be solved with linear programming techniques. A number of alternative formulations for this so-called *inverse shortest paths problem (ISP)* have been proposed in the literature [3,25]. In the following, we present the aggregated formulation used in our algorithm together with the arc-routing formulation for the master problem.

Let F be the given presumed unique shortest path forwarding. For each pair $(t, a) \in F$, arc $a = (u, v)$ is assumed to be on a *unique* shortest path from u to t. Hence, the arcs $a' \in \delta^+(u) \backslash \{a\}$ must not be on any shortest (u, t)-path. The set of all implied non shortest path node-arc pairs is $\bar{F} = \bigcup_{(t,(u,v)) \in F} (\delta^+(u) \backslash \{(u, v)\})$: For each pair $(t, a) \in \bar{F}$, arc $a = (u, v)$ must not be on a shortest path from u to t. (Note that we cannot simply assume $\bar{F} = V \times A \backslash F$, because F not necessarily prescribes the shortest paths between all node pairs. Arcs that are not relevant for the routing of the given commodities may or may not be on shortest paths.)

Our formulation of the inverse shortest paths problem uses a variable $w_a \in \mathbb{Z}$ for the length of each arc $a \in A$ and a variable $r_v^t \in \mathbb{R}$ for the potential of each node $v \in V$ with respect to each destination $t \in V$ and the metric $\mathbf{w}$. (If $r_t^t = 0$, the smallest possible potential r_v^t of node v is exactly the distance from v to t with respect to the arc lengths w_a.) With these variables, the inverse shortest paths problem for the given forwarding F, can be formulated as follows:

$$\min \quad w_{\max} \tag{3a}$$
$$\text{s.t.} \quad w_{(u,v)} - r_u^t + r_v^t = 0 \qquad (t, (u, v)) \in F \tag{3b}$$
$$w_{(u,v)} - r_u^t + r_v^t \geq 1 \qquad (t, (u, v)) \in \bar{F} \tag{3c}$$
$$w_{(u,v)} - r_u^t + r_v^t \geq 0 \qquad (t, (u, v)) \in (V \times A) \backslash F \backslash \bar{F} \tag{3d}$$
$$1 \leq w_a \leq w_{\max} \qquad a \in A \tag{3e}$$
$$r_v^t \in \mathbb{R} \qquad t \in V, v \in V \tag{3f}$$
$$w_a \in \mathbb{Z} \qquad a \in A . \tag{3g}$$

Constraints (3b),(3d), and (3e) ensure that the lengths w_a in any solution of (3) form a compatible metric for the given forwarding F. The term $w_{(u,v)} - r_u^t + r_v^t$

is the difference between the length of the shortest path starting in node u, passing through arc (u, v), and ending in node t, and the distance from node v to node t. This difference must be 0 for all arcs (u, v) that are on a shortest path and strictly greater than 0 for all arcs that must not be on a shortest path, as expressed in constraints (3b) and (3c). For all remaining arcs it must be non-negative. Formulation (3) has a solution if and only if there exist a compatible metric for the given forwarding F. Furthermore, there is a compatible metric with lengths in the range $\{1, 2, \ldots, M\}$ if and only if the optimal solution value $w_{\max}$ of formulation (3) is less or equal to M.

Note that formulation (3) is an integer program and may be computationally hard. In fact, Bley [8] proved that it is already $\mathcal{NP}$-hard to approximate its optimum value within a factor less than $9/8$ in general.

In our algorithm, we solve the linear relaxation of (3) in a first step and scale and round its optimal fractional solution to an integer feasible solution of (3) afterwards. It is not difficult to verify that the integer program (3) has a solution if and only if its linear relaxation has. Using the rounding scheme proposed by Ben-Ameur and Gourdin [3], we obtain lengths that exceed the minimal ones by a factor of at most $\min(|V|/2, |P_{\max}|)$, where $P_{\max}$ is the longest prescribed shortest path. For practically relevant network sizes, the weights computed with this approximate method easily fit into the admissible range of all modern routing protocols. So, we can safely ignore the integrality constraint (3g) in practice.

If the linear relaxation of (3) is infeasible, then the given solution $(\mathbf{x}, \mathbf{y}, L)$ of the (incomplete) master formulation is not a valid routing. In this case, the presumed forwarding F is no valid unsplittable shortest path forwarding. It contains at least one (irreducible) conflict $C \in \mathcal{C}$, whose corresponding inequality (2f) is violated by the given solution $(\mathbf{x}, \mathbf{y}, L)$. To find one of these conflicts, we iteratively try to remove each node-arc pair from F. In each iteration, we remove one pair (t, a) from F, update the set $\bar{F}$ of implied non-shortest path node-arc pairs, and solve the corresponding linear relaxation of (3). If this linear program remains infeasible, we remove the pair (t, a) permanently from F. Otherwise, we reinsert it into F and keep it permanently. If no more node-arc pair can be removed, the remaining set F defines an irreducible conflict, whose corresponding conflict inequality (2f) for $C = F$ is violated by the given solution $(\mathbf{x}, \mathbf{y}, L)$. In our implementation, we improved the practical performance of this procedure significantly by removing initially all those pairs $(t, (u, v))$ from F, for which the dual variables of the corresponding constraint (3b) and the dual variables of all constraints (3c) implied by $(t, (u, v)) \in F$ are 0. If these constraints are not active in the infeasible subsystem of (3), there is at least one (irreducible) conflict that is not related to the fact that $(t, (u, v)) \in F$.

Note that this iterative method finds an irreducible conflict inequality (2f), but not necessarily the most violated one. Finding the most violated such inequality is $\mathcal{NP}$-hard, even if the given solution of the master problem is integer [9]. Furthermore, note that this approach solves the separation problem over the conflict inequalities (2f) only for integer solutions $(\mathbf{x}, \mathbf{y}, L)$. For fractional solutions $(\mathbf{x}, \mathbf{y}, L)$, the presumed forwarding F is not well-defined. A separation heuristic based on an approximate integer programming model of the separation problem (for shortest multi-path routings), which can be applied for fractional solutions, has been proposed by Tomaszewski et al. [28]. Also, several subclasses of (2f) can be separated in polynomial time; see [9,11,13,14,28,29].

3.3   Implementation

From the theoretical point of view, the branch-and-cut approach presented above seems not very attractive. The integrality gap of the integer programming formulation (2) can be very large and the separation of the conflict inequalities (2f) is $\mathcal{NP}$-hard for fractional solutions of (2). Nevertheless, implemented carefully this approach works surprisingly well in practice. In the following, we briefly discuss the most important aspects of our implementation of this algorithm. Further details, including a description of all used cutting planes and separation algorithms, of the specially tailored branching schemes, and of the problem-specific primal heuristics, can be found in [9].

In our implementation, the initial formulation of the master problem contains only the arc-routing variables x_a^{st}, the congestion variable L, and the flow conservation and capacity constraints (2b) and (2c). All other constraints are separated. The degree constraints (2e) are separated by a simple enumerative algorithm searching through all node pairs $t, v \in V$. The conflict constraints (2f) are separated via the solution of the client problem as described in the previous section. However, the artificial variables y_a^t involved in these constraints and the linking constraints (2d) are not generated explicitly. Instead, we assume

$$y_a^t := \max\{x_a^{st} : s \text{ with } (s,t) \in K\} \text{ for all } t \in V \text{ and } a \in A, \qquad (4)$$

disaggregate each of the inequalities (2e) and (2f) into an equivalent set of inequalities on the arc-routing variables x_a^{st} instead of the forwarding variables y_t^a, and separate over the set of these disaggregated inequalities. This is done by applying the separation algorithms for the original inequalities to the values y_t^a defined as in (4). If a violated inequality is found, each variable y_t^a in this inequality is replaced by a variable $x_a^{st} = \arg\max\{x_a^{st} : s \text{ with } (s,t) \in K\}$, which yields one of the most violated disaggregated inequalities corresponding to the violated original inequality.

At each node of the master problem's branch-and-bound tree we solve the current LP relaxation and separate violated out-degree constraint and several other classes of inequalities.

Analogous to the out-degree inequalities (2e), which ensure that the routing paths towards each destination t form an anti-arborescence, we also separate in-degree inequalities, which ensure that the routing paths emanating from each source s form an arborescence. With the implicit, artificial variables $z_a^s := \max\{x_a^{st} : t \text{ with } (s,t) \in K\}$ for all $s \in V$ and $a \in A$, these inequalities can be easily formulated as

$$\sum_{a \in \delta^-(v)} z_a^s \leq 1 \qquad\qquad v, s \in V . \qquad (5)$$

Using the same disaggregation approach as for the out-degree constraints, we separate the disaggregated version of these inequalities with a simple enumerative algorithm.

Numerous types of valid inequalities can be derived from the so-called Bellman property (or subpath consistency) of shortest path routings. This property basically says the following: If both terminals s_1 and t_1 of a commodity $(s_1, t_1) \in K$ are contained in the routing path of another commodity $(s_2, t_2) \in K$, then the routing path of commodity (s_1, t_1) must be a subpath of commodity (s_2, t_2). Otherwise there is no metric such that the two different (sub-)paths between s_1 and t_1 are both unique shortest paths. In our algorithm, we use the following three types of inequalities that are implied by the Bellman property:

$$x_a^{s,v} - x_a^{s,t} + \sum_{e \in \delta^-(v)} x_e^{s,t} \le 1 \quad (s,t), (s,v) \in K, \, a \in A \, , \tag{6}$$

$$x_a^{v,t} - x_a^{s,t} + \sum_{e \in \delta^-(v)} x_e^{s,t} \le 1 \quad (s,t), (v,t) \in K, \, a \in A \, , \tag{7}$$

$$x_a^{s,v} + x_a^{v,t} - x_a^{s,t} - 2(1 - \sum_{e \in \delta^-(v)} x_e^{s,t}) \le 0 \quad (s,v), (v,t), (s,t) \in K, \, a \in A \, . \tag{8}$$

Although in general none of these inequalities is facet-defining for the polytope associated with (2), they all proved to be very useful in practice. In our implementation, we separate over each of these three classes with a straightforward enumerative algorithm.

In addition to these inequalities, which describe the valid routing path patterns independent of the given traffic demands and link capacities, our algorithm also uses cutting planes that are based on the resulting traffic flows and the link capacities. In practice, induced cover inequalities based on the precedence constrained knapsacks defined by a single arc capacity constraint (2c) and the subpath consistency among the paths across that arc proved to be very effective. Due to the space limitations in this extended abstract, we cannot discuss these inequalities here. A detailed description of these inequalities and the heuristic separation methods used in our algorithm is given in [9].

Whenever an integer solution candidate for the (incomplete) master formulation is found, we must solve the client problem to decide whether or not it defines a valid unsplittable shortest path routing and to find a compatible metric or a violated conflict inequality (2f). In our implementation, we solve the client problem not only for the fully integer solutions at the leaves of the master problem's branch-and-bound tree, but also for non-integer solutions arising within the branch-and-bound tree. In practice, this modification drastically reduced the running time of the overall algorithm.

At each node of the master problem's branch and bound tree, we consider the potential forwarding $F \subseteq V \times A$ defined by the integer and near integer routing variables. In our implementation, we let $F := \{(t,a) : y_a^t \ge 0.8\}$. We solve the client problem whenever this presumed forwarding differs from the one at the parent node in the branch-and-bound tree by more than two node-arc pairs, if

Table 1. Computational results for SNDlib problems

Problem	Nodes	Links	Demands	LP	LB	Sol	Nodes	Gap (%)	Time (s)
Atlanta	15	22	210	0.65	0.86	0.86	30	0.0	10.3
Dfn-bwin	10	45	90	0.34	0.69	0.69	89	0.0	26.5
Dfn-gwin	11	21	110	0.50	0.51	0.51	521	0.0	16.3
Di-yuan	11	42	22	0.25	0.62	0.62	33	0.0	1.8
France	25	45	300	0.60	0.71	0.74	76	5.0	10000.0
Germany50	50	88	662	0.64	0.64	0.73	56	12.7	10000.0
NewYork	16	49	240	0.44	0.62	0.62	15	0.0	54.9
Nobel-EU	28	41	378	0.44	0.44	0.45	75	0.3	10000.0
Nobel-GER	17	26	121	0.64	0.73	0.73	101	0.0	114.1
Nobel-US	14	21	91	0.48	0.49	0.49	77	0.0	20.4
Norway	27	51	702	0.54	0.54	0.62	99	14.9	10000.0
PDH	11	34	24	0.34	0.80	0.80	85	0.0	6.37
Polska	12	18	66	0.82	0.93	0.93	2149	0.0	200.2
TA1	24	55	396	0.30	0.93	0.93	11	0.0	289.2

the depth of the current node in the branch-and-bound is 2^k for some $k \in \mathbb{Z}$, or if all arc-routing variables are integer. If the linear relaxation of the client problem (3) is feasible for this forwarding F, the computed link lengths define a heuristic solution for the MIN-CON-USPR problem, which may improve on the best known solution. Otherwise, if a violated conflict inequality (2f) is found, this inequality may cut off the entire invalid branch at the current node in the branch-and-bound tree.

4 Results

The presented algorithm has been implemented as part of the network optimization library DISCNET [2]. The data structures and algorithms are based on the standard c++ library and LEDA [1], the linear programs arising in the solution process are solved with CPLEX 11.0 [21]. The master problem's branch-and-cut framework and all separation procedures are implemented directly in c++.

Table 1 shows computational results for a collection of benchmark problems taken from the Survivable Network Design Library [23]. All computations were performed on an Intel Pentium 4 machine with 2.66 GHz and 4 GB RAM running Linux 2.6. The algorithm was run with a total CPU time limit of 10,000 seconds on each problem instance. The underlying networks are bidirectional and have the same capacity for both directions of all links. The numbers of nodes, bidirected links and non-zero traffic demands are shown in the first columns of Table 1. Column LP shows the lower bound obtained by solving the initial linear relaxation of (2) at the root node of the master problem's branch-and-bound tree. The columns LB and Sol show the best proven lower bound and the best solution value found by our algorithm within the given time limit. The remaining columns show the number of explored branch-and-bound nodes, the residual optimality gap, and the total CPU time until either optimality was proven or the time limit was exceeded.

The results show that our algorithm can be used to solve real-world size problems. All small and medium size instances have been solved optimally within seconds or minutes. For large problems optimality cannot always be achieved. Instances with dense networks and lots of potential routing paths for most demand pairs are more difficult than those where the underlying networks are fairly sparse. For instances with dense networks, lots of violated conflict constraints are separated during the execution of the algorithms, which often drastically slows down the solution of the linear relaxation. For the most difficult problems, only few branch-and-bound nodes could be explored. Yet, even for those problem that could not be solved to optimality, our algorithm always found better solutions than length-based heuristic and Lagrangian approaches. Our algorithm also clearly outperforms all other integer programming approaches presented in the literature so far, which typically even fail to achieve gaps below 30% for networks larger than 10 nodes.

References

1. Algorithmic Solutions Software GmbH: LEDA – Library of Efficient Data types and Algorithms (2000–2007), http://www.algorithmic-solution.com/leda
2. atesio GmbH: DISCNET – Network optimization software library (2000–2007), http://www.atesio.de
3. Ben-Ameur, W., Gourdin, E.: Internet routing and related topology issues. SIAM Journal on Discrete Mathematics 17, 18–49 (2003)
4. Bley, A.: A Lagrangian approach for integrated network design and routing in IP networks. In: Ben-Ameur, W., Pertrowski, A. (eds.) 1st International Network Optimization Conference, pp. 107–113. Institut National des Télécommunications, Evry/Paris (2003)
5. Bley, A.: Finding small administrative lengths for shortest path routing. In: Gouveia, L., Mourão, C. (eds.) 2nd International Network Optimization Conference, pp. 121–128. Universidade de Lisboa, Lisbon (2005)
6. Bley, A.: On the approximability of the minimum congestion unsplittable shortest path routing problem. In: Jünger, M., Kaibel, V. (eds.) IPCO 2005. LNCS, vol. 3509, pp. 97–110. Springer, Heidelberg (2005)
7. Bley, A.: Approximability of unsplittable shortest path routing problems. Technical report ZR-06-02, Zuse Institute Berlin (2006)
8. Bley, A.: Inapproximability results for the inverse shortest paths problem with integer lengths and unique shortest paths. Networks 50, 29–36 (2007)
9. Bley, A.: Routing and capacity optimization for IP networks. PhD thesis, Technische Universität Berlin (2007)
10. Bley, A., Grötschel, M., Wessäly, R.: Design of broadband virtual private networks: Model and heuristics for the B-WiN. In: Dean, N., Hsu, D., Ravi, R. (eds.) Robust Communication Networks: Interconnection and Survivability. DIMACS Series in Discrete Mathematics and Theoretical Computer Science, vol. 53, pp. 1–16. AMS (1998)
11. Bley, A., Koch, T.: Integer programming approaches to access and backbone IP-network planning. In: 3rd International Conference on High Performance Scientific Computing, Hanoi, Vietnam (2006)

12. Bourquia, N., Ben-Ameur, W., Gourdin, E., Tolla, P.: Optimal shortest path routing for Internet networks. In: Ben-Ameur, W., Pertrowski, A. (eds.) 1st International Network Optimization Conference, pp. 119–125. Institut National des Télécommunications, Evry/Paris (2003)

13. Broström, P., Holmberg, K.: Determining the non-existence of compatibel OSPF weights. In: Nordic MPS 2004. Linköping Electronic Conference Proceedings, vol. 14, pp. 7–21. Linköping University Electronic Press (2004)

14. Broström, P., Holmberg, K.: Stronger necessary conditions for the existence of a compatible OSPF metric. Technical report LiTH-MAT-R-2004-08, Linköping University (2004)

15. Buriol, L., Resende, M., Ribeiro, C., Thorup, M.: A hybrid genetic algorithm for the weight setting problem in OSPF/IS-IS routing. Networks 46, 36–56 (2005)

16. Callon, R.: Use of OSI IS-IS for routing in TCP/IP and dual environments. IETF Internet RFC 1195 (1990)

17. Ericsson, M., Resende, M., Pardalos, P.: A genetic algorithm for the weight setting problem in OSPF routing. Journal of Combinatorial Optimization 6, 299–333 (2002)

18. Fortz, B., Thorup, M.: Increasing Internet capacity using local search. Computational Optimization and Applications 29, 13–48 (2004)

19. de Giovanni, L., Fortz, B., Labbé, M.: A lower bound for the Internet protocol network design problem. In: Gouveia, L., Mourão, C. (eds.) 2nd International Network Optimization Conference, pp. 402–408. Universidade de Lisboa, Lisbon (2005)

20. Holmberg, K., Yuan, D.: Optimization of Internet protocol network design and routing. Networks 43, 39–53 (2004)

21. ILOG CPLEX Division: CPLEX 11.0 (2007), http://www.ilog.com

22. Moy, J.: OSPF version 2. IETF Internet RFC 2328 (1998)

23. Orlowski, S., Pióro, M., Tomaszewski, A., Wessäly, R.: SNDlib 1.0 – Survivable Network Design Library. In: Fortz, B. (ed.) 3rd International Network Optimization Conference. Université Libre de Bruxels, Brussels (2007), http://sndlib.zib.de

24. Parmar, A., Ahmed, S., Sokol, J.: An integer programming approach to the OSPF weight setting problem. Optimization Online (2006)

25. Pióro, M., Medhi, D.: Routing, Flow, and Capacity Design in Communication and Computer Networks. Morgan Kaufmann, San Francisco (2004)

26. Pióro, M., Szentesi, A., Harmatos, J., Jüttner, A.: On OSPF related network optimization problems. In: 8th IFIP Workshop on Performance Modelling and Evaluation of ATM & IP Networks, Ilkley, UK, pp. 70/1–70/14 (2000)

27. Prytz, M.: On optimization in design of telecommunications networks with multicast and unicast traffic. Ph.D. thesis, Royal Institute of Technology, Stockholm, Sweden (2002)

28. Tomaszewski, A., Pióro, M., Dzida, M., Mycek, M., Zagożdżon, M.: Valid inequalities for a shortest-path routing optimization problem. In: Fortz, B. (ed.) 3rd International Network Optimization Conference. Université Libre de Bruxels, Brussels (2007)

29. Tomaszewski, A., Pióro, M., Dzida, M., Zagożdżon, M.: Optimization of administrative weights in IP networks using the branch-and-cut approach. In: Gouveia, L., Mourão, C. (eds.) 2nd International Network Optimization Conference, pp. 393–400. Universidade de Lisboa, Lisbon (2005)

A Constant-Approximate Feasibility Test
for Multiprocessor Real-Time Scheduling

Vincenzo Bonifaci[1,2,*], Alberto Marchetti-Spaccamela[1,**], and Sebastian Stiller[3]

[1] Sapienza Università di Roma, Italy
[2] Università degli Studi dell'Aquila, Italy
[3] Technische Universität Berlin, Germany

Abstract. We devise the first constant-approximate feasibility test for sporadic multiprocessor real-time scheduling. We give an algorithm that, given a task system and $\varepsilon > 0$, correctly decides either that the task system can be scheduled using the earliest deadline first algorithm on m speed-$(2 - 1/m + \varepsilon)$ machines, or that the system is infeasible for m speed-1 machines. The running time of the algorithm is polynomial in the size of the task system and $1/\varepsilon$. We also provide an improved bound trading off speed for additional machines.

Our analysis relies on a new concept for counting the workload of an interval, that might also turn useful for analyzing other types of task systems.

1 Introduction

We study the problem of scheduling recurring processes, or tasks, on a multiprocessor platform. An instance of the problem is given by a finite set I of tasks, which need to be executed by the system; each task generates a possibly infinite sequence of jobs. In the following we denote by n the cardinality of I.

In the *periodic* version of the problem, a task τ, $\tau \in I$, is characterized by a quadruple of positive numbers: an offset o_τ that represents the time instant when the first job generated by the task is released, a processing time c_τ, a relative deadline D_τ and a period T_τ. Each occurrence of task τ is represented by a job: the k-th occurrence of task τ is released at time $o_\tau + (k-1)T_\tau$, requires at most c_τ units of processor time and must complete its execution before time $o_\tau + (k-1)T_\tau + D_\tau$. Note that a task defines an infinite sequence of jobs, but a given set of tasks generates exactly one job sequence.

In the *sporadic* case, each task is characterized by a triple (c_τ, D_τ, T_τ) where c_τ, D_τ have the same meaning as in the periodic case, while T_τ denotes the *minimum* time interval between successive occurrences of the task. Note that in a sporadic task system the time instant when the next invocation of a task will be released after the minimal separation time has elapsed is unknown. Therefore, a given set of tasks can generate infinitely many sequences of jobs.

The correctness of a hard-real-time system requires that all jobs complete by their deadlines. A periodic (sporadic) task system is *feasible* if there is a feasible schedule for any possible sequence of jobs that is consistent with the period, deadline, and worst-case

---

* Research partially supported by the Future and Emerging Technologies Unit of EC (IST priority - 6th FP), under contract no. FP6-021235-2 (project ARRIVAL).
** Research supported by MIUR-FIRB project RBIN047MH9 Italy-Israel.

D. Halperin and K. Mehlhorn (Eds.): ESA 2008, LNCS 5193, pp. 210–221, 2008.

execution time constraints of the task system, and it is *schedulable* by a given algorithm if the algorithm finds a feasible schedule for every such sequence of jobs. In the sequel we focus on preemptive scheduling algorithms that are allowed to interrupt the execution of a job and resume it later.

Given a scheduling algorithm A, a *schedulability test* for A is an algorithm that takes as input a description of a task system and answers whether the system is schedulable by A or not. A schedulability test is *exact* if it correctly identifies all schedulable and unschedulable task systems and it is *sufficient* if it correctly identifies all unschedulable task systems, but may give a wrong answer for schedulable task systems. A sufficient schedulability test that can verify whether a given job set is schedulable is a natural requirement for a scheduling algorithm that must be used in hard-deadline real-time applications. In fact, from a practical point of view, there is no difference between a task system that is not schedulable and one that cannot be proven to be schedulable.

In the case of a single machine, the problem has been widely studied and effective scheduling algorithms are well understood [5,11]. In this paper we study scheduling algorithm for sporadic task systems on parallel machines. The problem is not only interesting from a theoretical point of view but is also relevant in practice. In fact, real-time multiprocessor systems are becoming common: there are single-chip architectures, characterized by a small number of processors and large-scale signal-processing systems with many processing units.

Related work
There is an extensive literature on real-time scheduling. We limit the following discussion to the results that are more relevant to our work.

Single machine scheduling. In the case of a single machine it is known [5,7,11] that the earliest deadline first scheduling algorithm (EDF), which at each instant in time schedules the available job with the smallest deadline (with ties broken arbitrarily), is an optimal scheduling algorithm for scheduling a periodic (or sporadic) task system in the following sense: if it is possible to preemptively schedule a given collection of independent jobs such that all the jobs meet their deadlines, then the schedule generated by EDF for this collection of jobs will meet all deadlines as well. Despite this positive result, we remark that the feasibility test for periodic task systems, although solvable in exponential time, is strongly co-NP-hard even in special cases [5,10].

Approximate feasibility tests have been proposed that allow the design of efficient feasibility tests (e.g. running in polynomial time) while introducing a small error in the decision process, that is controlled by an accuracy parameter. Such approaches have been developed for EDF scheduling and for other scheduling algorithms.

Two different paradigms can be used to define approximate feasibility tests: pessimistic and optimistic. If a pessimistic feasibility test returns "feasible", then the task set is guaranteed to be feasible. If the test returns "infeasible", the task set is guaranteed to be infeasible on a slower processor, of computing capacity $(1 - \varepsilon)$, where ε denotes the approximation guaranteed.

If an optimistic test returns "feasible", then the task set is guaranteed to be feasible on a $(1 + \varepsilon)$-speed processor. If the test returns "infeasible", the task set is guaranteed to be infeasible on a unit-speed processor [6].

Fully polynomial-time approximation schemes (FPTAS) are known for a single processor; in fact for any $\varepsilon > 0$ there exists a feasibility test that returns an ε-approximation; the running time of the algorithm is polynomial in the number of tasks and in $1/\varepsilon$ (see for example [1,2,6,8] and references therein).

Finally we observe that, in the case of one processor, the sporadic feasibility problem is known to reduce to a special case of the periodic problem, where all tasks have offset 0 (i.e. each task releases its first job at time zero).

Multiple machine scheduling. We first observe that in the multiprocessor case the previous analogy between sporadic and periodic problems is not true.

Regarding the analysis of EDF, it is known [12] that any *feasible* task system on m machines of unit capacity is EDF-schedulable on m machines of speed $2 - 1/m$. This result holds for EDF and other policies and has not been improved since then. Subsequent work has analyzed the advantage of trading speed for machines [9], while further work on conditions for the schedulability of EDF has been done by Baker [3].

Note that the result of [12] *does not* imply an efficient test for deciding when EDF (possibly with extra speed) can schedule a sporadic task system. Thus, the main open problem in order to apply the result of Phillips et al. [12] is the lack of a feasibility test.

The problem has attracted a lot of attention in recent years (see e.g. [4] and references therein for a thoroughly presentation). A number of special cases have also been studied; for example, when for each task the deadline is equal to the period (*implicit-deadline* task systems), it has been shown that

$$\sum_{\tau \in I} \frac{c_\tau}{T_\tau} \leq m \text{ and } \max_{\tau \in I} \frac{c_\tau}{T_\tau} \leq 1$$

gives a necessary and sufficient test for feasibility of the system.

However, not much was known regarding the feasibility of an arbitrary-deadline task system. A sufficient test in this case is given by

$$\sum_{\tau \in I} \frac{c_\tau}{\min(D_\tau, T_\tau)} \leq m \text{ and } \max_{\tau \in I} \frac{c_\tau}{\min(D_\tau, T_\tau)} \leq 1,$$

but this test is far from approximating a necessary condition, i.e., it does not provide a good approximate feasibility test in general (it is not hard to see that there exist feasible task systems for which $\sum_{\tau \in I} c_\tau / \min(D_\tau, T_\tau)$ can be $\Omega(m \log m)$).

To the best of our knowledge, no better bound is known. We refer the reader to the survey [4] for feasibility tests that are known for other special cases.

Our Contribution

We give the first constant-approximate feasibility test for sporadic multiprocessor real-time scheduling. Namely, we give a test that, given a sporadic multiprocessor instance I, decides whether it can be scheduled by EDF on m speed-$(2 - 1/m + \varepsilon)$ machines, or shows that the instance violates at least one of three basic conditions, which are necessary for schedulability on m speed-1-machines. In fact we give a slightly stronger result, allowing to trade some extra speed for extra machines. Note, that in general extra machines are less powerful than extra speed.

Two of the basic conditions are trivial. The third condition is new and provides a lower bound on the processing requirement of an interval. We call it the *forward forced demand*. This concept is strong enough to approximately capture the feasibility of scheduling a sporadic task system on a multiprocessor platform; however it is simple enough to be approximated in polynomial time up to an arbitrarily small $\varepsilon > 0$: in Section 4 we give an algorithm that checks the third condition in time polynomial in the input size of I and $1/\varepsilon$, for any desired error bound $\varepsilon > 0$.

2   The Model

An instance is a finite set of tasks I. Each task $\tau \in I$ is a triple of positive numbers, namely, a processing time c_τ, a relative deadline D_τ and a period or minimal separation time T_τ. Every job j belongs to a task τ_j, and has a release date $r_j \geq 0$. We write $c_j := c_{j_\tau}$, and $D_j := D_{j_\tau}$, and $T_j := T_{j_\tau}$, and we call $d_j := r_j + D_j$ the (absolute) deadline of j. We assume $D_\tau, c_\tau, T_\tau \in \mathbb{N}$.

A (sporadic) *job sequence R* of an instance I is an arbitrary, countable set of jobs, all belonging to tasks in I, with the following property: Any pair of distinct jobs j and k belonging to the same task τ satisfies $|r_j - r_k| \geq T_\tau$.

A feasible schedule for a job sequence R on m machines is a set of measurable functions $S_j : \mathbb{R}^+ \to \{0,\ldots,m\}$, one function for each job $j \in R$, satisfying:

- Everything is scheduled: $\forall j \in R : c_j = \sum_{p=1}^{m} |S_j^{-1}(p)|$.
- Deadlines and release dates are respected: $\forall j \in R : \bigcup_{p=1}^{m} S_j^{-1}(p) \subseteq [r_j, d_j]$.
- Each machine processes at most one job at a time: $\forall p \in \{1,\ldots,m\} : \forall j \neq g \in R : S_j^{-1}(p) \cap S_g^{-1}(p) = \emptyset$.
- Jobs of the same task are not scheduled in parallel:

$$\forall j \neq g \in R : \tau_j = \tau_g \Rightarrow \bigcup_{p=1}^{m} S_j^{-1}(p) \cap \bigcup_{p=1}^{m} S_g^{-1}(p) = \emptyset.$$

- No job is processed by two machines at the same time:

$$\forall j \in R, \forall p \neq q \in \{1,\ldots,m\} : S_j^{-1}(p) \cap S_j^{-1}(q) = \emptyset.$$

Preemption and migration of jobs are explicitly allowed.
Given a real number x we denote by x^+ its positive part, that is $x^+ := \max(x,0)$.

3   A Feasibility Test

Definition 1. *Consider a job j with release date r_j, absolute deadline d_j, and processing time c_j satisfying $d_j \geq r_j + c_j$ (i.e., for its task we have $D_{\tau_j} \geq c_{\tau_j}$). For a non-empty interval $\Delta = [t,t')$ with $d_j \in \Delta$, we call*

$$f(j,\Delta) := \left(c_j - (t - r_j)^+\right)^+$$

the forward forced demand *of j in Δ.*

Note that, for a job j and an interval Δ such that both deadline and release date lie in the interval (that is, $r_j, d_j \in \Delta$), the forward forced demand equals the processing time of the job ($f(j, \Delta) = c_j$). If $c_\tau \leq T_\tau$ for all tasks τ, then each pair of an interval Δ and a task τ can have at most one job j_τ with release date outside the interval ($r_{j_\tau} \notin \Delta$) that has positive forward forced demand ($f(j_\tau, \Delta) > 0$) in the interval.

Definition 2. *For a job sequence R of an instance I the necessary demand $\mathrm{ND}_R(\Delta)$ of a non-empty interval Δ is the sum of the forward forced demands of all jobs with absolute deadline in Δ. We use $\mathrm{ND}_R(\Delta, \tau)$ to denote the part of the necessary demand originating only from jobs of task τ. We write $\mathrm{ND}(\Delta)$ and $\mathrm{ND}(\Delta, \tau)$ when the sequence R is clear from the context.*

Observe that any algorithm working on any number of speed-1 machines must schedule in an interval at least the necessary demand of that interval.

We use the notation $\mathrm{EDF}_{(m+\mu, \sigma)}$ to denote the scheduling algorithm EDF executed on $(m + \mu)$ speed-σ machines, where ties can be broken arbitrarily.

Definition 3. *Given an instance I and a job sequence R. For a point in time t, a task τ, and a scheduling algorithm A, an interval $\Delta = [t', t)$ is called τ-A-busy before t, if executing the algorithm A on the sequence R yields for every point in Δ a positive remaining processing time for at least one of the jobs of task τ.*

Observe that the maximal τ-A-busy interval before t is unique, well defined, and starts with the release date of some job of τ, unless it is empty. Moreover, all demand from τ-jobs released before some maximal τ-A-busy interval Δ is processed by A strictly before Δ.

Theorem 1. *Let $\sigma \geq 1$. Given an instance I which satisfies $c_\tau \leq T_\tau$ and $c_\tau \leq D_\tau$ for all tasks τ. If there is some job sequence R which cannot be scheduled by $\mathrm{EDF}_{(m+\mu, \sigma)}$, then there is an interval Δ such that $\mathrm{ND}_R(\Delta)/|\Delta| > (m + \mu)(\sigma - 1) + 1$.*

Before giving the formal, slightly involved proof we convey the main intuitions. Knowing that $\mathrm{EDF}_{(m+\mu, \sigma)}$ fails, we will inductively construct an interval with high load. The interval will be composed of several subintervals. To each subinterval we associate a task such that the subinterval is EDF-busy for that task. Whenever EDF does not process a job of that task in the subinterval, it must have all machines busy. In order to conclude that the load of the whole interval is large, we must establish two things: First, that the fraction of a subinterval, in which its associated task is processed, is small, i.e., in a large part of the subinterval all machines must be busy. Second, everything processed in those busy subintervals is part of the necessary demand of the whole interval.

Proof. From now on we assume that R is a job sequence which cannot be scheduled by $\mathrm{EDF}_{(m+\mu, \sigma)}$, and that t_0 is the first point in time when $\mathrm{EDF}_{(m+\mu, \sigma)}$ fails a deadline.

We define inductively a finite sequence of pairs, comprised of a time t_i and a job j_i, for $1 \leq i \leq z$. For convenience define $\Delta_i := [t_i, t_0)$ and $\overline{\Delta}_i := [t_i, t_{i-1})$. Also the following notation for the work that $\mathrm{EDF}_{(m+\mu, \sigma)}$ does for a job j in a certain measurable subset S of $\mathbb{R}^+$ will be helpful: $\mathrm{EDF}_{(m+\mu, \sigma)}(j, S)$. To shorten we use $m' := (m + \mu)(\sigma - 1) + 1$.

For each pair (t_i, j_i) we define two subsets of the interval $\overline{\Delta}_i$, namely X_i and Y_i. The first subset X_i is the set of points in time between t_i and t_{i-1} when a job of task τ_{j_i} is processed. Due to the way $\mathrm{EDF}_{(m+\mu, \sigma)}$ schedules, X_i is a finite union of intervals. The other subset is its complement in the interval: $Y_i := \overline{\Delta}_i \setminus X_i$. Further, we set $x_i := |X_i|$ and $y_i := |Y_i|$.

Next, we define two values for each i. They will be interpreted later as certain parts of the work that $\text{EDF}_{(m+\mu,\sigma)}$ does or has to do. Let FAIL be the work that $\text{EDF}_{(m+\mu,\sigma)}$ failed to complete before t_0 for jobs of task τ_{j_1} (so FAIL > 0). We define $\widetilde{W}_i := (m + \mu)\sigma y_i + \sigma x_i$ and $W_i := \sum_{s=1}^{i} \widetilde{W}_s + \text{FAIL}$.

We will show the following properties for our sequence of intervals:

1. $t_0 > t_1 > \ldots > t_z$.
2. During each Y_i all machines are busy.
3. All jobs $\text{EDF}_{(m+\mu,\sigma)}$ schedules during Y_i have a deadline in Δ_i.
4. $W_i > m'|\Delta_i|$.
5. $\text{ND}(\Delta_z) \geq W_z$.

Property 2 implies that $(m + \mu)\sigma y_i = \sum_{j \in J} \text{EDF}_{(m+\mu,\sigma)}(j, Y_i)$ for some set J of jobs.

Basis of the induction. As job j_1 we pick one of the jobs $\text{EDF}_{(m+\mu,\sigma)}$ failed to finish at t_0, though they were due. Among these jobs, the job j_1 is one of those jobs j with largest maximal τ_j-$\text{EDF}_{(m+\mu,\sigma)}$-busy interval before t_0. We let $\overline{\Delta}_1 (= \Delta_1)$ be the maximal τ_{j_1}-$\text{EDF}_{(m+\mu,\sigma)}$-busy interval before t_0. This also defines t_1 as the lower endpoint of this interval. Clearly, $t_1 < t_0$ since relative deadlines cannot have zero length.

We have to verify property 2, 3 and 4 for (t_1, j_1). If at a certain time t in the τ_{j_1}-$\text{EDF}_{(m+\mu,\sigma)}$-busy interval $\overline{\Delta}_1$ no job of τ_{j_1} is processed by $\text{EDF}_{(m+\mu,\sigma)}$, then at that time all machines must be busy with jobs that have deadlines not later than t_0. This gives the first two properties. For property 4 we use that $\text{EDF}_{(m+\mu,\sigma)}$ failed at t_0 for j_1:

$$W_1 = \widetilde{W}_1 + \text{FAIL}$$
$$> (m + \mu)\sigma y_1 + \sigma x_1 = (m + \mu)\sigma(|\Delta_1| - x_1) + \sigma x_1.$$

So we get

$$\frac{W_1}{|\Delta_1|} > (m + \mu)\sigma - (m + \mu - 1)\frac{\sigma x_1}{|\Delta_1|}.$$

In Δ_1 the $\text{EDF}_{(m+\mu,\sigma)}$ schedule devotes x_1 units of time on jobs of task τ_{j_1} processing with speed-σ. Since the interval Δ_1 is maximally τ_{j_1}-$\text{EDF}_{(m+\mu,\sigma)}$-busy before t_0 and j_1 is not completed within t_0, we know that all those jobs must be released in the interval, and have their deadline in the interval.

The busy interval Δ_1 starts with the release date of some job of task τ_{j_1}. Therefore the number of τ_{j_1}-jobs with release date and deadline in Δ_1 is $\left\lfloor \frac{|\Delta_1| - D_{j_1} + T_{j_1}}{T_{j_1}} \right\rfloor$, and we can bound:

$$\frac{\sigma x_1}{|\Delta_1|} < \frac{c_{j_1}}{|\Delta_1|} \cdot \frac{|\Delta_1| - D_{j_1} + T_{j_1}}{T_{j_1}} \leq \max\left(\frac{c_{j_1}}{D_{j_1}}, \frac{c_{j_1}}{T_{j_1}}\right) \leq 1.$$

To verify the middle inequality one should distinguish the cases $(D_{j_1} \leq T_{j_1})$ and $(D_{j_1} > T_{j_1})$ using $|\Delta_1| \geq D_{j_1}$ for the former.

Combining the two bounds we get property 4:

$$\frac{W_1}{|\Delta_1|} > (m + \mu)(\sigma - 1) + 1 = m'.$$

The inductive step. Assume that the sequence of pairs up to $i-1$ satisfies the properties. We choose the job j_i as one having the following two properties:

1. The release date of j_i is strictly before t_{i-1}.
2.

$$\mathrm{EDF}_{(m+\mu,\sigma)}\left(j_i,\bigcup_{s=1}^{i-1}Y_s\right) > f(j_i,\Delta_{i-1}).$$

If no such job can be found, we set $z := i-1$ and return the interval Δ_{i-1} as one justifying the claim of the theorem. We will show later why this holds true. So assume such a j_i exists. Take $\overline{\Delta}_i$ as the maximal τ_{j_i}-$\mathrm{EDF}_{(m+\mu,\sigma)}$-busy interval before t_{i-1}, and accordingly set t_i as its lower endpoint.

Let us show the properties. As the release date of j_i is strictly before t_{i-1}, also $t_i < t_{i-1}$, and we have property 1. The next two properties again follow from the fact that $\overline{\Delta}_i$ is τ_{j_i}-$\mathrm{EDF}_{(m+\mu,\sigma)}$-busy. Here, take into account for property 3 that j_i has a deadline in Δ_{i-1} by induction.

To prove property 4 it suffices to show $\widetilde{W}_i \geq m'\left|\overline{\Delta}_i\right|$, because we have strict inequality in $W_{i-1} > m'|\Delta_{i-1}|$ by induction. By definition

$$\frac{\widetilde{W}_i}{\left|\overline{\Delta}_i\right|} = (m+\mu)\sigma - (m+\mu-1)\frac{\sigma x_i}{\left|\overline{\Delta}_i\right|}.$$

We want to establish $\sigma x_i \leq \left|\overline{\Delta}_i\right|$. Having this, property 4 follows as above.

For this part we simplify notation by setting $\tau := \tau_{j_i}$, $T := T_{\tau_{j_i}}$, $c := c_{\tau_{j_i}}$ and $D := D_{\tau_{j_i}}$. We distinguish the cases $\left|\overline{\Delta}_i\right| \geq T$ and $\left|\overline{\Delta}_i\right| < T$.

Case 1: $\left|\overline{\Delta}_i\right| \geq T$. We can bound σx_i by the amount of work released by τ during the maximal τ-$\mathrm{EDF}_{(m+\mu,\sigma)}$-busy interval $\overline{\Delta}_i$:

$$\sigma x_i \leq \left\lfloor\frac{\left|\overline{\Delta}_i\right|}{T}\right\rfloor \cdot c + \mathrm{EDF}_{(m+\mu,\sigma)}\left(j_i,\overline{\Delta}_i\right).$$

W.l.o.g. $\left|\overline{\Delta}_i\right|$ is not an integer multiple of T. Otherwise, the last released job could not contribute to the work done in X_i. But then, a slightly smaller value replacing $\left|\overline{\Delta}_i\right|$ would also give a valid bound on what is processed during $\overline{\Delta}_i$.

Recall that $f(j_i,\Delta_{i-1}) := \left(c_{j_i} - (t_{i-1} - r_{j_i})^+\right)^+$. By choice of j_i we know that more than its forced forward demand is done by $\mathrm{EDF}_{(m+\mu,\sigma)}$ in Δ_{i-1}. Therefore

$$\mathrm{EDF}_{(m+\mu,\sigma)}\left(j_i,\overline{\Delta}_i\right) \leq c - f(j_i,\Delta_{i-1}) \leq (t_{i-1} - r_{j_i}) \leq \left|\overline{\Delta}_i\right| - T\cdot\left\lfloor\frac{\left|\overline{\Delta}_i\right|}{T}\right\rfloor.$$

Note that the middle inequality is also true for $f(j_i,\Delta_{i-1}) = 0$. To verify the last inequality, assume first that j_i is the last job of task τ released in $\overline{\Delta}_i$. Then between the release of j_i and the end of $\overline{\Delta}_i$ at most $\left|\overline{\Delta}_i\right| - T\cdot\left\lfloor\frac{\left|\overline{\Delta}_i\right|}{T}\right\rfloor$ units of time may pass.

Now, say j_i is not the last job of task τ released in $\overline{\Delta}_i$. Remember that j_i is not finished by $\text{EDF}_{(m+\mu,\sigma)}$ within $\overline{\Delta}_i$. Therefore all jobs of τ released later are not processed within $\overline{\Delta}_i$ at all, because EDF implies FIFO for the jobs of a common task. If there is such a job released but not started in $\overline{\Delta}_i$, we can subtract its entire processing time from the upper bound on σx_i. This means to subtract at least as much as when we subtract $\text{EDF}_{(m+\mu,\sigma)}\left(j_i, \overline{\Delta}_i\right)$. Thus, we have

$$\sigma x_i \leq \left\lfloor \frac{|\overline{\Delta}_i|}{T} \right\rfloor \cdot c \leq \frac{|\overline{\Delta}_i|}{T} \cdot c \leq |\overline{\Delta}_i|.$$

To finish the case $\left(|\overline{\Delta}_i| \geq T\right)$ plug everything together:

$$\frac{\sigma x_i}{|\overline{\Delta}_i|} \leq \frac{\left\lfloor \frac{|\overline{\Delta}_i|}{T} \right\rfloor \cdot c + |\overline{\Delta}_i| - \left\lfloor \frac{|\overline{\Delta}_i|}{T} \right\rfloor \cdot T}{|\overline{\Delta}_i|} = 1 - \frac{(T-c)\left\lfloor \frac{|\overline{\Delta}_i|}{T} \right\rfloor}{|\overline{\Delta}_i|}.$$

As $T \geq c$ we have $\sigma x_i \leq |\overline{\Delta}_i|$.

Case 2: $|\overline{\Delta}_i| < T$. Assume $|\overline{\Delta}_i| < T$. Then only one job of task τ can be released during $|\overline{\Delta}_i|$, namely j_i. The choice of j_i gives

$$c = \sigma x_i + \text{EDF}_{(m+\mu,\sigma)}(j_i, \Delta_{i-1}) \geq \sigma x_i + \text{EDF}_{(m+\mu,\sigma)}\left(j_i, \bigcup_{s=1}^{i-1} Y_s\right) > \sigma x_i + f(j_i, \Delta_{i-1}).$$

As the release date of j_i is in $\overline{\Delta}_i$ we can use $t_{i-1} - r_{j_i} \leq |\overline{\Delta}_i|$ (indeed we have equality here) to conclude that

$$c > \sigma x_i + f(j_i, \Delta_{i-1}) = \sigma x_i + c - (t_{i-1} - r_{j_i}) \geq \sigma x_i + c - |\overline{\Delta}_i|,$$

which shows $0 > \sigma x_i - |\overline{\Delta}_i|$ for the case $f(j_i, \Delta_{i-1}) > 0$. Yet, if $f(j_i, \Delta_{i-1}) = 0$ we immediately have $|\overline{\Delta}_i| \geq c \geq \sigma x_i$. So again obtain $\sigma x_i \leq |\overline{\Delta}_i|$, yielding property 4.

The breaking condition. In each step from $i-1$ to i the interval is strictly extended backwards to the release date of at least one job which is released before t_0. As there are finitely many task, and all have positive minimum separation time T, there are finitely many such jobs, and we can make only finitely many steps. So at some point the breaking condition, namely that there is no job j_i with the two required properties, must hold.

If this holds we claim property 5 to be true, i.e., $\text{ND}(\Delta_z) \geq W_z$. In the value W_z we count σx_i for each X_i, because the whole τ-demand processed in a τ-$\text{EDF}_{(m+\mu,\sigma)}$-busy interval is part of the necessary demand of that interval. Also, the demand $\text{EDF}_{(m+\mu,\sigma)}$ failed to process before t_0 is part of the necessary demand of Δ_z. For each Y_i part we count $(m+\mu)\sigma y_i$, which is by property 2 exactly what is processed in those times by $\text{EDF}_{(m+\mu,\sigma)}$. By property 3 all jobs processed in some Y_i have their deadline in the interval Δ_i and therefore also in Δ_z. Finally, there is no job among those processed in some section Y_i with release date before t_z, which has been counted in the term $(m+\mu)\sigma y_i$ with more than its forced forward demand in Δ_i. The forced forward demand in the greater interval Δ_z can only be greater, and thus we count for no job more in W_z than in $\text{ND}(\Delta_z)$. $\qquad\square$

We required $c_\tau \leq T_\tau$ and $c_\tau \leq D_\tau$. Both are easy to test in linear time. In fact, the later condition is necessary for scheduling any job sequence on any number of machines with speed 1. The first condition is necessary for scheduling all job sequences on any number of speed-1 machines.

Now, consider $\sigma \geq 2 - \frac{1+\mu}{m+\mu}$. We get $m' = (m+\mu)(\sigma - 1) + 1 \geq m$. Then, if an instance I allows for a job sequence R with an interval Δ generating a necessary demand $\mathrm{ND}_R(\Delta) > m|\Delta|$ as in the theorem, then clearly it cannot be scheduled by any algorithm on m speed-1 machines. So, all three conditions of the theorem, $c_\tau \leq T_\tau$, $c_\tau \leq D_\tau$, and $\mathrm{ND}_R(\Delta) \leq m|\Delta|$, are necessary for scheduling on m speed-1 machines. By the theorem they are sufficient for scheduling on $(m+\mu)$ speed-σ machines. Therefore, all that is missing for an approximate feasibility test is a procedure testing whether an instance I can have a job sequence R with an interval Δ generating a necessary demand $\mathrm{ND}_R(\Delta) > m|\Delta|$. For this we will provide an FPTAS in the remainder. As this procedure determines the maximal load only up to an ε, we will have to choose σ slightly bigger than $2 - \frac{1+\mu}{m+\mu}$ in our final theorem.

4   An FPTAS for Load Estimation

The following observation facilitates the test:

Lemma 1. *Assume $c_\tau \leq T_\tau$ and $c_\tau \leq D_\tau$ for all tasks τ of an instance I. Then, over all intervals $\Delta = [t, t + \ell)$ of a fixed length ℓ and all job sequences R of I, the maximal necessary demand from a certain task τ is*

$$\mathrm{ND}_{R^*}(\Delta^*, \tau) = c_\tau k + [c_\tau + \ell - D_\tau - kT_\tau]^+, \text{ where } k = \left\lfloor \frac{\ell + T_\tau - D_\tau}{T_\tau} \right\rfloor.$$

Proof. Rewrite $c_\tau k + [c_\tau + \ell - D_\tau - kT_\tau]^+ = c_\tau k + [c_\tau - (T_\tau - (\ell - D_\tau - (k-1)T_\tau))]^+$. Make $t^* + \ell$ the deadline of some job j from τ and $t^* \geq T_\tau$. Further choose R^* such that all jobs of task τ released in $[t - T_\tau, t + \ell)$ precede their follower at the minimum distance T_τ. Then the necessary demand $\mathrm{ND}_{R^*}(\Delta^*, \tau)$ is as claimed.

To see that this is maximal, assume any interval Δ with $|\Delta| = \ell$ and any job sequence R of I with higher necessary demand than the one in the above construction. As $c_\tau \leq T_\tau$, at most $k+1$ jobs can contribute to $\mathrm{ND}_R(\Delta, \tau)$. Compressing the distances between all contributing jobs cannot diminish the forced forward demand in the interval for any of those jobs. Now push the compressed sequence of contributing jobs towards the right until the deadline of the last job coincides with the right boundary of Δ. This will not diminish the forced forward demand of any contributing job. Thus, we arrive at a job sequence and an interval as in the above construction which generate at least as much forced forward demand as the pair (R, Δ) with which we started. This contradicts that $\mathrm{ND}_R(\Delta, \tau) > c_\tau k + [c_\tau + \ell - D_\tau - kT_\tau]^+$.   □

The construction of the lemma also shows, that the maximal forced forward demand can be achieved for each task independently. As a consequence we only have to find the optimal length of an interval. Then we know how much forced forward demand a maximal pair of interval and job sequence has. We define for any instance I satisfying for all $\tau : c_\tau \leq T_\tau$ and $c_\tau \leq D_\tau$:

$$w := w_I : \mathbb{R}^+ \to \mathbb{R}^+, \ell \mapsto w(\ell) := w_I(\ell) := \sum_{\tau \in I} c_\tau k + [c_\tau + \ell - D_\tau - kT_\tau]^+$$

Lemma 1 states that $w_I(\ell)$ is the maximum forced forward demand of any job sequence of I in any interval of length ℓ.

The following algorithm finds a length ℓ' which approximates the maximum of $\frac{w(\ell)}{\ell}$ by a factor of ε in time polynomial in the input size of I and $1/\varepsilon$. In fact, we devise a function ϕ which pointwise approximates the load, i.e., $\forall \ell \in \mathbb{R}^+ : (1-\varepsilon)\frac{w(\ell)}{\ell} \leq \phi(\ell) \leq \frac{w(\ell)}{\ell}$. There is a polynomial size subset of $\mathbb{R}^+$, a priori determinable, in which the function ϕ must achieve its maximum. So, the approximation algorithm is straightforward.

Algorithm 1. Load Estimation(I, ε)

For each $\tau \in I$, compute:

$$\text{threshold}(\tau) := D_\tau + T_\tau/\varepsilon,$$
$$\text{points}(\tau) := \{\ell \in (0, \text{threshold}(\tau)] : \ell = q \cdot T_\tau + D_\tau \text{ for some } q \in \mathbb{N}\},$$
$$\text{points}'(\tau) := \{\ell \in (0, \text{threshold}(\tau)] : \ell = q \cdot T_\tau + D_\tau - c_\tau \text{ for some } q \in \mathbb{N}\}.$$

Compute $\text{POINTS} := \cup_{\tau \in I} \left(\text{points}(\tau) \cup \text{points}'(\tau) \cup \{\text{threshold}(\tau)\}\right).$

Output $\lambda := \max\left(\max_{\ell \in \text{POINTS}} \frac{w(\ell)}{\ell}, \sum_{\tau=1}^n \frac{c_\tau}{T_\tau}\right).$

Lemma 2. *For any instance I Algorithm 1 outputs a λ such that $(1-\varepsilon)\lambda^* \leq \lambda \leq \lambda^*$ where $\lambda^* = \sup_{\Delta,R} \frac{ND_R(\Delta)}{|\Delta|}$, and has running time polynomial in n and $1/\varepsilon$.*

Proof. We know that $\lambda^* = \sup_\ell \frac{w(\ell)}{\ell}$. We show that for all $\ell \geq 0$ the function

$$\phi(\ell) := \sum_{\tau:\text{threshold}(\tau) \geq \ell} \frac{w_\tau(\ell)}{\ell} + \sum_{\tau:\text{threshold}(\tau) < \ell} \left(1 - \frac{D_\tau}{\ell}\right)\frac{c_\tau}{T_\tau}$$

approximates the load $w(\ell)/\ell$ in the following sense:

$$(1-\varepsilon)\frac{w(\ell)}{\ell} \leq \phi(\ell) \leq \frac{w(\ell)}{\ell}.$$

Secondly, we will show that we can find the maximum of ϕ by only considering points in POINTS. The number of points in POINTS is obviously polynomial in the input, and so is the evaluation of ϕ for each point. This completes the proof.

Recall that

$$w_\tau(\ell) = c_\tau \left\lfloor \frac{\ell + T_\tau - D_\tau}{T_\tau} \right\rfloor + \left[c_\tau + \ell - D_\tau - \left\lfloor \frac{\ell + T_\tau - D_\tau}{T_\tau} \right\rfloor \cdot T_\tau\right]^+.$$

Therefore $w_\tau(\ell)T_\tau \geq c_\tau(\ell - D_\tau)$ and

$$\frac{w_\tau(\ell)}{\ell} \geq \frac{c_\tau}{T_\tau} \cdot \left(1 - \frac{D_\tau}{\ell}\right),$$

which summed over all tasks τ yields the upper bound on ϕ.

Concerning the lower bound, for $\ell >$ threshold(τ) we have $\ell > D_\tau + \frac{T_\tau}{\varepsilon}$ implying $\varepsilon > \frac{T_\tau}{\ell - D_\tau}$. Using again $w_\tau(\ell)T_\tau \geq c_\tau(l - D_\tau)$ gives $\varepsilon > \frac{c_\tau}{w_\tau(\ell)}$.

As the difference between the necessary demand of one task τ and the approximate demand $(\ell - D_\tau) \cdot \frac{c_\tau}{T_\tau}$ can at most be the execution time of the task, c_τ, we can substitute

$$\frac{w_\tau(\ell) - (\ell - D_\tau) \cdot \frac{c_\tau}{T_\tau}}{w_\tau(\ell)} < \varepsilon$$

and by rewriting we get

$$\frac{\ell - D_\tau}{\ell} \cdot \frac{c_\tau}{T_\tau} > (1 - \varepsilon)\frac{w_\tau(\ell)}{\ell}.$$

Again, summing over all tasks gives the claimed lower bound on ϕ.

To finish, observe that between two consecutive points $\ell_1, \ell_2 \in$ POINTS $\cup \{0\}$ we can write

$$\phi(\ell) = C_1/\ell + C_2 + \xi(\ell), \quad \forall \ell \in [\ell_1, \ell_2),$$

with

$$C_1 := \sum_{\tau:\text{threshold}(\tau) \geq \ell_1} w_\tau(\ell_1) - \sum_{\tau:\text{threshold}(\tau) < \ell_1} \frac{c_\tau D_\tau}{T_\tau}$$

$$C_2 := \sum_{\tau:\text{threshold}(\tau) < \ell_1} \frac{c_\tau}{T_\tau}$$

$$\xi(\ell) := (1/\ell) \cdot \sum_{\tau:\text{threshold}(\tau) \geq \ell_1} \left([c_\tau + \ell - D_\tau - k_1 T_\tau]^+ - [c_\tau + \ell_1 - D_\tau - k_1 T_\tau]^+\right)$$

where $k_1 := \left\lfloor \frac{\ell_1 + T_\tau - D_\tau}{T_\tau} \right\rfloor$.

By definition of POINTS, the function ξ can be written as $C/\ell + C'$ for some constants C, C'; this implies that the same is true for the function ϕ inside each interval $[\ell_1, \ell_2)$. Thus, a maximum of ϕ is always attained at an extreme point of such an interval. Also, beyond the maximum of POINTS, the function ϕ equals $\sum_{\tau \in I} \left(1 - \frac{D_\tau}{\ell}\right) \cdot \frac{c_\tau}{T_\tau}$. Therefore, the overall maximum of ϕ is attained at one of the points in POINTS or equals $\sum_{\tau \in I} \frac{c_\tau}{T_\tau}$, and the algorithm is correct. $\qquad \square$

Theorem 2. *There exists a feasibility test that, given a task system I, $\mu \in \mathbb{N}$ and $\varepsilon > 0$, decides whether I can be scheduled by EDF on $(m + \mu)$ speed-$(1 + \frac{m}{(m+\mu)(1-\varepsilon)} - \frac{1}{m+\mu})$ machines, or I cannot be scheduled at all on m speed-1 machines. The running time is polynomial in n, m and $1/\varepsilon$.*

Proof. With the help of Algorithm 1 we can verify in polynomial time the following conditions:

(C1) For all tasks $\tau \in I : c_\tau \leq \min(D_\tau, T_\tau)$.
(C2) There is $\lambda \leq m$, where $(1 - \varepsilon)\lambda^* \leq \lambda \leq \lambda^*$ and $\lambda^* = \sup_{R,\Delta} \frac{\mathrm{ND}_R(\Delta)}{|\Delta|}$.

Both are necessary for scheduling I on m speed-1 machines.

Condition (C2) implies that there is no job sequence R and interval Δ such $\mathrm{ND}_R(\Delta) > \frac{m}{1-\varepsilon}|\Delta|$. Choosing $\sigma \geq \left(1 + \frac{m}{(m+\mu)(1-\varepsilon)} - \frac{1}{m+\mu}\right)$ gives $(m+\mu)(\sigma - 1) + 1 \geq \frac{m}{(1-\varepsilon)}$, and the claim follows from Theorem 1. □

Corollary 1. *There exists a feasibility test that, given a task system I and $\varepsilon > 0$, decides whether I can be scheduled by EDF on m speed-$(2 - 1/m + \varepsilon)$ machines, or I cannot be scheduled at all on m speed-1 machines. Its running time is polynomial in n, m and $1/\varepsilon$.*

Acknowledgments. The authors acknowledge Enrico Bini for helpful discussions.

References

1. Albers, K., Slomka, F.: An event stream driven approximation for the analysis of real-time systems. In: Proc. 16th Euromicro Conference on Real-Time Systems, pp. 187–195 (2004)
2. Albers, K., Slomka, F.: Efficient feasibility analysis for real-time systems with EDF scheduling. In: Proc. Conf. on Design, Automation and Test in Europe, pp. 492–497 (2005)
3. Baker, T.P.: An analysis of EDF schedulability on a multiprocessor. IEEE Trans. Parallel Distrib. Syst. 16(8), 760–768 (2005)
4. Baker, T.P., Baruah, S.K.: Schedulability analysis of multiprocessor sporadic task systems. In: Son, S.H., Lee, I., Leung, J.Y.-T. (eds.) Handbook of Real-Time and Embedded Systems. CRC Press, Boca Raton (2007)
5. Baruah, S.K., Howell, R.R., Rosier, L.E.: Feasibility problems for recurring tasks on one processor. Theor. Comput. Sci. 118(1), 3–20 (1993)
6. Chakraborty, S., Künzli, S., Thiele, L.: Approximate schedulability analysis. In: Proc. 23rd IEEE Real-Time Systems Symp., pp. 159–168 (2002)
7. Dertouzos, M.L.: Control robotics: The procedural control of physical processes. In: Proc. IFIP Congress, pp. 807–813 (1974)
8. Fisher, N., Baruah, S.K.: A fully polynomial-time approximation scheme for feasibility analysis in static-priority systems with arbitrary relative deadlines. In: Proc. 17th Euromicro Conference on Real-Time Systems, pp. 117–126 (2005)
9. Lam, T.W., To, K.-K.: Trade-offs between speed and processor in hard-deadline scheduling. In: Proc. 10th Annual ACM-SIAM Symp. on Discrete Algorithms, pp. 623–632 (1999)
10. Leung, J.Y.-T., Merrill, M.L.: A note on preemptive scheduling of periodic, real-time tasks. Inf. Process. Lett. 11(3), 115–118 (1980)
11. Liu, C.L., Layland, J.W.: Scheduling algorithms for multiprogramming in a hard-real-time environment. J. ACM 20(1), 46–61 (1973)
12. Phillips, C.A., Stein, C., Torng, E., Wein, J.: Optimal time-critical scheduling via resource augmentation. Algorithmica 32(2), 163–200 (2002)

Tight Bounds and a Fast FPT Algorithm for Directed Max-Leaf Spanning Tree

Paul Bonsma[1,*] and Frederic Dorn[2]

[1] Technische Universität Berlin, Institut für Mathematik
Sekr. MA 5-1, Straße des 17. Juni 136, 10623 Berlin, Germany
bonsma@math.tu-berlin.de
[2] Humboldt-Universität zu Berlin, Institut für Informatik
Unter den Linden 6, 10099 Berlin, Germany
dorn@informatik.hu-berlin.de

Abstract. An out-tree T of a directed graph D is a rooted tree subgraph with all arcs directed outwards from the root. An out-branching is a spanning out-tree. By $\ell(D)$ and $\ell_s(D)$ we denote the maximum number of leaves over all out-trees and out-branchings of D, respectively. We give fixed parameter tractable algorithms for deciding whether $\ell_s(D) \geq k$ and whether $\ell(D) \geq k$ for a digraph D on n vertices, both with time complexity $2^{O(k \log k)} \cdot n^{O(1)}$. This proves the problem for out-branchings to be in FPT, and improves on the previous complexity of $2^{O(k \log^2 k)} \cdot n^{O(1)}$ for out-trees. To obtain the algorithm for out-branchings, we prove that when all arcs of D are part of at least one out-branching, $\ell_s(D) \geq \ell(D)/3$. The second bound we prove states that for strongly connected digraphs D with minimum in-degree 3, $\ell_s(D) \geq \Theta(\sqrt{n})$, where previously $\ell_s(D) \geq \Theta(\sqrt[3]{n})$ was the best known bound. This bound is tight, and also holds for the larger class of digraphs with minimum in-degree 3 in which every arc is part of at least one out-branching.

1 Introduction

Many important graph problems are well-studied on undirected graphs unlike their generalizations to directed graphs. One reason may be that despite their practical significance, it is generally harder to obtain similar results for directed graphs, since many standard tools are not available (see [2]) and thus problem specific approaches need to be used. MAX-LEAF SPANNING TREE is such a problem that has received a lot of study, both algorithmically and combinatorial. This optimization problem is defined as follows: given an undirected graph, find a spanning tree with maximum number of leaves. In the decision version of this problem, in addition an integer k is given, and we ask whether a spanning tree with at least k leaves exists (k-LEAF SPANNING TREE). In this paper we develop new techniques for solving the directed version of this problem and use these to find improved algorithms and bounds.

* Supported by the Graduate School "Methods for Discrete Structures" in Berlin, DFG grant GRK 1408.

D. Halperin and K. Mehlhorn (Eds.): ESA 2008, LNCS 5193, pp. 222–233, 2008.

For directed graphs or *digraphs* we use notions that are defined for undirected graphs, such as paths, trees, connectedness and vertex neighborhoods. These are defined as expected, where arc directions are ignored. An *out-tree* of a digraph D is a tree subgraph where every vertex has in-degree 1 except for one, the *root*, which has in-degree 0. An *out-branching* is a spanning out-tree. A *leaf* is a vertex with out-degree 0. In the directed generalization of the problem, one asks for an out-branching with maximum number of leaves. This problem is called MAX-LEAF OUT-BRANCHING. By $\ell(D)$ and $\ell_s(D)$ we denote the maximum number of leaves over all out-trees and out-branchings of D respectively (when considering $\ell_s(D)$ we assume that D has at least one out-branching). Clearly $\ell(D) \geq \ell_s(D)$ holds, but in contrast to undirected graphs, we do not always have equality here. Therefore, on digraphs, the problem of finding an out-tree with maximum number of leaves (MAX-LEAF OUT-TREE) is of independent interest. The corresponding decision problems where the question is asked whether $\ell_s(D) \geq k$ or whether $\ell(D) \geq k$ are called k-LEAF OUT-BRANCHING (k-LOB) and k-LEAF OUT-TREE (k-LOT), respectively. The related problem of finding out-branchings with *minimum* number of leaves has also been considered recently [12]. In the first part of this paper we are concerned with algorithmic questions, and in the second part we study the combinatorial question of finding lower bounds for $\ell(D)$ and $\ell_s(D)$. Throughout this section n denotes the number of vertices of the graph under consideration.

The NP-hardness of all problems above follows from the NP-completeness of k-LEAF SPANNING TREE. Whereas for the undirected problem, MAX-LEAF SPANNING TREE, a 2-approximation is known [15], the best known approximation result for MAX-LEAF OUT-BRANCHING is a very recent algorithm with ratio $O(\sqrt{\text{OPT}})$ [9]. In the algorithmic part of this work, we are interested in *fixed parameter tractable (FPT)* algorithms for the decision problems. We choose the desired number of leaves k as the parameter. Then an algorithm is an *FPT algorithm* if its time complexity is bounded by a function of the form $f(k) \cdot n^{O(1)}$, where the *parameter function* f may be any computable function only depending on k. See [11] for a recent introduction to FPT algorithms. The main indicator of the practicality of FPT algorithms is the growth rate of the parameter function. For the undirected problem k-LEAF SPANNING TREE many improvements have been made in this area (see e.g. [10,4]), which has also has been a large stimulus for research on related combinatorial questions. The current fastest FPT algorithm has a running time of $O^*(6.75^k) + O(m)$, with m being the number of edges [6].

Tackling two open problems posed by Fellows in 2005 [13], Alon et al. [2] were the first to show that k-LOT admits an FPT algorithm with parameter function $f(k) \in 2^{O(k^2 \log k)}$. Their method yields an FPT algorithm for k-LOB when restricted to digraph classes where out-trees with k leaves can always be extended to out-branchings with k leaves, which includes for instance strongly connected digraphs and acyclic digraphs. This algorithm again has a parameter function $f(k) \in 2^{O(k^2 \log k)}$. In [1], the same authors improve that function to $2^{O(k \log^2 k)}$ for strongly connected graphs, and $2^{O(k \log k)}$ for acyclic graphs. Note that even for acyclic digraphs, the problem is NP-hard, which is shown in the full version of [1]. The question whether the problem admits an FPT algorithm for all digraphs remained open, and was posed again in [1,2,7].

In this paper we present FPT algorithms for both k-LOT and k-LOB with parameter function $2^{O(k \log k)}$. This is the first FPT algorithm for k-LOB[1], and improves the complexity of all FPT algorithms for digraphs mentioned above, except for the algorithm for acyclic digraphs, which has the same complexity.

In another line of research, max-leaf problems have been studied in a purely combinatorial manner. For instance, for the undirected version, a well-known (tight) bound states that undirected graphs with minimum degree 3 have a spanning tree with at least $n/4 + 2$ leaves [14]. Similar bounds appear in [6,8]. For digraphs, it is much harder to obtain tight bounds, or even bounds that are tight up to a constant factor. Alon et al [1] showed that for strongly connected digraphs D with minimum in-degree 3, $\ell_s(D) \geq \sqrt[3]{n/4} - 1$ (this improves their previous bound from [2]). In addition they construct strongly connected digraphs D with minimum in-degree 3 with $\ell_s(D) \in O(\sqrt{n})$. Considering the gap between this lower bound and upper bound, it is asked in [1] what the minimum value of r is such that $\ell_s(D) \geq f(n) \in \Theta(\sqrt[r]{n})$ for all graphs in this class ($2 \leq r \leq 3$).

In this paper we answer this question by showing that for strongly connected digraphs D with minimum in-degree 3, $\ell_s(D) \geq \frac{1}{4}\sqrt{n}$. Considering the examples from [1], we see that this bound is tight (up to a constant factor). Furthermore we generalize this result by showing that $\ell_s(D) \geq f(n) \in \Theta(\sqrt{n})$ holds for the larger class of digraphs with minimum in-degree 3 in which every arc is part of an out-branching.

Overview of new techniques: For our algorithms we start with the general scheme that was introduced in [1,2]: starting with an arbitrary out-branching, small changes are made that increase the number of leaves, until a locally optimal out-branching T is obtained. *Back arcs* of T are those arcs of D that form a directed cycle together with a part of T (we omit the precise definitions used in [1]). If there are few back arcs, then a path decomposition of D can be constructed with small width, which allows for a dynamic programming procedure to be used. On the other hand, if the number of back arcs is large, an *out-tree* with at least k leaves exists. For graph classes like strongly connected digraphs this then yields an out-branching with at least k leaves.

However, without significant new ideas this scheme does not work for all digraphs, as is illustrated by the digraph D in Figure 1 (a): D has $\ell(D) = n - 2$, but the unique out-branching has only one leaf. More importantly, this example shows that the ratio between $\ell_s(D)$ on one hand, and the number of back arcs or the pathwidth on the other hand may be arbitrarily bad. But if one takes a closer look at the arcs of the out-tree, one may observe that they are irrelevant for the problem we consider; they do not appear in any out-branching. We will first remove all such arcs, which we call *useless arcs*. The following question is then immediate: for digraphs without useless arcs, what is the highest possible ratio $\ell(D)/\ell_s(D)$? Figure 1 (b) shows an example of a digraph without useless

---

[1] In an earlier unpublished technical report [5] we gave a different FPT algorithm for k-LOB, with parameter function $2^{O(k^3 \log k)}$.

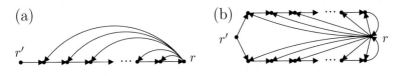

Fig. 1. Digraphs with $\ell(D)/\ell_s(D) \to \infty$ (a), and $\ell(D)/\ell_s(D) = 2$ (b)

arcs where $\ell(D)/\ell_s(D) = 2$. In the first of the two main bounds of this paper, we prove that this ratio cannot be much larger; we prove that if D contains no useless arcs, then $\ell(D)/\ell_s(D) \le 3$. Since this ratio is bounded by a constant, and since useless arcs can easily be removed in polynomial time, any algorithm for k-LOT then easily yields an algorithm for k-LOB with essentially the same complexity.

Our second algorithmic contribution is that we construct a tree decomposition instead of a path decomposition (the locally optimal out-branching that we start with serves as the skeleton for the tree decomposition), and use a better way to group back arcs. These improvements do not only make the algorithm conceptually simpler, but also allow us to decrease the parameter function $2^{O(k \log^2 k)}$ for k-LOT from [1] by a logarithmical factor in the exponent to $2^{O(k \log k)}$.

The paper is organized as follows. Definitions and preliminary observations are given in Section 2. In Section 3 and 4 we give the FPT algorithm for k-LOT and k-LOB, respectively. Section 4 also contains the proof that $\ell(D)/\ell_s(D) \le 3$ for digraphs without useless arcs. In Section 5 we give a lower bound for $\ell_s(D)$.

2   Preliminaries

For a digraph D, $V(D)$ denotes the set of vertices and $A(D)$ the set of arcs. Arcs are 2-tuples (u, v) where $u \in V(D)$ is called the *tail* and $v \in V(D)$ the *head*. For an arc set B, $\mathrm{HD}(B)$ is the set of heads of arcs in B. A digraph D is an *oriented graph* if $(u, v) \in A(D)$ implies $(v, u) \notin A(D)$. A *dipath* in a digraph D is a sequence of distinct vertices $v_1, v_2, \ldots, v_r$ such that $(v_i, v_{i+1}) \in A(D)$ for all $1 \le i \le r - 1$. This will also be called a (v_1, v_r)-*dipath*. The digraph consisting of these vertices and arcs will also be called a dipath. With such a dipath we associate an order from v_1 to v_r, for instance when talking about the first arc of the path that satisfies some property.

A *partial order* is a binary relation that is reflexive, antisymmetric and transitive. A *strict partial order* is irreflexive and transitive. Partial orders will be denoted by $\preceq$, and strict partial orders by $\prec$.

For digraphs we will use normal (undirected) tree decompositions. Hence we define a *tree decomposition* of a digraph D as a pair (X, U) where U is an (undirected) tree whose vertices we call *nodes*, and $X = (\{X_i : i \in V(U)\})$ is a collection of subsets of $V(D)$ (*bags*) such that

    1. $\bigcup_{i \in V(U)} X_i = V(D)$,
    2. for each $(v, w) \in A(D)$, there exists an $i \in V(U)$ such that $v, w \in X_i$,
    3. for each $v \in V(D)$, the set of nodes $\{i : v \in X_i\}$ forms a subtree of U.

The *width* of a tree decomposition (X, U) equals $\max_{i \in V(U)} \{|X_i| - 1\}$. For notational convenience, we will also allow the graph U in a tree decomposition (X, U) to be directed, in this case it should be understood that we actually consider the underlying undirected graph of U.

For an out-tree T, the vertices of out-degree at least two are called *branch vertices*. Let $L(T)$ denote the set of leaves of T, let $\mathrm{Br}(T)$ denote the set of branch vertices of T, and let $\mathrm{Bs}(T)$ be the vertices of T that have a branch vertex of T as in-neighbor.

Proposition 1. *For out-tree T, $|\mathrm{Bs}(T)| \le 2|L(T)| - 2$, $|\mathrm{Br}(T)| \le |L(T)| - 1$.*

The omitted proofs in this section are straightforward and/or can be found in [1,5]. If there exists a dipath in D from vertex u to vertex v, we say v is *reachable* from u (within D). The set of all vertices that are reachable from u within D is denoted by $R_D(u)$ (including u itself.)

Proposition 2. *Let T be an out-tree of a digraph D, with root r. Then D has an out-branching T' with root r, that contains T, if and only if $R_D(r) = V(D)$.*

Let T be an out-tree. Then we write $u \preceq_T v$ if $v \in R_T(u)$, and $u \prec_T v$ if in addition $v \ne u$. Note that the relation $\preceq_T$ is a partial order on $V(T)$. This important observation will be used implicitly throughout the paper.

A digraph H is *strongly connected* if for all pairs $u, v \in V(H)$, a (u, v)-dipath exists. A *strong component* is a maximal strongly connected subgraph. A strong component H of D is an *initial strong component* if there is no arc $(u, v) \in A(D)$ with $u \notin V(H)$, $v \in V(H)$.

Let T be an out-branching of D, and let $(u, v) \in A(D) \backslash A(T)$, where v is not the root of T. The *1-change for (u, v)* is the operation that yields $T + (u, v) - (w, v)$, where w is the unique in-neighbor of v in T. We call an out-branching T *1-optimal* if there is no 1-change for an arc of $A(D) \backslash A(T)$ that results in an out-branching T' with more leaves. Note that a 1-optimal out-branching can be found in polynomial time.

Proposition 3. *Let T be an out-branching of D, and let $(u, v) \in A(D) \backslash A(T)$.*

- The 1-change for (u, v) gives again an out-branching of D if and only if $v \not\preceq_T u$.
- The 1-change for (u, v) increases $|L(T)|$ if and only if $u \notin L(T)$ and $v \notin \mathrm{Bs}(T)$.

Proposition 4. *Let D be a digraph with a vertex r such that $R_D(r) = V(D)$. An arc (u, v) of D with $R_D(v) \ne V(D)$ is not useless if and only if there is a dipath in D starting at r that ends with (u, v).*

3   A Faster FPT Algorithm for k-LOT

We now show how back arcs of an out-tree are grouped, that is, how back arcs are assigned to vertices of the out-tree. Let T be an out-tree of D with $z \in V(T)$. Then

$$\mathrm{B}_D^T(z) = \{(u, v) \in A(D) : v \prec_T z \preceq_T u\}.$$

If it is clear what the graphs D and T in question are, the subscript and superscript will be omitted. When $|\text{HD}(\text{B}(z))| \geq k$ for some choice of z, an out-tree with at least k leaves is easily found.

Proposition 5. *Let T be an out-tree of D with $|\text{HD}(\text{B}_D^T(z))| \geq k$ for some $z \in V(T)$. Then D has an out-tree with at least k leaves.*

Proof. Start with the out-tree $T[R_T(z)]$, which is rooted at z. For every vertex in $v \in \text{HD}(\text{B}_D^T(z))$, add an arc from some vertex in $u \in R_T(z)$ to v (such an arc exists), making v a leaf.   □

Algorithm 1. An FPT algorithm for k-LOT

Input   : A digraph D and integer k.

for *every initial strong component C of D* **do**

1   Choose $r \in V(C)$, let $D' = D[R_D(r)]$.

2   Compute a 1-optimal out-branching T of D' with root r.

3   **if** $|L(T)| \geq k$ **then** Return(YES).

4   **if** *there exists a vertex z with $|\text{HD}(\text{B}_{D'}^T(z))| \geq k$* **then**
       Return(YES).

5   Construct a tree decomposition of D' with width at most $4k - 5$.

6   Do dynamic programming on the tree decomposition of D'.

7   **if** *an out-tree with at least k leaves is found* **then** Return(YES).

8 Return(NO)

This yields the correctness of Step 4 of the algorithm, which is shown in Algorithm 1. The construction of the tree decomposition of D' is as follows. For the tree of the tree decomposition, we simply use the 1-optimal out-branching T itself. For a vertex $v \in V(T)$ with $(u, v) \in A(T)$, the bag X_v of the tree decomposition is defined as $X_v = \{u, v\} \cup \text{Bs}(T) \cup L(T) \cup \text{HD}(\text{B}_{D'}^T(v))$.(If v is the root of T, simply omit u.) For verifying that (X, T) with $X = \{X_v : v \in V(T)\}$ is a tree decomposition, the 1-optimality of T and Proposition 3 can be used to show that for every arc $(u, v) \in A(D')$ the end vertices u, v appear in a common bag. By the transitivity of $\preceq_T$, it follows that the vertex set $B_v = \{u : v \in X_u\}$ induces a connected subgraph of T, for every $v \in V(T)$.

Lemma 1. *If T is a 1-optimal out-branching of D', then (X, T) as constructed above is a tree decomposition of D'.*

Proposition 6. *Let T be an out-branching of a digraph D with $|L(T)| \leq k - 1$. If for all vertices $z \in V(D)$ it holds that $|\text{HD}(\text{B}_D^T(z))| \leq k - 1$, then the tree decomposition (X, T) as constructed above has width at most $4k - 5$.*

Proof. This follows simply from $|X_u| = 2 + |L(T)| + |\text{Bs}(T)| + |\text{HD}(\text{B}(u))| \leq 2 + (k-1) + (2k-4) + (k-1) = 4k-4$, since $|\text{Bs}(T)| \leq 2|L(T)| - 2$ (Proposition 1).□

When a tree decomposition of D' is given, standard dynamic programming methods can be used to decide whether D' has an out-tree with at least k leaves (see also [3,12]). The time complexity of such a procedure is $2^{O(w \log w)} \cdot n$, where $n = |V(D')|$ and w is the width of the tree decomposition. Since in our case $w \leq 4k - 5$, and every step of the algorithm other than Step 6 can be done in polynomial time, the complexity of Algorithm 1 is $2^{O(k \log k)} \cdot n^{O(1)}$. If an out-tree with k leaves exists, it is part of $D[R_D(r)]$ for some r in an initial strong component, so YES will be returned. Thus:

Theorem 1. *For any digraph D with $n = |V(D)|$, Algorithm 1 solves k-LOT in time $2^{O(k \log k)} \cdot n^{O(1)}$.*

4   A Fast FPT Algorithm for k-LOB

Our algorithm for k-LOB is similar to Algorithm 1. We first check whether an out-branching exists for D, and if so we may remove all useless arcs to obtain D'. Then a 1-optimal out-branching T of D' is constructed. If $|\mathrm{H}_D(\mathrm{B}_{D'}^T(z))| \geq 3k$ holds for some vertex z, then an out-tree with at least $3k$ leaves exists (Proposition 5). In Theorem 3 below we show that this yields the existence of an out-branching with at least k leaves. On the other hand, if $|L(T)| < k$ and $|\mathrm{H}_D(\mathrm{B}_{D'}^T(z))| < 3k$ for all vertices z, the construction from Section 3 yields a tree decomposition with width $\leq 6k - 5$ (see also Proposition 6). At this point we can again apply dynamic programming.

Theorem 2. *For any digraph D with $n = |V(D)|$, k-LOB can be solved in time $2^{O(k \log k)} \cdot n^{O(1)}$.*

It remains to prove that if a graph D without useless arcs has $\ell(D) \geq 3k$, then $\ell_s(D) \geq k$. The proof of Theorem 3 can be turned into a polynomial time algorithm that constructs an out-branching, and therefore the algorithm for k-LOB can be made into a constructive FPT algorithm.

Theorem 3. *Let D be a digraph without useless arcs. If $\ell(D) \geq 3k$, then $\ell_s(D) \geq k$.*

Proof. Let T be an out-tree of D with at least $3k$ leaves, and let r be the root of T. If T contains at least one vertex v with $R_D(v) = V(D)$, then also $R_D(r) = V(D)$, so then T can be extended to an out-branching with at least $3k$ leaves (Proposition 2).

Otherwise, choose an arbitrary vertex r' with $R_D(r') = V(D)$ (which exists since there are non-useless arcs, and thus at least one out-branching), and let P be an (r', r)-dipath that contains a minimal number of vertices of $L(T)$. Let $L(T) \cap V(P) = \{l_1, \ldots, l_m\}$, labeled with decreasing labels along P. That is, if $i < j$, then $l_j \prec_P l_i$. These definitions are illustrated in Figure 2 (a). We distinguish two types of vertices l_i ($i \in \{1, \ldots, m\}$):

Type 1: $D - l_i$ contains an (x, y)-dipath for some $x, y \in V(P)$ with $x \prec_P l_i \prec_P y$, with no internal vertices in $V(P)$. **Type 2:** all other vertices l_i.

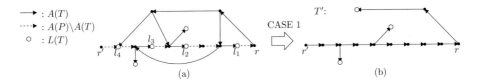

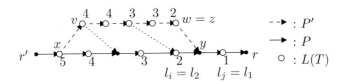

Fig. 2. (a) Out-tree T and (r',r)-dipath P, (b) the out-tree T' constructed in Case 1

Now we consider three cases: since $|L(T)| \geq 3k$, one of the following holds: (i) $|L(T)\backslash V(P)| \geq k$, (ii) the number of type 1 leaves is at least k, or (iii) the number of type 2 leaves is at least k. In all cases we will find an out-branching with at least k leaves.

CASE 1: $|L(T)\backslash V(P)| \geq k$. We use P and T to construct an out-tree T' of D. This is illustrated in Figure 2 (b). For all arcs $(u,v) \in A(P)$ with $v \notin V(T)$ or $v = r$, simply add (u,v) to the out-tree. For arcs $(u,v) \in A(P)\backslash A(T)$ with $v \in V(T)\backslash\{r\}$, do the 1-change for (u,v). Then T' is again an out-tree with at least k leaves, with root r' such that $R_D(r') = V(D)$. This is then easily extended to an out-branching with at least k leaves (Proposition 2).

Fig. 3. Definitions used in Case 2. Numbers indicate D_L.

CASE 2: *The number of type 1 leaves is at least k.* The definitions used in this case are illustrated in Figure 3. For every $v \in L(T)$, we define the following value: if $r \in R_D(v)$, then consider the (v,r)-dipath of D that contains the minimum number of $L(T)$-vertices. Then let $D_L(v)$ denote number of vertices in $L(T)$ on this path (including v itself). Note that since we chose P to contain the minimum number of $L(T)$-vertices, we have $D_L(l_i) = i$. In particular, all vertices l_i receive different values for D_L.

For every type 1 vertex l_i, we may consider an (x,y)-dipath P' in D with $x \prec_P l_i \prec_P y$ and no internal vertices in P. We can verify that P' contains a vertex $z \in L(T)\backslash V(P)$ with $D_L(z) = D_L(l_i)$. Since we assumed there are at least k type 1 vertices, and all of them receive different labels D_L, this proves that there are at least k vertices in $L(T)\backslash V(P)$, so by case 1 above, the desired out-branching exists.

CASE 3: *The number of type 2 leaves is at least k.* In this case we will use the fact that D contains no useless arcs. Let l_i be a type 2 vertex. Consider the unique (r,l_i)-dipath in T. Let (t_i,h_i) be the last arc of this path that is not in $A(P)$. Note that $h_i = l_i$ is possible. Note also that by choice of (t_i,h_i), we have $l_{i+1} \prec_P h_i \preceq_P l_i$. Since (t_i, h_i) is not useless and since we observed in the beginning of this proof that we may assume $R_D(h_i) \neq V(D)$, there is a dipath P' in D that starts in r' and ends with the arc (t_i, h_i) (Proposition 4). Let x_i be the last vertex on P' with $x_i \prec_P h_i$. Let y_i be out-neighbor of x_i on P'.

Using these definitions we can show how to construct an out-branching with at least k leaves. Construct T' as follows, starting with P. For every type 2 vertex l_i, if $y_i \notin V(P)$, then add (x_i, y_i). If $y_i \in V(P)$, then instead do the 1-change for (x_i, y_i). Since we do this only for type 2 vertices, it can be shown that T' is an out-tree with root r' with at least k leaves, which is easily extended to the desired out-branching (Proposition 2). We omit the details.   □

5   Lower Bounds for the Number of Leaves

The following lemma can be used for instance to find leafy out-branchings in digraphs D with minimum in-degree 3 (which is needed to satisfy the third condition). Its proof is postponed to the end of this section.

Lemma 2. *Let T be an out-branching of D, and let $P = v_0, \ldots, v_{p-1}$ be a dipath in T where (i) D contains no arcs (v_i, v_j) with $i \leq j - 2$, (ii) $V(P)$ contains no branch vertices of T, and (iii) every v_i has an in-neighbor in D other than v_{i-1} or v_{i+1}. Then D has an out-tree with at least $p/8$ leaves in $V(P)$.*

Lemma 2 is the key ingredient for our main result of this section. Apart from using this stronger lemma and a shorter formulation, the proof of the next theorem is similar to the one used in [1].

Theorem 4. *Let D be a digraph on n vertices with at least one out-branching. If D has minimum in-degree 3, or if D is an oriented graph with minimum in-degree 2, then $\ell(D) \geq \frac{1}{4}\sqrt{n}$.*

Proof. Let $k = \frac{1}{4}\sqrt{n}$. Consider a 1-optimal out-branching T of D. We only have to consider the case that $|L(T)| \leq k-1$, and thus $|\text{BR}(T)| < k-2$ (Proposition 1). Consider the set $\mathcal{P}$ of all maximal dipaths in T that contain no branch vertices. Note that every non-branch vertex of T is in exactly one such path, so the paths in $\mathcal{P}$ give a partition of $V(T)\backslash\text{BR}(T)$. It can easily be seen that the number of paths in $\mathcal{P}$ is bounded by $|L(T)| + |\text{BR}(T)| \leq 2k - 3$.

For every path $v_0, \ldots, v_{p-1}$ in $\mathcal{P}$ we may apply Lemma 2: since D either has minimum in-degree 3 or is an oriented graph with minimum in-degree 2, every v_i has an in-neighbor in D other than v_{i-1} or v_{i+1}. Since T is 1-optimal, there are no arcs (v_i, v_j) in D with $i \leq j - 2$ (Proposition 3). Hence if one of these paths contains at least $8k$ vertices, the desired out-tree exists (Lemma 2). So finally suppose every path in $\mathcal{P}$ has less than $8k$ vertices. This yields $n < 8k(2k - 3) + k - 2 < 16k^2$, a contradiction with our choice of k. Hence in every case an out-tree with at least $\frac{1}{4}\sqrt{n}$ leaves can be found.   □

Combining Theorem 4 with Proposition 2 and Theorem 3 respectively, we immediately obtain the following bounds for out-branchings.

Corollary 1. *Let D be a digraph on n vertices that has minimum in-degree 3, or has minimum in-degree 2 and is an oriented graph.*
-If D is strongly connected, then $\ell_s(D) \geq \frac{1}{4}\sqrt{n}$.
-If D contains no useless arcs, then $\ell_s(D) \geq \frac{1}{12}\sqrt{n}$.

It remains to prove Lemma 2. For this we will use the following lemma [5].

Lemma 3. *Let T be an out-branching of D with root r. Let Q be a dipath in D that starts at r. Then making all of the 1-changes for every arc in $A(Q)\backslash A(T)$ yields again an out-branching of D that contains Q.*

Proof of Lemma 2: Let T be an out-branching of a digraph D, and let P be a dipath in T that satisfies the properties stated in the lemma. Let r be the root of T. If v_{p-1} is not a leaf of T, then let v_p be the unique out-neighbor of v_{p-1} in T. In this case, we add the arc (r, v_p) to D (if it is not already present), and apply the 1-change for (r, v_p) to T. So in both cases, from now on we may conveniently assume that $R_T(v_i) = \{v_i, \ldots, v_{p-1}\}$. In the remainder of the proof we will use this to show that D has an out-branching with at least $p/4$ leaves in $V(P)$. From this the statement follows; if we added (r, v_p) then removing this arc from the out-branching will give two out-trees of the original digraph D, of which at least one has at least $p/8$ leaves in $V(P)$. If an arc (v_i, v_j) is present in $A(D)\backslash A(T)$, then $i > j$. Arcs of this type are called *back arcs*. (This is a subset of the arcs that were called back arcs in Section 1.)

We will now iteratively make changes to T until every $v_i \in V(P)$ is either a leaf, or is the tail of a back arc. The property of T being an out-branching will be maintained throughout. Changes to T are made in $p-1$ *stages*. During stage i ($i \in \{1, \ldots, p-1\}$), the goal is to make vertex v_{i-1} a leaf, if this is still possible. For this we consider a dipath Q_i that ends in the vertex v_i, and make 1-changes based on this path. The changes we make when considering the vertex v_i will only involve arcs that are incident with vertices of P with higher index, and vertices not in P. So in stages later than stage i, no changes are made to the arcs incident with v_j, for $j \leq i$. In particular, v_{i-1} will remain a leaf if it is made a leaf in stage i.

Before we define Q_i, we observe that the following properties hold for T. These properties will be maintained throughout the procedure, and will therefore be called *invariant properties*: (1) v_i has only out-neighbors in $\{v_1, \ldots, v_{i+1}\}$, for all $i \in \{0, \ldots, p-1\}$. (2) $R_T(v_i) \subseteq V(P)$. (Note that the second property follows from the first.)

The changes that will be made to T will consist of adding back arcs and adding arcs with tail not in P, and removing arcs of the form (v_j, v_{j+1}). Figure 4 (a) shows an example of how the out-branching may look after five stages (only the vertices of P are shown). Note that the invariant still holds even though the set of reachable vertices may change for a vertex v_i.

The operation of stage i, and the dipath Q_i that we use for it is defined as follows. Let T_i denote the out-branching as it is in the beginning of stage i, so $T_1 = T$. The changes in stage i will yield a new out-branching T_{i+1}. In Figure 4 an example is shown where T_7 is constructed from T_6. The dashed

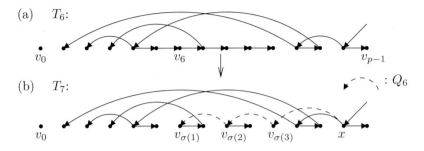

Fig. 4. Stage 6: constructing T_7 from T_6

arcs in Figure 4 (b) show the dipath Q_6. If v_{i-1} is already a leaf or a tail of a back arc in T_i, we do nothing, so $T_{i+1} = T_i$. Otherwise, v_i is the only out-neighbor of v_{i-1} in T_i (invariant Property 1). Then we consider a dipath $Q_i = x, v_{\sigma(q)}, v_{\sigma(q-1)}, \ldots, v_{\sigma(1)}$ in D that ends in v_i, and has $x \notin R_{T_i}(v_i)$, constructed as follows. Let $\sigma(1) = i$. By our assumption, v_i has an in-neighbor u in D that is not equal to v_{i-1} or v_{i+1}. Since all arcs between vertices in $V(P)$ are back arcs and $R_{T_i}(v_i) \subseteq V(P)$ (invariant Property 2), this vertex u is either not in $R_{T_i}(v_i)$ or it is equal to v_j for some $j \geq i + 2$. In the first case, $Q_i = u, v_i$. In the second case let $\sigma(2) = j$, and continue constructing the path using the same rule: v_j has an in-neighbor that is not in $R_{T_i}(v_j)$, or is equal to v_l for some $l \geq j + 2$, etc.

This process will terminate with a dipath $Q_i = x, v_{\sigma(q)}, \ldots, v_{\sigma(1)}$, where $v_{\sigma(1)} = v_i$, the function σ increases in steps of at least 2, and $x \notin R_{T_i}(v_i)$. It follows that if we make 1-changes for all arcs in Q_i, again an out-branching is obtained (Lemma 3, note that we can easily extend Q_i to start in r), and v_{i-1} becomes a leaf. Observe also that the invariant properties are maintained by these changes. This yields T_{i+1}. We omit the proof that an out-branching T_p constructed in this way contains at least $p/4$ leaves. □

6   Discussion

It seems that in order to significantly improve the parameter function of FPT algorithms for these problems further, a different approach is needed, one that is not based on dynamic programming over a tree decomposition. It is an interesting question whether different, significantly faster FPT algorithms are possible for these two problems, for instance FPT algorithms with a parameter function of the form c^k for some constant c. Such algorithms exist for the undirected version (with $c = 6.75$, see [6]). This was also asked in [12].

References

1. Alon, N., Fomin, F.V., Gutin, G., Krivelevich, M., Saurabh, S.: Better algorithms and bounds for directed maximum leaf problems. In: Arvind, V., Prasad, S. (eds.) FSTTCS 2007. LNCS, vol. 4855, pp. 316–327. Springer, Heidelberg (2007), Full version: http://arxiv.org/abs/0803.0701

2. Alon, N., Fomin, F.V., Gutin, G., Krivelevich, M., Saurabh, S.: Parameterized algorithms for directed maximum leaf problems. In: Arge, L., Cachin, C., Jurdziński, T., Tarlecki, A. (eds.) ICALP 2007. LNCS, vol. 4596, pp. 352–362. Springer, Heidelberg (2007)

3. Bodlaender, H.L.: A tourist guide through treewidth. Acta Cybernet. 11, 1–21 (1993)

4. Bonsma, P., Brüggemann, T., Woeginger, G.J.: A faster FPT algorithm for finding spanning trees with many leaves. In: Rovan, B., Vojtáš, P. (eds.) MFCS 2003. LNCS, vol. 2747, pp. 259–268. Springer, Heidelberg (2003)

5. Bonsma, P., Dorn, F.: An FPT algorithm for directed spanning k-leaf (2007), http://arxiv.org/abs/0711.4052

6. Bonsma, P., Zickfeld, F.: Spanning trees with many leaves in graphs without diamonds and blossoms. In: Laber, E.S., Bornstein, C., Nogueira, L.T., Faria, L. (eds.) LATIN 2008. LNCS, vol. 4957, pp. 531–543. Springer, Heidelberg (2008)

7. Demaine, E., Gutin, G., Marx, D., Stege, U.: 07281 Open problems – Structure theory and FPT algorithmics for graphs, digraphs and hypergraphs. In: Dagstuhl Seminar Proceedings 07281 (2007), http://drops.dagstuhl.de/opus/volltexte/2007/1254

8. Ding, G., Johnson, T., Seymour, P.: Spanning trees with many leaves. J. Graph Theory 37, 189–197 (2001)

9. Drescher, M., Vetta, A.: An approximation algorithm for the maximum leaf spanning arborescence problem (manuscript, 2007)

10. Fellows, M.R., McCartin, C., Rosamond, F.A., Stege, U.: Coordinatized kernels and catalytic reductions: An improved FPT algorithm for max leaf spanning tree and other problems. In: Kapoor, S., Prasad, S. (eds.) FST TCS 2000. LNCS, vol. 1974, pp. 240–251. Springer, Heidelberg (2000)

11. Flum, J., Grohe, M.: Parameterized Complexity Theory. Texts in Theoretical Computer Science. An EATCS Series. Springer, Berlin (2006)

12. Gutin, G., Razgon, I., Kim, E.J.: Minimum leaf out-branching problems. In: Fleischer, R., Xu, J. (eds.) AAIM 2008. LNCS, vol. 5034, pp. 235–246. Springer, Heidelberg (2008)

13. Gutin, G., Yeo, A.: Some parameterized problems on digraphs. Comput. J. 51, 363–371 (2008)

14. Kleitman, D.J., West, D.B.: Spanning trees with many leaves. SIAM J. Discrete Math. 4, 99–106 (1991)

15. Solis-Oba, R.: 2-approximation algorithm for finding a spanning tree with maximum number of leaves. In: Bilardi, G., Pietracaprina, A., Italiano, G.F., Pucci, G. (eds.) ESA 1998. LNCS, vol. 1461, pp. 441–452. Springer, Heidelberg (1998)

Engineering Tree Labeling Schemes: A Case Study on Least Common Ancestors*

Saverio Caminiti, Irene Finocchi, and Rossella Petreschi

Computer Science Department, *Sapienza* University of Rome
Via Salaria, 113 - 00198 Rome, Italy
{caminiti,finocchi,petreschi}@di.uniroma1.it

Abstract. We address the problem of labeling the nodes of a tree such that one can determine the identifier of the least common ancestor of any two nodes by looking only at their labels. This problem has application in routing and in distributed computing in peer-to-peer networks. A labeling scheme using $\Theta(\log^2 n)$-bit labels has been previously presented by Peleg. By engineering this scheme, we obtain a variety of data structures with the same asymptotic performances. We conduct a thorough experimental evaluation of all these data structures. Our results clearly show which variants achieve the best performances in terms of space usage, construction time, and query time.

1 Introduction

Effective representations of large, geographically dispersed communication networks should allow the users to efficiently retrieve information about the network in a distributed and localized way. Labeling schemes provide an answer to this problem by assigning labels to the network nodes in such a way that queries can be computed alone from the labels of the involved nodes, without any extra information source. The primary goal of a labeling scheme is to minimize the maximum label length, while keeping queries fast. Adjacency labeling schemes were first introduced by Breuer and Folkman in [5,6], and further studied in [12]. The interest in informative labeling schemes, however, was revived only more recently, after Peleg showed the feasibility of the design of efficient labeling schemes capturing distance information [16]. Since then, upper and lower bounds for labeling schemes have been proved on a variety of graph families and for a large variety of queries, including distance [2,9,11], tree ancestry [1,3], flow and connectivity [14]. In spite of a large body of theoretical works, to the best of our knowledge only few experimental investigations of the efficiency of informative labeling schemes have been addressed in the literature [9,13].

In this paper we focus on labeling schemes for answering least common ancestor queries in trees. Labeling schemes for least common ancestors can be easily

* Work partially supported by MIUR, the Italian Ministry of Education, University and Research, under Project MAINSTREAM ("Algorithms for Massive Information Structures and Data Streams").

D. Halperin and K. Mehlhorn (Eds.): ESA 2008, LNCS 5193, pp. 234–245, 2008.

exploited to answer distance queries and are mainly useful in routing messages on tree networks, processing queries in XML search engines and distributed computing in peer-to-peer networks (see, e.g., [3,4,13]). In [17], Peleg has proved that for the class of n-node trees there exists a labeling scheme for least common ancestors using $\Theta(\log^2 n)$-bit labels, which is also shown to be asymptotically optimal.

Peleg's labeling scheme hinges upon two main ingredients: a decomposition of the tree into paths, and a suitable encoding of information related to such paths into the node labels. Peleg's data structure uses an *ad hoc* path decomposition as well as an *ad hoc* label structure. In this paper we first discuss different path decomposition approaches and different ways of constructing node labels, with the aim of engineering Peleg's scheme and obtaining a variety of labeling schemes for least common ancestors. We then perform a thorough experimental evaluation of all these variants, also analyzing the effects of structural properties of the input tree (such as balancing and degree) on their performances. The main findings of our experiments can be summarized as follows:

- Among different path decompositions, those that generate the smallest number of paths (with the largest average path length) appear to be preferable in order to minimize the total size of the data structure.
- A variant of Peleg's scheme proposed in [7] achieves the best performances in terms of space usage and construction time.
- Peleg's scheme, used with a minor variant of the path decomposition originally proposed in [17], exhibits the fastest query times.
- All the data structures are very fast in practice. Although node labels have size $O(\log^2 n)$, only a small fraction of the labels is considered when answering random queries: typically, no more than a constant number of words per query is read in all our experiments. However, query times slightly increase with the instance size due to cache effects.
- Variants of the data structures carefully implemented with respect to alignment issues save 20% up to 40% of the space, but increase the query times approximately by a factor 1.3 on our data sets. The space saving reduces as the instance size gets larger.

The remainder of this paper is organized as follows. In Section 2 we describe the data structures being compared, focusing on path decomposition, label structure, and query algorithms. In Section 3 we give implementation details and discuss our experimental framework. The main findings of our experimental study are presented in Section 4.

2   Labeling Schemes for Least Common Ancestors

All the tree labeling schemes that we study in this paper follow the same basic approach: the tree is decomposed into a set of node disjoint paths, that we will call *solid paths*, and information related to the highest node in each path, called *head* of the path, is suitably encoded into the node labels. In the following we will consider different path decomposition approaches, then we will describe two possible ways of designing node labels. Different combinations of these two ingredients yield different labeling schemes: one of them coincides with the tree labeling scheme for least common ancestors originally proposed by Peleg in [17].

Path Decompositions. Let T be a tree with n nodes rooted at a given node r. For any node u, we denote its parent and its level in T by $p(u)$ and $\ell(u)$, respectively. We assume that the root has level 0. We also denote by T_u the subtree of T rooted at u and by $|T_u|$ the number of its nodes. In all the decompositions, for any solid path π, we denote by $head(\pi)$ the node of π with smallest level. We will also say that a solid path π is an *ancestral solid path* of a node u if $head(\pi)$ is an ancestor of u.

Decomposition by Large Child. This decomposition hinges upon the distinction between small and large nodes: a nonroot node v with parent u is called *small* if $|T_v| \leq |T_u|/2$, i.e., if its subtree contains at most half the number of nodes contained in its parents' subtree. Otherwise, v is called *large*. It is not difficult to see that any node has at most one large child: we will consider the edge to that large child, if any, as a solid edge. Solid edges induce a decomposition of the tree into solid paths: we remark that the head of any solid path π is always a small node, while all the other nodes in π must be large. Each node can have at most $\lceil \log n \rceil$ small ancestors, and thus at most $\lceil \log n \rceil$ ancestral solid paths (unless otherwise stated, all logarithms will be to the base 2).

Decomposition by Maximum Child. This is a minor variant of the previous decomposition, using a relaxed definition of large nodes: a nonroot node v with parent u is considered a *maximum child* of u if $|T_v| = \max_{w:(u,w)\in T} |T_w|$. If two or more children of u satisfy this condition, ties are broken arbitrarily. The edge to the maximum child is considered as a solid edge. We note that a large node is necessarily a maximum child; however, a maximum child exists even when all the children v of a node u are such that $|T_v| \leq |T_u|/2$. All the basic properties of the decomposition by large child remain valid in this variant.

Decomposition by Rank. In this decomposition, an edge (u, v) is solid if and only if $\lceil \log |T_u| \rceil = \lceil \log |T_v| \rceil$. It is not difficult to prove that for any node u there exists at most one child v such that (u, v) is solid (see, e.g., [10,15]). This implies that solid edges univocally partition the tree into disjoint paths. Some of these paths can consist of a single node: for instance, all the tree leaves are heads of solid paths of length 0. We remark that for all nodes v belonging to a given path π, the size of the subtree rooted at v satisfies the inequality $2^i \leq |T_v| < 2^{i+1}$, for some $i \geq 0$: we will say that i is the *rank* of path π. Since the rank of any path can be at most $\lceil \log n \rceil$, it follows that each node u can have at most $\lceil \log n \rceil$ ancestral solid paths.

Label Structure and Query Algorithms. We present two different ways of constructing node labels (the two approaches are extensively described in [17] and [7], respectively). When combined with any of the path decompositions, both schemes yield labels of size $O(\log^2 n)$. We also describe how information maintained in the node labels can be used to infer the least common ancestor of any two nodes.

Peleg's scheme. The first scheme [17] is based on a depth-first numbering of the tree T: as a preprocessing step, each node v is assigned an interval $Int(v) = [DFS(v); DFS(w)]$, where w is the last descendent of v visited by the depth-first tour and $DFS(x)$ denotes the depth-first number of node x. The label of each node v of the tree is defined as $label(v) = \ <Int(v), list(v)\ >$; where $list(v)$ contains information related to all the heads $(t_1, t_2, \ldots, t_h)$ of solid paths from the root of T to v: for each head t_i, $list(v)$ contains a quadruple $(t_i, \ell(t_i), p(t_i), succ_v(t_i))$, where $succ_v(t_i)$ is the unique child of t_i on the path to node v. We remark that this is slightly different (and optimized) with respect to the scheme originally proposed in [17].

We now describe the query algorithm: given two nodes u and v, the algorithm infers their least common ancestor $z = lca(u, v)$ using only information contained in $label(u)$ and $label(v)$. By well-known properties of depth-first search, we have that for every two nodes x and y of T, $Int(x) \subseteq Int(y)$ if and only if x is a descendent of y in T: this fact can be easily exploited to check whether the least common ancestor z coincides with any of the two input nodes u and v. If this is not the case, let $(u_1, u_2, \ldots, u_h)$ and $(v_1, v_2, \ldots, v_k)$ be the heads of solid paths from the root of T to u and v, respectively: information about these heads is maintained in the node labels. The algorithm finds the least common ancestor head h, which is identified by the maximum index i such that $u_i = v_i$. If $succ_u(h) \neq succ_v(h)$, then h must be the least common ancestor. Otherwise, the algorithm takes the node of minimum level between u_{i+1} and v_{i+1}, and returns its parent as the least common ancestor. We refer to [17] for a formal proof of correctness. Here, we limit to remark that both depth-first numbering and information about successors appear to be crucial in this algorithm.

CFP's scheme. This scheme [7] avoids the use of depth-first numbers and of successors. The label of each node v of the tree is now defined as $label(v) = \ <isHead(v), list(v)\ >$. The Boolean value $isHead(v)$ discriminates whether v is the head of its solid path or not. As in Peleg's scheme, $list(v)$ contains information related to all the heads $(t_1, t_2, \ldots, t_h)$ of solid paths from the root of T to v. In this case, the information for each head is less demanding and $list(v)$ consists just of a sequence of triples: $list(v) = [\ (t_1, \ell(t_1), p(t_1)), \ldots, (t_h, \ell(t_h), p(t_h)),$ $(v, \ell(v), p(v))\ ]$; where t_1 always coincides with the root of T. The sentinel triple $(v, \ell(v), p(v))$ is not necessary when v is head of its solid path, since $t_h = v$.

We now describe the query algorithm. Given any two nodes u and v, let $(u_1, u_2, \ldots, u_h)$ and $(v_1, v_2, \ldots, v_k)$ be the heads of solid paths from the root of T to u and v, respectively. Similarly to the previous data structure, the algorithm first identifies the lowest head h which is ancestor of both u and v: let i be such that $h = u_i = v_i$. If neither u nor v coincides with h (in this trivial case it would be $lca(u, v) = h$), the algorithm searches the least common ancestor in the solid path π with head h. At this aim, it identifies two candidates c_u and c_v and returns the highest of them. Notice that node u_{i+1} is either the sentinel of $list(u)$ or the head following u_i in $list(u)$: in the former case the candidate c_u is u itself, while in the latter case the candidate is the parent of u_{i+1}. The candidate c_v is computed similarly and the algorithm returns the highest level node among c_u and c_v. We refer the interested reader to [7] for a formal proof of correctness. We remark that this algorithm compensates for the absence of depth-first intervals and successor information thanks to the use of sentinel triples.

3   Experimental Framework

In this section we describe our experimental framework, discussing implementation details of the data structures being compared, performance indicators we consider, test sets, as well as our experimental setup. All implementations have been realized by the authors in ANSI C. The full package is available over the Internet at the URL: `http://www.dsi.uniroma1.it/~caminiti/lca/`.

Data Structure Implementation Issues. We implemented six different labeling schemes, obtained by combining the three path decompositions (`rank`, `largeChild`, and `maxChild`) and the two label structures (`Peleg` and `CFP`). The labeling scheme originally proposed in [17] corresponds to using Peleg's labels together with the decomposition by large child. It can be proved that all the obtained labeling schemes guarantee maximum label size $\Theta(\log^2 n)$ for trees with n nodes.

Each scheme comes in two variants, depending on alignment issues. In the `word` variant, every piece of information maintained in the node labels is stored at word-aligned addresses: some bytes are therefore used just for padding purposes. The actual sizes of nodes labels may be larger than the size predicted theoretically, but we expect computations on node labels to be fast. In the `bit` variant, everything is 1-bit aligned: this variant guarantees a very compact space usage, but requires operations for bit arithmetics that might have a negative impact on the running times of operations.

Performance Indicators. Main objectives that we considered to evaluate the data structures include space usage, construction time, and query time. Space usage is strictly related to the length of the lists in the node labels, i.e., to the number of entries in such lists: besides the total size of the data structure (measured in MB, unless otherwise stated), we have therefore taken into account also the average and maximum list length. Other structural measures have been used to study the effect of the different path decompositions on the labeling schemes: among them, we considered the number of paths in which the tree is decomposed, the average and maximum length of paths, and the variance of path lengths.

Test Sets. Problem instances consist both of synthesized, randomly generated trees and of real test sets. We used two random tree generators with different characteristics.

Uniformly distributed trees. This generator exploits the existence of a one-to-one correspondence between labeled rooted trees on n nodes and strings of length $n-1$: it first generates a random codeword of $n-1$ integers in the range $[1, n]$

and then applies a linear-time decoding algorithm [8] to obtain the tree. The approach guarantees that, if each integer is chosen uniformly at random in $[1, n]$, each tree will have the same probability to be generated.

Structured trees. This generator produces structured instances taking into account constraints on the degree and on the tree balancing. It works recursively and takes as input four arguments, named n, d, D, and β: n is the number of nodes of the tree T to be built; d and D are a lower and an upper bound for its degree, respectively; β is the unbalancing factor of T, i.e., a real number in $[0, 1]$ which indicates how much T must be unbalanced (the larger is β, the more unbalanced will be T).

Real test sets. Spanning trees of real networks have been obtained from data provided on the CAIDA (Cooperative Association for Internet Data Analysis) web site. Specifically, we exploited the network of Autonomous Systems monitored by the skitter project. We refer the interested reader to http://www.caida.org/ for detailed information about these datasets.

Experimental Setup. Our experiments have been carried out on a workstation equipped with two Dual Core Opteron processors with 2.2 GHz clock rate, 6 GB RAM, 1 MB L2 cache, and 64 KB L1 data/instruction cache. The workstation runs Linux Debian (Kernel 2.6.8). All programs have been compiled through the GNU gcc compiler version 3.3.5 with optimization level O3, using the C99 revised standard of the C programming language. Unless stated otherwise, in our experiments we averaged each data point on 1000 different instances. When computing running times of query operations, we averaged the time on (at least) 10^6 random queries.

4   Experimental Results

In this section we summarize our main experimental findings. We performed experiments using a wide variety of parameter settings and instance families, always observing the same relative performances of the data structures. Due to the lack of space, we do not explicitly report results on real data in this extended abstract: all measurements on these data sets completely confirm the results obtained on synthetic instances.

Path Decomposition. Our first aim was to analyze the effects of different path decomposition strategies on the size of node labels. A typical outcome of our experiments on trees generated uniformly at random is exemplified in Table 1. With respect to all measures, maxChild appears to be slightly preferable than largeChild and considerably better than rank. Consider first the structural measures: among the three decompositions, maxChild generates the smallest number of solid paths. Paths are therefore longer on the average, and their lengths exhibit a higher variance. On the opposite side, the number of paths generated by rank is almost twice as large for the parameter setting of this experiment, and their length is almost twice as small.

Table 1. Comparison of path decompositions. The results of this experiment are averaged over 500 random trees with $n = 10^7$ nodes. Only the **word** variant of the data structures is reported.

	maxChild	largeChild	rank
Number of paths	3678739	4172966	6803270
Average path length (and variance)	2.72(73.7)	2.4(61.2)	1.47(7.9)
Maximum path length	15352	15351	6346
Average list length (and variance) for Peleg	5.72(2.16)	5.89(2.32)	12.40(10.58)
Maximum list length for Peleg	15	15	24
Data structure size for Peleg	1179	1203	2199
Average list length (and variance) for CFP	6.36(2.06)	6.47(2.18)	12.7(10.44)2
Maximum list length for CFP	15	15	24
Data structure size for CFP	1033	1045	1761

Additional experiments were aimed at analyzing the effects of structural properties of the tree on the path decomposition: in all these tests, the relative ranking among the three strategies was always the same observed on uniformly distributed trees. The graphical outcome of two such experiments, obtained by increasing tree unbalancing and maximum degree, is reported in Figure 1. As the tree becomes more and more unbalanced, the advantages of using the maxChild decomposition drop: the number of solid paths obtained by largeChild and rank indeed decreases and, conversely, the average path length increases (see Figure 1a and Figure 1c). To explain this, let u be any node and let v be the child of u that is root of the maximum size subtree: the more T_u is unbalanced, the more $|T_u|$ and $|T_v|$ are close to each other and the edge (u, v) is likely to be solid. This reasoning cannot be applied to the maxChild strategy, according to which any internal node has always a solid child: for this reason curves related to maxChild exhibit an almost constant trend. Let us now analyze the effect of increasing the degree. Let T_1 and T_2 be two trees generated with the same fixed unbalancing factor β ($\beta = 0.9$ in the right column of Figure 1) and maximum degrees $D_1 < D_2$: for all strategies, we expect the number of solid paths in T_2 to be larger than the number of solid paths in T_1, since a larger degree implies a larger number of heads (not only among the children, but among all the descendants of each node). This intuition has been confirmed by the experiments with increasing maximum degree for all the decompositions, and explains the trend of the curves in Figure 1b and Figure 1d.

Size Comparison. Our next aim is to evaluate the requirements of Peleg's and CFP's schemes with respect to the space usage. Besides the total size of the data structure, we measured also the average number of solid heads in the lists associated to tree nodes (average list length). We performed experiments varying both structural properties of the input tree and the instance size.

At a first sight, it might appear that the average list length should be inversely proportional to the average path length: if paths are shorter on the average, the number of paths in any root-to-leaf path is expected to be larger, and so is

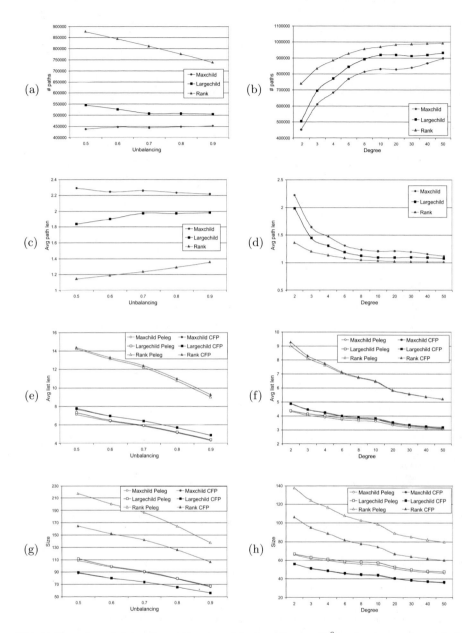

Fig. 1. Experimental results on structured trees with $n = 10^6$ nodes: increasing unbalancing factor β (left column, $d = 2 = D$) and increasing degree (right column, $d = D$, $\beta = 0.9$)

the number of heads in node labels (both for `Peleg` and `CFP`). While this was confirmed by the experiments on uniformly distributed trees (see Table 1), it is not necessarily the case on more structured instances: in particular, both the average

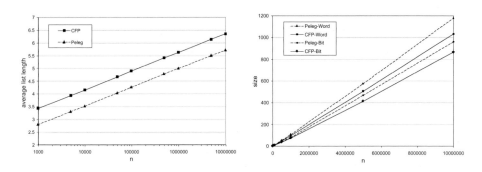

Fig. 2. Size comparison for `Peleg`'s and `CFP`'s schemes on uniformly distributed random trees: average list length and total size, measured in MB

path length (Figure 1d) and the average list length (Figure 1f) decrease as the maximum degree increases. A more refined analysis suggests that the topology of the tree should also be taken into account, and in particular the average height of tree nodes should be considered: the deeper a node, the larger the number of heads above it can be. As far as our generator works, trees with larger degree have smaller average node height and, according to Figure 1f, the effect of such smaller height appears to dominate on the shorter length of solid paths.

The total size of the data structure is directly proportional to the average list length, and curves related to these two measures exhibit the same trend (see Figure 1g and Figure 1h). However, it is worth observing that the data structure size in the case of `CFP` is considerably smaller than `Peleg`'s size, in spite of a slightly larger average list length. This is also evident from Figure 2, that reports on results obtained using the `maxChild` path decomposition on uniformly distributed random trees with a number of nodes increasing from 10^3 to 10^7 (from this point on we will omit the discussion of `rank` and `largeChild`, since `maxChild` proved to be consistently better in all the tests described so far). The smaller data structure size in the case of `CFP` depends on the fact that the lists are made of triples, instead of quadruples: the smaller list length in `Peleg`'s scheme (due to the absence of sentinel triples) is not sufficient to compensate for the presence of one more information in each element of the lists. We remark that lists are very short in practice for both schemes: they contain on the average 3 up to 6 elements for the data sets considered in this experiment. This value is very close to $\log_{10} n$, showing that the constant factors hidden by the asymptotic notation in the theoretical analysis are very small for the `maxChild` path decomposition. In Figure 2 we also distinguish between the `bit` and `word` versions of the data structures (there is no such difference with respect to the average list length): as expected, for both schemes the `bit` versions can considerably reduce the space usage. We will analyze further these data later in this section.

Running Times. According to the theoretical analysis, the construction times and the query times for the different labeling schemes are asymptotically the

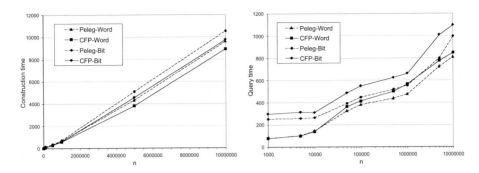

Fig. 3. Running time comparison for `Peleg`'s and `CFP`'s schemes on uniformly distributed random trees: construction time (in milliseconds) and average query time (in milliseconds per 10^6 queries)

same. A natural question is whether this is the case also in practice. Our experiments confirmed the theoretical prediction only in part, showing that the constant factors hidden by the asymptotic notation can be rather different for `Peleg`'s and `CFP`'s schemes. The charts in Figure 3, for instance, have been obtained on the same data sets used for the test reported in Figure 2: these charts show that `Peleg` is slower than `CFP` when considering initialization time, but faster when considering query times. The `bit` versions of the data structures are always slower than the corresponding `word` versions.

In order to explain the larger construction time of `Peleg`'s scheme, notice that `Peleg` makes use of a depth-first numbering of the tree, that is instead avoided by `CFP`: all the other operations performed by the initialization algorithms (i.e., path decomposition and list construction) are instead very similar. We also recall that Peleg's data structure is larger than `CFP`, and the size of a data structure is clearly a lower bound on its construction time. The larger amount of information maintained by `Peleg` in the list of each node is however efficiently exploited in order to get faster query times: as an example, if one of the two input nodes is ancestor of the other, the query algorithm used by `CFP` needs to scan the beginning of the nodes' lists, while the depth-first intervals directly provide the answer in the case of `Peleg` data structure.

To get a deeper understanding of the query times, we also measured the average number of list elements scanned by the query algorithms during a sequence of operations. This number turns out to be very small both for `Peleg` and for `CFP`, as shown by the left chart reported in Figure 4: on the average, slightly more than 2 elements are considered in each query even on the largest instances. `Peleg` considers less elements than `CFP`, especially for small values of n: on small trees, two nodes taken uniformly at random have indeed a higher probability to be one ancestor of the other, and for all these queries `Peleg` can avoid to scan the list at all, as we observed above. Quite surprisingly, however, for the largest values of n the number of scanned list elements remains almost constant for both data structures: this seems to be in contrast with the fact that the query times increase (see Figure 3), and suggests that the larger running times may

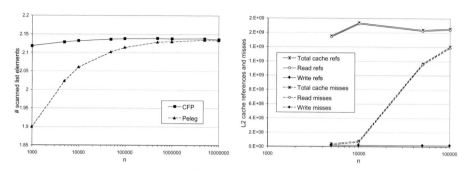

Fig. 4. Average number of list elements scanned by the query algorithms on uniformly distributed random trees (left chart); number of references to L2 cache and number of cache misses incurred by the CFP query algorithm on the same dataset (right chart)

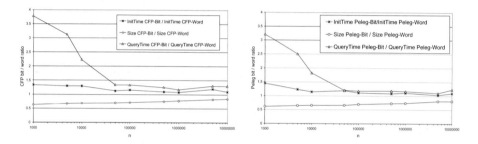

Fig. 5. Space/time saved by the bit/word versions: CFP (left chart) and Peleg (right chart). Tests are made on uniformly distributed random trees.

be mainly due to cache effects. To investigate this issue, we used the valgrind profiler to conduct a preliminary experimental analysis of the number of cache misses incurred by the query algorithms: the outcome of one such experiment, related to CFP, is reported in the right chart of Figure 4. The experiment confirms that the total number of cache references does not increase substantially with n (in agreement with the result on the number of scanned list elements), while the number of L2 cache read misses increases sharply, thus justifying the larger query times.

Trading Space for Time. The experimental results discussed up to this point show that the bit versions of the data structures require more space than the corresponding word versions, but have larger construction and query times. In Figure 5 we summarize the space-time tradeoffs, both for Peleg and for CFP. The charts show that, for all measures, the differences between bit and word versions tend to decrease as the instance size increases: this depends on the fact that, as n increases, the value $\log n$ becomes progressively closer to the word size specific of the architecture, and therefore the number of bits wasted by the word versions becomes smaller. The size of the bit versions ranges approximately from 60%

up to 80% of the size of the `word` versions on our data sets. On the other side, construction and query times of the `bit` versions are approximately 1.3 times higher than the `word` versions for the largest values of n (for small values of n the ratio is even larger).

References

1. Abiteboul, S., Alstrup, S., Kaplan, H., Milo, T., Rauhe, T.: Compact labeling schemes for ancestor queries. SIAM J. on Computing 35(6), 1295–1309 (2006)
2. Alstrup, S., Bille, P., Rauhe, T.: Labeling schemes for small distances in trees. SIAM J. on Discrete Mathematics 19(2), 448–462 (2005)
3. Alstrup, S., Gavoille, C., Kaplan, H., Rauhe, T.: Nearest common ancestors: a survey and a new distributed algorithm. In: Proc. ACM SPAA 2002, pp. 258–264 (2002)
4. Bonichon, N., Gavoille, C., Labourel, A.: Short labels by traversal and jumping. In: Flocchini, P., Gasieniec, L. (eds.) SIROCCO 2006. LNCS, vol. 4056, pp. 143–156. Springer, Heidelberg (2006)
5. Breuer, M.A.: Coding the vertexes of a graph. IEEE Transactions on Information Theory IT-12, 148–153 (1966)
6. Breuer, M.A., Folkman, J.: An unexpected result on coding the vertices of a graph. J. of Mathematical Analysis and Applications 20, 583–600 (1967)
7. Caminiti, S., Finocchi, I., Petreschi, R.: Concurrent data structures for lowest common ancestors (manuscript, 2008)
8. Caminiti, S., Finocchi, I., Petreschi, R.: On coding labeled trees. Theoretical Computer Science 382(2), 97–108 (2007)
9. Cohen, E., Halperin, E., Kaplan, H., Zwick, U.: Reachability and Distance Queries via 2-hop Labels. In: Proc. ACM-SIAM SODA 2002, pp. 937–946 (2002)
10. Cole, R., Hariharan, R.: Dynamic LCA Queries on Trees. SIAM J. on Computing 34(4), 894–923 (2005)
11. Gavoille, C., Peleg, D., Perennes, S., Raz, R.: Distance labeling in graphs. In: Proc. ACM-SIAM SODA 2001, pp. 210–219 (2001)
12. Kannan, S., Naor, M., Rudich, S.: Implicit representation of graphs. In: Proc. ACM STOC 1988, pp. 334–343 (1988)
13. Kaplan, H., Milo, T., Shabo, R.: A Comparison of Labeling Schemes for Ancestor Queries. In: Proc. ACM-SIAM SODA 2002, pp. 954–963 (2002)
14. Katz, M., Katz, N.A., Korman, A., Peleg, D.: Labeling schemes for flow and connectivity. SIAM J. on Computing 34(1), 23–40 (2004)
15. Kopelowitz, T., Lewenstein, M.: Dynamic weighted ancestors. In: Proc. ACM-SIAM SODA 2007, pp. 565–574 (2007)
16. Peleg, D.: Proximity-preserving labeling schemes and their applications. In: Widmayer, P., Neyer, G., Eidenbenz, S. (eds.) WG 1999. LNCS, vol. 1665, pp. 30–41. Springer, Heidelberg (1999)
17. Peleg, D.: Informative labeling schemes for graphs. In: Nielsen, M., Rovan, B. (eds.) MFCS 2000. LNCS, vol. 1893, pp. 579–588. Springer, Heidelberg (2000)

A Practical Quicksort Algorithm
for Graphics Processors

Daniel Cederman[*] and Philippas Tsigas[**]

Department of Computer Science and Engineering
Chalmers University of Technology, SE-412 96 Göteborg, Sweden
{cederman,tsigas}@chalmers.se

Abstract. In this paper we present GPU-Quicksort, an efficient Quicksort algorithm suitable for highly parallel multi-core graphics processors. Quicksort has previously been considered as an inefficient sorting solution for graphics processors, but we show that GPU-Quicksort often performs better than the fastest known sorting implementations for graphics processors, such as radix and bitonic sort. Quicksort can thus be seen as a viable alternative for sorting large quantities of data on graphics processors.

1 Introduction

In this paper, we present an efficient parallel algorithmic implementation of Quicksort, GPU-Quicksort, designed to take advantage of the highly parallel nature of graphics processors (GPUs) and their limited cache memory. Quicksort has long been considered as one of the fastest sorting algorithms in practice for single processor systems, but until now it has not been considered as an efficient sorting solution for GPUs [1]. We show that GPU-Quicksort presents a viable sorting alternative and that it can outperform other GPU-based sorting algorithms such as GPUSort and radix sort, considered by many to be two of the best GPU-sorting algorithms. GPU-Quicksort is designed to take advantage of the high bandwidth of GPUs by minimizing the amount of bookkeeping and inter-thread synchronization needed. It achieves this by using a two-phase design to keep the inter-thread synchronization low and by steering the threads so that their memory read operations are performed coalesced. It can also take advantage of the atomic synchronization primitives found on newer hardware, when available, to further improve its performance.

The obvious way to parallelize Quicksort is to take advantage of its inherent parallelism by just assigning a new processor to each new sequence created in the partitioning step. This means, however, that there will be very little parallelization at the beginning, when the sequences are few and long [2].

Another approach has been to divide each sequence to be sorted into blocks that can then be dynamically assigned to available processors [3,4]. However, this

---

[*] Supported by Microsoft Research through its European PhD Scholarship Programme.
[**] Partially supported by the Swedish Research Council (VR).

D. Halperin and K. Mehlhorn (Eds.): ESA 2008, LNCS 5193, pp. 246–258, 2008.

method requires extensive use of the atomic synchronization primitive Fetch-And-Add (FAA) which makes it too expensive to use on graphics processors.

Since most sorting algorithms are memory bandwidth bound, there is no surprise that there is currently a big interest in sorting on the high bandwidth GPUs. Purcell et al. [5] have presented an implementation of bitonic merge sort on GPUs based on an implementation by Kapasi et al. [6]. Kipfer et al. [7,8] have shown an improved version of the bitonic sort as well as an odd-even merge sort. Greß et al. [9] introduced an approach based on the adaptive bitonic sorting technique presented by Bilardi et al. [10]. Govindaraju et al. [11] implemented a sorting solution based on the periodic balanced sorting network method by Dowd et al. [12] and one based on bitonic sort [13]. They later presented a hybrid bitonic-radix sort that used both the CPU and the GPU to be able to sort vast quantities of data [14]. Sengupta et al. [1] have presented a radix-sort and a Quicksort implementation. Recently, Sintorn et al. [15] presented a sorting algorithm that combines bucket sort with merge sort.

2   The System Model

The algorithm has been implemented in CUDA, which is NVIDIA's initiative to enable general purpose computations on their graphics processors. It consists of a compiler for a C-based language which can be used to create kernels that can be executed on the GPU.

General Architecture. The high range graphics processors from NVIDIA that supports CUDA currently boasts 16 multiprocessors, each multiprocessor consisting of 8 processors that all execute the same instruction on different data in lock-step. Each multiprocessor supports up to 768 threads and has 16 KiB of fast local memory.

Scheduling. Threads are logically divided into *thread blocks* that are assigned to a specific multiprocessor. Depending on how many registers and how much local memory the block of threads requires, there could be multiple blocks running concurrently on a single multiprocessor. If more blocks are needed than there is room for, on any of the multiprocessors, the leftover blocks will be scheduled sequentially.

Synchronization. Threads within a thread block can use the multiprocessors local memory and a special thread barrier-function to communicate with each other. The barrier-function forces all threads in the same block to synchronize. Some newer graphics processors support atomic instructions such as Compare-And-Swap and FAA.

Memory. Data is stored in a large, global memory that supports both gather and scatter operations. There is no caching available when accessing this memory, but each thread block can use its own, very fast, shared local memory to temporarily copy and store data from the global memory and use it as a manual cache. By letting each thread access consecutive memory locations, it is possible to allow read and write operations to coalesce, which will increase performance.

3   The Algorithm

The following subsection gives an overview of GPU-Quicksort. Section 3.2 will then go into the algorithm in more detail.

3.1   Overview

The method used by the algorithm is to recursively *partition* the sequence to be sorted, i.e. to move all elements that are lower than a specific pivot value to a position to the left of the pivot and to move all elements with a higher value to the right of the pivot. This is done until the entire sequence has been sorted.

In each partition iteration a new pivot value is picked and as a result two new subsequences are created that can be sorted independently. After a while there will be enough subsequences available that each thread block can be assigned one of them. But before that point is reached, the thread blocks need to work together on the same sequences. For this reason, we have divided up the algorithm into two, albeit rather similar, phases.

First Phase. In the first phase, several thread blocks might be working on different parts of the same sequence of elements to be sorted. This requires appropriate synchronization between the thread blocks, since the results of the different blocks need to be merged together to form the two resulting subsequences.

Newer graphics processors provide access to atomic primitives that can aid somewhat in this synchronization, but they are not yet available on the high-end graphics processors. Because of that, there is still a need to have a thread block barrier-function between the partition iterations.

The reason for this is that the blocks might be executed sequentially and we have no way of knowing in which order they will be executed. The only way to synchronize thread blocks is to wait until all blocks have finished executing. Then one can assign new subsequences to them. Exiting and reentering the GPU is not expensive, but it is also not delay-free since parameters need to be copied from the CPU to the GPU, which means that we want to minimize the number of times we have to do that.

When there are enough subsequences so that each thread block can be assigned its own subsequence, we enter the second phase.

Second Phase. In the second phase, each thread block is assigned its own subsequence of input data, eliminating the need for thread block synchronization. This means that the second phase can run entirely on the graphics processor. By using an explicit stack and always recurse on the smallest subsequence, we minimize the shared memory required for bookkeeping.

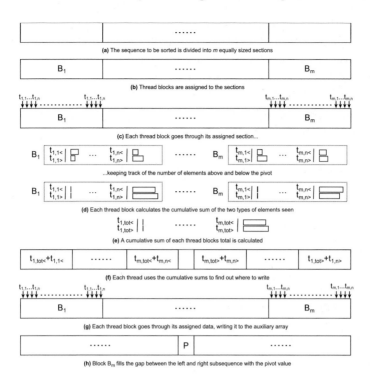

Fig. 1. Partitioning a sequence (m thread blocks with n threads each)

Hoare suggested in his paper [16] that it would be more efficient to use another sorting method when the subsequences are relatively small, since the overhead of the partitioning gets too large when dealing with small sequences. We decided to follow that suggestion and sort all subsequences that can fit in the available local shared memory using an alternative sorting method.

In-place. On conventional SMP systems it is favorable to perform the sorting in-place, since that gives good cache behavior. But on GPUs, because of their limited cache memory and the expensive thread synchronization that is required when hundreds of threads need to communicate with each other, the advantages of sorting in-place quickly fades away. Here it is better to aim for reads and writes to be coalesced to increase performance, something that is not possible on conventional SMP systems. For these reasons it is better, performance-wise, to use an auxiliary buffer instead of sorting in-place.

So, in each partition iteration, data is read from the primary buffer and the result is written to the auxiliary buffer. Then the two buffers switch places, with the primary becoming the auxiliary and vice versa.

Partitioning. The principle of two phase partitioning is outlined in Figure 1. The sequence to be partitioned is selected and it is then logically divided into m

equally sized sections (Step a), where m is the number of thread blocks available. Each thread block is then assigned a section of the sequence (Step b).

The thread block goes through its assigned data, with all threads in the block accessing consecutive memory so that the reads can be coalesced. This is important, since reads being coalesced will significantly lower the memory access time.

Synchronization. The objective is to partition the sequence, i.e. to move all elements that are lower than the pivot to a position to the left of the pivot in the auxiliary buffer and to move the elements with a higher value than the pivot to the right of the pivot. The problem here is to synchronize this in an efficient way. How do we make sure that each thread knows where to write in the auxiliary buffer?

Cumulative Sum. A possible solution is to let each thread read an element and then synchronize the threads using a barrier function. By calculating a cumulative sum[1] of the number of threads that want to write to the left and to the right of the pivot respectively, each thread would know that x threads with a lower thread id than its own are going to write to the left of the pivot and that y threads are going to write to the right of the pivot. Each thread then knows that it can write its element to either buf_{x+1} or $buf_{n-(y+1)}$, depending on if the element is higher or lower than the pivot.

A Two-Pass Solution. But calculating a cumulative sum is not free, so to improve performance we go through the sequence two times. In the first pass each thread just counts the number of elements it has seen that have value higher (or lower) than the pivot (Step c). Then when the block has finished going through its assigned data, we use these sums instead to calculate the cumulative sum (Step d). Now each thread knows how much memory the threads with a lower id than its own needs in total, turning it into an implicit memory-allocation scheme that only needs to run once for every thread block, in each iteration.

In the first phase, where we have several thread blocks accessing the same sequence, an additional cumulative sum need to be calculated for the total memory used by each thread block (Step e).

When each thread knows where to store its elements, we go through the data in a second pass (Step g), storing the elements at their new position in the auxiliary buffer. As a final step, we store the pivot value at the gap between the two resulting subsequences (Step h). The pivot value is now at its final position which is why it doesn't need to be included in any of the two subsequences.

3.2 Detailed Description

The First Phase The goal of the first phase is to divide the data into a large enough number of subsequences that can be sorted independently.

Work Assignment. In the ideal case, each subsequence should be of the same size, but that is often not possible, so it is better to have some extra subsequences

---

[1] The terms prefix sum or sum scan are also used in the literature.

procedure GPUQSORT($size, d^{prim}, d^{aux}$)

$minlength, flip \leftarrow \frac{size}{maxseq}, false$

$work, done \leftarrow \{(0, size, flip, piv)\}, \emptyset$

while $work \neq \emptyset \wedge |work| + |done| < maxseq$ **do**

$\quad ws, xs \leftarrow \sum_{v \in work} \frac{^v end - ^v beg}{maxseq}, \emptyset$

for all $v \in work$ **do**

$\quad x \leftarrow (v_{beg}, v_{end}, v, \lceil \frac{^v end - ^v beg}{ws} \rceil)$

$\quad xs \cup \{x\}$

$\quad$**for** $i \leftarrow 0, i < x^c - 1, i \leftarrow i + 1$ **do**

$\quad\quad beg \leftarrow x^s + ws \cdot i$

$\quad\quad bl \leftarrow bl \cup \{(x, beg, beg + ws)\}$

$\quad bl \leftarrow bl \cup \{(x, x^s + ws \cdot (x^c - 1), x^e)\}$

$gqsort(bl, d^{prim}, d^{aux})$;

for all $x \in xs$ **do**

$\quad ns_1 \leftarrow \{(x^{v beg}, x^s, flip, piv)\}$

$\quad ns_2 \leftarrow \{(x^e, x^v end, flip, piv)\}$

$\quad$**if** $x^s - x^{v beg} < minlength$ **then**

$\quad\quad done \leftarrow done \cup ns_1$

$\quad$**else**

$\quad\quad work \leftarrow work \cup ns_1$

$\quad$**if** $x^v end - x^e < minlength$ **then**

$\quad\quad done \leftarrow done \cup ns_2$

$\quad$**else**

$\quad\quad work \leftarrow work \cup ns_2$

$d^{prim}, d^{aux}, flip \leftarrow d^{aux}, d^{prim}, \neg flip$

if $flip$ **then**

$\quad d^{prim}, d^{aux} \leftarrow d^{aux}, d^{prim}$

$done \leftarrow done \cup work$

$lqsort(done, d^{prim}, d^{aux})$;

---

procedure GQSORT(bl, d^{prim}, d^{aux})

$b \leftarrow bl_{bid}$

$lt_{tid}, gt_{tid} \leftarrow 0, 0$

$i \leftarrow b^{beg} + tid$

for $i < b^{end}, i \leftarrow i + T$ **do**

$\quad$**if** $d_i^{prim} < b^{x^p}$ **then**

$\quad\quad lt_{tid} \leftarrow lt_{tid} + 1$

$\quad$**if** $d_i^{prim} > b.x.p$ **then**

$\quad\quad gt_{tid} \leftarrow gt_{tid} + 1$

$lt, gt \leftarrow accum(lt), accum(gt)$

$lbeg \leftarrow FAA(b^{x^s}, lt_T)$

$gbeg \leftarrow FAA(b^{x^e}, -gt_T)$

$lfrom_{tid} = lbeg + lt_{tid}$

$gfrom_{tid} = gbeg + gt_{tid}$

$i \leftarrow b^{beg} + tid$

for $i < b^{end}, i \leftarrow i + T$ **do**

$\quad$**if** $d_i^{prim} < pivot$ **then**

$\quad\quad d_{lfrom}^{aux} \leftarrow d_i^{prim}$

$\quad\quad lfrom \leftarrow lfrom + 1$

$\quad$**if** $ld > pivot$ **then**

$\quad\quad d_{gfrom}^{aux} \leftarrow d_i^{prim}$

$\quad\quad gfrom \leftarrow gfrom - 1$

if $FAA(b^{x^c}, -1) = 1$ **then**

$\quad$**for** $i \leftarrow b^{x^s}, i < b^{x^e}, i \leftarrow i + 1$ **do**

$\quad\quad d_i^{aux} \leftarrow b^{x^p}$

Fig. 2. Pseudocode for the first phase

and let the scheduler balance the workload. Based on that observation, a good way to partition is to only partition subsequences that are longer than $minlength = n/maxseq$ and to stop when we have $maxseq$ number of subsequences.

In the beginning of each iteration, all subsequences that are larger than the $minlength$ are assigned thread blocks relative to their size. In the first iteration, the original subsequence will be assigned all available thread blocks. The subsequences are divided so that each thread block gets an equally large section to sort, as can be seen in Figure 1 (Step a and b).

First Pass. When a thread block is executed on the GPU, it will iterate through all the data in its assigned sequence. Each thread in the block will keep track of the number of elements that are greater than the pivot and the number of elements that are smaller than the pivot. The data is read in chunks of T words, where T is the number of threads in each thread block. The threads read consecutive words so that the reads coalesce as much as possible.

procedure LQSORT(sl, d^{true}, d^{false})

$wset = \{sl_{bid}\}$

while $wset \neq \emptyset$ **do**
  $v \leftarrow minsize(wset)$
  where $v = (v^s, v^e, v^b)$
  $pivot \leftarrow med(d_{v^s}^{v^b}, d_{v^e}^{v^b}, d_{(v^s+v^e)/2}^{v^b})$
  $i, lt_{tid}, gt_{tid} \leftarrow v^s + tid, 0, 0$

  for $i < v^e, i \leftarrow i + T$ **do**
    if $d_i^{v^b} < pivot$ **then**
      $lt_{tid} \leftarrow lt_{tid} + 1$
    if $d_i^{v^b} > pivot$ **then**
      $gt_{tid} \leftarrow gt_{tid} + 1$

  $alt, agt \leftarrow accum(lt), accum(gt)$
  $alt_{tid}, agt_{tid} \leftarrow v^s + alt_{tid}, v^e - agt_{tid}$
  $i \leftarrow v^s + tid$

  for $i < v^e, i \leftarrow i + T$ **do**
    if $d_i^{v^b} < pivot$ **then**
      $d_{alt_{tid}}^{\neg v^b}, alt_{tid} \leftarrow d_i^{v^b}, alt_{tid} - 1$
    if $d_i^{v^b} > pivot$ **then**
      $d_{agt_{tid}}^{\neg v^b}, agt_{tid} \leftarrow d_i^{v^b}, agt_{tid} + 1$
    $i \leftarrow v^s + alt_T + tid$

  for $i < v^s - agt_T, i \leftarrow i + T$ **do**
    $d^{false} \leftarrow pivot$

  $r \leftarrow \{(v^s, alt_T), (v^e - agt_T, agt_T)\}$

  for all $s \in r$ **do**
    if $s^{len} < MINSIZE$ **then**
      $altsort(s^{beg}, s^{len}, d^{v^b}, d^{false})$
    else
      $wset \leftarrow wset \cup \{(s^f, s^f + s^{len}, \neg v^b)\}$

Fig. 3. Pseudocode for the second phase

Space Allocation. Once we have gone through all the assigned data, we calculate the cumulative sum of the two arrays. We then use the atomic FAA-function to calculate the cumulative sum for all blocks that have completed so far. This information is used to give each thread a place to store its result, as can be seen in Figure 1 (Step c-f).

FAA is as of the time of writing not available on all GPUs. An alternative, if one wants to run the algorithm on the older, high-end graphics processors, is to divide the kernel up into two kernels and do the block cumulative sum on the CPU instead. This would make the code more generic, but also slightly slower on new hardware.

Second Pass. Using the cumulative sum, each thread knows where to write elements that are greater or smaller than the pivot. Each block goes through its assigned data again and writes it to the correct position in the current auxiliary array. It then fills the gap between the elements that are greater or smaller than the pivot with the pivot value. We now know that the pivot values are in their correct final position, so there is no need to sort them anymore. They are therefore not included in any of the newly created subsequences.

Are We Done? If the subsequences that arise from the partitioning are longer than *minlength*, they will be partitioned again in the next iteration, provided we don't already have more than *maxseq* subsequences. If we do have more than *maxseq* subsequences, the next phase begins. Otherwise we go through another iteration. (See Algorithm 1).

The Second Phase. When we have acquired enough independent subsequences, there is no longer any need for synchronization between blocks. Because of this, the entire phase two can be run on the GPU entirely. There is however still the need for synchronization between threads, which means that we will use the same method as in phase one to partition the data. That is, we will count the number of elements that are greater or smaller than the pivot, do a cumulative sum so that each thread has its own location to write to and then move all elements to their correct position in the auxiliary buffer.

Stack. To minimize the amount of fast local memory used, there is a very limited supply of it, we always recurse on the smallest subsequence. By doing that, Hoare have showed [16] that the maximum recursive depth can never go below $\log_2(n)$. We use an explicit stack as suggested by Hoare and implemented by Sedgewick, always storing the smallest subsequence at the top [17].

Overhead. When a subsequence's size goes below a certain threshold, we use an alternative sorting method on it. This was suggested by Hoare since the overhead of Quicksort gets too big when sorting small sequences of data. When a subsequence is small enough to be sorted entirely in the fast local memory, we could use any sorting method that can be made to sort in-place, doesn't require much expensive thread synchronization and performs well when the number of threads approaches the length of the sequence to be sorted.

Theorem 1. *The average time complexity for GPU-Quicksort is $O(n \log(n))$.*

Theorem 2. *The space complexity for GPU-Quicksort is $2n + c$, where c is a constant.*

The proofs of the theorems above are simple and are not included in this version of the paper due to space constraints.

4   Experimental Evaluation

We ran the experiments on a dual-processor dual-core AMD Opteron 1.8GHz machine. Two different graphics processors were used, the low-end NVIDIA 8600GTS 256MiB with 4 multiprocessors and the high-end NVIDIA 8800GTX 768MiB with 16 multiprocessors. Since the 8800GTX provides no support for the atomic FAA operation we instead used an implementation of the algorithm that exits to the CPU for block-synchronization.

We compared GPU-Quicksort to the following state-of-the-art GPU sorting algorithms:

GPUSort. Uses bitonic merge sort [13].
Radix-Merge. Uses radix sort to sort blocks that are then merged [18].
Global Radix. Uses radix sort on the entire sequence [1].
Hybridsort. Uses a bucket sort followed by a merge sort [15].
STL-Introsort. This is the Introsort implementation found in the C++ Standard Library. Introsort is based on Quicksort, but switches to heap-sort when the recursion depth gets too large. Since it is highly dependent on the computer system and compiler used, we only included it to give a hint as to what could be gained by sorting on the GPU instead of on the CPU [19].

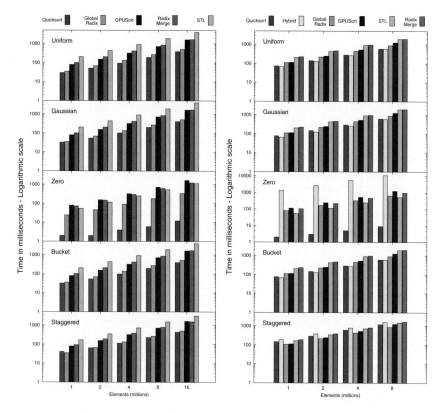

Fig. 4. Results on the 8800GTX   **Fig. 5.** Results on the 8600GTS

We could not find an implementation of the Quicksort algorithm used by Sengupta et al., but they claim in their paper that it took over 2 seconds to sort 4M uniformly distributed elements on a 8800GTX [1].

We only measured the actual sorting phase, we did not include in the result the time it took to setup the data structures and to transfer the data on and off the graphics memory. The reason for this is the different methods used to transfer data which wouldn't give a fair comparison between the GPU-based algorithms. Transfer times are also irrelevant if the data to be sorted are already available on the GPU. Because of those reasons, this way of measuring has become a standard in the literature.

On the 8800GTX we used 256 thread blocks, each block having 256 threads. When a subsequence dropped below 1024 elements in size, we sorted it using bitonic sort. On the 8600GTS we lowered the amount of thread blocks to 128 since it has fewer multiprocessors. All implementations were compiled with the -O3 optimization flag.

We used different pivot selection schemes for the two phases. In the first phase we took the average of the minimum and maximum element in the sequence and in the second we picked the median of the first, middle and last element as the pivot, a method suggested by Singleton[20].

The source code of GPU-Quicksort is available for non-commercial use [21].

For benchmarking we used the following distributions which are defined and motivated in [22]. These are commonly used yardsticks to compare the performance of different sorting algorithms. The source of the random uniform values is the Mersenne Twister [23].

Uniform. Values are picked randomly from $0 - 2^{31}$.

Zero. A constant value is used. The actual value is picked at random.

Bucket. The data set is divided into p blocks, where $p \in \mathbb{Z}^+$, which are then each divided into p sections. Section 1 in each block contains randomly selected values between 0 and $\frac{2^{31}}{p} - 1$. Section 2 contains values between $\frac{2^{31}}{p}$ and $\frac{2^{32}}{p} - 1$ and so on.

Gaussian. The Gaussian distribution is created by always taking the average of four randomly picked values from the uniform distribution.

Staggered. The data set is divided into p blocks, where $p \in \mathbb{Z}^+$. The staggered distribution is then created by assigning values for block i, where $i \leq \lfloor \frac{p}{2} \rfloor$, so that they all lie between $((2i - 1)\frac{2^{31}}{p})$ and $((2i)(\frac{2^{31}}{p} - 1))$. For blocks where $i > \lfloor \frac{p}{2} \rfloor$, the values all lie between $((2i - p - 2)\frac{2^{31}}{p})$ and $((2i - p - 1)\frac{2^{31}}{p} - 1)$.

We decided to use a p value of 128. The results presented in Fig. 4 and 5 are based on experiments sorting sequences of integers. We have done experiments using floats instead, but found no difference in performance.

4.1   Discussion

Quicksort has a worst case scenario complexity of $O(n^2)$, but in practice, and on average when using a random pivot, it tends to be close to $O(n \log(n))$, which is the lower bound for comparison sorts. In all our experiments GPU-Quicksort has shown the best performance or been among the best. There was no distribution that caused problems to the perfomance of GPU-Quicksort. As can be seen when comparing the performance on the two GPUs, GPU-Quicksort shows a speedup of approximately 3 on the higher-end GPU. The higher-end GPU has a memory bandwidth that is 2.7 times higher and has four times the number of multiprocessors, indicating that the algorithm is bandwidth bound and not computation bound, which was the case with the Quicksort in [1].

On the CPU, Quicksort is normally seen as a faster algorithm as it can potentially pick better pivot points and doesn't need an extra check to determine when the sequence is fully sorted. The time complexity of radix sort is $O(n)$, but that hides a potentially high constant which is dependent on the key size. Optimizations are possible to lower this constant, such as constantly checking if the sequence has been sorted, but that can be expensive when dealing with longer keys. Quicksort being a comparison sort also means that it is easier to modify it to handle different key types.

The hybrid approach uses atomic instructions that were only available on the 8600GTS. We can see that it outperforms both GPU-Quicksort and the global radix sort on the uniform distribution. But it loses speed on the staggered distributions and becomes immensely slow on the zero distribution. The authors state that the algorithm drops in performance when faced with already sorted data, so they suggest randomizing the data first, but this wouldn't affect the result in the zero distribution.

GPUSort doesn't increase as much in performance as the other algorithms when executed on the higher-end GPU. This is an indication that the algorithm is more computationally bound than the other algorithms. It goes from being much faster than the slow radix-merge to perform on par with and even a bit slower than it. The global radix sort showed a 3x speed improvement, as did GPU-Quicksort.

All algorithms showed about the same performance on the uniform, bucket and Gaussian distributions. GPUSort always shows the same result independent of distributions since it is a sorting network, which means it always performs the same number of operations regardless of the distribution. The staggered distribution was more interesting. On the low-end GPU the hybrid sorting was more than twice as slow as on the uniform distribution. GPU-Quicksort also dropped in speed and started to show the same performance as GPUSort. This can probably be attributed to the choice of pivot selection which was more optimized for uniform distributions. The zero distribution, which can be seen as an already sorted sequence, affected the algorithms to different extent. The STL reference implementation increased dramatically in performance since its two-way partitioning function always returned even partitions regardless of the pivot chosen. GPU-Quicksort shows the best performance as it does a three-way partitioning and can sort the sequence in $O(n)$ time.

5   Conclusions

In this paper we present GPU-Quicksort, a parallel Quicksort algorithm designed to take advantage of the high bandwidth of GPUs by minimizing the amount of bookkeeping and inter-thread synchronization needed. A significant conclusion, we think, that can be drawn from this work, is that Quicksort is a practical alternative for sorting large quantities of data on graphics processors.

Acknowledgements. We would like to thank Georgios Georgiadis, Marina Papatriantafilou and the anonymous referees for their valuable comments. We would also like to thank Ulf Assarsson and Erik Sintorn for insightful discussions regarding CUDA and for providing us with the source code to their hybrid sort.

References

1. Sengupta, S., Harris, M., Zhang, Y., Owens, J.D.: Scan Primitives for GPU Computing. In: Proceedings of the 22nd ACM Siggraph/Eurographics Symposium on Graphics Hardware, pp. 97–106 (2007)
2. Evans, D.J., Dunbar, R.C.: The Parallel Quicksort Algorithm Part 1 - Run Time Analysis. International Journal of Computer Mathematics 12, 19–55 (1982)

3. Heidelberger, P., Norton, A., Robinson, J.T.: Parallel Quicksort Using Fetch-And-Add. IEEE Transactions on Computers 39(1), 133–138 (1990)
4. Tsigas, P., Zhang, Y.: A Simple, Fast Parallel Implementation of Quicksort and its Performance Evaluation on SUN Enterprise 10000. In: Proceedings of the 11th Euromicro Conference on Parallel Distributed and Network-based Processing, pp. 372–381 (2003)
5. Purcell, T.J., Donner, C., Cammarano, M., Jensen, H.W., Hanrahan, P.: Photon Mapping on Programmable Graphics Hardware. In: Proceedings of the ACM Siggraph/Eurographics Symposium on Graphics Hardware, pp. 41–50 (2003)
6. Kapasi, U.J., Dally, W.J., Rixner, S., Mattson, P.R., Owens, J.D., Khailany, B.: Efficient Conditional Operations for Data-parallel Architectures. In: Proceedings of the 33rd annual ACM/IEEE International Symposium on Microarchitecture, pp. 159–170 (2000)
7. Kipfer, P., Segal, M., Westermann, R.: UberFlow: A GPU-based Particle Engine. In: Proceedings of the ACM Siggraph/Eurographics Conference on Graphics Hardware, pp. 115–122 (2004)
8. Kipfer, P., Westermann, R.: Improved GPU Sorting. In: Pharr, M. (ed.) GPUGems 2, pp. 733–746. Addison-Wesley, Reading (2005)
9. Greß, A., Zachmann, G.: GPU-ABiSort: Optimal Parallel Sorting on Stream Architectures. In: Proceedings of the 20th IEEE International Parallel and Distributed Processing Symposium (2006)
10. Bilardi, G., Nicolau, A.: Adaptive Bitonic Sorting. An Optimal Parallel Algorithm for Shared Memory Machines. SIAM Journal on Computing 18(2), 216–228 (1989)
11. Govindaraju, N.K., Raghuvanshi, N., Manocha, D.: Fast and Approximate Stream Mining of Quantiles and Frequencies Using Graphics Processors. In: Proceedings of the 2005 ACM SIGMOD International Conference on Management of Data, pp. 611–622 (2005)
12. Dowd, M., Perl, Y., Rudolph, L., Saks, M.: The Periodic Balanced Sorting Network. Journal of the ACM 36(4), 738–757 (1989)
13. Govindaraju, N., Raghuvanshi, N., Henson, M., Manocha, D.: A Cache-Efficient Sorting Algorithm for Database and Data Mining Computations using Graphics Processors. Technical report, University of North Carolina-Chapel Hill (2005)
14. Govindaraju, N.K., Gray, J., Kumar, R., Manocha, D.: GPUTeraSort: High Performance Graphics Coprocessor Sorting for Large Database Management. In: Proceedings of the 2006 ACM SIGMOD International Conference on Management of Data, pp. 325–336 (2006)
15. Sintorn, E., Assarsson, U.: Fast Parallel GPU-Sorting Using a Hybrid Algorithm. In: Workshop on General Purpose Processing on Graphics Processing Units (2007)
16. Hoare, C.A.R.: Quicksort. Computer Journal 5(4), 10–15 (1962)
17. Sedgewick, R.: Implementing Quicksort Programs. Communications of the ACM 21(10), 847–857 (1978)
18. Harris, M., Sengupta, S., Owens, J.D.: Parallel Prefix Sum (Scan) with CUDA. In: Nguyen, H. (ed.) GPU Gems 3. Addison-Wesley, Reading (August 2007)
19. Musser, D.R.: Introspective Sorting and Selection Algorithms. Software - Practice and Experience 27(8), 983–993 (1997)
20. Singleton, R.C.: Algorithm 347: an Efficient Algorithm for Sorting with Minimal Storage. Communications of the ACM 12(3), 185–186 (1969)

21. Cederman, D., Tsigas, P.: GPU Quicksort Library (December 2007),
    `www.cs.chalmers.se/~dcs/gpuqsortdcs.html`
22. Helman, D.R., Bader, D.A., JáJá, J.: A Randomized Parallel Sorting Algorithm
    with an Experimental Study. Journal of Parallel and Distributed Computing 52(1),
    1–23 (1998)
23. Matsumoto, M., Nishimura, T.: Mersenne Twister: a 623-Dimensionally Equidis-
    tributed Uniform Pseudo-Random Number Generator. Transactions on Modeling
    and Computer Simulation 8(1), 3–30 (1998)

Bloomier Filters: A Second Look

Denis Charles and Kumar Chellapilla

Microsoft Live Labs, One Microsoft Way, Redmond WA - 98052
`cdx@microsoft.com`, `kumarc@microsoft.com`

Abstract. A Bloom filter is a space efficient structure for storing static sets, where the space efficiency is gained at the expense of a small probability of false-positives. A *Bloomier filter* generalizes a Bloom filter to compactly store a function with a static support. In this article we give a simple construction of a Bloomier filter. The construction is linear in space and requires constant time to evaluate. The creation of our Bloomier filter takes linear time which is faster than the existing construction. We show how one can improve the space utilization further at the cost of increasing the time for creating the data structure.

1 Introduction

A *Bloom filter* is a compact data structure that supports set membership queries [1]. Given a set $S \subseteq D$ where D is a large set and $|S| = n$, the Bloom filter requires space $O(n)$ and has the following properties. It can answer membership queries in $O(1)$ time. However, it has one-sided error: Given $x \in S$, the Bloom filter will always declare that x belongs to S, but given $x \in D \backslash S$ the Bloom filter will, with high probability, declare that $x \notin S$. Bloom filters have found wide ranging applications [3,4,14,16]. There have also been generalizations in several directions of the Bloom filter [8,13,17,18]. More recently, Bloom filters have been generalized to "Bloomier" filters that compactly store functions [6]. In more detail: Given $S \subseteq D$ and a function $f : S \rightarrow \{0,1\}^k$ a Bloomier filter is a data structure that supports queries to the function value. It also has one-sided error: given $x \in S$, it always outputs the correct value $f(x)$ and if $x \in D \backslash S$ with high probability it outputs '$\perp$', a symbol not in the range of f. In [6] the authors construct a Bloomier filter that requires, $O(n \log n)$ time to create; $O(n)$ space to store and, $O(1)$ time to evaluate.

In this paper we give an alternate construction of Bloomier filters, which we believe is simpler than that of [6]. It has similar space and query time complexity. The creation is slightly faster, $O(n)$ vs. $O(n \log n)$. Changing the value of $f(x)$ while keeping S the same is slower in the worst case for our method, $O(\log n)$ vs. $O(1)$. For a detailed comparison we direct the reader to the extended version of this paper (see [7] §6). In §3 we discuss another construction that is very natural and has a smaller space requirement. However, this algorithm has a creation time of $O(n^3)$ which is too expensive. In §4 we discuss how bucketing can be used to reduce the construction time of this algorithm to $n \log^{O(1)} n$ and make it more practical. Recent independent results of [11] are related to this construction.

D. Halperin and K. Mehlhorn (Eds.): ESA 2008, LNCS 5193, pp. 259–270, 2008.

Due to space constraints we have omitted our experimental results comparing our construction to the previous construction. We refer the reader to [7] §7 for these results.

2 The Construction

2.1 A 1-Bit Bloomier Filter

We begin with the following simplified problem: Given a set S of n elements and a function $f : S \rightarrow \{0,1\}$, encode f into a space efficient data structure that allows fast access to the values of f. A simple way to solve this problem is to use a hash table (with open addressing) which requires $O(n)$ space and $O(1)$ time on average to evaluate f. If we want worst case $O(1)$ time for function evaluation, we could try different hash functions until we find one which produces few hash collisions on the set S. This solution however does not generalize to our ultimate goal which is to have a compact encoding of the function $\tilde{f} : D \rightarrow \{0,1,\perp\}$, where $\tilde{f}|_S = f$ and $\tilde{f}(x) = \perp$ with high probability if $x \notin S$. Thus if D is much larger than S, the solution using hash tables is not very attractive as it uses space proportional to D. To counter-act this one could use the hash table in conjunction with a Bloom filter for S. This is not the approach we will take[1].

Our approach to solving the simplified problem uses ideas from the creation of minimal perfect hashes (see [9]). We first map S onto the edges of a random (undirected) graph $G(V, E)$ constructed as follows. Let V be a set of vertices with $|V| \geq c|S|$, where $c \geq 1$ is a constant. Let $h_1, h_2 : D \rightarrow V$ be two hash functions. For each $x \in S$, we create an edge $e = (h_1(x), h_2(x))$ and let E be the set of edges formed in this way (so that $|E| = |S| = n$). If the graph G is not acyclic we try again with two independent hash functions h'_1, h'_2. It is known that if $c > 2$, then the expected number of vertices on tree components is $|V| + O(1)$ ([2] Theorem 5.7 ii). Indeed, in [10] the authors proved that if $G(V, E)$ is a random graph with $|V| = c|E|$ and $c > 2$, then with probability $\exp(1/c)\sqrt{(c-2)/c}$ the graph is acyclic. Thus, if $c > 2$ is fixed then the expected number of iterations till we find an acyclic graph is $O(1)$. In particular, if $c \geq 2.09$ then with probability at least $1/3$ the graph G is acyclic. Thus the expected number of times we will have to re-generate the graph until we find an acyclic graph is ≤ 3. Once we have an acyclic graph G, we try to find a function $g : V \rightarrow \{0,1\}$ such that $f(x) \equiv g(h_1(x)) + g(h_2(x)) \pmod 2$ for each $x \in S$. One can view this as a sequence of n equations for the variables $g(v)$, $v \in V$. The fact that G is acyclic implies that the set of equations can be solved by simple back-substitution in linear time. We then store the table of values $g(v)$ $(\in \{0,1\})$ for each $v \in V$. To evaluate the function f, given x, we compute $h_1(x)$ and $h_2(x)$ and add up the values stored in the table g at these two indices modulo 2. The expected creation time is $O(n)$, evaluation time is $O(1)$ (two hash function computations and two memory lookups to the table of values g) and the space utilization is $\lceil cn \rceil$ bits.

---

[1] The reason this is not optimal is because to achieve error probability ϵ, we will need to evalute $O(\log 1/\epsilon)$ hash functions.

Next, we generalize this approach to encoding the function $\tilde{f} : D \rightarrow \{0, 1, \bot\}$ that when restricted to S agrees with f and outside of S it maps to $\bot$ with high probability. Here again we will use the same construction of the random acyclic graph $G(V, E)$ together with a map from $S \rightarrow E$ via two hash functions h_1, h_2. Let $m \geq 2$ be an integer and $h_3 : D \rightarrow \mathbb{Z}/m\mathbb{Z}$ be another independent hash function. We solve for a function $g : V \rightarrow \mathbb{Z}/m\mathbb{Z}$ such that the equations $f(x) \equiv g(h_1(x)) + g(h_2(x)) + h_3(x) \pmod{m}$ holds for each $x \in S$. Again since the graph G is acyclic these equations can be solved using back-substitution. Note that back-substitution works even though we are dealing with the ring $\mathbb{Z}/m\mathbb{Z}$ which is not a field unless m is prime. To evaluate the function f at x we compute $h_i(x)$ for $1 \leq i \leq 3$ and then compute $g(h_1(x)) + g(h_2(x)) + h_3(x) \pmod{m}$. If the computed value is either 0 or 1 we output it otherwise, we output the symbol $\bot$. Algorithms 1 and 2 give the steps of the construction in more detail. It is clear that if $x \in S$ then the value output by our algorithm is the correct value $f(x)$. If $x \notin S$ then the value of $h_3(x)$ is independent of the values of $g(h_1(x))$ and $g(h_2(x))$ and uniform in the range $\mathbb{Z}/m\mathbb{Z}$. Thus $\Pr_{x \in D \setminus S}[g(h_1(x)) + g(h_2(x)) + h_3(x) \in \{0, 1\}] = \frac{2}{m}$.

Algorithm 1. Generate Table

Input: A set $S \subseteq D$ and a function $f : S \rightarrow \{0, 1\}$, $c > 2$, and an integer $m \geq 2$.
Output: Table g and hash functions h_1, h_2, h_3 such that $\forall s \in S : g[h_1(s)] + g[h_2(s)] + h_3(s) \equiv f(s) \mod m$.
Let $V = \{0, 1, \cdots, \lceil cn \rceil - 1\}$, where $n = |S|$
repeat
    Generate $h_1, h_2 : D \rightarrow V$ where h_i are chosen independently from $\mathcal{H}$ – a family of hash functions; Let $E = \{(h_1(s), h_2(s)) : s \in S\}$.
until $G(V, E)$ is a simple acyclic graph.
Let $h_3 : D \rightarrow \mathbb{Z}/m\mathbb{Z}$ be a third independently chosen hash function from $\mathcal{H}$.
for all T – a connected component of $G(V, E)$ **do**
    Choose a vertex $v \in T$ whose degree is non-zero.
    $F \leftarrow \{v\}; g[v] \leftarrow 0$.
    while $F \neq T$ **do**
        Let C be the set of nodes in $T \setminus F$ adjacent to nodes in F.
        for all $w = h_i(s) \in C$ **do**
            $g[w] \leftarrow f(s) - g[h_{3-i}(s)] - h_3(s) \mod m$.
        end for
        $F \leftarrow F \cup C$.
    end while
end for

In summary, we have proved the following:

Proposition 1. *Fix $c > 2$ and let $m \geq 2$ be an integer, the algorithms described above (Algorithms 1 and 2) implement a Bloomier filter for storing the function $\tilde{f} : D \rightarrow \{0, 1, \bot\}$ and the underlying function $f : S \rightarrow \{0, 1\}$ with the following properties:*

1. *The expected time for creation of the Bloomier filter is $O(n)$.*
2. *The space used is $\lceil cn \rceil \lceil \log_2 m \rceil$ bits, where $n = |S|$.*

3. *Computing the value of the Bloomier filter at $x \in D$ requires $O(1)$ time (3 hash function computations and 2 memory lookups).*
4. *Given $x \in S$, it outputs the correct value of $f(x)$.*
5. *Given $x \notin S$, it outputs $\bot$ with probability $1 - \frac{2}{m}$.*

2.2   General k-Bit Bloomier Filters

It is easy to generalize the results of the previous section to obtain Bloomier filters with range larger than just the set $\{0, 1\}$. Given a function $f : S \to \{0, 1\}^k$ it is clear that as long as the range $\{0, 1\}^k$ embeds into the ring $\mathbb{Z}/m\mathbb{Z}$ one can still use Algorithm 1 without any changes. This translates into the simple requirement that we take $m \geq 2^k$. Algorithm 2 needs a minor modification, namely, we check if $f = g(h_1(x)) + g(h_2(x)) + h_3(x) \pmod{m} \in \{0, 1\}^k$ and if so we output f otherwise, we output $\bot$. We encapsulate the claims about the generalization in the following theorem (the proof of which is similar to that of Proposition 1):

Theorem 1. *Fix $c > 2$ and let $m \geq 2^k$ be an integer, the algorithms described above implement a Bloomier filter for storing the function $\tilde{f} : D \to \{0, 1\}^k \cup \{\bot\}$, and the underlying function $f : S \to \{0, 1\}^k$ with the following properties:*

1. *The expected time for creation of the Bloomier filter is $O(n)$.*
2. *The space used is $\lceil cn \rceil \lceil \log_2 m \rceil$ bits, where $n = |S|$.*
3. *Computing the value of the Bloomier filter at $x \in D$ requires $O(1)$ time (3 hash function computations and 2 memory lookups).*
4. *Given $x \in S$, it outputs the correct value of $f(x)$.*
5. *Given $x \notin S$, it outputs $\bot$ with probability $1 - \frac{2^k}{m}$.*

Algorithm 2. Query function

Input: Table g, $h_1, h_2 : D \to \{0, \cdots, \lceil cn \rceil - 1\}$, $h_3 : D \to \mathbb{Z}/m\mathbb{Z}$ hash functions and $x \in D$.
Output: $0, 1$ or $\bot$ – the output of the Bloomier filter represented by the table g.
   $f \leftarrow g[h_1(x)] + g[h_2(x)] + h_3(x) \mod m$.
   if $f \in \{0, 1\}$ **then**
      Output f.
   else
      Output $\bot$.
   end if

2.3   Mutable Bloomier Filters

In this section we consider the task of handling changes to the function stored in the Bloomier filter produced by the algorithms in the previous section. We will only consider changes to the function $f : S \to \{0, 1\}^k$ where S remains the same but only the values taken by the function changes. In other words, the support of the function remains static.

Consider what happens when $f : S \to \{0,1\}^k$ is changed to the function $f' : S \to \{0,1\}^k$ where $f(x) = f'(x)$ except for a single $y \in S$. In this case we can change the values stored in the g-table so that we output the value of f' at y. We assume that the edges of the graph G are available (this is an additional $O(n \log n)$ bits). We begin with the observation that the values stored at $g(v)$ for vertices v not in the connected component containing the edge $e = (h_1(y), h_2(y))$ remain unaffected. Thus changing f to f' affects only the g values of the connected component, C (say), containing the edge e. Recomputing the g values corresponding to C would take time $O(|C|)$. How big can the largest connected component in G get? Our graph $G(V, E)$ built in Algorithm 1 is a sparse random graph with $|E| < \frac{1}{2}|V|$. A classical result due to Erdős and Rényi says that in this case the largest component is almost surely[2] $O(\log n)$ in size where $n = |E|$ (see [12] or [2]). Thus updates to the Bloomier filter take $O(\log n)$ time provided we ensure that the largest component in G is small when creating it. The result from [12] tells us that adding the extra condition while creating G will not change the expected running time of Algorithm 1. We call this modified algorithm Algorithm 1'.

Theorem 2. *The Bloomier filter constructed using algorithms 1' and 2 can accomodate changes to function values in time $O(\log n)$, provided the graph G is also retained. Moreover, the claims of Theorem 1 remain true for algorithms 1' and 2.*

3   Reducing the Space Utilization

If we are willing to spend more time in the creation phase of the Bloomier filter, we can further reduce the space utilization of the Bloomier filter. In this section we show how one can get a Bloomier filter for a function $f : S \to \{0,1\}^k$ with error rate $\frac{2^k}{m}$ using only $n(1 + \epsilon)\lceil \log_2 m \rceil$ bits of storage, where $n = |S|$ and $\epsilon > 0$ is a constant. In §2 we used a random graph generated by hash functions to systematically generate a set of equations that can be solved efficiently. The solution to these equations is then stored in a table which in turn encodes the function f. The main idea to reduce space usage further is to have a table $g[0], g[1], \cdots, g[N-1]$, where $N = (1+\epsilon)n$, and try to solve the following set of equations over $\mathbb{Z}/m\mathbb{Z}$:

$$\left(\sum_{1 \le i \le s} h_i(x)g[h_{i+s}(x)] \right) + h_0(x) = f(x), \quad x \in S \tag{1}$$

for the unknowns $g[0], \cdots, g[N-1]$. Here $s \ge 1$ is a fixed integer and $h_0, h_1, \cdots, h_{2s}$ are independent hash functions. Since s is fixed, look up of a function value will only take $O(1)$ hash function evaluations. These equations can be solved provided the determinant of the *sparse* matrix corresponding to these equations is a unit in $\mathbb{Z}/m\mathbb{Z}$. The next subsection gives an answer (under suitable conditions) to this question when m is a prime.

---

[2] This means that the probability that the condition holds is $1 - o(1)$.

3.1 Full Rank Sparse Matrices over a Finite Field

Let $\mathrm{GL}^s_{n\times r}(\mathbb{F}_p)$ be the *set* of full rank $n \times r$ matrices over $\mathbb{F}_p$[3] that have exactly s non-zero entries in each column. Our aim in this section is to get a lower bound for $\sharp\mathrm{GL}^s_{n\times r}(\mathbb{F}_p)$ (the cardinality of this set). We note the following lemma whose proof we omit.

Lemma 1. *Let $M^s_{n\times r}(\mathbb{F}_p)$ be the matrices over $\mathbb{F}_p$ where each column has exactly s non-zero entries. Then $\sharp M^s_{n\times r}(\mathbb{F}_p) = \left(\binom{n}{s}(p-1)^s\right)^r$.*

Before we begin the task of getting a lower bound for the sparse full rank matrices we briefly recall the method of proof for finding $\sharp\mathrm{GL}_n(\mathbb{F}_p)$ – the group of invertible $n \times n$ matrices over $\mathbb{F}_p$. One can build invertible matrices column by column as follows: Choose any non-zero vector for the first column, there are $p^n - 1$ ways of choosing the first column. The second column vector should not lie in the linear span of the first. Therefore there are $p^n - p$ choices for the second column vector. Proceeding in this way there are $p^n - p^j$ for the $j+1$ column. Thus we have $\sharp\mathrm{GL}_n(\mathbb{F}_p) = \prod_{1\le j\le n}(p^n - p^{n-j})$.

One can adapt this idea to get a bound on the invertible s-sparse matrices. There are $\binom{n}{s}(p-1)^s$ ways of choosing the first column. Inductively, suppose we have chosen the first i columns to be linearly independent, then we have a vector space $V_i \subseteq \mathbb{F}^n_p$ of dimension i spanned by the first i columns. One can grow this matrix to a rank $i+1$ matrix by augmenting it by any s-sparse vector $\mathbf{w} \notin V_i$. Thus we are faced with the task of finding an upper bound on the number of s-sparse vectors contained in V_i. We introduce some notation: suppose $\mathbf{w} = \langle w_1, w_2, \cdots, w_n \rangle^t \in \mathbb{F}^n_p$ is a vector then we define $\mathbf{w}^\oslash$ to be the vector $\langle w_n, w_1, \cdots, w_{n-1} \rangle^t$ (a cyclic shift of $\mathbf{w}$). Note that if $\mathbf{w}$ is s-sparse then so is $\mathbf{w}^\oslash$. Our approach is to show that under certain circumstances the vector space spanned by the orbit of a sparse vector under the circular shifts have high dimension and consequently, all the shifts cannot be contained in V_i (unless $i = n$). It is natural to expect that given a s-sparse vector $\mathbf{w}$, the vector space $W^\oslash$ spanned by all the circular shifts $\mathbf{w}, \mathbf{w}^\oslash, \cdots, \mathbf{w}^{\oslash^{n-1}}$ has dimension $\ge n - s$. Unfortunately, this is not so: For example, consider $\mathbf{w} = \langle 1, 0, 1, 0, 1, 0 \rangle$ whose cyclic shifts generate a vector space of dimension 2. This motivates the next lemma.

Lemma 2. *Suppose q is a prime number and $\mathbf{w} \in \mathbb{F}^q_p$ is an s-sparse vector with $0 < s < q$. Then the orbit $\{\mathbf{w}, \mathbf{w}^\oslash, \cdots, \mathbf{w}^{\oslash^{q-1}}\}$ has cardinality q.*

Proof. We have a natural action of the group $\mathbb{Z}/q\mathbb{Z}$ on the set of cyclic shifts of $\mathbf{w}$, via $a \mapsto \mathbf{w}^{\oslash^a}$. Suppose we have $\mathbf{w}^{\oslash^i} = \mathbf{w}^{\oslash^j}$ for $0 \le i \ne j \le q - 1$. Then we have $\mathbf{w}^{\oslash^{(i-j)}} = \mathbf{w} = \mathbf{w}^{\oslash^q}$. Since we have a group action this implies that $\mathbf{w}^{\oslash^{\gcd(i-j,p)}} = \mathbf{w}$. Since q is prime this means that $\mathbf{w}^\oslash = \mathbf{w}$. But $0 < s < q$ therefore $\mathbf{w}^\oslash \ne \mathbf{w}$ and we have a contradiction. $\square$

---

[3] Here p is a prime number and $\mathbb{F}_p$ is *the* finite field with p elements. Any two finite fields with p elements are isomorphic and the isomorphism is canonical. If the field has p^r, $r > 1$, elements then the isomorphism is not canonical.

One can show that the vector space spanned by the cyclic shifts of an s-sparse vector $(0 < s < n)$ has dimension at least n/s. However, this bound is not sufficient for our purpose. We need the following stronger conditional result whose proof is available in [7] (see Theorems 8 and 9 in the Appendix of [7]).

Theorem 3. *Let* $\mathbf{w} = \langle w_0, \cdots, w_{q-1} \rangle \in \mathbb{F}_p^q$, *where* p *is a prime that is a primitive root modulo* q *(i.e.,* p *generates the cyclic group* $\mathbb{F}_q^*$*). Suppose* $w_0 + w_1 \cdots + w_{q-1} \neq 0$ *and* w_i *are not all equal, then* $W^{\oslash}$ *(the vector space spanned by the cyclic shifts of* $\mathbf{w}$*) has dimension* q.

Let V_i be a vector space of dimension i contained in $\mathbb{F}_p^q$. We have $\frac{1}{q}\binom{q}{s}(p-1)^s$ orbits of size q under the action of $\mathbb{Z}/q\mathbb{Z}$ on the s-sparse vectors. If $s < n$ then all the coordinates cannot be identical. Once the s non-zero positions for an s-sparse vector are chosen there are $\geq (p-1)^s - (p-1)^{s-1}$ vectors whose coordinates do not sum to zero[4]. Now each of these orbits generates a vector space of rank q by the above theorem. In each orbit there are at most i vectors that can belong to V_i. Consequently, there are at least

$$\frac{1}{q}\binom{q}{s}\left((p-1)^s - (p-1)^{s-1}\right)(q-i) \tag{2}$$

s-sparse vectors that do not belong to V_i. We have thus proved the following theorem:

Theorem 4. *Let* q, p *be prime numbers such that* p *is congruent to a primitive root modulo* q. *Then*

$$\sharp \mathrm{GL}_{q \times r}^s(\mathbb{F}_p) \geq \prod_{0 \leq i \leq r-1} \left(\frac{1}{q}\binom{q}{s}\left((p-1)^s - (p-1)^{s-1}\right)(q-i)\right).$$

We note that the bound obtained above is almost tight[5] in the case $s = 1$, where the 1-sparse matrices are simply diagonal matrices (with non-zero entries) multiplied by permutation matrices.

3.2 The Algorithm

The outline of the algorithm is as follows. To create the Bloomier filter given $f : S \to \{0,1\}^k$, we consider each element x of S in turn. We generate a random equation as in (1) for x and check that the list of equations that we have so far has full rank. If not, we generate another equation using a different set of $2s$ hash functions. At any time, we keep the hash functions that have been used so far in blocks of $2s$ hash functions. When generating a new equation we always

---

[4] Indeed, it is not hard to show that the exact number of such vectors is $\frac{(p-1)\left((p-1)^s + (-1)^{s+1}\right)}{p}$.

[5] The bound is tight if we use the exact formula for the number of s-sparse vectors that do not sum to 0 in the derivation.

start with the first block of hash functions and try subsequent blocks only if the previous blocks failed to give a full rank system of equations. The results of the previous section show that the expected number of blocks of hash functions is bounded (provided the vector space has high dimension). Once we have a full rank set of equations for all the elements of S, we then proceed to solve the sparse set of equations. The solution to the equations is then stored in a table. At look up time, we generate the equations using each block of hash functions in turn and output the first time an equation generates a value in the range of f. At first glance it looks like this approach stores f with two-sided error, i.e., even when given $x \in S$ we might output a wrong value for $f(x)$. However, we show that the probability of error committed by the procedure on elements of S can be made so small that, by doing a small number of trials, we can ensure that we do not err on any element of S.

Algorithm 3. Setup parameters

Input: $n \geq 0$ integer given in unary, $m \geq 0$ integer, $\epsilon > 0$.
Output: q and p primes, p is a m-bit prime that is a primitive root modulo q.
   Let q be the first prime $\geq n(1 + \epsilon)$.
   Factor $q - 1$ and let $q_1, \cdots, q_k$ be the (distinct) prime factors of $q - 1$.
   repeat
      Choose a random $g \in \mathbb{F}_q$.
   until $g^{q_i} \not\equiv 1 \mod q$ for each $1 \leq i \leq k$.
   Let $g_i = g^i \mod q$ for $1 \leq i \leq q - 1$, $\gcd(i, q - 1) = 1$.
   repeat
      Choose a random m-bit integer p.
   until $p \equiv g_i$ for some i, and p is prime.

Analysis of Algorithm 3: It can be shown that Algorithm 3 has an expected running time of $\tilde{O}(n + m^4)$. We refer the reader to [7] for the details.

Analysis of Algorithm 4: The algorithm essentially mimics the proof of Theorem 4. It starts with a rank i matrix and grows the matrix to a rank $i + 1$ matrix by adding an s-sparse row using hash functions in B_j[6]. Let $n = |S|$ and suppose, $q \geq n(1 + \epsilon)$ for a fixed $\epsilon > 0$. Then equation (2) tells us that in $O(1/\epsilon)$ iterations we will find that the rank of the matrix increases. In more detail, the probability that a random s-sparse vector does not lie in V_i is at least $\frac{q-i}{q} \geq \epsilon$ since $i < n$ and $q \geq n(1 + \epsilon)$. Note that this requires rather strong pseudorandom properties from the hash family $\mathcal{H}$. As mentioned in the discussion following Lemma 4.2 in [6], a family of cryptographically strong hash functions is needed to ensure that the vectors generated by the hash function from the input behave as random and independent sparse vectors over the finite field. We will make this assumption on the hash family $\mathcal{H}$. Checking the rank can be done by Gaussian elimination keeping the resulting matrix at each stage. The inner-loop thus

---

[6] Strictly speaking the row could have $< s$ non-zero entries because a hash function could map to zero. But this happens with low probability.

Algorithm 4. Create Table

Input: A set $S \subseteq D$ and a function $f : S \to \{0,1\}^k$, two primes p, q, $\mathcal{H}$ a hash family, and $s \geq 2$.

Output: Table $\mathbf{g}$, h_0 a hash function and r blocks of $2s$ hash functions B_i.

$M \leftarrow (0)_{n \times q}$ (a $n \times q$ zero matrix).

Let h_0 be a random hash function from $\mathcal{H}$.

$i \leftarrow 0$.

for all $x \in S$ **do**

    $i \leftarrow i+1; j \leftarrow 0$.

    repeat

        if B_j is not defined **then**

            Generate $h_1, \cdots, h_{2s}$ random hash functions from $\mathcal{H}$.

            $B_j \leftarrow \{h_1, \cdots, h_{2s}\}$.

        end if

        Let $h_1, \cdots, h_{2s}$ be the hash functions in B_j.

        $M[i, h_{k+s}(x)] \leftarrow h_k(x)$ for $1 \leq k \leq s$; $j \leftarrow j+1$.

    until $\mathrm{Rank}(M) = i$

end for

Let $\mathbf{v} = \langle f(x) - h_0(x) : x \in S \rangle^t$.

Solve the system $M \times \mathbf{g} = \mathbf{v}$ for $\mathbf{g} = \langle g[i] : 1 \leq i \leq q \rangle^t$ over $\mathbb{F}_p$.

Return $\mathbf{g}$, h_0 and B_i.

---

runs in expected $O(n^2)$ time and the "for" loop takes $O(n^3)$ time on average. Solving the resulting set of sparse equations can be done in $O(n^2)$ time since the Gaussian elimination has already been completed. The algorithm also generates r blocks of hash functions, and by the earlier analysis the expected value of r is $O(1/\epsilon)$. In summary, the expected running time of Algorithm 4 is $O(n^3)$. We refer the reader to [7] for a discussion on why sparse matrix algorithms cannot be used in this stage, and also why $s = 1$ cannot be used here.

Analysis of Algorithm 5: In this algorithm we try the blocks of hash functions and output the first "plausible" value of the function (namely, a value in the range of the function f). If the wrong block, B_i, of hash functions was used then the probability that the resulting function value, y, belongs to the range $\{0,1\}^k$ is $\frac{2^k}{p}$. If the right block B_i was used then, of course, we get the correct value of the function and $y = f(x)$. If $x \in D \backslash S$, then again the probability that $y \in \{0,1\}^k$ is at most $\frac{r2^k}{p}$. Since r and s are $O(1)$ the algorithm requires $O(1)$ operations over the finite field : $\mathbb{F}_p$. This requires $O(\log^2 p)$ bit operations with the usual algorithms for finite field operations, and only $O(\log p \log \log p)$ bit operations if FFT multiplication is used.

How to get one-sided error: The analysis in the previous paragraph shows that the probability that we err on any element of S is $\leq \frac{n2^k}{p}$. Thus, if p is large we can construct a g table using Algorithm 4 and verify whether we give the correct value of f for all elements of S. If not, we can use Algorithm 4 again to

---

Algorithm 5. Query function

Input: Table g, hash functions $h_0, B_i, 1 \leq i \leq r, x \in D$.
Output: $y \in \{0,1\}^k$ or $\perp$.

  $i \leftarrow 1$
  while $i \leq r$ **do**
    Let $h_1, \cdots, h_{2s}$ be the hash functions in B_i.
    Let $y \leftarrow h_0(x) + \sum_{1 \leq j \leq s} h_i(x) g[h_{i+s}(x)]$.
    if $y \in \{0,1\}^k$ **then**
      Return y.
    end if
    $i \leftarrow i + 1$
  end while
  Return $\perp$.

---

construct another table g. The probability we succeed at any stage is $\geq 1 - \frac{n2^k}{p}$, and if p is taken large enough that this is $\geq \frac{1}{2}$, then the expected number of iterations is ≤ 2. We summarize the properties of the Bloomier filter constructed in this section below:

Theorem 5. *Fix $\epsilon > 0$ and $s \geq 2$ an integer, let $S \subseteq D$, $|S| = n$ and let m, k be positive integers such that $m \geq k$. Given $f : S \rightarrow \{0,1\}^k$, the Bloomier filter constructed, (with parameters ϵ, m and s) by Algorithms 3 and 4, and queried, using Algorithm 5, has the following properties:*

1. *The expected time to create the Bloomier filter is $\tilde{O}(n^3 + m^4)$.*
2. *The space utilized is $\lceil n(1 + \epsilon) \rceil m$ bits.*
3. *Computing the value of the Bloomier filter at $x \in D$ requires $O(1)$ hash function evaluations and $O(1)$ memory look ups.*
4. *If $x \in S$, it outputs the correct value of $f(x)$.*
5. *If $x \notin S$, it outputs $\perp$ with probability $1 - O(\frac{1}{\epsilon} 2^{k-m})$.*

4   Bucketing

The construction in §3 is space efficient but the time to construct the Bloomier filter is exhorbitant. In this section we show how to mitigate this with bucketing. To build a Bloomier filter for $f : S \rightarrow \{0,1\}^k$, one can choose a hash function $g : S \rightarrow \{0, 1, \cdots, b-1\}$ and then build Bloomier filters for the functions $f_i : S_i \rightarrow \{0,1\}^k$, for $i = 0, 1, \cdots, b-1$, where $S_i = g^{-1}(i)$ and $f_i(x) = f(x)$ for $x \in S_i$. The sets $|S_i|$ have an expected size of $|S|/b$ and hence results in a speedup for the construction time. The bucketing also allows one to parallelize of the construction process, since each of the buckets can in processed independently. To quantify the time saved by bucketing we need a concentration result for the size of the buckets produced by the hash function.

Fix a bucket b_i, $0 \leq b_i < b$ and define random variables $X_{s_1}^{(b_i)}, \cdots, X_{s_n}^{(b_i)}$ for $s_j \in S$ as follows: Pick a hash function $g : S \rightarrow \{0, 1, \cdots, b-1\}$ from a family of hash functions $\mathcal{H}$ and set $X_{s_j}^{(b_i)} = 1$ if $g(s_j) = b_i$ and set $X_{s_j}^{(b_i)} = 0$ otherwise. Under the assumption that the random variables $X_{s_j}^{(b_i)}$ are mutually independent, we obtain using Chernoff bounds that $\Pr\left[\sum_j X_{s_j}^{(b_i)} > (1+\delta)\frac{|S|}{b}\right] < 2^{-\frac{\delta|S|}{b}}$ provided $\delta > 2e - 1$. This bound holds for any bucket and consequently, $\Pr\left[\exists j \ : \ \sum_j X_{s_j}^{(b_i)} > (1+\delta)\frac{|S|}{b}\right] < b2^{-\frac{\delta|S|}{b}}$. Thus with probability $> 1 - b2^{-\frac{\delta|S|}{b}}$ all the buckets have at most $(1+\delta)\frac{|S|}{b}$ elements. Suppose we take the number of buckets b to be $\frac{|S|}{c\log|S|}$ for $c > 1$. Then the probability that all the buckets are of size $< c(1+\delta)\log|S|$ is at least $1 - 2^{(-c\delta\log|S|+\log|S|-c\log\log|S|)}$ which for large enough S is $> 1/2$. In other words, the expected number of trials until we find a hash function g that results in all the buckets being "small" is less than 2.

In the following discussion we adopt the notation from Theorem 5. We assume that we have a hash function g that results in all buckets have $O(\log n)$ elements. The time for creation of the Bloomier filter in §3 for each bucket is reduced to $O(\log^3 n + r^4)$. To query the bucketed Bloomier filter, given x, we first compute the bucket, $g(x)$, and then query the Bloomier filter for that bucket. Thus, querying requires one more hash function evaluation than the non-bucketing version. Suppose n_i is the number of elements of S that belonged to the bucket defined by b_i, then the Bloomier filter for this bucket requires $\lceil n_i(1+\epsilon)\rceil r$ bits. The total number of bits used is $\sum_{0\leq i<b}\lceil n_i(1+\epsilon)\rceil r \leq \sum_{0\leq i<b}(n_i(1+\epsilon)+1)r = n(1+\epsilon)r + br$, since $\sum_i n_i = n$. Since the number of buckets is $O(n/\log n)$, the number of bits used is $n(1+\epsilon)r + O(rn/\log n)$.

We summarize the properties of the bucketing variant of the construction in §3 in the following theorem.

Theorem 6. *Fix $\epsilon > 0$ and $s \geq 2$ an integer, let $S \subseteq D$, $|S| = n$ and let m, k be positive integers such that $m \geq k$. Given $f : S \to \{0,1\}^k$, bucketed using $|S|/c\log|S|$ buckets for a fixed $c > 1$, the Bloomier filter constructed on the buckets, (with parameters ϵ, m and s) by Algorithms 3 and 4, and queried (on the buckets), using Algorithm 5, has the following properties:*

1. *The expected time to create the Bloomier filter is $\tilde{O}(\frac{n}{\log n}(\log^3 n + m^4))$.*
2. *The space utilized is $n(1+\epsilon)m + O(mn/\log n)$ bits.*
3. *Computing the value of the Bloomier filter at $x \in D$ requires $O(1)$ hash function evaluations and $O(1)$ memory look ups.*
4. *If $x \in S$, it outputs the correct value of $f(x)$.*
5. *If $x \notin S$, it outputs $\perp$ with probability $1 - O(\frac{1}{\epsilon}2^{k-m})$.*

References

1. Bloom, B.: Space/time tradeoffs in hash coding with allowable errors. Comm. of the ACM 13, 422–426 (1970)
2. Bollobás, B.: The evolution of random graphs. Trans. Amer. Math. Soc. 286, 257–274 (1984)
3. Broder, A., Mitzenmacher, M.: Network applications of Bloom filters: a survey, Allerton (2002)

4. Byers, J., Considine, J., Mitzenmacher, M.: Informed content delivery over adaptive overlay networks. In: Proc. ACM SIGCOMM 2002. Comp. Communication Review, vol. 34(4), pp. 47–60 (2002)
5. Calkin, N.J.: Dependent sets of constant weight binary vectors. Combinatorics, Probability and Computing 6(3), 263–271 (1997)
6. Chazelle, B., Kilian, J., Rubinfeld, R., Tal, A.: The Bloomier filter: an efficient data structure for static support lookup tables. In: Proc. of the 15th Annual ACM-SIAM Symp. on Discrete Algorithms (SODA 2004), pp. 30–39 (2004)
7. Charles, D., Chellapilla, K.: Bloomier Filters: A second look (extended version) (2008) arXiv:0807.0928
8. Cohen, S., Matias, Y.: Spectral Bloom filters. In: ACM SIGMOD (2003)
9. Czech, Z., Havas, G., Majewski, B.S.: An optimal algorithm for generating minimal perfect hash functions. Information Processing Letters 43(5), 257–264 (1992)
10. Czech, Z., Havas, G., Majewski, B.S., Wormald, N.C.: Graphs, hypergraphs and hashing. In: van Leeuwen, J. (ed.) WG 1993. LNCS, vol. 790, pp. 153–165. Springer, Heidelberg (1994)
11. Dietzfelbinger, M., Pagh, R.: Succinct Data Structures for Retrieval and Approximate Membership. In: ICALP (to appear, 2008)
12. Erdős, P., Rényi, A.: On the evolution of random graphs. Publ. Math. Inst. Hungar. Acad. Sci. 5, 17–61 (1960)
13. Fan, L., Cao, P., Almeida, J., Broder, A.: Summary cache: a scalable wide-area web cache sharing protocol. IEEE/ACM Transactions on Networking 8, 281–293 (2000)
14. Fang, M., Shivakumar, N., Garcia-Molina, H., Motwani, R., Ullman, J.: Computing iceberg queries efficiently. In: Proc. 24th Int. Conf. on VLDB, pp. 299–310 (1998)
15. Geller, D., Kra, I., Popescu, S., Simanca, S.: On circulant matrices (manuscript), http://www.math.sunysb.edu/~sorin
16. Gremillion, L.L.: Designing a Bloom filter for differential file access. Comm. of the ACM 25, 600–604 (1982)
17. Mitzenmacher, M.: Compressed Bloom filters. IEEE Transactions on Networking 10 (2002)
18. Rhea, S.C., Kubiatowicz, J.: Proabilistic location and routing. In: Proceedings of INFOCOMM (2002)

Coupled Path Planning, Region Optimization, and Applications in Intensity-Modulated Radiation Therapy[*]

Danny Z. Chen[1], Shuang Luan[2], and Chao Wang[1,**]

[1] Department of Computer Science and Engineering, University of Notre Dame,
Notre Dame, IN 46556, USA
{chen,cwang1}@cse.nd.edu
[2] Department of Computer Science, University of New Mexico, Albuquerque, NM
87131, USA
sluan@cs.unm.edu

Abstract. The couple path planning (CPP) problem seeks the motion paths of the leaves of a multileaf collimator, to optimally reproduce the prescribed dose in intensity-modulated radiation therapy (IMRT). We study two versions of the CPP problem, constrained and unconstrained CPP, based on whether the starting and ending locations of the sought paths are prespecified. The unconstrained CPP problem models the leaf sequencing problem in dynamic IMRT delivery, while the set of all constrained CPP problem instances, in which all combinations of the starting and ending locations are considered, plays a key role in an emerging IMRT technique called arc-modulated radiation therapy. We give efficient algorithms for both the constrained and unconstrained CPP problems, and for computing the set of all constrained CPP problem instances. Our results are based on several new ideas and geometric observations, and substantially improve the solutions based on standard techniques. Implementation results show that our CPP algorithms run fast and produce better IMRT treatment plans than current methods.

1 Introduction

In this paper, we study an optimization problem in discrete geometry, called *coupled path planning* (CPP). The problem is defined on a uniform grid R_g of size $n \times H$ for some integers n and H such that the length of each grid edge is one unit. We say that a path on the plane is xy-monotone if it is monotone with respect to both the x-axis and the y-axis. For an integer $c > 0$, an xy-monotone (rectilinear) path p along the edges of R_g is said to be c-*steep* if every vertical segment of p is of a length at least c (i.e., formed by c or more grid edges) and every horizontal segment has a unit length. The CPP problem is defined as

---

[*] Supported in part by the National Science Foundation under Grants CCF-0515203 and CBET-0755054, and National Institutes of Health under Grant R01-CA117997.
[**] Corresponding author.

D. Halperin and K. Mehlhorn (Eds.): ESA 2008, LNCS 5193, pp. 271–283, 2008.

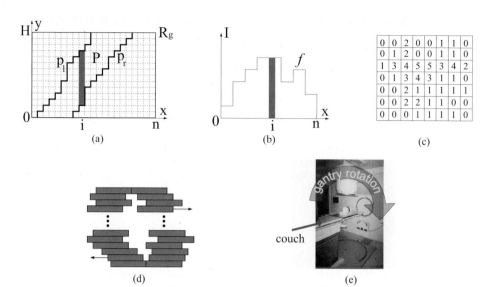

Fig. 1. (a) Illustrating the CPP problem: p_l and p_r are two non-crossing c-steep paths ($c = 1$); the darkened segment shows the vertical section on the i-th column of the region enclosed by the two paths, whose length corresponds to the amount of actually delivered radiation. (b) The input (intensity) function f for the CPP problem, defined on $\{1, 2, \ldots, n\}$; the darkened segment shows the value of f at the i-th cell, which specifies the amount of prescribed dose on that cell. (c) An IM (its 3rd row is described by the function f in (b)). (d) An MLC. (e) A radiation machine.

follows: Given a non-negative function f defined on the integer set $\{1, 2, \ldots, n\}$ and positive integers c and Δ ($\Delta \leq H$), find two non-crossing c-steep paths on R_g, each starting at the bottom boundary and ending at the top boundary of R_g, such that the two paths, possibly with the bottom and top boundaries of R_g, enclose a (rectilinear) region P in R_g such that (1) for any column C_i of R_g, the vertical length of the intersection between C_i and P approximates the function value $f(i)$ (i.e., the value of f at i) within the given error bound Δ (see Figs. 1(a)-1(b)), and (2) the total sum of errors on P is minimized.

We distinguish two versions of the CPP problem: (1) The **unconstrained CPP**, in which the starting and ending locations of the sought paths are not specified by the input; (2) the **constrained CPP**, where the starting and ending locations of the sought paths are given as part of the input.

Application Background. The CPP problems arise in *intensity-modulated radiation therapy* (IMRT) [26,27], a modern cancer treatment technique aiming to deliver prescribed conformal radiation dose to target tumors while sparing the surrounding normal tissue and critical structures. Effective IMRT treatment is hinged on the ability to *accurately* and *efficiently* deliver prescribed intensity distributions of radiation, called *intensity maps* (IMs). An IM is specified by an array of non-negative integers on a uniform 2-D grid I_g (see Fig. 1(c)). (We should point out that the two 2-D grids I_g and R_g represent different entities or objects.) The value in each cell of I_g indicates the prescribed intensity level of radiation to be delivered to the body region corresponding to that cell. One of the most advanced tools for IM delivery is the *multileaf collimator* (MLC) [26,27], which consists of many pairs of tungsten alloy leaves of the same rectangular shape and size (see Fig. 1(d)). The opposite leaves of each pair are aligned to each other. These leaves, controlled by a computer, can move left and right to enclose a rectilinear polygonal region called *MLC-aperture*. During treatment, the patient is positioned on and secured to the treatment couch (see Fig. 1(e)) and radiation beams are crossfired at the tumor from various directions. The direction of each radiation beam is controlled by rotating the gantry to the desired angle. The MLC is mounted on the gantry and the cross-section of a cylindrical radiation beam is shaped by an MLC-aperture to deliver a uniform dose to (a portion of) an IM. Each row of the IM is delivered by exactly one MLC leaf pair.

Two IMRT delivery approaches are commonly used, called *static* and *dynamic* IMRT [26,27]. In static IMRT, the MLC leaves do not move during irradiation of a beam, and are repositioned to form another beam shape only when the radiation is turned off. In dynamic IMRT, the MLC leaves keep moving across an IM field (normally, all from left to right) while the radiation remains on. In both approaches, the gantry is fixed when delivering an IM. Once an IM is delivered, the radiation is turned off and the gantry rotates to another angle to deliver the next IM, if any. Normally, a treatment session delivers 5 to 9 IMs. A key problem in IMRT delivery, called *leaf sequencing*, is to determine a *treatment plan* for a given IM, i.e., a description of how to position the MLC leaves and maintain the on/off states of the radiation in order to deliver the IM. Two key criteria are used to measure the quality of an IMRT treatment plan: (1) Delivery time (the efficiency): Minimizing the delivery time reduces machine wear and tear, lowers the treatment costs, and increases the patient throughput. Short delivery time also reduces the risk of treatment uncertainties. (2) Delivery error (the accuracy): For various reasons, there is a discrepancy between the prescribed IM and the actually delivered IM.

The unconstrained CPP problem models the *dynamic leaf sequencing* problem (i.e., leaf sequencing in dynamic IMRT delivery). Although an IM is delivered using many MLC leaf pairs, with each pair delivering one IM row, it suffices (as shown in [7,16] for Varian MLCs) to consider how to optimally deliver one IM row with one leaf pair. In the CPP problem, f is the intensity function specifying one row of a prescribed IM (see Fig. 1(b)), and the two output xy-monotone paths on R_g specify the moving trajectories of the two leaf ends of the MLC leaf pair, i.e., the leaf end positions (the x-coordinates) at any unit time (the y-coordinate). Due to the *maximum speed constraint* on the MLC leaf motion, i.e., the leaves cannot move faster than a threshold speed (e.g., 3cm/s for Varian MLCs), the paths must be c-steep for some $c > 0$. The vertical length of the segment on the i-th column of the region in R_g enclosed by the two paths equals the time duration the i-th cell of the IM row is exposed to irradiation, and is proportional to the intensity level actually delivered to that cell. To ensure the treatment quality, the delivered intensity level must be accurate enough (within an error of Δ to the prescribed intensity level at each IM cell). The total error over all columns of R_g gives the delivery error incurred to the IM row specified by f. Thus, the CPP problem seeks to deliver one IM row with the minimum error using exactly H units of delivery time.

The constrained CPP problem is a key to a newly emerging IMRT delivery technique called *arc-modulated radiation therapy* (AMRT) [29], which we have been developing jointly with Univ. of Maryland School of Medicine. AMRT differs from the common dynamic IMRT delivery in that both the beam direction (i.e., gantry angle) and MLC leaves keep moving, with the radiation source remained on. As shown in Sect. 5, the leaf sequencing problem in AMRT delivery can be solved by considering the set of all constrained CPP problem instances. More specifically, for all possible combinations of starting and ending leaf pair positions, we seek the optimal solutions for the corresponding constrained CPP problem instances (in total, there are $O(n^4)$ such instances).

Related Work. Algorithmic research for IMRT problems has been active in several areas such as medical physics [7,14,17,18,23,24,25,28], operations research [3,5,6,15], and computational geometry [9,10,11,12,13,19,20,21]. Most of the algorithms proposed so far were designed for the *static leaf sequencing* problem, i.e., the leaf sequencing problem in static IMRT delivery, and their solutions cannot be directly applied to the dynamic IMRT delivery due to different delivery constraints. Dynamic leaf sequencing (DLS) algorithms were mainly developed by the medical physics community [7,14,17,22,24,25] targeting at the exact delivery of an input IM with a short delivery time, under the maximum speed constraint. But, these DLS algorithms all assume that on each IM row, the corresponding MLC leaves always move from the left boundary of the leftmost non-zero cell to the right boundary of the rightmost non-zero cell, and hence their output may not be truly optimal in terms of the delivery time. For example, consider a $1 \times n$ IM filled with 1's, and assume that for each time unit, an MLC leaf can move across at most one IM cell. For the above algorithms, since the MLC leaves must move from the leftmost to the rightmost of the IM field, the minimum delivery time is $\Omega(n)$ time units. However, by fixing the left (resp., right) leaf end to the leftmost (resp., rightmost) of the IM field, only one time unit is needed for delivering this IM. For the AMRT delivery, no leaf sequencing algorithm was known except the heuristic back-and-forth sliding-window method proposed by Cameron [8].

The CPP problems are somewhat related to the *shape rectangularization* (SR) and *generalized shape rectangularization* (GSR) problems [9], which seek an optimal set of rectangles to exactly, or approximately, "build" an intensity functional curve. The SR and GSR problems are NP-hard [5,10]. Chen *et al.* [9] gave a polynomial time $(\frac{3}{2} + \epsilon)$-approximation SR algorithm and a pseudo-polynomial time dynamic programming algorithm for a key GSR case. Though the CPP problem can be viewed as finding a set of H rectangles, each corresponding to a row section of the region P (see Fig. 1(a)), to approximately build the input curve f, it differs from the SR and GSR problems in that all CPP rectangles are of the *same* height and form a *"smooth" increasing sequence*, i.e., no left or right edge can move more than 1 column in any c consecutive rectangles in the sequence.

Summary of Our Results. We present a unified approach, based on interesting geometric observations, for both the unconstrained and constrained CPP problems, substantially improving the solutions using standard techniques. One of our key ideas is to formulate these problems as computing shortest paths in a weighted directed acyclic graph of $O(nH\Delta)$ vertices and $O(nH^2\Delta^2)$ edges. We exploit a set of geometric properties, such as certain domination relations among the vertices, to speed up the shortest path computation, resulting in $O(nH\Delta)$ time algorithms for both the unconstrained and constrained CPP problems. To compute the set of all constrained CPP instances, instead of a simple approach to apply the $O(nH\Delta)$ time constrained CPP algorithm to each of the $O(n^4)$ problem instances (i.e., an $O(n^5H\Delta)$ time algorithm), we use a graph transformation scheme that allows a *batch fashion* computation of the instances. Further, we accelerate the shortest path computation by exploiting the Monge property of the transformed graphs. Consequently, we achieve an $O(n^4\Delta + n^2H\Delta^2)$ time algorithm for the set of all constrained CPP instances.

Note that in our CPP formulations, we seek to minimize the delivery error subject to a given amount of delivery time H. It is also useful to consider the dual problem of minimizing the delivery time subject to a given bound of delivery error. As shown in Sect. 2.3, for a given H, our CPP algorithms actually compute, in $O(nH\Delta)$ time, a *sequence* of H leaf trajectories (i.e., path pairs), the k-th ($1 \leq k \leq H$) of which corresponds to the optimal leaf trajectories (i.e., with the minimum error) for delivering the intensity function f in exactly k time units. This enables us to compute a tradeoff between the delivery time and delivery error. Consequently, for any error bound $\mathcal{E}$, in an exponential search manner, we can determine in $O(nH^*\Delta)$ time the minimum delivery time H^* required for delivering f with an error at most $\mathcal{E}$. In applications, one may use this feature to find a treatment plan with balanced delivery time and delivery error.

We implemented our CPP algorithms and developed new leaf sequencing softwares for common dynamic IMRT delivery as well as for the new AMRT delivery technique. Experimental results (in Sect. 5) on real medical data show that our CPP-based leaf sequencing software runs very fast and produces better quality treatment plans than the previously known methods.

2   Unconstrained Coupled Path Planning (UCPP)

2.1   The UCPP Problem Definition and Graph Modeling

We define the *height* of an xy-monotone path as the difference between the y-coordinates of its ending and starting points. For two non-crossing c-steep paths p_l and p_r of height H on the grid R_g (i.e., both paths start at the bottom and end at the top of R_g), denote by $P(p_\mathrm{l}, p_\mathrm{r})$ the rectilinear region in R_g enclosed by p_l, p_r, and the bottom and top boundaries of R_g. Denote by $\ell(i, p_l, p_r)$ the vertical length of the intersection of the i-th column C_i of R_g with $P(p_l, p_r)$. Let $\ell(i, p_l, p_r) := 0$ if $C_i \cap P(p_l, p_r) = \emptyset$.

Precisely, the **unconstrained coupled path planning** (UCPP) problem is: Given an $n \times H$ uniform grid R_g, a non-negative function f defined on the set $\{1, 2, \ldots, n\}$, and positive integers c and Δ ($\Delta \le H$), find two non-crossing paths p_l and p_r of height H along the edges of R_g to minimize the total error $\mathcal{E}(p_l, p_r) := \sum_{i=1}^{n} |\ell(i, p_l, p_r) - f(i)|$, subject to the following constraints: (1) (the *steepness constraint*) both p_l and p_r are *c-steep* paths, and (2) (the *closeness constraint*) $|\ell(i, p_l, p_r) - f(i)| \le \Delta$ for each $i = 1, 2, \ldots, n$.

For the UCPP problem, we can assume the two sought optimal c-steep paths p_l and p_r of height H are both *increasing* going from left to right. This is because we can vertically "flip" a decreasing path, i.e., by replacing the y-coordinate β of each point on the path by $H - \beta$ without changing its x-coordinate (see Fig. 2(a)-2(b)). This makes both paths non-crossing and increasing, with the same total error without violating the steepness and closeness constraints.

By considering only increasing c-steep paths, the region $P(p_l, p_r)$ is a rectilinear xy-monotone polygon in R_g, and can be uniquely mapped to a sequence of n vertical bars $B_1, B_2, \ldots, B_n$ (of unit width each), where the i-th bar B_i is the intersection between $P(p_l, p_r)$ and the i-th column, C_i, of R_g. If $C_i \cap P(p_l, p_r) = \emptyset$, then B_i is a bar of height 0, aligned with the bottom or top boundary of R_g, depending on if C_i is to the left or right of $P(p_l, p_r)$ (see Fig. 2(c)).

The following observations on the vertical bars $B_1, B_2, \ldots, B_n$ are useful. (1) Each vertical bar can be encoded as a point $(\alpha, \beta) \in \mathbb{Z}^2$, where α (resp., β) is the y-coordinate of its bottom (resp., top) edge, with $0 \le \alpha \le \beta \le H$. (2) The closeness constraint implies that for any vertical bar $B_i = (\alpha, \beta)$ ($1 \le i \le n$), $|\beta - \alpha - f(i)| \le \Delta$ holds. (3) The steepness constraint implies an interesting relation, called *c-dominance*, between any two consecutive vertical bars $B_i = (\alpha, \beta)$ and $B_{i+1} = (\alpha', \beta')$. More precisely, the c-dominance relation is defined on the set $S := \{(x, y) \in \mathbb{Z}^2 \mid 0 \le x \le y \le H\}$, and we say that (α', β') *c-dominates* (α, β) if and only if one of the following conditions holds: (i) $\alpha' = \alpha = \beta' = \beta = 0$; (ii) $\alpha' = \alpha = 0$ and $\beta' - \beta \ge c$; (iii) $\alpha' - \alpha \ge c$ and $\beta' - \beta \ge c$; (iv) $\alpha' = \alpha = 0$ and $\beta' = \beta = H$; (v) $\alpha' - \alpha \ge c$ and $\beta' = \beta = H$; (vi) $\alpha' = \alpha = \beta' = \beta = H$.

The above observations allow us to model the UCPP problem as a shortest path problem on a directed graph G, as follows. G contains n layers of vertices, $L_1, L_2, \ldots, L_n$, where the i-th layer L_i ($1 \le i \le n$) contains the vertices that represent all vertical bars on the column C_i whose lengths differ from $f(i)$ by at most Δ. That is, $L_i = \{(\alpha, \beta) \mid 0 \le \alpha \le \beta \le H$ and $|\beta - \alpha - f(i)| \le \Delta\}$. For each vertex $u = (\alpha, \beta) \in L_i$, we assign to it a weight $w(u) = |\beta - \alpha - f(i)|$. We also add to G two dummy vertices (of zero weight), the *source* s and *sink* t. The edges of G are defined as follows: (1) For any two vertices $u = (\alpha, \beta) \in L_i$ and $u' = (\alpha', \beta') \in L_{i+1}$, put a directed edge from u to u' if (α', β') c-dominates (α, β); (2) For any vertex $u' = (\alpha', \beta') \in L_1$, put an edge from the source s to u' if (α', β') c-dominates $(0, 0)$; (3) For any $u = (\alpha, \beta) \in L_n$, put an edge from u to the sink t if (H, H) c-dominates (α, β).

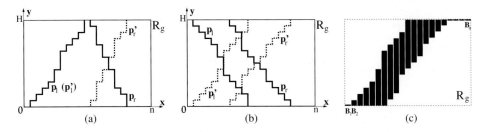

Fig. 2. (a) Flipping a decreasing path p_r to an increasing path p_r'. (b) Flipping two monotone decreasing paths p_l and p_r to two increasing paths p_l' and p_r'. The flipping in (a)-(b) affects neither the steepness nor the closeness constraint, and $\ell(i, p_l, p_r) = \ell(i, p_l', p_r')$ holds for each i, implying that the total error remains the same. (c) The xy-monotone region enclosed by the two paths p_l' and p_r' in (b) corresponds to a sequence of n vertical bars $B_1, B_2, \ldots, B_n$.

Clearly, G is a directed acyclic graph (DAG) with vertex weights. Each s-to-t path in G represents a sequence of vertical bars on R_g, which forms an xy-monotone rectilinear polygon and thus induces a pair of xy-monotone paths. The way in which the vertices and edges of G are defined guarantees that the induced pair of paths satisfies the steepness and closeness constraints, and thus is a feasible solution for the UCPP problem. It is also easy to argue that any feasible UCPP solution (p_l, p_r) corresponds to an s-to-t path p in G, and the total error $\mathcal{E}(p_l, p_r)$ is equal to the weight $w(p)$ of the path p, i.e., the sum of weights of all vertices in p. Hence we have the following lemma.

Lemma 1. *The UCPP problem is feasible if and only if there is a path from s to t in the DAG G. Moreover, an s-to-t shortest path in G defines an optimal solution for the UCPP problem.*

Note that the DAG G thus defined has $O(nH\Delta)$ vertices and $O(nH^2\Delta^2)$ edges. Hence an s-to-t shortest path in G can be computed in $O(nH^2\Delta^2)$ time straightforwardly in a topological sort fashion. In the next subsection, we show how to exploit the underlying geometric properties of the graph G to speed up the computation and obtain an $O(nH\Delta)$ time UCPP algorithm.

2.2   Speeding Up the Shortest Path Computation Using Geometry

We compute the single-source shortest paths in the DAG G layer by layer. For any vertex v of G, define $\text{In}(v) = \{w \mid (w, v) \text{ is an edge of } G\}$. Denote by $\text{length}(v)$ the length of the shortest s-to-v path in G. Since G is vertex-weighted, to compute $\text{length}(u)$ for a vertex $u = (\alpha, \beta)$, it suffices to find a vertex w^* that achieves $\min\{\text{length}(w) \mid w \in \text{In}(u)\}$. Our key idea for speeding up the computation is to exploit the geometric relations among the sets $\text{In}(u)$ for all vertices u in the same layer L_i.

Consider the i-th vertex layer L_i in G ($1 \leq i \leq n$). Recall that $L_i = \{(\alpha, \beta) \mid 0 \leq \alpha \leq \beta \leq H \text{ and } |\beta - \alpha - f(i)| \leq \Delta\}$. If we view each vertical

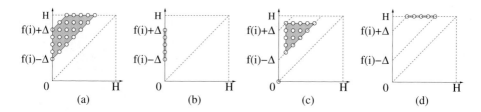

Fig. 3. (a) Illustrating the geometry of a vertex layer L_i of the DAG G. (b)-(d) Illustrating the geometry of a vertex layer L'_i of the DAG G' for (b) $l_{start} < i \leq r_{start}$, (c) $r_{start} < i \leq l_{end}$, and (d) $l_{end} < i \leq r_{end}$, respectively. In each figure, all vertices in the vertex layer L_i (or L'_i) are mapped to circled points in the 2-D plane; these points form all the lattice points in a convex polygon (possibly degenerated to a line segment) marked by the shaded area.

bar $(\alpha, \beta) \in L_i$ as a point in the 2-D plane, then L_i consists of all lattice points in a discrete convex polygon bounded by $O(1)$ discrete edges (see Fig. 3(a)). Recall that the edges of G are defined based on the c-dominance relation among the vertices in consecutive layers. Fix a vertex $u = (\alpha, \beta) \in L_i$. It is easy to show that $In(u) = L_{i-1} \cap D^c(\alpha, \beta)$, where $D^c(\alpha, \beta)$ is the c-dominated set of (α, β), i.e., the set of all points in S that are c-dominated by (α, β). (Figs. 4(a)-4(f) give examples of the typical c-dominated sets.) Our key observation here is that the c-dominated set $D^c(\alpha, \beta)$ always includes $D^c(\alpha - 1, \beta)$, $D^c(\alpha, \beta - 1)$, and $D^c(\alpha - 1, \beta - 1)$. Thus $In(u)$ always contains $In(v)$, for $v = (\alpha - 1, \beta), (\alpha, \beta - 1)$, and $(\alpha - 1, \beta - 1)$. The next lemma quantifies this inclusion relation (proof is left to the full paper).

Lemma 2. *For any vertex $u = (\alpha, \beta) \in L_i$, if $In(u) \neq \emptyset$, then the following properties hold:*
(2a) If $v = (\alpha - 1, \beta)$ (resp., $v = (\alpha, \beta - 1)$, $v = (\alpha - 1, \beta - 1)) \in L_i$, then $In(v) \subset In(u)$ and the set $In(u) \setminus In(v)$ can be enumerated in $O(\Delta)$ time.
(2b) If $v_1 = (\alpha-1, \beta) \in L_i$ and $v_2 = (\alpha, \beta-1) \in L_i$, then $In(v_1) \cup In(v_2) \subset In(u)$ and the set $In(u) \setminus (In(v_1) \cup In(v_2))$ can be enumerated in $O(1)$ time.

Lemma 2 implies the shortest path computation from s to the vertices in the layer L_i can be sped up by following an appropriate order of the vertices, in a dynamic programming fashion. Specifically, we visit (and compute the corresponding paths to) the vertices in L_i in the left-to-right and bottom-to-top order; here, L_i is viewed as a discrete convex polygon. Suppose length(u) has been computed for each vertex u in the previous layer L_{i-1}. For the first vertex of L_i visited, say v_0, since $In(v_0) \subset L_{i-1}$, length(v_0) can be computed in $O(|L_{i-1}|) = O(H\Delta)$ time. For each subsequent vertex in L_i, say $v = (\alpha, \beta)$, there are two possible cases. Case (I): (α, β) is on the boundary of L_i. By (2a) of Lemma 2, we can show that length(v) is computable in $O(\Delta)$ time. Case (II): (α, β) is in the interior of L_i. By (2b) of Lemma 2, we can show that length(v) is computable in $O(1)$ time. (Here, we assume it takes $O(1)$ time to report whether $In(v) \neq \emptyset$, which can be achieved by performing a breadth-first search in G at the beginning of the

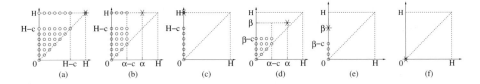

Fig. 4. Illustrating the typical types of c-dominated sets. In each figure, all the circled points form the c-dominated set of the point marked by an asterisk. (a) $\mathrm{D}^c(H, H)$. (b) $\mathrm{D}^c(\alpha, H)$ $(0 < \alpha < H)$. (c) $\mathrm{D}^c(0, H)$. (d) $\mathrm{D}^c(\alpha, \beta)$ $(0 < \alpha \leq \beta < H)$. (e) $\mathrm{D}^c(0, \beta)$ $(0 < \beta < H)$. (f) $\mathrm{D}^c(0, 0)$.

algorithm, in $O(nH\Delta)$ time.) Observing that L_i has $O(H\Delta)$ vertices and $O(H)$ of them are on the boundary of L_i (see Fig. 3(a)), the above process computes length(v) for all $v \in L_i$ in $O(H\Delta) + O(H) \times O(\Delta) + O(H\Delta) \times O(1) = O(H\Delta)$ time. Thus, we can obtain an s-to-t shortest path in G in $O(nH\Delta)$ time. By Lemma 1, the result below follows.

Theorem 1. *Given a non-negative function f defined on the integers in $\{1, 2, \ldots, n\}$ and positive integers c, H, and Δ $(\Delta \leq H)$, the UCPP problem is solvable in $O(nH\Delta)$ time.*

2.3 Extension

The above UCPP algorithm can be extended to computing a sequence of H path pairs, with the k-th $(1 \leq k \leq H)$ being an optimal path pair of height exactly k in an $n \times k$ grid, for approximating the input function f. The main idea is to replace the sink t in G by a layer L_{n+1} of H sink vertices $t_1, t_2, \ldots, t_H$, and associate with t_k a vertical bar (k, k) for $1 \leq k \leq H$. The edges from L_n to L_{n+1} are defined by the same c-domination relation. It is easy to show that an s-to-t_k shortest path in this new DAG specifies an optimal path pair of height exactly k. Using the same technique in this section, we can compute single-source shortest paths in the new DAG in $O(nH\Delta)$ time.

3   Constrained Coupled Path Planning (CCPP)

In this section, we study the **constrained coupled path planning** (CCPP) problem, in which the starting and ending points of the sought paths are pre-specified. Precisely, we are given positive integers $l_{\text{start}}, r_{\text{start}}, l_{\text{end}}, r_{\text{end}}$, and we require that the sought path p_{l} (resp., p_{r}) starts at $(l_{\text{start}}, 0)$ (resp., $(r_{\text{start}}, 0)$) and ends at (l_{end}, H) (resp., (r_{end}, H)).

Without loss of generality, we assume $l_{\text{start}} \leq l_{\text{end}}$ and $r_{\text{start}} \leq r_{\text{end}}$, so that p_{l} and p_{r} are both xy-monotone increasing paths. (Otherwise, we can transform the CCPP problem to a new CCPP problem that satisfies this condition: By flipping (see Figs. 2(a)-2(b)) one or both of the optimal paths for this new problem, we obtain two optimal paths for the original CCPP problem.) In the rest of this section, we present our CCPP algorithm for the case with $l_{\text{end}} \geq r_{\text{start}}$ (the algorithm can be easily adapted to handle the other case with $l_{\text{end}} < r_{\text{start}}$).

As for the UCPP problem in Sect. 2.1, the CCPP region $P(p_l, p_r)$ is an xy-monotone polygon in R_g and is made of a sequence of n vertical bars. Note that such vertical bars, if viewed as 2-D points, still satisfy the c-dominance relation. Thus, the problem can be solved in the same spirit as the UCPP algorithm, i.e., we can transform it to computing a shortest path in a DAG G'. The DAG G' has a source s, a sink t, and n layers of vertices, $L_1', L_2', \ldots, L_n'$, which are defined as follows to satisfy the additional geometric constraints of the CCPP problem:

$$L_i' = \begin{cases} \{(\alpha, \beta) \mid \alpha = \beta = 0 \text{ and } |\beta - \alpha - f(i)| \leq \Delta\} & \text{if } 1 \leq i \leq l_{\text{start}} \\ \{(\alpha, \beta) \mid 0 = \alpha < \beta \leq H - c \text{ and } |\beta - \alpha - f(i)| \leq \Delta\} & \text{if } l_{\text{start}} < i \leq r_{\text{start}} \\ \{(\alpha, \beta) \mid c \leq \alpha \leq \beta \leq H - c \text{ and } |\beta - \alpha - f(i)| \leq \Delta\} & \text{if } r_{\text{start}} < i \leq l_{\text{end}} \\ \{(\alpha, \beta) \mid c \leq \alpha < \beta = H \text{ and } |\beta - \alpha - f(i)| \leq \Delta\} & \text{if } l_{\text{end}} < i \leq r_{\text{end}} \\ \{(\alpha, \beta) \mid \alpha = \beta = H \text{ and } |\beta - \alpha - f(i)| \leq \Delta\} & \text{if } r_{\text{end}} < i \leq n \end{cases}$$

As the UCPP problem, the weight of a vertex $u = (\alpha, \beta) \in L_i'$ is defined as $w'(u) = |\beta - \alpha - f(i)|$ and the edges of G' are defined based on the c-domination relation. We can show that a shortest s-to-t path in G' corresponds to an optimal CCPP solution. Since G' has similar geometric properties as stated in Sect. 2.2 (see Figs. 3(b)-3(d)), the computation can be sped up in the same fashion as in the UCPP algorithm. Our final CCPP algorithm takes $O(nH\Delta)$ time.

4 Computing the Set of All CCPP Problem Instances

In this section, we discuss our algorithm for computing the set of all CCPP problem instances. More specifically, given f, n, H, Δ, and c, we solve the CCPP problem instances on $f, n, H, \Delta, c, l_{\text{start}}, r_{\text{start}}, l_{\text{end}}$, and r_{end} for all possible combinations of $l_{\text{start}}, r_{\text{start}}, l_{\text{end}}$, and r_{end}. Due to the space limit, we only sketch our ideas on solving the subset of CCPP instances with $l_{\text{start}} < l_{\text{end}} < r_{\text{start}} < r_{\text{end}}$.

Since $0 \leq l_{\text{start}} < r_{\text{start}} < l_{\text{end}} < r_{\text{end}} \leq n$, there are totally $N = \Theta(n^4)$ problem instances, which we denote by $\mathcal{I}_1, \mathcal{I}_2, \ldots, \mathcal{I}_N$. As discussed in Sect. 3, an instance $\mathcal{I}_k$ ($1 \leq k \leq N$) corresponds to a shortest path problem on a vertex-weighted DAG, denoted by G_k', of $O(nH\Delta)$ vertices and $O(nH^2\Delta^2)$ edges. Our key observation is that we can transform (details left to the full paper) G_k' to an edge-weighted DAG, denoted by $\hat{G}_k$, with only $O(\Delta)$ vertices and $O(\Delta^2)$ edges. The vertice set of $\hat{G}_k$ contains a subset of $O(1)$ vertex layers in G_k', and each edge (u, v) of $\hat{G}_k$ is defined by the shortest path between the u and v in G_k'. (Note that although $\hat{G}_k$ is of a much smaller size than G_k', the weights of the edges of $\hat{G}_k$ are costly to compute. Thus, solving a *single* CCPP problem instance by transforming G_k' to $\hat{G}_k$ will not lead to a faster CCPP algorithm.)

Our algorithm has two main steps:

(1) Prepare the weights of all edges in $\hat{G}_1, \hat{G}_2, \ldots$, and $\hat{G}_N$. By exploiting the properties of the graph transformation, we implicitly compute and store the weights of all the $O(n^4\Delta^2)$ edges in a batch fashion, in totally $O(n^2H\Delta^2)$ time, such that for any edge, its weight can be obtained in $O(1)$ time.

(2) Compute a shortest path in each of $\hat{G}_1, \hat{G}_2, \ldots, \hat{G}_N$. We show that each $\hat{G}_k$ $(1 \leq k \leq N)$ is a DAG satisfying the Monge property [1,2,4]. Since the weight of any edge can be obtained in $O(1)$ time, a shortest path in $\hat{G}_k$ takes only $O(\Delta)$ time to compute.

Our algorithm thus takes $O(n^2 H \Delta^2 + n^4 \Delta)$ time, improving the straightforward $O(n^5 H \Delta)$ time algorithm (i.e., by applying the CCPP algorithm $N = O(n^4)$ times) by a factor of $\min\{nH, \frac{n^3}{\Delta}\}$.

5 IMRT Applications

We implemented our CPP algorithms using the C programming language and developed new leaf sequencing softwares for common dynamic IMRT delivery and the new arc modulated radiation therapy (AMRT) [29]. Due to the space limit, we only present the application in AMRT.

AMRT is a new dynamic IMRT delivery technique, which we have been developing jointly with Univ. of Maryland School of Medicine. In an AMRT delivery, the beam source rotates along an arc path in 3-D, and for every θ degrees (usually $\theta = 10$), a prescribed IM is delivered to the target volume. A key problem to AMRT delivery, called *AMRT leaf sequencing*, is to optimally convert a given set of K IMs into MLC leaf trajectories. We model the AMRT leaf sequencing problem as a shortest path problem on a layered DAG $\tilde{G}$, constructed as follows. The vertices of the i-th (vertical) layer $\tilde{L}_i$ $(i = 1, 2, \ldots, K+1)$ of $\tilde{G}$ correspond to all possible leaf pair positions when the beam source is at angle $(i-1)\theta$ (assume that the source starts at angle 0). For any two vertices in adjacent layers, put a left-to-right directed edge, and let its weight be the minimum delivery error of the corresponding CCPP instance (with the head and tail of the edge specifying the starting and ending leaf positions, respectively). Also, add to $\tilde{G}$ two dummy vertices s and t, and put 0-weight edges from s to $\tilde{L}_1$ and from $\tilde{L}_{K+1}$ to t. Then computing the weights of all edges in $\tilde{G}$ is essentially computing K sets of all CCPP problem instances.

We developed an AMRT treatment planning software based on our CPP algorithm in Sect. 4, and tested the software using 18 clinical cancer cases with a wide range of treatment sites. All the tests were done on a Lenovo Thinkpad T61 laptop with a 2GHz Intel Core 2 Duo processor and 2GB of memory running Windows XP. On average, the AMRT leaf sequencing can be computed in 5 to 10 minutes using our CPP algorithm. We compared the CPP-based AMRT plans with AMRT plans based on the back-and-forth sliding-window (BFSW) method [8] and with the traditional IMRT plans produced by the commercial Pinnacle treatment planning system.

Comparisons between our CPP-based AMRT plans and the BFSW-based AMRT plans show that our CPP-based plans have similar tumor coverage but significantly better healthy structure sparing. For five prostate cases tested, the amount of undesired dose delivered to the three nearby healthy structures, bladder, rectum, and hips, is reduced on average by 25%, 40%, and 50%, respectively.

This is because using our CPP-based algorithm, we are able to reduce the delivery time by $40\% - 50\%$ through its tradeoff feature. The reduced delivery time in turn reduces the radiation leakage, resulting in significantly better quality plans.

Comparisons between our CPP-based AMRT plans and IMRT plans produced by the commercial Pinnacle planning system show that the two types of plans have comparable tumor coverage and healthy structure sparing. However, our CPP-based AMRT plans take much shorter delivery time: Delivering CPP-based AMRT plans on average takes 2 minutes for a prostate case and 4 minutes for a head-and-neck case, which are 3 to 5 times faster than the delivery of traditional IMRT plans.

References

1. Aggarwal, A., Klawe, M.M., Moran, S., Shor, P., Wilber, R.: Geometric Applications of a Matrix-Searching Algorithm. Algorithmica 2, 195–208 (1987)
2. Aggarwal, A., Park, J.: Notes on Searching in Multidimensional Monotone Arrays. In: Proc. 29th Annual IEEE Symp. on Foundations of Computer Science, pp. 497–512 (1988)
3. Ahuja, R.K., Hamacher, H.W.: A Network Flow Algorithm to Minimize Beam-on Time for Unconstrained Multileaf Collimator Problems in Cancer Radiation Therapy. Networks 45, 36–41 (2005)
4. Apostolico, A., Atallah, M.J., Larmore, L., McFaddin, H.S.: Efficient Parallel Algorithms for String Editing and Related Problems. SIAM J. Comput. 19, 968–988 (1990)
5. Baatar, D., Ehrgott, M., Hamacher, H.W., Woeginger, G.J.: Decomposition of Integer Matrices and Multileaf Collimator Sequencing. Discrete Applied Mathematics 152, 6–34 (2005)
6. Boland, N., Hamacher, H.W., Lenzen, F.: Minimizing Beam-on Time in Cancer Radiation Treatment Using Multileaf Collimators. Networks 43(4), 226–240 (2004)
7. Bortfeld, T.R., Kahler, D.L., Waldron, T.J., Boyer, A.L.: X-ray Field Compensation with Multileaf Collimators. Int. J. Radiat. Oncol. Biol. Phys. 28, 723–730 (1994)
8. Cameron, C.: Sweeping-Window Arc Therapy: An Implementation of Rotational IMRT with Automatic Beam-Weight Calculation. Phys. Med. Biol. 50(18), 4317–4336 (2005)
9. Chen, D.Z., Hu, X.S., Luan, S., Misiolek, E., Wang, C.: Shape Rectangularization Problems in Intensity-Modulated Radiation Therapy. In: Proc. 12th Annual Int. Symp. on Algorithms and Computation, pp. 701–711 (2006)
10. Chen, D.Z., Hu, X.S., Luan, S., Naqvi, S.A., Wang, C., Yu, C.X.: Generalized Geometric Approaches for Leaf Sequencing Problems in Radiation Therapy. International Journal of Computational Geometry and Applications 16(2-3), 175–204 (2006)
11. Chen, D.Z., Hu, X.S., Luan, S., Wang, C., Wu, X.: Geometric Algorithms for Static Leaf Sequencing Problems in Radiation Therapy. In: Proc. of 19th ACM Symposium on Computational Geometry, pp. 88–97 (2003)
12. Chen, D.Z., Hu, X.S., Luan, S., Wang, C., Wu, X.: Mountain Reduction, Block Matching, and Applications in Intensity-Modulated Radiation Therapy. In: Proc. of 21th ACM Symposium on Computational Geometry, pp. 35–44 (2005)

13. Chen, D.Z., Hu, X.S., Luan, S., Wu, X., Yu, C.X.: Optimal Terrain Construction Problems and Applications in Intensity-Modulated Radiation Therapy. Algorithmica 42, 265–288 (2005)
14. Convery, D.J., Rosenbloom, M.E.: The Generation of Intensity Modulated Fields for Conformal Radiotherapy by Dynamic Collimation. Phys. Med. Biol. 37, 1359–1374 (1992)
15. Engel, K.: A New Algorithm for Optimal Multileaf Collimator Field Segmentation. Discrete Applied Mathematics 152(1-3), 35–51 (2005)
16. Evans, P.M., Hansen, V.N., Swindell, W.: The Optimum Intensities for Multiple Static Collimator Field Compensation. Med. Phys. 24(7), 1147–1156 (1997)
17. Kallman, P., Lind, B., Brahme, A.: Shaping of Arbitrary Dose Distribution by Dynamic Multileaf Collimation. Phys. Med. Biol. 33, 1291–1300 (1988)
18. Kamath, S., Sahni, S., Palta, J., Ranka, S.: Algorithms for Optimal Sequencing of Dynamic Multileaf Collimators. Phys. Med. Biol. 49(1), 33–54 (2004)
19. Luan, S., Wang, C., Cao, D., Chen, D.Z., Shepard, D.M., Yu, C.X.: Leaf-Sequencing for Intensity-Modulated Arc Therapy Using Graph Algorithms. Medical Physics 35(1), 61–69 (2008)
20. Luan, S., Wang, C., Chen, D.Z., Hu, X.S., Naqvi, S.A., Wu, X., Yu, C.X.: An Improved MLC Segmentation Algorithm and Software for Step-and-Shoot IMRT Delivery without Tongue-and-Groove Error. Med. Phys. 33(5), 1199–1212 (2006)
21. Luan, S., Wang, C., Chen, D.Z., Hu, X.S., Naqvi, S.A., Yu, C.X., Lee, C.L.: A New MLC Segmentation Algorithm/Software for Step and Shoot IMRT. Med. Phys. 31(4), 695–707 (2004)
22. Ma, L., Boyer, A., Xing, L., Ma, C.M.: An Optimized Leaf-Setting Algorithm for Beam Intensity Modulation Using Dynamic Multileaf Collimators. Phys. Med. Biol. 43, 1629–1643 (2004)
23. Siochi, R.A.C.: Minimizing Static Intensity Modulation Delivery Time Using an Intensity Solid Paradigm. Int J. Radiation Oncology Biol. Phys. 43(3), 671–680 (1999)
24. Spirou, S.V., Chui, C.S.: Generation of Arbitrary Intensity Profiles by Dynamic Jaws or Multileaf Collimators. Med. Phys. 21, 1031–1041 (1994)
25. Stein, J., Bortfeld, T., Dorschel, B., Schlegel, W.: Dynamic X-ray Compensation for Conformal Radiotherapy by Means of Multileaf Collimations. Radiother. Oncol. 32, 163–173 (1994)
26. Webb, S.: The Physics of Three-Dimensional Radiation Therapy. Institute of Physics Publishing, Bristol (1993)
27. Webb, S.: The Physics of Conformal Radiotherapy — Advances in Technology. Institute of Physics Publishing, Bristol (1997)
28. Xia, P., Verhey, L.J.: MLC Leaf Sequencing Algorithm for Intensity Modulated Beams with Multiple Static Segments. Med. Phys. 25, 1424–1434 (1998)
29. Yu, C.X., Luan, S., Wang, C., Chen, D.Z., Earl, M.: Single-Arc Dose Painting: An Efficient Method of Precision Radiation Therapy. In: Provisional patent application, University of Maryland (2006)

A New Approach to Exact Crossing Minimization

Markus Chimani[1], Petra Mutzel[1], and Immanuel Bomze[2]

[1] Faculty of Computer Science, Dortmund University of Technology, Germany
{markus.chimani,petra.mutzel}@tu-dortmund.de
[2] Dep. of Statistics and Decision Support Systems, University of Vienna, Austria
immanuel.bomze@univie.ac.at

Abstract. The *crossing number* problem is to find the smallest number of edge crossings necessary when drawing a graph into the plane. Eventhough the problem is NP-hard, we are interested in practically efficient algorithms to solve the problem to provable optimality. In this paper, we present a novel integer linear programming (ILP) formulation for the crossing number problem. The former formulation [4] had to transform the crossing number polytope into a higher-dimensional polytope. The key idea of our approach is to directly consider the natural crossing number polytope and cut it with multiple linear-ordering polytopes. This leads to a more compact formulation, both in terms of variables and constraints.

We describe a Branch-and-Cut algorithm, together with a combinatorial column generation scheme, in order to solve the crossing number problem to provable optimality. Our experiments show that the new approach is more effective than the old one, even when considering a heavily improved version of the former formulation (also presented in this paper). For the first time, we are able to solve graphs with a crossing number of up to 37.

1 Introduction

A *drawing* of a graph $G = (V, E)$ in the plane is a one-to-one mapping of each vertex to a point in $\mathbb{R}^2$, and each edge to a curve between its two endpoints. The curve is not allowed to contain other vertices than its two endpoints. A *crossing* is a common point of two curves, other than their endpoints. We forbid common points of more than two curves, other than their endpoints. The *crossing number* $\mathrm{cr}(G)$ is the smallest number of crossings in any drawing of G. The NP-hard problem of finding $\mathrm{cr}(G)$ has been widely studied in the literature – see [20] for an extensive bibliography – both from the graph theoretic, as well as the algorithmic point of view.

Recently, Buchheim et al. [4] presented the first exact algorithm to solve this problem to provable optimality, based on an integer linear programming (ILP) formulation: The central idea in all these formulations is to have a variable $x_{\{e,f\}}$ for each pair of edges $e, f \in E$, which is 1 if these edges cross, and zero otherwise.

D. Halperin and K. Mehlhorn (Eds.): ESA 2008, LNCS 5193, pp. 284–296, 2008.

The convex hull of the feasible points of x form the *crossing number polytope* $\mathcal{P}_{cr}$. Unfortunately, there is no known way to describe $\mathcal{P}_{cr}$ directly, as already checking if a given solution $\bar{x}$ is feasible – known as the *Realizability* problem – is NP-complete [15,19]. If each edge is involved in only a single crossing, checking feasibility becomes simple: we can substitute each crossing by a *dummy vertex* of degree 4 and perform any planarity testing algorithm on the transformed graph. Hence the problem lies in edges e which are involved in multiple crossings, if we do not know the order of these crossings on e.

The formulation of [4] circumvents this problem by subdividing the graph such that each edge is replaced by a path of ℓ segments. Then, the formulation considers the *simple crossing number* instead, i.e., the smallest number of crossings in any drawing of G under the restriction that each edge-segment is involved in at most one crossing. Clearly, this solves the traditional crossing number problem on G if ℓ is large enough: since the optimal drawing of G might require all crossings to be on a single edge, we can select $\ell := \overline{cr}(G)$, some upper bound on the crossing number which may be obtained by a heuristic. Since $cr(G) = \mathcal{O}(|E|^2)$ and there are graphs with $cr(G) = \Omega(|E|^2)$, we obtain $\mathcal{O}(|E|^4)$ variables. We denote this formulation by SOCM, for *subdivision-based optimal crossing minimization*.

The enlarging of the input graph results in far too many variables to handle the problem efficiently, hence column generation schemes are proposed and compared in [8]: the therein presented *combinatorial column generation* – a scheme based on combinatorial and graph-theoretical arguments, rather than on algebraic concepts – offers a large improvement compared to traditional approaches based on reduced costs. Nonetheless, the approach, as presented in [8], was only suitable for relatively sparse graphs with roughly 70 nodes.

In this paper we present a competing ILP formulation based on *linear ordering* of crossings on any edge: we avoid the aforementioned graph expansion and require only $\mathcal{O}(|E|^3)$ instead of $\mathcal{O}(|E|^4)$ variables. We call this formulation OOCM, for *ordering-based optimal crossing minimization*. As the number of variables is still quite large, we furthermore present an efficient corresponding combinatorial column generation scheme.

From the polyhedral point of view, we can describe the situation as follows: checking the feasibility of a solution $\bar{x}$ is NP-complete and there is no known way to directly describe the feasible integer points of the polytope $\mathcal{P}_{cr}$. Hence, the SOCM formulation expands the input and considers the simpler polytope $\mathcal{P}_{scr}$ of the simple crossing number problem. In OOCM, we instead solve the problem directly in $\mathcal{P}_{cr}$, by cutting it with $O(|E|)$ many linear-ordering polytopes.

In the next section, we present the ILP formulation, while Section 3 describes the resulting Branch-and-Cut-and-Price algorithm and its sub-steps. In Section 4 we discuss extensions of OOCM for other types of crossing numbers and present recent improvements of SOCM which lead to improved performance compared to the results published in [4,8]. Finally, in Section 5 we compare the improved SOCM implementation to the novel OOCM implementation by way of experiment.

2   The OOCM ILP Formulation

It is a well-known fact that the crossing number of any graph is the sum of the crossing numbers of its biconnected components. Hence we can assume that the given graph G is at least 2-connected. Furthermore, we can confine ourselves to *simple* graphs, i.e., graphs without multi-edges or self-loops. While loops are irrelevant for the crossing number, we can get rid of multi-edges by introducing integer edge weights c. The crossing number can be obtained by counting $c_e \cdot c_f$ crossings for a crossing between the edges e and f. The need for these weights is further strengthened by the *non-planar core reduction* [7]: this preprocessing scheme shrinks a given 2-connected graph further without changing its crossing number, but introduces integer edge weights. Hence we will consider (G, c) as our input.

2.1   Variables and Linear Ordering

First, we orient all edges of G arbitrarily. For notational simplicity we continue to refer to the resulting graph as $G = (V, E)$. Let $E^{\langle k \rangle} := \{(e_1, \ldots, e_k) \mid \forall 1 \leq i < j \leq k : e_i, e_j \in E \land e_i \neq e_j\}$ be the set of all ordered k-tuples of pairwise distinct edges. We model the order of the crossings directly via variables:

$$x_{\{e,f\}} \in \{0,1\} \quad \forall \{e,f\} \in \binom{E}{2}, \quad y_{e,f,g} \in \{0,1\} \quad \forall (e,f,g) \in E^{\langle 3 \rangle} \quad (1)$$

A variable $x_{\{e,f\}}$ specifies whether or not the edges e and f cross. A variable $y_{e,f,g}$ is 1 if and only if both edges f and g cross e, and the crossing (e, f) is nearer to e's source node than the crossing (e, g). We say e is the *base* of the variable. The objective function of our ILP is then:

$$\min \sum_{\{e,f\} \in \binom{E}{2}} c_e \cdot c_f \cdot x_{\{e,f\}}$$

It is known that certain crossing-variables can be fixed to 0 as, e.g., there will never be crossings between adjacent edges. Any sensible implementation will ignore such variables.

Linear-Ordering Constraints. We define the set of *linear-order* (LO) constraints which ensure a consistent linear ordering over all edges:

$$x_{\{e,f\}} \geq y_{e,f,g}, \quad x_{\{e,g\}} \geq y_{e,f,g} \qquad \forall (e,f,g) \in E^{\langle 3 \rangle} \quad (2)$$

$$1 + y_{e,f,g} + y_{e,g,f} \geq x_{\{e,f\}} + x_{\{e,g\}} \qquad \forall (e,f,g) \in E^{\langle 3 \rangle} \quad (3)$$

$$y_{e,f,g} + y_{e,g,f} \leq 1 \qquad \forall (e,f,g) \in E^{\langle 3 \rangle} \quad (4)$$

$$y_{e,f,g} + y_{e,g,h} + y_{e,h,f} \leq 2 \qquad \forall (e,f,g,h) \in E^{\langle 4 \rangle} \quad (5)$$

We introduce *crossing-existence* constraints (2) which connect the x and y variables by ensuring that the x-vector specifies a crossing if the y-variables do. Vice

versa, the *order-existence* constraints (3) ensure that if x specifies two crossings on the same edge, the y-vector has to specify their order. The *mirror-order*
constraints (4) guarantee that two crossings are uniquely ordered if they exist.
Analogously, the *cyclic-order* constraints (5) ensure that the ordering is acyclic.
A solution $(\bar{x}, \bar{y})$ which satisfies the LO-constraints is called *LO-feasible*. Since
no two edges will ever cross more than once in any optimal solution, we have:

Proposition 1. *Let $\bar{x}$ be any optimal solution to the crossing number problem
of any graph G. There exists an assignment $\bar{y}$ for the vector y such that $(\bar{x}, \bar{y})$ is
LO-feasible.*

Checking feasibility. Let $(\bar{x}, \bar{y})$ be any integer LO-feasible solution. We replace
each crossing in G by a dummy vertex. Since we know the intended order of
these dummy vertices on each edge from the information in $(\bar{x}, \bar{y})$, the resulting
graph is the *(partial) planarization* of G, which we denote by $G[\bar{x}, \bar{y}]$. We can
check feasibility of $(\bar{x}, \bar{y})$ by testing $G[\bar{x}, \bar{y}]$ for planarity.

2.2   Kuratowski Constraints and Correctness of Oocm

The final class of constraints required to fully describe the feasible points of our
ILP are the *Kuratowski-constraints*. They guarantee that a computed integer
LO-feasible solution $(\bar{x}, \bar{y})$ corresponds to a feasible planarization, i.e., $G[\bar{x}, \bar{y}]$
is planar: the well-known theorem by Kuratowski [16] states that a graph is
planar if and only if it contains no *Kuratowski-subdivision* as a subgraph. A
Kuratowski-subdivision results from subdividing the edges of a K_5 (complete
graph on 5 nodes) or $K_{3,3}$ (complete bipartite graph with 3 nodes per partition)
into paths of length at least 1, called *Kuratowski-paths*. The original nodes not
obtained by the subdivision of the edges are called *Kuratowski-nodes*.

For any Kuratowski-subdivision K, we require at least one crossing between
the edges of K. Such a subdivision might not be a subgraph of the original
graph G, but might occur only in a partial planarization $G[\bar{x}, \bar{y}]$ for some integer
LO-feasible solution $(\bar{x}, \bar{y})$.

For Socm we simply use the crossings in such a planarization to "turn off"
Kuratowski-constraints that are only valid if these crossings are selected [4]. The
drawback is that these constraints are specifically tied to certain crossings, say
between the edges e and f_1. This unavoidably leads to a multitude of very similar
constraints, where, e.g., f_1 is replaced by another edge f_2, but f_1 and f_2 were
created by the graph enlargement and correspond to the same original edge.

We cannot reuse such a simple approach straight-forwardly for Oocm. But
now the additional effort is compensated for by constraints which correspond
to a whole class of similar Kuratowski-constraints in Socm. Let $(\bar{x}, \bar{y})$ be an
integer LO-feasible solution, and let K be a Kuratowski-subdivision in $G[\bar{x}, \bar{y}]$.
We define $\mathcal{Z}_K[\bar{x}, \bar{y}]$ as the set of crossings induced by $(\bar{x}, \bar{y})$ whose dummy nodes
form integral parts of K: any $\{e, f\} \in \mathcal{Z}_K[\bar{x}, \bar{y}]$ either induces a Kuratowski-
node or there exist a segment e' of e, a segment f' of f, and a Kuratowski-path
which contains $\langle e', f' \rangle$ as a subpath. We can then define the *crossing shadow*
$(\mathcal{X}_K[\bar{x}, \bar{y}], \mathcal{Y}_K[\bar{x}, \bar{y}])$ as a pair of sets as follows:

$\mathcal{Y}_K[\bar{x}, \bar{y}] := \{(e, f, g) \in \mathrm{E}^{\langle 3 \rangle} \mid \{e, f\}, \{e, g\} \in \mathcal{Z}_K[\bar{x}, \bar{y}] \wedge \bar{y}_{e,f,g} = 1 \wedge \nexists \{e, h\} \in$
$\mathcal{Z}_K : \bar{y}_{e,f,h} = \bar{y}_{e,h,g} = 1\}$, i.e., a triple (e, f, g) is in $\mathcal{Y}_K[\bar{x}, \bar{y}]$, if no other edge
crosses e between f and g. Thus $\mathcal{Y}_K[\bar{x}, \bar{y}]$ contains a minimal description of
all crossings and their orderings in K, except for crossings of two edges, both
not involved in multiple crossings; these are collected in the following set:
$\mathcal{X}_K[\bar{x}, \bar{y}] := \{\{e, f\} \in \mathcal{Z}_K[\bar{x}, \bar{y}] \mid \forall g \in E : (e, f, g), (e, g, f), (f, e, g), (f, g, e)\} \cap$
$\mathcal{Y}_K[\bar{x}, \bar{y}] = \emptyset\}$, i.e., all *singular crossings* in K not contained in $\mathcal{Y}_K[\bar{x}, \bar{y}]$.

Proposition 2. *For each integer LO-feasible solution $(\bar{x}, \bar{y})$ and each Kuratowski-subdivision K in $G[\bar{x}, \bar{y}]$ we have: the partial planarization of G only realizing the crossings (and their order) as defined by the crossing shadow, contains K as a Kuratowski-subdivision.*

Using this crossing shadow, we can define Kuratowski-constraints as

$$\sum_{\{e,f\} \in \mathrm{CrPairs}(K)} x_{\{e,f\}} \geq 1 - \sum_{a \in \mathcal{X}_K[\bar{x}, \bar{y}]} (1 - x_a) - \sum_{b \in \mathcal{Y}_K[\bar{x}, \bar{y}]} (1 - y_b) \qquad (6)$$

for all LO-feasible integer vectors $(\bar{x}, \bar{y})$ and all Kuratowski-subdivisions K in $G[\bar{x}, \bar{y}]$. Here and in the sequel, $\mathrm{CrPairs}(K)$ denotes all pairs of edges belonging to different paths p_1, p_2 in K which may cross in order to planarize K (i.e., the edges corresponding to p_1 and p_2 in the underlying K_5 or $K_{3,3}$ are non-adjacent). Our constraints require at least one crossing on every Kuratowski-subdivision if it exists; this existence is detected via the crossing shadow.

Lemma 1. *Each optimal solution to the crossing number problem of any graph G corresponds to a feasible integer solution vector.*

Proof. Clearly, any solution to the crossing number problem can be described by an integer LO-feasible solution $(\bar{x}, \bar{y})$ by construction, see Proposition 1. We show that this vector does not violate any constraint (6). Assume there is some $(\bar{x}, \bar{y})$ and K which induces a violated Kuratowski constraint. Then

$$\sum_{\{e,f\} \in \mathrm{CrPairs}(K)} x_{\{e,f\}} < 1 - \sum_{a \in \mathcal{X}_K(\bar{x}, \bar{y})} (1 - x_a) - \sum_{b \in \mathcal{Y}_K[\bar{x}, \bar{y}]} (1 - y_b)$$

Since we only consider integer solutions, the left-hand side is 0 while the right-hand side is 1. We thus have:

$$\forall \{e, f\} \in \mathrm{CrPairs}(K) : x_{\{e,f\}} = 0 \text{ , and} \qquad (7)$$

$$\forall a \in \mathcal{X}_K[\bar{x}, \bar{y}] : x_a = 1 \ \wedge \ \forall b \in \mathcal{Y}_K(\bar{x}, \bar{y}) : y_b = 1 .$$

But then, due to Proposition 2, the crossing shadow of $(\bar{x}, \bar{y})$ w.r.t. K specifies exactly the crossings which induce a graph $\bar{G}$ that contains K as a Kuratowski-subdivision. Due to (7) we know that there are no further crossings on K which would lead to a planarization of this non-planar subgraph. This is a contradiction to the feasibility of the original solution. $\square$

Lemma 2. *Every feasible solution to the ILP*

$$\min\left\{\sum_{\{e,f\}\in\binom{E}{2}} c_e c_f x_{\{e,f\}} \text{ subject to } (2),(3),(4),(5) \text{ and all } (6)\right\}$$

corresponds to a feasible solution of the crossing number problem.

Proof. We can interpret any integer LO-feasible solution $(\bar{x},\bar{y})$ as a (partial) planarization $\bar{G} := G[\bar{x},\bar{y}]$. Assume the solution vector satisfies all Kuratowski constraints, but $\bar{G}$ is non-planar. Then there exists a Kuratowski-subdivision in $\bar{G}$. Let K be such a subdivision with the smallest number of contained dummy nodes. We construct a crossing shadow $(\mathcal{X}_K[\bar{x},\bar{y}], \mathcal{Y}_K[\bar{x},\bar{y}])$ which describes the precise crossing configuration necessary to identify K. Since K is a non-planar (minimal) Kuratowski-subdivision, we know that there are no crossings on any pair of CrPairs(K). But then, (6) is violated for K and $(\mathcal{X}_K[\bar{x},\bar{y}], \mathcal{Y}_K(\bar{x},\bar{y}))$, as the left-hand side sums up to 0 and the right-hand side is 1. □

We therefore obtain:

Theorem 1. *Every optimal solution of the above ILP yields an optimal solution of the crossing number problem.*

3   Branch-and-Cut-and-Price Algorithm

The presented ILP

$$\min\left\{\sum_{\{e,f\}\in\binom{E}{2}} c_e c_f x_{\{e,f\}} \text{ subject to } (2),(3),(4),(5) \text{ and all } (6)\right\}$$

can be solved by a Branch-and-Cut framework: we start the computation with a subset of the above constraints and solve the LP-relaxations, i.e., we ignore the integer properties of the variables. Based on the thereby obtained fractional solution we start a *separation* routine to identify violated constraints not included in the current model. If we can find any, we add them to our model and iterate the process, computing the LP relaxation of this, now larger, model. If we cannot identify any more violated constraints but the solution is still not integer feasible, we have to resort to branching: we generate two subproblems, e.g., by fixing a variable to 0 and 1, respectively. Using the LP relaxations for lower bounds and some constructive heuristics for upper bounds, we can prune irrelevant subproblems.

Consider any optimal solution for any graph: at least half of the y-variables will be zero. Most graphs occurring in practice are far from being complete, and so actually most of the ILP variables will be zero in the optimal solution. Hence we augment the Branch-and-Cut framework with a column generation scheme, i.e., we start only with a subset of variables and assume that all other variables are zero. The task of the scheme is to detect which variables are necessary to add to the model, in order to guarantee overall optimality of the solution.

3.1   Upper Bounds and Integer Interpretation

To obtain upper bounds for our problem, we use the efficient planarization heuristic described in [11,12]. As the experiments in [8] showed, this heuristic is very good in practice, often finding the optimal solution. Before the actual ILP computation is started, we use the heuristic to obtain a first upper bound.

During the computation, we compute LO-feasible *integer interpretations* $(\tilde{x}, \tilde{y})$ of the current fractional solution $(\bar{x}, \bar{y})$. We can then construct $G[\tilde{x}, \tilde{y}]$ and solve the crossing number problem heuristically on this partial planarization. The union of the crossings in $(\tilde{x}, \tilde{y})$ and the heuristic solution on $G[\tilde{x}, \tilde{y}]$ then constitutes a heuristic solution for G.

Since we require the integer solution $(\tilde{x}, \tilde{y})$ to be LO-feasible in order to construct the planarization $G[\tilde{x}, \tilde{y}]$, we cannot use a simple rounding scheme on the y-variables. Our integer interpretation works as follows:

$\tilde{x}$-**variables:** We apply a traditional rounding scheme to $\bar{x}$. The variable $\tilde{x}_{\{e,f\}}$ is 1 iff $\bar{x}_{\{e,f\}} > \tau$. Here $\tau > 0.5$ is a fixed threshold value; in our experiments we used $\tau = 0.7$ and $\tau = 1 - \epsilon$ (for some very small $\epsilon > 0$) and compute two probably distinct planarizations for the subsequent steps.

$\tilde{y}$-**variables:** Based on $\tilde{x}$, we can then restrict the set of $\tilde{y}$-variables that may be 1. For each edge e, let $\mathcal{D}_e$ be the set of edges which cross e, according to $\tilde{x}$. We can set $\tilde{y}_{e,f,g} = 0$ for all variables with $\{f, g\} \not\subseteq \mathcal{D}_e$. If $|\mathcal{D}_e| \geq 2$, we define a complete bidirected weighted graph, using $\mathcal{D}_e$ as its vertex set. We choose the weight of an arc (f, g) as $\bar{y}_{e,f,g}$. Then we solve the linear ordering problem on this graph, using a straight-forward greedy heuristic [1]. Using this resulting order, we can decide the values for $\tilde{y}_{e,f,g}$, for all $\{f, g\} \subseteq \mathcal{D}_e$.

3.2   Initial Constraints and Separation

We start our ILP only with the 0/1 bounds on the x-variables. Initially, we do not need to add the LO-constraints (2),(3),(4), and (5) for the y-variables, as these variables do not enter the objective function, cf. Section 3.3. All required Kuratowski-constraints (6) will be added during our cutting step.

There is no known efficient method to identify violated Kuratowski-constraints in a fractional solution, hence we only separate heuristically. We re-use the integer interpretation of fractional solutions as described in the previous section, and run a linear planarity test on $G[\tilde{x}, \tilde{y}]$. State-of-the-art planarity testing algorithms can efficiently (i.e., in linear time) extract a Kuratowski-subdivision as a certificate for non-planarity. We use the method presented in [10], which is a significantly modified variant of the planarity testing algorithm of Boyer and Myrvold [3], to efficiently extract several such certificates in linear time. For each obtained Kuratowski-subdivision, we then can compute the corresponding crossing shadow and test whether the resulting Kuratowski-constraint is violated, adding it to the LP if necessary.

3.3 Combinatorial Column Generation

Our initial linear program only contains the x-variables. Note that only these variables enter the objective function: the values of the y-variables do not influence the solution value as they are only introduced to solve the ordering problems on the edges. Furthermore, we do not require y-variables if there is only a single crossing on all edges – then all y-variables are zero. Hence, conceptually, having some solution $\bar{x}$, we only require the y-variables with a base edge e, if there are multiple edges crossing over e. Since the separation routine does only use integer interpretations of the current solution, we only require the knowledge of the crossing order if $\sum_{f\in E\setminus\{e\}} \tilde{x}_{\{e,f\}} \geq 2$. Let F_e be the set of edges f with $\tilde{x}_{\{e,f\}} = 1$. The order of performing the variable generation prior to the separation routine is critical: we first obtain a fractional solution and check if the solution can be uniquely interpreted as a partial planarization, i.e., if all the variables $y_{e,f,g}$, with $\{f, g\} \subseteq F_e$, are contained in the current LP model. If there is at least one such y-variable missing in the current LP model, we add all required such variables, together with their corresponding LO-constraints, and resolve our LP model.

Hence, the variable generation takes place before we interpret a fractional solution as a partial planarization for the separation routine, and before the bounding heuristic. Therefore, for these steps we guarantee that all necessary y-variables are in the model, and the solution is LO-feasible.

3.4 Branching on K_5-Constraints

We can use Kleitman's parity argument for complete graphs with an odd number of vertices [13,14]: if a K_{2n+3}, $n \in \mathbb{N}^+$, has an even or odd crossing number, every possible drawing of K_{2n+3} will also have an even or odd number of crossings, respectively. Since we know that $\mathrm{cr}(K_5) = 1$, we have for every K_5-subdivision that if it is drawn with more than one crossing, it will require at least 3 crossings.

This jump in the crossing number can be used for branching. Most commonly, we would select a variable z and generate two subproblems with $z = 0$ and $z = 1$. Before we resort to this kind of branching, we check for any K_5-constraint of the type $p^T x + q^T y \geq 1$, with p and q being the coefficient vectors. We can then generate two subproblems, one with $p^T x + q^T y = 1$ and one with $p^T x + q^T y \geq 3$. Note that, theoretically, we can continue to branch on the latter constraint, generating $p^T x + q^T y = 3$ and $p^T x + q^T y \geq 5$, etc.

4 Further Remarks

Extending OOCM. The SOCM ILP was extended, e.g., to compute the bimodal crossing number [5], the minor-monotone and hypergraph crossing numbers [6], and the simultaneous crossing number [9]. The extensions for the first three problems can straight-forwardly be formulated within OOCM.

By contrast, extensions for the simultaneous crossing number, as well as potential extensions for the pairwise and the odd crossing number [18] are not straight-forward: they require that some edges cross multiple times, maybe even an exponential number of times. This states no problem for SOCM, as we can, theoretically, subdivide the edges into long enough paths and drop the one-crossing-per-edge-pair constraint. Anyhow, we cannot model such multiple crossings with the variables of OOCM.

Improvements to SOCM. The SOCM implementation of our experiments received improvements compared to the algorithm presented in [4,8]. Hence, the results are far better than previously reported. We denote the improved version of SOCM by iSOCM. The modifications include:
– The crossing minimization heuristic (used by both iSOCM and OOCM) improved, due to a more time-consuming but stronger post-processing scheme: in [11], the strongest post-processing was to remove and reinsert every edge, after obtaining a first full solution. The current implementation in OGDF [17] can remove and reinsert all edges after each single edge-insertion step.
– The branching on K_5-constraints, cf. Section 3.4, is also possible in iSOCM.
– The column generation scheme is now fine-tuned: originally, we introduced a new segment of the original edge e whenever the sum of crossings over the first segment of e is larger than 1 in the fractional solution. Now, we add this segment only if the sum is larger than 1 in the rounded solution that is used for the separation. This idea is then similar to the generation criterion in OOCM.
– As OOCM, iSOCM also uses the new extraction algorithm which finds multiple Kuratowski-subdivisions in linear time [10].

5   Experiments

The following experiments were conducted on an AMD Opteron 2.4 GHz with 2GB of RAM per process. SOCM, iSOCM, and OOCM are implemented in the open-source library OGDF [17], using ABACUS as a B&C framework and CPLEX 9.0 as LP solver. We applied a time limit of 30 minutes for each instance. The machine and the overall experimental setting is thus identical to the experiments reported in [4,8], which yielded the currently best known published results.

To compare the performance of both formulations, we chose the well-known *Rome* benchmark set [2], which is commonly used to assess algorithms for the crossing number and other graph drawing problems, e.g. [4,8,11]. It consists of over 11,500 real-world graphs emerging from software-engineering applications, with between 10 and 100 nodes. We use the non-planar core reduction [7] as a preprocessing step. We say graphs are *trivial*, if they are planar or if the heuristic achieves a planarization with only one crossing, as in these cases we need not prove optimality. The Rome library contains 7172 non-trivial graphs.

As we see in Figure 1, both new algorithms clearly outperform the old SOCM algorithm, which drops below a success-ratio of 50% for graphs with 70 nodes. While OOCM solves virtually all graphs with up to 60 nodes to provable optimality within the time limit, the formerly best algorithm already drops to a 70% success-ratio for graphs of size 60. The experiments also show that the new ILP formulation OOCM is able to solve more and larger graphs than iSOCM: while

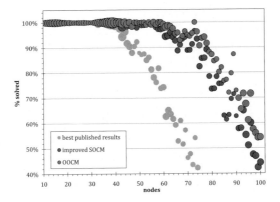

Fig. 1. Percentage of graphs solved to provable optimality within 30 minutes. The size of the circles denotes the number of instances per graph size. Therefore, larger circles correspond to statistically more reliable data points. The gray data points denote the previously best published results in [8] and the journal version of [4].

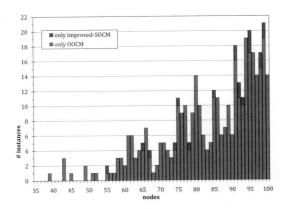

Fig. 2. The number of instances only solved by one of the approaches, but not by both

iSOCM only solves 84.4% of all non-trivial graphs within 30 minutes, OOCM finds and proves an optimal solution in 89.2% of all these instances, i.e., 93.3% over all benchmark instances. Even when OOCM has a time limit of only 10 and 5 minutes per non-trivial instance, it still solves 85.9% and 83.4%, respectively, and thus produces results comparable to 30 minutes of iSOCM computation in a 3–6x shorter period of time.

Note that there are only 19 instances solved by iSOCM but not by OOCM, within 30 minutes, but 361 instances which OOCM solved but iSOCM did not, cf. Figure 2. Most importantly, we can now solve over 50% of the largest graphs of the Rome library. Figure 3 further illustrates the strength of OOCM; it shows the average running times for graphs solved by both approaches; even for large graphs OOCM only requires roughly 100 seconds on average.

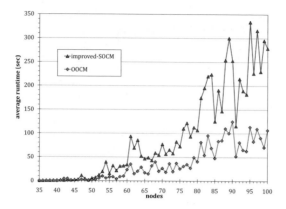

Fig. 3. The required running time, averaged over the instances solved by both OOCM and SOCM

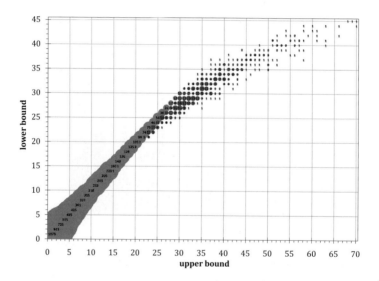

Fig. 4. The number of instances per combination of lower and upper bound after 30 minutes of OOCM, over all graphs of the Rome library. 9 instances are not shown as their lower or upper bounds do not fit into this diagram.

Figure 4 shows the dependency of the solvability on the crossing number: we see that OOCM solves all but 6 graphs with a crossing number of up to 20. It even solves a graph with a crossing number of 37. By contrast, iSOCM solves only all but 7 graphs with a crossing number of at most 12. Finally, Figure 5 shows a comparison of the number of required variables for the instances solved by both approaches: both algorithms start with the same initial variable set, but OOCM requires by far less additional variables during the computation of

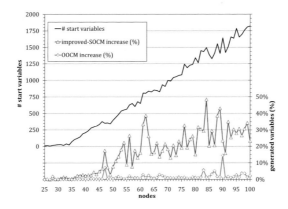

Fig. 5. The average factor by which the number of variables increases compared to the number of start variables, which is identical for OOCM and SOCM. The diagram also shows the average number of start variables per graph size.

the optimal solution. This seems to be the main reason why OOCM is faster and more efficient than SOCM and iSOCM.

References

1. Di Battista, G., Eades, P., Tamassia, R., Tollis, I.G.: Graph Drawing: algorithms for the visualization of graphs. Prentice-Hall, Englewood Cliffs (1999)
2. Di Battista, G., Garg, A., Liotta, G., Tamassia, R., Tassinari, E., Vargiu, F.: An experimental comparison of four graph drawing algorithms. Comput. Geom. Theory Appl. 7(5-6), 303–325 (1997)
3. Boyer, J.M., Myrvold, W.J.: On the cutting edge: Simplified $O(n)$ planarity by edge addition. Journal of Graph Algorithms an Applications 8(3), 241–273 (2004)
4. Buchheim, C., Chimani, M., Ebner, D., Gutwenger, C., Jünger, M., Klau, G.W., Mutzel, P., Weiskircher, R.: A branch-and-cut approach to the crossing number problem. Discrete Optimization 5, 373–388 (2008); (Memory of George B. Dantzig)
5. Buchheim, C., Jünger, M., Menze, A., Percan, M.: Bimodal crossing minimization. In: Chen, D.Z., Lee, D.T. (eds.) COCOON 2006. LNCS, vol. 4112, pp. 497–506. Springer, Heidelberg (2006)
6. Chimani, M., Gutwenger, C.: Algorithms for the hypergraph and the minor crossing number problems. In: Tokuyama, T. (ed.) ISAAC 2007. LNCS, vol. 4835, pp. 184–195. Springer, Heidelberg (2007)
7. Chimani, M., Gutwenger, C.: Non-planar core reduction of graphs. In: Healy, P., Nikolov, N.S. (eds.) GD 2005. LNCS, vol. 3843, pp. 223–234. Springer, Heidelberg (2006)
8. Chimani, M., Gutwenger, C., Mutzel, P.: Experiments on exact crossing minimization using column generation. In: Àlvarez, C., Serna, M. (eds.) WEA 2006. LNCS, vol. 4007, pp. 303–315. Springer, Heidelberg (2006)
9. Chimani, M., Jünger, M., Schulz, M.: Crossing minimization meets simultaneous drawing. In: Proc. IEEE PacificVis 2008 (2008)

10. Chimani, M., Mutzel, P., Schmidt, J.M.: Efficient extraction of multiple kuratowski subdivisions. In: Hong, S.-H., Nishizeki, T., Quan, W. (eds.) GD 2007. LNCS, vol. 4875, pp. 159–170. Springer, Heidelberg (2008)
11. Gutwenger, C., Mutzel, P.: An experimental study of crossing minimization heuristics. In: Liotta, G. (ed.) GD 2003. LNCS, vol. 2912, pp. 13–24. Springer, Heidelberg (2004)
12. Gutwenger, C., Mutzel, P., Weiskircher, R.: Inserting an edge into a planar graph. Algorithmica 41(4), 289–308 (2005)
13. Kleitman, D.J.: The crossing number of $K_{5,n}$. J. Comb. Theory 9, 315–323 (1970)
14. Kleitman, D.J.: A note on the parity of the number of crossings of a graph. J. Comb. Theory, Ser. B 21(1), 88–89 (1976)
15. Kratochvíl, J.: String graphs II: Recognizing string graphs is NP-hard. J. Combin. Theory Ser. B 52, 67–78 (1991)
16. Kuratowski, C.: Sur le problème des courbes gauches en topologie. Fund. Math. 15, 271–283 (1930)
17. OGDF – Open Graph Drawing Framework (2008), http://www.ogdf.net
18. Pach, J., Tóth, G.: Which crossing number is it anyway? J. Comb. Theory Ser. B 80(2), 225–246 (2000)
19. Schaefer, M., Sedgwick, E., Štefankovič, D.: Recognizing string graphs in NP. Journal of Computer and System Sciences 67(2), 365–380 (2003)
20. Vrt'o, I.: Crossing numbers of graphs: A bibliography (2007), ftp://ftp.ifi.savba.sk/pub/imrich/crobib.pdf

A Characterization of 2-Player Mechanisms for Scheduling[*]

George Christodoulou[1], Elias Koutsoupias[2], and Angelina Vidali[3]

[1] Max-Planck-Institut für Informatik, Saarbrücken, Germany
gchristo@mpi-inf.mpg.de
[2] Department of Informatics, University of Athens
elias@di.uoa.gr
[3] Department of Informatics, University of Athens
avidali@di.uoa.gr

Abstract. We study the mechanism design problem for scheduling unrelated machines and we completely characterize the decisive truthful mechanisms for two players when the domain contains both positive and negative values. We show that the class of truthful mechanisms is very limited: A decisive truthful mechanism partitions the tasks into groups so that tasks in each group are allocated independently of the other groups. Tasks in a group of size at least two are allocated by an affine minimizer and tasks in singleton groups by a task-independent mechanism. This characterization is about all truthful mechanisms, including those with unbounded approximation ratio.

A direct consequence of this approach is that the approximation ratio of mechanisms for two players is 2, even for two tasks. In fact, it follows that for two players, VCG is the unique algorithm with optimal approximation 2.

1 Introduction

Algorithmic mechanism design is an important area between computer science and economics. The two most fundamental problems in this area are the problem of scheduling unrelated machines [25] and the problem of combinatorial auctions [19,12,7]. Here we are dealing with the scheduling problem, but our main result which is the characterization of truthful mechanisms for two players extends naturally to the more general domain of combinatorial auctions. In the scheduling problem, there are n players (machines) and m tasks to be executed on these machines. Each task j needs time t_{ij} on machine i. We want to allocate the tasks to machines in a way that minimizes the makespan (the time required to finish all tasks). The problem is that the machines are selfish and will not reveal the true values (we assume that only machine i knows the true values t_{ij}).

A mechanism consists of two parts, the allocation algorithm and the payment functions, one for each player. Each player i declares its own execution times t_i.

---

[*] Supported in part by IST-15964 (AEOLUS) and the Greek GSRT.

D. Halperin and K. Mehlhorn (Eds.): ESA 2008, LNCS 5193, pp. 297–307, 2008.

The mechanism collects all the declarations t and allocates the tasks according to an allocation function $a : R^{n \times m} \to \{1, \ldots, n\}^m$ from the set of all execution times to the set of partitions of m tasks to n players. It is more convenient to denote an allocation using the characteristic variables: a_{ij} is an indicator variable for task j to be allocated to machine i. The mechanism also pays each player i a payment p_i. The payment depends on the declared values t and indirectly on the allocation. A mechanism is truthful, if every player has no incentive to lie. We are dealing here with the standard and more restricted notion of truthfulness, dominant truthfulness, in which a player has no incentive to lie for every value of the other players. It is well-known that in truthful mechanisms, the payment to player i depends on the values t_{-i} of the other players and on the allocation a_i of player i: $p_i = p_i(a_i, t_{-i})$.

The allocation of the mechanism to player i is given by the argmin expression $a_i = \text{argmin}_a \{a_i \cdot t_i - p_i(a_i, t_{-i})\}$. The allocations to players must be consistent, i.e., every task is allocated to exactly one machine. The question is what type of allocation algorithms and payment schemes satisfy this property.

There is a simple answer to this question: A mechanism is truthful if and only if it satisfies the *Monotonicity Property*: If a and a' are the allocations of the mechanism for inputs t and t' which differ only on the values of player i, then we must have $\sum_{j=1}^{m}(a_{ij} - a'_{ij})(t_{ij} - t'_{ij}) \leq 0$. One nice property of this characterization is that it does not involve the payments at all. Since we usually care about the allocation part of mechanisms, this property focuses exactly on the interesting part. Unfortunately, although this is a necessary and sufficient condition [26], it is not very useful because it is a local and indirect property. The best way to clarify this point is to consider the case of mechanism design in unrestricted domains. In such domains, the same monotonicity property characterizes the truthful mechanisms. However, there is a much more direct characterization due to Roberts [16]: The class of truthful mechanisms for the unrestricted domain is very limited and contains exactly the class of affine maximizers. An important open problem is to come up with a similar characterization for the scheduling problem and combinatorial auctions. This work resolves this question for 2 players.

For the scheduling problem, very few mechanisms are known to be truthful. The principal example is the VCG mechanism [27,11,15] (or second-price mechanism) and its generalization, the affine minimizers [19]. The VCG mechanism allocates each task independently to the machine with minimum value, and pays the machine the second minimum value. VCG can be generalized in two ways and retain its truthfulness. The first generalization is the task-independent mechanisms, which allocate each task independently of the rest. The second generalization is the affine minimizers, which multiply the value of each player by some constant, but more importantly, they alter the value of each allocation by a constant. It is this set of additive constants, one per allocation, which make this generalization different than the first generalization.

Both these generalizations are known to be truthful, but they make very poor algorithms. The reason is that they allocate each task independently, or almost independently. The question is whether there are other truthful mechanisms. The answer appears at first to be negative: For example, the mechanism that allocates all tasks to one player, the one with minimum sum of execution times, is truthful but it is neither affine minimizer nor task-independent. However, this negative answer is not satisfactory because some allocations are never used, no matter how high or low are the values of the players. (One of the undesired properties of these mechanisms is that they have unbounded approximation ratio.) In contrast, we usually require that mechanisms have a much stronger property: decisiveness. A mechanism is called *decisive* when a player can enforce an outcome (allocation), by declaring very high or very low values.

A natural question is to characterize the decisive truthful algorithms. Unfortunately, by restricting our interest to decisive algorithms, we leave out important truthful specimens because some affine minimizers are not decisive: in some cases, a task will not be allocated to a player even when he declares 0 value for the task. To circumvent this problem, we allow negative values and we characterize the decisive truthful mechanisms for the domain of real values (both positive and negative). These algorithms include the affine minimizers and the task-independent algorithms; furthermore, every such algorithm is also truthful (but not necessarily decisive) for the nonnegative domain. By allowing negative values, we obtain not only a clean characterization but a useful one too, because we can still use it to argue about the approximation ratio for nonnegative values.

In our presentation we deal a lot with payments and, since we are only interested in the difference of payments, we will use the following notation

$$f^i_{a:a'}(t_{-i}) = p_i(a'_i, t_{-i}) - p_i(a_i, t_{-i}).$$

For simplicity, we write $f_{a:a'}$ in place of $f^1_{a:a'}$. We also represent the allocations using only the allocation of player 1, since the allocation of player 2 can be inferred. For example, we write $f_{00:10}$ for the difference in payments of player 1 when he gets only task 1 and when he gets no task. There is an extra reason to define $f_{a:a'}$: at some point in our proof, we will use the inverse function $f^{-1}_{a:a'}$.

The main reason for using negative values in our characterization is that the values $f_{a:a'}$, being the differences of payments, can take negative values.

As we mentioned, the allocation of a mechanism can be expressed with argmin expressions, one for every player: $a_i = \text{argmin}_a\{a_i \cdot t_i - p_i(a_i, t_{-i})\}$. For two players and two tasks, we essentially seek the payments that satisfy the following equation, which expresses the fact that the allocations for the two players must be consistent (i.e. each task is allocated exactly once):

$$\text{argmin}\{t_{11} + t_{12} - p_1(11, t_2), t_{11} - p_1(10, t_2), t_{12} - p_1(01, t_2), -p_1(00, t_2)\} =$$
$$\text{argmin}\{-p_2(11, t_1), t_{22} - p_2(10, t_1), t_{21} - p_2(01, t_1), t_{21} + t_{22} - p_2(00, t_1)\}.$$

Therefore the problem of characterizing the argmin mechanisms for two players and two tasks boils down to the following simple question: Which payments p satisfy the above equation? This is precisely the problem that we are trying to solve here.

The following theorem provides the answer, which applies also to any number of tasks. But first we give a precise definition of the affine minimizers:

Definition 1 (Affine minimizers). *A mechanism is an affine minimizer if there are constants $\lambda_i > 0$ (one for each player i) and γ_a (one for each of the n^m allocations) such that the mechanism selects the allocation a which minimizes $\sum_i \lambda_i a_i t_i + \gamma_a$.*

We now state our main result:

Theorem 1. *For the scheduling problem with real values every decisive truthful mechanism for 2 players is a collection of, independent from each other, affine minimizers and task-independent mechanisms.*

By combining the theorem with the fact that non-decisive mechanisms have unbounded approximation ratio (see Section 5), one can show that even for 2 players and 2 tasks, the approximation ratio of every truthful mechanism is at least 2. In fact, we don't need the full power of our characterization for this result, but only Lemma 1 below.

2   Related Work

The scheduling problem on unrelated machines is one of the most fundamental problems in combinatorial optimization. Here we study its mechanism design version which was introduced by Nisan and Ronen in their paper [25] that initiated the algorithmic theory of Mechanism Design. They gave a truthful n-approximate (polynomial-time) algorithm (where n is the number of machines); they also showed that no mechanism (polynomial-time or not) can achieve approximation ratio better than 2 when there are at least three tasks. We strengthen this result by proving that it holds even for only two tasks.

The lower bound for deterministic mechanisms has been improved in [10] to 2.41 (this is the best-known lower bound for 3 machines) and [17] to 2.618 for $n \to \infty$ machines.

There is a lot of work on randomized truthful mechanisms for the scheduling problem [25,23,21], on fractional truthful mechanisms [9], on the discrete-domain case [20], and on the special case of related machines [24,4,2,1,18]. Much more work has been done in the context of combinatorial auctions (see for example [3,7,8,12,6,13] and the references within).

Our approach of aiming at a complete characterization of truthful mechanisms, regardless of approximation ratio, is analogous to Roberts [16] result for unrestricted domains, but also resembles the approach in [19,5], and it was influenced by the limitations of the current methods in establishing lower bounds [25,10,17].

Saks and Yu [26] proved that the monotonicity property is necessary and sufficient for truthful mechanisms of convex domains, which applies to the scheduling problem. Monderer [22] shows that the domain cannot be further generalized in the case of quasi-linear utility functions.

A very recent paper [14] by Dobzinski and Sundararajan is very close in spirit to this work. Dobzinski and Sundararajan restrict their attention to mechanisms with bounded approximation ratio. They show that the truthful mechanisms with bounded approximation ratio are task-independent. In contrast, our work provides a more complete characterization of all mechanisms including those with unbounded approximation ratio.

3   The Characterization of Decisive Mechanisms for 2 Tasks

Our main result is based on the following theorem which applies to 2 players and 2 tasks and which is the subject of this section.

Theorem 2. *For the scheduling problem with real values the decisive truthful mechanisms for 2 players and 2 tasks are either task-independent or affine minimizers.*

We proceed in our proof carefully, revealing gradually the properties of $f_{a:a'}$. We assume here that the payments take real (positive or negative) values, so that $f_{a:a'}$ is also a real function. An indispensable part of the proof is the following lemma.

Lemma 1. *For allocations a and a' that differ in only one task, the quantity $f_{a:a'}(t_2)$ depends only on $(a - a') \cdot t_2$ (and therefore it depends on only one variable).*

Proof. This lemma holds for every number of tasks. We will first prove the lemma for $m = 2$ tasks. We will focus on the case of $a = 00$ and $a' = 10$ since the other cases are very similar.

We will show by contradiction that $f_{00:10}(t_{21}, t_{22})$ does not depend on t_{22}. Suppose that there are t_{21}, t_{22}, and t'_{22} with $t_{22} \neq t_{22'}$ with $f_{00:10}(t_{21}, t_{22}) < f_{00:10}(t_{21}, t'_{22})$.

From the definition of $f_{00:10}(t_{21}, t_{22})$, the tasks of the form

$$\begin{pmatrix} f_{00:10}(t_{21}, t_{22}) + \epsilon & \infty \\ t_{21} \star & t_{22} \star \end{pmatrix}$$

have the indicated allocation for every $\epsilon > 0$, *where $infty$ indicates an arbitrarily high value* which guarantees that the second task will not be allocated to player 1 (i.e., ∞ is greater than $\max\{f_{00:01}(t_2), f_{00:11}(t_2)\}$).

Similarly, the tasks of the form

$$\begin{pmatrix} f_{00:10}(t_{21}, t'_{22}) - \epsilon \star & \infty \\ t_{21} & t'_{22} \star \end{pmatrix}$$

have the indicated allocation for every $\epsilon > 0$. As we mentioned before, ∞ denotes an arbitrarily high value. We assume of course that the two occurrences of this symbol above denote the same value.

By the Monotonicity Property, if we decrease the values of t_{22} to t'_{22} to $\min\{t_{22}, t'_{22}\}$, the allocations remain the same.

This leads to a contradiction when $\epsilon = (f_{00:10}(t_{21}, t'_{22}) - f_{00:01}(t_{21}, t_{22}))/2$, because the task

$$\left(\begin{matrix} \frac{f_{00:10}(t_{21}, t_{22}) + f_{00:10}(t_{21}, t'_{22})}{2} & \infty \\ t_{21} & \min\{t_{22}, t'_{22}\} \star \end{matrix} \right)$$

would have two allocations.

The proof can be extended to the case of $m > 2$ tasks: We reduce it to the $m = 2$ case by fixing all tasks except of two. For example, for every $t_2 = (t_{21}, t_{22}, t_{23})$ and $t'_2 = (t_{21}, t'_{22}, t'_{23})$ we have: $f_{000:100}(t_{21}, t_{22}, t_{23}) = f_{000:100}(t_{21}, t'_{22}, t_{23}) = f_{000:100}(t_{21}, t'_{22}, t'_{23})$.

Corollary 1. *The quantities $c_1 = f_{01:11}(t_2) - f_{00:10}(t_2)$ and $c_2 = f^2_{10:00}(t_2) - f^2_{11:01}(t_2)$ do not depend on t_2.*

We can now define the regions of truthful mechanisms. For fixed t_2, let R_{11} denote the set of values t_1 for which the mechanism allocates both tasks to player 1. Region R_{11} which is defined by the following constraints:

$$t_{11} < f_{10:11}(t_{21})$$
$$t_{12} < f_{01:11}(t_{22})$$
$$t_{11} + t_{12} < f_{01:11}(t_{21}) + f_{00:01}(t_{22}).$$

There are similar constraints that define the other regions R_{00}, R_{10}, and R_{01}. What happens at the boundaries, where the inequality becomes an equality is not determined by the Monotonicity Property. These undetermined values are a major source of difficulty in the characterization of the mechanisms.

From the above inequalities we get that the boundary between regions R_{00} and R_{11}, if it exists, is of the form $t_{11} + t_{12} = f_{01:11}(t_{21}) + f_{00:10}(t_{22})$. Since a similar constraint holds for player 2 (in which the sum $t_{21} + t_{22}$ appears), one could be tempted to conclude that the boundary between allocations 00 and 11 is of the form $t_{11} + t_{12} = h(t_{21} + t_{22})$ for some function h. *Although this conclusion is exactly the one that we will eventually reach, the above argument is not rigorous.*

To proceed to the characterization of mechanisms, we need to understand the functions $f_{00:10}$ and $f_{00:01}$. To this end, we prove a series of lemmas (the proofs which are similar in spirit to the proof of Lemma 1 are omitted from this extended abstract).

Lemma 2. *The functions $f_{01:11}$ and $f_{00:01}$ are nondecreasing.*

For most reasonable mechanisms, a stronger statement seems to apply for these two functions: that they are strictly increasing. This however is not generally true. But we can show that the functions $f_{01:11}$ and $f_{00:01}$ are indeed strictly increasing when $c_1 \neq 0$. In fact, we show in the next lemma that either the functions are strictly increasing or they are like the following mechanism, which is not a decisive mechanism.

Example 1 (Mechanism with some oblivious player). Consider the mechanism with $f_{00:10}(t_{21}) = b_1$, $f_{00:01}(t_{22}) = b_2$ where b_1, b_2, and c_1 are constants. In this mechanism the first player decides independently of the values of the second player. For given values t_1 of the first player, the second player has the same allocation for every t_2. This mechanism is not decisive, since the second player cannot force all allocations.

Lemma 3. *In a truthful mechanism with $c_1 \neq 0$ the functions $f_{01:11}$ and $f_{00:01}$ are either both strictly increasing or both constant. (The same holds for the pair $f_{00:10}$ and $f_{10:11}$.)*

The above lemma establishes that the mechanisms with $c_1 \neq 0$ are either one of the mechanisms of the Example 1 or both functions $f_{01:11}$ and $f_{00:01}$ are strictly increasing. As we consider decisive mechanisms, from now on we will consider only strictly increasing functions.

Lemma 4. *If $c_2 \neq 0$ then the functions $f_{01:11}$ and $f_{00:01}$ are bijections from $\mathbb{R}$ to $\mathbb{R}$.*

The assumption $c_2 \neq 0$ is essential in the above lemma. When $c_2 = 0$, there are mechanisms in which $f_{00:10}$ and $f_{00:01}$ are not bijections.

Lemma 5. *The constants c_1 and c_2 are either both positive, both negative, or both 0.*

Lemma 6. *For $c_1 \neq 0$, the functions $f_{00:10}$ and $f_{00:01}$ are semiperiodic and in particular they satisfy $f_{00:10}(t_{21} + c_2) = f_{00:10}(t_{21}) + c_1$ and $f_{00:01}(t_{22} + c_2) = f_{00:01}(t_{22}) + c_1$.*

We will focus on the case of $c_1 > 0$ as the case $c_1 < 0$ is very similar. Consider the diagonal boundary between the regions R_{11} and R_{00}. This boundary is on the line $t_{11} + t_{12} = f_{01:11}(t_{21}) + f_{00:01}(t_{22})$. We have $f_{00:11}(t_{21}, t_{22}) = f_{01:11}(t_{21}) + f_{00:01}(t_{22})$. The heart of the characterization is that the function $f_{00:11}(t_{21}, t_{22})$ depends only on the sum of $t_{21} + t_{22}$.

Lemma 7. *The function $f_{00:11}(t_{21}, t_{22}) = f_{01:11}(t_{21}) + f_{00:01}(t_{22})$ depends only on $t_{21} + t_{22}$, i. e., there is some function h such that $f_{00:11}(t_{21}, t_{22}) = h(t_{21} + t_{22})$.*

Proof. Suppose not. That is suppose that there are t_2 and t_2' such that $t_{21} + t_{22} = t_{21}' + t_{22}'$ and yet $f_{00:11}(t_{21}, t_{22}) < f_{00:11}(t_{21}', t_{22}')$. If the values differ, they have to differ for some t_{21} and t_{21}' that are very close.

Without loss of generality then we assume that $t_{21} < t_{21}' < t_{21} + c_2$. This implies that $t_{22}' < t_{22} < t_{22'} + c_2$ and therefore

$$f_{00:01}(t_{22}) < f_{00:01}(t_{22}' + c_2) = f_{00:01}(t_{22}') + c_1.$$

Let ϵ be a positive parameter with $\epsilon < f_{00:11}(t_{21}', t_{22}') - f_{00:11}(t_{21}, t_{22})$ and $\epsilon < f_{01:11}(t_{22}') - f_{00:01}(t_{22})$. By the above inequalities, ϵ belongs to an open interval and more specifically it can take at least two distinct values. Consider then the values

$$t_{11} = f_{01:11}(t_{21}) \qquad\qquad t_{12} = f_{00:01}(t_{22}) + \epsilon$$

We can easily verify that the following inputs satisfy the boundary constraints of the appropriate regions (R_{00} and R_{11}) and have the indicated allocations:

$$\begin{pmatrix} t_{11} & t_{12} \\ t_{21} \star & t_{22} \star \end{pmatrix} \qquad \begin{pmatrix} t_{11} \star & t_{12} \star \\ t'_{21} & t'_{22} \end{pmatrix}$$

This means that, when we fix t_1, the points t_2 and t'_2 are on the boundary between regions R_{11} and R_{00} of player 2. Equivalently, that

$$t_{21} + t_{22} = f_{01:11}^{-1}(t_{11}) + f_{00:01}^{-1}(t_{12} - \epsilon).$$

(A similar equation holds for t'_2 which however is not different since we assumed that $t_{21} + t_{22} = t'_{21} + t'_{22}$). This equality should hold for every ϵ in some open interval. But this contradicts the fact that $f_{00:01}^{-1}$ is strictly increasing.

From the last lemma, we get that $h(t_{21}+t_{22}) = f_{01:11}(t_{21}) + f_{00:01}(t_{22})$. We claim that the functions involved are affine as the following lemma (which is based on the Cauchy functional equation) shows.

Lemma 8. *If for some real functions h, h_1, h_2 which are continuous at some point, we have $h(x + y) = h_1(x) + h_2(y)$, then all three functions are affine, i. e., they are of the form $ax + b$ for some constants a and b.*

We have established that the functions $f_{01:11}$ and $f_{00:01}$ are affine but we can say more about their coefficients:

Lemma 9. *When $c_1 \neq 0$, the payments of the first player (up to a common additive term which depends on t_2) are of the form $p_1(a_1, t_2) = -\lambda \cdot a_2 \cdot t_2 - \gamma_a$, for some constants $\lambda > 0$ and γ_a.*

With the above payments, the mechanism is the following affine minimizer: $\operatorname{argmin}_a\{a_1 \cdot t_1 + \lambda \cdot a_2 \cdot t_2 + \gamma_a\}$.

4   The Case of Many Tasks

The generalization of the characterization to more than two tasks is almost straightforward. Fix a truthful mechanism. For two distinct tasks j_1 and j_2 we will write $j_1 \sim j_2$ when there are some values for the other $m-2$ tasks such that the mechanism restricted to tasks j_1 and j_2 is an affine minimizer (i.e., with the associated constant $c_1 \neq 0$). It should be stressed that we require the mechanism restricted to these two tasks to be an affine minimizer for *some* values of the other tasks, not necessarily for all values, but we are going to see that the two are equivalent.

Our aim is to show that the relation $\sim$ is transitive; since it is clearly symmetric, it essentially partitions the tasks into equivalence classes with the exception that classes of size one are not affine minimizer but task-independent mechanisms. Assume that $j_1 \sim j_2$ and $j_2 \sim j_3$. That is, assume that when we fix some values of the other tasks, the mechanism for tasks j_1 and j_2 is an affine minimizer and when we fix some (not necessarily the same) values of the other tasks the mechanism for tasks j_2 and j_3 is also an affine minimizer, not necessarily with consistent coefficients. Our aim is to show that the coefficients are consistent. We show the following lemma, first for two tasks, and then for 3 or more tasks (the proof is omitted).

Lemma 10. *When $j_1 \sim j_2$, $j_2 \sim j_3$, $\ldots$, $j_{k-1} \sim j_k$, the payments of player 1 satisfy the following for allocations a and b that agree on all other tasks (i.e., not in $\{j_1, \ldots, j_k\}$):*

$$p_a(t_2) - p_b(t_2) = \lambda_{j_1,\ldots,j_k} \cdot (a - b)t_2 + \zeta_{a:b},$$

where $\lambda_{j_1,\ldots,j_k} > 0$ and $\zeta_{a:b}$ are constants.

The relation $\sim$ is symmetric and transitive and it partitions the tasks into equivalence classes. Suppose for simplicity that all tasks belong to one class. Then the mechanism is an affine minimizer (when there are at least 2 tasks). This follows from the last lemma: Fix $b = 1$, i.e. in b all tasks are allocated to player 1. The payment p_b can be set arbitrarily, so we set it to some arbitrary constant γ_b. Then $p_a(t_2) = \lambda \cdot (a - b) \cdot t_2 + \zeta_{a:b} + p_b(t_2) = -\lambda \cdot a_2 \cdot t_2 - \gamma_a$, where we defined $\gamma_a = -\zeta_{a:b} + \gamma_b$ (a constant) and used $\lambda > 0$ as an abbreviation of $\lambda_{1,\ldots,m}$. Then the allocation for player 1 is given by

$$\operatorname*{argmin}_{a_1}\{a_1 t_1 - p_a(t_2)\} = \operatorname*{argmin}_{a_1}\{a_1 t_1 + \lambda a_2 t_2 + \gamma_a\},$$

with λ and γ_a constants.

The above lemma allows as to partition the tasks so that each part is independent of the other parts. Parts that have 2 or more tasks are affine minimizers. Parts that have only 1 task are not necessarily affine minimizers.

5   Lower Bound for 2 Tasks

Although our characterization involves only decisive mechanisms and negative values, it can be extended directly to show that the approximation ratio even for two tasks is at least 2. The following claim from [14] shows a non-decisive mechanism for positive values has unbounded ratio:

Suppose for example that the allocation 10 does not occur for some t_2, and take the input $\begin{pmatrix} \epsilon & \infty \\ t_{21} \star & t_{22} \star \end{pmatrix}$. Since the allocation of the first player cannot be 10 the allocation is indicated by the stars. By monotonicity the allocation is the same for the instance $\begin{pmatrix} \epsilon & \infty \\ t_{21} \star & \epsilon \star \end{pmatrix}$. But this gives approximation ratio $1 + t_{21}/\epsilon \to \infty$.

The following theorem reproduces the result in [14] for any number $m \geq 2$ of tasks.

Theorem 3. *No truthful mechanism for 2 players with $c_1 \neq 0$ can have a bounded approximation ratio. Consequently any mechanism for 2 players with bounded approximation ratio is a task independent mechanism.*

In fact, for two tasks, we can show (proof omitted):

Theorem 4. *For 2 players and 2 tasks, the only truthful mechanism which achieves approximation ratio 2 is the VCG mechanism.*

References

1. Andelman, N., Azar, Y., Sorani, M.: Truthful approximation mechanisms for scheduling selfish related machines. In: STACS, pp. 69–82 (2005)
2. Archer, A.: Mechanisms for Discrete Optimization with Rational Agents. PhD thesis, Cornell University (January 2004)
3. Archer, A., Papadimitriou, C.H., Talwar, K., Tardos, É.: An approximate truthful mechanism for combinatorial auctions with single parameter agents. In: SODA, pp. 205–214 (2003)
4. Archer, A., Tardos, É.: Truthful mechanisms for one-parameter agents. In: FOCS, pp. 482–491 (2001)
5. Archer, A., Tardos, É.: Frugal path mechanisms. In: SODA (2002)
6. Babaioff, M., Lavi, R., Pavlov, E.: Mechanism design for single-value domains. In: AAAI, pp. 241–247 (2005)
7. Bartal, Y., Gonen, R., Nisan, N.: Incentive compatible multi unit combinatorial auctions. In: TARK, pp. 72–87 (2003)
8. Briest, P., Krysta, P., Vöcking, B.: Approximation techniques for utilitarian mechanism design. In: STOC, pp. 39–48 (2005)
9. Christodoulou, G., Koutsoupias, E., Kovács, A.: Mechanism design for fractional scheduling on unrelated machines. In: Arge, L., Cachin, C., Jurdziński, T., Tarlecki, A. (eds.) ICALP 2007. LNCS, vol. 4596, pp. 40–52. Springer, Heidelberg (2007)
10. Christodoulou, G., Koutsoupias, E., Vidali, A.: A lower bound for scheduling mechanisms. In: SODA, pp. 1163–1169 (2007)
11. Clarke, E.: Multipart pricing of public goods. Public Choice 8, 17–33 (1971)
12. Dobzinski, S., Nisan, N., Schapira, M.: Approximation algorithms for combinatorial auctions with complement-free bidders. In: STOC, pp. 610–618 (2005)
13. Dobzinski, S., Nisan, N., Schapira, M.: Truthful randomized mechanisms for combinatorial auctions. In: STOC, pp. 644–652 (2006)
14. Dobzinski, S., Sundararajan, M.: On characterizations of truthful mechanisms for combinatorial auctions and scheduling. In: EC (2008)
15. Groves, T.: Incentives in teams. Econometrica 41, 617–631 (1973)
16. Kevin, R.: The characterization of implementable choice rules. In: Aggregation and Revelation of Preferences, pp. 321–348 (1979)
17. Koutsoupias, E., Vidali, A.: A lower bound of $1+\phi$ for truthful scheduling mechanisms. In: Kučera, L., Kučera, A. (eds.) MFCS 2007. LNCS, vol. 4708, pp. 454–464. Springer, Heidelberg (2007)
18. Kovács, A.: Fast Algorithms for Two Scheduling Problems. PhD thesis, Universität des Saarlandes (2007)

19. Lavi, R., Mu'alem, A., Nisan, N.: Towards a characterization of truthful combinatorial auctions. In: FOCS, pp. 574–583 (2003)
20. Lavi, R., Swamy, C.: Truthful mechanism design for multi-dimensional scheduling via cycle monotonicity. In: EC, pp. 252–261 (2007)
21. Lu, P., Yu, C.: An improved randomized truthful mechanism for scheduling unrelated machines. In: STACS, pp. 527–538 (2008)
22. Monderer, D.: Monotonicity and implementability. In: EC (2008)
23. Mu'alem, A., Schapira, M.: Setting lower bounds on truthfulness. In: SODA, pp. 1143–1152 (2007)
24. Myerson, R.B.: Optimal auction design. Mathematics of Operations Research 6(1), 58–73 (1981)
25. Nisan, N., Ronen, A.: Algorithmic mechanism design. Games and Economic Behavior 35, 166–196 (2001)
26. Saks, M.E., Yu, L.: Weak monotonicity suffices for truthfulness on convex domains. In: Proceedings 6th ACM Conference on Electronic Commerce (EC), pp. 286–293 (2005)
27. Vickrey, W.: Counterspeculations, auctions and competitive sealed tenders. Journal of Finance 16, 8–37 (1961)

A Local-Search 2-Approximation for 2-Correlation-Clustering*

Tom Coleman, James Saunderson, and Anthony Wirth

The University of Melbourne

Abstract. CORRELATIONCLUSTERING is now an established problem in the algorithms and constrained clustering communities. With the requirement that at most two clusters be formed, the minimisation problem is related to the study of *signed graphs* in the social psychology community, and has applications in statistical mechanics and biological networks.

Although a PTAS exists for this problem, its running time is impractical. We therefore introduce a number of new algorithms for 2CC, including two that incorporate some notion of local search. In particular, we show that the algorithm we call PASTA-TOSS is a 2-approximation on complete graphs.

Experiments confirm the strong performance of the local search approaches, even on non-complete graphs, with running time significantly lower than rival approaches.

1 Introduction

The TWO-CORRELATION-CLUSTERING (2CC) problem asks us to partition a dataset into two clusters given only *advice* about *pairs* of points in the dataset. This *advice* comes in the form of soft *must-link* and *cannot-link* constraints. The aim is to minimise the number of such constraints violated in forming the clusters.

1.1 The 2CC Problem

The CORRELATIONCLUSTERING problem [1] asks us to form a clustering of a signed graph that minimises the number of edges that are not respected. In the 2CC variant, the number of clusters is restricted to two. This bears some similarity to the MAXCUT problem. Formally, the input is a graph $G = (V, E)$ and a labelling on edges $l : E \rightarrow \{-1, +1\}$. The output is a clustering of the vertices $c : V \rightarrow \{-1, +1\}$. The aim is to choose a clustering that minimises the number of edges that disagree with the labelling, viz.

$$|\{e = (v, w) \in E \text{ s.t. } l(e) \neq c(v) \cdot c(w)\}|.$$

* This work was supported by the Australian Research Council through Discovery Grant DP0663979.

D. Halperin and K. Mehlhorn (Eds.): ESA 2008, LNCS 5193, pp. 308–319, 2008.

We refer to this as the *cost of the clustering c under labelling l* or just the *cost* if the clustering and labelling are clear from the context. Note that *labelling* refers to edges, whereas *clustering* refers to vertices, and that n refers to $|V|$.

If the graph is not two-connected, then each two-connected component can be considered independently. Without loss of generality, we will therefore assume that the input graph is two-connected.

1.2 Related Work

Initial work on signed graphs [2,3] focused on graph theory, rather than optimisation. Early results [4] demonstrated that 2CC is an NP-complete problem, both on complete graphs, and in general.

Bansal *et al.* [1] put forward the first approximation algorithm for MIN-2CC on *complete* graphs, with factor 3. Giotis and Guruswami [5] completed the picture, from a *theoretical* viewpoint, for 2CC on complete graphs by developing a PTAS (polynomial time approximation scheme) for both the maximisation and minimisation versions of the problem. For CORRELATIONCLUSTERING on complete graphs, a PTAS exists for maximisation, but minimisation is APX-hard [6]. The best known upper bound for MIN-CORRELATIONCLUSTERING on complete graphs is a 5/2-approximation developed by Ailon *et al.* [7].

On *general* graphs, the problem is more difficult to solve. There is a direct relationship between 2CC and the classic MAXCUT problem: replace all + edges on the signed graph with a pair of − edges meeting at a new vertex. The classic SDP-based approximation algorithm, by Goemans and Williamson [8], achieves a 0.878-approximation for MAXCUT. Dasgupta *et al.* [9] extend this result to the maximization version of the 2CC problem, achieving the same approximation factor. Note that CORRELATIONCLUSTERING on general graphs and MINIMUM MULTICUT reduce to one another, leading to $O(\log n)$ approximations [6]. Finally, Huffner *et al.* [10] use a fixed parameter algorithm, and some data reduction rules, to solve 2CC exactly in greatly reduced time compared to a brute force algorithm. However, such algorithms are still exponential in running time.

1.3 History of the 2CC Problem

The 2CC problem has been repeatedly rediscovered, and renamed, since it was first defined by Harary [2] in 1950. Harary introduced the *signed graph*: an undirected graph with +1 or −1 labels on the edges (corresponding to must-link and cannot-link advice). He also introduced the notion of *imbalance* in a signed graph, which corresponds to the 2CC cost of the graph, the number of violated constraints. Harary considered a psychological interpretation of the problem: positive edges correspond to pairs of people who like one another, and negative edges to pairs who dislike one another. His aim was to find two highly *cliquey* groups.

Apart from social psychology, the study of signed graphs has many other applications, notably in statistical mechanics, where it relates to energy configurations of the Ising model with no external field. Solé and Zaslavsky [3] show a connection to coding theory: between signings of a graph and the cutset code defined by that graph. Also, Dasgupta *et al.* [9] apply the problem to the decomposition of large-scale biological networks into monotonic subsystems.

1.4   Layout of the Paper

In Section 2, we outline the majority of the algorithms used in this paper. In Section 3, we show that the PASTA-TOSS algorithm is a 2-approximation. Section 4 explains a more involved algorithm, PASTA-FLIP, which is similar in structure to PASTA-TOSS. Finally, Section 5 outlines the experiments we conducted to validate the practical performance of these algorithms.

2   Algorithms to Solve 2CC

In this section, we provide details about most of the algorithms for 2CC that we will run experiments on. This includes both existing work and two new algorithms: PAST and SPECTRAL.

2.1   Pick-a-Vertex Type Algorithms

The Pick-a-Vertex Algorithm. Bansal *et al.* [1] outline a simple approximation algorithm for 2CC, which we call PICK-A-VERTEX. It provides the inspiration for a number of algorithms that we introduce in this paper. First some notation: let $N^+(v)$ be the set of vertices that share a positive-labelled edge with v, and $N^-(v)$ those that share a negative edge. So PICK-A-VERTEX is

> For each vertex v, there is an associated partitioning: one cluster being $\{v\} \cup N^+(v)$, the other $N^-(v)$. Of these n partitionings, return the one that minimises the number of disagreements with the labels.

Bansal *et al.* demonstrate that this simple algorithm is a 3-approximation for the 2CC problem on complete graphs. It turns out that the 3-approximation is tight, a fact not mentioned in the original paper. Consider a *complete* graph, consisting solely of positive edges, apart from a Hamiltonian cycle of negative edges. The optimal solution (placing all vertices together) has cost n, whilst any PICK-A-VERTEX solution will have cost $3n - 10$.

Notice that the PICK-A-VERTEX clustering described above is *not* a local optimum. This fact is the inspiration for some of the algorithms we introduce.

The PAST Algorithm. The PICK-A-VERTEX algorithm was designed for complete graphs. There is no obvious extension to incomplete graphs, as there may not be candidate vertices v that are adjacent to every other vertex.

In the complete case, the edges incident to v form a *spanning tree* of the underlying graph G. Now, any spanning tree of G induces a unique clustering that is consistent with the tree. From this perspective, PICK-A-VERTEX is considering spanning tree-based clusterings. We therefore propose the PAST (Pick-a-Spanning-Tree) algorithm:

For each vertex v, perform a breadth first search from v to find a spanning tree, and use that tree to induce a clustering. Return the *best* of the n clusterings.

By using breadth-first-search trees, PAST chooses the same spanning trees as PICK-A-VERTEX on complete graphs, and is thus a generalisation.

2.2   Local Search

Local-search algorithms have been successful in practice for many years, and more recently as approximation algorithms [11], for various combinatorial problems. For the 2CC problem, the obvious local improvement to make to is to move (*toss*) a vertex from one cluster to the other if, by doing so, the cost of the clustering is lowered.

Given a clustering c, the clustering c_v represents the same clustering as c, except with $v \in V$ in the opposite cluster. We then define $\lambda_v = \text{cost}(c) - \text{cost}(c_v)$, the improvement caused by the change (non-negative, if there is some improvement). With this in mind, we define LOCALSEARCH as follows:

Given a clustering c, let w be the vertex with maximum λ_w. If $\lambda_w \leq 0$, stop, otherwise let $c \leftarrow c_w$ and repeat.

Counter Example for Local Search Approximation. The LOCALSEARCH algorithm, used naively, has no good approximation guarantee. Consider a complete graph with $n/2$ disjoint edges labelled $-$ (all other edges are labelled $+$). The global minimum here has cost $n/2$, however, there is a local minimum—which cuts across each minus-edge—that has cost $n(n-2)/4$.

2.3   The PASTA-toss Algorithm

PASTA-TOSS is defined in the following way:

Generate n breadth-first-search trees, one emanating from each vertex. For each such tree T, after finding the 2-clustering ^Tc consistent with T, run LOCALSEARCH on ^Tc. Return the best locally-optimal solution.

Clearly the PASTA-TOSS algorithm will return a solution no worse than the PAST algorithm. In Section 3 we show that PASTA-TOSS is a two-approximation on complete graphs.

2.4   A Spectral Algorithm

In an earlier paper [12], we formulated 2CC as an eigenvalue problem, similar to the spectral clustering approach. We refer the reader to that paper for a full exposition of that algorithm, which we will refer to as SPECTRAL.

2.5   The PTAS

Giotis and Guruswami [5] discovered a PTAS (polynomial time approximation scheme) for the k-CORRELATIONCLUSTERING problem, with arbitrary k. They first take a random sample of the vertices and then use each possible clustering of the sample as a basis for a clustering of the entire data set.

Giotis and Guruswami's scheme provides a $(1 + \varepsilon)$-factor approximation algorithm that runs in time $2^{O(1/\varepsilon^3)}$. However, the constants involved are large enough that the smallest possible sample size is greater than 4000. In practice, checking every sample clustering is infeasible. We investigated using the same techniques with smaller sample sizes. Consequently, there are no approximation guarantees, but we anticipated similar behaviour to the full-blown PTAS.

3   PASTA-toss Is a 2-Approximation

In this section we develop some theoretical results, leading to a proof that PASTA-TOSS is a 2-approximation. To begin, we need the concept of a switching class.

3.1   Switching

The notion of *switching* in signed graphs is well established [13]. Given a labelling l, we generate another labelling l_v by selecting a vertex v and flipping the labels on the edges incident to v. We may repeat this switching operation at other vertices, generating further labellings. The family of all possible labellings can be partitioned into equivalence classes under this (multiple) switching operation: we refer to labellings in the same class as *switching equivalent*.

In this paper we also introduce the notion of switching on 2-clusterings: we *switch* a clustering c to c_v by tossing v to the other cluster. In this way, every clustering can be obtained by a series of switching steps from c.

Lemma 1. *The cost of c under l is the same as the cost of c_v under l_v.*

Proof. The only edges affected by these operations are edges incident to v. For such an edge $e = (v, u)$, $l(e) = -l_v(e)$, and $c(v) = -c_v(v)$, whilst $c(u) = c_v(u)$. Thus the cost of such an edge is unchanged.   □

Lemma 1 tells us that if l has a solution of cost k, l_v also has a solution of cost k. Also as $(l_v)_v = l$, the converse is true. Consequently, we see the following useful corollaries.

Corollary 1. *The optimal costs of all labellings in a switching class are the same. In particular, if c^* is an optimal clustering for l, then c_v^* is an optimal clustering for l_v.*

Corollary 2. *For a given labelling l, there exists a labelling l', switching equivalent to l, for which placing all vertices together in one cluster is optimal.*

Note that the optimal cost for l' in Corollary 2 equals the number of negative edges in l'.

3.2   Switching-Invariant Algorithms

Imagine we knew that an algorithm behaved in essentially the same way on all switching-equivalent labellings. Then Corollary 2 tells us that we can focus on labellings in which the optimum has all elements in one cluster.

Definition 1. *An algorithm is* switching invariant *if, whenever it produces c on input l, it produces c_v on input l_v.*

We now investigate the behaviour of two key algorithms under switching.

Lemma 2. PAST *is switching invariant.*

Proof. Let T be any spanning tree of G inducing a clustering T_c under PAST. Consider two vertices u and x in V. Whether they are clustered together depends only on the parity of the number of negative edges on the path between u and x in tree T. If v is not on this path, clearly the parity is unchanged. If v is on the path, the parity is changed only if u or x is v.

So under l_v, the clustering based on T is switching invariant. Lemma 1 tells us that the spanning tree that induces the best clustering on l also induces the best clustering on l_v.   □

We can now infer an interesting fact about spanning trees.

Lemma 3. *For a given labelling l on a graph G, there exists a spanning tree T that induces an optimal clustering.*

Proof. Consider labelling l' as defined in Corollary 2. The positively-labelled edges in l' form a subgraph that is connected and spans G: if they did not, then there would be a non-trivial cut of G with only l'-negative edges. This would imply that the optimum clustering must use two clusters, contradicting the definition of l'. Hence, we can find a spanning tree T of positively-labelled edges in l': this induces a solution with all vertices in one cluster.

The proof of Lemma 2, combined with Corollary 1 shows that T will induce the optimum solution on l.   □

LocalSearch is not exactly switching invariant, but we can prove a similar result.

Lemma 4. *If* LocalSearch *is given l as input and uses c as a starting point, resulting in solution $\bar{c}$, then given input l_v and starting point c_v,* LocalSearch *produces solution $(\bar{c})_v$.*

Proof. Consider running two simultaneous instances of LocalSearch, one starting from c and the other starting from c_v. To begin with, the only edges that could possibly be different are the edges incident to v. The proof of Lemma 1 shows that the edges that incur a cost are the same in (l_v, c_v) as they are in (l, c). So in both cases, λ_u is the same, for all $u \in V$. Therefore the same sequence of vertices will be chosen to be tossed.   □

The following lemma is an immediate consequence of Lemmas 2 and 4.

Lemma 5. PASTA-toss *is switching invariant.*

3.3   Proof That PASTA-toss Is a 2-Approximation

Since PASTA-TOSS is switching invariant, we can analyse its behaviour on in-put labellings in which the optimum places all vertices in one cluster (refer to Corollaries 1 and 2). For such a labelling, no vertex has minus-degree more than $n/2$, and the optimum cost is simply the total number of minus-edges in the graph. If we let β be the minimum of the minus-degree of all the vertices, then $\text{cost}^* \geq \beta n/2$.

To analyse the performance of PASTA-TOSS consider the iteration where PASTA-TOSS uses the spanning tree from v, a node of minus-degree β. Initially, the algorithm splits the vertices into two sets, $X_0 = \{v\} \cup N^+(v)$ and $Y_0 = N^-(v)$. As the local search progresses, vertices will be tossed from one set to the other (call them X and Y). Consider the point at which the first vertex is tossed from X to Y. Note that this means $|Y| \leq \beta$.

We can compare the cost of the clustering (X, Y) to cost^* in a fashion similar to Bansal $et\ al.$. We can form an estimate of the difference by counting the number of $+$ edges between X and Y, discounting the $-$ edges. For a vertex $v \in V$, and a set A, define A_v^+ to be the number of $+$ edges from v to A. A_v^- is defined in the analogous way. Then

$$\text{cost}(X, Y) - \text{cost}^* = \sum_y X_y^+ - \sum_y X_y^- = \sum_y \text{pull}_y \leq \beta \max_{y \in Y} \text{pull}_y \quad (1)$$

Where $\text{pull}_y = X_y^+ - X_y^-$ is the "pull" that X exerts on y.

If we let $\text{push}_y = Y_y^- - Y_y^+$ (the "push" that Y exerts on y), the local improvement of swapping any node $y \in Y$ is given by

$$\text{imp}_y = \text{pull}_y + \text{push}_y \quad (2)$$

So we can use a bound on the local improvement of swapping a node (from X) to get a contradictory bound on pull_y for any y.

Theorem 1. PASTA-TOSS $is\ a\ 2$-$approximation\ on\ complete\ graphs.$

$Proof.$ We claim at this point, when the first node to be swapped is from X, that $\text{cost}(X, Y) \leq 2\text{cost}^*$.

Arguing by contradiction, suppose that $\text{cost}(X, Y)$ is not within a factor 2 of cost^*. Then there must be some $y_0 \in Y$ such that $\text{pull}_{y_0} > n/2$.

Let x_0 be the vertex from X that is about to be swapped. By definition,

$$Y_{x_0}^+ + Y_{x_0}^- = |Y| \text{ and } X_{x_0}^+ + X_{x_0}^- = n - |Y| - 1$$

Since we have assumed that the optimum solution places all vertices together, x_0 is incident to at most $n/2$ negative edges, and so $X_{x_0}^- \leq n/2$. So we have

$$\text{imp}_{x_0} = X_{x_0}^- + Y_{x_0}^+ - X_{x_0}^+ - Y_{x_0}^- \leq 2X_{x_0}^- - (X_{x_0}^- + X_{x_0}^+) + (Y_{x_0}^+ + Y_{x_0}^-),$$

which is at most $2|Y| + 1$. Given x_0 is the vertex which is about to be swapped, $\text{imp}_{y_0} \leq \text{imp}_{x_0} \leq 2|Y| + 1$.

Alternatively, if the algorithm ends without ever swapping an $x \in X$, at the conclusion, $\text{imp}_{y_0} \leq 0 < 2|Y| + 1$.

So, using (2) and our assumption, we have

$$\text{push}_{y_0} = \text{imp}_{y_0} - \text{pull}_{y_0} < 2|Y| - 1 - n/2 \tag{3}$$

Now we use the fact that y_0 has to have at least β minus-edges to show a contradictory lower-bound on push_{y_0}. We have

$$\begin{aligned}
\text{push}_y &= Y_{y_0}^- - Y_{y_0}^+ \\
&= 2Y_{y_0}^- - |Y| + 1 \\
&\geq |Y| - 2X_{y_0}^- + 1 \\
&= |Y| + X_{y_0}^+ - X_{y_0}^- - (X_{y_0}^+ + X_{y_0}^-) + 1 \\
&> 2|Y| + 1 - n/2
\end{aligned}$$

The first equality follows as $Y_{y_0}^- + Y_{y_0}^+ = |Y| - 1$, the first inequality as the minus-degree of y_0, $Y_{y_0}^- + X_{y_0}^-$ is at least $\beta \geq |Y|$, and the second as $X_{y_0}^+ + X_{y_0}^- = n - |Y|$ and $X_{y_0}^+ - X_{y_0}^- = \text{pull}_{y_0} > n/2$.   □

4   The PASTA-flip Algorithm

The PASTA-FLIP algorithm is another local-search approach, but rather more involved than tossing vertices between clusters.

4.1   Removing Bad Cycles

By removing bad cycles, defined below, we will produce a graph that is trivial to cluster.

Definition 2. A bad cycle *is a cycle C in G in which there is an odd number of negative-labelled edges.*

These cycles are called *bad* as there is no clustering of the vertices in C that satisfies all the labels of C's edges. On the other hand, if there are no bad cycles in a graph, solving the problem is easy.

Lemma 6. *Suppose l is a labelling that causes G to have no bad cycles. Then there is a clustering of the vertices with cost zero.*

Proof. Choose some vertex v and assign every other vertex u to a cluster based on the parity of the number of negative edges on the paths between u and v. Note that the parity is uniquely defined: if not, there would be a cycle with an odd number of negative edges. This proves the lemma, as all paths (and edges, as length one paths) are respected.   □

The basic principle of PASTA-FLIP is that it might be a good idea to flip the label on an edge that is involved in many bad cycles: the cycles would then become good. If this process could be repeated in an organised way so that no bad cycles remained, then the clustering problem would be trivial. This approach has two drawbacks. Firstly, it is conceivable that there is a scenario where there exists a bad cycle, yet there is no edge to flip that will reduce the number of bad cycles. More importantly, there are too many cycles to consider (possibly an exponential number).

Cycle Bases. Let us represent a set of edges by an $|E|$-dimensional vector with entries in $\mathbb{Z}_2$. The set of all cycles is a subspace of this vector space. Standard results show that the cycle space has dimension $|E|-|V|+1$ and can be generated by a spanning tree T of G. We obtain a *fundamental basis* of the cycles by forming a cycle C_e for each edge $e = (v, w) \notin T$: C_e is e plus the path in T from v to w.

4.2   The PASTA-flip Algorithm

Consider such a fundamental cycle basis. Each edge $e \notin T$ will only be involved in a single cycle in the basis, C_e. So there is one straightforward technique to ensure that each cycle in the basis is good: if C_e is bad, simply flip e. At the end of this process, the labellings on the T-edges will be respected, which is exactly the PAST algorithm.

However this is wasteful—edges inside T are involved in many basis cycles. Flipping one of these edges could potentially fix a number of bad cycles (in the basis), and thus mean fewer flips. Each flip represents a disagreement between the output clustering and the (original) edge labelling. With this in mind, we define the PASTA-FLIP (PICK-A-SPANNING TREE AND FLIP) algorithm as follows:

> For each vertex v create a breadth-first-search tree T_v. While there is an edge $e \in T_v$ which is involved in more bad cycles than good, flip e. When there are no more such edges, flip edges outside of T_v. Return the solution found of lowest cost.

The action of "flipping" never worsens the 2CC cost, giving the following lemma.

Lemma 7. *The cost of the solution returned by* PASTA-FLIP *is no greater than the cost of the solution returned by* PAST.

5   Experimental Work

5.1   Algorithms Tested

In our experimental work, we tested all algorithms mentioned in Section 2, along with PASTA-FLIP. As mentioned, the PTAS was not feasible to implement, so we tested a PTAS-like algorithm, called PTAS-k, where k is the sample size. Also, the algorithm we refer to below as LOCALSEARCH takes n randomised starting clusterings, and produces the best clustering found after toss-based search from each. This is to compare it to PASTA-TOSS, which uses n PAST-style starting clusterings. Also we experimented with PASTA-FLIP+TOSS, which performs PAST, and for each tree flips edges (until no more flips are possible) and then tosses vertices. Additionally we used the code provide by Dasgupta *et al.* [9] to test the Goemans-Williamson style SDP algorithm that they developed.

5.2   Datasets

For our experimental work, we used three datasets: the regulatory network of human epidermal growth factor (EGFR), as used by both Dasgupta *et al.* [9] and Huffner *et al.* [10] in their investigations, and two synthetic datasets.

Each synthetic dataset was generated randomly subject to two parameters, which were independent over each edge. The first, p_e, is the probability that an edge exists (with either sign), and given the edge exists. The second, p, is the probability that the edge agrees to a randomly generated initial clustering.

The first data set, called SPARSE, had problems of size 200, a p_e value of 0.05, and a p value of 0.3, which was an attempt to approximate the EGFR dataset. The second data set, called COMPLETE, had problems of size 100, $p_e = 1$—thus all graphs are complete—and $p = 0.45$. We found empirically that lower values of p result in 2CC problems that are easy to solve.

All experiments were run on a 2 GHz Intel Core 2 Duo machine with 2GB of RAM, running MAC OS X 10.5.2. All algorithms were implemented in C, apart from SPECTRAL and GW-SDP, which were run in Matlab 7.4.0. Note that this means the times recorded for the Matlab algorithms perhaps were not entirely appropriate for comparison.

5.3   Results

Figures 1 and 2 show the relative performances of the algorithms discussed in this paper on the EGFR and COMPLETE datasets. These plots compare the

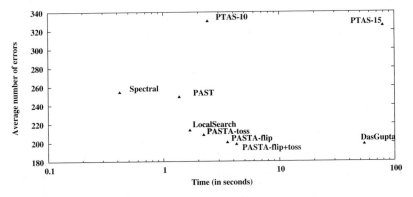

Fig. 1. The time/effectiveness profile on the EGFR Dataset

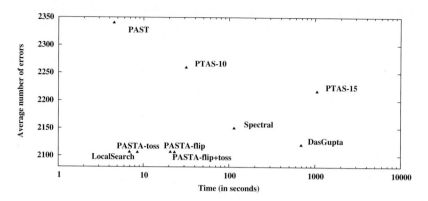

Fig. 2. The time/effectiveness profile on 100 instances of *complete* signed graphs, $n = 100$ and $p = 0.45$

Table 1. The results of running all algorithms on all datasets. We report the average of the percentage (%) relative difference between the number of errors compared to LOCALSEARCH, over all problem instances in the dataset. The running time is measured in seconds.

Algorithm	EGFR Cost	EGFR Time	SPARSE Cost	SPARSE Time	COMPLETE Cost	COMPLETE Time
DASGUPTA	**-0.070**	54.01	-0.011	26.28	0.006	689.01
SPECTRAL	0.192	0.42	0.224	2847.70	0.021	114.35
PAST	0.169	1.37	0.298	29.16	0.111	4.54
PASTA-FLIP	-0.061	3.55	-0.033	80.60	0.000	20.77
PASTA-TOSS	-0.023	2.22	-0.020	54.82	**-0.000**	8.54
PASTA-FLIP+TOSS	**-0.070**	4.25	**-0.042**	99.62	-0.000	23.18

algorithmic performance (number of errors) to the time taken to achieve that performance. As we can see, the PTAS algorithms and PAST perform poorly as a rule; DASGUPTA can achieve good results, but is very slow in comparison to our algorithms. Although the SPECTRAL technique can be quite fast on sparse graphs, its performance is not great. Table 5.2 summarises the results on all three datasets.

6   Conclusions

In this paper, we have introduced some new algorithms for solving the 2CC problem: PASTA-TOSS, PASTA-FLIP, and the spectral method. The PASTA-TOSS algorithm is a 2-approximation on complete graphs. In general, performances of the local-search enhanced algorithms are impressive, with comparatively low running times. Certainly, they form a more practical approach than the existing PTAS, whilst retaining some proved performance bounds.

6.1   Further Work

Is it possible to apply these methods to solve CORRELATIONCLUSTERING problems in which the required number of clusters is fixed at a number larger than two? Although the local search step generalises easily, it is not at all clear how to generalise the spanning tree approach.

We have no example showing that the 2-approximation result for PASTA-TOSS is tight. We suspect that the proof technique for the approximation performance of PASTA-TOSS extends to PASTA-FLIP, but have not yet investigated this in detail. The approximability of 2CC on general graphs is not well understood: the results for MAXCUT also apply, but they tell us little about the minimisation problem. The good performance of our algorithms on general graphs suggest that we may obtain something better than the reduction to MINIMUM MULTICUT of the generic CORRELATIONCLUSTERING problem.

References

1. Bansal, N., Blum, A., Chawla, S.: Correlation clustering. Machine Learning 56(1), 89–113 (2004)
2. Harary, F.: On the notion of balance of a signed graph. Michigan Mathematical Journal 2, 143–146 (1953)
3. Solé, P., Zaslavsky, T.: A coding approach to signed graphs. SIAM Journal on Discrete Mathematics 7, 544–553 (1994)
4. Shamir, R., Sharan, R., Tsur, D.: Cluster graph modification problems. Discrete Applied Mathematics 144(1-2), 173–182 (2004)
5. Giotis, I., Guruswami, V.: Correlation clustering with a fixed number of clusters. In: Proceedings of the 17th Annual ACM-SIAM Symposium on Discrete Algorithms, pp. 1167–1176 (2006)
6. Charikar, M., Guruswami, V., Wirth, A.: Clustering with qualitative information. Journal of Computer and System Sciences 71(3), 360–383 (2005)
7. Ailon, N., Charikar, M., Newman, A.: Aggregating inconsistent information: Ranking and clustering. In: Proceedings of the 37th annual ACM Symposium on Theory of Computing, pp. 684–693 (2005)
8. Goemans, M., Williamson, D.: Improved approximation algorithms for maximum cut and satisfiability problems using semidefinite programming. Journal of the ACM 42(6), 1115–1145 (1995)
9. DasGupta, B., Enciso, G., Sontag, E., Zhang, Y.: Algorithmic and complexity results for decompositions of biological networks into monotone subsystems. BioSystems 90(1), 161–178 (2007)
10. Huffner, F., Betzler, N., Niedermeier, R.: Optimal edge deletions for signed graph balancing. In: Proceedings of the 6th Workshop on Experimental Algorithms, pp. 297–310 (2007)
11. Arya, V., Garg, N., Khandekar, R., Meyerson, A., Munagala, K., Pandit, V.: Local search heuristics for k-median and facility location problems. SIAM Journal on Computing 33(3), 544–562
12. Coleman, T., Saunderson, J., Wirth, A.: Spectral clustering with inconsistent advice. In: Proceedings of the 25th Annual International Conference on Machine Learning, pp. 152–159 (2008)
13. Zaslavsky, T.: Signed Graphs. Discrete Applied Mathematics 4, 47–74 (1982)

The Alcuin Number of a Graph

Péter Csorba, Cor A.J. Hurkens, and Gerhard J. Woeginger

Department of Mathematics and Computer Science
TU Eindhoven, P.O. Box 513, 5600 MB Eindhoven, The Netherlands

Abstract. We consider a planning problem that generalizes Alcuin's river crossing problem (also known as: The wolf, goat, and cabbage puzzle) to scenarios with arbitrary conflict graphs. We derive a variety of combinatorial, structural, algorithmical, and complexity theoretical results around this problem.

Keywords: Transportation problem; scheduling; graph theory.

1   Introduction

Alcuin's river crossing problem. The Anglo-Saxon monk Alcuin (735–804 A.D.) was one of the leading scholars of his time. He served as head of Charlemagne's Palace School at Aachen, he developed the Carolingian minuscule (a script which has become the basis of the way the letters of the present Roman alphabet are written), and he wrote a number of elementary texts on arithmetic, geometry, and astronomy. His book *"Propositiones ad acuendos iuvenes"* (Problems to sharpen the young) is perhaps the oldest collection of mathematical problems written in Latin. It contains the following well-known problem.

> A man had to transport to the far side of a river a wolf, a goat, and a bundle of cabbages. The only boat he could find was one which would carry only two of them. For that reason he sought a plan which would enable them all to get to the far side unhurt. Let him, who is able, say how it could be possible to transport them safely?

In a safe transportation plan, neither wolf and goat nor goat and cabbage can be left alone together. Alcuin's river crossing problem differs significantly from other mediaeval puzzles, since it is neither geometrical nor arithmetical but purely combinatorial. Biggs [3] mentions it as one of the oldest combinatorial puzzles in the history of mathematics. Ascher [1] states that the problem also shows up in Gaelic, Danish, Russian, Ethiopian, Suaheli, and Zambian folklore. Borndörfer, Grötschel & Löbel [4] use Alcuin's problem to provide the reader with a leisurely introduction into integer programming.

Graph-theoretic model. We consider the following generalization of Alcuin's problem to arbitrary graphs $G = (V, E)$. Now the man has to transport a set V of items/vertices across the river. Two items are connected by an edge in

D. Halperin and K. Mehlhorn (Eds.): ESA 2008, LNCS 5193, pp. 320–331, 2008.

E, if they are *conflicting* and thus cannot be left alone together without human supervision. The available boat has capacity $b \geq 1$, and thus can carry the man together with any subset of at most b items. A *feasible schedule* is a finite sequence of triples $(L_1, B_1, R_1), (L_2, B_2, R_2), \ldots, (L_s, B_s, R_s)$ of subsets of the item set V that satisfies the following conditions (FS1)–(FS3). The odd integer s is called the *length* of the schedule.

(FS1) For every k, the sets L_k, B_k, R_k form a partition of V. The sets L_k and R_k form stable sets in G. The set B_k contains at most b elements.

(FS2) The sequence starts with $L_1 \cup B_1 = V$ and $R_1 = \emptyset$, and the sequence ends with $L_s = \emptyset$ and $B_s \cup R_s = V$.

(FS3) For even $k \geq 2$, we have $B_k \cup R_k = B_{k-1} \cup R_{k-1}$ and $L_k = L_{k-1}$. For odd $k \geq 3$, we have $L_k \cup B_k = L_{k-1} \cup B_{k-1}$ and $R_k = R_{k-1}$.

Intuitively speaking, the kth triple encodes the kth boat trip: L_k contains the items on the left bank, B_k the items in the boat, and R_k the items on the right bank. Odd indices correspond to forward boat trips from left to right, and even indices correspond to backward trips from right to left. Condition (FS1) states that the sets L_k and R_k must not contain conflicting item pairs, and that set B_k must fit into the boat. Condition (FS2) concerns the first boat trip (where the man has put the first items into the boat) and the final trip (where the man transports the last items to the right bank). Condition (FS3) says that whenever the man reaches a bank, he may arbitrarily re-divide the set of items that currently are on that bank and in the boat.

---

1. $w, c \mid g \rightarrow \quad \mid \emptyset$		2. $w, c \mid \leftarrow \emptyset \mid g$
3. $w \mid c \rightarrow \quad \mid g$		4. $w \mid \leftarrow g \mid c$
5. $g \mid w \rightarrow \quad \mid c$		6. $g \mid \leftarrow \emptyset \mid w, c$
7. $\emptyset \mid g \rightarrow \quad \mid w, c$		

Fig. 1. A solution for Alcuin's river crossing puzzle. The partitions L_k, B_k, R_k are listed as $L_k \mid B_k \mid R_k$; the arrows $\rightarrow$ and $\leftarrow$ indicate the current direction of the boat.

We are interested in the smallest possible capacity of a boat for which a graph $G = (V, E)$ possesses a feasible schedule; this capacity is called the *Alcuin number* $\text{ALCUIN}(G)$ of the graph. In our graph-theoretic model Alcuin's river crossing problem corresponds to the path P_3 with three vertices w(olf), g(oat), c(abbage) and two edges $[w, g]$ and $[g, c]$. Figure 1 lists one possible feasible schedule for a boat of capacity $b = 1$. This implies $\text{ALCUIN}(P_3) = 1$.

A natural problem variant puts a hard constraint on the length of the schedule: Let $t \geq 1$ be an odd integer. The smallest possible capacity of a boat for which G possesses a feasible schedule with at most t boat trips is called the *t-trip constrained* Alcuin number $\text{ALCUIN}_t(G)$. Of course, $\text{ALCUIN}_1(G) = |V|$ holds for any graph G. For our example in Figure 1, it can be seen that $\text{ALCUIN}_1(P_3) = 3$, that $\text{ALCUIN}_t(P_3) = 2$ for $t \in \{3, 5\}$, and that $\text{ALCUIN}_t(P_3) = 1$ for $t \geq 7$.

Known results. The idea of generalizing Alcuin's problem to arbitrary conflict graphs goes back (at least) to Prisner [13] and Bahls [2]: Prisner introduced it in 2002 in his course on Discrete Mathematics at the University of Maryland, and Bahls discussed it in 2005 in a talk in the Mathematics Seminar at the University of North Carolina.

Bahls [2] (and later Lampis & Mitsou [9]) observed that it is NP-hard to compute the Alcuin number exactly; Lampis & Mitsou [9] also showed that the Alcuin number is hard to approximate. These negative results follow quite easily from the close relationship between the Alcuin number and the vertex cover number; see Lemma 1. The papers [2,9] provide a complete analysis of the Alcuin number of trees. Finally, Lampis & Mitsou [9] proved that the computation of the trip constrained Alcuin number $\text{ALCUIN}_3(G)$ is NP-hard.

Our results. We derive a variety of combinatorial and algorithmical results around the Alcuin number. As a by-product, our results also settle several open questions from [9].

Our main result is the structural characterization of the Alcuin number in Section 3. This characterization yields an NP-certificate for the Alcuin number. It also yields that every feasible schedule (possibly of exponential length) can be transformed into a feasible schedule of linear length.

The close relationship between the Alcuin number and the vertex cover number of a graph (see Lemma 1) naturally divides graphs into so-called *small-boat* and *big-boat* graphs. In Section 4 we derive a number of combinatorial lemmas around the division line between these two classes. All these lemmas fall out quite easily from our structural characterization. Standard techniques yield that computing the Alcuin number belongs to the class FPT of fixed-parameter tractable problems; see Section 5.

In Section 6 we discuss the computational hardness of the Alcuin number. First, we provide a new NP-hardness proof for this problem. Other proofs of this result are already in the literature [2,9], but we think that our three-line argument is considerably simpler than all previously published arguments. Secondly, we establish the NP-hardness of distinguishing small-boat graphs from big-boat graphs. Thirdly, we prove NP-hardness of computing the t-trip constrained Alcuin number $\text{ALCUIN}_t(G)$ for every fixed value $t \geq 3$.

In Section 7 we finally apply our machinery to chordal graphs, trees, and planar graphs, for which we get concise descriptions of the division line between small-boat and big-boat graphs. We also show that the Alcuin number of a bipartite graph can be determined in polynomial time.

2   Definitions and Preliminaries

We first recall some basic definitions. A set $S \subseteq V$ is a *stable* set for a graph $G = (V, E)$, if S does not induce any edges. The *stability number* $\alpha(G)$ of G

is the size of a largest stable set in G. A set $W \subseteq V$ is a *vertex cover* for G if $V - W$ is stable. The *vertex cover number* $\tau(G)$ of G is the size of a smallest vertex cover for G. We denote the set of neighbors of a vertex set $V' \subseteq V$ by $\Gamma(V')$.

The Alcuin number of a graph is closely related to its vertex cover number.

Lemma 1. *(Prisner [13]; Bahls [2]; Lampis & Mitsou [9])*
Every graph G satisfies $\tau(G) \leq \text{ALCUIN}(G) \leq \tau(G) + 1$.

Indeed during the first boat trip of any feasible schedule, the man leaves a stable set L_1 on the left bank and transports a vertex cover B_1 with the boat. This implies $b \geq \tau(G)$. And it is straightforward to find a schedule for a boat of capacity $\tau(G) + 1$: The man permanently keeps a smallest vertex cover $W \subseteq V$ in the boat, and uses the remaining empty spot to transport the items in $V - W$ one by one to the other bank.

The following observation follows from the inherent symmetry in conditions (FS1)–(FS3).

Lemma 2. *If $(L_1, B_1, R_1), \ldots, (L_s, B_s, R_s)$ is a feasible schedule for a graph G and a boat of capacity b, then also (R_s, B_s, L_s), $(R_{s-1}, B_{s-1}, L_{s-1})$, $\ldots$, (R_1, B_1, L_1) is a feasible schedule.*

3   A Concise Characterization

The definition of a feasible schedule does not a priori imply that the decision problem *"Given a graph G and a bound A, is $\text{ALCUIN}(G) \leq A$?"* is contained in the class NP: Since the length s of the schedule need not be polynomially bounded in the size of the graph G, this definition does not give us any obvious NP-certificate. The following theorem yields such an NP-certificate.

Theorem 1. *(Structure theorem)*
A graph $G = (V, E)$ possesses a feasible schedule for a boat of capacity $b \geq 1$, if and only if there exist five subsets X_1, X_2, X_3, Y_1, Y_2 of V that satisfy the following four conditions.

   (i) The three sets X_1, X_2, X_3 are pairwise disjoint. Their union $X := X_1 \cup X_2 \cup X_3$ forms a stable set in G.
   (ii) The (not necessarily disjoint) sets Y_1, Y_2 are non-empty subsets of the set $Y := V - X$, which satisfies $|Y| \leq b$.
   (iii) $X_1 \cup Y_1$ and $X_2 \cup Y_2$ are stable sets in G.
   (iv) $|Y_1| + |Y_2| \geq |X_3|$.

If these four conditions are satisfied, then there exists a feasible schedule of length at most $2|V| + 1$. This bound $2|V| + 1$ is the best possible (for $|V| \geq 3$).

As an illustration for Theorem 1, we once again consider Alcuin's problem with $b = 1$; see Figure 1. The corresponding sets in conditions (i)–(iv) then are

$X_1 = X_2 = \emptyset$, $X_3 = \{w, c\}$, and $Y_1 = Y_2 = \{g\}$. The rest of this section is dedicated to the proof of Theorem 1.

For the (only if)-part, we consider a feasible schedule (L_k, B_k, R_k) with $1 \le k \le s$. Without loss of generality we assume that $B_{k+1} \ne B_k$ for $1 \le k \le s - 1$. Lemma 1 yields that there exists a vertex cover $Y \subseteq V$ with $|Y| = b$ (which is not necessarily a vertex cover of minimum size). Then the set $X = V - Y$ is stable. We branch into three cases.

In the first case, there exists an index k for which $L_k \cap Y \ne \emptyset$ and $R_k \cap Y \ne \emptyset$. We set $Y_1 = L_k \cap Y$, $X_1 = L_k \cap X$, and $Y_2 = R_k \cap Y$, $X_2 = R_k \cap X$, and $X_3 = B_k \cap X$. This construction yields $X = X_1 \cup X_2 \cup X_3$, and obviously satisfies conditions (i), (ii), (iii). Since

$$|Y| = b \ge |B_k \cap X| + |B_k \cap Y| = |X_3| + (|Y| - |Y_1| - |Y_2|),$$

we also derive the inequality $|Y_1| + |Y_2| \ge |X_3|$ for condition (iv).

In the second case, there exists an index k with $1 < k < s$ such that $B_k = Y$. If index k is odd (and the boat is moving forward), our assumption $B_{k-1} \ne B_k \ne B_{k+1}$ implies that $L_{k-1} \cap Y \ne \emptyset$ and $R_{k+1} \cap Y \ne \emptyset$. We set $Y_1 = L_{k-1} \cap Y$, $X_1 = L_{k-1} \cap X$, and $Y_2 = R_{k+1} \cap Y$, $X_2 = R_{k+1} \cap X$, and $X_3 = (B_{k-1} \cup B_{k+1}) \cap X$. Then X_1, X_2, X_3 are pairwise disjoint, and conditions (i), (ii), (iii) are satisfied. Furthermore,

$$|Y| = b \ge |B_{k-1} \cap X| + |B_{k-1} \cap Y| = |B_{k-1} \cap X| + (|Y| - |Y_1|)$$

implies $|B_{k-1} \cap X| \le |Y_1|$, and a symmetric argument yields $|B_{k+1} \cap X| \le |Y_2|$. These two inequalities together imply $|Y_1| + |Y_2| \ge |X_3|$ for condition (iv). If the index k is even (and the boat is moving back), we proceed in a similar way with the roles of $k - 1$ and $k + 1$ exchanged.

The third case covers all remaining situations: All k satisfy $L_k \cap Y = \emptyset$ or $R_k \cap Y = \emptyset$, and all k with $1 < k < s$ satisfy $B_k \ne Y$. We consider two subcases. In subcase (a) we assume $R_s \cap Y \ne \emptyset$. We define $Y_1 = R_s \cap Y$ and $X_1 = R_s \cap X$, and we set $Y_2 = Y_1$, $X_2 = \emptyset$, and $X_3 = B_s \cap X$. Then conditions (i), (ii), (iii) are satisfied. Since

$$|Y| = b \ge |B_s \cap X| + |B_s \cap Y| = |X_3| + (|Y| - |Y_1|),$$

also condition (iv) holds. In subcase (b) we assume $R_s \cap Y = \emptyset$. We apply Lemma 2 to get a symmetric feasible schedule with $L_1 \cap Y = \emptyset$. We prove by induction that this new schedule satisfies $R_k \cap Y \ne \emptyset$ for all $k \ge 2$. First, $L_1 \cap Y = \emptyset$ implies $Y \subseteq B_1$, and then $B_2 \ne B_1$ implies $R_2 \cap Y \ne \emptyset$. In the induction step for $k \ge 3$ we have $R_{k-1} \cap Y \ne \emptyset$, and hence $L_{k-1} \cap Y = \emptyset$. If k is odd, then $R_k = R_{k-1}$ and we are done. If k is even, then $R_k \cap Y = \emptyset$ would imply $B_k = Y$, a contradiction. This completes the inductive argument. Since the new schedule has $R_s \cap Y \ne \emptyset$, we may proceed as in subcase (a). This completes the proof of the (only if)-part.

The proof of the (if)-part can be found in the full version of this paper.

4 Small Boats Versus Big Boats

By Lemma 1 every graph G has either $\text{ALCUIN}(G) = \tau(G)$ or $\text{ALCUIN}(G) = \tau(G) + 1$. In the former case we call G a *small-boat* graph, and in the latter case we call G a *big-boat* graph. Note that for a small-boat graph G with $b = \tau(G)$, the stable set X in Theorem 1 is a maximum size stable set and set Y is a minimum size vertex cover.

The following three lemmas provide tools for recognizing small-boat graphs.

Lemma 3. *Let $G = (V, E)$ be a graph, and let set $C \subseteq V$ induce a subgraph of G with stability number at most 2. If the graph $G - C$ has at least two non-trivial connected components, then G is a small-boat graph.*

PROOF. Let $V_1 \subseteq V$ denote the vertex set of a non-trivial connected component of $G - C$, and let $V_2 = V - (V_1 \cup C)$ be the vertex set of all other components. Let X be a stable set of maximum size in G.

We set $X_1 = V_1 \cap X$, $X_2 = V_2 \cap X$, and $X_3 = C \cap X$; note that $X_1 \cup X_2 \cup X_3 = X$ and $|X_3| \leq 2$. Since V_1 and V_2 both induce edges, $V_1 - X$ and $V_2 - X$ are non-empty. We put a single vertex from $V_2 - X$ into Y_1, and a single vertex from $V_1 - X$ into Y_2. This satisfies all conditions of the Structure Theorem 1. □

Lemma 4. *Let $G = (V, E)$ be a graph with a minimum vertex cover Y and a maximum stable set $X = V - Y$. If Y contains two (not necessarily distinct) vertices u and v that have at most two common neighbors in X, then G is a small-boat graph.* □

Lemma 5. *Let $G = (V, E)$ be a graph that has two distinct stable sets $S_1, S_2 \subseteq V$ of maximum size (or equivalently: two distinct vertex covers of minimum size). Then G is a small-boat graph.* □

The following lemma allows us to generate a plethora of small-boat and big-boat graphs.

Lemma 6. *Let $G = (V, E)$ be a graph with $\alpha(G) = s$, let I be a stable set on $q \geq 1$ vertices that is disjoint from V, and let G' be the graph that results from G and I by connecting every vertex in V to every vertex in I.*

Then G' is a small-boat graph if $s/2 \leq q \leq 2s$, and a big-boat graph if $q \geq 2s + 1$. □

The following Corollary 1 follows from Lemma 6. It also illustrates that the statement of Lemma 6 cannot be extended in any meaningful way to the cases with $1 \leq q < s/2$: If we join the graph $G = K_{s,s}$ with stability number s to a stable set I on q vertices, then the resulting tri-partite graph $K_{q,s,s}$ is a small-boat graph. On the other hand, if we join the graph $G = K_{q,s}$ with stability number s to a stable set I on q vertices, then the resulting tri-partite graph $K_{q,q,s}$ is a big-boat graph.

Corollary 1. *Let $k \geq 2$ and $1 \leq n_1 \leq n_2 \leq \cdots \leq n_k$ be positive integers. Then the complete k-partite graph $K_{n_1,\ldots,n_k}$ is a small-boat graph if $n_k \leq 2n_{k-1}$, and it is a big-boat graph otherwise.*

The following observation is a consequence of Lemma 3 (with $C = \emptyset$) and the Structure Theorem 1. It allows us to concentrate our investigations on connected graphs.

Lemma 7. *A disconnected graph G with $k \geq 2$ connected components is a big-boat graph, if and only if $k - 1$ components are isolated vertices, whereas the remaining component is a big-boat graph (which might be another isolated vertex).*

5   An Algorithmic Result

The following theorem demonstrates that determining the Alcuin number of a graph belongs to the class FPT of fixed-parameter tractable problems.

Theorem 2. *For a given graph G with n vertices and m edges and a given bound A, we can decide in $O(4^A mn)$ time whether $\textsc{Alcuin}(G) \leq A$.*

PROOF. The proof can be found in the full version of this paper. $\square$

6   Hardness Results

The reductions in this section are from the NP-hard VERTEX COVER and from the NP-hard STABLE SET problem; see Garey & Johnson [5]. Slightly weaker versions of the statements in Lemma 8 and 9, and also the restriction of Theorem 4 to three boat trips have been derived by Lampis & Mitsou [9].

The following observation implies that finding the Alcuin number is NP-hard for planar graphs and for graphs of bounded degree.

Lemma 8. *Let $\mathcal{G}$ be a graph class that is closed under taking disjoint unions. If the vertex cover problem is NP-hard for graphs in $\mathcal{G}$, then it is NP-hard to compute the Alcuin number for graphs in $\mathcal{G}$.*

PROOF. For a graph $G \in \mathcal{G}$, we consider the disjoint union G' of two independent copies of G. Then $\tau(G') = 2\,\tau(G)$, and Lemma 1 yields $2\,\tau(G) \leq \textsc{Alcuin}(G') \leq 2\,\tau(G) + 1$. Hence, we can deduce the vertex cover number $\tau(G)$ from $\textsc{Alcuin}(G')$. $\square$

The *approximability threshold* of a minimization problem $\mathcal{P}$ is the infimum of all real numbers $R \geq 1$ for which problem $\mathcal{P}$ possesses a polynomial time approximation algorithm with worst case ratio R. The approximability threshold of the vertex cover problem is known to lie somewhere between 1.36 and 2, and it is widely conjectured to be exactly 2; see for instance Khot & Regev [8].

Lemma 9. *The approximability threshold of the vertex cover problem coincides with the approximability threshold of the Alcuin number problem.*

PROOF.   First, we show that an approximation algorithm with worst case ratio R for VERTEX COVER implies an approximation algorithm with worst case ratio R for the Alcuin number problem. For an input graph G, we call the approximation algorithm for vertex cover and simply output its approximation of $\tau(G)$ as approximation A' of ALCUIN(G). Then Lemma 1 yields $A' \leq R \cdot \tau(G) \leq R \cdot$ ALCUIN(G).

Secondly, we show that an approximation algorithm with worst case ratio R for the Alcuin number problem implies an approximation algorithm with worst case ratio $R + \varepsilon$ for the VERTEX COVER, where $\varepsilon > 0$ can be brought arbitrarily close to 0. For an input graph G we first check whether $\tau(G) \leq R/\varepsilon$ holds. If it holds, then we compute the value $\tau(G)$ exactly in polynomial time; see Section 5. If it does not hold, then we call the approximation algorithm for the Alcuin number, and output its approximation of ALCUIN(G) as approximation τ' of $\tau(G)$. Then Lemma 1 yields $\tau' \leq R \cdot$ ALCUIN(G) $\leq R \cdot (\tau(G) + 1) \leq (R + \varepsilon)$ $\tau(G)$.   □

Theorem 3. *It is NP-hard to decide whether a given graph is a small-boat graph.*

PROOF. We show that if small-boat graphs can be recognized in polynomial time, then there existis a polynomial time algorithm for computing the stability number of a graph.

Indeed, consider a graph $G = (V, E)$ on $n = |V|$ vertices. For $q = 1, \ldots, 2n+1$, let I_q be a stable set on q vertices that is disjoint from V, and let G_q be the graph that results from G and I_q by connecting every vertex in V to every vertex in I_q. We check for every q whether G_q is small-boat, and we let q^* denote the largest index q for which G_q is small-boat. Lemma 6 yields that the stability number of G equals $q^*/2$.   □

Since the Structure Theorem 1 produces feasible schedules of length at most $2|V| + 1$, we have ALCUIN$_t(G) =$ ALCUIN(G) for all $t \geq 2|V| + 1$. Consequently, computing the t-trip constrained Alcuin number is NP-hard, if t is part of the input. The following theorem shows that this problem is NP-hard for every fixed $t \geq 3$.

Theorem 4. *Let $r \geq 1$ be a fixed integer bound. Then it is NP-hard to decide for a given graph and a given boat capacity, whether there exists a feasible schedule that only uses $2r + 1$ boat trips.*

PROOF. The proof can be found in the full version of this paper.   □

7   Special Graph Classes

In this section we discuss Alcuin number, small-boat graphs, and big-boat graphs in several classes of specially structured graphs.

7.1   Chordal Graphs and Trees

A *split graph* is a graph $G = (V, E)$ whose vertex set can be partitioned into a clique and a stable set; see Golumbic [6]. An equivalent characterization states that a graph is a split graph, if and only if it does not contain C_4, C_5, and $2K_2$ (= two independent edges) as induced subgraphs. *Chordal graphs* are the graphs in which every cycle of length exceeding three has a chord, that is, an edge joining two non-consecutive vertices in the cycle; see Golumbic [6]. An equivalent characterization states that a graph is chordal, if and only if every minimal vertex separator induces a clique. Note that split graphs and trees are special cases of chordal graphs.

The following lemma provides a complete charaterization of chordal small-boat graphs.

Lemma 10. *Let $G = (V, E)$ be a connected chordal graph. Then G is a small-boat graph, if and only if one of the following holds:*

(1) G is a split graph with a maximum stable set X and a clique $Y = V - X$, such that there exist two (not necessarily distinct) vertices u, v in Y that have at most two common neighbors in X.

(2) G is not a split graph. □

As a special case, Lemma 10 contains the following classification of trees (which has already been derived in [2,9]). Stars $K_{1,k}$ with $k \geq 3$ leaves are split graphs that do not satisfy condition (1) of Lemma 10; therefore they are big-boat graphs (note that this also follows from Lemma 6). All remaining trees T are small-boat graphs: Either such a tree T has two independent edges (and thus is small-boat), or it is of the following form: There are vertices $a_0, \ldots, a_k$ and $b_0, \ldots, b_\ell$ with $k, \ell \geq 0$, and edges $[a_0, a_i]$ for all $i > 0$, and edges $[b_0, b_j]$ for all $j > 0$. Then T is a split graph with clique $\{a_0, b_0\}$ that satisfies condition (1); hence T is small-boat.

7.2   Bipartite Graphs

The proof of the following theorem is centered around submodular functions. We recall that a function $f : 2^X \to \mathbb{R}$ over a set X is *submodular*, if $f(A) + f(B) \geq f(A \cup B) + f(A \cap B)$ holds for all $A, B \subseteq X$; see for instance Grötschel, Lovász & Schrijver [7] or Schrijver [14]. Standard examples of submodular functions are $f(A) = c|A|$ for any real parameter c, and the function $f(A) = |\Gamma(A)|$ that assigns to a subset $A \subseteq V$ of vertices the number of neighbors in an underlying graph. If $f(A)$ is submodular, then also $f_{\min}(A) = \min\{f(B) \mid B \subseteq A\}$ and $f'(A) = f(X - A)$ are submodular. Also the sum of two submodular functions is submodular. The minimum of a submodular function f can be determined in polynomial time [7,14].

Theorem 5. *For a bipartite graph $G = (V, E)$, the Alcuin number can be computed in polynomial time.*

PROOF. It is well-known that the stability number and the vertex cover number of a bipartite graph G can be computed in polynomial time; see for instance Lovász & Plummer [10]. Hence it is also easy to decide whether G has a unique maximum size stable set (for instance, by finding some maximum size stable set X, and by checking for every $x \in X$ whether $G - x$ has a stable set of cardinality $|X|$). If G possesses two distinct maximum size stable sets, then Lemma 5 yields $\text{ALCUIN}(G) = \tau(G)$. Hence, in the light of Theorem 1 the only interesting situation is the following: The graph G has a unique maximum size stable set X and a unique minimum size vertex cover $Y = V - X$. Do there exist sets X_1, X_2, X_3 and Y_1, Y_2 that satisfy conditions (i)–(iv)?

Let $V = V_1 \cup V_2$ denote a bipartition of V with $E \subseteq V_1 \times V_2$. If $Y \cap V_1 \neq \emptyset$ and $Y \cap V_2 \neq \emptyset$, then we may choose $X_1 = X \cap V_1$, $X_2 = X \cap V_2$, $X_3 = \emptyset$, and $Y_1 = Y \cap V_1$, $Y_2 = Y \cap V_2$. Otherwise $Y \subseteq V_1$ or $Y \subseteq V_2$ holds, and Y is also stable. Hence, we may concentrate on the case where $X = V_1$ and $Y = V_2$ form the bipartition. Our problem boils down to identifying the two disjoint sets X_1 and X_2: Then $X_3 = X - (X_1 \cup X_2)$ is fixed. By condition (iv), Y_1 should be chosen as large as possible and hence should be equal to $Y - \Gamma(X_1)$; symmetrically we set $Y_2 = Y - \Gamma(X_2)$. Condition (iv) can now be rewritten into

$$|\Gamma(X_1)| - |X_1| + |\Gamma(X_2)| - |X_2| \leq 2|Y| - |X|.$$

We define a function $f : 2^X \to \mathbb{R}$ by $f(X_1) = |\Gamma(X_1)| - |X_1|$, and a function $g : 2^X \to \mathbb{R}$ by $g(X_1) = \min\{f(X_2) \mid X_2 \subseteq X - X_1\}$. Since functions f, g, and their sum $f + g$ are submodular, the minimum of $f + g$ can be determined in polynomial time. If the corresponding minimum value is at most $2|Y| - |X|$, then $\text{ALCUIN}(G) = \tau(G)$. Otherwise $\text{ALCUIN}(G) = \tau(G) + 1$. □

7.3   Planar Graphs

Next, let us turn to planar and outer-planar graphs. Outer-planar graphs are easy to classify: Any outer-planar graph G with $\tau(G) = 1$ is a star, and hence a small-boat if and only if it has at most two leaves; see Section 7.1. Any outer-planar graph G with $\tau(G) \geq 2$ satisfies the conditions of Lemma 4 and thus is small-boat: Two arbitrary vertices u and v in a minimum vertex cover cannot have more than two common neighbors, since otherwise $K_{2,3}$ would occur as a subgraph. The behavior of general planar graphs is more interesting.

Lemma 11. *Every planar graph* $G = (V, E)$ *with* $\tau(G) \geq 5$ *is a small-boat graph.*

PROOF. Let $Y = \{y_1, \dots, y_t\}$ with $t \geq 5$ be a vertex cover of minimum size, and let $X = V - Y$ denote the corresponding stable set. For $y \in Y$ we denote by $\Gamma_x(y)$ the set of neighbors of y in X. If there exist two indices i, j with $1 \leq i < j \leq 5$ such that $\Gamma_x(y_i) \cap \Gamma_x(y_j)$ contains at most two vertices, then G is small-boat by Lemma 4. We will show that no other case can arise.

Suppose for the sake of contradiction that for every two indices i, j with $1 \leq i < j \leq 5$, the set $\Gamma_x(y_i) \cap \Gamma_x(y_j)$ contains at least three vertices. Then let a, b, c be three vertices in $\Gamma_x(y_1) \cap \Gamma_x(y_2)$. In any planar embedding of G the three paths $y_1 - a - y_2$, $y_1 - b - y_2$, $y_1 - c - y_2$ divide the plane into three regions. If two of y_3, y_4, y_5 would lie in different regions, they could not have three common neighbors; a contradiction. Hence y_3, y_4, y_5 all lie in the same region, say in the region bounded by $y_1 - a - y_2 - b - y_1$, and hence vertex c is not a neighbor of y_3, y_4, y_5. An analogous argument yields that for any $1 \leq i < j \leq 5$, the two vertices y_i and y_j have a common neighbor that is not adjacent to the other three vertices in $\{y_1, y_2, y_3, y_4, y_5\}$. This yields that G contains a subdivision of K_5, the desired contradiction.   □

The condition $\tau(G) \geq 5$ in Lemma 11 cannot be dropped, since there exists a variety of planar graphs G with $\tau(G) \leq 4$ that are big-boat. Consider for instance the following planar graph G: The vertex set contains four vertices y_1, y_2, y_3, y_4, and for every i, j with $1 \leq i < j \leq 4$ a set V_{ij} of $t \geq 3$ vertices. The edge set connects every vertex in V_{ij} to y_i and to y_j. It can be verified that G is planar, that $\tau(G) = 4$, and that $\text{ALCUIN}(G) = 5$.

Lemma 11 implies that there is a polynomial time algorithm that decides whether a planar graph G is small-boat or big-boat: In case G has a vertex cover of size at most 4 we use Theorem 2 to decide whether $\text{ALCUIN}(G) = \tau(G)$, and in case G has vertex cover number at least 5 we simply answer YES.

Summarizing, this yields the following (perhaps unexpected) situation: Although it is NP-hard to compute the Alcuin number and the vertex cover number of a planar graph, we can determine in polynomial time whether these two values coincide.

8   Conclusions

In this paper we have derived a variety of combinatorial, structural, algorithmical, and complexity theoretical results around a graph-theoretic generalization of Alcuin's river crossing problem.

Our investigations essentially revolved around three algorithmic problems: (1) Computation of the stability number; (2) Computation of the Alcuin number; (3) Recognition of small-boat graphs. All three problems are polynomially solvable, if the input graph has bounded treewidth (the Alcuin number can be computed along the lines of the standard dynamic programming approach).

Question 1. Does there exist a graph class $\mathcal{G}$, for which computing the stability number is easy, whereas computing the Alcuin number is hard?

In particular, the case of perfect graphs remains open. A graph is *perfect*, if for every induced subgraph the clique number coincides with the chromatic number; see for instance Golumbic [6]. Trees, split graphs, and chordal graphs are special cases of perfect graphs.

Question 2. Is there a polynomial time algorithm for computing the Alcuin number of a perfect graph?

Also the computational complexity of recognizing small-boat graphs remains unclear.

Question 3. Is the problem of recognizing small-boat graphs contained in NP?

We have proved that this problem is NP-hard, but there is no reason to assume that it lies in NP: To demonstrate that a graph is small-boat in a straightforward way, we have to show that its Alcuin number is small (NP-certificate) and that its vertex cover number is large (coNP-certificate). This mixture of NP- and coNP-certificates suggests that the problem might be located in one of the complexity classes above NP (see for instance Chapter 17 in Papadimitriou's book [12]); the complexity class DP might be a reasonable guess.

Acknowledgement. This research has been supported by the Netherlands Organisation for Scientific Research (NWO), grant 639.033.403; by DIAMANT (an NWO mathematics cluster); and by BSIK grant 03018 (BRICKS: Basic Research in Informatics for Creating the Knowledge Society).

References

1. Ascher, M.: A river-crossing problem in cross-cultural perspective. Mathematics Magazine 63, 26–29 (1990)
2. Bahls, P.: The wolf, the goat, and the cabbage: A modern twist on a classical problem. University of North Carolina Asheville (unpublished manuscript, 2005)
3. Biggs, N.L.: The roots of combinatorics. Historia Mathematica 6, 109–136 (1979)
4. Borndörfer, R., Grötschel, M., Löbel, A.: Alcuin's transportation problems and integer programming. In: Charlemagne and his heritage. 1200 years of civilization and science in Europe, Brepols, Turnhout, vol. 2, pp. 379–409 (1998)
5. Garey, M.R., Johnson, D.S.: Computers and Intractability: A Guide to the Theory of NP-Completeness. Freeman, San Francisco (1979)
6. Golumbic, M.C.: Algorithmic Graph Theory and Perfect Graphs. Academic Press, New York (1980)
7. Grötschel, M., Lovász, L., Schrijver, A.: Geometric algorithms and combinatorial optimization. Springer, New York (1988)
8. Khot, S., Regev, O.: Vertex cover might be hard to approximate to within $2 - \varepsilon$. Journal of Computer and System Sciences 74, 335–349 (2008)
9. Lampis, M., Mitsou, V.: The ferry cover problem. In: Crescenzi, P., Prencipe, G., Pucci, G. (eds.) FUN 2007. LNCS, vol. 4475, pp. 227–239. Springer, Heidelberg (2007)
10. Lovász, L., Plummer, M.D.: Matching Theory. Annals of Discrete Mathematics, vol. 29. North-Holland, Amsterdam (1986)
11. Niedermeier, R.: Invitation to Fixed-Parameter Algorithms. Oxford University Press, New York (2006)
12. Papadimitriou, C.H.: Computational Complexity. Addison-Wesley, Reading (1994)
13. Prisner, E.: Generalizing the wolf-goat-cabbage problem. Electronic Notes in Discrete Mathematics 27, 83 (2006)
14. Schrijver, A.: A combinatorial algorithm minimizing submodular functions in strongly polynomial time. Journal of Combinatorial Theory, Series B 80, 346–355 (2000)

Time-Dependent SHARC-Routing*

Daniel Delling

Universität Karlsruhe (TH), 76128 Karlsruhe, Germany
delling@ira.uka.de

Abstract. During the last years, many speed-up techniques for DIJK-
STRA's algorithm have been developed. As a result, computing a shortest
path in a *static* road network is a matter of microseconds. However, only
few of those techniques work in *time-dependent* networks. Unfortunately,
such networks appear frequently in reality: Roads are predictably con-
gestured by traffic jams, and efficient timetable information systems rely
on time-dependent networks. Hence, a fast technique for routing in such
networks is needed. In this work, we present an *exact* time-dependent
speed-up technique based on our recent SHARC-algorithm. As a result, we are able to efficiently compute shortest paths in time-dependent
continental-sized transportation networks, both of roads and of railways.

1 Introduction

Computing shortest paths in graphs is used in many real-world applications like
route planning in road networks, timetable information for railways, or scheduling for airplanes. In general, DIJKSTRA's algorithm [1] finds a shortest path
between a given source s and target t. Unfortunately, the algorithm is far too
slow to be used on huge datasets. Thus, several speed-up techniques have been
developed yielding faster query times for typical instances, e.g., road or railway
networks. See [2] for an overview. A major drawback of most existing speedup techniques is that their correctness depends on the fact that the network is
static, i.e., the network does *not* change between queries. Only [3,4] showed how
preprocessing can be updated if a road network is perturbed by a relatively small
number of traffic jams.

However, in real-world road networks, many traffic jams are predictable. This
can be modeled by a time-dependent network, where the travel time depends on
the departure time τ. Moreover, a very efficient model for timetable information
relies on time-dependent networks (cf. [5] for details) as well. Unfortunately,
none of the speed-up techniques yielding high speed-ups can be used in a time-
dependent network in a straight-forward manner. Moreover, possible problem
statements for shortest paths become even more complex in such networks. A
user could ask at what time she should depart in order to spend as little time
traveling as possible.

---

* Partially supported by the Future and Emerging Technologies Unit of EC (IST
priority – 6th FP), under contract no. FP6-021235-2 (project ARRIVAL).

D. Halperin and K. Mehlhorn (Eds.): ESA 2008, LNCS 5193, pp. 332–343, 2008.

Related Work. As already mentioned, a lot of speed-up techniques for static scenarios have been developed during the last years. Due to space limitations, we direct the interested reader to [2], which gives a good overview over static routing techniques. Much less work has been done on time-dependent routing. In [6], DIJKSTRA's algorithm is extended to the time-dependent case based on the assumption that the network fulfills the FIFO property. The FIFO property is also called the *non-overtaking property*, because it basically states that if A leaves an arbitrary node s before B, B cannot arrive at any node t before A. Computation of shortest paths in FIFO networks is polynomially solvable [7], while it is NP-hard in non-FIFO networks [8].

Goal-directed search, also called A^* [9], has been adapted to the previously described scenario; an efficient version for the static case has been presented in [10]. In [3], unidirectional ALT is evaluated on time-dependent graphs (fulfilling the FIFO property) yielding mild speed-ups of a factor between 3 and 5, depending on the degree of perturbation. Goal-directed search has also successfully been applied to time-dependent timetable networks [5,11]. Recently, it has been shown that time-dependent ALT can be used in a bidirectional manner [12]. However, in order to obtain faster queries than in the unidirectional case, the user has to accept approximative solutions. Moreover, our old implementation of static SHARC [13] already allowed fast *approximative* queries in a time-dependent scenario.

Our Contribution. In this work, we show how our recently developed SHARC-algorithm [13] can be generalized in such a way that we are able to perform exact shortest-path queries in time-dependent networks. The key observation is that the concept of SHARC stays untouched. However, at certain points we augment static routines to time-dependent ones. Moreover, we slightly adapt the intuition of Arc-Flags [14]. And finally, we deal with the problem that adding shortcuts to the graph is more expensive than in static scenarios. As a result, we are able to perform *exact* time-dependent queries in road and railway networks.

We start our work on time-dependent routing in Section 2 by introducing basic definitions and a short review of SHARC in static scenarios. Basic work on modeling time-dependency in road and railway networks is located in Section 3. Furthermore, we introduce basic algorithms that our preprocessing routines rely on. The preprocessing routine itself and the query algorithms of time-dependent SHARC are located in Section 4. We hereby show how the two main ingredients of SHARC, i.e., graph contraction and arc-flags computation, have to be altered for time-dependent networks. It turns out that the adaption of contraction is straight-forward, while arc-flags computation gets more expensive: The key observation is that we have to alter the intuition of arc-flags slightly for correct routing in time-dependent networks. We also show how SHARC can be used to compute a shortest path between two points for all possible departure times.

In order to show that time-dependent SHARC performs well in real-world environments, we present an extensive experimental evaluation in Section 5. Section 6 concludes our work with a summary and possible future research.

2   Preliminaries

The major difference between static and time-dependent routing is the usage of functions instead of constants for specifying edge weights. Throughout the whole work, we restrict ourselves to a function space $\mathbb{F}$ consisting of positive *periodic* functions $f : \Pi \to \mathbb{R}^+, \Pi = [0, p], p \in \mathbb{N}$ such that $f(0) = f(p)$ and $f(x) + x \leq f(y) + y$ for any $x, y \in \Pi, x \leq y$. In the following, we call Π the *period* of the input. The composition of two functions $f, g \in \mathbb{F}$ is defined by $(f \oplus g)(x) := f(x) + g((f(x) + x) \bmod p)$. Moreover, we need to *merge* functions. The merged function h of two functions f, g is defined by $h(x) = \min\{f(x), g(x)\}$. Comparison of functions is defined as follows: $f < g$ means that $f(x) < g(x)$ holds for all $x \in \Pi$. The upper bound of f is noted by $\overline{f} = \max_{x \in \Pi} f(x)$, the lower by $\underline{f} = \min_{x \in \Pi} f(x)$. An underapproximation $\downarrow f$ of a function f is a function such that $\downarrow f(x) \leq f(x)$ holds for all $x \in \Pi$. An overapproximation $\uparrow f$ is defined analogously. We also restrict ourselves to simple, directed graphs $G = (V, E)$ with time-dependent length functions $len : E \to \mathbb{F}$. Note that our networks fullfill the FIFO-property if we interpret the length of an edge as travel times due to our choice of $\mathbb{F}$. The reverse graph $\overline{G} = (V, \overline{E})$ is the graph obtained from G by substituting each $(u, v) \in E$ by (v, u). The 2-core of an undirected graph is the maximal node induced subgraph of minimum node degree 2. The 2-core of a directed graph is the 2-core of the corresponding simple, unweighted, undirected graph. A *partition* of V is a family $\mathcal{C} = \{C_0, C_1, \ldots, C_k\}$ of sets $C_i \subseteq V$ such that each node $v \in V$ is contained in exactly one set C_i. An element of a partition is called a *cell*. A *multilevel partition* of V is a family of partitions $\{\mathcal{C}^0, \mathcal{C}^1, \ldots, \mathcal{C}^l\}$ such that for each $i < l$ and each $C_n^i \in \mathcal{C}^i$ a cell $C_m^{i+1} \in \mathcal{C}^{i+1}$ exists with $C_n^i \subseteq C_m^{i+1}$. In that case the cell C_m^{i+1} is called the *supercell* of C_n^i. The supercell of a level-l cell is V. The *boundary nodes* B_C of a cell C are all nodes $u \in C$ for which at least one node $v \in V \setminus C$ exists such that $(v, u) \in E$ or $(u, v) \in E$.

By $d(s, t, \tau)$ we denote the distance between $s, t \in V$ if departing from s at time τ. The distance-label, i.e., the distance between s and t for all possible departure times $\in \Pi$, is given by $d_*(s, t)$. Note that the distance-label is a function $\in \mathbb{F}$. In the following, we call a query for determining $d(s, t, \tau)$ an *s-t time-query*, while a query for computing $d_*(s, t)$ is denoted by *s-t profile-query*.

Static SHARC-Routing. The classic arc-flag approach [14] first computes a partition $\mathcal{C}$ of the graph and then attaches a *label* to each edge e. A label contains, for each cell $C_i \in \mathcal{C}$, a flag $AF_{C_i}(e)$ which is *true* iff a shortest path to a node in C_i starts with e. A modified DIJKSTRA then only considers those edges for which the flag of the target node's cell is *true*. SHARC [13] extends and combines ideas of Arc-Flags and hierarchical approaches [18,17]. Preprocessing of static SHARC is divided into three sections. During the *initialization* phase, we extract the 2-core of the graph and perform a *multi-level* partition of G. Then, an *iterative* process starts. At each step i we first *contract* the graph by *bypassing* low-degree nodes and set the arc-flags *automatically* for each removed edge. On the contracted graph we compute the arc-flags of level i by growing a *partial* centralized shortest-path tree from each cell C_j^i. At the end of each step we *prune* the input by detecting those edges that already have their final arc-flags assigned. In the *finalization* phase, we assemble the output-graph, refine arc-flags of edges removed during contraction and finally reattach the nodes removed at the beginning. The query of static SHARC is a multi-level Arc-Flags DIJKSTRA adapted from a two-level Arc-Flags setup [14].

3   Models and Basic Algorithms

In this section, we introduce our approach how to model time-dependency in road and railway networks efficiently. In particular, we present our label-correcting algorithm, which is a main ingredient of time-dependent SHARC-preprocessing.

Modeling Time-Dependency. We apply two types of edge-functions, one for road networks, the other one for timetable information.

In *road networks*, we use a piece-wise linear function for modeling time-dependency. Each edge gets assigned a number of sample points that depict the travel time on this road at the specific time. Evaluating a function at time τ is then done by linear interpolation between the points left and right to τ. Let $P(f)$ be the number of interpolation points of f. Then the composed function $f \oplus g$, modeling the duration for traversing g after f, may have up to $P(f) + P(g)$ number of interpolation points in worst case. This is one of the main problems when routing in time-dependent graphs: Almost all speed-up techniques developed for static scenarios rely on adding long shortcuts to the graph. While this is "cheap" for static scenarios, the insertion of time-dependent shortcuts yields a high amount of preprocessed data. Even worse, merging travel-functions, modeling the merge of two parallel edges into one, increases $|P|$ as well.

In *timetable graphs*, time-dependent edges model several trains running on the same route from one station to another. For each such connection, we add an interpolation point to the corresponding edge. The timestamp σ of the interpolation point is the departure time, the weight w the travel time. When we want to evaluate a time-dependent edge at a specific time τ, we identify the interpolation point with minimum $\sigma - \tau \geq 0$. Then the resulting traveltime is $w + \sigma - \tau$, i.e., the waiting time for the next connection plus its travel duration.

Note that composing two timetable edge-functions f, g is less expensive than in road networks. More precisely, $P(f \oplus g) = \min\{P(f), P(g)\}$ holds as the number of relevant departure times is dominated by the edge with less connections. Merging functions, however, may increase the number of interpolation points.

Label-Correcting Algorithms. As already mentioned, computing $d(s, t, \tau)$ can be solved by a modified DIJKSTRA [6]. However, computing $d_*(s, t)$ is more expensive but can be computed by a label-correcting algorithm [15]. Such an algorithm can be implemented very similarly to DIJKSTRA. The source node s is initialized with a constant label $d_*(s, s) = 0$, any other node u with a constant label $d_*(s, u) = \infty$. Then, in each iteration step, a node u with minimum

$d_*(s, u)$ is removed from the priority queue. Then for all outgoing edges (u, v) a temporary label $l(v) = d_*(s, u) \oplus len(u, v)$ is created. If $l(v) \geq d_*(s, v)$ does *not* hold, $l(v)$ yields an improvement. Hence, $d_*(s, v)$ is updated to $\min\{l(v), d_*(s, v)\}$ and v is inserted into the queue. We may stop the routine if we remove a node u from the queue with $\underline{d}(s, u) \geq \overline{d}(s, t)$. If we want to compute $d_*(s, t)$ for many nodes $t \in V$, we apply a label-correcting algorithm and stop the routine as soon as our stopping criterion holds for all t. Note that we may reinsert nodes into the queue that have already been removed by this procedure. Also note that when applied to a graph with constant edge-functions, this algorithm equals a normal DIJKSTRA. An interesting result from [15] is the fact that the runtime of label-correcting algorithms highly depends on the complexity of the edge-functions.

In the following, we construct *shortest-path DAGs*, i.e., compute $d_*(s, u)$ for a given source s and all nodes $u \in V$, with our label-correcting algorithm. We call an edge (v, u) a *DAG-edge* if $d_*(s, v) \oplus (v, u) > d_*(s, u)$ does *not* hold. In other words, (u, v) is a DAG-edge iff it is part of a shortest path from s to v for at least one departure time.

4   Exact Time-Dependent SHARC

In static scenarios, a true arc-flag $AF_C(e)$ denotes whether e has to be considered for a shortest-path query targeting a node within C. In other words, the flag is set if e is important for (at least one target node) in C. In a time-dependent scenario, we use the following intuition to set arc-flags: an arc-flag $AF_C(e)$ is set to true, if e is important for C at least once during Π. In the following, we show how to adapt preprocessing of SHARC in order to reflect this intuition correctly. Moreover, we present the time-dependent query algorithm.

4.1   Time-Dependent Preprocessing

Initialization. In a first step, we extract the 2-core from the graph since we can directly assign correct arc-flags to all edges outside the 2-core: Edges targeting the 2-core get full flags assigned, others only get the own-cell flag set to true. Note that this procedure is independent from edge weights. Next, we perform a multi-level partitioning—using SCOTCH [16]—of the *unweighted* graph.

Iteration. Next, an iterative process starts. Each iteration step is divided into three parts, described in the following: contraction, edge reduction, arc-flag computation.

Contraction. Our time-dependent contraction routine works very similar to a static one [2,17]: We iteratively *bypass* nodes until no node is *bypassable* any more. To bypass a node n we first remove n, its incoming edges I and its outgoing edges O from the graph. Then, for each combination of $e_i \in I$ and $e_o \in O$, we introduce a new edge of the length $len(e_i) \oplus len(e_o)$. Note that we explicitly allow multi-edges. Hence, each shortcut represents exactly one path in the graph, making shortcut unpacking easier. We call the number of edges of the path that a shortcut represents on the graph at the beginning of the current iteration step the *hop number* of the shortcut. Note that in road networks, contraction gets more expensive in terms of memory consumption because the number of interpolation points of an added shortcut is roughly the sum of the number of interpolation points of the arcs the shortcuts is assembled from. Moreover, merging a short-cut with an existing edge may increase the number of interpolation points even further. Hence, the choice of which node to bypass next is even more important for the time-dependent scenario than for the static one. We use a heap to determine the next bypassable node [17]. Let #*shortcut* of *new* edges that would be inserted into the graph if n is bypassed and let $\zeta(n) =$#shortcut$/(|I| + |O|)$ be the *expansion* [17] of node n. Furthermore, let $h(n)$ be the hop number of the hop-maximal shortcut, and let $p(n)$ be the number of interpolation points of the shortcut with most interpolation points, that would be added if n was bypassed. Then we set the key of a node n within the heap to $h(n)+p(n)+10\cdot\zeta(n)$, smaller keys have higher priority. By this ordering for bypassing nodes we prefer nodes whose removal yield few additional shortcuts with a small hop number and few interpolation points.

To keep the costs of shortcuts limited we do not bypass a node if its removal would either result in a shortcut with more than 200 interpolation points or a hop number greater than 10. We say that the nodes that have been bypassed belong to the *component*, while the remaining nodes are called *core-nodes*. Note that in order to guarantee correctness, we have to use *cell-aware* contraction, i.e., a node n is never marked bypassable if any of its neighboring nodes is *not* in the same cell as n.

Edge-Reduction [4]. Note that our contraction potentially adds shortcuts not needed for keeping the distances in the core correct. Hence, we perform an edge reduction directly after each contraction. We grow a shortest-path DAG from each node u of the core. We stop the growth as soon as all neighbors t of u have their final label assigned. Then we check all neighbors whether $d_*(u,t) < len(u,t)$ holds. If it holds, we can remove (u,t) from the graph because for all possible departure times, the path from u to t does not include (u,t). In order to limit the running time of this procedure, we restrict the number of priority-queue removals to 100. Hence, we may leave some unneeded edges in the graph.

Arc-Flags. We have to set arc-flags for all edges of our output-graph, including those which we remove during contraction. Like for static SHARC, we can set arc-flags for all removed edges automatically. We set the arc-flags of the current and all higher levels depending on the source node s of the deleted edge. If s is a core node, we only set the own-cell flag to *true* (and others to false) because this edge can only be relevant for a query targeting a node in this cell. If s belongs to the component, all arc-flags are set to *true* as a query has to leave the component in order to reach a node outside this cell.

Setting arc-flags of those edges not removed from the graph is more expensive. A straight-forward adaption of computing arc-flags in a time-dependent graph is to grow a shortest-path DAG in $\overline{G}$ for all boundary nodes $b \in B_C$ of all cells C at level i. We stop the growth as soon as $d_*(u, b) \geq \overline{d_*}(v, b)$ holds for all nodes v in the supercell of C and all nodes u in the priority queue. Then we set $AF_C(u, v) = true$ if (u, v) is a DAG-edge for at least one DAG grown from all boundary nodes $b \in B_C$.

However, this approach would require to compute a full label-correcting algorithm on the backward graph from each boundary node yielding too long preprocessing times for large networks. Recall that the running time of growing DAGs is dominated by the complexity of the function. Hence, we may grow two DAGs for each boundary node, the first uses $\uparrow len$ as length functions, the latter $\downarrow len$. As we use approximations with a constant number of interpolation points (we use 48), growing two such DAGs is faster than growing one exact one. We end up in two distance labels per node u, one being an overapproximation, the other being an underapproximation of the correct label. Then, we set $AF_C(u, v) = true$ if $len(u, v) \oplus \uparrow d_*(v, b_C) > \downarrow d_*(u, b_C)$ does not hold. If networks get so big that even setting approximative labels is prohibited due to running times, one can even use upper and lower bounds for the labels. This has the advantage that building two shortest-path trees per boundary node is sufficient for setting correct arc-flags. The first uses $\overline{len}$ as length function, the other $\underline{len}$. Note that by approximating arc-flags the quality of them may decrease but correctness is untouched. Thus, queries remain correct but may become slower.

Finalization. The last phase of our preprocessing-routine first assembles the output graph. It contains the original graph, shortcuts added during preprocessing and arc-flags for all edges of the output graph. However, some edge may have no arc-flag set to true, which we can safely remove from the output graph.

Arc-Flags Refinement. During the iteration-phase we set sub-optimal arc-flags to edges originating from component nodes. However, a query starting from a node u being part of the a component has to leave the component via core-nodes. We call those nodes the exit nodes of u. The idea of arc-flags refinement is to propagate the flags from the exit nodes to edges outgoing from u. For details, see [13]. This routine can directly be adapted to a time-dependent scenario by growing shortest-paths DAGs from each u. However, we limit the growth of those DAGs to 1000 priority-queue removals due to performance. In order to preserve correctness, we then may only propagate the flags from the exit nodes to u if the stopping criterion is fulfilled before this number of removals.

Shortcut-Removal. As already mentioned, time-dependent shortcuts are very space-consuming. Hence, we try to remove shortcuts as the very last step of preprocessing. The routine works as follows. For each added shortcut (u, v) we analyze the shortest path it represents. If all nodes on this shortest path have a degree less than 3, we remove (u, v) from the graph and all edges being part of the shortest path additionally inherit the arc-flags from (u, v).

4.2   Query

Time-dependent SHARC allows time- and profile-queries. For computing $d_\tau(s, t)$, we use a modified DIJKSTRA that operates on the output graph. The modifications are as follows: When settling a node n, we compute the lowest level i on which n and the target node t are in the same supercell. In order to keep the effort for this operation as small as possible we use such a numbering of cells such that the common level can be computed by the most significant bit of current and target cell. Moreover, we consider only those edges outgoing from n having a set arc-flag on level i for the corresponding cell of t. In other words, we *prune* edges that are not important for the current query. We stop the query as soon as we settle t. For computing $d_*(s, t)$, we use a modified variant of our label-correcting algorithm (see Section 3) that also operates on the output graph. The modifications are the same as for time-queries and the stopping criterion is the standard one explained in Section 3.

SHARC adds shortcuts to the graph in order to accelerate queries. If the complete description of the path is needed, the shortcuts have to be unpacked. As we allow multi-edges during contraction, each shortcut represents exactly one path in the network, and hence, we can directly apply the unpacking routine from Highway Hierarchies [18].

5   Experiments

In this section, we present our experimental evaluation. To this end, we evaluate the performance of time-dependent SHARC for road and railway networks. Our implementation is written in C++ using solely the STL. As priority queue we use a binary heap. Our tests were executed on one core of an AMD Opteron 2218 running SUSE Linux 10.3. The machine is clocked at 2.6 GHz, has 16 GB of RAM and 2 x 1 MB of L2 cache. The program was compiled with GCC 4.2, using optimization level 3.

Default Setting. Unless otherwise stated, we use a 7-level partition with 4 cells per supercell on levels 0 to 5 and 104 cells on level 6 for road networks. As railway networks are smaller, we use a 3-level setup with 8 cells per supercell on levels 0 to 1 and 112 cells on level 2 for such networks. We use $c = 2.5$ as contraction parameter for the all levels. The hop-bound of our contraction is set to 10, the interpolation-bound to 200.

In the following, we report preprocessing times and the overhead of the pre-processed data in terms of *additional* bytes per node. Moreover, we report two types of queries: *time-queries*, i.e., queries for a specific departure time, and *profile-queries*, i.e., queries for computing $d_*(s, t)$. For each type we provide the average number of settled nodes, i.e., the number of nodes taken from the priority queue, and the average query time. For *s-t* profile-queries, the nodes s and t are picked uniformly at random. Time-queries additionally need a departure time τ as well, which we pick uniformly at random as well. All figures in this paper are based on 1 000 random *s-t* queries and refer to the scenario that only the lengths of the shortest paths have to be determined, without outputting a complete description of the paths. However, our shortcut expansion routine needs less than 1 ms to output the whole path; the additional space overhead is ≈ 4 bytes per node.

5.1 Time-Dependent Timetable Information

Our timetable data—provided by Hacon for scientific use—of Europe consists of 30 516 stations and 1 775 482 elementary connections. The period is 24 hours. The resulting realistic, i.e., including transfer times, time-dependent network (cf. [5] for details on modeling issues) has about 0.5 million nodes and 1.4 million edges. Table 1 reports the performance of time-dependent SHARC using this input. We report the performance of two variants of SHARC: the economical version computes DIJKSTRA-based arc-flags on all levels, while our generous variant computes *exact* flags during the last iteration step. Note that we do *not* use additional techniques in order to improve query performance, e.g. the *avoid binary search* technique (cf. [5] for details). For comparison, we also report the results for plain DIJKSTRA and unidirectional ALT [3].

We observe a good performance of SHARC in general. Queries for a specific departure times are up to 29.7 times faster than plain DIJKSTRA in terms of search space. This lower search space yields a speed-up of a factor of 26.6. This gap originates from the fact that SHARC operates on a graph enriched by shortcuts. As shortcuts tend to have many interpolation points, evaluating them is more expensive than original edges. As expected, our economical variant is slower than the generous version but preprocessing is almost 8 times faster. Recall that the only difference between both version is the way arc-flags are computed during the last iteration step. Although the number of heap operations is nearly the same for running one label-correcting algorithm per boundary node as for growing two DIJKSTRA-trees, the former has to use functions as labels. As composing and merging functions is more expensive than adding and comparing integers, preprocessing times increase significantely.

Table 1. Performance of time-dependent DIJKSTRA, uni-directional ALT and SHARC using our timetable data as input. Preprocessing times are given in hours and minutes, the overhead in bytes per node. Moreover, we report the increase in edge count over the input. #delete mins denotes the number of nodes removed from the priority queue, query *times* are given in milliseconds. Moreover, *speed-up* reports the speed-up over the corresponding value for plain DIJKSTRA.

technique	PREPRO time [h:m]	space [B/n]	edge inc.	TIME-QUERIES #delete mins	speed up	time [ms]	speed up	PROFILE-QUERIES #delete mins	speed up	time [ms]	speed up
Dijkstra	0:00	0	0%	260 095	1.0	125.2	1.0	1 919 662	1.0	5 327	1.0
uni-ALT	0:02	128	0%	127 103	2.0	75.3	1.7	1 434 112	1.3	4 384	1.2
eco SHARC	1:30	113	74%	32 575	8.0	17.5	7.2	181 782	10.6	988	5.4
gen SHARC	12:15	120	74%	8 771	29.7	4.7	26.6	55 306	34.7	273	19.5

Comparing time- and profile-queries, we observe that computing d_* instead of d yields an increase of about factor $4-7$ in terms of heap operations. Again, as composing and merging functions is more expensive than adding and comparing integers, the loss in terms of running times is much higher. Still, both our SHARC-variants are capable of computing d_* for two random stations in less than 1 second.

5.2   Time-Dependent Road Networks

Unfortunately, we have no access to *large* real-world time-dependent road networks. Hence, we use available *real-world* time-independent networks and generate synthetic rush hours. As network, we use the largest strongly connected component of the road network of Western Europe, provided by PTV AG for scientific use. The graph has approximately 18 million nodes and 42.6 million edges and edge lengths correspond to (time-independent) travel times. Each edge belongs to one of five main categories representing motorways, national roads, local streets, urban streets, and rural roads. In order to generate synthetic time-dependent edge costs, we use the generator introduced in [12]. The methods developed there are based on statistics gathered using real-world data on a limited-size road network. The period is set to 24 hours. For details, see [12]. We additionally adjust the degree of perturbation by assigning time-dependent edge-costs only to specific categories of edges. In a *low traffic* scenario, only motorways are time-dependent. The *medium traffic* scenario additionally includes congested national roads, and for the *high traffic* scenario, we pertube all edges except local and rural roads. For comparison, we also report the performance of *static* SHARC in a *no traffic* scenario, i.e., all edges are time-independent.

Table 2 reports the results of SHARC in our different scenarios. Note that we use the same parameters for all inputs and also report the speed-up over DIJKSTRA's algorithm in terms of query performance. Unfortunately, it turned out that this input is too big to use a label-correcting algorithm for computing arc-flags. Hence, we use DIJKSTRA-based approximation of arc-flags for all levels. Note that this type of preprocessing equates our economical variant from the last section. We observe that the degree of perturbation has a high influence on both preprocessing and query performance of SHARC. Preprocessing times increase if more edges are time-dependent. This is mainly due to our

Table 2. Performance of SHARC on our time-dependent European road network instance. Note that profile-queries are reported in *seconds*, while time-queries are given in *milliseconds*. Also note that we apply static SHARC for the no traffic scenario.

	PREPRO			TIME-QUERIES				PROFILE-QUERIES	
	time	space	edge	#delete	speed	time	speed	#delete	time
scenario	[h:m]	[B/n]	inc.	mins	up	[ms]	up	mins	[s]
no traffic	0:41	13.7	27%	997	8830	0.42	13369	–	–
low traffic	4:03	27.2	31%	34123	261	26.12	214	37980	35.28
medium traffic	6:10	45.6	32%	51738	173	38.05	148	57761	61.05
high traffic	8:31	112.4	34%	84234	105	75.33	76	92413	154.32

refinement phase that uses partial label-correcting algorithms in order to improve the quality of arc-flags. The increase in overhead derives from the fact that the number of additional interpolation points for shortcuts increases. Analyzing time-query performance of SHARC, we observe that in a our scenario where only motorways are time-dependent, SHARC provides speed-ups of up to 214 over DIJKSTRA. However, this values drops to 76 if more and more edges become time-dependent. The reason for this loss in query performance is the bad quality of our DIJKSTRA-based approximation. If more edges are time-dependent, upper- and lower-bounds are less tight than in a scenario with only few time-dependent edges. Comparing time- and profile-queries, we observe that the search-space only increases by $\approx 10\%$ when running profile- instead of the time-queries. However, due to the high number of interpolation points of the labels propagated through the network, profile-queries are up to 1200 times slower than time-queries. Comparing the figures from Tab. 1 and 2, we observe that speed-ups for time-queries in road networks are higher than in railway networks. However, the situation changes when running profile-queries. Here, timetable queries are much faster than queries in road networks. The reason for this is that composing functions needed for timetables is cheaper than those needed for road networks.

Summarizing, average time-query times are below 100 ms for all scenarios, while plain DIJKSTRA has query times of about 5.6 seconds. Moreover, for the probably most important scenario, i.e., the medium traffic scenario, SHARC provides query times of about 38 ms being sufficient for many applications. Moreover, SHARC allows profile-queries that cannot be handled by a plain label-correcting algorithm due to memory consumption.

6   Conclusion

In this work, we presented the first efficient speed-up technique for exact routing in large time-dependent transportation networks. We generalized the recently introduced SHARC-algorithm by augmenting several static routines of the preprocessing to time-dependent variants. In addition, we introduced routines to handle the problem of expensive shortcuts. As a result, we are able to run fast queries on continental-sized transportation networks of both roads and of railways. Moreover, we are able to compute the distances between two nodes for all possible departure times.

Regarding future work, one could think of faster ways of composing, merging, and approximating piece-wise linear functions as this would directly accelerate preprocessing and, more importantly, profile-queries significantly. Another interesting question is, whether SHARC is helpful to run multi-criteria queries in time-dependent graphs. The good performance of the multi-metric variant of static SHARC [13] might be a good indicator that this works well. This is very interesting for timetable information systems as users may be willing to accept longer travel times if the required number of transfers is smaller.

Acknowledgments. The author thanks Veit Batz, Reinhard Bauer, Robert Görke, Riko Jacob, Bastian Katz, Ignaz Rutter, Peter Sanders, Dominik Schultes and Dorothea Wagner for interesting discussions on time-dependent routing. Moreover, I thank Giacomo Nannicini for providing me with his time-dependent edge-cost generator, and Thomas Pajor for his work on timetable data parsers.

References

1. Dijkstra, E.W.: A Note on Two Problems in Connexion with Graphs. Numerische Mathematik 1, 269–271 (1959)
2. Schultes, D.: Route Planning in Road Networks. PhD thesis, Uni. Karlsruhe (2008)
3. Delling, D., Wagner, D.: Landmark-Based Routing in Dynamic Graphs. In: Demetrescu, C. (ed.) WEA 2007. LNCS, vol. 4525, pp. 52–65. Springer, Heidelberg (2007)
4. Schultes, D., Sanders, P.: Dynamic Highway-Node Routing. In: Demetrescu, C. (ed.) WEA 2007. LNCS, vol. 4525, pp. 66–79. Springer, Heidelberg (2007)
5. Pyrga, E., Schulz, F., Wagner, D., Zaroliagis, C.: Efficient Models for Timetable Information in Public Transportation Systems. ACM J. of Exp. Al. 12, 2–4 (2007)
6. Cooke, K., Halsey, E.: The Shortest Route Through a Network with Time-Dependent Intermodal Transit Times. Journal of Mathematical Analysis and Applications, 493–498 (1966)
7. Kaufman, D.E., Smith, R.L.: Fastest Paths in Time-Dependent Networks for Intelligent Vehicle-Highway Systems Application. Journal of Intelligent Transportation Systems 1, 1–11 (1993)
8. Orda, A., Rom, R.: Shortest-Path and Minimum Delay Algorithms in Networks with Time-Dependent Edge-Length. Journal of the ACM 37, 607–625 (1990)
9. Hart, P.E., Nilsson, N., Raphael, B.: A Formal Basis for the Heuristic Determination of Minimum Cost Paths. IEEE Transactions on Systems Science and Cybernetics 4, 100–107 (1968)
10. Goldberg, A.V., Harrelson, C.: Computing the Shortest Path: A* Search Meets Graph Theory. In: 16th Annual ACM–SIAM Symposium on Discrete Algorithms (SODA), pp. 156–165 (2005)
11. Disser, Y., Müller-Hannemann, M., Schnee, M.: Multi-Criteria Shortest Paths in Time-Dependent Train Networks. In: McGeoch, C.C. (ed.) WEA 2008. LNCS, vol. 5038, pp. 347–361. Springer, Heidelberg (2008)
12. Nannicini, G., Delling, D., Liberti, L., Schultes, D.: Bidirectional A* Search for Time-Dependent Fast Paths. In: McGeoch, C.C. (ed.) WEA 2008. LNCS, vol. 5038, pp. 334–346. Springer, Heidelberg (2008)
13. Bauer, R., Delling, D.: SHARC: Fast and Robust Unidirectional Routing. In: 10th Workshop on Algorithm Engineering and Experiments (ALENEX), pp. 13–26 (2008)
14. Hilger, M., Köhler, E., Möhring, R.H., Schilling, H.: Fast Point-to-Point Shortest Path Computations with Arc-Flags. In: 9th DIMACS Implementation Challenge - Shortest Paths (2006)
15. Dean, B.C.: Continuous-Time Dynamic Shortest Path Algorithms. Master's thesis, Massachusetts Institute of Technology (1999)
16. Pellegrini, F.: SCOTCH: Static Mapping, Graph, Mesh and Hypergraph Partitioning, and Parallel and Sequential Sparse Matrix Ordering Package (2007)
17. Goldberg, A.V., Kaplan, H., Werneck, R.F.: Better Landmarks Within Reach. In: Demetrescu, C. (ed.) WEA 2007. LNCS, vol. 4525, pp. 38–51. Springer, Heidelberg (2007)
18. Delling, D., Sanders, P., Schultes, D., Wagner, D.: Highway Hierarchies Star. In: 9th DIMACS Implementation Challenge - Shortest Paths (2006)

Detecting Regular Visit Patterns

Bojan Djordjevic[1,2], Joachim Gudmundsson[2], Anh Pham[1,2],
and Thomas Wolle[2]

[1] School of Information Technologies, University of Sydney, NSW 2006, Australia
bojan@cs.usyd.edu.au, vinhanh@gmail.com
[2] NICTA* Sydney, Locked Bag 9013, Alexandria NSW 1435, Australia
{joachim.gudmundsson,thomas.wolle}@nicta.com.au

Abstract. We are given a trajectory T and an area A. T might intersect A several times, and our aim is to detect whether T visits A with some regularity, e.g. what is the longest time span that a GPS-GSM equipped elephant visited a specific lake on a daily (weekly or yearly) basis, where the elephant has to visit the lake *most* of the days (weeks or years), but not necessarily on *every* day (week or year).

During the modelling of such applications, we encounter an elementary problem on bitstrings, that we call LDS (LONGESTDENSESUBSTRING). The bits of the bitstring correspond to a sequence of regular time points, in which a bit is set to 1 iff the trajectory T intersects the area A at the corresponding time point. For the LDS problem, we are given a string s as input and want to output a longest substring of s, such that the ratio of 1's in the substring is at least a certain threshold.

In our model, LDS is a core problem for many applications that aim at detecting regularity of T intersecting A. We propose an optimal algorithm to solve LDS, and also for related problems that are closer to applications, we provide efficient algorithms for detecting regularity.

1 Introduction

Recent technological advances of location-aware devices and mobile phone networks provide increasing opportunities to trace moving individuals. As a result many different areas including geography, market research, database research, animal behaviour research, surveillance, security and transport analysis involve to some extent the study of movement patterns of entities [1,6,10]. This has triggered an increasing amount of research into developing algorithms and tools to support the analysis of trajectory data [7]. Examples are detection of flock movements [3,5,8], leadership patterns [4], commuting patterns [11,12,13] and identification of popular places [9].

In this paper, we introduce and study a problem called the *Longest Dense Substring* problem, which originally stems from a problem concerning the analysis of trajectories, namely detecting regular visits to an area. As an example,

---

* NICTA is funded by the Australian Government's Backing Australia's Ability initiative, in part through the Australian Research Council.

D. Halperin and K. Mehlhorn (Eds.): ESA 2008, LNCS 5193, pp. 344–355, 2008.

consider a person whose locations are tracked over time. It is easy to detect which areas are important for her, such as home, work, local shopping areas and the cricket ground. But it would be interesting to find out if she goes to the cricket ground with some regularity, for example batting practice every Wednesday night. Note that the visits may be regular even though the cricket ground is not visited *every* Wednesday evening. It might be a regular event even though it only takes place 50% of all Wednesday evenings.

The above examples give rise to the following problem, as illustrated in Fig. 1. Given an area $\mathcal{A}$ in some space and a trajectory $\mathcal{T}$, one can generate a sequence of n time intervals $\mathcal{I} = \langle I_1 = [t_1^s, t_1^e], \ldots, I_n = [t_n^s, t_n^e] \rangle$ for which $\mathcal{T}$ intersects the area $\mathcal{A}$. Some of these intervals might be important for our application, while others are not (e.g. a person's visit to the cricket ground on a Sunday to watch a match is not interesting for detecting regular practice that occurs on Wednesdays). Hence, we look at whether $\mathcal{T}$ intersects $\mathcal{A}$ for a sequence of regular time points. For modelling regularity among the sequence of time points, we introduce two important notions: the *period length* p and the *offset* o. For fixed period length p and offset o (with $o < t_1^s + p$), we have a sequence of time points between t_1^s and t_n^e uniquely defined in the following way: All time points are equidistant with distance p and the first time point is at time o (e.g. if o is chosen to be a 'Wednesday at 19:30', and p equals 7 days, then all these time points correspond to all 'Wednesday at 19:30' for all weeks). Having the entire sequence of regular time points, the problem is to find the longest subsequence of consecutive time points such that $\mathcal{T}$ intersects $\mathcal{A}$ with high density (e.g. among the last three years, find the longest time span that a person was at the cricket ground on Wednesdays at 19:30). The density allows us to model exceptional occurrences of $\mathcal{T}$ not intersecting $\mathcal{A}$ (we still would like to detect the regular Wednesday's practice, even though the person called in sick on some Wednesdays). We model the density as a value $c \in [0, 1]$ and require that $\mathcal{T}$ intersects $\mathcal{A}$ for at least $(100 \cdot c)\%$ of the times. To further formalise the above, we associate to each regular time point a value in $\{0, 1\}$. This value is 1 iff there exists an interval $I \in \mathcal{I}$ such that the time point is inside I, (this can be extended to 'approximate' versions where the value is set to 1 if $\mathcal{A}$ is visited approximately at this time point). These values *generate* the bitstring $s(o, p)$ for fixed p and o (for the example of batting practice, the bits indicate that a person has or has not been at the cricket ground on the corresponding Wednesday at 19:30). Now the aim is to compute a longest substring s^{opt} of $s(o, p)$ with the ratio of 1's being at least c. We refer to such an optimal substring s^{opt} as a *longest dense substring*. A longest dense substring represents a longest time span, where $\mathcal{T}$ visited $\mathcal{A}$ with regularity and high density (defined by o, p and c). This gives the following problem. Let $length(s)$ denote the length of bitstring s, and $ratio(s)$ is the number of 1's in s divided by $length(s)$.

Problem: LDS (LONGESTDENSESUBSTRING)
Input: A string s and a real number $c \in (0, 1]$.
Question: What is a longest dense substring $s^{opt} \subseteq s$, i.e. what is a longest substring s^{opt} of s with $ratio(s^{opt}) \geq c$?

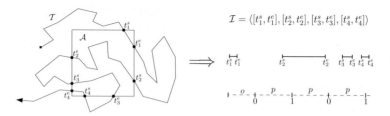

Fig. 1. A trajectory $\mathcal{T}$ and an area $\mathcal{A}$ is shown. From this, we derive the sequence of intervals $\mathcal{I}$ from which we obtain the sequence of regular time points and also $s(o, p)$.

LDS plays an important role for most of our applications for detecting regularity. Despite the fact that it seems fundamental, nothing is known about it to the best of the authors' knowledge. Motivated from the analysis of trajectories, we have different variants for our applications. For an application, we may or may not be given a set of offsets and/or a set of period lengths. Thus together with the LDS-problem, we will also focus on finding the offsets and/or period lengths that generate the string that contains a longest dense substring. The perhaps given offsets and/or period lengths then generate an entire set of strings. Depending on the application and our approach, we can then compute a longest dense substring *for each string* or *over all strings* in this set of strings. The exact definitions are given in the appropriate section.

In Section 2, we propose an optimal algorithm to solve LDS. This algorithm is used in Section 3, where we consider the case when both a set of possible offsets and a set of possible period lengths are given as input. For example if we know the first time of the period we would have a fixed offset, or set of possible offsets. In the most common scenario, one is given a set of possible period lengths. This variant is considered in Sections 4 and 5. In Section 6, we consider the general version, where nothing is known regarding the offset and only a lower bound is given for the period length. We conclude the paper with some final remarks in Section 7. Due to space constraints, detailed proofs are omitted.

2   Optimally Solving LDS

We present an algorithm to solve LDS for a string $s(o, p)$, for given period length p, offset o and density ratio c. Note that the length of the string $s(o, p)$ can be much larger than the number of intervals in $\mathcal{I}$. Hence, we study a flavour of LDS that deals with compressed strings, where runs of 1s or 0s are compressed.

A compressed bit-string is easy to obtain from a normal bitstring or a set $\mathcal{I}$ of intervals: runs of 0s or 1s are represented as pairs $(count, value)$; for example, a run (of maximal length) of x bits whose value is 0 is represented by $(x, 0)$. A compressed bitstring s^{comp} that arises from $\mathcal{I}$ for an offset o and a period length p is a sequence of such pairs:

$$s^{comp}(o, p) = (count_1, value_1)(count_2, value_2)...(count_k, value_k)$$

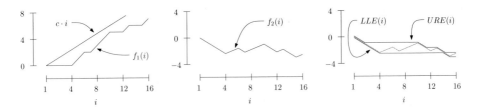

Fig. 2. Exemplary illustrations of $f_1(i)$, $f_2(i)$, $LLE(i)$ and $URE(i)$ for $c = 0.6$ and the compressed bit string $(4,0)(2,1)(1,0)(3,1)(2,0)(1,1)(2,0)(1,1)$

The number of bits in s^{comp} is $\sum_{i=1}^{k} count_i$, where the number k of pairs depends on the intervals and on o and p. The advantage of a compressed bit-string which is derived from a set of n intervals, is that its size is linear in n. The results of this section carry over to the problem with non-compressed bitstrings.

Problem: LDS^{comp}
Input: A compressed string s^{comp} of k pairs and a real number $c \in (0, 1]$.
Question: What is a compressed longest dense substring $s^{opt} \subseteq s^{comp}$ with $ratio(s^{opt}) \geq c$?

Our general approach to solve LDS^{comp} is to transform it in the following way. We consider a function $f_1(i)$ that is the number of 1's in s^{comp} from the first position to position i, see Fig. 2(a). We then define a second function f_2 that is obtained from f_1 by skewing the coordinate system: $f_2(i) := f_1(i) - c \cdot i$, see Fig. 2(b). We observe that a longest dense substring in s^{comp} corresponds to two indices $i_1 \leq i_2$, such that $i_2 - i_1$ is as large as possible and $f_2(i_1) \leq f_2(i_2)$. To compute such indices efficiently, we define a *lower left envelope* $LLE(i) := \min_{1 \leq j \leq i} f_2(j)$. In a symmetric way, we also define an *upper right envelope* $URE(i) := \max_{i \leq j} f_2(j)$. These envelopes are indicated in Fig. 2(c). Finding two indices $i_1 \leq i_2$ where $i_2 - i_1$ is as large as possible and $f_2(i_1) \leq f_2(i_2)$ can be done by a 'walking along' these envelopes with two pointers i_1 and i_2, initially both are at bit position 1. With i_2 we walk along URE as long as $URE(i_2) \geq LLE(i_1)$. We then walk forward with i_1 on LLE and repeat the process until both pointers reached the end of the envelopes. During this process, we keep track of the largest difference between these two pointers.

Theorem 1. *Let s^{comp} be a compressed bitstring represented by k pairs. There is an $\mathcal{O}(k)$ time algorithm to solve LDS^{comp} for s^{comp}, for a given c.*

3 Given Offsets and Period Lengths

If we are given a sequence $\mathcal{I}$ of n intervals, a set P of period lengths and a set O of offsets, we can use the results in Section 2 and run the algorithm of Theorem 1 on every string $s(o, p)$ that is generated by any combination of $p \in P$ and $o \in O$. We obtain the following lemma.

Lemma 1. *Let O be a set of offsets and P be a set of period lengths. In $\mathcal{O}(|O| \cdot |P| \cdot n)$ time, we can compute the overall longest dense substring over all $p \in P$ and $o \in O$. In the same time, we can compute the longest dense substrings for all combinations of $p \in P$ and $o \in O$.*

4 Given Period Lengths (Approximate)

Here, we are given a set of period lengths P together with the set of intervals $\mathcal{I}$. We propose an efficient algorithm that computes for *each* period length $p \in P$ all approximate longest dense substrings – one for each possible offset. The general approach is to run an algorithm for every $p \in P$. For a fixed p, the algorithm is as follows: We cut the time-line and intervals between t_1^s and t_n^e into $\frac{t_n^e - t_1^s}{p}$ pieces of length p, see Fig. 4(a). We arrange all the pieces into a two dimensional structure by putting them above each other, see Fig. 4(b). Now we scan this structure from left to right with a vertical scan line. The scan line stops at *events*, which are moments during the scan, where the scan line leaves or enters any interval of any piece. At each event, we perform certain computations. We can interpret inside an interval as bit 1 and outside as bit 0. Hence, each vertical position o of the scan line cutting through the pieces represents a bit-string $s(o, p)$ of length $\frac{t_n^e - t_1^s}{p}$. Note that this bitstring does not change in between two events; and hence, we only have at most $2 \cdot n$ offsets to consider.

We observe that from one event to the next, exactly one bit will flip in $s(o, p)$. (In the case that two or more intervals have the same endpoint modulo p, we define an order on them according to their absolute time.) In the just mentioned approach, we spend $\mathcal{O}(\frac{t_n^e - t_1^s}{p})$ time for each bitstring, even though this bitstring differs only by one bit from the previous bitstring. We will present an approximation algorithm that spends $\mathcal{O}(\log \frac{t_n^e - t_1^s}{p})$ time per bitflip. The main idea is that the bitstring $s(o, p)$ is represented in the leaves of a binary tree T. For a bitflip, we have to update the corresponding leaf of T and also information stored in nodes along the path from that leaf to the root of T. After that we can query the tree T to find an approximate solution for the current bitstring. Updating and querying can be done in logarithmic time, if T is balanced. In addition to T, we store in an event queue the $\mathcal{O}(n)$ events in sorted order. We have one event for each endpoint of an interval, each of which causes a bitflip.

For our approximation algorithm, we assume that we are given a constant real ε, $0 < \varepsilon < 1$. To clarify what we mean by an approximation, let s_{opt} be an optimal solution to the LDS problem on a string s. A $(1 - \varepsilon)$-*approximate solution* to this problem is a string $s' \subseteq s$ with $ratio(s') \geq (1 - \varepsilon) \cdot c$ and $length(s') \geq length(s_{opt})$. Note that s_{opt} and s' can be disjoint and that s' can be much longer than s_{opt}, and $\frac{ratio(s')}{ratio(s_{opt})}$ can be smaller than $(1 - \varepsilon)$.

The Data Structure T: The structure T is a binary tree with the leaves representing the bits of the current string s, see Fig. 3. To ease the description, we assume w.l.o.g. that T is a complete binary tree. We define leaves of T to

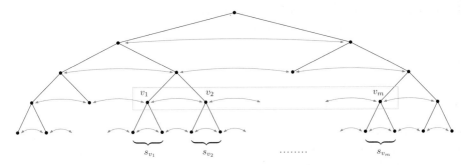

Fig. 3. The tree T for string s is shown (grey arrows are the level-links). Also the list of m nodes $v_1, ..., v_m$ on the same level as v_1 and starting with v_1 is indicated (grey rectangle), as well as the substrings corresponding to those nodes.

have height-level 0 and the root of T has height-level $\log(length(s))$. Each node v_1 of the tree represents a substring s_{v_1} of s that contains exactly those bits of s that are represented in the leaves of the subtree rooted at v_1. The length of s_{v_1} depends on the height-level $level(v_1)$ of v_1, i.e. $length(s_{v_1}) = 2^{level(v_1)}$.

Each node in T will store four values and two links as described next. For each node v_1, we store the ratio $ratio(s_{v_1})$ and the length $length(s_{v_1})$ of the corresponding string s_{v_1}. We also create *level-links* (indicated in Fig. 3) that connect consecutive nodes in T on the same height-level into a doubly-linked list. On top of that, we attach two other values to every node v_1. Since the tree is level-linked, we can easily access the nodes $v_2, v_3, ...$ on the same height-level as v_1 and to the right of v_1 in T, see Fig. 3. Hence, we can easily compute the ratio and length of the substrings obtained by concatenating ('∘'-operation) the substrings $s_{v_1}, s_{v_2}, ..., s_{v_i}$. For $1 \leq i \leq m$, we obtain m such substrings, where $m := \lceil \frac{4}{\varepsilon} - 4 \rceil$. And among those we store at v_1 the length $length_{max}(v_1)$ of the longest such substring with ratio at least $(1 - \varepsilon) \cdot c$. Note that $length_{max}(v_1)$ is always a multiple of $length(s_{v_1})$. Additionally, we store at v_1 the maximum $length_{max}^{tree}(v_1)$ of this value over all nodes of the subtree rooted at v_1. Using elementary techniques and results, we can conclude with the following lemma.

Lemma 2. *Constructing the tree T and the event queue can be done in $\mathcal{O}(\frac{1}{\varepsilon^2} \cdot \frac{t_n^e - t_1^s}{p} + n \log n)$ time and $\mathcal{O}(\frac{t_n^e - t_1^s}{p} + n)$ space.*

Once we have the tree T for string s, we will see that an optimal solution $s_{opt} \subseteq s$ to the LDS problem can be approximated by concatenating at most m substrings that correspond to consecutive tree-nodes on the same height-level.

Lemma 3. *Let lvl be the smallest height level in T such that $length(s_{opt}) \leq m \cdot 2^{lvl}$. Among the nodes of T on level lvl, let v_1 be the left-most node with $s_{v_1} \cap s_{opt} \neq \emptyset$, and let v_i be the right-most node with $s_{v_i} \cap s_{opt} \neq \emptyset$. Then $ratio(s_{v_1} \circ ... \circ s_{v_i}) \geq (1 - \varepsilon) \cdot c$ and $s_{opt} \subseteq s_{v_1} \circ ... \circ s_{v_i}$.*

Note that the previous lemma also holds for any string with ratio at least c. Nevertheless, we formulated it with respect to an optimal solution s_{opt}, and we can conclude the existence of approximate solutions. For finding an approximate solution, recall that for each node v in T, we store the $length_{max}(v)$ values.

Lemma 4. *Let lvl and $v_1, ..., v_i$ be defined as in Lemma 3, and let s' be the string defined by $s' := s_{v_1} \circ s_{v_2} \circ ...$ and $length(s') = length_{max}(v_1)$. Then $s' \supseteq s_{v_1} \circ ... \circ s_{v_i} \supseteq s_{opt}$.*

So far, we have considered the approximate longest dense substrings only for one string for the current position of the scan line. Now, we will move the scan line to the right until it either leaves an interval or enters a new interval. This results in one bitflip, and we have to update T accordingly.

Lemma 5. *For a single bitflip, T can be updated in $\mathcal{O}(\frac{1}{\varepsilon^2} \cdot \log \frac{t_n^e - t_1^s}{p})$ time.*

Given the tree at any time, an approximate solution to the LDS problem can be found by following the path from the root of the tree to children with highest $length_{max}^{tree}$ value. From this and Lemmas 4 and 5, we derive the following theorem.

Theorem 2. *Let P be a set of period lengths and $\mathcal{I}$ be a set of n intervals. We can compute approximate solutions for all longest dense substrings for all period lengths in P and all possible offsets in $\mathcal{O}(|P| \cdot (n(\log n + \frac{1}{\varepsilon^2} \log(t_n^e - t_1^s)) + (t_n^e - t_1^s)))$ time and $\mathcal{O}((t_n^e - t_1^s) + n)$ space.*

5   Given Period Lengths (Exact)

As in the previous section we are given a set of period lengths P together with the set of intervals $\mathcal{I} = \langle I_1 = [t_1^s, t_1^e], ..., I_n = [t_n^s, t_n^e] \rangle$, see Fig. 4(a). We refer to the intervals in $\mathcal{I}$ as *grey intervals* and to the intervals between them as *white intervals*. We give an efficient algorithm that computes a longest dense substring for *each* period length $p \in P$ over all possible offsets. The general approach is also the same as in the previous section: run an algorithm for every $p \in P$. For a fixed p, the algorithm is as follows: we cut the time-line and intervals between t_1^s and t_n^e into $\rho = \frac{t_n^e - t_1^s}{p}$ *pieces* of length p, denoted $\ell_1, ..., \ell_\rho$. The last piece might have length less than p. We arrange all the pieces into a two dimensional structure by putting them above each other, as shown in Fig. 4(b).

Transform into a weighted range query problem: We will show how the original problem can be transformed into the problem of finding the tallest grounded rectangle among a set of weighted points such that the total weight of the points within the rectangle is at least zero. A grounded rectangle is a rectilinear rectangle whose bottom left corner lies at $(0, o')$ for some offset o'. The tallest rectangle is the one with the maximum height. Subsequently, we show how this problem can be solved efficiently.

The part of a piece that is grey or white is called a *grey part* or *white part*, respectively, see Fig. 4(b). Each part has an index i that indicates the position along the vertical axis. The problem now is to find a longest vertical segment

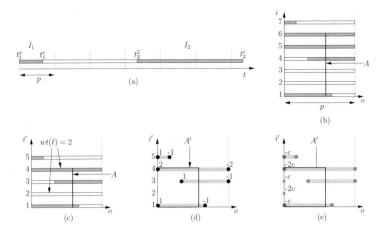

Fig. 4. (a) Input is a set of intervals and a period length p. (b) Cut off pieces of length p and place them above each other. (c) Compressed segments and best line. (d) Segments replaced by their endpoints, best line becomes best grounded rectangle. (e) The additional points.

$A = \{o'\} \times [i_1, i_2]$ that intersects at least $c(i_2 - i_1 + 1)$ grey parts. Note that a grey or white interval that is much longer than p would create a large number of adjacent pieces that each contain just one grey or white part of length p, such as pieces 2 to 3 and 5 to 6 in Fig. 4(b). To overcome this problem, we compress them into a single piece with just one grey or white part. The pieces at $i = 2$ and $i = 3$ (respectively at $i = 5$ and $i = 6$) get compressed into the piece at $i' = 2$ (respectively at $i' = 4$) in Fig. 4(c). When pieces are compressed, all pieces on top are moved downward to fill the gap. Each compressed piece ℓ' is assigned a weight $wt(\ell')$, equal to the number of pieces that were compressed. For each uncompressed piece ℓ' we let $wt(\ell') = 1$. Note that this compression is valid since an optimal pattern will always contain either all or none of the grey parts in a compressed piece. The obtained set of pieces is denoted $\Lambda = \langle \ell'_1, \ldots, \ell'_{\rho'} \rangle$. We further assign to each grey piece l the weight $wt(l)$, equal to the weight $wt(\ell')$ of the compressed piece ℓ' it belongs to.

When pieces with indices in the range $[i_1, i_2]$ are compressed into a single piece at i', we lose information about the vertical position of pieces. So we define two mappings $\alpha_1(i')$ and $\alpha_2(i')$ that return the lowest and highest index of the compressed pieces, i.e. $\alpha_1(i')$ returns i_1 and $\alpha_2(i')$ returns i_2. Note that we can go from the input in Fig. 4(a) to the compressed version in Fig. 4(c) directly in $\mathcal{O}(n)$ time.

We can now rewrite the original problem as follows. Find an offset o' and integers i'_1 and i'_2 such that $\alpha_2(i'_2) - \alpha_1(i'_1)$ is maximised and the sum of the weights over all grey parts intersected by the segment $\{o'\} \times [i'_1, i'_2]$ is at least $c(\alpha_2(i'_2) - \alpha_1(i'_1) + 1)$. Since there are only $\mathcal{O}(n)$ different offsets that might give different bitstrings we can use the approach presented in Section 3 to obtain the following observation.

Observation 1. *A longest pattern for any offset can be computed in $\mathcal{O}(n^2)$ time.*

In the rest of this section we will prove that the running time can be improved to $\mathcal{O}(n^{\frac{3}{2}}\log^2 n)$. We replace each grey part l by two points $q_{left}(l)$ and $q_{right}(l)$. The point $q_{left}(l)$ has weight $wt(l)$ and is placed at the left endpoint of l and $q_{right}(l)$ has weight $-wt(l)$ and is placed at the right endpoint of l, as illustrated in Fig. 4(d). The set of weighted points is denoted Λ'. We observe that the sum over all the weights of the grey parts in Λ intersected by a vertical segment A is equal to the sum over the points in Λ' in the rectilinear rectangle A' with top right corner at the top endpoint of A, bottom right corner at the bottom endpoint of A and unbounded to the left, see Fig. 4(c) and (d). The condition on A' is that $\sum_{q\in A'} wt(q) \geq c(\alpha_2(i'_2) - \alpha_1(i'_1) + 1)$.

Finally, for each piece ℓ', insert into Λ' a point $(0, i')$, where i' is the index of ℓ', as shown in Fig. 4(e), with weight $-wt(\ell') \cdot c$. The sum over the new points in the region A' will be equal to $-c(\alpha_2(i'_2) - \alpha_1(i'_1) + 1)$, so the constraint on A' becomes that the sum over all points in A' is at least zero. Note that the constraint on the sum is now independent of the height of A', i.e. i'_1 and i'_2. We have now transformed the original problem into the following problem:

Problem:
Input: A set of weighted points in the plane.
Question: What is a grounded rectangle $[0, o'] \times [i'_1, i'_2]$ of total weight at least zero that maximises $\alpha_2(i'_2) - \alpha_1(i'_1)$?

Finding a longest pattern: Partition the points in Λ' with respect to their i'-coordinates into $\sqrt{n}$ sets $\Lambda'_1, \ldots, \Lambda'_{\sqrt{n}}$, each set having at most $\sqrt{n}$ points, as shown in Fig. 5(a). An optimal solution will either only contain points from a set Λ'_i, for some $1 \leq i \leq \sqrt{n}$, or contain points from several consecutive sets. In the former case we can find an optimal solution by simply running the quadratic time algorithm from Observation 1 on each set Λ'_i, to find the longest pattern that does not cross a boundary between the sets. It remains to handle the case when the optimal solution contains points from several consecutive sets. Recall that the height of A in the uncompressed setting is $\alpha_2(i'_2) - \alpha_1(i'_1)$. For a bottom side fixed at i'_1, finding the tallest rectangle is equivalent to finding one that maximises i'_2. We do this for every value of i'_1 and at the end report the rectangle with the largest height in the uncompressed setting. We first need to define a new problem. A point q dominates a point q' if and only if $q_x \geq q'_x$ and $q_y \geq q'_y$. Let $\text{dom}(q)$ be the set of points dominated by a point q. We define the dominance sum, denoted $\sigma(q)$ to the be sum of $wt(q')$ over all points q' dominated by q. Finally, the *Highest Valid Dominance Point*, or $HVDP(x_1, x_2, S)$, is the point q with the following properties: $\sigma(q) \geq S$, $q_x \in [x_1, x_2)$, and q_y is maximised.

Lemma 6. *We can preprocess a set of n weighted points in $\mathcal{O}(n\log^2 n)$ time using $\mathcal{O}(n\log n)$ space s.t. HVDP queries can be answered in $\mathcal{O}(\log^2 n)$ time.*

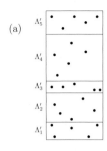

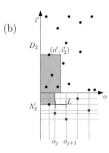

Fig. 5. (a) The points in Λ' are split into $\sqrt{n}$ sets. (b) The grounded rectangle is split into two quadrants. Any point on L covers the same set of points in Λ'_i.

Now, for each set Λ'_i, $1 \leq i < \sqrt{n}$, we build a HVDP data structure D_i on all the points in $\Lambda'_{i+1}, \ldots, \Lambda'_{\sqrt{n}}$. We are going to search for grounded rectangles with the bottom edge in Λ'_i and the top edge using the structure D_i. Note that such a rectangle can be partitioned into a top left quadrant in Λ'_i and a bottom left quadrant in D_i, as shown in Fig. 5(b).

Let $o_1 < \ldots < o_m$ be the ordered set of o-coordinates of the points in Λ'_i, where $m \leq \sqrt{n}$, and let I' be the set of the corresponding i'-coordinates. For a fixed $i'_1 \in I'$ we partition the horizontal line $i' = i'_1$ into $\mathcal{O}(\sqrt{n})$ half-open segments $\langle L_1 = [o_1, o_2) \times \{i'_1\}, \ldots, L_{m-1} = [o_{m-1}, o_m) \times \{i'_1\}, L_m = [o_m, \infty) \times \{i'_1\}\rangle$, such as segment L in Fig. 5(b). Let q be a point and $\mathrm{dom}'(q_o, q_{i'})$ be the set of points q' in Λ'_i with $q'_o \leq q_o$ and $q'_{i'} \geq q_{i'}$, i.e. the set of points in the top-left quadrant from q. Note that $\mathrm{dom}'(q_o, q_{i'})$ will be the same for any point q on the half-open segment $[o_a, o_{a+1}) \times \{i'_1\}$, and will therefore be equal to $\mathrm{dom}'(o_a, i'_1)$.

For each segment L_j we want to find the tallest rectangle with the bottom right corner on L_j. Let S be the sum over points in $\mathrm{dom}'(x_j, i'_1)$, which we can find using semigroup dominance searching using standard techniques [2]. Now we query D_i for the highest point (o', i'_2) with $o' \in [o_j, o_{j+1})$ and whose dominance sum is at least $-S$. We calculate the uncompressed height of each rectangle, $\alpha_2(i'_2) - \alpha_1(i'_1)$, and report only the tallest one. This process is repeated for each $i'_1 \in I'$. We summarise by stating the main result of this section.

Theorem 3. *Let P be a set of period lengths and $\mathcal{I}$ be a set of n intervals. For each period length in P, we can compute a longest dense substring over all possible offsets in $\mathcal{O}(|P| \cdot n^{\frac{3}{2}} \log^2 n)$ time and $\mathcal{O}(n \log n)$ space.*

6   Nothing Given

Even if we are not given a set of possible offsets nor a set of possible period lengths, we still can tackle the problem of computing the *overall* longest dense substring over all period lengths and over all offsets.

We solve this problem under the following assumptions: the period length p can be any value in $[0, t_n^e - t_1^s]$, the offset can be any value between t_1^s and $t_1^s + p$, and the period length p is larger than any interval. Hence, a single visit can only contribute once to a bit-string. Usually the lower bound is related to the length of the shortest interval between two visits. We believe that considering these constraints is meaningful from an application point of view. We observe that it is sufficient to check $\mathcal{O}(\frac{n^3}{c})$ period lengths, one of which leads to a bit string with overall longest dense substring. For these period lengths, we can apply the algorithm in Section 5 (respectively, Observation 1) to obtain the following theorem.

Theorem 4. *There exists an* $\mathcal{O}(\frac{n^5}{c})$ *time and* $\mathcal{O}(n)$ *space algorithm, and an* $\mathcal{O}(\frac{n^{\frac{9}{2}}}{c})$ *time and* $\mathcal{O}(n \log n)$ *space algorithms to compute an overall longest dense substring, assuming that the period length* p *can be any value in* $[0, t_n^e - t_1^s]$, *the offset can be any value between* t_1^s *and* $t_1^s + p$, *and that the intervals are shorter than the period length.*

7   Concluding Remarks

In our applications, we look for regularities when a trajectory $\mathcal{T}$ intersects an area $\mathcal{A}$. To this end, we generate a bit string from $\mathcal{T}$ and $\mathcal{A}$ that reflects regularity by specifying a period length and an offset. The here proposed approaches are not confined to regular visit patterns, but can be used for finding regularities in anything that can be expressed as a bit string.

During the course of this application driven research, we encountered the elementary problem, called LDS, of computing a longest dense substring, which is at the core of many applications. We provided an optimal algorithm to solve this basic LDS problem, see Theorem 1. To solve our more applied problems, we proposed efficient (approximation) algorithms that compute longest dense substrings, and hence, longest regular visit patterns for the cases where we are given a set of possible offsets and/or a set of possible period lengths.

It is often a topic for discussion to specify what our algorithms should produce as output. We chose to maximise the length of a substring, while the density has to be above a certain threshold. From an application point of view it might be a good choice to output all substrings of a string of which the length *and* the density are above certain thresholds. Some of our algorithms can be easily extended (with increased running time) to this *report all* version of our problems, while other algorithms require more research for such an extension.

When generating bit strings, we used a sequence of *time points* to define the bit values. It is also possible to use *time spans* instead (e.g. each bit represents an entire day and is set to 1, iff the person has been to the cricket ground on that day at *any* time). This is appropriate for many applications, and because our results also hold for this modelling, we can conclude the practical relevance of our algorithms.

Worthwhile directions for further research include the consideration of LDS and the related applications when we have streaming data. Also if we do not know the area(s) $\mathcal{A}$, we can consider the problem of computing the area(s) $\mathcal{A}$ that are visited with regularity (perhaps specified by length and density thresholds).

Acknowledgements

We would like to thank Mark de Berg, Sergio Cabello and Damian Merrick for sharing their insights and for very useful discussions. Some of these discussions took place during the GADGET Workshop on Geometric Algorithms and Spatial Data Mining, funded by the Netherlands Organisation for Scientific Research (NWO) under BRICKS/Focus grant number 642.065.503.

References

1. Wildlife tracking projects with GPS GSM collars (2006),
   http://www.environmental-studies.de/projects/projects.html
2. Agarwal, P., Erickson, J.: Geometric range searching and its relatives (1999)
3. Al-Naymat, G., Chawla, S., Gudmundsson, J.: Dimensionality reduction for long duration and complex spatio-temporal queries. In: Proceedings of the 22nd ACM Symposium on Applied Computing, pp. 393–397. ACM, New York (2007)
4. Andersson, M., Gudmundsson, J., Laube, P., Wolle, T.: Reporting leaders and followers among trajectories of moving point objects. GeoInformatica (2007)
5. Benkert, M., Gudmundsson, J., Hübner, F., Wolle, T.: Reporting flock patterns. Computational Geometry—Theory and Applications (2007)
6. Frank, A.U.: Socio-Economic Units: Their Life and Motion. In: Frank, A.U., Raper, J., Cheylan, J.P. (eds.) Life and motion of socio-economic units. GISDATA, vol. 8, pp. 21–34. Taylor & Francis, London (2001)
7. Gudmundsson, J., Laube, P., Wolle, T.: Encyclopedia of GIS, chapter Movement Patterns in Spatio-temporal Data, pp. 726–732. Springer, Heidelberg (2008)
8. Gudmundsson, J., van Kreveld, M.: Computing longest duration flocks in trajectory data. In: Proceedings of the 14th ACM Symposium on Advances in GIS, pp. 35–42 (2006)
9. Gudmundsson, J., van Kreveld, M., Speckmann, B.: Efficient detection of motion patterns in spatio-temporal sets. GeoInformatica 11(2), 195–215 (2007)
10. Güting, R.H., Schneider, M.: Moving Objects Databases. Morgan Kaufmann Publishers, San Francisco (2005)
11. Lee, J.-G., Han, J., Whang, K.-Y.: Trajectory clustering: a partition-and-group framework. In: SIGMOD 2007: Proceedings of the 2007 ACM SIGMOD international conference on Management of data, pp. 593–604. ACM Press, New York (2007)
12. Mamoulis, N., Cao, H., Kollios, G., Hadjieleftheriou, M., Tao, Y., Cheung, D.: Mining, indexing, and querying historical spatiotemporal data. In: Proceedings of the 10th ACM SIGKDD International Conference On Knowledge Discovery and Data Mining, pp. 236–245. ACM, New York (2004)
13. Vlachos, M., Kollios, G., Gunopulos, D.: Discovering similar multidimensional trajectories. In: Proceedings of the 18th International Conference on Data Engineering (ICDE 2002), pp. 673–684 (2002)

Improved Approximation Algorithms
for Relay Placement

Alon Efrat[1], Sándor P. Fekete[2], Poornananda R. Gaddehosur[1],
Joseph S.B. Mitchell[3], Valentin Polishchuk[4], and Jukka Suomela[4]

[1] Department of Computer Science, University of Arizona
`alon@email.arizona.edu, poorna@email.arizona.edu`
[2] Department of Computer Science, Braunschweig University of Technology
`s.fekete@tu-bs.de`
[3] Department of Applied Mathematics and Statistics, Stony Brook University
`jsbm@ams.stonybrook.edu`
[4] Helsinki Institute for Information Technology HIIT,
University of Helsinki and Helsinki University of Technology
`valentin.polishchuk@cs.helsinki.fi, jukka.suomela@cs.helsinki.fi`

Abstract. In the *relay placement problem* the input is a set of sensors and
a number $r \geq 1$, the communication range of a relay. The objective is to
place a minimum number of relays so that between every pair of sensors
there is a path through sensors and/or relays such that the consecutive
vertices of the path are within distance r if both vertices are relays and
within distance 1 otherwise. We present a 3.11-approximation algorithm,
and show that the problem admits no PTAS, assuming P $\neq$ NP.

1 Introduction

A sensor network consists of a large number of low-cost autonomous devices,
called *sensors*. Communication between the sensors is performed by wireless
radio with very limited range, e.g., via the Bluetooth protocol. To make the
network connected, a number of additional devices, called *relays*, must be judi-
ciously placed within the sensor field. Relays are typically more advanced and
expensive than sensors. For instance, in addition to a Bluetooth chip, each relay
may be equipped with a WLAN transceiver, enabling communication between
distant relays. The problem we study in this paper is that of placing a *minimum
number* of relays to ensure the connectivity of a sensor network.

Two models of communication have been considered in the literature
[1,2,3,4,5,6,7,8]. In both models, a sensor and a relay can communicate if the
distance between them as at most 1, and two relays can communicate if the
distance between them is at most r, where $r \geq 1$ is a given number. The models differ in whether direct communication between sensors is allowed. In the
one-tier model two sensors can communicate if the distance between them is at
most 1. In the *two-tier* model the sensors do not communicate at all, no matter
how close they are. In other words, in the two-tier model the sensors may only
link to relays, but not to other sensors.

D. Halperin and K. Mehlhorn (Eds.): ESA 2008, LNCS 5193, pp. 356–367, 2008.

Formally, the input to the relay placement problem is a set of sensors, identified with their locations in the plane, and a number $r \geq 1$, the communication range of a relay (w.l.o.g. the communication range of a sensor is 1). The objective in the *one-tier* relay placement is to place a minimum number of relays so that between every pair of sensors there exists a path, *through sensors and/or relays*, such that the consecutive vertices of the path are within distance r if both vertices are relays, and within distance 1 otherwise. The objective in the *two-tier* relay placement is to place a minimum number of relays so that between every pair of sensors there exists a path *through relays only* such that the consecutive vertices of the path are within distance r if both vertices are relays, and within distance 1 if one of the vertices is a sensor and the other is a relay (going directly from a sensor to a sensor is forbidden).

The current best approximation ratio of 7 for one-tier relay placement is due to Lloyd and Xue [5]. For the two-tier version, Lloyd and Xue [5] suggested a $(5 + \varepsilon)$-approximation algorithm for arbitrary $r \geq 1$; Srinivas et al. [6] gave a $(4 + \varepsilon)$-approximation for the case $r \geq 2$. In this paper, we present a polynomial-time 3.11-approximation algorithm for the one-tier relay placement, and show that it admits no PTAS unless P = NP (assuming that r is part of the input). In the full version, we will present a PTAS for the two-tier version; the PTAS works for arbitrary $r \geq 1$.

2   Blobs, Clouds, Stabs, Hubs, and Forests

For two points x, y in the plane let $|xy|$ be the Euclidean distance between them. Let V be a given set of sensors (points in the plane). We form a unit disk graph $\mathcal{G} = (V, E)$ and a disk graph $\mathcal{F} = (V, F)$ where $E = \{\{u, v\} : |uv| \leq 1\}$, $F = \{\{u, v\} : |uv| \leq 2\}$; see Fig. 1.

We define a *blob* to be the union of the unit disks centered at the sensors that belong to the same connected component of $\mathcal{G}$. We use B to refer to a blob, and $\mathcal{B}$ for the set of all blobs.

Analogously, we define a *cloud* $C \in \mathcal{C}$ as the union of the unit disks centered at the sensors that belong to the connected component of the graph $\mathcal{F}$. The sensors in a blob can communicate with each other without relays, while the ones in a cloud might not, even though their disks may overlap. Each cloud

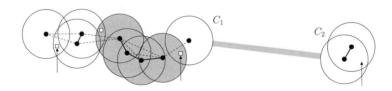

Fig. 1. Dots are sensors in V, solid lines are edges in E and F, and dashed lines are edges in F only. There are 5 blobs in $\mathcal{B}$ (one of them highlighted) and 2 clouds $C_1, C_2 \in \mathcal{C}$. Arrows are stabs, and small rectangles are hubs. The wide grey line is the only edge in $\mathrm{MStFN}(\mathcal{C})$, which happens to be equal to $\mathrm{MSFN}(\mathcal{C})$ here.

$C \in \mathcal{C}$ consists of one or more blobs $B \in \mathcal{B}$; we use $\mathcal{B}_C$ to denote the blobs that form the cloud C.

We define a *stab* to be a relay with an infinite communication range ($r = \infty$), and a *hub* as a relay without the ability to communicate with the other relays (thus hubs can enable communication within one cloud, but are of no use in communicating between clouds). As will be shown, a solution to stab or hub placement can be used as a step towards a solution for relay placement.

If we are placing stabs, it is necessary and sufficient to have a stab in each blob to ensure communication between all sensors (to avoid trivialities we assume there is more than one blob). Thus, stab placement is equivalent to the set cover problem: the universe is the blobs, and the subsets are sets of blobs that have a point in common. In the example in Fig. 1 arrows show an optimal solution to the stab placement problem; 3 stabs are enough.

If we are placing hubs, it is necessary (assuming more than one blob in the cloud), but not sufficient, to have a hub in each blob to ensure communication between sensors within one cloud. In fact, hub placement can be interpreted as a special case of the *connected* set cover problem [9,10]. In the example in Fig. 1 small rectangles show an optimal solution to the hub placement problem for the cloud $C = C_1$; in this particular case, 2 stabs within the cloud C were sufficient to "pierce" each blob in $\mathcal{B}_C$, however, an additional hub is required to "stitch" the blobs together. The next lemma shows that, in general, the number of additional hubs needed is less than the number of stabs:

Lemma 1. *Given a feasible solution S to stab placement on $\mathcal{B}_C$, we can obtain in polynomial time a feasible solution to hub placement on $\mathcal{B}_C$ with $2|S| - 1$ hubs.*

Proof. Let $\mathcal{H}$ be the graph, whose nodes are the sensors in the cloud C and the stabs in S, and whose edges connect two devices if either they are within distance 1 from each other or if both devices are stabs (i.e., there is an edge between *every* pair of the stabs). Switch off communication between the stabs, thus turning them into hubs. Suppose that this breaks $\mathcal{H}$ into k connected components. There must be a stab in each connected component. Thus, $|S| \geq k$.

If $k > 1$, by the definition of a cloud, there must exist a point where a unit disk covers at least two sensors from two different connected components of $\mathcal{H}$. Placing a hub at the point decreases the number of the connected components by at least 1. Thus, after putting at most $k - 1$ additional hubs, all connected components will merge into one. □

2.1   Steiner Forests and Spanning Forests with Neighbourhoods

Let $\mathcal{P}$ be a collection of planar sets; call them *neighbourhoods*. (In Section 3 the neighbourhoods will be "clusters" of clouds.) For a plane graph G, let $\mathcal{G}_\mathcal{P} = (\mathcal{P}, E(G))$ be the graph whose vertices are the neighbourhoods and two neighbourhoods $P_1, P_2 \in \mathcal{P}$ are adjacent whenever G has a vertex in P_1, a vertex in P_2, and a path between the vertices.

The *Minimum Steiner Forest with Neighbourhoods* on $\mathcal{P}$, denoted MStFN($\mathcal{P}$), is a *minimum-length* plane graph G such that $\mathcal{G}_{\mathcal{P}} = (\mathcal{P}, E(G))$ is connected. The MStFN is a generalisation of the Steiner tree of a set of points. Note that MStFN is slightly different from Steiner tree with neighbourhoods (see, e.g., [11]) in that we are only counting the part of the graph *outside* $\mathcal{P}$ towards its length (since it is not necessary to connect neighbourhoods beyond their boundaries).

Consider a complete weighted graph whose vertices are the neighbourhoods in $\mathcal{P}$ and whose edge weights are the distances between them. A minimum spanning tree in the graph is called the *Minimum Spanning Forest with Neighbourhoods* on $\mathcal{P}$, denoted MSFN($\mathcal{P}$). A natural embedding of the edges of the forest is by the straight-line segments that connect the corresponding neighbourhoods; we will identify MSFN($\mathcal{P}$) with the embedding. (As with MStFN, we count the length of MSFN only *outside* $\mathcal{P}$.)

We denote by $|$MStFN($\mathcal{P}$)$|$ and $|$MSFN($\mathcal{P}$)$|$ the total length of the edges of the forests. It is known that $|$MSFN$(P)| \leq (2/\sqrt{3})|$MStFN$(P)|$ for a *point* set P, where $2/\sqrt{3}$ is the *Steiner ratio* [12]. The following lemma generalises this to neighbourhoods.

Lemma 2. *For any* $\mathcal{P}$, $|$MSFN($\mathcal{P}$)$| \leq (2/\sqrt{3})|$MStFN($\mathcal{P}$)$|$.

Proof. If $\mathcal{P}$ is erased, MStFN($\mathcal{P}$) falls off into a forest, each tree of which is a minimum Steiner tree on its leaves; its length is within the Steiner ratio of minimum spanning tree length. $\square$

3   A 3.11-Approximation Algorithm

In this section we give a 3.11-approximation algorithm for one-tier relay placement. We focus on nontrivial instances with more than one blob.

Note that the *number* of relays in a solution may be exponential in the size of the input (number of bits). Our algorithm produces a succinct representation of the solution, given by a set of points and a set of line segments; the relays are placed on each point and equally-spaced along each segment.

3.1   Overview

The basic steps of our algorithm are as follows:

1. Compute optimal stabbings for clouds which can be stabbed with few relays.
2. Connect the blobs in each of these clouds, using Lemma 1.
3. Greedily connect all blobs in each of the remaining clouds ("stitching").
4. Greedily connect clouds into clusters, using 2 additional relays per cloud.
5. Connect the clusters by a spanning forest.

The algorithm constructs a set A_r of "red" relays (for connecting blobs in a cloud, i.e., relays added in steps 1–3), a set A_g of "green" relays (two per cloud, added in steps 4–5) and a set A_y of "yellow" relays (outside of sensor range, added in step 5). In the analysis, we compare an optimal solution R^* to our approximate one by subdividing the former into a set R_d^* of "dark" relays that are within reach of sensors, and into a set R_ℓ^* of "light" relays that are outside of sensor range. We compare $|R_d^*|$ with $|A_r| + |A_g|$, and $|R_\ell^*|$ with $|A_y|$, showing in both cases that the ratio is less than 3.11.

3.2 Clouds with Few Stabs

For any constant k, it is straightforward to check in polynomial time whether all blobs in a cloud $C \in \mathcal{C}$ can be stabbed with $i < k$ stabs. (For any subset of i cells of the arrangement of unit disks centered on the sensors in C, we can consider placing the relays in the cells and check whether this stabs all blobs.) Using Lemma 1, we can connect all blobs in such a cloud with at most $2i - 1$ red relays. We denote by $\mathcal{C}^i$ the set of clouds where the minimum number of stabs is i, and by $\mathcal{C}^{k+}$ the set of clouds that need at least k stabs.

3.3 Stitching a Cloud from $\mathcal{C}^{k+}$

We focus on one cloud $C \in \mathcal{C}^{k+}$. For a point y in the plane, let $\mathcal{B}(y) = \{B \in \mathcal{B}_C : y \in B\}$ be the set of blobs that contain the point; obviously $|\mathcal{B}(y)| \le 5$ for any y. For any subset of blobs $\mathcal{T} \subseteq \mathcal{B}_C$, define $\mathcal{S}(\mathcal{T}, y) = \mathcal{B}(y) \setminus \mathcal{T}$ to be the set of blobs *not from* $\mathcal{T}$ containing y, and define $V(\mathcal{T})$ to be the set of sensors that form the blobs in $\mathcal{T}$.

Within C, we place a set of red relays $A_r^C = \{y_j : j = 1, 2, \dots\}$, as follows:

1. Choose arbitrary $B_0 \in \mathcal{B}_C$.
2. Initialise $j \leftarrow 1$, $\mathcal{T}_j \leftarrow \{B_0\}$.
3. While $\mathcal{T}_j \ne \mathcal{B}_C$:

$$y_j \leftarrow \arg\max_y \{|\mathcal{S}(\mathcal{T}_j, y)| : \mathcal{B}(y) \cap \mathcal{T}_j \ne \emptyset\},$$
$$\mathcal{S}_j \leftarrow \mathcal{S}(\mathcal{T}_j, y_j),$$
$$\mathcal{T}_{j+1} \leftarrow \mathcal{T}_j \cup \mathcal{S}_j,$$
$$j \leftarrow j + 1.$$

By induction on j, after each iteration, there exists a path through sensors and/or relays between any pair of sensors in $V(\mathcal{T}_j)$. By the definition of a cloud, there is a line segment of length at most 2 that connects $V(\mathcal{T}_j)$ to $V(\mathcal{B}_C \setminus \mathcal{T}_j)$; the midpoint of the segment is a location y with $\mathcal{S}(\mathcal{T}_j, y) \ne \emptyset$. Since each iteration increases the size of $\mathcal{T}_j$ by at least 1, the algorithm terminates in at most $|\mathcal{B}_C| - 1$ iterations, and $|A_r^C| \le |\mathcal{B}_C| - 1$. The sets $\mathcal{S}_j$ form a partition of $\mathcal{B}_C \setminus \{B_0\}$.

We prove the following performance guarantee.

Lemma 3. *For each cloud C we have $|A_r^C| \le 37|R_d^* \cap C|/12 - 1$.*

Proof. For each $B \in \mathcal{B}_C \setminus \{B_0\}$, define the weight $w(B) = 1/|\mathcal{S}_j|$, where $\mathcal{S}_j$ is the unique set for which $B \in \mathcal{S}_j$. We also set $w(B_0) = 1$. We have

$$\sum_{B \in \mathcal{B}_C} w(B) = |A_r^C| + 1. \tag{1}$$

Consider a relay $z \in R_d^* \cap C$, and find the smallest ℓ with $\mathcal{T}_\ell \cap \mathcal{B}(z) \neq \emptyset$, that is, $\ell = 1$ if $B_0 \in \mathcal{B}(z)$, and otherwise $y_{\ell-1}$ is the first relay that pierced a blob from $\mathcal{B}(z)$. Partition the set $\mathcal{B}(z)$ into $\mathcal{U}(z) = \mathcal{T}_\ell \cap \mathcal{B}(z)$ and $\mathcal{V}(z) = \mathcal{B}(z) \setminus \mathcal{U}(z)$. Note that $\mathcal{V}(z)$ may be empty, e.g., if $y_{\ell-1} = z$.

First, we show that

$$\sum_{B \in \mathcal{U}(z)} w(B) \leq 1.$$

We need to consider two cases. It may happen that $\ell = 1$, which means that $B_0 \in \mathcal{B}(z)$ and $\mathcal{U}(z) = \{B_0\}$. Then the total weight assigned to the blobs in $\mathcal{U}(z)$ is, by definition, 1. Otherwise $\ell > 1$ and $\mathcal{U}(z) \subseteq S_{\ell-1}$, implying $w(B) = 1/|S_{\ell-1}| \leq 1/|\mathcal{U}(z)|$ for each $B \in \mathcal{U}(z)$.

Second, we show that

$$\sum_{B \in \mathcal{V}(z)} w(B) \leq \frac{1}{|\mathcal{V}(z)|} + \frac{1}{|\mathcal{V}(z)| - 1} + \cdots + \frac{1}{1}.$$

Indeed, at iterations $j \geq \ell$, the algorithm is able to consider placing the relay y_j at the location z. Therefore $|S_j| \geq |S(\mathcal{T}_j, z)|$. Furthermore, $S(\mathcal{T}_j, z) \setminus S(\mathcal{T}_{j+1}, z) = \mathcal{B}(z) \cap S_j = \mathcal{V}(z) \cap S_j$. Whenever placing the relay y_j makes $|S(\mathcal{T}_j, z)|$ decrease by k, exactly k blobs of $\mathcal{V}(z)$ get connected to $\mathcal{T}_j$. Each of them is assigned the weight $w(C) \leq 1/|S(\mathcal{T}_j, z)|$. Thus, $\sum_{B \in \mathcal{V}(z)} w(B) \leq k_1/(k_1 + k_2 + \cdots + k_n) + k_2/(k_2 + k_3 + \cdots + k_n) + \cdots + k_n/k_n$, where $k_1, k_2, \ldots, k_n$ are the number of blobs from $\mathcal{V}(z)$ that are pierced at different iterations, $\sum_i k_i = |\mathcal{V}(z)|$. The maximum value of the sum is attained when $k_1 = k_2 = \cdots = k_n = 1$ (i.e., every time $|\mathcal{V}(z)|$ is decreased by 1, and there are $|\mathcal{V}(z)|$ summands).

Finally, since $|\mathcal{B}(z)| \leq 5$, and $\mathcal{U}(z) \neq \emptyset$, we have $|\mathcal{V}(z)| \leq 4$. Thus,

$$W(z) = \sum_{B \in \mathcal{U}(z)} w(B) + \sum_{B \in \mathcal{V}(z)} w(B) \leq 1 + \frac{1}{4} + \frac{1}{3} + \frac{1}{2} + \frac{1}{1} = \frac{37}{12}. \qquad (2)$$

The sets $\mathcal{B}(z)$, $z \in R_d^* \cap C$, form a cover of $\mathcal{B}_C$. Therefore, from (1) and (2),

$$\frac{37}{12}|R_d^* \cap C| \geq \sum_{z \in R_d^* \cap C} W(z) \geq \sum_{B \in \mathcal{B}_C} w(B) = |A_r^C| + 1. \qquad \square$$

3.4   Green Relays and Cloud Clusters

At any stage of the algorithm, we say that a set of clouds is *interconnected* if, with the current placement of relays, the sensors in the clouds can communicate with each other. Now, when all clouds have been stitched (so that the sensors within any one cloud can communicate), we proceed to interconnecting the clouds. First we greedily form the collection of cloud *clusters* (interconnected clouds) as follows. We start by assigning each cloud to its own cluster. Whenever it is possible to interconnect two clusters by placing one relay within each of the two clusters, we do so. These two relays are coloured green. After it is no longer possible to interconnect 2 clusters by placing just 2 relays, we repeatedly place 4 green relays wherever we can use them to interconnect clouds from 3 different clusters. Finally, we repeat this for 6 green relays which interconnect 4 clusters.

On average we place 2 green relays every time the number of connected components in the communication graph on sensors plus relays decreases by one.

3.5   Interconnecting the Clusters

Now, when the sensors in each cloud and the clouds in each cluster are interconnected, we interconnect the clusters by MSFN. We find MSFN on the clusters and place relays along edges of the forest. Specifically, for each edge e of the forest, we place 2 green relays at the endpoints of e, and $\lfloor |e|/r \rfloor$ yellow relays every r units starting from one of the endpoints (and when we find MSFN, we minimise the total number of yellow relays that we need). As with interconnecting clouds into the clusters, when interconnecting the clusters we use 2 green relays each time the number of connected components of the communication graph decreases by one. Thus, overall, we use at most $2|\mathcal{C}| - 2$ green relays.

3.6   Analysis: Red and Green Relays

Recall that for $i < k$, $\mathcal{C}^i$ is the class of clouds that require precisely i relays for stabbing, and $\mathcal{C}^{k+}$ is the class of clouds that need at least k relays for stabbing. An optimal solution R^* therefore contains at least $|R_d^*| \geq k|\mathcal{C}^{k+}| + \sum_{i=1}^{k-1} i|\mathcal{C}^i|$ dark relays (relays inside clouds, i.e., relays within reach of sensors). Furthermore, $|R_d^* \cap C| \geq 1$ for all C.

Our algorithm places at most $2i - 1$ red relays per cloud in $\mathcal{C}^i$, and not more than $37/12|R_d^* \cap C| - 1$ red relays per cloud in $\mathcal{C}^{k+}$. Adding a total of $2|\mathcal{C}| - 2$ green relays used for clouds interconnections, we get

$$
\begin{aligned}
|A_r| + |A_g| &\leq \sum_{C \in \mathcal{C}^{k+}} (37|R_d^* \cap C|/12 - 1) + \sum_{i=1}^{k-1}(2i - 1)|\mathcal{C}^i| + 2|\mathcal{C}| - 2 \\
&\leq 37(|R_d^*| - \sum_{i=1}^{k-1} i|\mathcal{C}^i|)/12 + |\mathcal{C}^{k+}| + \sum_{i=1}^{k-1}(2i + 1)|\mathcal{C}^i| - 2 \\
&\leq 37|R_d^*|/12 + |\mathcal{C}^{k+}| < (3.084 + 1/k)|R_d^*|.
\end{aligned}
$$

3.7   Analysis: Yellow Relays

Let $\mathcal{R}$ be the communication graph on the optimal set R^* of relays alone, i.e., without sensors taken into account; two relays are connected by an edge in $\mathcal{R}$ if and only if they are within distance r from each other. In $\mathcal{R}$ there exists a forest $\mathcal{R}'$ that makes the clusters interconnected. Let $R' \subset R^*$ be the relays that are vertices of $\mathcal{R}'$. We partition R' into "black" relays $R_b^* = R' \cap R_d^*$ and "white" relays $R_w^* = R' \cap R_\ell^*$ – those inside and outside the clusters, resp.

Two black relays cannot be adjacent in $\mathcal{R}'$: if they are in the same cluster, the edge between them is redundant; if they are in different clusters, the distance between them must be larger than r, as otherwise our algorithm would have placed two green relays to interconnect the clusters into one. By a similar reasoning, there cannot be a white relay adjacent to 3 or more black relays in $\mathcal{R}'$, and there cannot be a pair of adjacent white relays such that each of them is adjacent to 2 black relays. Finally, the maximum degree of a white relay is 5. Using these observations, we can prove the following lemma.

Lemma 4. *There is a spanning forest with neighbourhoods on cloud clusters that requires at most* $(4/\sqrt{3}+4/5)|R_w^*| < 3.11|R_w^*|$ *yellow relays on its edges.*

Proof. Let $\mathcal{D}$ be the set of cloud clusters. We partition $\mathcal{R}'$ into edge-disjoint trees induced by maximal connected subsets of white relays and their adjacent black relays. It is enough to show that for each such tree T which interconnects a subset of clusters $\mathcal{D}' \subseteq \mathcal{D}$, there is a spanning forest on $\mathcal{D}'$ such that the number of yellow relays on its edges is at most 3.11 times the number of white relays in T. As no pair of black relays is adjacent in $\mathcal{R}'$, these edge-disjoint trees interconnect all clusters in $\mathcal{D}$. The same holds for the spanning forests, and the lemma follows.

Trees with only one white relay (and thus exactly two black relays) are trivial: the spanning forest needs only one edge with one yellow relay (and one green in each end). Therefore assume that T contains at least two white relays.

We introduce yet another colour. For each white relay with two black neighbours, arbitrarily choose one of the black relays and change it into a "grey" relay. Let w be the number of white relays, let b be the number of remaining black relays, and let g be the number of grey relays in T.

First, we clearly have $b \leq w$. Second, there is no grey–white–white–grey path, each white relay is adjacent to another white relay, and the maximum degree of a white relay is 5 (geometry). Therefore the ratio $(b+g)/w$ is at most $9/5$. To see this, let w_2 be the number of white relays with a grey and a black neighbour, let w_1 be the number of white relays with a black neighbour but no grey neighbour, and let w_0 be the number of white relays without a black neighbour. By degree bound, $w_2 \leq 4w_1+5w_0 = 4w_1+5(w-w_2-w_1)$; therefore $5w \geq 6w_2+w_1$. We also know that $w \geq w_2+w_1$. Therefore $(9/5)w \geq (1/5)(6w_2 + w_1)+(4/5)(w_2 + w_1) = (w_2 + w_1) + w_2 = b + g$. (The worst case is a star of $1 + 4$ white relays, 5 black relays and 4 grey relays.)

Now consider the subtree induced by the black and white relays. It has fewer than $b + w$ edges, and the edge length is at most r. By Lemma 2, there is a spanning forest on the black relays with total length less than $(2/\sqrt{3})(b + w)r$; thus we need fewer than $(2/\sqrt{3})(b + w)$ yellow relays on the edges.

Now each pair of black relays in T is connected. It is enough to connect each grey relay to the nearest black relay: the distance is at most 2, and one yellow relay is enough. In summary, the total number of yellow relays is less than $(2/\sqrt{3})(b + w) + g \leq (2/\sqrt{3} - 1)2w + (14/5)w = (4/\sqrt{3} + 4/5)w < 3.11w.$ □

Then it follows that $|A_y| < 3.11|R_w^*| \leq 3.11|R_\ell^*|$. This completes the proof that the approximation ratio of our algorithm is less than 3.11.

4   Inapproximability of One-Tier Relay Placement

We have improved the best known approximation ratio for one-tier relay placement from 7 to 3.11. A natural question to pose at this point is whether we could make the approximation ratio as close to 1 as we wish. In this section, we show that no PTAS exists, unless P = NP.

Theorem 1. *It is NP-hard to approximate one-tier relay placement within factor $1 + 1/687$.*

The reduction is from minimum vertex cover in graphs of bounded degree. Let $\mathcal{G} = (V, E)$ be an instance of vertex cover; let $\Delta \leq 5$ be the maximum degree of $\mathcal{G}$. We construct an instance $\mathcal{J}$ of the relay placement problem which has a feasible solution with $|C| + 2|E| + 1$ relays if and only if $\mathcal{G}$ has a vertex cover of size k.

Fig. 2 illustrates the construction. Fig. 2a shows the *vertex gadget*; we have one such gadget for each vertex $v \in V$. Fig. 2b shows the *crossover gadget*; we have one such gadget for each edge $e \in E$. Small dots are sensors in the relay placement instance; each solid edge has length at most 1. White boxes are *good locations* for relays; dashed lines show connections for relays in good locations.

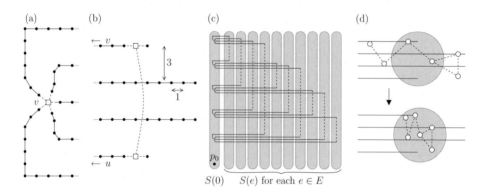

Fig. 2. (a) Vertex gadget for $v \in V$. (b) Crossover gadget for $\{v, u\} \in E$. (c) Reduction for K_5. (d) Normalising a solution, step 1.

We set $r = 16(|V| + 1)$, and we choose $|E| + 1$ disks of diameter r such that each pair of these disks is separated by a distance larger than $|V|r$ but at most poly($|V|$). One of the disks is called $S(0)$ and the rest are $S(e)$ for $e \in E$. All vertex gadgets and one isolated sensor, called p_0, are placed within disk $S(0)$. The crossover gadget for edge e is placed within disk $S(e)$. There are noncrossing paths of sensors that connect the crossover gadget $e = \{u, v\} \in E$ to the vertex gadgets u and v; all such paths (*tentacles*) are separated by a distance at least 3. Good relay locations and p_0 cannot be closer than 1 unit to a disk boundary.

Fig. 2c is a schematic illustration of the overall construction in the case of $\mathcal{G} = K_5$; the figure is highly condensed in x direction. There are 11 disks. Disk

$S(0)$ contains one isolated sensor and 5 vertex gadgets. Each disk $S(e)$ contains one crossover gadget. Outside these disks we have only parts of tentacles.

There are $4|E|+1$ blobs in $\mathcal{I}$. The isolated sensor p_0 forms one blob. For each edge there are 4 blobs: two tentacles from vertex gadgets to the crossover gadget, and two isolated sensors in the crossover gadget.

Theorem 1 now follows from the following two lemmata.

Lemma 5. *Let C be a vertex cover of $\mathcal{G}$. Then there is a feasible solution to relay placement problem $\mathcal{I}$ with $|C|+2|E|+1$ relays.*

Proof. For each $v \in C$, place one relay at the good location of the vertex gadget v. For each $e \in E$, place two relays at the good locations of the crossover gadget e. Place one relay at the isolated sensor p_0. $\square$

Lemma 6. *Assume that there exists a feasible solution to relay placement problem $\mathcal{I}$ with $k+2|E|+1$ relays. Then $\mathcal{G}$ has a vertex cover of size at most k.*

Proof. If $k \geq |V|$, then the claim is trivial: $C = V$ is a vertex cover of size at most k. We therefore focus on the case $k < |V|$.

Let R be a solution with $k+2|E|+1$ relays. We transform the solution into a canonical form R' of the same size and with the following additional constraints: there is a subset $C \subseteq V$ such that at least one relay is placed at the good relay location of each vertex gadget $v \in C$; two relays are placed at the good locations of each crossover gadget; one relay is placed at p_0; and there are no other relays. If R' is a feasible solution, then C is a vertex cover of $\mathcal{G}$ with $|C| \leq k$.

Now we show how to construct the canonical form R'. We observe that there are $2|E|+1$ isolated sensors in $\mathcal{I}$: sensor p_0 and two sensors for each crossover gadget. In the feasible solution R, for each isolated sensor p, we can always identify one relay within distance 1 from p (if there are several relays, pick one arbitrarily). These relays are called *bound relays*. The remaining $k < |V|$ relays are called *free relays*.

Step 1. Consider the communication graph formed by the sensors in $\mathcal{I}$ and the relays R. Since each pair of disks $S(i)$, $i \in \{0\} \cup E$, is separated by a distance larger than $|V|r$, we know that there is no path that extends from one disk to another and consists of at most k free relays (and possibly one bound relay in each end). Therefore we can shift each connected set of relays so that it is located within one disk (see Fig. 2d). While doing so, we do not break any relay–relay links: all relays within the same disk can communicate with each other. We can also maintain each relay–blob link intact.

Step 2. Now we have a clique formed by a set of relays within each disk $S(i)$, there are no other relays, and the network is connected. We move the bound relay in $S(0)$ so that it is located exactly on p_0. For each $e \in E$, we move the bound relays in $S(e)$ so that they are located exactly on the good relay locations. Finally, any free relays in $S(0)$ can be moved to a good relay location of a suitable vertex gadget. These changes may introduce new relay–blob links but they do not break any existing relay–blob or relay–relay links.

Step 3. What remains is that some disks $S(e)$, $e \in E$, may contain free relays. Let x be one of these relays. If x can be removed without breaking connectivity, we can move x to the good relay location of any vertex gadget. Otherwise x is adjacent to exactly one blob of sensors, and removing it breaks the network into two connected components: component A which contains p_0, and component B. Now we simply pick a vertex $v \in V$ such that the vertex gadget v contains sensors from component B, and we move x to the good relay location of this vertex gadget; this ensures connectivity between p_0 and B.   □

Proof of Theorem 1. Let $\Delta, A, B, C \in \mathbb{N}$, with $\Delta \leq 5$ and $C > B$. Assume that there is a factor $\alpha = 1 + (C - B)/(B + \Delta A + 1)$ approximation algorithm $\mathcal{A}$ for relay placement. We show how to use $\mathcal{A}$ to solve the following *gap-vertex-cover* problem for some $0 < \varepsilon < 1/2$: given a graph $\mathcal{G}$ with An nodes and maximum degree Δ, decide whether the minimum vertex cover of $\mathcal{G}$ is smaller than $(B+\varepsilon)n$ or larger than $(C - \varepsilon)n$.

If $n < 2$, the claim is trivial. Otherwise we can choose a positive constant ε such that $\alpha - 1 < (C - B - 2\varepsilon)/(B + \varepsilon + \Delta A + 1/n)$ for any $n \geq 2$. Construct the relay placement instance $\mathcal{I}$ as described above.

If minimum vertex cover of $\mathcal{G}$ is smaller than $(B + \varepsilon)n$, then by Lemma 5, the algorithm $\mathcal{A}$ returns a solution with at most $b = \alpha((B + \varepsilon)n + 2|E| + 1)$ relays. If minimum vertex cover of $\mathcal{G}$ is larger than $(C - \varepsilon)n$, then by Lemma 6, the algorithm $\mathcal{A}$ returns a solution with at least $c = (C - \varepsilon)n + 2|E| + 1$ relays. As $2|E| \leq \Delta An$, we have $c - b \geq (C - \varepsilon)n + 2|E| + 1 - \alpha((B + \varepsilon)n + 2|E| + 1) \geq (C - B - 2\varepsilon - (\alpha - 1)(B + \varepsilon + \Delta A + 1/n))n > 0$, which shows that we can solve the gap-vertex-cover problem in polynomial time.

For $\Delta = 4$, $A = 152$, $B = 78$, $C = 79$, and any $0 < \varepsilon < 1/2$, the gap-vertex-cover problem is NP-hard [13, Thm. 3].   □

Remark 1. We remind that throughout this work we assume that radius r is part of the problem instance. Our proof of Theorem 1 heavily relies on this fact; in our reduction, $r = \Theta(|V|)$. It is an open question whether one-tier relay placement admits a PTAS for a small, e.g., constant, r.

Acknowledgments

We thank Guoliang Xue for suggesting the problem to us and for fruitful discussions, and Marja Hassinen for comments and discussions. We thank the anonymous referees for their helpful suggestions. Parts of this research were conducted at the Dagstuhl research center. AE is supported by NSF CAREER Grant 0348000. JM is partially supported by grants from the National Science Foundation (CCF-0431030, CCF-0528209, CCF-0729019), NASA Ames, and Metron Aviation. JS is supported in part by the Academy of Finland grant 116547, and Helsinki Graduate School in Computer Science and Engineering (Hecse). VP is supported in part by the Academy of Finland grant 118653 (ALGODAN).

References

1. Chen, D., Du, D.Z., Hu, X.D., Lin, G.H., Wang, L., Xue, G.: Approximations for Steiner trees with minimum number of Steiner points. Journal of Global Optimization 18(1), 17–33 (2000)
2. Chen, D., Du, D.Z., Hu, X.D., Lin, G.H., Wang, L., Xue, G.: Approximations for Steiner trees with minimum number of Steiner points. Theoretical Computer Science 262(1–2), 83–99 (2001)
3. Cheng, X., Du, D.Z., Wang, L., Xu, B.: Relay sensor placement in wireless sensor networks. Wireless Networks (to appear, 2007)
4. Liu, H., Wan, P.J., Jia, X.: Fault-tolerant relay node placement in wireless sensor networks. In: Wang, L. (ed.) COCOON 2005. LNCS, vol. 3595, pp. 230–239. Springer, Heidelberg (2005)
5. Lloyd, E.L., Xue, G.: Relay node placement in wireless sensor networks. IEEE Transactions on Computers 56(1), 134–138 (2007)
6. Srinivas, A., Zussman, G., Modiano, E.: Mobile backbone networks – construction and maintenance. In: Proc. 7th ACM International Symposium on Mobile Ad Hoc Networking and Computing, MobiHoc, Florence, Italy, May 2006, pp. 166–177. ACM Press, New York (2006)
7. Zhang, W., Xue, G., Misra, S.: Fault-tolerant relay node placement in wireless sensor networks: Problems and algorithms. In: Proc. 26th IEEE International Conference on Computer Communications, INFOCOM, Anchorage, Alaska, USA, May 2007, pp. 1649–1657. IEEE, Piscataway (2007)
8. Bredin, J.L., Demaine, E.D., Hajiaghayi, M., Rus, D.: Deploying sensor networks with guaranteed capacity and fault tolerance. In: Proc. 6th ACM International Symposium on Mobile Ad Hoc Networking and Computing, MobiHoc, Urbana-Champaign, IL, USA, May 2005, pp. 309–319. ACM Press, New York (2005)
9. Cerdeira, J.O., Pinto, L.S.: Requiring connectivity in the set covering problem. Journal of Combinatorial Optimization 9(1), 35–47 (2005)
10. Shuai, T.P., Hu, X.D.: Connected set cover problem and its applications. In: Cheng, S.-W., Poon, C.K. (eds.) AAIM 2006. LNCS, vol. 4041, pp. 243–254. Springer, Heidelberg (2006)
11. Yang, Y., Lin, M., Xu, J., Xie, Y.: Minimum spanning tree with neighborhoods. In: Kao, M.-Y., Li, X.-Y. (eds.) AAIM 2007. LNCS, vol. 4508, pp. 306–316. Springer, Heidelberg (2007)
12. Du, D.Z., Hwang, F.: An approach for proving lower bounds: Solution of Gilbert–Pollak's conjecture on Steiner ratio. In: Proc. 31st Annual Symposium on Foundations of Computer Science, FOCS, St. Louis, MO, USA, October 1990, pp. 76–85. IEEE, Piscataway (1990)
13. Berman, P., Karpinski, M.: On some tighter inapproximability results. In: Wiedermann, J., Van Emde Boas, P., Nielsen, M. (eds.) ICALP 1999. LNCS, vol. 1644, pp. 200–209. Springer, Heidelberg (1999)

Selfish Bin Packing

Leah Epstein and Elena Kleiman

Department of Mathematics, University of Haifa, 31905 Haifa, Israel
lea@math.haifa.ac.il, elena.kleiman@gmail.com

Abstract. Following recent interest in the study of computer science problems in a game theoretic setting, we consider the well known bin packing problem where the items are controlled by selfish agents. Each agent is charged with a cost according to the fraction of the used bin space its item requires. That is, the cost of the bin is split among the agents, proportionally to their sizes. Thus, the selfish agents prefer their items to be packed in a bin that is as full as possible. The social goal is to minimize the number of the bins used. The social cost in this case is therefore the number of bins used in the packing.

A pure Nash equilibrium is a packing where no agent can obtain a smaller cost by unilaterally moving his item to a different bin, while other items remain in their original positions. A Strong Nash equilibrium is a packing where there exists no subset of agents, all agents in which can profit from jointly moving their items to different bins. We say that all agents in a subset profit from moving their items to different bins if all of them have a strictly smaller cost as a result of moving, while the other items remain in their positions.

We measure the quality of the equilibria using the standard measures *PoA* and *PoS* that are defined as the worst case worst/best asymptotic ratio between the social cost of a (pure) Nash equilibrium and the cost of an optimal packing, respectively. We also consider the recently introduced measures *SPoA* and *SPoS*, that are defined similarly to the *PoA* and the *PoS*, but consider only Strong Nash equilibria.

We give nearly tight lower and upper bounds of 1.6416 and 1.6428, respectively, on the *PoA* of the bin packing game, improving upon previous result by Bilò, and establish the fact that *PoS* = 1. We show that the bin packing game admits a Strong Nash equilibrium, and that *SPoA=SPoS*. We prove that this value is equal to the approximation ratio of a natural greedy algorithm for bin packing.

1 Introduction

Motivation and framework. In the last few decades, we have witnessed the tremendous development of the Internet and its penetration into almost any aspect of our lives, influencing the society on a scope not known before. The emergence of the Internet created a major shift in our view of computational networking systems. Traditional system design assumes that all participants behave according to some protocol that serves the intentions of the system designers and the users often have to sacrifice some of their own performance for the

D. Halperin and K. Mehlhorn (Eds.): ESA 2008, LNCS 5193, pp. 368–380, 2008.

sake of the entire network. Unlike any other distributed system, the Internet is built, operated and used by various autonomous and self-interested entities, in different levels of competition and cooperation relationship with one another. These entities (or *agents*) have diverse sets of interests and aim at achieving their individual goals as opposed to obtaining a global optimum of the system. Hence, selfishness is an inherent characteristic of the Internet. Also, there exists no central authority that can enforce a certain policy or regulation on the participants of the system. Under these assumptions, network optimization problems that model situations where rational agents compete each other over network resources while seeking to satisfy their individual requirements at minimum cost, can be viewed as non-cooperative strategic games considered by the classical Game Theory. It becomes natural to revisit various aspects concerning networking under a Game-Theoretic perspective, using the tools that the Game Theory provides us with. In particular, we are interested in quantifying the loss to the system performance caused by the lack of cooperation and the selfishness of the players. This is achieved by analyzing the *Nash equilibrium* (the main concept of stability in Game Theory) of the game and comparing it to the social optimum.

In reality, in many networking applications the multitude of entities that use and operate the system are not completely autonomous. They interact with each other and form *coalitions*, members of which agree to coordinate their actions in a mutually beneficial way. Of course, these entities still remain selfish. Thus, each agent will agree to participate, if at all, in a coalition that ensures him a benefit from participation in that coalition. This scenario evokes the Coalitional Game Theory and the concept of *Strong Nash equilibrium*. Considering the possibility of players to gather in coalitions allows us to separate the effect incurred to the system performance due to selfishness from that of lack of coordination (which disappears if we let the participants of the game to cooperate).

In this paper, we consider the well-known Bin Packing problem (see e.g. [16], [17], [7] for surveys). The basic Bin Packing problem consists of packing a set of objects with sizes in $(0,1]$ into a set of unit-capacity bins while using as few bins as possible. Among other important real-life applications, such as multiprocessor scheduling and stock cutting, the Bin Packing problem can be met in a great variety of network problems. For example, the packet scheduling problem (the problem of packing a given set of packets into a minimum number of time slots for fairness provisioning), the bandwidth allocation problem (signals have usually a small size and several of them can be transmitted in the same frame so as to minimize bandwidth consumption) and the problem of packing the data for Internet phone calls into ATM packets (filling fixed-size frames to maximize the amount of data that they carry), to mention only a few. Therefore, the study of this problem from a Game-Theoretic standpoint is clearly well motivated.

Definitions and notations. To establish notation, we will briefly introduce the basic concepts from Game Theory. A non-cooperative strategic game is a tuple $G = \langle N, (S_i)_{i \in N}, (c_i)_{i \in N} \rangle$, where N is a non-empty, finite set of players, each player $i \in N$ has a non-empty, finite set S_i of *strategies* (actions) and a cost function c_i. Each player chooses a strategy independently of the choices of the other players. The choices of all players can thus be thought to be made simultaneously. It is assumed that each player has a full knowledge over all strategy sets of all the players. In a setting of *pure* strategies, each player chooses exactly one strategy (with probability one); in a setting of *mixed* strategies, each player uses a probability distribution over the strategies. A combination of strategies chosen by the players $s = (x_j)_{j \in N} \in \times_{j \in N} S_j$, is called a *strategy profile* or a *configuration*. $X = \times_{j \in N} S_j$ denotes the set of the strategy profiles. Let $i \in N$. $X_{-i} = \times_{j \in N \setminus \{i\}} S_j$ denotes the strategy profiles of all players except player i. Let $A \subseteq N$. $X_A = \times_{j \in A} S_j$ denotes the set of strategy profiles of players in A. Strategy profiles $s = (x_j)_{j \in N} \in X$ will be denoted by (x_i, x_{-i}) or $(x_A, x_{N \setminus A})$ if the strategy choice of player i or of the set A of players needs stressing. The cost function $c_i : X \to \mathbb{R}$ specifies for each strategy profile $s \in X$ the cost charged from player i, $c_i(x) \in \mathbb{R}$. The cost charged from each player depends not only on his own strategy but also on the strategies chosen by all other players. Each player $i \in N$ would prefer to chose a strategy that minimizes his cost. The accepted concept of rationality in a game is the *Nash equilibrium* [24]. Throughout the paper, the Nash equilibrium is considered only in the setting of pure strategies.

Definition 1. *A strategy profile $s \in X$ is called a pure Nash equilibrium (NE) if for every i and for all $x'_i \in S_i$, $x'_i \neq x_i$, $c_i(x_i, x_{-i}) \leq c_i(x'_i, x_{-i})$ holds. That is, no player can reduce his cost by unilaterally changing his strategy, while the strategies of all other players remain unchanged.*

Nash equilibrium (perhaps only in mixed strategies) exists in every finite game [24]. A game can have several Nash equilibria, with different social cost values. If only pure strategies are allowed, there may exist no Nash equilibrium at all. The set of pure Nash equilibria of a game G is denoted by $NE(G)$.

Games as defined above assume that players can not negotiate and cooperate with each other. *Coalitional Game Theory* considers cooperative games, where the notion of players is replaced by the set of possible coalitions (i.e., groups of players) rather than individuals. A participation in a coalition is voluntary. Each coalition can achieve a particular value (the smallest possible sum of costs among players in the coalition, against worst-case behavior of players outside the coalition). Aumann [4] introduced the concept of Strong Nash equilibrium. Since each player can either participate or decline to participate in a coalition, given the strategy he will be obligated to choose in case he does, and the cost he will be charged with as a result, the Strong Nash equilibrium is studied only for settings that involve no randomization, that is, only pure strategies are considered.

Definition 2. *A strategy profile $s \in X$ is called a Strong Nash equilibrium (SNE) if for every $S \subseteq N$ and for all strategy profiles $y_S \in X_S$, there is at least one player $i \in S$ such that $c_i(x_S, x_{-S}) \leq c_i(y_S, x_{-S})$. That is, no subset of players can deviate by changing strategies jointly in a manner that reduces the costs charged from all its members, given that nonmembers stick to their original strategies.*

The set of Strong Nash equilibria of a game G is denoted by $SNE(G)$. Every Strong Nash equilibrium is a Nash equilibrium (by definition). Hence, $SNE(G) \subseteq NE(G)$. The opposite does not usually hold. A game can have no Strong Nash equilibrium at all. Several specific classes of congestion games were shown in [15,27] to possess Strong Nash equilibria. For any other game, the existence of Strong equilibria should be checked specifically in each case. Other variants of Strong equilibria studied consider static predefined coalitions [14,12] and coalitions that are not subject to deviations by subsets of their own members [29].

The *social cost* of a game G, is an objective function $SC(s) : X \to \mathbb{R}$ that numerically expresses the 'social cost' of an outcome of the game for a strategy profile $s \in X$. The *social optimum* of a game G, is the game outcome that optimizes the social cost function. It is denoted by $OPT(G)$, and defined by $OPT(G) = \min_{s \in X} SC(s)$.

2   The Bin Packing Game

The model. The bin packing problem consists of packing a set N of items, each item $i \in N$ having a size $a_i \in (0, 1]$, into a set of unit-capacity bins while using as few bins as possible. The induced bin packing game BP is defined by a tuple $BP = \langle N, (B_i)_{i \in N}, (c_i)_{i \in N} \rangle$, where N is the set of selfish players. Each player $i \in N$ controls a single item with size $a_i \in (0, 1]$ and selects the bin to which this item is packed. We identify the player with the item he wishes to pack. Thus, the set of players corresponds to the set of items. The set of strategies B_i for each item $i \in N$ is the set of all possible open bins. Each item can be assigned to one bin only. Splitting items among several bins is not allowed. The outcome of the game is a particular assignment $(b_j)_{j \in N} \in \times_{j \in N} B_j$ of items to bins of equal capacity. Let X denote the set of all possible assignments. All the bins have the same fixed cost which equals their capacity and the cost of a bin is shared among all the items it contains. The cost function of item i is c_i. If we scale the cost and the size of each bin to one, the cost paid by item i for choosing to be packed in bin $\mathcal{B}_j$ such that $j \in B_i$ is defined by $c_i(j, b_{-i}) = \dfrac{a_i}{\sum_{k:b_k=j} a_k}$, when $b_{-i} \in X_{-i}$;

i.e, an item is charged with a cost which is proportional to the portion of the bin it occupies in a given packing. We consider the cost charged from an item for being packed in a bin in which it does not fit to be ∞. The items are interested in being packed in a bin so as to minimize their cost. Thus, item i packed into $\mathcal{B}_j$ in a particular assignment $(b_j)_{j \in N}$ will migrate from $\mathcal{B}_j$ each time it will detect another bin $\mathcal{B}_{j'}$ such that $c_i(j', b_{-i}) < c_i(j, b_{-i})$. This inequality holds for each j' such that $\sum_{k:b_k=j'} a_k + a_i > \sum_{k:b_k=j} a_k$, thus an item will perform an improving step each time it will detect a strictly more loaded bin in which it fits. At a Nash equilibrium, no item can unilaterally reduce its cost by moving to a different bin. The social cost function that we want to minimize is the number of used bins.

In the cooperative version of the game, we consider all possible (non-empty) groups of items $A \subseteq N$. A group can contain a single item. The cost functions of the players are defined the same as in the non-cooperative case. Each group of items is interested to be packed in a way so as to minimize the costs of all group members. Thus, given a particular assignment, all members of group A will perform a joint improving step if there is a configuration in which, for each member, the new bin will admit a strictly greater load than the bin of origin. The costs of the non-members may be enlarged as a result of this step.

At a Strong Nash equilibrium, no group of items can reduce the costs of its members by jointly moving to a different bin. The social cost function remains the same one we consider in the non-cooperative setting.

Measuring the inefficiency of the equilibria. It is well-known that Nash equilibrium does not always optimize the social cost function. Even in very simple settings, selfish behavior can lead to highly inefficient outcome. Our bin packing game is no exception: an equilibrium packing does not necessarily have minimum cost. Note also that not every optimal solution is an equilibrium.

The quality of an equilibrium is measured with respect to the social optimum. In the bin packing game, the social optimum is the number of bins used in a coordinated optimal packing. In the computer science literature, the Price of Anarchy *(PoA)* [20,25] (also referred to as the Coordination Ratio *(CR)*) and the Price of Stability *(PoS)* [3,2] (also called optimistic price of anarchy) have become prevalent measures of the quality of the equilibria reached with uncoordinated selfish players. The Price of Anarchy/ Price of Stability of a game G are defined to be the ratio between the cost of the worst/best Nash equilibrium and the social optimum, respectively. Formally,

$$PoA(G) = \sup_{s \in NE(G)} \frac{SC(s)}{OPT(G)}, \quad PoS(G) = \inf_{s \in NE(G)} \frac{SC(s)}{OPT(G)}.$$

The former quantifies the worst possible loss to performance incurred by selfish uncoordinated agents, and the latter measures the minimum penalty in performance required to ensure a stable equilibrium outcome.

The bin packing problem is usually studied via asymptotic measures. The asymptotic *PoA* and *PoS* of the bin packing game *BP* are defined by

$$PoA(BP) = \limsup_{OPT(G) \to \infty} \sup_{G \in BP} PoA(G), \quad PoS(BP) = \limsup_{OPT(G) \to \infty} \sup_{G \in BP} PoS(G).$$

Recent research by Andelman et al. [1] initiated a study of measures that separate the effect of the lack of coordination between players from the effect of their selfishness. The measures considered are the Strong Price of Anarchy *(SPoA)* and the Strong Price of Stability *(SPoS)*. These measures are defined similarly to the *PoA* and the *PoS*, but only Strong equilibria are considered. We define the Strong Price of Anarchy/ Strong Price of Stability of a game G as the ratio between the cost of the worst/best Strong Nash equilibrium and the social optimum, respectively. Formally,

$$SPoA(G) = \sup_{s \in SNE(G)} \frac{SC(s)}{OPT(G)}, \quad SPoS(G) = \inf_{s \in SNE(G)} \frac{SC(s)}{OPT(G)},$$

As before, we define the asymptotic *SPoA* and *SPoS* of the bin packing game *BP* by

$$SPoA(BP) = \limsup_{OPT(G) \to \infty} \ \sup_{G \in BP} \ SPoA(G)$$

$$SPoS(BP) = \limsup_{OPT(G) \to \infty} \ \sup_{G \in BP} \ SPoS(G).$$

3   Related Work and Our Contributions

Related work. The application of concepts and techniques borrowed from Game Theory to various problems in computer science, specifically, to network problems, was initiated in [20,25]. Since then, issues like *routing* [28,23,8], *bandwidth allocation* [30], and *congestion control* [18], to name only a few, have been analyzed from a Game-Theoretic perspective. The studied models are simplification of problems arising in real networks, that seem appropriate for describing basic network problems. The bin packing problem discussed in this paper belongs to a class of problems induced by selfish flow routing in non-cooperative networks. The first model studied in that context is the KP model introduced by Koutsoupias and Papadimitriou in [20]. This model features a network consisting of two nodes, a source and a destination, connected by a set of parallel links, all with the same bandwidth capacity, and a set of selfish users, each wishing to route a certain amount of flow from the source to the destination. The delay suffered by each user for utilizing a link equals to total amount of flow routed through this link. Hence, the more flow routed on a specific link, the longer the delay. For such a reason, users, which are assumed to be selfish, want to route their flow on the least loaded link. The goal is minimize the greatest delay. The resulting problem can be viewed as a selfish job scheduling problem. The bounds on the *PoA* for the aforementioned model were initially analyzed both in pure and mixed strategies setting in [20]. They were later improved by [23], and definitively characterized in [9,19]. The existence of pure Nash equilibrium in this setting was proved in [11]. The cooperative version of the job scheduling problem was first studied in [1]. The authors proved that job scheduling games admit Strong equilibria, established the fact that $SPoS = 1$ as for every instance of the scheduling game there exists an optimal solution which is a Strong equilibrium, and gave non-tight bounds on the $SPoA$ that were later definitively characterized in [10]. Since then, many variants and generalizations of this basic model have been studied, with different network topology, different social costs, different nature of the flow, etc.. See for example [28,26,22].

The selfish bin packing problem defined above can also be interpreted as a routing problem. Consider a network consisting of two nodes, a source and a destination, connected by a potentially infinite number of parallel links having the same bandwidth capacity, and a set of users wishing to send a certain amount of unsplittable flow between the two nodes. To establish a link, one has to pay a fixed cost which equals the capacity of the link. The cost of each link is shared

Table 1. Summary of the results

		Lower Bound	Upper Bound
PoA	Bilò [5]	1.6	1.6667
	Our paper	1.6416	1.6428
$SPoA=SPoS$	Our paper	1.6067	1.6210
PoS	Our paper	1	1

among the users routing their flow on that link according to the normalized fraction of its utilized bandwidth. For such a reason, users, who are assumed to be selfish, want to route their traffic on the most loaded link. The goal is to minimize the number of links used. This model resembles the KP model with different cost and social functions. It was suggested by Bilò in [5].

Bilò [5] was the first to study the bin packing problem under game theoretic perspective. He proved that the bin packing game admits pure Nash equilibria and provided non-tight bounds on the Price of Anarchy. He also proved that the bin packing game converges to a pure Nash equilibrium in a finite sequence of selfish improving steps, starting from any initial configuration of the items.

The *Subset Sum*[1] algorithm for bin packing we refer to in the sequel of this paper, is a greedy algorithm that repeatedly solves a one-dimensional knapsack problem for packing each bin in turn. It was originally suggested by Prim and first mentioned by Graham [13], who also gave a lower bound of $\sum_{k=1}^{\infty} \frac{1}{2^k-1} = 1.6067$ on its asymptotic worst-case performance. An upper bound of 1.6210 was proved only recently by Caprara and Pferschy in [6].

Our results and organization of the paper. In this paper we consider the pin packing game, in a variant originally proposed and analyzed by Bilò in [5]. We establish that for every instance of bin packing game there exists an optimal *NE* packing where the social cost is equal to the social optimum; in other words, $PoS = 1$. We also give improved (and nearly tight) lower and upper bounds on the *PoA* of the bin packing game. We extend the results in [5] and show that bin packing game admits Strong Nash equilibria as well. Moreover, we show that the aforementioned *Subset Sum* algorithm in fact produces an assignment that admits Strong equilibrium. Therefore, we provide an exponential time deterministic algorithm with guaranteed (asymptotic) worst-case performance ratio [6] that actually calculates the Strong Nash assignment for each bin. Interestingly, the *SPoA* equals the *SPoS*, and we prove this value is equal to the approximation ratio of the *Subset Sum* algorithm. Thus, we provide bounds on the *SPoA* and the *SPoS* of the game.

Our results for the *PoA* improve upon previous results of Bilò [5]. The other concepts were not addressed to the bin packing framework prior to this paper, to the best of our knowledge. Our contributions can therefore be summarized in Table 1. Some of the proofs were omitted due to space constraints.

---

[1] Also called *fill bin* or *minimum bin slack* in the literature.

4   The Price of Stability

In our first result, we establish that for every instance of the bin packing game there always exists a packing, among the optimal ones, which is a *NE*. We do it by introducing an order relation similar to the one used by Fotakis et al. in [11] between the different configurations and showing that an optimal packing which is the "highest" among all optimal packings according to this order is always a *NE*. Specifically, in this section we prove the following theorem.

Theorem 1. *For every instance of the bin packing game there is a NE packing which is optimal.*

Definition 3. *For a configuration b, the load vector is an n-tuple $L(b) = (L_1(b), L_2(b), \ldots, L_n(b))$, where each component $L_i(b)$ is the load of bin $\mathcal{B}_i$ in a packing defined by b.*

Definition 4. *A vector $u = (u_1, u_2, \ldots, u_n)$ is greater than $v = (v_1, v_2, \ldots, v_n)$ lexicographically, if there is some $k \geq 1$ such that $u_i = v_i$ for $i = 1, \ldots k-1$, and $u_k > v_k$.*

We define a sorted lexicographic order on the configurations via the lexicographic order on the vectors.

Definition 5. *Let b and b' be two configurations with the corresponding load vectors $L(b) = (L_1(b), L_2(b), \ldots, L_n(b))$ and $L(b') = (L_1(b'), L_2(b'), \ldots, L_n(b'))$. A configuration b' is greater than b lexicographically, if and only if the load vector $L(b')$ sorted in non-increasing order is greater lexicographically than $L(b)$, sorted in non-increasing order. We denote this relation by $b' \succ_L b$.*

The sorted lexicographic order $\succ_L$ defines a total order on the configurations. Next, we show that when an item migrates, we move to a "higher" configuration in the order.

Lemma 1. *The sorted lexicographic order of the load vector always increases when an item migrates.*

Lemma 2. *For any instance of the bin packing game, the lexicographically maximal optimal packing b^* is a NE.*

Theorem 1 now follows from Lemmas 1 and 2. An immediate conclusion from Theorem 1 is that the upper bound on the Price of Stability (*PoS*) of the bin packing game is 1. Combined with the fact that $PoS(G) \geq 1$ for any $G \in BP$ as no equilibrium point can be better than the social optimum, we conclude that $PoS(BP) = 1$.

5   The Price of Anarchy

We now provide a lower bound for the Price of Anarchy of the bin packing game and also prove a very close upper bound.

5.1   A Lower Bound: Construction

In this section, we present our main technical contribution, which is a lower bound on the *PoA*. We start with presenting a set of items. The set of items consists of multiple levels. Such constructions are sometimes used to design lower bounds on specific bin packing algorithms (see e.g., [21]). Our construction differs from these constructions since the notion of order (in which packed bins are created) does not exist here, and each bin must be stable with respect to all other bins. The resulting lower bound on the *PoA* is different from any bounds known on the asymptotic approximation ratio of well known algorithms for bin packing. Since we prove an almost matching upper bound, we conclude that the *PoA* is probably not related directly to any natural algorithm. We prove the following theorem.

Theorem 2. *The Price of Anarchy of the bin packing game is at least the sum of the following series:* $\sum_{j=1}^{\infty} 2^{-j(j-1)/2}$, *which is equal to approximately* 1.64163.

Proof. Let $s > 2$ be an integer. We define a construction with s phases of indices $1 \leq j \leq s$, where the items of phase j have sizes which are close to $\frac{1}{2^j}$, but can be slightly smaller or slightly larger than this value.

We let $OPT = n$, and assume that n is a large enough integer, such that $n > 2^{s^3}$. We use a sequence of small values, δ_i such that $\delta_j = \frac{1}{(4n)^{3s-2j}}$. Note that this implies $\delta_{j+1} = (4n)^2 \delta_j$ for $1 \leq j \leq s - 1$. We use two sequences of positive integers $r_j \leq n$ and $d_j \leq n$, for $2 \leq j \leq s$, and in addition, $r_1 = n$ and $d_1 = 0$. We define $r_{j+1} = \frac{r_j - 1}{2^j}$, for $1 \leq j \leq s - 1$, and $d_{j+1} = r_j - r_{j+1} = \frac{(2^j-1)r_j+1}{2^j} = (2^j - 1)r_{j+1} + 1$.

Proposition 1. *For each* $1 \leq j \leq s$, $\frac{n}{2^{j(j-1)/2}} - 1 < r_j \leq \frac{n}{2^{j(j-1)/2}}$.

Phase 1 simply consists of r_1 items of size $\sigma_1 = \frac{1}{2} + 2(d_1 + 1)\delta_1$. For $j \geq 2$, phase j consists of the following $2d_j + r_j$ items. There are r_j items of size $\sigma_j = \frac{1}{2^j} + 2(d_j+1)\delta_j$, and for $1 \leq i \leq d_j$, there are two items of sizes $\pi_j^i = \frac{1}{2^j} + (2i-1)\delta_j$ and $\theta_j^i = \frac{1}{2^j} - 2i\delta_j$. Note that $\pi_j^i + \theta_j^i = \frac{1}{2^{j-1}} - \delta_j$.

The packing will contain d_j bins of level j, for $2 \leq j \leq s$, and the remaining bins are of level $s + 1$, where a bin of level j, contains only items of phases $1, \ldots, j$.

To show that we can allocate these numbers of bins, and to calculate the number of level $s+1$ bins, note that $\sum_{j=2}^{s} d_j = r_1 - r_s = n - r_s$. Thus, the number of level $s + 1$ bins is (at most) r_s.

The packing of a bin of a given level is defined as follows. For $2 \leq j \leq s$, a level j bin contains one item of each size σ_k for $1 \leq k \leq j - 1$, and in addition, one pair of items of sizes π_j^i and θ_j^i for a given value of i such that $1 \leq i \leq d_j$. A bin of level $s + 1$ contains one item of each size σ_k for $1 \leq k \leq j - 1$.

Proposition 2. *This set of items can be packed into* n *bins, i.e.,* $OPT \leq n$

We next define an alternative packing, which is a *NE*. In the sequel, we apply a modification to the input by removing a small number of items. Clearly, $OPT \leq n$ would still hold for the modified input.

Our modification to the input is the removal of items π_j^1 and $\theta_j^{d_j}$ for all $2 \leq j \leq s$. We construct r_j bins for phase j items. A bin of phase j consists of $2^j - 1$ items, as follows. One item of size $\sigma_j = \frac{1}{2^j} + 2(d_i + 1)\delta_i$, and $2^{j-1} - 1$ pairs of items of phase j. A pair of items of phase j is defined to be the items of sizes π_j^{i+1} and θ_j^i, for some $1 \leq i \leq d_j - 1$. The sum of sizes of this pair of items is $\frac{1}{2^j} + (2i + 1)\delta_j + \frac{1}{2^j} - 2i\delta_j = \frac{1}{2^{j-1}} + \delta_j$. Using $d_j = (2^{j-1} - 1)r_j + 1$ we get that all phase j items are packed. The sum of items in every such bin is $1 - \frac{1}{2^{j-1}} + (2^{j-1} - 1)\delta_j + \frac{1}{2^j} + 2(d_j + 1)\delta_j = 1 - \frac{1}{2^j} + \delta_j(2^{j-1} + 1 + 2d_j)$.

Proposition 3. *The loads of the bins in the packing defined above are monotonically increasing as a function of the phase.*

Proposition 4. *The packing as defined above is a valid NE packing.*

Finally, we bound the *PoA* as follows. The cost of the resulting *NE* is $\sum_{j=1}^{s} r_j$. Using Proposition 1 we get that $\sum_{j=1}^{s} r_j \geq \sum_{j=1}^{s} (\frac{n}{2^{j(j-1)/2}} - 1)$ and since $OPT = n \gg s$, we get a ratio of at least $\sum_{j=1}^{s} 2^{-j(j-1)/2}$. Letting s tend to infinity as well results in the claimed lower bound. $\qquad\square$

5.2   An Upper Bound

To bound the *PoA* from above, we prove the following theorem.

Theorem 3. *For any instance of the bin packing game $G \in BP$: Any NE packing uses at most $1.64286 \cdot OPT(G) + 2$ bins, where $OPT(G)$ is the number of bins used in a coordinated optimal packing.*

6   Bounding the SPoA and the SPoS

The *SPoA* and the *SPoS* measures are well defined only when a Strong equilibrium exists. Our Bin Packing game does not belong to the set of games that were already shown to admit a Strong equilibrium. Thus, in order to analyze the *SPoA* and the *SPoS* of the Bin Packing game, we must first prove that a Strong equilibrium exists in our specific setting.

Theorem 4. *For each instance of the bin packing game, the set of Strong Nash equilibria is non-empty.*

Proof. We give a constructive proof to this theorem, by providing a deterministic algorithm that, for each instance of the bin packing game, produces a packing which admits *SNE*. This is the well-known *Subset Sum* algorithm, that proceeds by filling one bin at a time with a set of items that fills the bin as much as possible. We will show a stronger result; For the Bin Packing game introduced above, the set of *SNE* and the set of outcomes of *Subset Sum* algorithm coincide. A proof of this result is given in two parts.

Proposition 5. *The output of the Subset Sum algorithm is always a SNE.*

Proposition 6. *Any SNE is an output of some execution of the Subset Sum algorithm.*

As the *Subset Sum* algorithm is deterministic, Proposition 5 shows that an *SNE* always exists.   □

Now, we would like to show that for the bin packing game, $SPoA$ equals $SPoS$, and that this value is equal to the approximation ratio of the *Subset Sum* algorithm. For shortening notation, from now on, we refer to the *Subset Sum* algorithm as to algorithm C, and denote its approximation ratio by R_C.

Theorem 5. *For the bin packing game introduced above, $SPoA = SPoS = R_C$.*

Theorem 5 implies that the problem of bounding the $SPoA$ and the $SPoS$ of the bin packing game is equivalent to the problem of bounding the approximation worst-case ratio R_C of the well known *Subset Sum* algorithm for bin packing. The latter was tackled by Caprara and Pferschy, who used a novel and non-trivial method to show $1.6067 \leq R_C \leq 1.6210$, thus determining the exact value of R_C within a relative error smaller than 1% (see [6]). This exact value is yet to be found. We conclude that $1.6067 \leq SPoS(BP) = SPoA(BP) \leq 1.6210$.

7   Summary and Conclusions

We have studied the Bin Packing problem, where the items are controlled by selfish agents, and the cost charged from each bin is shared among all the items packed into it, both in non-cooperative and cooperative versions. We proved a tight bound on the PoS and provided improved and almost tight upper and lower bounds on the PoA of the induced game. We have also provided a simple deterministic algorithm that computes the SNE assignment for any instance of the Bin Packing game, and proved that the asymptotic worst-case performance of this algorithm equals the $SPoA$ and the $SPoS$ values of the game. Two open problems in that context are closing of the small gaps between upper and lower bounds for the PoA and the $SPoA/SPoS$ of the bin packing game. The latter, if achieved, will result in giving a tight bound on the worst-case performance of the *Subset Sum* algorithm for bin packing, as we proved these two problems are equivalent. This probably would not be an easy task, as finding tight bound on the approximation ratio of the *Subset Sum* algorithm, though very nearly approximated by Caprara and Pferschy in [6], remains open problem since 70's.

References

1. Andelman, N., Feldman, M., Mansour, Y.: Strong price of anarchy. In: SODA, pp. 189–198 (2007)
2. Anshelevich, E., Dasgupta, A., Kleinberg, J.M., Tardos, É., Wexler, T., Roughgarden, T.: The price of stability for network design with fair cost allocation. In: FOCS, pp. 295–304 (2004)
3. Anshelevich, E., Dasgupta, A., Tardos, É., Wexler, T.: Near-optimal network design with selfish agents. In: STOC, pp. 511–520 (2003)
4. Aumann, R.J.: Acceptable points in general cooperative n-person games. In: Tucker, A.W., Luce, R.D. (eds.) Contributions to the Theory of Games IV, Annals of Mathematics Study, vol. 40, pp. 287–324. Princeton University Press, Princeton (1959)
5. Bilò, V.: On the packing of selfish items. In: IPDPS. IEEE, Los Alamitos (2006)
6. Caprara, A., Pferschy, U.: Worst-case analysis of the subset sum algorithm for bin packing. Oper. Res. Lett. 32(2), 159–166 (2004)
7. Coffman Jr., E., Csirik, J.: Performance guarantees for one-dimensional bin packing. In: Gonzalez, T.F. (ed.) Handbook of Approximation Algorithms and Metaheuristics, ch. 32, pp. (32–1)–(32–18). Chapman & Hall/Crc (2007)
8. Czumaj, A.: Selfish routing on the internet. In: Leung, J. (ed.) Handbook of Scheduling: Algorithms, Models, and Performance Analysis, ch. 42, CRC Press, Boca Raton (2004)
9. Czumaj, A., Vöcking, B.: Tight bounds for worst-case equilibria. ACM Transactions on Algorithms 3(1) (2007)
10. Fiat, A., Kaplan, H., Levy, M., Olonetsky, S.: Strong price of anarchy for machine load balancing. In: Arge, L., Cachin, C., Jurdziński, T., Tarlecki, A. (eds.) ICALP 2007. LNCS, vol. 4596, pp. 583–594. Springer, Heidelberg (2007)
11. Fotakis, D., Kontogiannis, S.C., Koutsoupias, E., Mavronicolas, M., Spirakis, P.G.: The structure and complexity of nash equilibria for a selfish routing game. In: Widmayer, P., Triguero, F., Morales, R., Hennessy, M., Eidenbenz, S., Conejo, R. (eds.) ICALP 2002. LNCS, vol. 2380, pp. 123–134. Springer, Heidelberg (2002)
12. Fotakis, D., Kontogiannis, S.C., Spirakis, P.G.: Atomic congestion games among coalitions. In: Bugliesi, M., Preneel, B., Sassone, V., Wegener, I. (eds.) ICALP 2006, Part I. LNCS, vol. 4051, pp. 572–583. Springer, Heidelberg (2006)
13. Graham, R.L.: Bounds on multiprocessing anomalies and related packing algorithms. In: Proceedings of the 1972 Spring Joint Computer Conference, pp. 205–217 (1972)
14. Hayrapetyan, A., Tardos, É., Wexler, T.: The effect of collusion in congestion games. In: STOC, pp. 89–98 (2006)
15. Holzman, R., Law-Yone, N.: Strong equilibrium in congestion games. Games and Economic Behavior 21(1-2), 85–101 (1997)
16. Coffman Jr., E.G., Galambos, J., Martello, S., Vigo, D.: Bin packing approximation algorithms: Combinatorial analysis. In: Du, D.-Z., Pardalos, P.M. (eds.) Handbook of Combinatorial Optimization. Kluwer Academic Publishers, Amsterdam (1998)
17. Coffman Jr., E.G., Garey, M., Johnson, D.: Approximation algorithms for bin-packing: An updated survey. In: Ausiello, M.L.G., P.S. (eds.) Algorithm Design for Computer Systems Design. Springer, New York (1984)
18. Karp, R.M., Koutsoupias, E., Papadimitriou, C.H., Shenker, S.: Optimization problems in congestion control. In: FOCS, pp. 66–74 (2000)

19. Koutsoupias, E., Mavronicolas, M., Spirakis, P.G.: Approximate equilibria and ball fusion. Theory of Computing Systems 36(6), 683–693 (2003)
20. Koutsoupias, E., Papadimitriou, C.H.: Worst-case equilibria. In: Meinel, C., Tison, S. (eds.) STACS 1999. LNCS, vol. 1563, pp. 404–413. Springer, Heidelberg (1999)
21. Lee, C.C., Lee, D.T.: A simple online bin packing algorithm. J. ACM 32, 562–572 (1985)
22. Lücking, T., Mavronicolas, M., Monien, B., Rode, M.: A new model for selfish routing. In: Diekert, V., Habib, M. (eds.) STACS 2004. LNCS, vol. 2996, pp. 547–558. Springer, Heidelberg (2004)
23. Mavronicolas, M., Spirakis, P.G.: The price of selfish routing. In: STOC, pp. 510–519 (2001)
24. Nash, J.: Non-cooperative games. Annals of Mathematics 54(2), 286–295 (1951)
25. Papadimitriou, C.H.: Algorithms, games, and the internet. In: STOC, pp. 749–753 (2001)
26. Roughgarden, T.: Designing networks for selfish users is hard. In: FOCS, pp. 472–481 (2001)
27. Tennenholtz, M., Rozenfeld, O.: Strong and correlated strong equilibria in monotone congestion games. In: Spirakis, P.G., Mavronicolas, M., Kontogiannis, S.C. (eds.) WINE 2006. LNCS, vol. 4286, pp. 74–86. Springer, Heidelberg (2006)
28. Roughgarden, T., Tardos, É.: How bad is selfish routing? In: FOCS, pp. 93–102 (2000)
29. Whinston, M., Bernheim, B., Peleg, B.: Coalition-proof nash equilibria: I concepts. Journal of Economic Theory 42, 1–12 (1987)
30. Yaïche, H., Mazumdar, R., Rosenberg, C.: A game theoretic framework for bandwidth allocation and pricing in broadband networks. IEEE/ACM Trans. Netw. 8(5), 667–678 (2000)

Improved Randomized Results for That Interval Selection Problem

Leah Epstein[1] and Asaf Levin[2]

[1] Department of Mathematics, University of Haifa, 31905 Haifa, Israel
lea@math.haifa.ac.il
[2] Department of Statistics, The Hebrew University, Jerusalem, Israel
levinas@mscc.huji.ac.il

Abstract. Online interval selection is a problem in which intervals arrive one by one, sorted by their left endpoints. Each interval has a length and a non-negative weight associated with it. The goal is to select a non-overlapping set of intervals with maximal total weight and run them to completion. The decision regarding a possible selection of an arriving interval must be done immediately upon its arrival. The interval may be preempted later in favor of selecting an arriving overlapping interval, in which case the weight of the preempted interval is lost. We follow Woeginger [10] and study the same models. The type of instances we consider are C-benevolent instances, where the weight of an interval in a monotonically increasing (convex) function of the length, and D-benevolent instances, where the weight of an interval in a monotonically decreasing function of the length. Some of our results can be extended to the case of unit length intervals with arbitrary costs. We significantly improve the previously known bounds on the performance of online randomized algorithms for the problem, namely, we introduce a new algorithm for the D-benevolent case and for unit intervals, which uses a parameter θ and has competitive ratio of at most $\frac{\theta^2 \ln \theta}{(\theta-1)^2}$. This value is equal to approximately 2.4554 for $\theta \approx 3.513$ being the solution of the equation $x - 1 = 2 \ln x$. We further design a lower bound of $1 + \ln 2 \approx 1.693$ on the competitive ratio of any randomized algorithm. The lower bound is valid for any C-benevolent instance, some D-benevolent functions and for unit intervals. We further show a lower bound of $\frac{3}{2}$ for a wider class of D-benevolent instances. This improves over previously known lower bounds. We also design a barely random online algorithm for the D-benevolent case and the case of unit intervals, which uses a single random bit, and has a competitive ratio of 3.22745.

1 Introduction

We consider the following online problem. The input is a sequence of intervals arriving at arbitrary times. We denote an interval by $I_j = (r_j, w_j, p_j)$, where $r_j \geq 0$ is its release time, $w_j > 0$ is its value, and $p_j > 0$ is its length. Two such intervals I_j, I_k are said to be *non-overlapping* if $[r_j, r_j + p_j) \cap [r_k, r_k + p_k) = \emptyset$ (i.e., either $r_k \geq r_j + p_j$ or $r_j \geq r_k + p_k$). The goal of the problem is to

D. Halperin and K. Mehlhorn (Eds.): ESA 2008, LNCS 5193, pp. 381–392, 2008.
© Springer-Verlag Berlin Heidelberg 2008

select a maximum (total) weight subset of non-overlapping intervals. The online algorithm is allowed to preempt an interval when a new interval arrives, but in this case the weight of the preempted interval is lost. See [6,7] for recent surveys on (offline and online) interval selection problems.

We note that interval selection problems can be seen as scheduling problems, where intervals are seen as jobs to be processed. The jobs must be run during a fixed interval in time, and the left and right endpoints of an interval are its release time and completion time, respectively. Kovalyov, Ng, and Cheng [7] describe the applications of interval scheduling problems as follows. "These problems arise naturally in various real-life operations planning situations, including the assignment of transports to loading/unloading terminals, work planning for personnel, computer wiring, bandwidth allocation of communication channels, printed circuit board manufacturing, gene identification, and examining computer memory structures".

For an algorithm $\mathcal{A}$, we denote its cost by $\mathcal{A}$ as well. The cost of an optimal offline algorithm that knows the complete sequence of intervals is denoted by OPT. Since the problem is scalable, we consider the absolute competitive ratio criterion. The competitive ratio of $\mathcal{A}$ is the infimum $\mathcal{R}$ such that for any input, OPT $\leq \mathcal{R} \cdot \mathcal{A}$. If $\mathcal{A}$ is randomized, the last inequality is replaced by OPT $\leq \mathcal{R} \cdot E(\mathcal{A})$. If the competitive ratio of an online algorithm is at most $\mathcal{C}$ we say that it is $\mathcal{C}$-competitive. If an algorithm has an unbounded competitive ratio, we say that it is not competitive.

It is known [2,10] that the general case of the problem defined above does not have a competitive algorithm (in [10] this result was shown for deterministic algorithms, and in [2] it was shown for randomized algorithms). These negative results motivate the search of special cases that admit competitive algorithms. Note that the special case where all intervals have unit weight was studied in [4,3]. This case admits a deterministic online algorithm which produces an optimal solution for any instance of the problem.

Woeginger [10] has further identified three such special cases. The first one is called *C-benevolent* in which $w_j = f(p_j)$ (the weight of an interval depends only on its length), and f satisfies the following conditions: $f(0) = 0$, $f(p) > 0$ for all $p > 0$, and f is (strictly) monotonically increasing, continuous and convex function in $(0, \infty)$. Note that if we do not require strict monotonicity, then the only type of functions this would add are constant functions. This case is equivalent to the case of unit weights that is discussed above. The second case is called *D-benevolent* where $w_j = f(p_j)$ and f satisfies $f(0) = 0$, $f(p) > 0$ for all $p > 0$, and f is a monotonically non-increasing function in $(0, \infty)$. The third case is called the *unit interval case* is where $p_j = 1$ for all j. For all these three cases he showed a (deterministic) 4-competitive algorithm. In the C-benevolent case and in the unit interval case, he showed that no deterministic algorithm can perform better (which holds for *any* C-benevolent function). Moreover, for any D-benevolent function f, such that f is surjective onto $\mathbb{R}_0^+$, he presented a lower bound of 3 on the competitive ratio of any (deterministic) online algorithm, and showed that there can be no lower bound on the competitive ratio that applies for any D-benevolent function. He concluded his paper by raising the following open question, "We leave it as major open problem whether randomization can help to construct heuristics for OSI with better (randomized) worst case ratio" (where OSI is the name of this problem in his paper).

Since the publication of [10] there has been some progress in finding the answer to this last question. More precisely, there are later works designing better online algorithms for some special cases, and better lower bounds for randomized online algorithms. We discuss this related work next.

Seiden [9] presented an online algorithm for the C-benevolent case and the D-benevolent case with competitive ratio of $2 + \sqrt{3} < 3.73206$. This is still the best known upper bound for the C-benevolent case. Seiden has raised the question of the existence of a lower bound (on the performance of randomized algorithms) for these cases as his first open problem.

Miyazawa and Erlebach [8] considered the case of unit intervals. They designed a (randomized) 3-competitive algorithm for the special case where the sequence of arriving intervals has monotonically non-decreasing weight, as a function of the arrival times. They also designed a lower bound of $\frac{5}{4}$ on the competitive ratio of online randomized algorithm for each of the three cases defined above (that is, it holds for unit intervals, for any C-benevolent function, and for D-benevolent functions such that there exist a pair of values p_1 and p_2 where $f(p_2) = 2 \cdot f(p_1)$).

The last previous work is due to Fung, Poon and Zheng [5]. They considered the unit interval case, and presented a randomized algorithm with competitive ratio of $\frac{\sqrt{5}+5}{2} \approx 3.618$ and a lower bound of $\frac{4}{3}$ (which can be adapted for all C-benevolent and some D-benevolent instances). This algorithm uses a single random bit. Fung et al. showed in [5] that such an algorithm cannot have competitive ratio smaller than 2.

In this paper we significantly improve most previous results by presenting a new randomized algorithm for D-benevolent case and the unit interval case. This algorithm uses a parameter θ and has a competitive ratio of at most $\frac{\theta^2 \ln \theta}{(\theta-1)^2}$. This results in an upper bound of approximately 2.4554 using $\theta \approx 3.513$ which is the solution of the equation $x - 1 = 2 \ln x$. This improves the upper bound 3.732 of Seiden [9] for the D-benevolent case, and the upper bound 3.618 of Fung, Poon and Zheng [5] for unit intervals. We note that our upper bound improves also the upper bound of [8] for the special case of unit intervals discussed in [8]. We show that a simplified version of our randomized algorithm that uses a single random bit has a competitive ratio of $\frac{51\sqrt{17}-107}{32} \approx 3.227$ for the D-benevolent case and the case of unit intervals. This result improves the current best algorithm which uses a single random bit for the unit interval case [5].

We introduce an improved lower bound of $1 + \ln 2 \approx 1.6931$ on the competitive ratio of any randomized algorithm for all three cases, C-benevolent functions, D-benevolent functions and unit length intervals. The lower bound is general in the sense that it is valid for *any* C-benevolent function. We then show a lower bound of $\frac{3}{2}$ for any D-benevolent function f such that f is surjective onto $(c, +\infty)$ for some constant $c \geq 0$. Our lower bounds improve upon the previous lower bound $\frac{4}{3}$ of [5].

Paper outline.   We present the algorithm and its analysis in Section 2, and the lower bound in Section 3. We conclude this paper in Section 4 by presenting some directions for future research.

2   The Algorithm

Let $\theta > 1$ be a parameter to be defined later. We design the following randomized algorithm ROUND. The algorithm picks a value $\tau \in (0, 1]$ uniformly at random. τ is used as a parameter in a rounding scheme for the weights. From this point on (given the rounded weights), the algorithm is deterministic (it is similar to the one of [10], only our inputs have a restricted set of possible weights, due to the rounding). We define the algorithm as a function of τ.

Upon arrival of a new interval I_j, we let $w'_j = \max\{\theta^{p+\tau} | \theta^{p+\tau} \leq w_j, p \in \mathbb{Z}\}$. If the algorithm is not processing an interval, then it starts the interval I_j. Otherwise, if it is running an interval I_s, such that $w'_s < w'_j$, I_s is preempted and the algorithm starts I_j (due to the rounding, in this case we actually have $w'_j \geq \theta \cdot w'_s$). Otherwise, if $r_j + p_j < r_s + p_s$ (i.e., I_j can be completed before I_s) and $w'_j = w'_s$, then I_s is preempted, and the algorithm starts I_j. Otherwise, the algorithm rejects I_j.

In this section, each time that we consider an optimal solution for some input (the original input or a rounded input), we always assume that this is an optimal solution which minimizes the total length of completed intervals, among all optimal solutions, if more than one optimal solution exists.

We follow [10] and note that when we analyze the worst case performance of ROUND, we can restrict ourselves to input sequences such that the case where $r_j + p_j < r_s + p_s$ and $w'_j = w'_s$ never occurs. If we are dealing with unit intervals, then a later coming interval also ends later, so this condition can never hold for $r_j \geq r_s$. Note that if several unit intervals have the exact same start point, the algorithm selects one of them with a maximum rounded weight, already by the first rule.

Finally, for the D-benevolent case, the swap may be done by ROUND if the rounded weights of the two intervals are identical. We first show that the optimal solution considered here does not select I_s. Assume by contradiction that I_s is selected by our optimal solution OPT. Replace I_s by I_j in OPT. This results in a feasible solution since I_j is contained in I_s. Moreover, $w_j \geq w_s$, since I_j is shorter than I_s, and we are considering a D-benevolent function. We also have $w'_j = w'_s$, and thus the same claim holds for the optimal solution for the rounded instance. We get a contradiction with the choice of an optimal solution of minimum total length of intervals. Consider next a modified instance where I_s is replaced with an interval I'_s, where its release time is r_s, and its length is $r_j + p_j - r_s$, that is, it ends at the same point as I_j. Since this length is in the range $[p_j, p_s]$, its rounded weight is identical to the one of I_j and I_s. Running the algorithm on the modified instance will result in the same output except for possibly the replacement of I_j by I'_s, in case that I_j was a part of the output of the original instance. OPT does not change as a result of the modification by the same arguments as above.

Hence, the modified instance results in a competitive ratio which is at least as high as the competitive ratio of the original input. This modification can be applied repeatedly and thus for the sake of analysis, we assume that no such interval j exists.

We use the following notations. The benefit of ROUND on an input σ and a value $\tau \in (0, 1]$, using the rounded weights, is denoted by $\text{ROUND}_\tau(\sigma)$. The benefit of an optimal offline algorithm with the weights rounded according to the value τ, for the sequence σ is denoted by $\text{OPT}_\tau(\sigma)$. The benefit of an optimal offline algorithm is denoted by $\text{OPT}(\sigma)$, and the expected benefit of ROUND (over all choices of τ) is denoted by $\text{ROUND}(\sigma)$. We use ROUND_τ, OPT_τ, OPT and ROUND if the sequence σ is clear from the context. Our goal is to prove $\text{ROUND} \geq \frac{(\theta-1)^2}{\theta^2 \ln \theta} \text{OPT}$ for every sequence σ. We prove a sequence of lemmas.

Lemma 1. $\text{ROUND} \geq E(\text{ROUND}_\tau)$, where $E(\text{ROUND}_\tau)$ is the expected benefit of ROUND on the rounded weights, taken over all values of τ.

Proof. Since for every interval and every choice of τ, we have $w_j \geq w'_j$, the inequality holds for every value of τ separately, and thus also in expectation. $\square$

Given a specific value of τ, and a sequence σ, let $J_1, J_2, \ldots, J_m$ be a set of intervals completed by ROUND. For a given interval J_t, let $J_t^1, J_t^2 \ldots, J_t^{p_t}$ be a maximal sequence of intervals, such that J_t^1 is either the first interval ever started by ROUND, or the first interval started after a completed interval, each interval in the sequence is preempted by the previous interval, and $J_t^{p_t} = J_t$ is completed ($p_t - 1$ is the number of intervals that are preempted by J_t directly or indirectly).

Lemma 2. *Consider either the D-benevolent case and the unit interval case, then $\frac{\theta}{\theta-1} \cdot E(\text{ROUND}_\tau) \geq E(\text{OPT}_\tau)$, where $E(\text{OPT}_\tau)$ is the expected benefit of OPT on the rounded weights, taken over all values of τ.*

Proof. We consider the subsequence of intervals that are completed by OPT_τ, denoted by $\mathcal{A} = \{A_1, \ldots, A_k\}$. We may assume that without loss of generality, an optimal schedule only runs intervals to completion. We define a mapping from $\mathcal{A}$ to the set $\{J_b^a | 1 \leq b \leq m, 1 \leq a \leq p_b\}$. An interval A_j is mapped to an interval J_b^a that is run by the algorithm at the time that A_j is released, which is denoted by r'_j. Specifically, we map A_j to J_b^a if $r'_j \in [r_b^a, f_b^a)$ where r_b^a is the release time of J_b^a and f_b^a is either the time that it is preempted or the time that it is completed.

We show that the mapping is well defined and injective (but not necessarily bijective). We clearly map every interval of OPT_τ to at most one interval of ROUND_τ. Assume by contradiction that there exists no interval run by ROUND_τ at the time that some interval A_j is released. By the definition of the algorithm, it must start A_j, so A_j is mapped to itself. To show that this is an injection, note that for the unit interval case $f_b^a - r_b^a \leq 1$, thus OPT_τ can only start one interval during this time slot. For the D-benevolent case if there are two intervals of OPT_τ that start in the interval $[r_b^a, f_b^a)$ then the first such interval is (fully) contained in $[r_b^a, f_b^a)$ and hence its rounded weight is not smaller than the one of J_b^a contradicting the fact that ROUND did not process it, and hence also in this case OPT$_\tau$ can only start one interval during this time slot.

We now claim that no interval of OPT$_\tau$ is mapped to an interval of ROUND$_\tau$ with smaller rounded weight. The reason here is that by definition, ROUND$_\tau$ preempts an interval for an interval of larger rounded weight. So an interval A_j is either mapped to itself, or to an interval J_b^a that ROUND$_\tau$ could preempt in favor of running A_j.

We conclude that the benefit of OPT$_\tau$ is not larger than the total rounded weight of intervals started by ROUND$_\tau$. By the definition of the algorithm, we have for a sequence of intervals $J_t^1, J_t^2 \ldots, J_t^{p_t}$ that the rounded weight of each interval is strictly smaller than the previous interval, and hence it is actually smaller by a factor of at least θ. Thus $\sum_{j=1}^{p_t} w_j' \leq w_{p_t}' \cdot \frac{\theta}{\theta-1}$. We get that OPT$_\tau \leq \frac{\theta}{\theta-1}$ROUND$_\tau$, hence this is true for the expected benefits as well. $\qquad \square$

Remark 1. We note that the proof of Lemma 2 does not hold for the C-benevolent case. This is so because when we consider the C-benevolent case, it is no longer true that the defined mapping is injective (as there might be an interval of OPT$_\tau$ that is fully contained in $J_t^{p_t}$).

Lemma 3. *For a given interval I_j with weight w_j, we have $\frac{\theta \ln \theta}{\theta-1} \cdot E(w_j') \geq w_j$.*

Proof. We denote by w_j^τ the value w_j' for a given choice of τ. Let p be an integer, and $0 < \alpha \leq 1$ such that $w_j = \theta^{p+\alpha}$. Then for $\tau \leq \alpha$, $w_j^\tau = \theta^{p+\tau}$, and for $\tau > \alpha$, $w_j^\tau = \theta^{p-1+\tau}$, thus the expected profit from I_j over the choices of τ is $\int_0^\alpha \theta^{p+\tau} d\tau + \int_\alpha^1 \theta^{p-1+\tau} d\tau = \frac{1}{\ln \theta} \cdot \left(\theta^p(\theta^\alpha - 1) + \theta^{p-1}(\theta - \theta^\alpha)\right) = w_j(1 - \frac{1}{\theta})\frac{1}{\ln \theta}$, and the claim follows. $\qquad \square$

Lemma 4. *For the D-benevolent case and the unit interval case we have $\frac{\theta \ln \theta}{\theta-1} \cdot E(\text{OPT}_\tau) \geq \text{OPT}$.*

Proof. We consider an optimal solution for the original weights. We define by OFF$_\tau$ a solution with rounded weights according to τ, which has the same structure as OPT with respect to the set of completed intervals. Clearly, OFF$_\tau \leq$ OPT$_\tau$. Since the structure of all solutions we consider here is the same, we can compute the expected profit from an interval I_j that OPT completes, in the solutions OFF$_\tau$. By Lemma 3, this expected profit satisfies $\frac{\theta \ln \theta}{\theta-1} \cdot E(w_j') \geq w_j$. Summing up the last inequalities for all j such that I_j is selected by OPT we get $E(\text{OFF}_\tau) \geq \frac{\theta-1}{\theta \ln \theta}$OPT. $\qquad \square$

Combining Lemmas 1, 2 and 4 we conclude that for the D-benevolent case and the unit interval case

$$\text{ROUND} \geq E(\text{ROUND}_\tau) \geq \frac{\theta-1}{\theta} E(\text{OPT}_\tau) \geq \frac{(\theta-1)^2}{\theta^2 \ln \theta} \text{OPT}.$$

The maximizer of the function $\frac{(\theta-1)^2}{\theta^2 \ln \theta}$ is $\theta \approx 3.513$ which is a root of the equation $\theta - 1 - 2 \ln \theta = 0$. The resulting competitive ratio of ROUND for this value of θ is approximately 2.4554. Therefore, we conclude the following theorem.

Theorem 1. *There is a randomized 2.4554-competitive algorithm for the D-benevolent case and for the unit intervals case.*

2.1 Barely Random Algorithms

In this section we study a simplified version of the algorithm which requires the usage of a single random bit. Such an algorithm (that uses a constant number of random bits) is called *barely random*. The 3.618-competitive algorithm of [5] has this property and uses a single random bit. Our analysis is valid only for the D-benevolent case and the unit interval case.

The algorithm acts the same as ROUND, only the choice of τ is done uniformly at random on the set $\{\frac{1}{2}, 1\}$. Lemmas 1 and 2 are still valid, since they hold for any fixed choice of τ. Instead of Lemma 4 we prove the following lemma.

Lemma 5. $\frac{2\theta}{\sqrt{\theta}+1} \cdot E(\text{OPT}_\tau) \geq \text{OPT}$.

Proof. We consider an optimal solution for the original weights. We define by OFF_τ a solution with rounded weights according to τ, which has the same structure as OPT regarding the intervals that are completed. Clearly, $\text{OFF}_\tau \leq \text{OPT}_\tau$. Since the structure of all solutions we consider here is the same, we can compute the expected profit from an interval I_j that OPT completes, in the solutions OFF_τ. Let p be an integer, and $0 \leq \alpha < 1$ such that $w_j = \theta^{p+\alpha}$.

Assume first that $\alpha \geq \frac{1}{2}$. If $\tau = \frac{1}{2}$, then $w'_j = \theta^{p+\frac{1}{2}}$, and otherwise $w'_j = \theta^p$. In the first case $w'_j \geq \frac{w_j}{\sqrt{\theta}}$ and in the second case $w'_j \geq \frac{w_j}{\theta}$. Hence the expected value of w'_j is at least $\frac{1}{2} \cdot \frac{w_j}{\sqrt{\theta}} + \frac{1}{2} \cdot \frac{w_j}{\theta}$.

Now assume that $\alpha < \frac{1}{2}$. If $\tau = \frac{1}{2}$, then $w'_j = \theta^{p-\frac{1}{2}}$, and otherwise $w'_j = \theta^p$. In the first case $w'_j \geq \frac{w_j}{\theta}$ and in the second case $w'_j \geq \frac{w_j}{\sqrt{\theta}}$. Hence the expected value of w'_j is at least $\frac{1}{2} \cdot \frac{w_j}{\sqrt{\theta}} + \frac{1}{2} \cdot \frac{w_j}{\theta}$ in this case as well.

Summing up the inequalities for intervals I_j that are selected by OPT we get $E(\text{OPT}_\tau) \geq \frac{\sqrt{\theta}+1}{2\theta} \cdot \text{OPT}$. □

Combining the inequalities of Lemmas 1, 2 and 5 we conclude that,

$$\text{ROUND} \geq E(\text{ROUND}_\tau) \geq \frac{\theta-1}{\theta} E(\text{OPT}_\tau) \geq \frac{\theta-1}{\theta} \cdot \frac{\sqrt{\theta}+1}{2\theta} \cdot \text{OPT}.$$

The maximizer of the function $\frac{\theta-1}{\theta} \cdot \frac{\sqrt{\theta}+1}{2\theta}$ is $\theta = \frac{9-\sqrt{17}}{2} \approx 2.43845$. The resulting competitive ratio of the algorithm for this value of θ is approximately $\frac{51\sqrt{17}-107}{32} \approx 3.22745$. Therefore, we conclude the following theorem.

Theorem 2. *There is a barely random algorithm that uses a single random bit with a competitive ratio of 3.22745 for the D-benevolent case and the unit interval case.*

3   The Lower Bound

Our lower bound proofs follow Yao's principle [11] (see also Chapter 8.3.1 in [1]). Yao's principle states that given a probability measure, defined over a set of input sequences, a lower bound on the competitive ratio of any online algorithm (for a maximization problem) is implied by a lower bound on the ratio between the expected value of an optimal solution divided by the expected value of a deterministic algorithm (both expectations are taken with respect to the probability distribution defined for the random choice of the input sequence).

We start by considering the unit interval case. Later we show how to modify our construction to the other cases.

To use Yao's principle we need to define a probability measure over a set of input sequences. Our constructions uses a notion of phases, where in our construction, we have up to N phases. In each phase, the input has k intervals, where k and N are large numbers defined later. Our probability measure will be defined using conditional probability.

The sequence starts by presenting k intervals of phase 1 where the j-th such interval is denoted by I_1^j, its starting time is $\frac{j}{k+1}$ and its weight is $a_{1,j} = \frac{1}{\frac{1}{2} + \frac{k-j}{2(k-1)}}$.
Then, with probability $\frac{1}{2}$ the sequence stops, and the index j is chosen with probability $\frac{1}{2(k-1)}$ for every $j \in \{1, 2, \ldots, k-1\}$.

Assume that in phase $i-1$ (for $i = 2, \ldots, N$) we decided to continue by selecting index j, and assume that the right endpoint of interval I_{i-1}^j is b_j and the right endpoint of interval I_{i-1}^{j+1} is $b_j + \varepsilon_{i,j}$ where $\varepsilon_{i,j} > 0$ (the condition on the value $\varepsilon_{i,j}$ clearly holds in the first phase, and we keep an invariant throughout the construction, that no two intervals have the same right endpoint), then in phase i we present k new intervals $I_i^1, \ldots, I_i^k$ where $I_i^{j'}$ has the starting point $b_j + \frac{\varepsilon_{i,j} \cdot j'}{k+1}$ and the weight $a_{i,j'} = 2^{i-1} \cdot \frac{1}{\frac{1}{2} + \frac{k-j'}{2(k-1)}}$ (note that the weights of the new intervals are independent of j). Then, for $i \leq N - 1$ with conditional probability of $\frac{1}{2}$ we stop the sequence after i phases (the conditional probability is conditioned on the event that we actually reach phase i), and otherwise we pick an index $j = 1, 2, \ldots, k-1$ uniformly at random, and continue to the next phase. For $i = N$, the sequence stops at phase N (with conditional probability 1).

We note that the marginal probability of stopping the sequence at phase i is $\frac{1}{2^i}$ for $i = 1, 2, \ldots, N-1$, and $\frac{1}{2^{N-1}}$ for $i = N$, and the marginal probability of reaching phase i is $\frac{1}{2^{i-1}}$ for all i. Thus the marginal probability of choosing an index j in a phase i is $\frac{1}{2^i(k-1)}$.

We further note that if an online algorithm chooses interval I_i^j at phase i, and the sequence continues to phase $i+1$ with the index j' such that $j' < j$, then all new k intervals overlap with I_i^j, and all have a weight that is not smaller. The interval I_{i+1}^1 has at least the same weight as I_i^j and it intersects with exactly the same set of future intervals as I_i^j. We get that preempting I_i^j in favor of I_{i+1}^1 does not reduce the goal function of the resulting solution with respect to the possibility of keeping this interval, no matter if the sequence stops or continues further afterwards. Thus it is always better to preempt interval I_i^j in favor of a new interval. Therefore, an online algorithm gains weight from interval I_i^j of phase i in one of the following events, either the sequence stops at phase i, or it continues to phase $i + 1$ and at this time it picks an index j' such that $j' \geq j$. This event happens with a marginal probability of $\frac{1}{2^{i-1}} \cdot \left(\frac{1}{2} + \frac{k-j}{2(k-1)} \right)$. Note that if we define the weight of phase i to be the weight that the online algorithm gains from intervals of phase i, if phase i exists, and if such a phase does not exist (i.e., the construction was stopped earlier) to be 0, then the expected weight of phase i is exactly 1 (if $i < N$) independently of the action that the algorithm takes (i.e., independently of which of the k intervals it selects. The additional expected weight of intervals of phase N is at most $2^N \cdot \frac{1}{2^{N-1}} = 2$ (the maximum occurs when the interval with largest weight is selected). Therefore, the total expected weight of the online algorithm is at most $N + 1$.

We now lower bound the expected total weight of the optimal solution. For a phase $i < N$ such that the algorithm stops at this phase, the optimal solution picks the maximum weight interval, which is I_i^k. This happens with a marginal probability of $\frac{1}{2^i}$, resulting an expected weight of 1. For $i = N$ the optimal solution again picks interval I_N^k resulting an additional expected weight of 2. Consider phase i, where the sequence continues by selecting index j. Then, the optimal solution picks interval I_i^j, since it is the most profitable interval that does not overlap with intervals of future phases. This event happens with a marginal probability of $\frac{1}{2^i} \cdot \frac{1}{k-1}$. Hence, by linearity of expectation the total expected weight (in all phases) of the optimal solution is:

$$\sum_{i=1}^{N-1} \left(1 + \sum_{j=1}^{k-1} \frac{1}{2^i} \cdot \frac{1}{k-1} \cdot 2^{i-1} \cdot \frac{1}{\frac{1}{2} + \frac{k-j}{2(k-1)}} \right) + 2$$

$$= \sum_{i=1}^{N-1} \left(1 + \sum_{j=1}^{k-1} \frac{1}{2(k-1)} \cdot \frac{1}{\frac{k-1+k-j}{2(k-1)}} \right) + 2 = N + 1 + (N-1) \cdot \sum_{j=1}^{k-1} \frac{1}{2k-j-1}$$

$$= N + 1 + (N-1) \cdot \sum_{\ell=1}^{k-1} \frac{1}{k+\ell-1} = N + 1 + (N-1) \cdot \left(\sum_{p=1}^{2k-2} \frac{1}{p} - \sum_{p=1}^{k-1} \frac{1}{p} \right).$$

When k is arbitrarily large the right hand side becomes approximately $N + 1 + (N-1) \cdot (\ln(2k-2) - \ln(k-1)) = N + 1 + (N-1) \ln 2$, and the ratio between the expected weight of the optimal solution to the expected weight of the online algorithm tends to $1 + \ln 2 \approx 1.6931$ as N goes to infinity. Therefore, we established the following theorem.

Theorem 3. *Any randomized online algorithm for the case of unit intervals has a competitive ratio of at least $1 + \ln 2$.*

We next note that one can easily change our lower bound construction to obtain similar results for the C-benevolent and D-benevolent cases. To do so, we let $\delta > 0$ be infinitisimally small positive value (more precisely we consider a series of counter-examples for different values of δ where the series of δ tends to zero, and we consider the limit of the lower bounds obtained for these values of δ). Then, we change the length of an interval with weight w_j in the above construction to be $1 + \delta \cdot w_j$. For δ sufficiently small, this does not change the feasibility of solutions. We now have a weight function f, that is defined by $f(p) = \frac{p-1}{\delta}$. This function is linearly increasing in p and convex, thus we conclude that this instance is C-benevolent. By the above theorem, we conclude the result for the C-benevolent case. For D-benevolent case we change the length of an interval with weight w_j in the above construction to be $1 - \delta \cdot w_j$. For sufficiently small δ, this does not change the feasibility of solutions (i.e., it does not allow the algorithm to keep its selection of an interval I_i^j, if the index picked for the next phase is smaller than j) . Since now we have a weight function f defined as $f(p) = \frac{1-p}{\delta}$ that is linearly decreasing in p, we conclude that this instance is D-benevolent. By the above theorem, we conclude the result for the D-benevolent case. Therefore, we established the following theorem.

Theorem 4. *There is no randomized algorithm that can be applied for any C-benevolent instance or an algorithm that can be applied to any D-benevolent instance, that achieves a competitive ratio smaller than $1 + \ln 2$.*

The above result for C-benevolent instances shows that there is a C-benevolent function f for which no online algorithm has a competitive ratio better than $1 + \ln 2$. We next show that our construction actually holds not only for a specific function, but for all C-benevolent functions. Consider such a function f. f is monotonically non-decreasing and hence once we place two intervals I_i^j and I_i^{j+1} such that the left endpoint of I_i^j is smaller than the left endpoint of I_i^{j+1}, then we can conclude that the right endpoint of I_i^j is smaller than the right endpoint of I_i^{j+1}. The claim follows by noting that f is continuous and approaches infinity when its argument goes to infinity, and hence for every non-negative weight, we can always find an interval with this exact weight that is necessary for our construction. Hence, we conclude the following.

Proposition 1. *For any C-benevolent function f, there is no online algorithm with competitive ratio smaller than $1 + \ln 2$.*

A similar result for D-benevolent functions cannot hold as a function f that is $f(0) = 0$ and $f(p) = 1$ for all $p > 0$ is D-benevolent, and for this function the problem is exactly the one solved optimally by the online algorithm of [4,3] (a similar argument is given in [10] for deterministic online algorithms). There is a wide class of D-benevolent functions whose range is contained a bounded interval $[a, b]$, and for these functions, a deterministic $\frac{b}{a}$-competitive algorithm follows directly from the results of [4,3], by treating all intervals as if they have identical weights.

We next show how to get a lower bound of $\frac{3}{2}$ on the competitive ratio of any algorithm designed for any specific D-benevolent function, that satisfies some natural assumptions. Assume that f is D-benevolent function that satisfies the additional property that f is surjective onto $(c, +\infty)$ for some constant $c \geq 0$.

We first multiply the weight of all intervals in our previous construction by c and we fix $k = 2$. Then, for every weight of an interval defined by our construction there is a length that has this weight. Specifically, for a given value of N, we are interested in intervals having the weights $c \cdot 2^i$ for $0 \leq i \leq N$. Let $\ell_i = f^{-1}(c \cdot 2^i)$.

Let $\delta > 0$ be a small value which satisfies $\delta < \min\limits_{0 \leq i \leq N} \frac{\ell_i}{2(i+2)}$. We next modify the starting points of the intervals as follows. The construction is adapted in a way that the overlap between the two intervals of phase i, I_i^1 and I_i^2 (if this phase is reached) is exactly $2i\delta$, and the common overlap between the three intervals I_i^1, I_i^2 and I_{i-1}^2, for $i \geq 2$, is exactly δ. The specific construction is a follows. I_1^1 is placed at time 0. I_1^2 is placed such that the length of the intersection between I_1^1 and I_1^2 is 2δ. Assume that the construction satisfies the above conditions up to phase $i - 1$. Assume now that after phase $i - 1$ (for some $i = 2, \ldots, N$) the sequence continues to the next phase (and since $k = 2$, this can only mean that the index 1 is chosen), and assume that the right endpoint of interval I_{i-1}^1 is b_i and the right endpoint of interval I_{i-1}^2 is $b_i + \varepsilon_i$. By the properties of the construction, the overlap between these two intervals is $2(i - 1)\delta$ and since $\ell_{i-2} \geq \ell_{i-1} > 2(i+1)\delta$, we get $\varepsilon_i > 4\delta$. Thus $\varepsilon_i > 0$. In phase i, we present $k = 2$ new intervals I_i^1, I_i^2 where I_i^1 has a starting point $b_i + \delta$ and I_i^2 has a starting point of $b_i + \varepsilon_i - \delta$. Since I_{i-1}^2 and I_i^1 both have the same length ℓ_{i-1}, the overlap between these two intervals is $\ell_{i-1} - (2i-1)\delta > 3\delta$. We get that the left endpoint of I_i^1 is smaller than the left endpoint of I_i^2, and the overlap between them is $(2i - 1)\delta + \delta = 2i\delta$. Since $\ell_i > 2(i+2)\delta$, the right endpoint of I_i^2 is strictly larger than the right endpoint of I_i^1. We conclude that the construction is correct. To calculate the value of the resulting lower bound, technical difficulties require us to to set $k = 2$ and not $k \to \infty$. We have showed that for every value of k the online algorithm has an expected weight of at most $N + 1$ and the optimal solution has an expected weight of at least $N + 1 + (N - 1) \cdot \sum\limits_{j'=1}^{k-1} \frac{1}{k+j'-1}$ that equals (when $k = 2$) to $N + 1 + \frac{N-1}{2} = \frac{3N+1}{2}$, and when N goes to infinity the resulting lower bound tends to $\frac{3}{2}$. Hence, we established the following.

Theorem 5. *For any f such that f is D-benevolent function and surjective onto $(c, +\infty)$ for some constant $c \geq 0$, there is no randomized online algorithm with competitive ratio smaller than $\frac{3}{2}$.*

4   Concluding Remarks

We note that our upper bound holds also for proper interval graphs. To see this claim note that these graphs are equivalent to unit interval graphs and the algorithm we presented acts the same on a proper interval graph as it does not depend on the exact value of the coordinates of the endpoints of the intervals, but only on the relative order of these endpoints.

Our lower bounds on the performance of randomized algorithms as well as the lower bounds of Woeginger [10], indicate that for some D-benevolent functions

f, the problem is significantly easier than the general one. The study of the exact boundaries of these easier instances is left for future research.

Our randomized algorithm has a competitive ratio better than the previous results only for the D-benevolent case and the unit interval case. Therefore, improving the upper bound of Seiden [9] for the C-benevolent case is still left as a major open question. To understand why our algorithm and its analysis fails to improve the result for the C-benevolent case, we note that whereas for the D-benevolent case and the unit interval case setting $\tau = 1$ (in a deterministic way) results an alternative 4-competitive algorithm, this is not the case for the C-benevolent case, where we can only show that such a deterministic algorithm is 6-competitive. Now, randomization in the selection of τ helps to reduce the resulting competitive ratio below 6 but not enough to get below the competitive ratio of [9] (or even below 4) for this case.

We considered only the three special cases which are the C-benevolent and D-benevolent cases and the case of unit intervals, that were all studied by Woeginger [10]. Identifying other special cases for which there exists a (constant) competitive algorithms is also left for future research.

References

1. Borodin, A., El-Yaniv, R.: Online Computation and Competitive Analysis. Cambridge University Press, Cambridge (1998)
2. Canetti, R., Irani, S.: Bounding the power of preemption in randomized scheduling. SIAM Journal on Computing 27(4), 993–1015 (1998)
3. Carlisle, M.C., Lloyd, E.L.: On the k-coloring of intervals. Discrete Applied Mathematics 59(3), 225–235 (1995)
4. Faigle, U., Nawijn, W.M.: Note on scheduling intervals on-line. Discrete Applied Mathematics 58(1), 13–17 (1995)
5. Fung, S.P.Y., Poon, C.K., Zheng, F.: Online interval scheduling: randomized and multiprocessor cases. In: Lin, G. (ed.) COCOON 2007. LNCS, vol. 4598, pp. 176–186. Springer, Heidelberg (2007)
6. Kolen, A.W.J., Lenstra, J.K., Papadimitriou, C.H., Spieksma, F.C.R.: Interval scheduling: A survey. Naval Research Logistics 54(5), 530–543 (2007)
7. Kovalyov, M.Y., Ng, C.T., Cheng, T.C.E.: Fixed interval scheduling: Models, applications, computational complexity and algorithms. European Journal of Operational Research 127(2), 331–342 (2007)
8. Miyazawa, H., Erlebach, T.: An improved randomized online algorithm for a weighted interval selection problem. Journal of Scheduling 7(4), 293–311 (2004)
9. Seiden, S.S.: Randomized online interval scheduling. Operetions Research Letters 22(4-5), 171–177 (1998)
10. Woeginger, G.J.: On-line scheduling of jobs with fixed start and end times. Theoretical Computer Science 130(1), 5–16 (1994)
11. Yao, A.C.C.: Probabilistic computations: towards a unified measure of complexity. In: Proc. of the 18th Symposium on Foundations of Computer Science (FOCS 1977), pp. 222–227 (1977)

Succinct Representations of Arbitrary Graphs

Arash Farzan and J. Ian Munro

Cheriton School of Computer Science,
University of Waterloo,
Waterloo, Ontario, Canada
{afarzan,imunro}@cs.uwaterloo.ca

Abstract. We consider the problem of encoding a graph with n vertices and m edges compactly supporting adjacency, neighborhood and degree queries in constant time in the $\log n$-bit word RAM model. The adjacency query asks whether there is an edge between two vertices, the neighborhood query reports the neighbors of a given vertex in constant time per neighbor, and the degree query reports the number of incident edges to a given vertex.

We study the problem in the context of succinctness, where the goal is to achieve the optimal space requirement as a function of n and m, to within lower order terms. We prove a lower bound in the cell probe model that it is impossible to achieve the information-theory lower bound within lower order terms unless the graph is too sparse (namely $m = o\left(n^\delta\right)$ for any constant $\delta > 0$) or too dense (namely $m = \omega\left(n^{2-\delta}\right)$ for any constant $\delta > 0$).

Furthermore, we present a succinct encoding for graphs for all values of n, m supporting queries in constant time. The space requirement of the representation is always within a multiplicative $1 + \epsilon$ factor of the information-theory lower bound for any arbitrarily small constant $\epsilon > 0$. This is the best achievable space bound according to our lower bound where it applies. The space requirement of the representation achieves the information-theory lower bound tightly within lower order terms when the graph is sparse ($m = o\left(n^\delta\right)$ for any constant $\delta > 0$).

1 Introduction

A succinct representation of a combinatorial object is an encoding which supports a reasonable set of operations on the object in constant time and has a storage requirement matching the information-theory lower bound to within lower order terms. We use the usual model, namely a $\log n$-bit word RAM model where n is the size of the object (see for example [1]).

In this paper, we study the problem of representing a given graph with n vertices and m edges with vertex labels from $[n] = \{1, \ldots, n\}$ to support adjacency, degree, and neighborhood queries in constant time. We mainly consider directed graphs in this paper, however we discuss in section 5 that all of our results apply to undirected graphs. We assume that there are no multiple edges in the graph and thus there is only one edge from vertex i to vertex j for each order pair i, j (edges (i, j) and (j, i) can be simultaneously present as can the loop edge (i, i)).

D. Halperin and K. Mehlhorn (Eds.): ESA 2008, LNCS 5193, pp. 393–404, 2008.

Supporting these queries give the functionality of both an adjacency matrix and an adjacency list to our encoding. An *adjacency query* on a pair of vertices (i, j) determines whether (i, j) is an edge. This query is supported easily in constant time by an adjacency matrix but not an adjacency list. A *neighborhood query* has the functionality to iterate through vertices incident to given a vertex i in constant time per neighbor. A crucial point is that the representation must be able to iterate through either the *in-neighbors* and *out-neighbors* of a given vertex (though we do not insist on any particular order). Finally, the *degree query* is to output the in-degree and out-degree of a vertex in constant time. Neighborhood and degree queries are supported easily by an adjacency list but not an adjacency matrix. Therefore, the representation can be used in lieu of the adjacency list and matrix combined while supporting the same queries they provide in constant time.

The storage requirement of such a representation is the main issue of the paper. A counting argument suggests that the information-theory lower bound for the space requirement of any representation with encodes graphs with n vertices and m edges is $\lg \binom{n^2}{m}$ bits. However, we prove a lower bound in section 3 that where $n^\delta < m < n^{2-\delta}$ for a constant $\delta > 0$, it is impossible to achieve this space within lower order terms. Therefore, the best storage requirement has to be a multiplicative factor away from the information-theory bound. We match this lower bound by presenting an encoding in section 4 that requires $(1 + \epsilon) \lg \binom{n^2}{m}$ bits for an arbitrary small constant $\epsilon > 0$. In the case where $m < n^\delta$ for any constant $\delta > 0$, the space of the representation matches the information-theory lower bound tightly within lower order terms. For extremely large values of m, where $n^2 / \lg^{1/3} n < m < n^2/2$, the space requirement of the representation again matches the information theory-bound (cases where $m > n/2$ edges are symmetrical to $n - m$ edges).

1.1   Related Work

There is a large body of literature on space-efficient representations of graphs most of which deal with graphs with certain properties: such as graphs with limited arboricity or c-decomposable graphs [2], separable graphs [3], planar graphs [4,5,6,7], triconnected and/or triangulated planar graphs [8].

Raman *et al.* [9] study the problem of indexable dictionary and in the extended version of the paper, they observe a given graph can be represented by having a dictionary structure for each vertex containing the endpoints of all its incident edges. Using this approach to be able to report both in-neighbors and out-neighbors of a vertex in constant time per neighbor, we need to include in the dictionary of a vertex both its in and out neighbors. This is space inefficient as it may double the storage requirement.

A problem closely related to representation of graphs is binary relations whose succinct encodings has been studied [10,11]. Binary relations associate r objects to s labels such that objects can be associate to multiple labels and a particular label can be assigned to multiple objects. According to this definition a graph is essentially a binary relation from objects in $[n]$ to labels in $[n]$. The supported operations are rank and select on objects and labels. It is not hard to verify that we can implement adjacency, neighborhood, and degree queries using these operations. Their representation requires $r \lg s + o\left(r \log s\right)$ bits, however the operations do not perform in constant time. Golynski [12] proved that any representation with the same storage requirement within lower order terms cannot perform these operations in constant time. Nevertheless, the operations we require to navigate on graphs are weaker than the full rank and select operations and therefore, the infeasibility result does not hold for our purposes.

2   Preliminaries

We view the problem of encoding a graph with n vertices and m edges as compactly encoding its adjacency matrix. Given boolean matrix A of size $n \times n$ containing m ones, we wish to represent the matrix succinctly so it supports the access and successor queries. The adjacency query in the graph corresponds to access query in the matrix and the neighborhood query corresponds to successor query. The degree query in the graph corresponds to reporting the number of ones in a given row or column.

Definition 1. *The* access(i,j) *query simply reports the content of* $A[i,j]$. r-successor(i,0) *gives the position of a one in row* i *(if there is one).* r-successor(i,j) *(where* $A[i,j] = 1$*) gives the entry one in row* i *that "follows" the one in position* (i,j)*. By "follows" we permit the encoding to iterate through ones in row* i *in any order.* c-successor(.,.) *is defined identically on columns.* successor(r/c, ., .) *query encapsulates* r-successor *and* c-successor *queries as its first parameter is a switch* r *or* c: successor(r, i, j) = r-successor(i, j), *and* successor(c, i, j) = c-successor(i, j).

We use succinct dictionaries extensively throughout this paper. We state the results on succinct dictionaries. The first dictionary structure that we use is the fully indexable dictionary (FID) [9] (we note that there is a more space-efficient version [13]). This structure is essentially equivalent to a bit-vector supporting rank and select on both zeros and ones. The structure is very powerful (*e.g.* predecessor queries [14] are supported in constant time), and thus it is rather space inefficient:

Theorem 1. *[9] Given a subset* S *of a universe* U, *there is a* fully indexable dictionary **(FID)** *structure which requires* $\lg \binom{|U|}{|S|} + O\left(|U| \log \log |U| / \log |U|\right)$ *bits and supports rank and select queries both on members and nonmembers of* S *in constant time.*

The second dictionary structure is an indexable dictionary (ID). This structure is more efficient but its supports for queries is limited. It is essentially equivalent to a bit vector supporting rank and select, however rank can only be performed on one bits and not on zero bits:

Theorem 2. *[9] Given a subset S of a universe U, there is an* indexable dic-
tionary **(ID)** *structure which requires* $\lg \binom{|U|}{|S|} + o(|S|) + O(\log \log |U|)$ *bits and
supports rank and select queries only on members of S in constant time.*

At the heart of our representation sits a succinct encoding of functions allowing
forward and reverse navigation, partial rank, and select in constant time.

Definition 2. *Given a function $f : [n] \rightarrow [m]$, forward navigation is, given
$i \in [n]$ to compute $f(i)$. The* select(i,j) *operation determines the i-th largest
element k such that $f(k) = j$. We can use this operation to report the set $f^{-1}(j)$
in constant time per element for any given j. We refer to this as the reverse navigation capability of the function. The* partial_rank(i) *operation is determines
the rank of i among all elements k such that $f(k) = f(i)$.*

The problem of representing a function $f : [n] \rightarrow [m]$ supporting the set of
described operations is equivalent to representing a string S of length n over
an alphabet of size m. The equivalent operations are string access (to report
$S[i]$), string select (to determine the location of the i-th occurrence of a symbol),
and partial rank (given a location i, to determine the number of $S[i]$ symbols
occurring before location i). Golynski *et al.* [15] studied a stronger version of the
problem where we require support for full rank (given any position i, to determine
the number of occurrences of another given symbol before i). Their space matches
the information theory bound of $n \lg m$ within lower order terms, however the
operations do not perform in constant time. It is not clear that constant time
operations are possible even if we relax the space bound to $(1 + \epsilon)n \lg m$ for any
constant $\epsilon > 0$. However, we obtain constant time support for *partial* rank, select,
and access operations with $(1 + \epsilon)n \lg m$ storage requirement for any constant
$\epsilon > 0$ by a slight modification of their representation. We omit the details of the
needed modifications and state the result:

Theorem 3. *Given a function $f : [n] \rightarrow [m]$, there is a succinct encoding of f
which requires $(1 + \epsilon)n \log m$ bits of space for any constant $\epsilon > 0$ and supports
forward navigation, select, and partial rank (definition 2) in constant time.* □

3   Space Lower Bounds

For the purpose of proving lower bounds, we assume the cell probe model where
the size of a word is $w = \lg n$ bits. For all values of n, m, we prove lower bounds
as a function of n and m on the worst-case space requirement of representations
of $n \times n$ boolean matrices with m ones supporting access and successor queries
as described in definition 1.

There is a trivial information theory bound which comes directly from a counting argument and it holds for any representation regardless of the queries it can
support:

Theorem 4. *Any representation of $n \times n$ boolean matrices contain m ones requires $\lg \binom{n^2}{m}$ bits in the worse case for some matrices.* □

The main purpose of this section is to show that for a reasonably large range of values of m in comparison to n, it is infeasible to achieve the optimal information theory bound in theorem 4 within lower order terms while supporting the desired queries in constant time (namely for values $n^\delta < m < n^{2-\delta}$ for an arbitrary small constant δ). This implies that in this range, the space requirement must be at least a constant multiplicative factor away from the information theory bound. We give a representation in section 4 that makes the multiplicative factor arbitrarily small to $1 + \epsilon$ for any constant $\epsilon > 0$.

We distinguish two cases depending on relative values of n, m and study each case separately: (1) the moderate case: $m = \Omega(n)$ and $m = O(n^{2-\delta})$ for any constant $\delta > 0$, and (2) the Sparse case: $m = o(n)$. In either case, we give matching upper bounds in section 4. A discussion is in order in section 5 for the remaining values of m which are extremely close to n^2.

3.1   Lower Bound for the Moderate Case

This section proves lower bounds for the moderate case where $m = \Omega(n)$ and $m = O(n^{2-\delta})$ for a constant $\delta > 0$. We use ideas from Golynski [12] which proved an infeasibility result for succinct representation of permutations. It proved that not all permutations $\pi : [n] \to [n]$ can be encoded in the information theory optimal bound of $n \lg n$ bits within lower order terms supporting π and π^{-1} in constant time. In fact, this result shows a lower bound directly for our problem when $m = n$. Therefore, our lower bound is an extension of that work.

Theorem 5. *If $m = \Omega(n)$ and $m = O(n^{2-\delta})$ for a constant $\delta > 0$, there is a $n \times n$ boolean matrix containing m ones which cannot be encoded in $\lg \binom{n^2}{m} + o\left(\lg \binom{n^2}{m}\right)$ supporting the* access *and* successor *queries as described in definition 1 in constant time.*

Proof. Assume such structure S exists in the cell probe model for any such boolean matrix M which performs the queries in constant time. We derive a contradiction by showing an encoding for M in less than $\lg \binom{n^2}{m}$ bits.

Structure S works in the cell probe model and requires $\lg \binom{n^2}{m} + o\left(\lg \binom{n^2}{m}\right) = m \lg(n^2/m) + o\left(m \lg(n^2/m)\right)$ bits which is $m \lg_n(n^2/m) + o\left(m \lg_n(n^2/m)\right) = O(m)$ cells. We show that a constant fraction of these cells can be safely deleted while the rest of the structure still describes the original matrix uniquely.

successor queries iterate through ones in a column and a row and report them in an order. We denote by $q_{successor}(i,j)$ the successor query that obtains the successor one from location (i,j). We denote by $q_{access}(i,j)$ the access(i,j) query. As queries take constant time, all such queries probe a constant number of cells. We denote by $\mathcal{C}[q_{access}(i,j)]$ and $\mathcal{C}[q_{successor}(i,j)]$ the set of cells that these queries probe, and define $\mathcal{C}[q(i,j)]$ as their union: i.e. $\mathcal{C}[q(i,j)] = \mathcal{C}[q_{access}(i,j)] \cup \mathcal{C}[q_{successor}(i,j)]$.

Consider all sets $\mathcal{C}[q(i,j)]$ for all entries (i,j) where there is a one in the matrix ($M(i,j) = 1$). There are m such sets each of which containing a constant number of cells. Since, there are $O(m)$ cells, there is at least a constant fraction of cells which occur in at most $r = O(1)$ of the sets (for r a suitable large constant). We denote by C_r the set of all such cells which appear in at most r sets ($|C_r| = \Omega(m)$). The goal is to select a large subset $\mathcal{D} \subset C_r$ of these cells to remove from the structure S in such a manner that the matrix is constructible given the rest of the cells.

We start by an empty $\mathcal{D}$ and add cells from C_r in an incremental fashion. We maintain some invariants which allow us to recover the matrix after deletion of cells in $\mathcal{D}$. The first invariant is that for any matrix entry (i, j) such that $M[i, j] = 1, \mathcal{C}[q(i, j)] \cap \mathcal{D}$ is either empty or it contains a single element. Therefore, we can label each one entry in the matrix with $\mathcal{C}[q(i, j)] \cap \mathcal{D}$ such that each entry is labeled either empty or a single cell. Furthermore, we maintain the invariant that if an entry (i, j) is labeled c, then its predecessor and successor in row and column i as well as its predecessor and successor in row and column j are assigned label empty or c.

We remove an arbitrary cell $c \in C_r$ and include it in $\mathcal{D}$. If $c \in \mathcal{C}[q(i, j)]$ for any (i, j) and $(a, b), (a', b')$ are the predecessor and successor to (i, j) in row/column i and $(c, d), (c', d')$ are the predecessor and successor to (i, j) in row/column j, we remove all elements of $\mathcal{C}[q(a, b)]$, $\mathcal{C}[q(a', b')]$, $\mathcal{C}[q(c, d)]$, and $\mathcal{C}[q(c', d')]$ from C_r, and add another arbitrary cell from C_r to D and continue in this greedy manner. Since $\mathcal{C}[q(i, j)]$ has constant size, at each step we remove a constant number of cells from C_r, and hence, the number of cells added to $\mathcal{D}$ is a constant fraction of C_r. It is easy to verify that the deletions from C_r maintain the invariants throughout the procedure.

We are now ready to delete cells of $\mathcal{D}$ from structure S by adding some auxiliary structures. We form a bit vector `deleted_cells` of length $O(m)$ bits corresponding to the cells of structure S in order; its bits are one if the corresponding cell belongs to $\mathcal{D}$ (and therefore deleted) and zero otherwise. For a cell $c \in \mathcal{D}$, we refer to a one matrix entry (i, j) as *affected by* c, if $c \in \mathcal{C}[q(i, j)]$. We note that only a constant number (r) of entries are affected by c. We refer to a row or a column as affected by c, if they contain an entry affected by c. For each $c \in \mathcal{D}$, the projected matrix on affected rows and columns by c is stored explicitly (each matrix requires a constant number of bits less than r^2). Finally the cells of $\mathcal{D}$ are removed from S and remaining cells are stored consecutively.

A constant fraction of the number cells ($O(m)$) are deleted ($O(m \log n)$ bits) and auxiliary structures stored require $O(m)$ bits. Therefore, the total size of the final structure is less than $\lg \binom{n^2}{m}$. The contradiction is derived from the fact that the matrix is fully recoverable from the final structures.

Given the `deleted_cells` vector and the retained cells of the structures, one can simulate a query on the original structure S. The only issue arises where a query *fails* as it wants to probe a cell in $\mathcal{D}$ which is deleted. To recover the matrix given these structures, we exhaustively perform all **access** queries over all possible entries (i, j) and fill in the matrix where the queries succeed. We now simulate all **successor** queries on previously discovered ones in the matrix repeatedly in to exhaust all one entries these queries can recover. We form an affected list for all rows and columns which are initially empty. If a `successor` query fails on an entry (i, j) as it needs access to cell c, we add c to the affected list of cells for row i and column j. The invariants guarantee that each row/column completely discovers the set of cells by which it is affected. For each cell $c \in \mathcal{D}$, we fill in the sub-matrix projected on the rows and columns affected by c, using the pre-stored sub-matrix for c. Therefore, all one entries are discovered and hence the matrix is fully recovered.

3.2   Lower Bound for the Sparse Case

In this section, we give a lower bound for the case where $m = o(n)$:

Theorem 6. *If $m = o(n)$, there is a $n \times n$ boolean matrix containing m ones whose encoding requires at least $\lg \binom{n^2}{m} + \epsilon m \lg m$ bits to support the* `access` *and* `successor` *queries as described in definition 1 in constant time.*

Proof. We omit the proof due to space constraints. The proof is analogous to that of the lower bound for permutations by Golynski [12] with minor modifications.

Theorem 6 suggests that where $m > n^{\delta}$ for a constant $\delta > 0$, the space requirement is at least $(1 + \epsilon) \lg \binom{n^2}{m}$ bits for some constant $\epsilon > 0$.

4   Upper Bound: The Representation

Given a $n \times n$ boolean matrix A containing m ones, this section shows how to represent the matrix succinctly so it supports the `access`, `successor`, and `degree` queries in constant time. Given our representation, the support for degree queries is straightforward, thus we mainly focus on implementation of the `access` and `successor` queries in this section.

Depending on the density of the matrix, we distinguish four cases which we discuss in four subsequent sections: (1) Over half full: $m > n^2/2$ (2) Dense: $n^2/2 \geq m > n^2/\lg^{1/3} n$. (3) Moderate: $n^2/\lg^{1/3} n \geq m > n/2$ (4) Sparse: $n/2 \geq m$.

4.1   The over Half Full Case

If more than half of the matrix entries are one $(m > n^2/2)$, we simply negate the matrix by changing zeros to ones and vice versa. In the new flipped matrix, less than half of the entries are one and thus the problem is reduced to one of the other three density cases. The `access` query is answered by simply negating the result of the `access` query on the flipped matrix. The `successor` query however is more involved. This query translates into `successor` queries on zeros in the negated matrix. We perform this query by supporting `successor` queries on zeros as well as ones in each of the three following cases.

4.2   The Dense Case

There are $m > n^2/\lg^{1/3} n$ ones in the matrix, we divide the matrix into tiny square matrices of size $\frac{1}{2}\sqrt{\lg n} \times \frac{1}{2}\sqrt{\lg n}$ and represent each tiny square by a reference to a look-up table.

The look-up table exhaustively lists all square matrices of size $\frac{1}{2}\sqrt{\lg n} \times \frac{1}{2}\sqrt{\lg n}$ ordered by the number of ones. It moreover contains answers to access and successor queries for all different possible parameters of these queries. The space of the table is clearly $o(n)$ and negligible.

A tiny matrix is encoded by a reference to a look-up table. The reference is a pair (t, i) where t is the number of ones in the matrix and i distinguishes the matrix among all matrices with the same number of ones. To account for the space of references, we calculate the space for t and i fields separately. Fields t amount to $O\left(n^2 \log \log n / \log n\right) = o(m)$ which is negligible. The i fields have a space requirement which is dominant in the overall space bound. In a tiny matrix T_i with k_i ones, the i field requires $\left\lceil \lg \binom{\lg n/4}{k_i} \right\rceil$ bits. Therefore, over all the tiny matrices these fields occupy $\sum_{i=1}^{4n^2/\lg n} \left\lceil \lg \binom{\lg n/4}{k_i} \right\rceil = \lg \binom{n^2}{m} + o\left(\lg \binom{n^2}{m}\right)$ bits.

Thus far, we can answer our desired queries in tiny matrices. To extend this power to the entire matrix, we simply use summary bits for rows and column of tiny matrices. We form a bit vector of length $2n/\sqrt{\lg n}$ for each row of the matrix. Bit i of the vector is a summary bit for the corresponding row of the tiny matrix; it is set to one if there is at least a one in that row. Similarly, we form a bit vector for each column of the matrix which contains summary bits for the columns of tiny matrices. We represent these bit vectors using the FID structure of theorem 1. These structures together require $O\left(n^2/\sqrt{\log n}\right)$ which is a lower order term. Using these structures, implementation of queries is straightforward:

Theorem 7. *A boolean matrix of size $n \times n$ with $m > n^2/\lg^{1/3} n$ ones can be represented in $\lg \binom{n^2}{m} + o\left(\lg \binom{n^2}{m}\right)$ bits supporting access query and successor query on both ones and zeros in constant time.* $\qquad\square$

4.3   The Moderate Case

This is the case where $n^2/\lg^{1/3} n \geq m > n/2$. We divide the matrix into smaller square matrices of size $n^2/(2m) \times n^2/(2m)$. As in the dense case (section 4.2), we store summary bits to be able to confine our attention to within individual $n^2/(2m) \times n^2/(2m)$ matrices. For each row of the matrix, we form a bit vector of length $n/(n^2/2m) = 2m/n$. Bit i of the vector is one if there is at least a one in the corresponding row of small matrix i in the row. Similarly, there is a bit vector of the same length for each column of the matrix. Moreover to support navigation on zeros, there are symmetrical summary row and column bit vectors for zeros as opposed to ones; these summary bits are one if all entries of the row or column of the small matrix are one and zero if there is at least one zero there. These bit vectors are represented using the FID structure (theorem 1). Therefore, queries reduce to queries within small matrices. We state the bounds of our representation for small matrices and prove it in the following section:

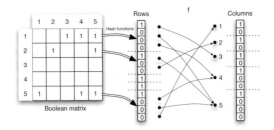

Fig. 1. Structures used to represent a small matrix

Lemma 1. *A boolean matrix of size $u \times u$ containing r ones can be encoded in $(1+\epsilon)r \lg u + O(u)$ bits for any constant $\epsilon > 0$ supporting* access *and* successor *queries on both ones and zeros in constant time.*

Therefore, we obtain the following to represent a moderate case matrix:

Theorem 8. *A $n \times n$ boolean matrix with m ones such that $n^2 / \lg^{1/3} n \geq m > n/2$ can be represented in $(1 + \epsilon) \lg \binom{n^2}{m}$ bits for any constant $\epsilon > 0$ supporting* access *query and* successor *query on both ones and zeros in constant time.* $\square$

Representing small matrices: lemma 1. We use a minimal perfect hash function on each row that hashes u cells on the row to a set of r_i cells where r_i is the number of ones in the cell. The matrix is traversed in a row-major fashion and the ones in each row are traversed in the order the hash function dictates Hence after the traversal ones are (implicitly) assigned a number from $[r]$.

  We store a function $f : [r] \rightarrow [u]$ where ones in the matrix map their assigned numbers from $[r]$ to their corresponding columns. In other words, an entry in row i and column j which is assigned t in the traversal, maps t to j ($f(t) = j$). This function is represented using theorem 3 which supports forward navigation, select, and partial rank operations in constant time. Structures of this section are illustrated in figure 1.

  Furthermore, a bit vector Rows of length $u+r$ is stored containing descriptions of r_i's in order in unary format; for each row i in order, there is a one bit followed by r_i zero bits. Similarly, we stored a bit vector Columns of length $u + r$ which contains c_i's in order in unary format where c_i is the number of ones in column i. These bit vectors are encoded using the FID structure of theorem 1.

  We now explain how queries can be implemented. To respond to an access(i, j) query, we perform a select(i) on bit vector Rows to find the first assigned number on row i. We use the perfect hash function h_i of row i to get the offset from which the entry (i, j) is hashed to; the assigned number to entry (i, j) is $t =$ select(i)$+h_i(j)$. Now the function is used and if $f(t) = j$ then the content (i, j) of the matrix is one and it is zero otherwise.

  To implement successor queries, we need to find ones in a row or a column in constant time per element. We first explain how we can translate a location in Rows to the corresponding location in Columns and vice versa. Given a location in Rows, we determine the corresponding row by a rank query and determine the corresponding column by using the function. We use the `partial_rank` capability and determine the rank of the cell in the column. The corresponding entry in `Columns` bit vector is determined by a select query in `Columns` to go to the start of the appropriate column and we add to that the rank in the column to find the correct entry. Backward translation is performed similarly using the `select` capability of the function.

Determining a successor one in a row is easy as consecutive locations in `Rows` contain all ones in a row and similarly determining a successor one in a column is easy as consecutive locations in `Columns` contain all ones in a column. Given the translation capability, we can find the row and column number of an entry in `Rows` or `Columns`.

Thus far we showed how `successor` query is performed on ones. As we mentioned in section 4.1, we also need to show `successor` query on zeros. This part is more involved and we must add structures to be able to support these queries in constant time. We store bit vectors `Row_next` and `Column_next` of length `u+r` corresponding to bit vectors `Rows` and `Columns` respectively. If an entry in `Rows` corresponds to cell (i, j) in the matrix, we set the corresponding entry in `Rows_next` to zero if cell $(i, j + 1)$ is a zero and we set it to one otherwise. Similarly, if an entry in `Columns` corresponds to cell (i, j) in the matrix, we set the corresponding entry in `Columns_next` to zero if $(i + 1, j)$ is a zero and we set it to one otherwise. This bit vectors essentially mark either ends of runs of ones and therefore can be used to find zero successors. To determine a zero successor to (i, j) $(M[i, j] = 0)$ in the column j, we first determine the content of cell $(i + 1, j)$; if it is a zero then we are done as we have found a zero successor. Otherwise, if $(i + 1, j)$ contains a one, we find its corresponding entry to in `Columns` and therefore `Columns_next`. We only need to determine the first position after the entry in `Columns_next` which contains a zero (indicating that its proceeding entry is a zero). This task is easily performed by the FID structure. Determining a zero successor in a row is essentially similar. The only difference stems from the fact that ones in a row are not listed in order and thus entries corresponding to `Rows` are not sorted. Nevertheless, the same method works but zero successors are not determined in order and follow the order the perfect hash function dictates.

The perfect hash functions together require $O(u + r \log \log u)$ bits (see for example [16]). Representation of bit vectors uses $\lg \binom{r+u}{u} + o(r + u)$ by theorem 1. The representation of the function uses $(1 + \epsilon)r \log u$ bits. Thus all together the space requirement of our representation is $(1 + \epsilon)r \log u + O(u)$ which concludes the proof of lemma 1.

4.4   The Sparse Case

This case is the case where there is $m \leq n/2$ ones in the matrix. Therefore, there exists columns or rows containing no ones. We handle this case simply by projecting the matrix into non-empty rows and columns and representing the projected matrix using one of the other previous cases (dense or moderate).

To project the matrix, we form two bit vectors R,C of length n which encode empty rows and columns respectively. Bit i of R is zero if row i is empty and one otherwise. Similarly, bit i of C is zero if column i is empty and one otherwise. We represent these bit vectors using the ID structure of theorem 2 using $2m \lg(n/m) + o(m)$ bits. We represent the sub-matrix formed on non-empty rows and columns using either of representations of sections 4.1, 4.2, or 4.3 depending on its sparsity. This representation uses at most $(1 + \epsilon)m \lg m$ bits for any constant $\epsilon > 0$. Given these structures, implementation of queries is straightforward:

Theorem 9. *A boolean matrix of size $n \times n$ with m ones such that $m \leq n/2$ can be represented in $\lg \binom{n^2}{m} + \epsilon m \lg m$ bits for any constant $\epsilon > 0$ supporting* access *query and* successor *query on both ones and zeros in constant time.* $\square$

Theorem 9 implies that where $m < n^\delta$ for any constant $\delta > 0$, the information theory lower bound of $\lg \binom{n^2}{m}$ bits is achieved, and for the remaining values of m in the range $(1 + \epsilon) \lg \binom{n^2}{m}$ bits are used.

5   Conclusion and Final Remarks

We considered the problem of encoding a directed labeled graph with n vertices and m edges compactly supporting adjacency, neighborhood and degree queries. Measuring the storage requirement of representations as a function of n and m, we showed that the information-theoretic lower bound of $\lg \binom{n^2}{m}$ is not achievable for most cases by proving a better lower bound. More precisely, We proved impossible to achieve the information-theory lower bound within lower order terms unless the number of edges in the graph is such that $m = o\left(n^\delta\right)$ or $m = \omega\left(n^{2-\delta}\right)$ for any constant $\delta > 0$. We furthermore matched the lower bound in its applicable range by presenting an encoding with the worst case storage requirement of $(1 + \epsilon) \lg \binom{n^2}{m}$ for any $\epsilon > 0$. Where $m = o\left(n^\delta\right)$ for any constant $\delta > 0$, the representation matches the information theoretic lower bound within lower order terms and requires $\lg \binom{n^2}{m} + o\left(\lg \binom{n^2}{m}\right)$ bits. The information-theory lower bound is also matched where $n^2/\lg^{1/3} n < m < n^2/2$. This leaves a small gap where $n^{2-\delta} < m < n^2/\lg^{1/3} n$ for any constant $\delta > 0$ where our lower and upper bounds are a multiplicative factor $1 + \epsilon$ apart for any arbitrary small constant $\epsilon > 0$, which we leave as an open problem. We showed that the case where $m \geq n/2$ is symmetrical to previous cases by replacing m with $n - m$.

We argue briefly how the results extrapolate to undirected graphs. One can transform an undirected graph to a directed graph and support all queries by orienting an edge towards the incident vertex with the larger label (in other words taking the upper triangle of the adjacency matrix). The information theory lower bound for space requirement of representations is clearly $\lg \binom{n^2/2}{m}$. This change does not affect any upper or lower bounds except for the dense case where $n^2/\lg^{1/3} n < m < n^2/4$ where the same representation with trivial modifications achieve the information theory bound.

References

1. Munro, J.I.: Succinct data structures. Electronic Notes in Theoretical Computer Science 91, 3 (2004)
2. Kannan, S., Naor, M., Rudich, S.: Implicit representation of graphs. SIAM J. Discrete Math. 5(4), 596–603 (1992)
3. Blandford, D.K., Blelloch, G.E., Kash, I.A.: Compact representations of separable graphs. In: SODA, pp. 679–688 (2003)
4. Turán, G.: On the succinct representation of graphs. Discrete Applied Mathematics 8, 289–294 (1984)
5. Keeler, Westbrook: Short encodings of planar graphs and maps. DAMATH: Discrete Applied Mathematics and Combinatorial Operations Research and Computer Science 58 (1995)
6. Munro, J.I., Raman, V.: Succinct representation of balanced parentheses, static trees and planar graphs. In: IEEE Symposium on Foundations of Computer Science, pp. 118–126 (1997)
7. Chuang, R.C.N., Garg, A., He, X., Kao, M.Y., Lu, H.I.: Compact encodings of planar graphs via canonical orderings and multiple parentheses. In: Larsen, K.G., Skyum, S., Winskel, G. (eds.) ICALP 1998. LNCS, vol. 1443, pp. 118–129. Springer, Heidelberg (1998)
8. Aleardi, L.C., Devillers, O., Schaeffer, G.: Optimal succinct representations of planar maps. In: Amenta, N., Cheong, O. (eds.) Symposium on Computational Geometry, pp. 309–318. ACM, New York (2006)
9. Raman, R., Raman, V., Rao, S.S.: Succinct indexable dictionaries with applications to encoding k-ary trees and multisets. In: SODA 2002: Proceedings of the thirteenth annual ACM-SIAM symposium on Discrete algorithms, Philadelphia, PA, USA, pp. 233–242 (2002)
10. Barbay, J., He, M., Munro, J.I., Rao, S.S.: Succinct indexes for strings, binary relations and multi-labeled trees. In: Bansal, N., Pruhs, K., Stein, C. (eds.) SODA, pp. 680–689. SIAM, Philadelphia (2007)
11. Barbay, J., Golynski, A., Munro, J.I., Rao, S.S.: Adaptive searching in succinctly encoded binary relations and tree-structured documents. In: Lewenstein, M., Valiente, G. (eds.) CPM 2006. LNCS, vol. 4009, pp. 24–35. Springer, Heidelberg (2006)
12. Golynski, A.: Upper and lower bounds for Text Indexing Data Structures. PhD thesis, University of Waterloo, Waterloo, Ontario, Canada (2007)
13. Golynski, A., Grossi, R., Gupta, A., Raman, R., Rao, S.S.: On the size of succinct indices. In: Arge, L., Hoffmann, M., Welzl, E. (eds.) ESA 2007. LNCS, vol. 4698, pp. 371–382. Springer, Heidelberg (2007)
14. Beame, P., Fich, F.E.: Optimal bounds for the predecessor problem and related problems. J. Comput. Syst. Sci. 65(1), 38–72 (2002)
15. Golynski, A., Munro, J.I., Rao, S.S.: Rank/select operations on large alphabets: a tool for text indexing. In: Proceedings of the seventeenth annual ACM-SIAM symposium on Discrete algorithm, pp. 368–373. ACM, New York (2006)
16. Hagerup, T., Tholey, T.: Efficient minimal perfect hashing in nearly minimal space. In: Ferreira, A., Reichel, H. (eds.) STACS 2001. LNCS, vol. 2010, pp. 317–326. Springer, Heidelberg (2001)

Edge Coloring and Decompositions of Weighted Graphs[*]

Uriel Feige[1] and Mohit Singh[2]

[1] Weizmann Institute, Rehovot, Israel
uriel.feige@weizmann.ac.il
[2] Tepper School of Business, Carnegie Mellon University, Pittsburgh, USA
mohits@andrew.cmu.edu

Abstract. We consider two generalizations of the edge coloring problem in bipartite graphs. The first problem we consider is the WEIGHTED BIPARTITE EDGE COLORING problem where we are given an edge-weighted bipartite graph $G = (V, E)$ with weights $w : E \to [0, 1]$. The task is to find a *proper weighted coloring* of the edges with as few colors as possible. An edge coloring of the weighted graph is called a *proper weighted coloring* if the sum of the weights of the edges incident to a vertex of any color is at most one. We give a polynomial time algorithm for the WEIGHTED BIPARTITE EDGE COLORING problem which returns a proper weighted coloring using at most $\lceil 2.25n \rceil$ colors where n is the maximum total weight incident at any vertex. This improves on the previous best bound of Correa and Goemans [5] which returned a coloring using $2.557n + o(n)$ colors. The second problem we consider is the BALANCED DECOMPOSITION OF BIPARTITE GRAPHS problem where we are given a bipartite graph $G = (V, E)$ and $\alpha_1, \ldots, \alpha_k \in (0, 1)$ summing to one. The task is to find a partition $E_1, \ldots, E_k$ of E such that $deg_{E_i}(v)$ is close to $\alpha_i deg_E(v)$ for each $1 \le i \le k$ and $v \in V$. We give an alternate proof of the result of Correa and Goemans [5] that there is a decomposition such that $\lfloor \alpha_i deg_E(v) \rfloor - 2 \le deg_{E_i}(v) \le \lceil \alpha_i deg_E(v) \rceil + 2$ for each $v \in V$ and $1 \le i \le k$. Moreover, we show that the additive error can be improved from two to one if only upper bounds or only lower bounds on the degree are present. All our results hold also for bipartite multigraphs, and the decomposition results hold also for general graphs.

1 Introduction

Edge coloring problems have been crucial in the development of different algorithmic techniques and have also been used to model various scheduling problems. In this paper, we consider two edge coloring problems which have been inspired from study of Clos networks [4] and also generalize classical coloring problems. Clos network were introduced by Clos [4] in the context of designing interconnection networks used to route telephone calls and have found various applications [2,10]. We refer the reader to Correa and Goemans [5] for the relationship between the problems considered here and Clos networks.

---

[*] Part of this work was performed at Microsoft Research, Redmond, Washington.

D. Halperin and K. Mehlhorn (Eds.): ESA 2008, LNCS 5193, pp. 405–416, 2008.
© Springer-Verlag Berlin Heidelberg 2008

The first problem we consider is the WEIGHTED BIPARTITE EDGE COLORING problem where we are given an edge-weighted bipartite graph $G = (V, E)$ with weights $w : E \to [0, 1]$. The task is to find a *proper weighted coloring* of the edges with as few colors as possible. An edge coloring of the weighted graph is called a *proper weighted coloring* if the sum of the weights of the edges incident to a vertex of any color is at most one. If all the edges have weight one then the problem reduces to the classical bipartite edge coloring problem. König's Theorem [12] gives an optimal coloring in this case where the number of colors used is exactly the maximum degree of the graph. For the weighted bipartite edge coloring problem, Chung and Ross [3] gave the following conjecture.

Conjecture 1. Given an instance of the WEIGHTED BIPARTITE EDGE COLORING problem, there is a proper weighted coloring using at most $2n - 1$ colors where n denotes the maximum over all the vertices of the number of unit-sized bins needed to pack the weights of edges incident at the vertex.

The following is a stronger version of the Conjecture 1.

Conjecture 2. Given an instance of the WEIGHTED BIPARTITE EDGE COLORING problem, there is a proper weighted coloring using at most $2n - 1$ colors where n is the smallest integer greater than the maximum over all the vertices of the total weight of edges incident at the vertex.

Conjecture 2 is the best possible since there are instances where any proper weighted coloring takes $2n - 1$ colors. Melen and Turner [15] showed that the Conjecture 2 is true when all edge-weights are at most $\frac{1}{2}$. Moreover when all weights are strictly more than $\frac{1}{2}$, Conjecture 2 is also true and follows simply from König's Theorem.

One of our main results in the paper makes progress towards the resolution of Conjecture 2 and therefore Conjecture 1.

Theorem 1. *There is a polynomial time algorithm for the* WEIGHTED BIPARTITE EDGE COLORING *problem which returns a proper weighted coloring using at most* $\lceil 2.25n \rceil$ *colors where* n *is the maximum total weight incident at any vertex.*

Theorem 1 improves on the previous best result given by Correa and Goemans [5] who give a coloring using at most $2.557n + o(n)$ colors. Correa and Goemans [5] also give an algorithm which returns a proper weighted coloring with $2.5480n + o(n)$ colors where n denotes the maximum over all the vertices of the number of unit-sized bins needed to pack the weights of incident edges. Theorem 1 implies the improved bound of $\lceil 2.25n \rceil$ for this variant as well.

The second problem we consider is the BALANCED DECOMPOSITION OF BIPARTITE GRAPHS problem where we are given a bipartite graph $G = (V, E)$ and $\alpha_1, \ldots, \alpha_k \in (0, 1)$ summing to one. The task is to find a partition $E_1, \ldots, E_k$ of E such that $deg_{E_i}(v)$ is close to $\alpha_i deg_E(v)$ for each $1 \le i \le k$ and $v \in V$. Correa and Goemans [5] gave the following conjecture.

Conjecture 3. Given an instance of BALANCED DECOMPOSITION OF BIPARTITE GRAPH problem there exists a decomposition such that

$$\lfloor \alpha_i deg_E(v) \rfloor \leq deg_{E_i}(v) \leq \lceil \alpha_i deg_E(v) \rceil$$

for each $1 \leq i \leq k$ and each $v \in v$.

Correa and Goemans [5] proved a relaxed version of the conjecture in which both the upper and lower bounds are relaxed by two, i.e, the decomposition guarantees that $\lfloor \alpha_i deg_E(v) \rfloor - 2 \leq deg_{E_i}(v) \leq \lceil \alpha_i deg_E(v) \rceil + 2$.

We give an alternate proof of the result of Correa and Goemans [5] using linear programming methods and then show that the violation can be bounded by an additive one if only upperbound (or lowerbound) are present.

Theorem 2. *Given an instance of* BALANCED DECOMPOSITION OF BIPARTITE GRAPH *problem there exists a decomposition* $E_1, \ldots, E_k$ *of E such that*

$$\lfloor \alpha_i deg_E(v) \rfloor - 2 \leq deg_{E_i}(v) \leq \lceil \alpha_i deg_E(v) \rceil + 2$$

for each $1 \leq i \leq k$ and each $v \in V$. Moreover, there are decompositions $F_1, \ldots, F_k$ and $G_1, \ldots G_k$ such that

$$deg_{F_i}(v) \leq \lceil \alpha_i deg_E(v) \rceil + 1$$

$$deg_{G_i}(v) \geq \lfloor \alpha_i deg_E(v) \rfloor - 1$$

for each $1 \leq i \leq k$ and $v \in V$.

1.1   Previous Work

Two classical results on edge coloring are König's theorem [12] for coloring a bipartite graph with Δ colors and the Vizing's theorem [18] for coloring any simple graph with $\Delta + 1$ colors where Δ is the maximum degree of the graph.

Before we review some of the existing literature on the problems discussed in this paper, we introduce some notation. Given a weighted bipartite graph $G = (A \cup B, E)$ with weights $w : E \to [0, 1]$, let $\chi'_w(G)$ denote the minimum number of colors needed to obtain a proper weighted coloring of G. Given positive integers n and r, let $M(n, r) = max_G \chi'_w(G)$ where the maximum is taken over all bipartite graphs $G = (A \cup B, E)$ with $|A| = |B| = r$ and $max_{v \in V} \sum_{e \in \delta(v)} w_e \leq n$. In this notation, Conjecture 2 can be reformulated to claim that $M(n, r) \leq 2n - 1$.

Given positive integers n and r, let $m(n, r) = max_G \chi'_w(G)$ where the maximum is taken over all bipartite graphs $G = (A \cup B, E)$ with $|A| = |B| = r$ and where n is the maximum over all the vertices of the number of unit-sized bins needed to pack the weights of incident edges. Conjecture 1 can be reformulated to claim that $m(n, r) \leq 2n - 1$. It is easy to see that Conjecture 2 implies Conjecture 1 since $m(n, r) \leq M(n, r)$ for each n and r.

If the weight function is restricted to $w : E \to I$ for some interval $I \subseteq [0, 1]$, then we let the minimum number of colors be denoted by $M_I(n, r)$ an $m_I(n, r)$

respectively. Melen and Turner [15] proved that $m_{[0,1/2]}(n,r) \leq M_{[0,1/2]}(n,r) \leq 2n-1$ and in general showed that

$$m_{[0,B]}(n,r) \leq M_{[0,B]}(n,r) \leq \frac{n}{1-B}$$

Improving the bounds for $m(n,r)$ and $M(n,r)$ has received considerable attention [3,5,8,15,16,17] and the previous best bounds known were

$$\frac{5n}{4} \leq m(n,r) \leq 2.548n + o(n)$$

$$2n-1 \leq M(n,r) \leq 2.557n + o(n)$$

where both the upper bounds are by Correa and Goemans [5]. The lower bound on $m(n,r)$ is due to Ngo and Vu [16] and lower bound on $M(n,r)$ is due to Du et al [8]. Our results improve the upper bounds for both $m(n,r)$ and $M(n,r)$ to $\lceil 2.25n \rceil$ making progress towards resolution of Conjecture 1 and Conjecture 2.

The BALANCED DECOMPOSITION OF BIPARTITE GRAPHS problem was introduced by Correa and Goemans [5] who proved a relaxed version of the Conjecture 3 as mentioned above. Some special cases of Conjecture 3 are known to be true. When $k = 2$, Conjecture 3 is true and the decomposition was given by Hoffman [9]. When each α_i is equal to $\frac{1}{k}$ then de Werra [7] showed that the conjecture is true. The conjecture is also true when G is regular or when $\alpha_i deg_E(v)$ is an integer for each i and v and follows from König's edge coloring theorem [12].

1.2   Bipartite Versus General Graphs

In all results stated in the paper, there is no distinction between bipartite graphs and bipartite multigraphs (allowing parallel edges): the proofs apply without change also to bipartite multigraphs. Conjectures 2 and 3 do not hold as stated for arbitrary (non-bipartite) graphs. We elaborate on this here, and explain which of the results in this paper extend to general graphs.

Consider the Petersen graph which is a regular graph of degree 3 whose edges cannot be properly colored by 3 colors. Give every edge a weight 2/3. In the setting of Conjecture 2 this corresponds to a value of $n = 2$ and a requirement for a proper weighted coloring with 3 colors, which is impossible. This shows that when general graphs are concerned, the term $2n-1$ in the conjecture needs to be raised to at least $2n$.

If one allows parallel edges, then having odd cycles has a more dramatic effect. Consider for example a triangle with k parallel edges between any two vertices. Give each edge a weight of $(k+1)/2k$. Now n corresponds to $k+1$, whereas any proper weighted coloring requires $3k$ colors. Hence as k grows, the bound in Conjecture 1 approaches $3n$ (if the graph is non-bipartite and has parallel edges).

Applications of Conjecture 2 often involve bipartite graphs with parallel edges. And indeed, our proof of Theorem 1 works without change even if the bipartite graph has parallel edges. For general (non-bipartite) graphs, our proof of Theorem 1 easily extends to give a bound of $\lceil 2.25n \rceil + r$, where r is the maximum multiplicity of any edge (and in particular, $r = 1$ in simple graphs). In counting multiplicity of an edge, one may first merge parallel copies of an edge if the sum of their weights does not exceed 1. Hence r need never exceed $2n$.

Conjecture 3 does not hold for all graphs, a counter example being the triangle and $\alpha_1 = \alpha_2 = \frac{1}{2}$. Nevertheless, our proof of Theorem 2 holds with no change for general graphs. The previous proof of Correa and Goemans 3, that is cited after the statement of Conjecture 3, makes use of the bipartiteness of the underlying graph, but it is possible to modify their proof technique, using the results of Kano and Saito [11], such that that it works also for general graphs (see also [6]). Unlike the nonbipartite version of Theorem 1 (discussed in the previous paragraph), multiplicity of edges has no effect on Theorem 2.

2 Edge-Coloring Weighted Bipartite Graphs

In this section we give a proof of Theorem 1. The algorithm is a combination of König's Theorem [12] with the greedy algorithm. We state the König's Theorem since we use it as a subroutine in our algorithm.

Theorem 3. *[12] Given a bipartite (multi) graph $G = (V, E)$ there exists a coloring of edges with $\Delta = max_{v \in V} deg_E(v)$ colors such that all edges incident at a common vertex receive a distinct color. Moreover, such a coloring can be found in polynomial time.*

The algorithm giving the guarantee of Theorem 1 is given in Figure 1. Observe that in Step 3 of the algorithm, F can indeed be decomposed into $\lceil tn \rceil$ matchings, using Theorem 3 (because the maximum degree of F is $\lceil tn \rceil$).

We now show that the algorithm in Figure 1 gives a proper weighted coloring for $t = \frac{9}{4}$. Since the algorithm only uses $\lceil tn \rceil = \lceil \frac{9}{4}n \rceil$ colors, it is enough to show that each edge will be colored in either Step (2) when it is included in F or Step (4) of the algorithm. We prove this by a series of claims which follow.

---

1. $F \leftarrow \emptyset$, $t \leftarrow \frac{9}{4}$.
2. Include edges in F in non-increasing order of weight maintaining the property that $deg_F(v) \leq \lceil tn \rceil$ for all $v \in V$.
3. Decompose F into $r = \lceil tn \rceil$ matchings $M_1, \ldots, M_r$ and color them using colors $1, \ldots, r$. Let $F_i \leftarrow M_i$ for each $1 \leq i \leq r$.
4. Greedily add remaining edges to any of the F_i's maintaining that weighted degree of each color at each vertex is at most one, i.e, $\sum_{e \in \delta(v) \cap F_i} w_e \leq 1$ for each $v \in V$ and $1 \leq i \leq r$.

Fig. 1. Algorithm for Edge Coloring Weighted Bipartite Graphs

Claim. Each edge of weight at least $\frac{1}{t}$ is in F.

Proof. Let $e = \{u, v\}$ be an edge such that $w_e \geq \frac{1}{t}$. If e cannot be added to F then $deg_F(v) \geq \lceil tn \rceil$ or $deg_F(u) \geq \lceil tn \rceil$ when e is considered in Step (2) of the algorithm. But edges added in F, before e is considered in Step (2), have weight larger than the weight of e. Therefore, the total weight at the endpoint with degree at least $\lceil tn \rceil$ is at least $tn \cdot \frac{1}{t} + w_e > n$. A contradiction.

Lemma 1. *If $t \geq \frac{9}{4}$ then each edge can be colored with one of the colors.*

Proof. For sake of contradiction suppose some edge cannot be colored in Step (3) or Step (4). Let $e = \{u, v\}$ be such an edge and let $w_e = \alpha$. From Claim 2, we have that $\alpha < \frac{1}{t}$. Moreover, when e is considered in Step (2), the degree of either u or v is already $\lceil tn \rceil$ else we would have included e in F. Without loss of generality let that vertex be u, i.e, $deg_F(u) = \lceil tn \rceil$.

For each color $1 \leq i \leq \lceil tn \rceil$, we must have that $\sum_{f \in \delta(v) \cap F_i} w_f > 1 - \alpha$ or $\sum_{f \in \delta(u) \cap F_i} w_f > 1 - \alpha$ else we can color e in Step (4).

Let $L_v = \{i | \sum_{f \in \delta(v) \cap F_i} w_f > 1 - \alpha\}$ and $k = |L_v|$. Then we have

$$n > \sum_{i \in L_v} \sum_{f \in \delta(v) \cap F_i} w_f > k(1 - \alpha) \tag{1}$$

Now for each color $i \notin L_v$, we have $\sum_{f \in \delta(u) \cap F_i} w_f > 1 - \alpha$. Moreover, $deg_F(u) = \lceil tn \rceil$ and each of these edges weighs at least $w_e = \alpha$. Hence, for each color $1 \leq i \leq \lceil tn \rceil$, there is an edge incident at u colored with color i with weight at least α. Therefore

$$n > \sum_{f \in \delta(u)} w_f \geq \sum_{1 \leq i \leq \lceil tn \rceil} \sum_{f \in \delta(u) \cap F_i} w_f \tag{2}$$

$$= \sum_{i \in L_v} \sum_{f \in \delta(u) \cap F_i} w_f + \sum_{i \notin L_v} \sum_{f \in \delta(u) \cap F_i} w_f \tag{3}$$

$$\geq \sum_{i \in L_v} \alpha + \sum_{i \notin L_v} (1 - \alpha) = k\alpha + (\lceil tn \rceil - k)(1 - \alpha) \tag{4}$$

$$\geq k\alpha + (tn - k)(1 - \alpha). \tag{5}$$

Let $\beta = \frac{k}{n}$. By scaling Inequation (1), Inequation (5) and from Claim 2, we have

$$\beta(1 - \alpha) < 1 \tag{6}$$

$$\beta(2\alpha - 1) + t(1 - \alpha) < 1 \tag{7}$$

$$\alpha < \frac{1}{t}. \tag{8}$$

We now show that for $t = \frac{9}{4}$, we have a contradiction to the above inequalities.

The expression $\beta(2\alpha - 1) + t(1 - \alpha)$ is a decreasing function of β as $2\alpha - 1 < 0$ since $\alpha < \frac{1}{t} < \frac{1}{2}$. Thus the expression $\beta(2\alpha - 1) + t(1 - \alpha)$ has a minimum value at largest possible β which is at most $\frac{1}{1-\alpha}$ and at $\beta = \frac{1}{1-\alpha}$, we have

$$\beta(2\alpha - 1) + t(1 - \alpha) = \frac{1}{1 - \alpha}(2\alpha - 1) + t(1 - \alpha) = \frac{1}{1 - \alpha} - 2 + t(1 - \alpha). \tag{9}$$

Let $g(\alpha) = \frac{1}{1-\alpha} - 2 + t(1-\alpha)$. We claim that $g(\alpha) \geq 1$ for each $\alpha \in [0, \frac{1}{t})$ which gives the desired contradiction. Since, $g(\alpha)$ is a differentiable function of α in the range $[0, \frac{1}{t})$ the global minimum will occur at either a local minimum or at boundary of the interval. The derivative $g'(\alpha) = \frac{1}{(1-\alpha)^2} - t$. Thus the local minima can occur at $\alpha = 1 - \frac{1}{\sqrt{t}}$. But then

$$g(0) = t - 1 \geq 1 \tag{10}$$

$$g(\frac{1}{t}) = \frac{t}{t-1} - 2 + t - 1 = \frac{(t-2)^2}{t-1} + 1 \geq 1 \tag{11}$$

$$g(1 - \frac{1}{\sqrt{t}}) = \sqrt{t} - 2 + \sqrt{t} = 2(\sqrt{t} - 1) \geq 1 \tag{12}$$

where the last inequality holds for $t \geq \frac{9}{4}$. Thus $g(\alpha) \geq 1$ for each $\alpha \in [0, \frac{1}{t})$ which contradicts inequation (7).

3   Partitioning Bipartite Graphs

In this section we prove Theorem 2. First, we give an algorithm where we show a decomposition which matches the guarantee of Correa and Goemans [5] and violates the bounds by at most two. We then show how to modify the algorithm to obtain the stronger guarantee where violation is bounded by at most one when only upper or lower bounds are present. Our algorithms use linear programming methods and the techniques have close resemblance to result of Beck and Fiala [1] on discrepancy of sets. We also note that the proofs do not use the fact that the graphs are bipartite or simple and all our results in this section also hold for general graphs with parallel edges.

Theorem 4. *[5] Given an instance of* BALANCED DECOMPOSITION OF BIPARTITE GRAPH *problem there exists a decomposition such that*

$$\lfloor \alpha_i deg_E(v) \rfloor - 2 \leq deg_{E_i}(v) \leq \lceil \alpha_i deg_E(v) \rceil + 2$$

for each $1 \leq i \leq k$ and each $v \in v$.

Proof. We formulate a feasibility linear program for the following generalization of the decomposition problem. For each edge e, we are given a set of allowable colors $C_e \subseteq \{1, \ldots, k\}$ and for each vertex v, we have a degree bound for every color from a set of colors $K_v \subseteq \{1, \ldots, k\}$. We let the binary variable x_e^i denote whether an edge e belongs to E_i for each edge $e \in E$ and $i \in C_e$. We initialize $C_e = \{1, \ldots, k\}$, $K_v = \{1, \ldots, k\}$ for each $v \in V$ and degree bound $B_v^i = \alpha_i deg_E(v)$ for each $1 \leq i \leq k$, $v \in V$ which corresponds to the required decomposition in Conjecture 3.

$$\text{(LP)} \qquad \text{minimize} \qquad 0 \tag{13}$$

$$\text{subject to} \qquad \sum_{e \in \delta(v): i \in C_e} x_e^i = B_v^i \qquad \forall\, v \in V,\ \forall\, i \in K_v \tag{14}$$

$$\sum_{i \in C_e} x_e^i = 1 \qquad \forall e \in E \qquad (15)$$

$$x_e \geq 0 \qquad \forall e \in E \qquad (16)$$

Observe that the fractional solution $x_e^i = \alpha_i$ for each $1 \leq i \leq k$ and $e \in E$ is a fractional feasible solution to the linear program.

We give an iterative algorithm which rounds the above linear program into an integral decomposition. The integral decomposition will violate the degree bounds by an additive error of 2 giving us Theorem 4. The algorithm iteratively constructs the partition $E^1, \ldots, E^k$ of E and is given in Figure 2.

---

1. Let $E^i \leftarrow \emptyset$ for each $1 \leq i \leq k$. While $E \neq \emptyset$ do
    (a) Find an extreme point optimal solution x to (LP).
    (b) If there is a variable $x_e^i = 0$ then remove variable x_e^i and let $C_e \leftarrow C_e \setminus \{i\}$.
    (c) If $x_e^i = 1$ then
        - $E^i \leftarrow E^i \cup \{e\}$
        - $E \leftarrow E \setminus \{e\}$
        - $B_v^i \leftarrow B_v^i - 1$ for each $v \in e$.
    (d) If there exists a vertex $v \in V$ and $1 \leq i \leq k$ such that $i \in K_v$ and there are at most 3 edges incident at v with non-zero x_e^i then remove the constraint at vertex v for i, i.e, $K_v \leftarrow K_v \setminus \{i\}$.
2. Return E^i for $1 \leq i \leq k$.

Fig. 2. Decomposition Algorithm I

First we show that if the algorithm reaches Step (2), then the solution returned by the algorithm satisfies the guarantees claimed in Theorem 4. In Step (1c) we reduce B_v^i whenever we select an edge e in E^i incident at v. Therefore, the bound for E^i at any vertex v can only be violated if the constraint for v and i is removed in Step (1d) We maintain the property that the constraint for vertex v and i is removed only if there are at most three edges incident at vertex v which can possibly be included in E^i. Therefore, it follows that the number of edges selected in E^i incident at v is strictly less than $B_v^i + 3$ and hence at most $\lceil B_v^i \rceil + 2$. Moreover, we have already selected strictly more than $B_v^i - 3$ edges incident at v in E^i when we remove the constraint for vertex v and color i. Hence, the number of edges in E^i incident at v is at least $\lfloor B_v^i \rfloor - 2$.

To complete the proof we show that the algorithm indeed reaches Step (2). Observe that Steps (1b), (1c) and (1d) all make progress in the sense that they reduce either the number of variables or the number of constraints. Lemma 2 implies that whenever Step (1a) is not applicable (because we are already at an extreme point of the current LP), at least one of these three other steps is indeed available. Since between every two applications of Step (1a) there must be an application of one of the other three steps, Step (2) must be reached eventually.

Lemma 2. *Given an extreme point solution x such that $0 < x_e^i < 1$ for each $e \in E$ and $i \in C_e$ there must exist a vertex v and color i satisfying the conditions of Step (1d).*

Proof. Suppose for the sake of contradiction there is no vertex $v \in V$ and color $i \in K_v$ with at most three edges incident at v with non-zero x_e^i. Since x is an extreme point, the number of tight independent constraints equals the number of variables. We will show a contradiction to this fact by showing that the number of tight independent constraints at x are strictly less than the number of variables.

We first count the number of variables. For each edge e, we must have $|C_e| \geq 2$ since $x_e^i < 1$ for each edge e and $i \in C_e$ and $\sum_{i \in C_e} x_e^i = 1$. Hence,

$$\# \text{ of variables} \geq 2|E|. \tag{17}$$

For each vertex $v \in V$ and $i \in K_v$, let D_v^i denote the number of variables of form x_e^i where $v \in e$. Since the condition of Step (1d) is not applicable we must have $D_v^i \geq 4$ for each vertex $v \in V$ and $i \in K_v$.

Hence,

$$\# \text{ of variables} \geq \frac{1}{2} \sum_{v \in V} \sum_{i=1}^{k} D_v^i \geq 2 \sum_v |K_v|. \tag{18}$$

A simple averaging gives that the

$$\# \text{ of variables} \geq |E| + \sum_v |K_v| \tag{19}$$

Observe that if equality must hold in inequations (18) and (19) then $i \in K_v$ whenever $i \in C_e$ for some $e \in \delta(v)$.

Now we bound the total number of tight independent constraints. Since $0 < x_e^i < 1$ for each e and $i \in C_e$, these integrality constraints cannot be tight at x. The number of other constraints is exactly $|E| + \sum_v |K_v|$. Thus all of these constraints must be at equality at x and linearly independent. We now show that this cannot be the case and derive a linear dependence in the tight constraints.

Summing up all the edge constraints we obtain that

$$\sum_{e \in E} \sum_{i \in C_e} x_e^i = |E| \tag{20}$$

where LHS is the sum of the all the variables. Summing up all the vertex constraints we obtain

$$\sum_{v \in V, i \in K_v} \sum_{e \in \delta(v): i \in C_e} x_e^i = \sum_{v \in V, i \in K_v} B_v^i \tag{21}$$

where each variable occurs exactly twice in the LHS. Thus equation (21) is exactly twice of equation (20) giving us a dependence in the tight constraints which is a contradiction.

This completes the proof of the Theorem 4.

We now prove the second guarantee in Theorem 2.

Theorem 5. *Given an instance of* BALANCED DECOMPOSITION OF BIPARTITE GRAPH *problem, there are decompositions* $F_1, \ldots, F_k$ *and* $G_1, \ldots G_k$ *such that*

$$deg_{F_i}(v) \le \lceil \alpha_i deg_E(v) \rceil + 1$$

$$deg_{G_i}(v) \ge \lfloor \alpha_i deg_E(v) \rfloor - 1$$

for each $1 \le i \le k$ *and* $v \in V$.

Proof. We first show how to construct the decomposition $F_1, \ldots, F_k$ which satisfies the upper bounds within an additive error of 1. The algorithm is very similar to the algorithm given in Figure 2 with the following difference. The relaxation step (1d) is modified and the constraint for $i \in K_v$ is removed whenever $D_v^i \le \lceil B_v^i \rceil + 1$ where D_v^i is the number of variables of the form x_e^i for some edge e incident at v.

---

1. Let $F^i \leftarrow \emptyset$ for each $1 \le i \le k$. While $E \ne \emptyset$ do
   (a) Find an extreme point optimal solution x to (LP).
   (b) If there is a variable $x_e^i = 0$ then remove variable x_e^i and let $C_e \leftarrow C_e \setminus \{i\}$.
   (c) If $x_e^i = 1$ then
       - $F^i \leftarrow F^i \cup \{e\}$
       - $E \leftarrow E \setminus \{e\}$
       - $B_v^i \leftarrow B_v^i - 1$ for each $v \in e$.
   (d) If there exists a vertex $v \in V$ and i such that $i \in K_v$ and $D_v^i \le \lceil B_v^i \rceil + 1$ then remove the constraint at vertex v for color i, i.e, $K_v \leftarrow K_v \setminus \{i\}$. Here $D_v^i = |\{e \in \delta(v) : x_e^i > 0\}|$.
2. Return F^i for $1 \le i \le k$.

Fig. 3. Decomposition Algorithm II

If the modified algorithm reaches Step (2) then it gives the claimed guarantee since the bound for color i at vertex v is violated only when the corresponding constraint is removed in Step (1d). In such a case we have $D_v^i \le \lceil B_v^i \rceil + 1$ and hence the total number of edges in F^i incident at v are bounded by $\lceil B_v^i \rceil + 1$ as desired.

To complete the proof of the Theorem 5 we show that the algorithm reaches Step (2). As in the discussion preceding Lemma 2, this will follow from the following lemma.

Lemma 3. *Given an extreme point solution x such that $0 < x_e^i < 1$ for each $v \in V$ and $i \in K_v$ there must exist a vertex v and color i such that $D_v^i \le \lceil B_v^i \rceil + 1$ where D_v^i is the number of variables of the form x_e^i for some edge e incident at v.*

Proof. Suppose for sake of contradiction we have $D_v^i \geq \lceil B_v^i \rceil + 2$ for each $i \in K_v$. We give a contradiction to the fact that the number of tight independent constraints is equal to the number of variables in x.

The contradiction is shown by a counting argument. We give one token to each variable which redistributes its token to the constraints. We then collect one token for each tight independent constraint and still have extra tokens, giving us the contradiction. The redistribution is given by the following two rules.

- **Rule 1:** Each variable x_e^i gives x_e^i tokens to the constraint for edge e.
- **Rule 2:** Each variable x_e^i gives $\frac{1-x_e^i}{2}$ tokens to the constraint for each endpoint v of e and i.

Observe that each edge gives a total of one token.

Now, we count the number of tokens received by each constraint. Edge constraint for an edge e receives $\sum_{i \in C_e} x_e^i$ tokens from Rule 1 which is exactly one from the edge constraint of e in (LP). Hence, each edge constraint receives one token in the redistribution.

Consider a constraint for vertex $v \in V$ and $i \in K_v$. It receives $\frac{1-x_e^i}{2}$ tokens for each $e \in \delta(v)$ such that $x_e^i > 0$ by Rule 2 or equivalently each edge counting towards D_v^i. Hence, the total number of tokens received by the constraint is at least

$$\sum_{e \in \delta(v), x_e^i > 0} \frac{1 - x_e^i}{2} = \frac{1}{2}(D_v^i - \sum_{e \in \delta(v), x_e^i > 0} x_e^i) \geq \frac{1}{2}(D_v^i - B_v^i) \geq 1$$

where the last inequality follows since $D_v^i \geq B_v^i + 2$. Thus each degree constraint also receives at least one token. Moreover, if any of the constraints receives more than token or there is a vertex $v \in V$ and color $i \notin K_v$ such that $x_e^i > 0$ for some edge $e \in \delta(v)$ then $\frac{1-x_e^i}{2}$ token given by Rule 2 is extra and gives us the contradiction. Otherwise, for any color i and vertex v, we must have that $i \in K_v$ whenever $i \in C_e$. But then the sum of all the edge constraints exactly equals the sum of the all the degree constraints, contradicting the requirement that the constraints are linearly independent.

This completes the proof that there exists a decomposition $F_1, \ldots, F_k$ satisfying the upper bounds within additive error of one.

We now show how to construct the decomposition $G_1, \ldots, G_k$ which satisfies the lower bounds within an additive error of one. The algorithm is exactly similar to one in Figure 3 except that we modify Step (1d) in the following manner. We delete the constraint for vertex $v \in V$ and $i \in K_v$ only when $\lfloor B_v^i \rfloor \leq 1$. Observe that with this modification it is easy to verify that the solution returned satisfies the lowerbound within an additive error of 1. This follows from the fact that at least $\lfloor B_v^i \rfloor - 1$ edges incident at v are in G_i before we remove the degree constraint for vertex v and color i.

We now show that algorithm will make progress with the modified Step (1d) in the following lemma. The proof of Lemma 4 is omitted and appears in the full version of the paper.

Lemma 4. *Given an extreme point solution x such that $0 < x_e^i < 1$ for each $v \in V$ and $i \in K_v$ there must exist a vertex v and color i such that $\lfloor B_v^i \rfloor \leq 1$.*

This completes the proof of Theorem 5.

References

1. Beck, J., Fiala, T.: "Integer-Making" Theorems. Discrete Applied Mathematics 3, 1–8 (1981)
2. Beetem, J., Denneau, M., Weingarten, D.: The GF11 Supercomputer. In: Proceedings of the 12th annual international symposium on Computer architecture, Boston, Massachusetts, United States, June 17-19, pp. 108–115 (1985)
3. Chung, S.-P., Ross, K.W.: On Nonblocking Multirate Interconnection Networks. SIAM Journal of Computing 20(4), 726–736 (1991)
4. Clos, C.: A Study of Nonblocking Switching Networks. Bell System Technical Journal 32(2), 406–424 (1953)
5. Correa, J., Goemans, M.X.: Improved Bounds on Nonblocking 3-Stage Clos Networks. SIAM Journal of Computing 37, 870–894 (2007)
6. Correa, J.R., Matamala, M.: Some Remarks About Factors of Graphs. Journal of Graph Theory 57, 265–274 (2008)
7. de Werra, D.: On Some Combinatorial Problems arising in Scheduling. Operations Research Society Journal 8, 165–175 (1970)
8. Du, D.Z., Gao, B., Hwang, F.K., Kim, J.H.: On Multirate Rearrangeable Clos Networks. SIAM Journal on Computing 28(2), 463–470 (1999)
9. Hoffman, A.J.: Generalization of a theorem of König. Journal of the Washington Academy of Science 46, 211–212 (1956)
10. Itoh, A., Takahashi, W., Nagano, H., Kurisaka, M., Iwasaki, S.: Practical Implementation and Packaging Technologies for a Large-Scale ATM Switching System. Journal of Selected Areas in Communications 9, 1280–1288 (1991)
11. Kano, M., Saito, A.: [a,b]-factors of graphs. Discrete Mathematics 47, 113–116 (1983)
12. König, D.: Graphok és Alkalmazásuk a Determinánsok és a Halmazok Elméletére. Mathematikai és Termszettudományi értesitö 34, 104–119 (1916)
13. Lin, G.-H., Du, D.-Z., Hu, X.-D., Xue, G.: On Rearrangeability of Multirate Clos Networks. SIAM Journal on Computing 28(4), 1225–1231 (1999)
14. Lin, G., Du, D., Wu, W., Yoo, K.: On 3-Rate Rearrangeability of Clos Networks. DIMACS Series in Discrete Mathematics and Theoretical Computer Science 42, 315–333 (1998)
15. Melen, R., Turner, J.S.: Nonblocking Multirate Networks. SIAM Journal on Computing 18(2), 301–313 (1989)
16. Ngo, H.Q., Vu, V.H.: Multirate Rearrangeable Clos Networks and a Generalized Edge Coloring Problem on Bipartite Graphs. In: Proceedings of the fourteenth annual ACM-SIAM symposium on Discrete algorithms, Baltimore, Maryland, January 12-14 (2003)
17. Slepian, D.: Two Theorems on a Particular Crossbar Switching (unpublished manuscript, 1958)
18. Vizing, V.G.: On an Estimate of the Chromatic Class of a p-Graph (in Russian). Diskret. Analiz 3, 23–30 (1964)

The Complexity of Sorting with Networks of Stacks and Queues

Stefan Felsner[1] and Martin Pergel[2],[*]

[1] Institut für Mathematik,
Technische Universität Berlin
`felsner@math.tu-berlin.de`
[2] Department of Applied Mathematics (KAM),
Charles University Prague
`perm@kam.mff.cuni.cz`

Abstract. We consider a sorting problem on networks whose nodes are storage elements of type stack or queue. A railway switchyard could be an instance of such a network. Given is an input node where a permutation of items 1 to n is delivered and an output node where they are expected in sorted order. How many moves, where an item is transfered from one node to an adjacent node, are needed in the worst case for the sorting? Among others we have the following results: A characterization of networks where the sorting complexity is $\Theta(n \log n)$. A lower bound of $\Omega(n^{2-\epsilon})$ for the network consisting of only two stacks that can exchange items.

1 Introduction

In 1972 Tarjan published the article "Sorting Using Networks of Queues and Stacks" [8]. Tarjan's model consists of an acyclic directed graph, alternatively called *network* or *switchyard*, with a designated input node s and output node t and additional nodes representing storage buffers of type Q (queue) or S (stack). Suppose a permutation $i_1, i_2, \ldots, i_n$ of items $1, \ldots, n$ is entered at the source node of the network, the question is whether they can be sorted, i.e., whether there is a sequence of moves such that the items arrive at the output node in the correct order. A *move* consists of choosing an edge $e = (i, j)$ and transferring the item that can be extracted at i through e and insert it into the storage at j.

The question could be answered for some special types of networks. The first result being Knuth's characterization of permutations that can be sorted with a single stack as those avoiding the pattern 231, see [5, Exercises 2.2.1.2–6]. This line of research leads to the study of permutation classes, c.f. Bóna [3,4]. A related line of research deals with token passing, in this model the nodes of the network are allowed to hold only a single item, again characterizations of sortable permutations are a central topic, e.g. Atkinson et al. [2]. Amato et al. [1] study the problem of reversing a train with a spur line just large enough to hold a single car. They have results for several cost models.

---

[*] Support of grant GAUK 154907 is gladly acknowledged.

D. Halperin and K. Mehlhorn (Eds.): ESA 2008, LNCS 5193, pp. 417–429, 2008.

In this paper we shift the focus from existence to complexity. Quoting Tarjan: *"A circuit in the switchyard will allow us to sort any sequence"*, thus when looking at 'cyclic' networks we may ask the questions:

How many moves are needed in the worst case to sort a permutation of n items in a given network?

We feel that the question is well motivated from a practical point of view, after all switchyards are cyclic in general and a specific order of the wagons of a train may be requested. Figure 1 shows a network with two stacks. The ability to use the track connecting the two stacks in two directions transforms the classical 2-stack problem into a 'cyclic' 2-stack problem as investigated in Theorem 3.

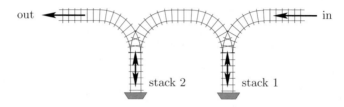

Fig. 1. If the track between the stacks is directed we have 2 stacks in series, the permutation 2435761 is unsortable, making the track bidirectional allows to sort every input

We were motivated to investigate the problem by discussions with König and Lübbecke [6]. They ask for approximation algorithms for a problem in steel processing where steel slabs are moved into a warehouse where they have to be placed on a fixed number of stacks. The aim is to allow extraction of the slabs in a prescribed order such that the amount of rearrangement (stack to stack transfers) is minimized. The hardness of the optimization problem is shown in [7].

In Section 2 we consider networks consisting of k communicating stacks, i.e., there is a directed edge between each ordered pair of stacks. We determine the asymptotic worst case for the number of moves required to sort in such a network for different choices of k. For $k \geq 3$ constant the complexity is $\Theta(n \log n)$, for $k \sim \log n$ it is $\Theta(\frac{n \log n}{\log \log n})$ and for $k = \sqrt{n}$ it is exactly $3n - \sqrt{n}$. In the case $k = 2$ we complement the trivial upper bound of $O(n^2)$ with a lower bound of $\Omega(n^{2-\epsilon})$ for all $\epsilon > 0$.

Section 3 deals with general networks. We identify two simple substructures of networks that allow sorting with $O(n \log n)$ moves. Networks avoiding these substructures are 'almost acyclic'. We show that the sorting complexity on such networks depends on the length of certain paths. In the conclusion we have collected some open problems.

2 Communicating Stacks

In this section we analyze the sorting complexity for networks of k communicating stacks. Such a network consists of input and output nodes s and t and k

additional nodes each representing an unbounded stack, i.e., a storage of last-in-first-out type. There are edges (s, i), (i, j) and (j, t) for all $i, j \neq s, t$. Recall that we assume that the input to the sorting network consists of some permutation π of items numbered $1, 2, \ldots, n$.

2.1   The Upper Bound

Let us begin considering the case $k = 3$ and let S_0, S_1 and S_2 be the three stacks. The idea for the algorithm is to sort by recursive splitting. First the input is distributed on the stacks such that S_0 contains a block consisting of the $n/3$ smallest items, the block on S_1 consists the middle third of the items and the block on S_2 consists of the largest third of the items. The three blocks will be sorted and sent to the output one after the other. To begin with the block B_0 from S_0 is extracted. The smaller half of the items, i.e., those with a number smaller than the median of B_0, are moved to S_2 and the larger half the items, i.e., the remaining ones, are moved to S_1. This makes new blocks B_2' and B_1' on top of the blocks B_2 and B_1. Recursively first sort B_2' and then B_1'. If a block to be sorted in the recursive process is of size 1, then this item is sent to the output.

For a more formal description we need to enhance each block B with information about the items in it, in particular we need $\min(B)$ and $\max(B)$ to be the smallest and largest numbers of items in B and $\mathsf{stack}(B)$ to be the index of the stack of B, we use arithmetic modulo 3 on these indices. Here is a code describing the recursion.

```
sort(B)
     if |B| = 1 then output this item
     else
          i ← stack(B)
          m ← ⌊(min(B)+max(B))/2⌋
          create a new block B₋ on Sᵢ₋₁
               min(B₋) ← min(B) and max(B₋) ← m
          create a new block B₊ on Sᵢ₊₁
               min(B₊) ← m + 1 and max(B₊) ← max(B)
          for b ∈ B do
               if b ≤ m then move b to B₋ else move b to B₊
          sort(B₋)
          sort(B₊)
```

Correctness of the procedure follows from the fact that the algorithm always acts on the block containing the smallest items that have not yet been moved to the output. For the complexity note that when an element is moved, then it is transfered from a block B to a block whose size is only half of the size of B.

Hence after $\log_2 n$ move operations the element is in a block of size 1 and will be output.

The procedure is easily generalized to the case of networks with $k > 3$ communicating stacks. In that case a block can be split into $k - 1$ parts and the total number of moves between stacks is bounded by $n \log_{k-1}(n)$. Note that in this analysis we have already included the cost of moving items from the input to their initial blocks. Adding one unit per item for the move to the output we obtain a bound of $n(\log_{k-1}(n) + 1)$ for the total number of moves. The following simple observation allows to improve this slightly. Whenever, sort(B) is called the smallest element of the block can be moved directly to the output. Doing this saves at least one move for every recursive call. The number of recursive calls equals the number of inner nodes of a full $(k - 1)$-ary tree with n leaves, i.e., it is $\frac{n-1}{k-2}$.

Theorem 1. *Every permutation π of $1, \ldots, n$ can be sorted in a network of $k \geq 3$ communicating stacks with at most $n \log_{k-1}(n) + n - \frac{n-1}{k-2}$ moves.*

Let us look at two particular values.

If $k = \log(n) + 1$ the cost per item is $a = \log_{\log(n)}(n) = \frac{\log n}{\log \log n}$.

If $k = \sqrt{n} + 1$ the cost per item is $a = \log_{\sqrt{n}}(n)$, i.e., $(\sqrt{n})^a = n$ and $a = 2$. From the theorem we get the upper bound $3n - \sqrt{n}$ for the number of moves. This number of moves is also enough if we have one stack less, i.e., for $k = \sqrt{n}$: Split the elements into $\sqrt{n}$ blocks of size $\sqrt{n}$, when processing a block the smallest goes to the output and the others are intermediately placed in the $\sqrt{n} - 1$ other stacks. Hence $\sqrt{n}$ items are moved only twice and all others three times. Note that an additional smallest element 0 can be processed with two additional moves. When it arrives it is immediately moved to the output.

For completeness some word about the case $k = 2$. In this case sorting can be accomplished by keeping all items together in one block which is moved hence and forth between the two stacks. In each transfer of the block the smallest remaining element is directly moved to the output. Hence the size of the block is decreasing and the overall complexity is at most $\binom{n+1}{2}$.

2.2   Lower Bounds

For the lower bound we only consider permutations with the least element last. This property implies that all elements have to be inserted into the stacks before the first element can be moved to the output. This restriction is natural when the stacks model the store at some transportation hub. Following König and Lübbecke we refer to the restriction as the *midnight constraint*.

The idea for the lower bounds is to define an encoding for a sorting procedure. Different input permutations shall require differently encoded sorting procedures. Hence the number of different encodings of sorting procedures for n items must be at least $n!$. In the computations we use Stirling's formula $n! \approx (\frac{n}{e})^n \sqrt{2\pi n}$ to approximate $n!$.

A move of an item from stack i to stack j will be encoded as a pair (i, j). A move from the input to stack i or from this stack to the output will be encoded as

(i, i). A sorting procedure is a sequence of moves, hence, a list of such pairs. Since we have k^2 pairs there are k^{2t} possible sequences that potentially encode a sorting with t moves. The inequality $k^{2t} \geq n! > (\frac{n}{e})^n$ yields $2t \geq n \log_k(n) - O(n)$, i.e., for n large t has to get arbitrarily close to $\frac{n \log(n)}{2 \log(k)}$.

For $k \geq 3$ we thus obtain upper and lower bounds differing only by the small factor $\frac{2 \log(k)}{\log(k-1)}$, that is by a factor ≤ 3.2.

Theorem 2. *The worst case complexity for sorting n elements in a network of $k \geq 3$ communicating stacks is at least $\frac{n}{2} \log_k(n) - O(n)$.*

For $k = \sqrt{n}$ we can point to a specific permutation that maximizes the number of moves required. Consider the permutation $\pi = 1, 2, 3, \ldots, n, 0$. The element 0 at the end enforces the midnight constraint. Consider the position of the n items in the stacks right after inserting element 0. For a consecutive pair a below b on any of these stacks we either have $a < b$ and b has to be displaced before a can be output or we have $a > b$ and if $b \neq 0$ it has been moved after the arrival of a. Hence, there is a stack to stack move for all elements except 0 and the lowest of each stack. This gives a total of at least $3(n + 1) - \sqrt{n} - 1 = 3n - \sqrt{n} + 2$ moves. Together with the sorting described in the previous subsection we have the proposition.

Proposition 1. *The worst case complexity for sorting $n + 1$ elements in a network of $\sqrt{n}$ communicating stacks is precisely $3n - \sqrt{n} + 2$.*

2.3   Two Communicating Stacks

Again we assume the midnight constraint, i.e., the largest element comes last. Consider the position of the n elements in the two stacks at *midnight*, i.e., right before the first element is moved out. Imagine the two stacks horizontally sticked together top to top, this shows a permutation of all the elements, this is the midnight permutation σ of the process. Remarkably the pair (π, σ) uniquely describes a sorting $\pi \to id$ on the two stacks network. A good way of visualizing the process is to keep the stacks sticked together linearly from the beginning and to think of an operating head moving left and right over this linear structure, push and pop operations always take place at the position of the head. Figure 2 shows an example.

To encode the sorting process we describe the movement of the head between consecutive in- resp. out-moves. Such a movement is readily described by a direction $a \in \{\ell, r\}$ indicating whether the head moves left or right and a distance b for the move, clearly with $0 \leq b \leq n - 1$. In total we have $2n$ such pairs (a_i, b_i), $i = 1, .., 2n$. Actually, there are only $2n - 2$ movements of the head but such details disappear in the asymptotic analysis, hence, we will continue ignoring them. The total complexity of the sorting is $t = 2n + \sum_i b_i$. For a fixed t we may consider $(b_i)_i$ as a composition of the number $t - 2n$ with $2n$ parts. Therefore, there are at most $2^{2n} \binom{t}{2n}$ choices of $2n$ pairs (a_i, b_i) respecting the sum constraint. Sorting codes of different permutations have to be different, therefore, t has to be large enough for $2^{2n} \binom{t}{2n} \geq n!$.

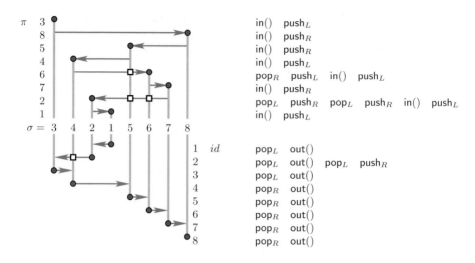

Fig. 2. Sorting the input permutation $\pi = 38546721$ via $\sigma = 34215678$. Time corresponds to the vertical axis, movements of the head are horizontal arrows. The four extra moves where an element has to switch between stacks are indicated by squares. On the right we give the sequence of stack operations for sorting π via σ.

If t satisfies $2^{2n}\binom{t}{2n} \geq n!$ then $2^{2n}\frac{t^{2n}}{(2n)!} \geq n!$, hence, $2^{2n}t^{2n} \geq \left(\frac{n}{e}\right)^n \left(\frac{2n}{e}\right)^{2n}$ and $t^{2n} \geq \left(\frac{n}{e}\right)^{3n}$. Taking the $2n$th root yields $t \geq c\, n^{3/2}$. This is already well above the $\Theta(n \log(n))$ complexity obtained for $k \geq 3$ stacks. With an additional idea we will squeeze more out of this approach.

The idea is that if π is effectively sortable via the midnight permutation σ and σ' is close to σ, then the cost of sorting π via σ' will not be much higher, hence, an effectively sortable π has many effective sortings. To make this precise we begin with a notion of closeness: Given a parameter $0 < \alpha < 1$ we say that σ and σ' are α-*close* if they have the same elements in the interval between positions $\lfloor p n^\alpha \rfloor$ and $\lfloor (p+1)\, n^\alpha \rfloor - 1$ for each $p \geq 0$. The concept is illustrated in Figure 3. For later use we note that the equivalence classes of α-closeness are of size $(n^\alpha)!^{\,n/n^\alpha} = (n^\alpha)!^{\,n^{1-\alpha}} \geq \left(\frac{n^\alpha}{e}\right)^n$.

Lemma 1. *If sorting π with midnight permutation σ requires at most $c\,n^{1+\alpha}$ moves and σ' is α-close to σ, then the sorting of π with midnight permutation σ' requires at most $(c+4)\, n^{1+\alpha}$ moves.*

Proof. By exchanging σ and σ' the distance of each of the $2n$ movements of the head can increase by no more than $2n^\alpha$. This adds up to no more than $4n^{1+\alpha}$.

$\square$

Being interested mainly in the exponent $1 + \alpha$ of the sorting complexity we may thus assume that every permutation has $(n^\alpha)!^{\,n^{1-\alpha}}$ different sortings of this

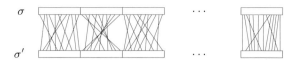

Fig. 3. A typical pair of α-close permutations, each of the $n^{1-\alpha}$ blocks of length n^α is permuted independently

complexity. For the required number t of moves we need $2^{2n} \binom{t}{2n} / (n^\alpha)!\, n^{1-\alpha} \geq n!$. This allows to estimate t as follows:

$$2^{2n} \frac{t^{2n}}{(2n)!} \geq n! \left(\frac{n^\alpha}{e}\right)^n \implies 2^{2n} t^{2n} \geq \left(\frac{n}{e}\right)^n \left(\frac{2n}{e}\right)^{2n} \left(\frac{n^\alpha}{e}\right)^n$$

$$\implies t^{2n} \geq \left(\frac{n^{3+\alpha}}{e^4}\right)^n \implies t \geq \frac{1}{e^2} n^{\frac{3+\alpha}{2}}$$

Any t satisfying the last inequality is in $\Omega(n^{1+\alpha})$, i.e., the additional moves for replacing a midnight permutation σ by an α-close σ' can be afforded. The bound for t holds for every $\alpha < 1$ we thus obtain:

Theorem 3. *The worst case complexity for sorting n elements in a network of two communicating stacks is at least $\Omega(n^{2-\epsilon})$ for all $\epsilon > 0$.*

3   General Networks

To avoid trivialities we assume that every node of a given network is contained in some directed $s - t$ path and that a stack-node never has a loop. In the first part of this section We identify two simple substructures $\mathcal{S}_1$, and $\mathcal{S}_2$ of networks that allow sorting with $O(n \log n)$ moves.

Networks avoiding the substructures $\mathcal{S}_1$ and $\mathcal{S}_2$ will be called *almost acyclic*. They have strongly connected components of very restricted type only. For such networks with a path containing r components that do not consist of a single node without loop we prove that sorting is possible in $O(n^{1+\frac{1}{r}})$ moves. If every $s - t$ path intersects at most r strong components, then there is a lower bound of $\Omega(n^{1+\frac{1}{2r}})$.

3.1   Strong Substructures

We first describe the two substructures allowing fast sorting. They are:

($\mathcal{S}_1$) Three stacks S_1, S_2 and S_3 and paths $p_1 : S_1 \to S_2$, $p_2 : S_2 \to S_3$ and $p_3 : S_3 \to S_1$.

($\mathcal{S}_2$) A queue Q, an a second node T, either stack or queue, with paths $p_1 : Q \to T$, $p_2 : T \to Q$ and in the case where T is a queue an additional path $q : Q \to Q$ that avoids T, q may be a loop. In the case where T is a stack the concatenation of p_1 and p_2 can replace q.

The analysis for case $\mathcal{S}_1$ is an obvious reduction to the situation with three communicating stacks analyzed in Section 2. Move all items from s to one of the stacks and then use the splitting scheme from Subsection 2.1. When an item has to be moved from a block on stack S_i to a block on stack S_j we move them along an appropriate concatenation of the paths p_1, p_2, p_3. This yields a sorting with $cn \log n$ moves, where c depends on the length of the paths p_i.

A sorting strategy for case $\mathcal{S}_2$ also uses blocks and splitting. The block B that has to be processed will be in the front of Q. Small elements from B are moved via q to the back of Q where the block B_- is created. Large elements are parked in the block B_+ on T. When the processing of B is complete the content of T is also moved to the back of Q. The start is with a single block consisting of all elements on B. A *round* is a period of time in which every element is moved into a new block. The size of the blocks is essentially halved in each round. When blocks have size 1 we have a completely sorted list on Q and are done. The complexity is $c\,n$ times the number of rounds, i.e., $c\,n \log n$.

Note that the argument preceding Theorem 2 applies to arbitrary networks with a constant number k of nodes and thus yields a general lower bound of order $\Omega(n \log n)$ for the worst case sorting complexity.

Proposition 2. *The sorting complexity on networks with a constant number k of nodes that contain a substructure of type $\mathcal{S}_1$ or $\mathcal{S}_2$ is $\Theta(n \log n)$.*

3.2   Almost Acyclic Networks

Networks avoiding the substructures $\mathcal{S}_1$ and $\mathcal{S}_2$ are called *almost acyclic*. Their strong components are either trivial, i.e., consisting of a single node without loop, or they consist of a simple cycle of queues, this may also be a single queue with a loop, or they consist of two communicating stacks.

Let us consider a network with an $s - t$ path containing k nontrivial strong components. Let $C_1, \ldots, C_k$ be the order of the components on the path. In the following description of a sorting procedure we again use the terminology of blocks. At the beginning all items form a single block on C_1. When a component is empty it may receive a new block from the preceding component. A block sent from C_i to C_{i+1} always consists of (approximately) a_i items, where $a_i = n^{1-\frac{i}{k}}$. When component C_i is non-empty and C_{i+1} is allowed to receive a block, then C_i looks at all items it holds and sends the a_i smallest. The numbers are set up such that C_k will send singletons to the output. Since at every moment of time, when two components C_i and C_j with $i < j$ are non-empty, all items on C_i are larger than any item on C_j it follows that the process yields the sorted sequence at the output.

Every block received by C_i is of size $a_{i-1} = n^{\frac{1}{k}} a_i$ and every block sent by C_i is of size a_i. Therefore, each element is 'looked at' at most $n^{\frac{1}{k}}$ times within the component. The number of moves of an element in a component is proportional to the number of looks at it. This makes a cost of $O(n^{1+\frac{1}{k}})$ per component. This makes a total of $O(k\, n^{1+\frac{1}{k}})$ moves. For k constant this is $O(n^{1+\frac{1}{k}})$ while for $k \sim \log n$ it is $O(n \log n)$.

Theorem 4. *Almost acyclic networks with an $s-t$ path containing k nontrivial strong components can sort with $O(k\,n^{1+\frac{1}{k}})$ moves.*

In Subsection 3.3 we deal with a special class of almost acyclic networks where the result of the theorem is best possible. First, however, we go for a general lower bound. Again, the method of choice is to use an appropriate encoding.

We start considering a network consisting of a linearly arranged sequence of k strong components. Collapsing the strong components this reduces to a single $s-t$ path with k nodes. To encode a sorting consisting of t moves we first break the sequence at *transition moves*, i.e. moves where an element is transfered from one component to the next. We assume that the sorting is normalized in the sense that between a transition move bringing an item from C_i to C_{i+1} and the next transition move there are only moves within C_i and C_{i+1}. From the structure of the strong components it follows that for each component all that matters is the direction of the movement and the number of elements moved. Hence, we can encode the transition move with the index i of the component and the action on C_i and C_{i+1} by two bits b, b' and two numbers x and y. There is a total of kn transition moves, hence, we get a sequence of kn encoding tuples $(i_j, b_j, b'_j, x_j, y_j)$. For the bits and the leading indices there are at most $(4\,k)^{kn}$ choices. The numbers satisfy $\sum_j x_j + y_j < t$, hence, there are at most $\binom{t}{2kn}$ possibilities for them.

The computation that follows is similar to what we did in Subsection 2.2. Requiring that t is large enough such that all input permutations consisting of n items can be sorted implies an inequality:

$$(4\,k)^{kn}\binom{t}{2kn} \geq n! \implies (4\,k)^{kn}\frac{t^{2kn}}{(2kn)!} \geq n! \implies$$

$$(2\sqrt{k}\,t)^{2kn} \geq \left(\frac{n}{e}\right)^n\left(\frac{2kn}{e}\right)^{2kn} \implies t^{2kn} \geq \left(\frac{n}{e}\right)^{(2k+1)n}k^{kn} \implies t \geq c\,n^{\frac{(2k+1)}{2k}}.$$

Consider an arbitrary almost acyclic network with a constant number k of strong components. There is 'only' a constant, say k^k, number of $s-t$ path in the network. Therefore, in a sorting of n items there is a path taken by linearly many of the items. Applying the previous consideration to this path we conclude:

Theorem 5. *An almost acyclic network containing a constant number k of strong components requires $\Omega(n^{1+\frac{1}{2k}})$ moves for sorting.*

In the following subsection we consider two special cases of almost acyclic networks. In both cases we can improve upon the lower bound of the theorem.

3.3 Sequences of Looped Queues and Doublestacks

In this subsection we consider almost acyclic networks consisting of a single $s-t$ path of k strong components. We investigate two particular instances:

(1) Each strong component is a cycle of queues or a single queue with a loop.

(2) Each strong component is a doublestack, i.e., a pair of communicating stacks.

Let NQ_k be the first of these instances, and let Z_i, $i = 1, .., k$, denote the ith cycle of queues along the path. The input permutation is $\pi = n, n-1, \ldots 2, 1$. It will be shown that a sorting of π in NQ_k requires at least $\Omega(n^{1+\frac{1}{k}})$ moves.

Consider a sorting procedure and associate a vector $q(x) \in \mathbb{N}^k$ with every number $x \in \{1, .., n\}$. The component $q_i(x)$ of this vector records the number of rounds item x makes on Z_i during the sorting. To account for the move of the element from Z_i to Z_{i+1} the actual value of $q_i(x)$ is one more than the number of rounds. Hence, in the case where each Z_i consists of a single queue with a loop, the total number of moves of the sorting is exactly $\sum_{i,x} q_i(x)$.

Observe that during a sorting for every given pair of numbers $x < y$ there is an i such that y is overtaken by x in Z_i, i.e., x arrives later in Z_i but leaves earlier, in particular $q_i(x) < q_i(y)$. This implies that the vectors $q(x)$ are pairwise different.

Lemma 2. *There is a constant c_k depending only on k such that*

$$\sum_{x=1}^{n} \sum_{i=1}^{k} q_i(x) \geq c_k \, n^{1+\frac{1}{k}}$$

for every set of n pairwise different vectors $q(x) \in \mathbb{N}^k$.

Before proving the lemma we shall point to its consequence. We get a lower bound matching the upper bound from Theorem 4:

Proposition 3. *Sorting the reverse permutation π on the network NQ_k consisting of k cycles of queues along a path requires $\Omega(n^{1+\frac{1}{k}})$ moves.*

Proof of the lemma. A set $\mathcal{Q}$ of n different positive vectors minimizing the sum has to be packed in the sense that there is a k-dimensional simplex $\Delta_k^0(r)$ spanned by $\mathbf{0}$ and the k vectors $r\,\mathbf{e}_i$ such that all integral points in the open interior of $\Delta_k^0(r)$ belong to $\mathcal{Q}$ and no point outside of $\Delta_k^0(r)$ belongs to $\mathcal{Q}$.

Every $q \in \mathcal{Q}$ is the maximal corner of a unit-cube C_q contained in $\Delta_k^0(r)$, therefore,

$$\frac{r^k}{k!} = \mathsf{Vol}_k(\Delta_k^0(r)) \geq n \quad \Longrightarrow \quad r \geq \frac{k}{e} n^{\frac{1}{k}}.$$

¿From $\sum_i q_i \geq \int_{C_q} (\sum_i x_i)\, dx$ for every $q \in \mathcal{Q}$ we get

$$\sum_{q \in \mathcal{Q}} \sum_i q_i \geq \int_{\Delta_k^0(r)} \left(\sum_i x_i \right) dx = \int_{t=0}^{\frac{r}{\sqrt{k}}} t \cdot \mathsf{Vol}_{k-1}(\Delta_{k-1}(t))\, dt,$$

where $\Delta_{k-1}(t)$ is the $(k-1)$-dimensional simplex spanned by the k vectors $t\,\mathbf{e}_i$, i.e., $\Delta_{k-1}(t)$ is a regular simplex with sidelength $\sqrt{2}t$. The volume of the regular

k-dimensional simplex with sidelength one is $\frac{\sqrt{k+1}}{\sqrt{2^k}\,k!}$, hence, $\mathsf{Vol}_{k-1}(\Delta_{k-1}(t)) = \frac{\sqrt{k}}{(k-1)!}\,t^{k-1}$. Using this in the above integral and substituting for r yields the final inequalities:

$$\sum_{q \in Q}\sum_i q_i \geq \frac{k\sqrt{k}}{(k+1)!}\left(\frac{r}{\sqrt{k}}\right)^{k+1} \geq \frac{k\sqrt{k}}{(k+1)!}\frac{k^{k+1}}{(e\sqrt{k})^{k+1}}\,n^{\frac{k+1}{k}} = c_k\,n^{1+\frac{1}{k}}.$$

$\square$

Let NS_k be an almost acyclic networks consisting of a single $s - t$ path of k doublestacks. A lower bound for the number of moves required to sort on NS_k was given in Theorem 5. To improve upon this bound we use terminology and the idea from the proof of Theorem 3. We assume that the input permutation has the least element last, i.e., the midnight constraint is enforced. Consider the arrangement of items on doublestack i at midnight, this is a sequence σ_i. The concatenation of these sequences is a permutation σ split into k pieces $\sigma = (\sigma_1, \sigma_2, \ldots, \sigma_k)$, in the following we refer to such a permutation as *splitted (midnight) permutation*. Two splitted permutations σ and σ' are α-close if for all i: σ_i and σ'_i contain the same items and they are α-close in the old sense, i.e., they contain the same items in their buckets of length n^α. Equivalence classes of α closeness are of size at least $(n^\alpha)!^{n/n^\alpha - k}$. Since k is a constant we may still estimate this size as $(\frac{n^\alpha}{e})^n$.

Lemma 3. *If sorting π on NS_k with splitted midnight permutation σ requires at most $c\,n^{1+\alpha}$ moves and σ' is α-close to σ, then there is a sorting of π with splitted midnight permutation σ' that requires at most $(c + 4 + k)\,n^{1+\alpha}$ moves.*

Proof. The sorting with σ' reproduces the original sorting with σ as close as possible, i.e, the sequence of moves where elements are sent to the next doublestack are identical, moreover, if x is an element belonging to piece σ_j, then then position of x in the sequence of each doublestack i with $i \neq j$ is exactly the same in both sortings. Hence, all additional moves that are associated with x occur when x is inserted or removed from doublestack j. These additional moves are of two types:

- The head is passing an element y that belongs to the block of x, i.e., to the interval of length n^α on σ_j containing x. There are at most $2n^\alpha$ such moves associated with the insertion of x into doublestack j and again $2n^\alpha$ moves associated with the removal.

- The head is passing an element z belonging to a piece σ_i with $i \neq j$. For this to happen it must be that in one of the two sortings x is left of z and in the other it is right of z, i.e., the position of z is in the range spanned by elements the block of x. This kind of move is assigned to z. While sitting on doublestack i element z can cause at most n^α such moves. Altogether there are at most $k\,n^\alpha$ such moves assigned to z.

Summing over all x and z we can bound the number of additional moves by $n\,(4 + k)\,n^\alpha$.

$\square$

Given the lemma we can redo the computation preceding Theorem 5:

$$(4\,k)^{kn}\binom{t}{2kn} \geq n!(\frac{n^\alpha}{e})^n \implies t \geq cn^{1+\frac{1+\alpha}{2k}}.$$

The choice of α is restricted by the condition that there is additional work of order $n^{1+\alpha}$. Hence we need $1+\alpha \leq 1+\frac{1+\alpha}{2k}$, i.e., the best we can do is to choose $\alpha = \frac{1}{2k-1}$. This yields the proposition:

Proposition 4. *Sorting n elements on the network NS_k consisting of k doublestacks along a path requires at least $\Omega(n^{1+\frac{1}{2k-1}})$ moves in the worst case.*

4   Conclusion

We have analyzed the sorting complexity of networks of stacks and queues. In most cases we could prove upper and lower bounds that are at least reasonably close. Some questions are left open or raised by our results. To us the single most intriguing problem is the following:

- Is it possible to sort on two communicating stacks with $o(n^2)$ moves?

One of the aspects where networks of queues and networks of stacks differ is that in the former case we could get lower bounds by analyzing a specific input permutation while in the second case we had to rely on counting arguments. It would be interesting to get hand on explicit permutations that are hard to sort on a given network of stacks, e.g., on NS_k.

A related line of questions is opened if we fix an input permutation and ask for the optimal sorting on a given network. As mentioned in the introduction some instances of the problem have been shown to be computationally hard by König et al. [7]. Again the case of the network consisting of two stacks seems to be challenging.

- Is it hard to compute an optimal sorting for an input permutation π on a network of two communicating stacks?

- Is it possible to approximate the sorting complexity of π on a network of two communicating stacks in polynomial time?

References

1. Amato, N., Blum, M., Irani, S., Rubinfeld, R.: Reversing trains: a turn of the century sorting problem. J. Alg. 10, 413–428 (1989)
2. Atkinson, M.D., Livesy, M.J., Tulley, D.: Permutations generated by token passing in graphs. Theor. Comput. Sci. 178, 103–118 (1997)
3. Bóna, M.: A survey of stack-sorting disciplines. Electr. J. Combin. 9(2), 16 pages (2003)
4. Bóna, M.: Combinatorics of Permutations. Chapman & Hall, Boca Raton (2004)
5. Knuth, D.E.: The Art of Computer Programming, 3rd edn., vol. 1. Addison-Wesley, Reading (updated and revised) (1997)

6. König, F.G., Lübbecke, M.E.: Sorting with Complete Networks of Stacks, TU Berlin, Mathematik (preprint, 036-2007)
7. König, F.G., Lübbecke, M.E., Möhring, R.H., Schäfer, G., Spenke, I.: Solutions to real-world instances of Pspace-complete stacking. In: Arge, L., Hoffmann, M., Welzl, E. (eds.) ESA 2007. LNCS, vol. 4698, pp. 729–740. Springer, Heidelberg (2007)
8. Tarjan, R.: Sorting using networks of queues and stacks. J. Assoc. Comput. Mach. 19, 341–346 (1972)

Faster Steiner Tree Computation in Polynomial-Space

Fedor V. Fomin[1,*], Fabrizio Grandoni[2,**], and Dieter Kratsch[3]

[1] Department of Informatics, University of Bergen, N-5020 Bergen, Norway
`fomin@ii.uib.no`
[2] Dipartimento di Informatica, Sistemi e Produzione, Università di Roma "Tor Vergata", via del Politecnico 1, 00133, Roma, Italy
`grandoni@disp.uniroma2.it`
[3] LITA, Université Paul Verlaine-Metz, 57045 Metz Cedex 01, France
`kratsch@univ-metz.fr`

Abstract. Given an n-node graph and a subset of k terminal nodes, the NP-hard Steiner tree problem is to compute a minimum-size tree which spans the terminals. All the known algorithms for this problem which improve on trivial $O(1.62^n)$-time enumeration are based on dynamic programming, and require exponential space.

Motivated by the fact that exponential-space algorithms are typically impractical, in this paper we address the problem of designing faster polynomial-space algorithms. Our first contribution is a simple polynomial-space $O(6^k n^{O(\log k)})$-time algorithm, based on a variant of the classical tree-separator theorem. This improves on trivial $O(n^{k+O(1)})$ enumeration for, roughly, $k \leq n/4$.

Combining the algorithm above (for small k), with an improved branching strategy (for large k), we obtain an $O(1.60^n)$-time polynomial-space algorithm. The refined branching is based on a charging mechanism which shows that, for large values of k, convenient local configurations of terminals and non-terminals must exist. The analysis of the algorithm relies on the Measure & Conquer approach: the non-standard measure used here is a linear combination of the number of nodes and number of non-terminals.

As a byproduct of our work, we also improve the (exponential-space) time complexity of the problem from $O(1.42^n)$ to $O(1.36^n)$.

1 Introduction

The *Steiner tree problem* is one of the best-known optimization problems: Given a connected graph $G = (V, E)$ on $n = |V|$ nodes, edge costs $c : E \to \mathbb{R}^+$ and a set $T \subseteq V$ of $k = |T|$ *terminals*, the objective is to find a subtree S of G spanning T such that the cost of S (i.e. the total cost of its edges) is minimum. Steiner trees are important in various applications such as VLSI routings [22],

---

* Supported by the Norwegian Research Council.
** Partially supported by MIUR under project MAINSTREAM.

D. Halperin and K. Mehlhorn (Eds.): ESA 2008, LNCS 5193, pp. 430–441, 2008.

phylogenetic tree reconstruction [21] and network routing [24]. We refer to the book of Prömel and Steger [27] for an overview of the results and applications of the Steiner tree problem.

The Steiner tree problem is known to be NP-hard [18]. Furthermore, it is APX-complete, even when the graph is complete and all edge costs are either 1 or 2 [3]. Finding the best approximation algorithm for the Steiner tree problem has been a challenge and many papers have been written on this subject. The currently best polynomial-time approximation algorithm for the Steiner tree problem, due to Robins and Zelikovsky, has approximation ratio $1 + (\ln 3)/2 < 1.55$ [28]. Among other results, Robins and Zelikovsky establish an approximation ratio of 1.28 for complete graphs with edge costs 1 or 2. The Steiner tree problem remains NP-hard for Euclidean and rectilinear metrics [17]. On the positive side, Arora established polynomial-time approximation schemes for those two important variants of the Steiner tree problem [1].

The Steiner tree problem plays a crucial role also in parameterized algorithms [9,12,26]. The aim here is designing the fastest possible algorithm under the (realistic) assumption that $k \ll n$. For more than 30 years the fastest parameterized algorithm for the Steiner Tree problem was the classical $O^*(3^k)$ dynamic programming algorithm by Dreyfus and Wagner [10].[1] Dreyfus-Wagner's algorithm is still probably the most popular algorithm used for solving different variants of the Steiner tree problem in practice [8,16]. This algorithm and its variations are also used as a subroutine in many other algorithms. For example, recent applications of it can be found in fixed parameter tractable algorithms for certain vertex cover problems [19] and for near-perfect phylogenetic tree reconstruction [6]. Recent progress in parameterized complexity and exact algorithms led to new insights on the Steiner tree problem. Mölle, Richter, and Rossmanith [25] (see also [15]) improved the running time to $O^*((2+\epsilon)^k)$, for any constant $\epsilon > 0$. More recently, Björklund, Husfeldt, Kaski, and Koivisto [5] obtained an $O^*(2^k)$ time algorithm for the version of the problem where edges have bounded integer weights. All the mentioned algorithms are based on a dynamic programming approach: they store useful auxiliary information for every subset of the terminal set, and thus use exponential space $\Omega(2^k)$.

For arbitrary values of k, the fastest known $O^*(1.4143^n)$-time (exponential-space) algorithm for the Steiner tree problem is obtained by combining the algorithm by Mölle et al. [25] (for small k) with trivial enumeration (for large k).

Exponential-space versus polynomial-space. The situation with exact algorithms for the Steiner tree problem is quite typical for a number of other NP-hard problems: the best exponential time complexity is achieved by algorithms with exponential space complexity [29]. However, algorithms with very high space complexity are unlikely to be fast in practice, especially when external memory accesses are frequent. This kind of phenomena is not captured by the standard RAM model. Hence it makes sense to search for algorithms with

---

[1] Throughout this paper we use the O^* notation which suppresses polynomial factors: for any polynomial $p(n)$, $O(p(n)f(n))$ is $O^*(f(n))$.

low memory requirements, even if they are asymptotically slower than their exponential-space counterpart. Polynomial-space exact algorithms have been studied for various NP-hard problems, among them Hamiltonian Path [2,20,23] and Coloring [4].

For $k = \omega(\log n)$, the existing parameterized algorithms for the Steiner tree problem are not polynomial-space. Under that assumption, the fastest known polynomial-space algorithm is the (almost) trivial enumerative algorithm, based on the following observation. Since all the leaves of any optimal Steiner tree are terminals, the number of Steiner nodes T' of degree 3 or larger is at most k. Given T', the Steiner tree problem is equivalent to the minimum spanning tree problem on $G_M[T \cup T']$, where G_M is the metric closure of G. Such problem can be solved in polynomial time. Hence it is sufficient to list all the subsets $T' \subseteq N := V \setminus T$ of size at most k, and then apply the observation above. This takes time $O(\sum_{i=1}^{k} \binom{n-k}{i} n^{O(1)})$. For $k \ll n$ this running time is $O^*(n^k)$, while for arbitrary values of k it is $O^*(1.6181^n)$.

Our Results and Techniques. Motivated by the practical limitations of exponential-space algorithms and by the theoretical interest of the topic itself, in this paper we address the problem of designing faster polynomial-space exact algorithms for the Steiner tree problem. In particular, we present an exact algorithm for the cardinality version of the problem (where every edge is of weight one), of running time $O^*(1.5949^n)$. This result is achieved in three steps:

• We describe a new, easy-to-implement, Steiner tree algorithm, taking $O(5.96^k n^{O(\log k)})$ time and polynomial space. This means an improvement on known polynomial-space results for $\omega(\log n) = k \leq 0.269\, n$, which covers many real-world instances. Our result is based on a simple variant of the classical tree-separator theorem: shortly, there is a node in every Steiner tree which separates two *balanced* subsets of terminals. This can be exploited in a top-down recursive implementation of the classical algorithm by Dreyfus and Wagner, hence achieving running time $O((27/4)^k n^{O(\log k)})$ and polynomial-space. The running time can be refined to $O(5.96^k n^{O(\log k)})$ by exploiting the properties of the Steiner separators in combination with a more careful branching. This algorithm works also in the weighted case, and might be of independent, practical interest[2].

• We design an improved branching strategy, based on the following idea. When k is small, it is convenient to use the algorithm above. Otherwise, there must be clusters of terminals "close" to each other. This property can be used to guide the branching process. From the technical point of view, we use a simple charging mechanism to show that, for large k's, the graph must contain one of a small list of local configurations of terminals and non-terminals. On such configurations we are able to branch better than trivially.

• We analyze the algorithm above with the Measure & Conquer technique described in [13,14], and based on the quasiconvex analysis of multivariate recurrences by Eppstein [11]. The basic idea is designing a convenient (non-trivial)

---

[2] An experimental analysis of our algorithms is postponed to future work.

measure of the size of the problem. This measure is used to bound in a tighter way the progress made by the recursive algorithm considered at each branching step. The running time obtained with respect to the refined measure is eventually turned into the equivalent running time in terms of the standard measure considered (typically the number of nodes or edges for graph problems). As it will be clearer from the analysis, a convenient measure in our case is a linear combination of the number n of nodes and number $n_N = n - k$ of non-terminals in the graph.

Preliminaries. In the following $st_G(T)$ denotes the minimum number of edges of a Steiner tree of graph G over terminal set T. When the graph G is clear from the context, we will simply write $st(T)$. By *contracting* a subset of nodes V', we mean (i) removing V' from the graph, (ii) adding a new node v', and (iii) adding one edge between v' and each neighbor of V' not in V'. The following lemma is easy to verify.

Lemma 1. (Contraction Lemma) *Let (G, T) be an instance of the cardinality Steiner tree problem. Also let V' be a connected component of terminals, G' be the graph resulting from contracting V' in a unique node v', and $T' = T \cup \{v'\} \setminus V'$. Then*

$$st_G(T) = |V'| - 1 + st_{G'}(T').$$

The rest of this paper is organized as follows. In Section 2 we present our $O(5.96^k n^{O(\log k)})$ polynomial-space algorithm. The refined branching strategy based on the charging argument is described in Section 3, and analyzed in Section 4 with the Measure & Conquer technique.

2   Steiner Tree Via Steiner Separators

In this section we describe a simple polynomial-space algorithm for the Steiner tree problem of running time $O((27/4)^k n^{O(\log k)})$. We later show how to reduce the time complexity to $O(5.96^k n^{O(\log k)})$. We remark that, with minor modifications, this algorithm works also in the weighted case.

Our algorithm is inspired by the classical dynamic programming algorithm D&W by Dreyfus and Wagner [10], which takes $O^*(3^k)$ time and exponential space. Algorithm D&W is based on the following observation. Consider any Steiner tree S on the set of terminals T, $|T| \geq 3$. There must be an internal node $s \in S$, not necessarily a terminal, such that the subtrees of S rooted at s can be partitioned in two forests $\mathcal{R}_1$ and $\mathcal{R}_2$, each one containing at least one terminal. Let T_i be the terminals in $\mathcal{R}_i$, $i \in \{1, 2\}$. If we compute optimal Steiner trees on terminals $T_1 \cup \{s\}$ and $T_2 \cup \{s\}$, and we merge them, we obtain an optimal Steiner tree for the original problem. Of course we do not know s nor (T_1, T_2) a priori, but we can guess them by enumerating all the possible cases. Recall that $st_G(T) = st(T)$ is the minimum cost of a Steiner tree of G on terminals T. The following equation holds:

$$st(T) = \min_{s \in V} \min_{(T_1, T_2) \in \mathcal{P}(s, T)} \{st(T_1 \cup \{s\}) + st(T_2 \cup \{s\})\}, \tag{1}$$

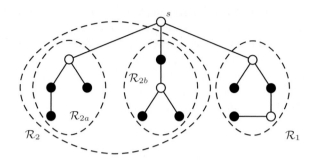

Fig. 1. Tight example for Lemma 2 (black nodes are terminals): a Steiner separator s, and the corresponding forests $\mathcal{R}_1$ and $\mathcal{R}_2$ with $|T_1| = k/3$ and $|T_2| = 2k/3$ terminals, respectively. Note that in $\mathcal{R}_2 \cup \{s\}$, node s separates two perfectly balanced forests $\mathcal{R}_{2a}$ and $\mathcal{R}_{2b}$.

where $\mathcal{P}(s,T)$ is the set of possible partitions (T_1, T_2) of $T \setminus \{s\}$ in two non-empty subsets. Algorithm D&W simply applies Equation (1) to any subset of T, in a bottom-up fashion, storing each partial solution computed for later computations. Storing the partial solutions takes $\Omega(2^k)$ space.

A simple-minded approach to obtain a polynomial-space variant of D&W is to apply Equation (1) recursively, in a top-down fashion, without storing any partial solution. When $|T| \leq 2$, the problem is solved trivially in polynomial time and space (*base case*). Unfortunately, this approach leads to a very high running time. The main reason is that, by applying Equation (1) as it is, one generates some subproblems with almost the same number of terminals as in the original problem.

This problem can be circumvented by exploiting a variant of the classical tree-separator theorem. It is well known that any n-node tree contains a node s (*separator*) whose removal divides the tree in two forests, each one containing at most $2n/3$ nodes. The same basic result holds if we put weights on the nodes [7]. In particular, the following lemma holds (see Figure 1 for a tight example).

Lemma 2. [7] *Consider any Steiner tree S on the set of terminals T, $|T| = k \geq 3$. Then there exists an internal node $s \in S$ (Steiner-separator), not necessarily a terminal, whose removal divides the tree in two forests, each one containing at most $2k/3$ terminals.*

As a consequence of Lemma 2, when applying Equation (1), we do not really need to consider all the partitions in $\mathcal{P}(s,T)$, but it is sufficient to consider only the subset $\mathcal{B}(s,T) \subseteq \mathcal{P}(s,T)$ of ("almost balanced") partitions (T_1, T_2) where $|T_1| \leq |T_2| \leq 2k/3$:

$$st(T) = \min_{s \in V} \min_{(T_1, T_2) \in \mathcal{B}(s,T)} \{st(T_1 \cup \{s\}) + st(T_2 \cup \{s\})\}. \qquad (2)$$

Using Equation (2) instead of (1) makes no substantial difference with the dynamic programming approach by Dreyfus and Wagner: in fact, the most frequent partitions (which determine the running time) contain a balanced number of terminals, and such partitions are contained both in $\mathcal{B}(s,T)$ and in $\mathcal{P}(s,T)$. The situation changes drastically in the top-down recursive implementation of the algorithm: here the running time is essentially determined by the most *unbalanced* partitions. Hence, replacing $\mathcal{P}(s,T)$ with $\mathcal{B}(s,T)$ has a tremendous impact on the performance of the algorithm.

The following Steiner tree algorithm summarizes the discussion above:

- **(base case)** If $T = \{v\}$, return v. If $T = \{v,w\}$, return the shortest path from v to w.
- **(recursive case)** For every $s \in V$ and for every partition (T_1, T_2) of $T \setminus \{s\}$, $|T_1| \leq |T_2| \leq 2k/3$, compute recursively optimal Steiner trees S_1 and S_2 over $T_1 \cup \{s\}$ and $T_2 \cup \{s\}$, respectively. Return the cheapest Steiner tree $S_1 \cup S_2$ obtained.

Theorem 1. *The Steiner tree algorithm above takes time $O((27/4)^k n^{O(\log k)})$ and polynomial space.*

Proof. The correctness of the algorithm follows from the discussion above, and its space complexity is trivially polynomial. Let $P(k)$ be the number of base instances generated by the algorithm to solve the problem. The time complexity of the algorithm is $O(P(k)n^{O(1)}\log k) = O(P(k)n^{O(1)})$, where we used the fact that each branching step takes polynomial time and the depth of the recursion is $O(\log k)$.

It remains to bound $P(k)$. We will show by induction that $P(k) \leq Cn^{c\ln k}\alpha^k$, for some constants $C > 0$, $c > 0$, and $\alpha \geq 4$. Clearly the condition is true for $k \leq 2$. Now assume it is satisfied for every $h \leq k-1$, and consider an instance with k terminals. For a given partition (T_1, T_2), the number of base instances generated is $P(|T_1|+1) + P(|T_2|+1)$. By construction, $k/2 \leq |T_2| \leq 2k/3$ and $|T_1| + |T_2| \leq k$. Hence, for sufficiently large constants C and c and for $\alpha = 8$, the following inequalities hold:

$$P(k) \leq n \sum_{i=k/2}^{2k/3} \binom{k}{i}(P(i+1) + P(k-i+1)) \leq 2n \sum_{i=k/2}^{2k/3} \binom{k}{i} P(i+1)$$

$$\leq 2n\,P(2k/3+1) \sum_{i=k/2}^{2k/3} \binom{k}{i} \leq 2n\,Cn^{c\ln(2k/3+1)}\alpha^{2k/3+1}2^k$$

$$\leq Cn^{c\ln k}(2\alpha^{2/3})^k \leq Cn^{c\ln k}\alpha^k.$$

Above we used the fact that $2\alpha^{2/3} = \alpha$ for $\alpha = 8$. In order to obtain a better value of α, we use the following observation.

Fact 1. *For every fixed $x \geq 4$, function $f(y) = \dfrac{x^y}{y^y(1-y)^{1-y}}$ is increasing on interval $(0, 2/3]$.*

From Stirling's formula and Fact 1, for $i \in [k/3, 2k/3]$,

$$\binom{k}{i} P(i+1) \leq \frac{C n^{c\ln(i+1)} \alpha^{i+1}}{((i/k)^{i/k}(1-i/k)^{1-i/k})^k} \leq \frac{(\alpha^{i/k})^k \alpha \, C \, n^{c\ln(2k/3+1)}}{((i/k)^{i/k}(1-i/k)^{1-i/k})^k}$$

$$\leq \alpha \, C \, n^{c\ln(2k/3+1)} \left(\frac{\alpha^{2/3}}{(2/3)^{2/3}(1/3)^{1/3}} \right)^k = \alpha \, C \, n^{c\ln(2k/3+1)} \left(\frac{3\alpha^{2/3}}{2^{2/3}} \right)^k.$$

It follows that

$$P(k) \leq 2n \sum_{i=k/2}^{2k/3} \binom{k}{i} P(i+1) \leq 2n \, k \, \alpha \, C \, n^{c\ln(2k/3+1)} \left(\frac{3\alpha^{2/3}}{2^{2/3}} \right)^k \leq C \, n^{c\ln k} \alpha^k,$$

for sufficiently large constants C and c and for $\alpha = 27/4$. The claim follows.

2.1 A Refined Algorithm

The algorithm of the previous section can be refined thanks to the following observation. Let S be an optimal Steiner tree. Consider the Steiner-separator $s \in S$ leading to the most balanced partition (T_1, T_2) of the terminals, $|T_1| \leq |T_2|$. In case of a tie, we choose s such that the forest $\mathcal{R}_2$ associated to T_2 contains the smallest possible number of nodes. In the worst possible case, $|T_1| = k/3$ and $|T_2| = 2k/3$. Note that in such case the forest $\mathcal{R}_2$ cannot be formed by a unique subtree of S. This is because otherwise the root s' of such a subtree would contradict the minimality of s. It follows that we can further partition $\mathcal{R}_2$ in two sub-forests $\mathcal{R}_{2a}$ and $\mathcal{R}_{2b}$. Let T_{2x} be the terminals of $\mathcal{R}_{2x}$, $x \in \{a, b\}$. Without loss of generality, we assume that $|T_{2a}| \leq |T_{2b}|$. Again by the minimality of s, we have $|T_{2b}| \leq |T_1| = k/3$. In fact, otherwise the partition $(T_{2b}, T_{2a} \cup T_1)$ would be more balanced than $(T_1, T_2) = (T_1, T_{2a} \cup T_{2b})$. It follows that $|T_{2a}| = |T_{2b}|$, that is in the subproblem induced by T_2 there is a perfectly balanced partition (see Figure 1 for an example).

This argument can be generalized in the following way. Let $\gamma \in (0, 1/6)$ be a given parameter. With the same notation as above, suppose $|T_2| \geq (2/3 - \gamma)k$. Then it must be $|T_{2a}| \leq |T_{2b}| \leq |T_1| \leq (1/3 + \gamma)k$. As a consequence, $\frac{|T_{2b}|}{|T_2|} \leq \frac{1/3+\gamma}{2/3-\gamma}$. For $\gamma < 1/15$ this gives a more balanced partition than the one guaranteed by Lemma 2 (which ensures $|T_{2b}|/|T_2| \leq 2/3$ only).

The idea is then to modify the algorithm of the previous section in the following way:

- For any partition (T_1, T_2) considered, if $|T_2| \geq (2/3 - \gamma)k$, then in the sub-problem corresponding to T_2 consider only partitions (T_{2a}, T_{2b}) satisfying $|T_{2a}| \leq |T_{2b}| \leq \frac{1/3+\gamma}{2/3-\gamma}|T_2|$.

We can ideally partition the subproblems generated in two classes: (i) the subproblems with $|T_2| < (2/3 - \gamma)k$ and (ii) the subproblems with $|T_2| \geq (2/3 - \gamma)k$. For subproblems of type (i) the larger is γ, the better is the recurrence obtained in the current step. For subproblems of type (ii), the smaller is γ, the better is the recurrence obtained in the following step. Optimizing $\gamma \in (0, 1/15)$ we obtain the following result, whose proof is omitted for lack of space.

Theorem 2. *For a proper choice of the parameter* γ, *the algorithm above solves the Steiner tree problem in time* $O(5.96^k n^{O(\log k)})$ *and polynomial space.*

In the following we will denote by `smallST` the algorithm of Theorem 2. We remark that `smallST` is *not* fixed-parameter-tractable because of the factor $n^{O(\log k)}$ in its running time. Finding a polynomial-space fixed-parameter-tractable algorithm for Steiner tree is left as a challenging open problem.

3   Branching on Small-Load Terminals

In this section we describe a simple, recursive algorithm `steiner` for the Steiner tree problem, taking $O(1.5949^n)$ time and polynomial space. Our algorithm computes the size $st_G(T)$ of an optimal Steiner tree, but it can be easily modified in order to produce one optimal Steiner tree.

The main idea behind our approach is as follows. If $k \leq cn$ for a suitable constant $c < 1$, it is convenient to use the $O(5.96^k n^{O(\log k)})$ algorithm from Section 2. Otherwise, there must be a terminal t which is at distance at most one from "many" other terminals. Thus, if by branching we add to T one or more non-terminals adjacent to t, we can contract a "large" connected component of terminals afterwards (using the Contraction Lemma 1). This phenomenon is not exploited in trivial enumeration, and it is at the base of our refined branching algorithm.

In order to formalize in a convenient way the mentioned phenomenon, we introduce the following definition of *load* of a terminal. Let each non-terminal node $s \in N := V \setminus T$ be initially assigned a load one. Node s evenly distributes its load among the terminals adjacent to it (if any). The final load $w(t)$ of each terminal t is the sum of the loads received by its non-terminal neighbors. As it will be clearer from the analysis, we can branch efficiently on terminals of small load.

We are now ready to describe algorithm `steiner`:

1. **(base)** If $|T| \in \{0, 1\}$, $st_G(T) = 0$:
$$\texttt{steiner}(G, T) = 0.$$

2. **(contraction)** If there is a connected component V' of at least 2 terminals, we apply Lemma 1. Let G' be the graph obtained from G by contracting V' in a node v', and let $T' = T \cup \{v'\} \setminus V'$. Then
$$\texttt{steiner}(G, T) = |V'| - 1 + \texttt{steiner}(G', T').$$

3. **(reduction)** If there is a terminal t adjacent to a unique (non-terminal) node s, we add s to the terminals since s must belong to any Steiner tree (being $k \geq 2$):
$$\texttt{steiner}(G, T) = \texttt{steiner}(G, T \cup \{s\}).$$

4. (**small k**) If $k \leq n/4$, we apply our algorithm smallST:

$$\texttt{steiner}(G,T) = \texttt{smallST}(G,T).$$

5. (**simple branch**) If there is a non-terminal s adjacent to at least 3 terminals, we simply branch by either removing s from the graph, or by adding it to the terminals:

$$\texttt{steiner}(G,T) = min\{\texttt{steiner}(G \setminus \{s\}, T), \texttt{steiner}(G, T \cup \{s\})\}.$$

6. (**multiple branch**) Let t be a terminal of minimum load according to the definition above, and let $s_1, \ldots, s_p$ be the (not-terminal) neighbors of t, sorted in decreasing number of adjacent terminals. We branch on the p subproblems obtained by removing $s_1, \ldots, s_{i-1}$, and adding s_i to the terminals, for $i \in \{1, \ldots, p\}$:

$$\texttt{steiner}(G,T) = \min_{i \in \{1,\ldots,p\}} \{\texttt{steiner}(G \setminus \{s_1, \ldots, s_{i-1}\}, T \cup \{s_i\})\}.$$

Observe that Algorithm steiner does not work in the weighted case. This is essentially due to the fact that the Contraction Lemma 1 does not extend to such case. Finding an improved algorithm for the weighted Steiner tree problem is an interesting open problem.

4   Analysis

We next analyze algorithm steiner with the Measure & Conquer technique described in [13,14]. Recall that $n_N = n - k$ is the number of non-terminals.

Theorem 3. *Algorithm* steiner *solves the Steiner tree problem in* $O(1.6011^n)$ *time and polynomial space.*

Proof. The correctness of the algorithm is not hard to check. For $k \leq n/4$ the running time of the algorithm is $O^*(5.96^k) = O^*(5.96^{n/4}) = O^*(1.5625^n)$, so assume that initially $k > n/4$. We let $h := n + n_N$ be the *size* of the problem, and denote by $T(h)$ the time required to solve a problem of size h. We will show by induction that $T(h) = O^*(1.3086^h)$. The claim follows since, being $n_N \leq 3n/4$ by assumption, $O^*(1.3086^h) = O^*(1.3086^{7n/4}) = O^*(1.6011^n)$.

Let $poly(n)$ be the maximum (polynomial) time spent at each step of the algorithm (excluding the recursive calls). For $h = 0$, $k = 0$ and hence $T(h) \leq poly(n) = O^*(1)$. Assume now that $T(h') = O^*(1.3086^{h'})$ for any $h' < h$, and consider the different steps of the algorithm.

Case 1 (base). The problem is solved directly: $T(h) \leq poly(h)$.

Case 2 (contraction). The algorithm generates a unique subproblem containing at most $n - 1$ nodes and n_N non-terminals:

$$T(h) \leq poly(h) + T(h-1) = poly(h) + O^*(1.3086^{h-1}) = O^*(1.3086^h).$$

Table 1. Feasible values of $(m_1, \ldots, m_p)$ for multiple branch, with the corresponding load (strictly smaller than 3), and number of nodes removed in each subproblem. The number of non-terminals removed in the ith subproblem is i.

$(m_1, \ldots, m_p)$	load	nodes removed
$(1, 1)$	$4/2$	$1, 2$
$(2, 1)$	$3/2$	$2, 2$
$(2, 2)$	$2/2$	$2, 3$
$(2, 1, 1)$	$5/2$	$2, 2, 3$
$(2, 2, 1)$	$4/2$	$2, 3, 3$
$(2, 2, 2)$	$3/2$	$2, 3, 4$
$(2, 2, 2, 1)$	$5/2$	$2, 3, 4, 4$
$(2, 2, 2, 2)$	$4/2$	$2, 3, 4, 5$
$(2, 2, 2, 2, 2)$	$5/2$	$2, 3, 4, 5, 6$

Case 3 (reduction). The algorithm adds s to the set of terminals (and hence removes one node from the non-terminals), and then removes at least one node by Case 2:

$$T(h) \le 2poly(h) + T(h - 2) = 2poly(h) + O^*(1.3086^{h-2}) = O^*(1.3086^h).$$

Case 4 (small k). The problem is solved by applying algorithm smallST, in time $O^*(5.96^k)$. Observe that, being $k \le n/4$, $k = (n + n_N)\frac{n - n_N}{n + n_N} = h\frac{k}{2n-k} \le h\frac{n/4}{7n/4} = \frac{h}{7}$. Hence the running time is $T(h) = O^*(5.96^k) = O^*(5.96^{h/7}) = O^*(1.2905^h)$.

Case 5 (single branch). Let $p \ge 3$ be the number of terminals adjacent to the selected non-terminal s. The algorithm generates two subproblems. In the first subproblem it removes s from the graph. In the second one it adds s to the terminals, and then it removes p nodes by Case 2. Hence

$$T(h) \le 2poly(h) + T(h - 2) + T(h - 1 - p) \le 2poly(h) + T(h - 2) + T(h - 4)$$

$$= 2poly(h) + O^*(1.3086^{h-2}) + O^*(1.3086^{h-4}) = O^*(1.3086^h).$$

Case 6 (multiple branch). Observe that, being $k > n/4$ by Case 4, the minimum load of a node is at most $\frac{n-k}{k} < \frac{3n/4}{n/4} = 3$. In particular, for the selected terminal t, $w(t) < 3$. Recall that $s_1, \ldots, s_p$ are the (non-terminal) neighbors of t, in decreasing order $m_1, \ldots, m_p$ of the number of adjacent terminals. Note that the load assigned by s_i to t is exactly $1/m_i$. By Case 5 it must be $m_i \in \{1, 2\}$ for each i (each non-terminal has between 0 and 2 terminal neighbors). It follows by $w(t) < 3$ and by a simple case enumeration that the sequence $(m_1, \ldots, m_p)$ must be one of the sequences in Table 1.

In the ith subproblem, $i \in \{1, \ldots, p\}$, the algorithm removes nodes $s_1, \ldots, s_{i-1}$ from the graph, and adds node s_i to the terminals, which later determines the removal of m_i nodes by Case 2. Note that in the ith step i non-terminals are removed. Hence, by an easy case-by-case check,

$$T(h) \le (1 + p)poly(h) + \sum_{i=1}^{p} T(h - (i - 1) - m_i - i)$$

$$= O^*\left(\sum_{i=1}^{p} 1.3086^{h - (i-1) - m_i - i}\right) = O^*(1.3086^h).$$

4.1   A Refined Measure

The running-time analysis can be refined (without modifying the algorithm) by defining the size of the subproblems as $h := n + \alpha\, n_N$, for a proper constant $\alpha > 0$. Choosing $\alpha = 0.7297$, and by essentially the same analysis as in Theorem 3, we obtain the following result.

Theorem 4. *Algorithm* steiner *solves the Steiner tree problem in* $O(1.5949^n)$ *time and polynomial space.*

4.2   An Exponential-Space Algorithm

As a by-product of our approach, we are able to improve on the current best $O^*(1.4143^n)$ exponential-space algorithm as well. This is achieved by modifying algorithm steiner in the following way.

- In Step 4 replace smallST with the $O^*(2^k)$ algorithm of [5], and increase the corresponding threshold from $k \le n/4$ to $k \le 3n/7$.
- In Step 5 increase the threshold number of adjacent terminals from 3 to 5.

As a consequence of these changes, in Step 6 the minimum load of a terminal is strictly less than $\frac{n - 3n/7}{3n/7} = \frac{4}{3}$ (instead of 3), and each non-terminal can have between 0 and 4 (instead of 2) adjacent terminals. Note that this implies a different list of feasible local configurations. The same kind of analysis as in Theorem 3 leads to the following result.

Theorem 5. *Algorithm* steiner, *modified as above, solves the Steiner tree problem in time* $O(1.3533^n)$ *and exponential space.*

References

1. Arora, S.: Polynomial time approximation schemes for Euclidean TSP and other geometric problems. J. ACM 45, 753–782 (1998)
2. Bax, E.T.: Inclusion and exclusion algorithm for the hamiltonian path problem. Information Proc. Letters 47, 203–207 (1993)
3. Bern, M., Plassmann, P.: The Steiner tree problem with edge lengths 1 and 2. Information Proc. Letters 32, 171–176 (1989)
4. Björklund, A., Husfeldt, T.: Inclusion-exclusion algorithms for counting set partitions. In: FOCS 2006, pp. 575–582. IEEE, Los Alamitos (2006)
5. Björklund, A., Husfeldt, T., Kaski, P., Koivisto, M.: Fourier meets Möbious: Fast subset convolution. In: STOC 2007, pp. 67–74. ACM Press, New York (2007)
6. Blelloch, G.E., Dhamdhere, K., Halperin, E., Ravi, R., Schwartz, R., Sridhar, S.: Fixed parameter tractability of binary near-perfect phylogenetic tree reconstruction. In: Bugliesi, M., Preneel, B., Sassone, V., Wegener, I. (eds.) ICALP 2006. LNCS, vol. 4051, pp. 667–678. Springer, Heidelberg (2006)
7. Bodlaender, H.L.: A partial k-arboretum of graphs with bounded treewidth. Theor. Comp. Sci. 209, 1–45 (1998)

8. Deneen, L.L., Shute, G.M., Thomborson, C.D.: A probably fast, provably optimal algorithm for rectilinear Steiner trees. Random Structures and Algorithms 5(4), 535–557 (1994)

9. Downey, R.G., Fellows, M.R.: Parameterized complexity. Springer, New York (1999)

10. Dreyfus, S.E., Wagner, R.A.: The Steiner problem in graphs. Networks 1, 195–207 (1971/1972)

11. Eppstein, D.: Quasiconvex analysis of multivariate recurrence equations for backtracking algorithms. ACM Transactions on Algorithms 2(4), 492–509 (2006)

12. Flum, J., Grohe, M.: Parameterized Complexity Theory. Springer, Berlin (2006)

13. Fomin, F., Grandoni, F., Kratsch, D.: Measure and conquer: domination - a case study. In: Caires, L., Italiano, G.F., Monteiro, L., Palamidessi, C., Yung, M. (eds.) ICALP 2005. LNCS, vol. 3580, pp. 191–203. Springer, Heidelberg (2005)

14. Fomin, F., Grandoni, F., Kratsch, D.: Measure and conquer: a simple $O(2^{0.288\,n})$ independent set algorithm. In: SODA 2006, pp. 18–25. ACM Press, New York (2006)

15. Fuchs, B., Kern, W., Mölle, D., Richter, S., Rossmanith, P., Wang, X.: Dynamic programming for minimum Steiner trees. Theory of Computing Systems (to appear, 2008)

16. Ganley, J.L.: Computing optimal rectilinear Steiner trees: a survey and experimental evaluation. Discrete Applied Mathematics 90(1-3), 161–171 (1999)

17. Garey, M.R., Johnson, D.S.: The rectilinear Steiner tree problem is NP-complete. SIAM J. on Applied Mathematics 32, 826–834 (1977)

18. Garey, M.R., Johnson, D.S.: Computers and Intractability. A Guide to the Theory of NP-Completeness. Freeman, New York (1979)

19. Guo, J., Niedermeier, R., Wernicke, S.: Parameterized complexity of generalized vertex cover problems. In: Dehne, F., López-Ortiz, A., Sack, J.-R. (eds.) WADS 2005. LNCS, vol. 3608, pp. 36–48. Springer, Heidelberg (2005)

20. Gurevich, Y., Shelah, S.: Expected computation time for Hamiltonian path problem. SIAM J. Computing 16(3), 486–502 (1987)

21. Hwang, F.K., Richards, D.S., Winter, P.: The Steiner Tree Problem. North-Holland, Amsterdam (1992)

22. Kahng, A., Robins, G.: On Optimal Interconnections for VLSI. Kluwer, Dordrecht (1995)

23. Karp, R.M.: Dynamic programming meets the principle of inclusion and exclusion. Operation Research Letters 1, 49–51 (1982)

24. Korte, B., Prömel, H.J., Steger, A.: Steiner trees in VLSI-layout. In: Paths, Flows, and VLSI-Layout, pp. 185–214 (1990)

25. Mölle, D., Richter, S., Rossmanith, P.: A faster algorithm for the Steiner tree problem. In: Durand, B., Thomas, W. (eds.) STACS 2006. LNCS, vol. 3884, pp. 561–570. Springer, Heidelberg (2006)

26. Niedermeier, R.: Invitation to fixed-parameter algorithms. Oxford Lecture Series in Mathematics and its Applications, vol. 31. Oxford University Press, Oxford (2006)

27. Prömel, H.J., Steger, A.: The Steiner tree problem. Advanced Lectures in Mathematics. Friedr. Vieweg & Sohn, Braunschweig (2002)

28. Robins, G., Zelikovsky, A.: Improved Steiner tree approximation in graphs. In: SODA 2000, pp. 770–779. ACM Press, New York (2000)

29. Woeginger, G.: Space and time complexity of exact algorithms: Some open problems. In: Downey, R.G., Fellows, M.R., Dehne, F. (eds.) IWPEC 2004. LNCS, vol. 3162, pp. 281–290. Springer, Heidelberg (2004)

Fitting a Step Function to a Point Set

Hervé Fournier[1] and Antoine Vigneron[2]

[1] Laboratoire PRiSM
CNRS UMR 8144 and Université de Versailles St-Quentin en Yvelines
45 av. des États-Unis, 78035 Versailles, France
herve.fournier@prism.uvsq.fr
[2] INRA, UR 341 Mathématiques et Informatique Appliquées
78352 Jouy-en-Josas, France
antoine.vigneron@jouy.inra.fr

Abstract. We consider the problem of fitting a step function to a set of points. More precisely, given an integer k and a set P of n points in the plane, our goal is to find a step function f with k steps that minimizes the maximum vertical distance between f and all the points in P. We first give an optimal $\Theta(n \log n)$ algorithm for the general case. In the special case where the points in P are given in sorted order according to their x-coordinates, we give an optimal $\Theta(n)$ time algorithm. Then, we show how to solve the weighted version of this problem in time $O(n \log^4 n)$. Finally, we give an $O(nh^2 \log h)$ algorithm for the case where h outliers are allowed, and the input is sorted. The running time of all our algorithms is independent of k.

1 Introduction

In this paper, we consider the problem of fitting a step function to a point set in $\mathbb{R}^2$. (See Figure 1 for an example.) For a given number of steps k, we find the step function whose maximum vertical distance to a point set P is minimized.

The motivation for this work is to find a concise representation of a large set of points by a step-function with few steps. This type of representation of point-sets by step-functions (also called *histograms*) is used in Database Management Systems, for *query optimization*: there can be many different ways of answering a complex query involving several attributes of the data, and query optimization consists in predicting the fastest way to answer a query, before this query is performed. This prediction is done using some statistics on the data, which usually consists of histograms. Several types of histograms have been used in databases [13]; the histograms that correspond to our optimal step-functions are called *maximum error histograms*, and have recently been studied in the database community [4,10,14].

We give optimal algorithms for computing the optimal step-function in our model; in other words, we give optimal algorithms for computing maximum error histograms. We also give efficient algorithms for two generalizations. First, we consider the more general case where each point is weighted, and its contribution to the distance computation is multiplied by this weight. Second, we introduce a generalization of our problem to the case where outliers are allowed; that is, we allow our algorithm to ignore h input

D. Halperin and K. Mehlhorn (Eds.): ESA 2008, LNCS 5193, pp. 442–453, 2008.

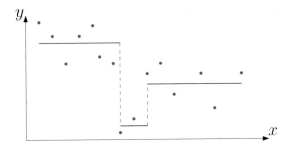

Fig. 1. A set of points in $\mathbb{R}^2$ and an optimal approximation by a 3-step function

points, where h is an input parameter. The motivation is to make the algorithm more robust to noise in the input point set.

1.1 Problem Formulations

A function $f : [a, b) \to \mathbb{R}$ is called a k-*step function* if there exists a real sequence $a = a_0 < a_1 < \cdots < a_k = b$ such that the restriction of f to each interval $[a_i, a_{i+1})$ is a constant. We use $\mathrm{d}(p, f)$ to denote the vertical distance between a point $p \in \mathbb{R}^2$ and f; in other words when $p = (x, y)$, we have $\mathrm{d}(p, f) = |f(x) - y|$. Let P denote a set of n points in $\mathbb{R}^2$. We define the distance $\mathrm{d}(P, f)$ between P and a step function f as follows:

$$\mathrm{d}(P, f) = \max\{\mathrm{d}(p, f) \mid p \in P\}.$$

We will consider the following three problems. The first one is the problem that we already mentioned and the second one is the weighted version. The third one is a generalization where we allow h outliers, which means that we allow a given number h of points from P to be far from f.

- MIN-DIST : Given an integer $k > 0$ and a set P of n points in $\mathbb{R}^2$, find a k-step function f^* such that $\varepsilon^* = \mathrm{d}(P, f^*)$ is minimized.
- weighted-MIN-DIST : a generalization of MIN-DIST where we are given a set of weighted points, and the distance between f and a point p with weight μ is $\mu \cdot \mathrm{d}(p, f)$. The goal is still to minimize the maximum of these distances for a given k.
- OUTLIER : Given $P \subseteq \mathbb{R}^2$, an integer $k > 0$ and $h \in \mathbb{N}$, find a k-step function f and a subset $P' \subseteq P$ such that $|P'| \leqslant h$ and $\mathrm{d}(P \setminus P', f)$ is minimized.

1.2 Previous Work

Algorithms for fitting a polyline to a dataset have been extensively studied. For instance, Goodrich [9] gave an $O(n \log n)$ time algorithm for fitting an x-monotone polyline with k edges to a set of points, under the same criterion as ours: minimizing the maximum vertical distance between the input point set and the polyline. Goodrich's work was motivated by applications to geographic information systems and image processing, where one wants to simplify a curve using a polyline with few edges. References to related work can be found in Goodrich's article [9]. There has also been extensive research in algorithms for fitting a step function to a point set under criterions that are different from ours: for instance, minimizing the sum of the squared vertical distances. The interested reader can find references to these results in Guha and Shim's article [10]. We are not aware of any work for fitting a step function or a polyline that explicitly handles outliers in the same way as we do, but it has been considered for other shape fitting problems. See for instance the work of Har-Peled et al. [1,11] on the minimum width annulus and related problems, or the recent paper by Atanassov et al. [3] on outliers removal minimizing parameters such as diameter, perimeter of parallel-axis bounding box, or area of the convex hull.

We now mention results that are more directly related to this paper. Diáz-Báñez and Mesa [17] showed that the dual problem where we want to minimize the number of steps k for a fixed error bound ε can be solved in $O(n)$ time by a greedy approach. This algorithm can be used as a decision algorithm for the MIN-DIST problem, and since the optimal distance ε^* in the MIN-DIST problem is realized by half the difference between two y-coordinates in P, then by sorting these $O(n^2)$ values and applying binary search, Diáz-Báñez and Mesa [17] obtained an $O(n^2 \log n)$ algorithm. This result was improved to $O(n^2)$ by Wang [18], and then by Mayster and Lopez [16] who gave an $O(\min(n^2, nk \log n))$ algorithm for the MIN-DIST problem. Chazal and Das [5] designed an algorithm with running time $O(n \log n + k^2 \log(\frac{n}{k})^2)$ for the same problem. Recently, Guha and Shim [10] found an algorithm with running time $O(n + k^2 \log^3 n)$ when the input points are given in sorted order, by increasing x-coordinate. Their algorithm also applies to a model of maximum relative error and to the case where points are weighted. For the latter case, the bound becomes $O(n \log n + k^2 \log^6 n)$; for large k, this was later improved by Lopez and Mayster [15] who gave an algorithm with running time $O(n^2)$.

Finally, we mention two recent articles from the database community on maximum error histograms. (Which, in our terminology, is the MIN-DIST problem.) Karras et al. [14] give an $O(nL)$-time algorithm for MIN-DIST with sorted input, where in the worst case, L is the number of bits used for representing each coordinate of the input points. They achieve it using the greedy decision algorithm by Diáz-Báñez and Mesa [17], together with binary search. Buragohain et al. [4] gave an efficient algorithm for computing maximum error histograms over data streams.

1.3   Our Results

In Section 2, we give a simple $O(n \log n)$ time algorithm for MIN-DIST . We achieve it by combining the technique of Frederickson and Johnson [7] for searching a sorted matrix, with the linear-time decision algorithm by Diáz-Báñez and Mesa [17]. When the input points are not given in sorted order, our algorithm is optimal, and it improves on all previous algorithms [5,10,16,17,18] in the worst case. In particular, our algorithm is the first one to be truly subquadratic, as previous algorithms run in time $\Omega(n^2)$, $\Omega(k^2)$, or $\Omega(nk)$ in the worst case. It is particularly significant for applications to databases, where n and k could be large enough to make a quadratic running time unacceptable.

In Section 3, we give a more general formulation of Frederickson's path partitioning algorithm [6]. In Section 4, we combine this technique with the data structure of Gabow et al. [8] for reporting range maxima, and we obtain a linear time algorithm for the MIN-DIST problem where the input points are given in sorted order, by increasing x-coordinates. It is the first optimal algorithm for this problem.

Our approach also gives an $O(n \log^4 n)$ algorithm for weighted-MIN-DIST . (See Section 5.) It is the first truly subquadratic algorithm for this problem, and it improves on the $O(n \log n + k^2 \log^6 n)$ algorithm of Guha and Shim [10] when $k = \omega(\sqrt{n}/\log n)$.

Finally, our algorithms extend to the OUTLIER problem, where up to h input points can be ignored. When the input points are given in sorted order according to their x-coordinate, we give an $O(nh^2 \log h)$ algorithm. It improves on the obvious $O(h^2 n^2)$ dynamic programming approach.

2   A Simple Optimal Algorithm for MIN-DIST with Unsorted Input

In this section we present our algorithm for the MIN-DIST problem. We first present the sorted matrix searching technique [6,7], then we give the greedy, linear time decision algorithm for sorted input (which is essentially the algorithm by Diáz-Báñez and Mesa [17] for the dual problem), and then we combine these two results to get an $O(n \log n)$ time optimization algorithm.

2.1   Searching in a Sorted Matrix

In this section we quickly describe the technique of Frederickson and Johnson for searching in a sorted matrix [6,7]. Suppose we are given an $n \times n$ sorted matrix M—by sorted, we mean that $i \leqslant i'$ and $j \leqslant j'$ implies that $M_{i,j} \leqslant M_{i',j'}$. We assume that we can access in constant time the value of each element $M_{i,j}$.

Let $g : \mathbb{R} \to \{\text{TRUE, FALSE}\}$ be a monotone function in the sense that if $x < y$ and $g(x) = \text{TRUE}$, then $g(y) = \text{TRUE}$. Our goal is to find the smallest element $M_{i,j}$ of the matrix M such that $g(M_{i,j}) = \text{TRUE}$; we call this problem the *optimization problem*. The *decision problem* is to compute the mapping g: given $x \in \mathbb{R}$, compute the value of $g(x)$. If we assume that the decision problem can be solved in time D, the optimization problem can be trivially solved in time $O(n^2 \log n + D \log n)$ by sorting $\{M_{i,j} \mid 1 \leqslant i, j \leqslant n\}$ and then performing a binary search over these values. The technique of Frederickson and Johnson allows to improve it to $O(n + D \log n)$ time as follows.

The algorithm maintains a collection $\mathcal{M}$ of submatrices of M, and initially we set $\mathcal{M} = \{M\}$. At each step, we partition each matrix in $\mathcal{M}$ into four equal-size square matrices. We do not maintain these matrices explicitly (which would require quadratic time): we only keep the range of indices in the original matrix M that corresponds to each submatrix. Then about half of these matrices are discarded, and we repeat the process until $O(1)$ elements remain, and thus we can find the optimal element by brute force.

We still need to explain how submatrices are discarded. For each submatrix in $\mathcal{M}$, we compute the smallest element (which of course is at upper left corner). Then we compute the median $\lambda_{\min}$ of these smallest elements. We also compute the median $\lambda_{\max}$ of the largest elements. Suppose now that $g(\lambda_{\min}) = $ TRUE. Then clearly, we can discard all the submatrices whose smallest element is larger than $\lambda_{\min}$. We handle in a similar way the other cases: $g(\lambda_{\min}) = $ FALSE, and the same with $\lambda_{\max}$. For more details, we refer to the papers by Frederickson and Johnson [6,7] and the survey by Agarwal and Sharir [2, Section 3.3]

2.2   A Decision Algorithm for Sorted Input

In this section, we assume that P is given as a set of points $p_i = (x_i, y_i)$ for $1 \leqslant i \leqslant n$ sorted from left to right: we assume that for all i, we have $x_i < x_{i+1}$. (To simplify the exposition, we assume that no two points have same x-coordinate.) We denote $P[i,j] = \{p_i, \ldots p_j\}$, $Y[i,j] = \{y_i, \ldots y_j\}$ and $\Delta[i,j] = (\max Y[i,j] - \min Y[i,j])/2$. In other words, $\Delta[i,j]$ is the distance between $P[i,j]$ and the closest 1-step function.

Our decision algorithm takes as input the point set P, an integer k and $\varepsilon \geqslant 0$. It returns TRUE if there exists a k-step function f such that $\mathrm{d}(f, P) \leqslant \varepsilon$, and returns FALSE otherwise. We define a function $\mathrm{next}_\varepsilon$ as follows: if $\Delta[i,n] \leqslant \varepsilon$, then $\mathrm{next}_\varepsilon(i) = \infty$ and otherwise, $\mathrm{next}_\varepsilon(i)$ is the smallest integer $j > i$ such that $\Delta[i,j] > \varepsilon$. We first observe that for all i, we can compute $\mathrm{next}_\varepsilon(i)$ in time $O(\mathrm{next}_\varepsilon(i) - i)$ by traversing $P[i,n]$ from left to right with a pointer i', while maintaining the value of $\max Y[i,i']$ and $\min Y[i,i']$. We are now ready to give the decision algorithm:

Algorithm DECIDE(P, k, ε)
1. $i_1 \leftarrow 1$.
2.   **for** $j \leftarrow 1$ **to** k
3.   **do** $i_{j+1} \leftarrow \mathrm{next}_\varepsilon(i_j)$.
4.   **if** $i_{j+1} = \infty$
5.   **then return** TRUE.
6.   **return** FALSE.

From our observation that $\mathrm{next}_\varepsilon(i)$ can be computed in time $O(\mathrm{next}_\varepsilon(i) - i)$, we can see that algorithm DECIDE runs in $O(n)$ time. Now we still need to prove its correctness. The exact value of the x_i's plays no role in our problem, only their order matters, so in the proof below, we assume that $x_i = i$ for all i. We will first prove that, if our algorithm returns TRUE, then the answer to the decision problem is positive. Then we will show the converse, that is, if the answer to the decision problem is positive, then our algorithm returns TRUE.

First assume that our algorithm returns TRUE. Let j' denote the last value of j before DECIDE returns TRUE. Now consider the step function defined by $f_0(x) = (\max Y[i_j, i_{j+1} - 1] + \min Y[i_j, i_{j+1} - 1])/2$ for all $x \in [i_j, i_{j+1})$ and $j \in \{1, \ldots, j' - 1\}$, and $f_0(x) = (\max Y[i_{j'}, n] + \min Y[i_{j'}, n])/2$ for all $x \in [i_{j'}, n+1)$. Then clearly f_0 is a j'-step function such that $\mathrm{d}(f_0, P) \leqslant \varepsilon$, and since $j' \leqslant k$, it implies that the answer to the decision problem is positive.

Conversely, assume that the answer to the decision problem is positive. Let k' be the smallest integer such that there exists a k'-step function at distance at most ε from P. We denote by f_0 such a k'-step function, defined over $[1, n+1)$, and which is at distance at most ε from P. We denote by $1 = a_0 < a_1 < \cdots < a_{k'} = n+1$ the numbers such that f_0 is constant over $[a_i, a_{i+1})$ for all i. There could be several such functions; we choose f_0 such that $(a_0, a_1, \ldots a_{k'})$ is maximal in lexicographic order. First notice that a_i is the x-coordinate of some point in P for all $i < k'$, so we have $a_i \in \{1, \ldots, n\}$. Then we will show that $a_i = \text{next}_\varepsilon(a_{i-1})$ for all $i < k'$, which clearly implies that our algorithm returns TRUE. So now, we assume for a contradiction that it is not the case. Let j denote the first index such that $a_j \neq \text{next}_\varepsilon(a_{j-1})$. Then $a_j < \text{next}_\varepsilon(a_{j-1})$ and $P[a_j, n]$ can be approximated (within distance ε) by a $(k' - j)$-step function. So $P[\text{next}_\varepsilon(a_{j-1}), n]$ can also be approximated by a $(k' - j)$-step function f_1. Now consider the function f_2 that coincides with f_0 over $[1, a_{j-1})$, that is equal to $(\max Y[a_{j-1}, \text{next}_\varepsilon(a_{j-1}) - 1] + \min Y[a_{j-1}, \text{next}_\varepsilon(a_{j-1}) - 1])/2$ over $[a_{j-1}, \text{next}_\varepsilon(a_{j-1}))$, and coincides with f_1 over $[\text{next}_\varepsilon(a_{j-1}), n+1)$. Then $\mathrm{d}(f_2, P) \leqslant \varepsilon$ and f_2 is larger than f_0 in lexicographic order, a contradiction.

Lemma 1. *Given a sorted point set P, an integer k and $\varepsilon > 0$, the algorithm* DECIDE(P, k, ε) *decides in $O(n)$ time whether there exists a k-step function f such that $\mathrm{d}(f, P) \leqslant \varepsilon$.*

2.3   Optimization Algorithm

We denote by E the set of half-differences between y-coordinates in P:

$$E = \left\{ \frac{y - y'}{2} \mid (x, y) \in P \text{ and } (x', y') \in P \right\}$$

It is easy to see that the error ε^* of the solution to the MIN-DIST problem is in this set. The MIN-DIST problem can be solved by sorting E in $O(n^2 \log n)$ time, and then looking for the optimal value ε^* using the decision algorithm and binary search.

In order to avoid a quadratic running time, we will apply the sorted matrix searching technique (Section 2.1). This is made possible by the fact that E can be written as follows:

$$E = Y + (-Y) \text{ where } Y = \left\{ \frac{y}{2} \mid (x, y) \in P \right\}.$$

Thus we first sort Y and obtain a non-decreasing sequence (b_i) such that $Y = \{b_1 \leqslant b_2 \ldots \leqslant b_n\}$. Then we represent the elements of E as the set of elements of a sorted matrix M defined by $M_{i,j} = \frac{1}{2}b_i - \frac{1}{2}b_{n+1-j}$.

So our optimization algorithm works as follows. We first place in a sorted array the elements of Y, which takes $O(n \log n)$ time. It will allow us to compute elements of M in constant time. Then we sort P according the x-coordinates, which, by Lemma 1, will allow us to run the decision algorithm in $O(n)$ time for any value of ε. So, applying the sorted matrix searching technique (see Section 2.1), we obtain the following result:

Theorem 1. *The* MIN-DIST *problem can be solved in $O(n \log n)$ time.*

A simple reduction from sorting shows that it is optimal when the input point-set P is not given in sorted order: given the input $(x_1, \ldots, x_n)$, take $P = \{(x_i, x_i) \mid 1 \leqslant i \leqslant n\}$ and $k = n$. The sequence of y-values taken by an optimal k-step function corresponds to $(x_1, \ldots, x_n)$ in sorted order.

3   Frederickson's Algorithm for Min-Max Partitioning

Frederickson [6] gave a linear time algorithm for the following path partitioning problem: given an integer $k > 0$ and n positive real numbers $\omega_1, \ldots, \omega_n$, compute a partition of $\{1, \ldots, n\}$ into k intervals $I_1, \ldots, I_k$ such that $\max_{j \in \{1,\ldots,k\}} \sum_{i \in I_j} \omega_i$ is minimized.

Notice that a simple reduction allows to use it to solve the sorted-MIN-DIST problem in the special case where the x_i's are distinct and $y_1 < y_2 < \ldots < y_n$. Our goal is to extend this algorithm to solve sorted-MIN-DIST in the general case.

Let us first formulate Frederickson's min-max partition problem in a more general setting. Let Σ be a set (not necessarily finite); we shall call it the alphabet. We denote by Σ^* the set of words over Σ, and the empty word is denoted by e. For $v, w \in \Sigma^*$, vw denotes the concatenation of v and w. Let us suppose we have a mapping $\theta : \Sigma^* \to \mathbb{R}^+$ such that $\theta(e) = 0$. We are interested in the following problem: given $w \in \Sigma^*$, compute a factorization $w = w_1 w_2 \ldots w_k$ (where $w_i \in \Sigma^*$) such that $\max_{i \in \{1,\ldots,k\}} \theta(w_i)$ is minimized. We shall call this problem MIN-MAX PARTITION(θ). Note that the problem of Frederickson corresponds to MIN-MAX PARTITION(S) with $\Sigma = \mathbb{R}^+$ and $S(\omega_i \ldots \omega_j) = \omega_i + \ldots + \omega_j$. The following result gives sufficient conditions on θ which allow to apply Frederickson's technique to solve MIN-MAX PARTITION(θ).

Theorem 2. *Let Σ be a set, and $\theta : \Sigma^* \to \mathbb{R}^+$ be a mapping such that $\theta(e) = 0$. Suppose that θ has the following properties:*

(i) θ is non-decreasing, that is, $\theta(v) \leqslant \theta(uvw)$ for all $u, v, w \in \Sigma^*$.
(ii) We can preprocess $a_1 \ldots a_n \in \Sigma^n$ in time $\pi(n)$ so that, given any query (i, j), we can compute $\theta(a_i \ldots a_j)$ in time $\kappa(n)$.

Then MIN-MAX PARTITION(θ) *can be solved in time $O(\pi(n) + n\kappa(n))$.*

To see why this theorem holds, one just has to reformulate the proof of Frederickson [6] using our more general framework. As it would be quite technical, we only reprove what corresponds to the $O(n \log \log n)$ algorithm given by Frederickson, which gives an $O(\pi(n) + n(\log \log n)\kappa(n))$ time bound in our case. The rest of the proof in Frederickson's paper extends directly to our case, which proves Theorem 2.

To simplify the presentation, we assume that $\kappa(n) = O(1)$ in the remainder of this section. The lemma below shows that conditions (i) and (ii) yield a linear time algorithm for the decision problem.

Lemma 2 (Naive decision algorithm). *Under the hypothesis of Theorem 2, after the preprocessing step corresponding to condition (ii), there exists a linear time algorithm for the decision problem relative to* MIN-MAX PARTITION(θ).

Proof. Once the preprocessing on θ has been done, a greedy algorithm for the decision problem can be achieved by a single sweep from left to right. It is essentially the same algorithm as the decision algorithm for MIN-DIST presented in Section 2.2, and the proof carries over to this case.   □

Now we still need to design an algorithm to compute the optimal value ε^*. The algorithm to compute this value relies on the technique of matrix searching. We recall the main result in its general version as it appears in Frederickson's article [6], but restricted to the case of square matrices of the same size.

Theorem 3 (Matrix Searching). *Let $\mathcal{M}$ be a collection of N sorted matrices $\{M_1, \ldots, M_N\}$ in which matrix M_j is of size $m \times m$. Let s be a non-negative integer (called the stopping count). The number of calls to the decision algorithm that are needed by the matrix searching algorithm to discard all but at most s of the elements is $O(\max\{\log m, \log(Nm/(s+1))\})$, and the total time of the Matrix Searching algorithm exclusive of the calls to the decision algorithm is $O(Nm)$.*

Given an input $w = a_1 \ldots a_n \in \Sigma^n$ and $k > 0$ (both fixed from now on), we define $\theta_{i,j} = \theta(a_i \ldots a_j)$ for all $i \leqslant j$. Let us define the $n \times n$ matrix M by $M_{i,j} = \theta_{n+1-i,j}$ when $i + j < n + 1$ and $M_{i,j} = 0$ otherwise. Because of property (i), M is a sorted matrix: it is non-decreasing along each line and each column. Let ε^* be the optimal value of MIN-MAX PARTITION(θ) on input (w, k). Of course $\varepsilon^* \in M$. Condition (ii) allows to query any entry of the matrix M defined above in time $O(1)$ with preprocessing time $\pi(n)$ on the input $(a_1, \ldots, a_n)$. Note that we never do any other preprocessing of this type: all matrices occurring in the algorithm are seen as a product of two intervals of $\{1, \ldots, n\}$, and querying these matrices is performed via a query on the big matrix M. For the next two lemmas, we assume the preprocessing corresponding to condition (ii) of Theorem 2 has been done, and we only consider the running times after this step.

The main idea to obtain the $O(n \log \log n)$-time optimization algorithm is to get a faster decision algorithm by doing some additional preprocessing on w. Then ε^* is computed by applying the technique of matrix searching on M, using this improved decision algorithm.

The preprocessing is performed as follows. Let r be an integer (to be chosen later). The input w is divided into $\lceil n/r \rceil$ factors v_i of length r, thus we have $w = v_1 \ldots v_{n/r}$. The family of sorted matrices $\mathcal{M} = \{M_1, \ldots, M_{n/r}\}$ is created, where M_i contains the values of θ over v_i. Then a first phase of matrix searching is performed on $\mathcal{M}$ with stopping count n/r^2. While doing this search, the decision algorithm is run for several values of ε. We denote by λ_1 the largest such value of ε that is not feasible, and we denote by λ_2 the smallest one that is feasible. Hence, we have $\lambda_1 < \varepsilon^* \leqslant \lambda_2$. At most n/r^2 factors v_p have (at least) an element $\theta_{i,j}$ of their matrix M_p lying in $[\lambda_1, \lambda_2]$; we call these factors *active*. The other factors are called non-active.

We shall carry out some preprocessing on the non-active factors. Let us consider a factor $v_i = a_p \ldots a_q$. For $t \in \{p, \ldots, q\}$, we define $\mathrm{ncut}(t)$ to be the minimum index ℓ such that there exists a partition $a_t \ldots a_q = u_1 \ldots u_{\ell+1}$ such that $\max_i \theta(u_i) \leqslant \lambda_1$. Moreover, we define $\mathrm{rem}(t)$ to be the maximum of j where $u_{\ell+1} = a_j \ldots a_q$ over all these partitions. Notice that these two parameters $\mathrm{ncut}(t)$ and $\mathrm{rem}(t)$ are the ones obtained by applying the greedy decision algorithm given in Lemma 2 on $a_p \ldots a_q$ and λ_1. The next lemma explains how to compute these values efficiently.

Lemma 3 (Preprocessing factors). *Given an interval of $\{1, \ldots, n\}$ of length r, computing $\mathrm{rem}(t)$ and $\mathrm{ncut}(t)$ for all $t \in I$ can be done in time $O(r)$.*

Proof. For $t \in I$, we define $\text{next}_{\lambda_1}(t)$ to be the smallest t' such that $\theta_{t,t'} > \lambda_1$. All values of $\text{next}_{\lambda_1}(t)$ can be computed in time $O(r)$ by scanning from left to right, while maintaining a pointers to t and a pointer to $\text{next}_{\lambda_1}(t)$. Then, $\text{ncut}(t)$ and $\text{rem}(t)$ can be computed by a single scan from right to left. At each step of this scan, we compute $\text{ncut}(t)$ and $\text{rem}(t)$ in constant time by accessing $t' := \text{next}_{\lambda_1}(t)$, and then using the already computed values $\text{ncut}(t')$ and $\text{rem}(t')$. □

Once this preprocessing has been done, we obtain a sublinear decision algorithm.

Lemma 4 (Sublinear decision algorithm). *After the preprocessing of Lemma 3 has been done, we have an $O((n/r) \log r)$ time algorithm to solve the decision problem relative to* MIN-MAX PARTITION(θ).

Proof. We can assume that $\lambda_1 < \varepsilon < \lambda_2$, because if $\varepsilon \leqslant \lambda_1$ we can immediately return FALSE, and if $\varepsilon \geqslant \lambda_2$ we can return TRUE. The idea is to implement the greedy approach faster, by jumping inside non-active factors; on the other hand, we still operate by brute force within active factors. So let's assume that the naive, greedy approach yields a factorization $w = u_1 \ldots u_q$.

Consider the maximum sequence $u_i \ldots u_j$ (possibly the empty word) which entirely lies in the p-th subsequence v_p of w. Hence we can write $v_p = uu_i \ldots u_j u'$. Assume that v_p is non-active. For all $i \leqslant i' \leqslant j$, we have $\theta(u_{i'}) \leqslant \varepsilon$, so by definition of non-active factors, we have $\theta(u_{i'}) < \lambda_1$. It follows that, if a_t is the first letter in u_i, we have that $j - i = \text{ncut}(t)$ and u' starts at index $\text{rem}(t)$.

As a result, we can implement the greedy algorithm in $O(\log r)$ time within a non-active factor v_p. First we find by binary search the index t of first cut inside z_p, using the index of the previous cut. Then we find the number of cuts needed inside v_p using $\text{ncut}(t)$. Finally, we know that the last cut inside v_p is at $\text{rem}(t)$.

There are at most n/r^2 active factors, so our improved greedy algorithm spends a total of $O(n/r)$ time on them. On the other hand, it spends time $O(\log r)$ on each non-active interval, and there are less than n/r of them. It yields the desired time bound. □

We can now describe the whole $O(\pi(n) + n \log \log n)$-time algorithm. First the preprocessing corresponding to condition (ii) is performed on the input w. The sorted matrix M is created. Then we choose $r = \lfloor \log n \rfloor$ and we create the family of sorted matrices $\mathcal{M}$ corresponding to the n/r factors $v_1, \ldots, v_{n/r}$ of length r of w. A first phase of matrix searching is performed on $\mathcal{M}$ using the naive decision algorithm (Lemma 2) and stopping count n/r^2; it provides new bounds $\lambda_1 < \varepsilon^* \leqslant \lambda_2$. Then we perform the preprocessing (Lemma 3) with respect to λ_1 on all non-active factors. The last step of the algorithm consists in a matrix search on the big matrix M with stopping count $O(1)$, using the sublinear decision algorithm (Lemma 4). This gives the optimal value ε^*. It is easy to check that the running time of this algorithm is $O(\pi(n) + n \log \log n)$, thanks to our improved decision algorithm that runs in time $O(n(\log \log n)/\log n)$.

Frederickson's $O(\pi(n) + n)$-time algorithm is based on clever pruning techniques, and cutting the intervals recursively (with finely tuned parameters) to obtain faster decision algorithms at each step. A careful reading of the proof of Frederickson shows that conditions (i) and (ii) are sufficient to be able to apply these techniques exactly in the same way. We do not rewrite this proof here; the interested reader can check the original paper of Frederickson [6] to complete the proof of Theorem 2.

4   A Linear Time Algorithm for MIN-DIST with Sorted Input

In this section, we give an optimal, linear-time algorithm for the MIN-DIST problem with sorted input. We achieve it by combining our reformulation of Frederickson's technique (Theorem 2) with efficient data structures for range reporting.

The input of sorted-MIN-DIST is an integer k, and a set $P = \{(x_1, y_1), \ldots, (x_n, y_n)\}$ of n points in the plane. These points are given as a sequence, sorted according to their x-coordinates, so we have $x_1 \leqslant \ldots \leqslant x_n$. This problem can be reduced in linear time to the case where at most two points have the same x-coordinate: we only need to rewrite the input under the form $((x_1, y_1, y_1'), \ldots, (x_n, y_n, y_n'))$ with $x_1 < \ldots < x_n$ and $y_i \leqslant y_i'$ for all i. The x-coordinates obviously play no role in this problem, so we are left with an input which is a positive integer k, and a sequence of intervals of the real line $([y_1, y_1'], \ldots, [y_n, y_n'])$. The sorted-MIN-DIST problem corresponds to MIN-MAX PARTITION(Δ) with $\Sigma = \{(a, b) \in \mathbb{R}^2 \mid a \leqslant b\}$ and

$$\Delta([z_1, z_1'], \ldots, [z_p, z_p']) := (\max(z_1', \ldots, z_p') - \min(z_1, \ldots, z_p))/2.$$

The mapping Δ is obviously non-decreasing, that is, it satisfies property (i) of Theorem 2. Let us now show that it satisfies property (ii). Given an input $([y_1, y_1'], \ldots, [y_n, y_n'])$ and k, we define $\Delta_{i,j} := \Delta([y_i, y_i'], \ldots, [y_j, y_j'])$. After $O(n)$ preprocessing time, we need to be able to compute $\Delta_{i,j}$ in time $O(1)$ for any given i and j. To this end, we use an algorithm for the range maxima problem obtained by Gabow, Bentley and Tarjan [8] and by Harel and Tarjan [12]. More precisely, given a sequence of numbers $(a_1, \ldots, a_n)$, it allows us to answer any query $(i, j) \mapsto \max(a_i, \ldots, a_j)$ in constant time, after preprocessing time $O(n)$. After preprocessing $(y_1', \ldots, y_n')$ in this way, we can query $\max(y_i', \ldots, y_j')$ in time $O(1)$. In the same way, we can preprocess $(y_1, \ldots, y_n)$ in linear time with respect to the query $(i, j) \mapsto \min(y_i, \ldots, y_j)$. It allows us to compute $\max(y_i', \ldots, y_j')$ and $\min(y_i, \ldots, y_j)$, and thus $\Delta_{i,j}$, in $O(1)$ time per query after preprocessing time $O(n)$. Thus Δ has property (ii) with $\pi(n) = O(n)$ and $\kappa(n) = O(1)$. So by Theorem 2, we have proved the following:

Theorem 4. *The sorted-MIN-DIST problem can be solved in linear time.*

This algorithm is optimal, since no algorithm can solve this optimization problem without reading the y-coordinates of all the input points. Suppose indeed that an algorithm returns a function f on the input (P, k) without accessing the y-coordinate of the point p_{i_0}. Consider $\tilde{P}$ to be same as P except that the y-coordinate of p_{i_0} is replaced with z. This algorithm will return the same function f on input $(\tilde{P}, k)$, but f is not optimal anymore if z is large enough. This gives an $\Omega(n)$ lower bound on this problem and shows the optimality of the linear time algorithm.

5   MIN-DIST with Weighted Inputs

In this section, we give a near-linear time algorithm for the weighted version of the MIN-DIST problem. Again, it is an application of Theorem 2. We also use an efficient data structure by Guha and Shim [10] for the related query problem.

Let us recall the weighted MIN-DIST problem defined by Guha and Shim [10]—where it is called Maximum Error Histogram. Given a collection of points in the plane $\{(x_1, y_1), \ldots, (x_n, y_n)\}$ with positive weights $\mu_1, \ldots, \mu_n$ and an integer $k > 0$, compute a k-step function f such that $\max_{1 \leqslant i \leqslant n} \mu_i |f(x_i) - y_i|$ is minimized. Guha and Shim [10] give an algorithm to solve weighted-MIN-DIST in time $O(n \log n + k^2 \log^6 n)$ and space $O(n \log n)$. We obtain the following alternative result, which is better when $k = \omega(\sqrt{n}/\log n)$.

Theorem 5. *The weighted* MIN-DIST *problem can be solved in time* $O(n \log^4 n)$ *and space* $O(n \log n)$.

Proof. To avoid technicalities, we assume that no two points have the same x-coordinate. Without loss of generality we assume that the points are sorted with respect to their x-coordinates. Thus the input consists in $k > 0$ and $((x_1, y_1, \mu_1), \ldots, (x_n, y_n, \mu_n))$ with $x_1 < \ldots < x_n$. Since the x_i's play no role, we suppose that the input is reduced to k and $((y_1, \mu_1), \ldots, (y_n, \mu_n))$. Thus the weighted MIN-DIST problem corresponds to MIN-MAX PARTITION(H) with $D = \mathbb{R} \times \mathbb{R}^+$ and

$$H((z_1, \mu_1), \ldots, (z_r, \mu_r)) = \max_{1 \leqslant i \leqslant r} \mu_i |z_i - \hat{z}|$$

where $\hat{z}$ is defined as the value of z that minimizes $\max_{1 \leqslant i \leqslant r} \mu_i |z_i - z|$. Obviously the cost function H is non-decreasing, that is, it satisfies condition (i) of Theorem 2.

The algorithm given in [10] relies on a preprocessing step requiring $O(n \log n)$ time and $O(n \log n)$ space which allows to perform the queries $(i, j) \mapsto H((y_i, \mu_i), \ldots, (y_j, \mu_j))$ in time $O(\log^4 n)$. So Theorem 2 yields the desired result.

□

6   Handling Outliers

We can also consider a generalization of the MIN-DIST problem where at most h points are allowed to be at distance more than ε from P. These points are outliers in the datasets and are removed to make our algorithm more robust to noise. This corresponds to the OUTLIER problem formally defined in Section 1.3. Using Frederickson's method, we obtain:

Theorem 6. *The* OUTLIER *problem with sorted input can be solved in time* $O(nh^2 \log h)$.

The proof of this theorem is omitted due to space limitation.

Acknowledgment

We thank the anonymous referees for their helpful comments.

References

1. Agarwal, P.K., Har-Peled, S., Yu, H.: Robust shape fitting via peeling and grating coresets. In: Proc. 17th Annual ACM-SIAM Symposium on Discrete Algorithms, pp. 182–191 (2006)
2. Agarwal, P.K., Sharir, M.: Efficient algorithms for geometric optimization. Computing Surveys 30 (1998)
3. Atanassov, R., Bose, P., Couture, M., Maheshwari, A., Morin, P., Paquette, M., Smid, M., Wuhrer, S.: Algorithms for optimal outlier removal. Journal of Discrete Algorithms (to appear)
4. Buragohain, C., Shrivastava, N., Suri, S.: Space efficient streaming algorithms for the maximum error histogram. In: 23rd International Conference on Data Engineering, pp. 1026–1035 (2007)
5. Chazal, F., Das, S.: An efficient algorithm for fitting rectilinear x - monotone curve to a point set in a plane. Technical report (August 2006),
   `http://math.u-bourgogne.fr/IMB/chazal/publications.htm`
6. Frederickson, G.N.: Optimal algorithms for tree partitioning. In: Proc. 2nd Annual ACM-SIAM Symposium on Discrete Algorithms, pp. 168–177 (1991)
7. Frederickson, G.N., Johnson, D.B.: Generalized selection and ranking: Sorted matrices. SIAM Journal on Computing 13(1), 14–30 (1984)
8. Gabow, H.N., Bentley, J.L., Tarjan, R.E.: Scaling and related techniques for geometry problems. In: Proc. 16th Annual ACM Symposium on Theory of Computing, pp. 135–143 (1984)
9. Goodrich, M.T.: Efficient piecewise-linear function approximation using the uniform metric. Discrete and Computational Geometry 14(4), 445–462 (1995)
10. Guha, S., Shim, K.: A note on linear time algorithms for maximum error histograms. IEEE Transactions on Knowledge and Data Engineering 19(7), 993–997 (2007)
11. Har-Peled, S., Wang, Y.: Shape fitting with outliers. SIAM Journal on Computing 33(2), 269–285 (2004)
12. Harel, D., Tarjan, R.E.: Fast algorithms for finding nearest common ancestors. SIAM Journal on Computing 13(2), 338–355 (1984)
13. Ioannidis, Y., Poosala, V.: Histogram-based solutions to diverse database estimation problems. IEEE Data Eng. Bull. 18(3), 10–18 (1995)
14. Karras, P., Sacharidis, D., Mamoulis, N.: Exploiting duality in summarization with deterministic guarantees. In: 13th ACM SIGKDD International Conference on Knowledge Discovery and Data Mining, pp. 380–389 (2007)
15. Lopez, M., Mayster, Y.: Weighted rectilinear approximation of points in the plane. In: Laber, E.S., Bornstein, C., Nogueira, L.T., Faria, L. (eds.) LATIN 2008. LNCS, vol. 4957, pp. 642–653. Springer, Heidelberg (2008)
16. Mayster, Y., Lopez, M.A.: Approximating a set of points by a step function. Journal of Visual Comunication and Image Represententation 17(6), 1178–1189 (2006)
17. Díaz-Báñez, J.M., Mesa, J.A.: Fitting rectilinear polygonal curves to a set of points in the plane. European Journal of Operational Research 130(1), 214–222 (2001)
18. Wang, D.P.: A new algorithm for fitting a rectilinear x-monotone curve to a set of points in the plane. Pattern Recognition Letters 23(1-3), 329–334 (2002)

Faster Swap Edge Computation in Minimum Diameter Spanning Trees*

Beat Gfeller

Institute of Theoretical Computer Science, ETH Zurich, Switzerland
gfeller@inf.ethz.ch

Abstract. In network communication systems, frequently messages are routed along a minimum diameter spanning tree (MDST) of the network, to minimize the maximum travel time of messages. When a *transient* failure disables an edge of the MDST, the network is disconnected, and a temporary replacement edge must be chosen, which should ideally minimize the diameter of the new spanning tree. Preparing for the failure of any edge of the MDST, the all-best-swaps (ABS) problem asks for finding the best swap for every edge of the MDST. Given a 2-edge-connected weighted graph $G = (V, E)$, where $|V| = n$ and $|E| = m$, we solve the ABS problem in $O(m \log n)$ time and $O(m)$ space, thus considerably improving upon the decade-old previously best solution, which requires $O(n\sqrt{m})$ time and $O(m)$ space, for $m = o(n^2 / \log^2 n)$.

1 Introduction

For communication in computer networks, often only a subset of the available connections is used to communicate at any given time. If all nodes are connected using the smallest possible number of links, the subset forms a spanning tree of the network. When an edge in a communication tree fails, routing information becomes wrong and message transmission is interrupted. For transient failures that are expected to be repaired quickly, the idea of online point-of-failure rerouting has gained popularity recently [2, 3, 6, 8]: Instead of changing a lot of routing information, only one alternative (so-called *swap*) edge is used to reconnect the disconnected parts of the tree. For the corresponding change in routing information to be fast, a swap edge for each failing edge needs to be readily available, as the result of an earlier computation. Among all possible swap links for a failing edge, one should choose a *best swap* link, that is, a swap edge which reconnects the two disconnected parts of the tree in such a way that the resulting *swap tree* is best w.r.t. some objective.

We show in the following that the common computation of *all best swaps (ABS)* has the further advantage of gaining efficiency (against computing swap edges individually), because dependencies between the computations for different failing edges can be exploited.

* We gratefully acknowledge the support of the Swiss SBF under contract no. C05.0047 within COST-295 (DYNAMO) of the European Union.

D. Halperin and K. Mehlhorn (Eds.): ESA 2008, LNCS 5193, pp. 454–465, 2008.

In this paper, we are interested in using a *Minimum Diameter Spanning Tree* (MDST) as the communication tree, i.e., a tree that minimizes the largest distance between any pair of nodes, thus minimizing the worst case length of any transmission path, even if edge lengths are not uniform. Consequentially, a best swap edge in our case minimizes the diameter of the resulting swap tree. Interestingly, this choice of swapping against adjusting the entire tree even comes at a moderate loss in diameter: The swap tree diameter is at most a factor of $5/2$ larger than the diameter of an entirely adjusted tree [9].

Related Work. During the last decade, the ABS problem has been investigated for spanning trees with various objectives [1, 8, 9, 10, 11, 12].

Computing all best swaps of a MDST was one of the first swap problems that were studied. In [9], an algorithm for this problem is given which requires $O(n\sqrt{m})$ time and $O(m)$ space, where the given underlying 2-edge-connected communication network $G = (V, E)$ has $n = |V|$ nodes and $m = |E|$ edges. For each of the $n - 1$ different tree edges, their algorithm uses somewhat augmented topology trees to select $O(\sqrt{m})$ best swap candidates, then evaluates the quality of each of the $O(\sqrt{m})$ candidate swap edges in $O(1)$ amortized time, and selects the best among them. In order to obtain the $O(1)$ amortized time for computing the diameter of the swap tree associated with a given swap edge, information from a preprocessing phase is used, and combined with an inductive computation that uses path compression.

Contribution. In this paper, we present an algorithm for computing all best swap edges for a MDST, leading to a proof of our

Main Theorem 1. *Given a graph $G = (V, E)$ with $n = |V|$ nodes and $m = |E|$ edges, and a Minimum Diameter Spanning Tree T of G, all best swap edges of T can be computed in $O(m \log n)$ time and $O(m)$ space.*

For $m = o\left(n^2/\log^2 n\right)$, this significantly improves upon the time complexity of the previously best known solution [9], using $O(n\sqrt{m})$ time and $O(m)$ space, without increasing the space complexity. Our techniques can also be used to solve the $\{r, \max\}$-problem of [10], which asks for all best swap edges in a shortest paths tree, in time $O(m \log n)$ instead of $O(n\sqrt{m})$.

This improvement over the previous bounds is based on two key ingredients: First, partitioning the set of tree edges into two particular sets, and computing their best swap edges separately using two different techniques, and second, utilizing an essential observation (Lemma 2) to simplify the computation of the diameter in a given swap tree. Our new observations allow for a simpler algorithm than the previous; we use only fundamental data structures.

2   Terminology

A communication network is a 2-edge-connected, undirected graph $G = (V, E)$, with $n = |V|$ nodes and $m = |E|$ edges. Each edge $e \in E$ has a non-negative rational[1] *length* $l(e)$. The length $|\mathcal{P}|$ of a path $\mathcal{P} = \langle p_1, \ldots, p_r \rangle$, $p_i \in V$, is the sum of the lengths of its edges, and the *distance* $d(x, y)$ between two nodes x, y is the length of a shortest path between x and y. Throughout the paper, we are only dealing with *simple* paths. The following notation is illustrated in Fig. 1. Given a spanning tree $T = (V, E_T)$ of G, let $\mathcal{D}(T) := \langle d_1, d_2, \ldots, d_k \rangle$ denote a *diameter* of T, that is, a longest path in T. From now on, we measure distances in the given spanning tree T, not in the underlying graph G itself. T is said to be a *minimum diameter spanning tree* (MDST) of G if it has minimum diameter among all the spanning trees of G. For the rest of the paper, we assume that T is a particular MDST of G. If we consider T to be rooted at a node on the diameter, say s, then for each node $x \neq s$, let node $p(x)$ be the *parent* of x and $C(x)$ the set of its *children*. Furthermore, let $T_x = (V(T_x), E(T_x))$ be the subtree of T rooted at x, including x.

The removal of any edge $e \in E_T$ partitions the spanning tree into two disjoint trees. A *swap edge* f for e is any edge in $E \backslash E_T$ that (re-)connects the two trees, i.e., for which $T_{e/f} := (V, (E_T \backslash \{e\}) \cup \{f\})$ is a spanning tree of $G - e = (V, E \backslash \{e\})$. We denote by $\mathcal{P}_{e/f}$ a longest path in $T_{e/f}$ that goes through swap edge f. Let $F(e)$ be the set of swap edges for e. A *best swap edge* (with respect to the diameter) for e is any edge $f \in F(e)$ for which $|\mathcal{D}(T_{e/f})|$ is minimum. The *all-best-swaps* (ABS) problem for a MDST is the problem of finding for every edge $e \in E_T$ a best swap edge. Throughout the paper, let e denote a failing edge and f a swap edge.

In Section 3, we start with some crucial observations, which are used to compute all best swaps for failing diameter edges in Section 4, and all best swaps for failing non-diameter edges in Section 5. Due to space restrictions, we omit some details of the latter, which can be found in [5].

3   The Quality of a Swap Edge f for a Failing Edge e

We start with a number of observations, all of which are used in our algorithm. Our first observation is that if the diameter of $T_{e/f}$ is longer than $|\mathcal{D}(T)|$, then the new diameter must go through f. More precisely:

Lemma 1 (Proved in [6]). *For a given failing edge e of the MDST T, the length of the diameter of $T_{e/f}$ is $|\mathcal{D}(T_{e/f})| = \max\{|\mathcal{D}(T)|, |\mathcal{P}_{e/f}|\}$.*

In our algorithm, we always judge swap edges only according to $|\mathcal{P}_{e/f}|$, instead of $|\mathcal{D}(T_{e/f})|$. This causes no problem because any swap edge f for which $|\mathcal{P}_{e/f}| < |\mathcal{D}(T_{e/f})|$ is a best swap edge for e, since in this case $|\mathcal{D}(T_{e/f})| = |\mathcal{D}(T)|$.

For a given tree $T = (V, E_T)$, and a given node $r \in T$, let $\mathcal{L}(T, r)$ denote the length of a longest simple path in T which starts in node r. Note that for $f = (u, v)$, $\mathcal{P}_{e/f}$ is composed of three parts: the longest path in $T - e$ starting in u, the longest path in $T - e$ starting in v, and the edge f itself. Thus, we have

---

[1] Assuming the Real-RAM model, our algorithms would also work for non-negative real weights.

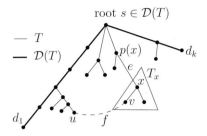
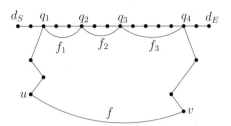

Fig. 1. A MDST T rooted at a node s on its diameter $\mathcal{D}(T)$, a failing edge e, and a swap edge $f = (u, v)$ for e. The bold line segments denote the diameter $\mathcal{D}(T)$ of T.

Fig. 2. Replacing a swap edge f by three virtual swap edges f_1, f_2, f_3

$|\mathcal{P}_{e/f}| = l(f) + \mathcal{L}(T - e, u) + \mathcal{L}(T - e, v)$. The following lemma shows how to compute $\mathcal{L}(T, r)$ efficiently for any given node $r \in V$.

Lemma 2 (Proof in [5]²). *Let $T = (V, E_T)$ be a weighted tree, and let $\mathcal{D}(T) = \langle d_S, \ldots d_E \rangle$ be a diameter of T with endpoints d_S and d_E. The length of a longest simple path inside T starting in $r \in V$ is $\mathcal{L}(T, r) = \max \left\{ d(r, d_S), d(r, d_E) \right\}$.*

We now show how, given the endpoints of a diameter of T, one can compute $\mathcal{L}(T, r)$ for any given node r in constant time, after a preprocessing step requiring $O(n)$ time. We root the tree T at any node, and augment it with (i) a labeling of the nodes which allows to obtain the nearest common ancestor (called $\mathrm{nca}(a, b)$ for two nodes a, b) of two given nodes in constant time [7]; (ii) in every node x, store its distance to the root, called $\mathrm{toRoot}(x)$.

This information allows to compute the distance between two arbitrary nodes a and b in the tree T (and thus $\mathcal{L}(T, r)$) in constant time: $d(a, b) = d(a, \mathrm{nca}(a, b)) + d(b, \mathrm{nca}(a, b)) = \mathrm{toRoot}(a) + \mathrm{toRoot}(b) - 2 \cdot \mathrm{toRoot}(\mathrm{nca}(a, b))$.

In our algorithm, we distinguish between failing edges on the diameter, called *diameter edges*, and failing edges not on the diameter, called *non-diameter* edges. If the given tree has several diameters, we select one and use the same throughout the algorithm. This guarantees that each edge is either a diameter edge or a non-diameter edge, and that this classification is consistent.

4   Best Swap Edges for Failing Diameter Edges

In this section, we show how to compute the best swap edges for all failing edges which lie on the diameter $\mathcal{D}(T)$ in time $O(m \log n)$ and $O(m)$ space.

Due to Lemma 1, a given swap edge f for a failing edge e can be evaluated by computing the lengths of the two longest paths starting at its endpoints. It turns out that these lengths can always be found by only considering paths which visit the diameter:

---

² Due to lack of space, we only present a selection of proofs, and refer to [5] for further details.

Lemma 3 (Proof in [5]). *Consider a tree $T = (V, E_T)$, a diameter $\mathcal{D}(T)$ of it with endpoints d_S, d_E, a failing edge e on $\mathcal{D}(T)$, and an arbitrary node $r \in V$. Let u be the node on $\mathcal{D}(T)$ closest to r. One of the longest paths in $T - e$ starting from r contains the node u.*

Due to the above lemma, a longest path starting in any endpoint r of a given swap edge can always be found by first going to the node $u \in \mathcal{D}(T)$ closest to r. From there, a longest path may either continue to the end of the diameter (d_S or d_E), or cross at least one edge towards the failing edge e, and possibly leave the diameter again. Note that going from u towards d_S, but leaving the diameter again, cannot be longer than continuing until d_S.

For finding the length of a longest path starting from u efficiently, we compute two values $\mu_S(d_i, d_{i+1})$ and $\mu_E(d_i, d_{i+1})$ for every node d_i, $i = 1, \ldots, k-1$ on the diameter. By $\mu_S(d_i, d_{i+1})$ (respectively $\mu_E(d_i, d_{i+1})$), we denote the length of a longest path in T starting at d_S (d_E) and not crossing the edge (d_i, d_{i+1}). Formally, we have ($d_S := d_1, d_E := d_k$):

$$\mu_S(d_1, d_2) = \mu_E(d_{k-1}, d_k) = 0$$
$$\mu_S(d_i, d_{i+1}) = \max\{\mu_S(d_{i-1}, d_i), d(d_S, d_i) + h(d_i)\} \text{ for } i = 2, 3, \ldots, k-1, \text{ and}$$
$$\mu_E(d_i, d_{i+1}) = \max\{\mu_E(d_{i+1}, d_{i+2}), d(d_E, d_{i+1}) + h(d_{i+1})\} \text{ for } i = k-2, \ldots, 1.$$

where $h(d_i)$ denotes the length of a longest path starting in d_i, and not using any edges on the diameter $d_S, \ldots d_E$. It is easy to see that if T is rooted at a node on the diameter, then $h(d_i)$ can be computed for all d_i on the diameter in $O(n)$ time by traversing T in postorder. Thus, the values $\mu_S(d_i, d_{i+1}), \mu_E(d_i, d_{i+1})$ can be computed for all d_i on the diameter in $O(n)$ time.

The following lemma describes how to efficiently compute the longest path in $T - (d_i, d_{i+1})$ starting from any node r.

Lemma 4 (Proof in [5]). *Consider any fixed diameter $d_S, \ldots, d_E$ of a tree T, any node r of T, and a failing edge (d_i, d_{i+1}) on the diameter. Let u be the node on the diameter closest to r. The length of a longest path in $T - (d_i, d_{i+1})$ starting in r is given by $d(r, u) + \max\{d(u, d_S), \mu_S(d_i, d_{i+1}) - d(u, d_S)\}$ if r lies in the same connected component of $T - (d_i, d_{i+1})$ as d_S, and $d(r, u) + \max\{d(u, d_E), \mu_E(d_i, d_{i+1}) - d(u, d_E)\}$ otherwise.*

4.1   Using Virtual Swap Edges

For any node v, let $nc(v)$ be the node on the diameter which is closest to v (possibly, $nc(v) = v$). According to Lemma 4, the value $|\mathcal{P}_{e/f}|$ of a particular swap edge $f = (u, v)$ for any failing edge e on the diameter is one of the following four terms (assuming that u lies in the same component of $T - e$ as d_S, and v lies in the same component of $T - e$ as d_E):

1. $d(u, d_S) + d(v, d_E) + l(f)$
2. $d(u, d_S) + \mu_E(e) - d(nc(v), d_E) + d(v, nc(v)) + l(f)$
3. $\mu_S(e) - d(nc(u), d_S) + d(u, nc(u)) + d(v, d_E) + l(f)$
4. $\mu_S(e) - d(nc(u), d_S) + d(u, nc(u)) + \mu_E(e) - d(nc(v), d_E) + d(v, nc(v)) + l(f)$.

Note that in all above terms, the part depending on the failing edge e is independent of f. Thus, if two swap edges f' and f'' for edge e are such that their values $|\mathcal{P}_{e/f'}|$ and $|\mathcal{P}_{e/f''}|$ both correspond to the same of the four terms above, then we can omit the terms $\mu_S(e)$ and $\mu_E(e)$ when comparing their quality, without affecting the comparison. Furthermore, note that since $\mu_S(d_i, d_{i+1})$ is monotonically increasing in i, all the failing edges (d_i, d_{i+1}) for which $\max\{d(u, d_S), \mu_S(d_i, d_{i+1}) - d(u, d_S)\} = d(u, d_S)$ form a connected path, as do all the failing edges for which $\max\{d(u, d_S), \mu_S(d_i, d_{i+1}) - d(u, d_S)\} = \mu_S(d_i, d_{i+1}) - d(u, d_S)$ (the same holds for d_E). Thus, for a given swap edge $f = (u, v)$, the set of diameter edges can be divided into at most three sets, each composing a path, such that for each set, f's value is defined by a specific one of the four terms above. We denote the endpoints of these paths by q_1, q_2, q_3, q_4. Note that $q_1 = \text{nc}(u)$ and $q_4 = \text{nc}(v)$.

The above observations lead to the idea of introducing *virtual swap edges* which replace the original swap edges, as follows (see also Fig. 2): A virtual swap edge f_i consists of its two endpoints, its *type*, and its *value*. The two endpoints define a path on the spanning tree T, which is equal to the set of diameter edges for which f_i is a swap edge. The type of a virtual swap edge is a number in $1, 2, 3, 4$. By definition, two virtual swap edges can only be compared if they have the same type. The value of a virtual swap edge is a rational number. By construction, the quality of each virtual swap edge for a given failing edge e is identical to the quality of the original swap edge which it is replacing. Each swap edge f is replaced by at most three "virtual" swap edges f_1, f_2, f_3 in the following way:

- The endpoints are: $f_1 = (q_1, q_2)$, $f_2 = (q_2, q_3)$, $f_3 = (q_3, q_4)$.
- For every failing edge e on $\mathcal{D}(T)$ such that $f \in F(e)$, exactly one of f_1, f_2, f_3 is a swap edge.
- The value of each $f_i = (u, v)$ is one of the terms shown above, except for the part depending on e. Thus, it is either of
  1. $d(u, d_S) + d(v, d_E) + l(f)$,
  2. $d(u, d_S) - d(\text{nc}(v), d_E) + d(v, \text{nc}(v)) + l(f)$,
  3. $d(v, d_E) - d(\text{nc}(u), d_S) + d(u, \text{nc}(u)) + l(f)$,
  4. $-d(\text{nc}(u), d_S) + d(u, \text{nc}(u)) - d(\text{nc}(v), d_E) + d(v, \text{nc}(v)) + l(f)$.

  The number of the term used to compute this value corresponds to the *type* of the virtual swap edge f_i.

Note that although there are four different types of virtual swap edges, each individual (original) swap edge is replaced by at most three different virtual swap edges, whose types are all different. In the following, we assume that a swap edge f is replaced by exactly three virtual swap edges; if fewer virtual swap edges are required, the adaptation of the method we describe is straightforward. Let us summarize.

Lemma 5 (Proof in [5]). *The set of all swap edges can be replaced by at most three times as many virtual swap edges, each having one of four types and a value, such that the quality of two swap edges of the same type can be compared* *based solely on their values. Moreover, this transformation can be carried out using $O(m \log n)$ time and $O(m)$ space.*

Using the virtual swap edges, we compute, for each of the four types $t \in \{1, 2, 3, 4\}$ separately, the best virtual swap edge for all failing edges on the diameter in $O(m \log n)$ time and $O(m)$ space, with the following simple scanline algorithm:

1. Initialize an empty Heap H_t. The virtual swap edges which are later inserted into H_t are to be ordered by their values.
2. Consider all failing edges $e_i = (d_i, d_{i+1})$ on the diameter sequentially, for $i = 1, 2, \ldots, k$. For each $e_i = (d_i, d_{i+1})$:
   - add to H_t all those virtual swap edges whose left endpoint (i.e., the one closer to d_1) is d_i.
   - remove from H_t all those virtual swap edges whose right endpoint is d_i.
   - store the current minimum of H_t as $best(e_i, t)$.

Then, for each e_i and each type t, replace the virtual swap edge $best(e_i, t)$ by its corresponding swap edge. This yields at most four potential best swap candidates for each diameter edge e_i, among which a best swap is contained. The best swap edges are then found in time $O(n)$ by simply computing $|\mathcal{P}_{e/f}|$ explicitly (and in constant time) for each of these selected $O(n)$ candidates.

As we show below, replacing each and every swap edge by its virtual swap edges requires $O(m \log n)$ time and $O(m)$ space, and increases the number of swap edges by a factor of at most three. Summarizing, we have:

Theorem 2. *All best swap edges for failing edges on a chosen diameter can be computed in $O(m \log n)$ time and $O(m)$ space[3].*

5   Swap Edges for Failing Non-diameter Edges

In this section, we describe an algorithm to compute the best swap edges for those tree edges which do not lie on the chosen diameter $\mathcal{D}(T)$ of the given MDST T. We will show that this algorithm runs in $O(m \log n)$ time and requires $O(m)$ space.

For our approach, we root T in an arbitrary node *on the diameter*, and label all edges by their occurrence in a postorder traversal.

To begin, let $f = (u, v)$ be an edge in $E \backslash E_T$ such that u is a descendant of v in T, and such that the path from u to v in T does not contain any edge of the diameter $\mathcal{D}(T)$. We call such an edge a *backedge*. For a backedge $f = (u, v)$, we call the endpoint u the *lower* endpoint of f, and v the *upper* endpoint of f. In the following, we assume for ease of exposition that all edges in $E \backslash E_T$ are backedges. In Section 5.3, we describe how to adapt our algorithm to work without this assumption.

---

[3] With a transmuter data structure, a running time of $O(m\alpha(m, n))$ could be achieved here. However, the algorithm in Section 5 requires $\Omega(m \log n)$ time, and hence the asymptotic running time of the complete algorithm would not decrease.

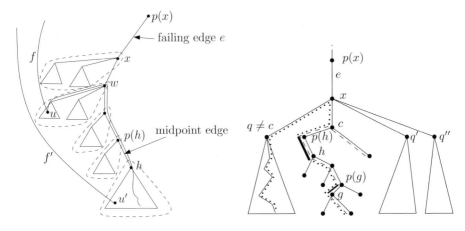

Fig. 3. Grouping of swap edges according to their endpoints in T_x. Sets of endpoints whose swap edges are grouped together are enclosed in dashed shapes.

Fig. 4. A failing edge $e = (x, p(x))$, the midpoint edge $(h, p(h))$ of $\mathcal{D}(T_x)$, the child $c \in C(x)$ whose subtree contains h, and the midpoint edge $(g, p(g))$ of $\mathcal{D}(T_c)$

Consider the sequence of (non-diameter) tree edges $e_1, \ldots, e_k$ in the path from u to v, starting with the edge adjacent to u: how does $|\mathcal{P}_{e_i/f}|$ depend on the e_i? Since the failing edge e_i is not on the diameter $\mathcal{D}(T)$, the connected component of $T - e_i$ containing v still contains $\mathcal{D}(T)$. According to Lemma 2, the longest path in $T - e_i$ starting in v is therefore the same for all edges $e_1, \ldots, e_k$, and thus $\mathcal{L}(T - e_i, v) = \mathcal{L}(T, v)$.

On the other hand, the longest path in $T - e_i$ starting in u may be different for different failing edges e_i. To characterize the structure of these paths, we introduce a new concept: The *midpoint edge* of a tree's diameter is the edge on the diameter which contains the center of the diameter. More precisely, this is the diameter edge whose removal splits it into two parts whose difference in length is minimum (there could be two edges satisfying this definiton; any of them can be chosen). Note that the position of the midpoint edge determines in which direction a longest path starting in a particular node goes (again using Lemma 2): all longest paths which start on one side of the midpoint edge go to the opposite end of the diameter.

We now focus on a particular failing (non-diameter) edge $e = (x, p(x))$ for which the best swap is to be computed. Let $(h, p(h))$ be the midpoint edge of $\mathcal{D}(T_x)$. By Lemma 2, the longest path starting in u inside T_x will contain $(h, p(h))$. This fact allows to partition the set $F(e)$ of swap edges for e into groups as follows (see Fig. 3):

– All swap edges having their lower endpoint below the midpoint edge $(h, p(h))$ will have a longest path going up towards this edge, and then further on to the furthest node in T_x (this furthest node is the endpoint of the diameter of T_x which lies outside of T_h, and which is precomputed). We call this the *lower* group, and denote it by $\mathcal{G}_{\text{lower}}(x)$. Formally, $\mathcal{G}_{\text{lower}}(x) := \{(u, v) \in E \backslash E_T | u \in T_h \wedge v \notin T_x\}$.

- All swap edges having their lower endpoint u above the midpoint edge (i.e., not in T_h) will have a longest path which first leads to some node on the path from $p(h)$ to x, then continue down towards the midpoint edge, and finally going into a deepest leaf in T_h (this node is the endpoint of T_x's diameter which lies inside T_h, which is also precomputed). We partition these swap edges into groups distinguished by the node $w = \text{nca}(u, h)$, the first node on the path from $p(h)$ to x contained in their longest path in $T - e$ starting in u. These groups are called the *upper* groups, and denoted by $\mathcal{G}_{\text{upper}}(x, w)$. Formally: $\mathcal{G}_{\text{upper}}(x, w) := \{(u, v) \in E \backslash E_T | u \in T_x \backslash T_h \wedge \text{nca}(u, h) = w \wedge v \notin T_x\}$.

This grouping is helpful for computing best swap edges, due to the following fact:

Lemma 6. *In any group $\mathcal{G}_{\text{upper}}(x, w)$ or $\mathcal{G}_{\text{lower}}(x)$, a best swap candidate for the failing edge $e = (x, p(x))$ is a swap edge $f = (u, v)$ for which $\mathcal{L}(T, v) + l(f) + \text{toRoot}(u)$ is minimum.*

Proof. For swap edges in the lower group, all "longest paths" in T_x are identical after crossing the midpoint edge. For each upper group corresponding to some node w, all "longest paths" in T_x are identical after reaching w.   □

In order to compare the best candidates from different upper groups, an additional offset has to be added to each candidate's value, such that the so-called *updated value* of a candidate f is exactly equal to $|\mathcal{P}_{e/f}|$. For $f = (u, v)$ with $\text{nca}(u, h) = w$, this updated value is

$$\mathcal{L}(T, v) + l(f) + \text{toRoot}(u) - \text{toRoot}(w) + d(w, v_{deep}), \tag{1}$$

where v_{deep} is the endpoint of $\mathcal{D}(T_x)$ in T_h. For the following, it is useful to denote by $\mathcal{GR}(x)$ the union of all groups associated with a given edge $e = (x, p(x))$.

5.1   Relations between Groups for Different Non-diameter Edges

There is a close connection between the midpoint edges of a subtree T_x rooted at a node x and the midpoint edges of the subtrees of this node's children. Indeed, the following lemma is easy to prove:

Lemma 7 (Proof omitted). *Consider a tree edge $e = (x, p(x))$ and the child $c \in C(x)$ for which the midpoint edge of $\mathcal{D}(T_x)$ is either (c, x) or an edge in T_c. Then, the midpoint edge of $\mathcal{D}(T_x)$ lies on the path from the midpoint edge of $\mathcal{D}(T_c)$ to e (possibly, the midpoint edges of $\mathcal{D}(T_c)$ and of $\mathcal{D}(T_x)$ are identical).*

Thus, the midpoint edge only moves "upwards" when failing edges are visited in postorder: it never occurs that the midpoint edge of T_x lies below the midpoint edge of T_d for any descendant d of x. This implies that for any particular backedge $f = (u, v)$, if a longest path in $T - e_i$ starting in u does not visit any child of u, then nor will a longest path in any $T - e_j$, $j > i$.

Recall that we consider all (non-diameter) failing edges in a postorder. In the following, we show how the groups of swap edges for a non-diameter tree edge $e = (x, p(x))$ relate to the groups of previously considered failing edges. Later, we exploit these relations using a collection of suitable data structures.

The set of swap edges for edge $e = (x, p(x))$ can be expressed as

$$F(e) = \text{start-at}(x) \cup \Big\{ \bigcup_{q \in C(x)} F((q, x)) \Big\} \setminus \text{end-at}(x),$$

where start-at(x) is the set of swap edges whose lower endpoint is x, and where end-at(x) is the set of swap edges whose upper endpoint is x. We now describe how $F(e)$ is partitioned into the lower group and all the upper groups of e. Let $c \in C(x)$ be the child of x for which the midpoint edge of $\mathcal{D}(T_x)$ is either (c, x) or an edge in T_c. Furthermore, let $(g, p(g))$ be the midpoint edge of $\mathcal{D}(T_c)$ and let $(h, p(h))$ be the midpoint edge of $\mathcal{D}(T_x)$ (see Fig. 4). Clearly, all swap edges which belong to the upper group of e associated with $w = x$ are

$$\mathcal{G}_{\text{upper}}(x, x) = \text{start-at}(x) \cup \Big\{ \bigcup_{q \in C(x), q \neq c} \mathcal{G}\mathcal{R}(q) \Big\} \setminus \text{end-at}(x).$$

For any $w \neq x$ on the path from $p(h)$ to c, thanks to Lemma 7, we can express the set of swap edges in the upper group of e associated with w as $\mathcal{G}_{\text{upper}}(x, w) = \mathcal{G}_{\text{upper}}(c, w) \setminus \text{end-at}(x)$. Finally, the swap edges belonging to the lower group of e are

$$\mathcal{G}_{\text{lower}}(x) = \Big(\mathcal{G}_{\text{lower}}(c) \cup \Big\{ \bigcup_{d \in \langle p(g), \dots, h \rangle} \mathcal{G}_{\text{upper}}(c, d) \Big\} \Big) \setminus \text{end-at}(x).$$

5.2   Our Data Structure and Our Inductive Approach

Our approach visits all non-diameter tree edges in postorder, and computes a best swap edge for each of them sequentially. In order to leverage our observations about connections between best swaps for different edges, we associate a data structure, denoted by GroupsDS(x), with each considered edge $e = (x, p(x))$. This structure contains a representation of the group $\mathcal{G}_{\text{lower}}(x)$ and all groups $\mathcal{G}_{\text{upper}}(x, w)$ for $w \in \langle p(h), \dots, x \rangle$ (recall $(h, p(h))$ denotes the midpoint edge), from which a best swap for e can be extracted in constant time. Moreover, it is designed such that GroupsDS(x) can be efficiently composed of their counterparts of previously visited edges.

Lemma 7 implies that by visiting the (non-diameter) failing edges in postorder results in a corresponding midedge sequence which is also postorder (although this may be only a subset of all tree edges). This is crucial for the correctness of our approach, because once we used a data structure GroupsDS(x') associated with a previously visited edge $(x', p(x'))$, to compute GroupsDS(x), GroupsDS(x') is no longer available. In GroupsDS(x), each group is represented by a Minimum Fibonacci-Heap (short *F-Heap* in the following) [4]. Each swap edge f contained in a group $\mathcal{G}$ is stored in the corresponding F-Heap, using the value $\mathcal{L}(T, v) + l(f) + \text{toRoot}(u)$, which we call the *invariant value* of f, as its key[4]. Note crucially, that this value is independent of the failing edge, and according to Lemma 6 the minimum element in the F-Heap corresponding to a group is the best swap (in this group) for the currently considered failing edge. Furthermore, even when this F-Heap is later altered, by inserting or deleting some swap edges, or by merging the F-Heap with another, the value associated with a given swap edge need never be changed. In particular, GroupsDS(x) contains (see [5] for more details):

1. a list heaplist(x) of F-Heaps, containing, for each node w on the path from $p(h)$ to x, an F-Heap $\text{FH}_{\text{upper}}(x, w)$ of all swap edges in $\mathcal{G}_{\text{upper}}(x, w)$. The order of the F-Heaps in the list corresponds to the order of the respective nodes w (lowest node first).
2. an F-Heap $\text{FH}_{\text{lower}}(x)$ of all swap edges whose lower endpoint lies in T_h.

In principle, the best swap for e is found by choosing the candidate with minimum updated value among the best of each group. Doing this naively would require at least linear time in the number of groups, i.e., at least linear in the number of nodes between e and the midpoint edge. To expedite this process during the induction, we use an ordinary Minimum Heap which contains the updated values of the best candidate from each upper group. The best swap edge is then either the minimum element in this heap, or the best candidate from the lower group. Thus, GroupsDS(x) additionally contains the following item:

3. an ordinary Minimum Heap CandHeap(x), containing for each F-Heap in heaplist(x) the best swap candidate, ordered by their quality (i.e., their $\mathcal{P}_{e/f}$- lengths as defined in Equation 1).

From this information, a best swap edge for $(x, p(x))$ is found in constant time by comparing the best candidate in CandHeap(x) with the best candidate in $\text{FH}_{\text{lower}}(x)$, and taking the better of the two. Moreover, using the insights of Section 5.1, we can efficiently compute GroupsDS(x) for each node x in postorder, by composing it from the GroupsDS(c_1), ..., GroupsDS(c_k) associated with its children $c_1, \ldots, c_k$. More precisely, we have (see [5] for the details):

Theorem 3. *All best swap edges for failing edges not lying on the chosen diameter can be computed in $O(m \log n)$ time and $O(m)$ space.*

5.3   Transforming Non-tree Edges to Backedges

So far, we have assumed that all swap edges are backedges. We now describe to replace any edge f by at most two "virtual" backedges, whose lengths are defined in such a way that the best swap edge computed by our algorithm is

---

[4] Technically speaking, the key must be made unique by using the tuple $(\mathcal{L}(T, v) + l(f) + \text{toRoot}(u), f)$ as key, where comparisons are based mainly on the first component, and the second is only used to break ties. We omit this detail in the main text for ease of exposition.

correct. That is, if the computed best swap for a given failing edge e is a virtual backedge, then replacing the virtual backedge by the edge f it represents yields a (non-backedge) swap edge for e with the same quality. Formally, we replace $f = (u, v)$ by $f_1 := (u, v_1)$ and $f_2 := (v, u_2)$ (recall that these tuples are ordered), with lengths $l(f_1) := l(f) + d(v, v_1)$ and $l(f_2) := d(u, u_2)$. If the path from u to v in T uses one or more edges of $\mathcal{D}(T)$, we define $v_1 := \mathrm{nc}(u)$ and $v_2 := \mathrm{nc}(v)$. Otherwise, we define $v_1 := \mathrm{nca}(u, v)$ and $u_2 := \mathrm{nca}(u, v)$. If it happens that $u = v_1$, we omit f_1, and if $v = u_2$, we omit f_2. To see why this replacement works, note that in both cases f_1 represents f exactly for all failing edges on the path in T from u to v_1, and f_2 represents f exactly for all edges from v to u_2 (i.e., for each non-diameter tree edge, one of f_1, f_2 represents f). Furthermore, the lengths of f_1 and f_2 are defined exactly such that for any failing edge e for which f_i is a swap edge, it holds $|\mathcal{D}(T_{e/f_i})| = |\mathcal{D}(T_{e/f})|$.

References

[1] Di Salvo, A., Proietti, G.: Swapping a Failing Edge of a Shortest Paths Tree by Minimizing the Average Stretch Factor. Theor. Comp. Sci. 383(1), 23–33 (2007)

[2] Flocchini, P., Enriques, A.M., Pagli, L., Prencipe, G., Santoro, N.: Point-of-failure Shortest-path Rerouting: Computing the Optimal Swap Edges Distributively. IEICE Transactions on Information and Systems E89-D(2), 700–708 (2006)

[3] Flocchini, P., Pagli, L., Prencipe, G., Santoro, N., Widmayer, P.: Computing All the Best Swap Edges Distributively. Journal of Parallel and Distributed Computing (in press, 2008)

[4] Fredman, M.L., Tarjan, R.E.: Fibonacci Heaps and Their Uses in Improved Network Optimization Algorithms. J. ACM 34(3), 596–615 (1987)

[5] Gfeller, B.: Faster swap edge computation in minimum diameter spanning trees. Technical Report 597, ETH Zurich (June 2008),
http://www.inf.ethz.ch/research/disstechreps/techreports

[6] Gfeller, B., Santoro, N., Widmayer, P.: A Distributed Algorithm for Finding All Best Swap Edges of a Minimum Diameter Spanning Tree. In: Pelc, A. (ed.) DISC 2007. LNCS, vol. 4731, pp. 268–282. Springer, Heidelberg (2007)

[7] Harel, D., Tarjan, R.E.: Fast Algorithms for Finding Nearest Common Ancestors. SIAM Journal on Computing 13(2), 338–355 (1984)

[8] Ito, H., Iwama, K., Okabe, Y., Yoshihiro, T.: Single Backup Table Schemes for Shortest-path Routing. Theor. Comp. Sci. 333(3), 347–353 (2005)

[9] Nardelli, E., Proietti, G., Widmayer, P.: Finding All the Best Swaps of a Minimum Diameter Spanning Tree Under Transient Edge Failures. Journal of Graph Algorithms and Applications 5(5), 39–57 (2001)

[10] Nardelli, E., Proietti, G., Widmayer, P.: Swapping a Failing Edge of a Single Source Shortest Paths Tree Is Good and Fast. Algorithmica 35(1), 56–74 (2003)

[11] Proietti, G.: Dynamic Maintenance Versus Swapping: An Experimental Study on Shortest Paths Trees. In: Näher, S., Wagner, D. (eds.) WAE 2000. LNCS, vol. 1982, pp. 207–217. Springer, Heidelberg (2001)

[12] Wu, B.Y., Hsiao, C.-Y., Chao, K.-M.: The Swap Edges of a Multiple-Sources Routing Tree. Algorithmica 50(3), 299–311 (2008)

The Partial Augment–Relabel Algorithm for the Maximum Flow Problem

Andrew V. Goldberg

Microsoft Research – Silicon Valley, 1065 La Avenida, Mountain View, CA 94062
goldberg@microsoft.com

Abstract. The maximum flow problem is a classical optimization problem with many applications. For a long time, HI-PR, an efficient implementation of the highest-label push-relabel algorithm, has been a benchmark due to its robust performance. We propose another variant of the push-relabel method, the partial augment-relabel (PAR) algorithm. Our experiments show that PAR is very robust. It outperforms HI-PR on all problem families tested, asymptotically in some cases.

1 Introduction

The maximum flow problem and its dual, the minimum cut problem, are classical combinatorial optimization problems with applications in many areas of science and engineering. For this reason, the problem has been studied both from theoretical and practical viewpoints for over half a century. The problem is to find a maximum flow from the source to the sink (a minimum cut between the source and the sink) given a network with arc capacities, the source, and the sink. Below we denote the number of vertices and arcs in the input network by n and m, respectively. Theoretical line of research led to the development of augmenting path [16], network simplex [12], blocking flow [14], and push-relabel [20] methods. The best currently known time bounds appear in [25,19].

From the practical point of view, good implementations of Dinic's blocking flow method [10,21] proved superior to the network simplex and the augmenting path algorithms. The blocking flow method remained the method of choice until the development of the push-relabel method [20], which was quickly recognized as practical. Within a year of its invention, the method had been used in a physics application [28]. A parallel implementation of the method, including some speed-up heuristics applicable in the sequential context as well, has been studied in [17]. Implementations of variants of the method has been studied during the First DIMACS Implementation Challenge [23,2,27]. This work showed that using the global update and gap heuristics (discussed in detail in Section 3), one gets an implementation superior to the efficient implementations of Dinic's algorithm. Another conclusion was that, except in degenerate cases, the dynamic tree data structure, used in the most theoretically efficient algorithms, does not help in practice, where its overhead exceeds the corresponding performance gains [4]. The Challenge also led to the development of the DIMACS problem families.

D. Halperin and K. Mehlhorn (Eds.): ESA 2008, LNCS 5193, pp. 466–477, 2008.

Subsequent work of Cherkassky and Goldberg [11] showed that, with a proper choice of data structures, the combination of global update and gap heuristics is more robust than the individual heuristics, and the high-level selection rule outperforms other popular selection rules. This implementation, PRF, and its later version, HI-PR, has been used for over a decade in many applications. Several subsequent implementations, such as [26], use the combination of gap and global update and differ by low-level data structures or initialization strategies.

A number of attempts have been made to develop an implementation that is more robust than HI-PR. The ideas behind the binary blocking flow algorithm in particular appear practical, and Hagerup et al. [22] show that this algorithm outperforms Dinic' blocking flow algorithm. However, although the algorithm has a better worst-case time bound and performs better on specific bad instances, all attempts so far to produce an implementation of this algorithm that is more robust than HI-PR failed.

Some maximum flow algorithms developed for specific applications outperform HI-PR in these applications. For example, minimum cuts are being used extensively in vision applications. Boykov and Kolmogorov [5] developed an algorithm that is superior to the highest level and FIFO push-relabel implementations on many vision problems. Their implementation is extensively used by the vision community. See [5,6] for surveys of the vision applications.

In this paper we describe a new *partial augment-relabel (PAR)* variant of the push-relabel method. In our comparison of PAR to HI-PR, the former code is consistently faster, in some cases asymptotically so. The push-relabel algorithm implementations had significant impact on applications and experimental work in the area for over a decade. In this context, the superior performance of PAR is significant. Furthermore, the push-relabel algorithm is the basis for efficient implementations of algorithms for the minimum-cost flow [18], global minimum cut [8], and parametric flow [3] problems. The ideas presented in this paper apply to these problems, and may improve performance of the corresponding implementations.

2   Definitions and Notation

Input to the maximum flow problem is (G, s, t, u), where $G = (V, A)$ is a directed graph, $s, t \in V$, $s \neq t$ are the *source* and the *sink*, respectively, $u : A \Rightarrow [1, \ldots, U]$ is the *capacity function*, and U is the *maximum capacity*.

Let a^R denote the *reverse* of an arc a. let A^R be the set of all reverse arcs, and let $A' = A \cup A^R$. Note that we add a reverse arc for every arc of A; in particular, if A contains both $a = (v, w)$ and $b = (w, v)$, then a^R is an arc parallel to but different from b. A function g on A' is *anti-symmetric* if $g(a) = -g(a^R)$. Extend u to be an anti-symmetric function on A', i.e., $u(a^R) = -u(a)$.

A flow f is an anti-symmetric function on A' that satisfies *capacity constraints* on all arcs and *conservation constraints* at all vertices except s and t. The capacity constraint for $a \in A$ is $0 \leq f(a) \leq u(a)$ and for $a \in A^R$ it is $-u(a^R) \leq f(a) \leq 0$. The conservation constraint for v is $\sum_{(u,v) \in A} f(u, v) = \sum_{(v,w) \in A} f(v, w)$. The *flow value* is the total flow into the sink: $|f| = \sum_{(v,t) \in A} f(v, t)$.

A *cut* is a partitioning of vertices $S \cup T = V$ with $s \in S, t \in T$. Capacity of a cut is defined by $u(S,T) = \sum_{v \in S, w \in T, (v,w) \in A} u(v,w)$.

A *preflow* is a relaxation of a flow that satisfies capacity constraints and a relaxed version of conservation constraints $\sum_{(u,v) \in A} f(u,v) \geq \sum_{(v,w) \in A} f(v,w)$. We define flow *excess* of v by $e_f(v) = \sum_{(u,v) \in A} f(u,v) - \sum_{(v,w) \in A} f(v,w)$. For a preflow f, $e_f(v) \geq 0$ for all $v \in V - \{s,t\}$.

Residual capacity is defined by $u_f(a) = u(a) - f(a)$ for $a \in A$ and $u_f(a) = f(a^R)$ for $a \in A^R$. Note that if f satisfies capacity constraints, then u_f is non-negative. The *residual graph* $G_f = (V, A_f)$ is induced by the arcs in A' with strictly positive residual capacity. An *augmenting path* is an s–t path in G_f.

A distance labeling is an integral function d on V that satisfies $d(t) = 0$. Given a preflow f, we say that d is valid if for all $(v,w) \in A_f$ we have $d(v) \leq d(w) + 1$. Unless mentioned otherwise, we assume that a distance labeling is valid with respect to the current preflow in the graph. We say that an arc (v,w) is *admissible* if $(v,w) \in A_f$ and $d(v) = d(w) + 1$, and denote the set of admissible arcs by A_d.

3   The Push-Relabel Method

The push-relabel method [20][1] maintains a preflow and a distance labeling, which are modified using two *basic operations*:

Push(v,w) applies if $e_f(v) > 0$ and $(v,w) \in A_d$. The operation chooses $\delta : 0 < \delta \leq \min(u_f(v,w), e_f(v))$, increases $f(v,w)$ and $e_f(w)$ by δ and decreases $e_f(v)$ and $f((v,w)^R)$ by δ. A push is *saturating* if after the push $u_f(v,w) = 0$ and *non-saturating* otherwise.

Relabel(v) applies if $d(v) < n$ and v has no outgoing admissible arcs. A relabel operation increases $d(v)$ to the maximum value allowed by the distance labeling constraints: $1 + \min_{(v,w) \in A_f} d(w)$ or to n if v has no outgoing residual arcs.

The method can start with any feasible preflow and distance labeling. Unless mentioned otherwise, we assume the following simple initialization: f is zero on all arcs except for arcs out of s, for which the flow is equal to the capacity; $d(s) = n$, $d(t) = 0$, $d(v) = 1$ for all $v \neq s,t$. For a particular application, one may be able to improve algorithm performance using an application-specific initialization. After initialization, the method applies push and relabel operations until no operation applies.

When no operation applies, the set of all vertices v such that t is reachable from v in G_f defines a minimum cut, and the excess at the sink is equal to the maximum flow value. For applications that need only the cut, the algorithm can terminate at this point. For applications that need the maximum flow, we run the second stage of the algorithm. One way to implement the second stage is to first reduce flow around flow cycles to make the flow acyclic, and then to return flow excesses to the source by reducing arc flows in the reverse topological order

---

[1] Sometimes it is referred to as preflow-push, which is misleading: e.g., Karzanov's implementation [24] of the blocking flow method uses preflows and the push operation.

with respect to this acyclic graph. See [29]. Both in theory and in practice, the first stage of the algorithm dominates the running time.

The *current arc* data structure [20] is important for algorithm efficiency; it works as follows. Each vertex maintains a current arc $a(v)$. Initially, and after each relabeling of v, the arc is the first arc on $v's$ arc list. When we examine $a(v)$, we check if it is admissible. If not, we advance $a(v)$ to the next arc on the list. The definition of basic operations implies that only relabeling v can create new admissible arcs out of v. Thus as $a(v)$ advances, arcs behind it on the list are not admissible. When the arc advances past the end of the list, v has no outgoing admissible arcs and therefore can be relabeled. Thus the current arc data structure allows us to charge to the next relabel operation the searches for admissible arcs to apply push operations to. We say that a vertex $v \neq s, t$ is *active* if $d(v) < n$ and $e_f > 0$. The highest-label variant of the method, which at each step selects an active vertex with the highest distance label, runs in $O(n^2\sqrt{m})$ time [9,30].

HI-PR Implementation. Next we review the HI-PR implementation [11] of the push-relabel algorithm. It uses the highest-label selection rule, and global update and gap heuristics.

To facilitate implementation, the method uses a *layers of buckets* data structure. The layers correspond to distance labels i. Each layer i contains two buckets, *active* and *inactive*. A vertex v with $d(v) = i$ is in one of these buckets: in the former if $e_f(v) > 0$ and in the latter otherwise. Active buckets are maintained as singly linked lists and support insert and extract-first operations. Inactive buckets are maintained as doubly linked lists and support insert and delete operations. The layer data structure is an array of records, each containing two pointers – to the active and the inactive buckets of the layer. A pointer is `null` if the corresponding bucket is empty. To implement the highest-level selection, we maintain the index of the highest layer with non-empty active bucket.

The gap heuristic [13] is based on the following observation. Suppose for $0 < i < n$, no vertex has a distance label of i but some vertices w have distance labels $j : i < j < n$. The validity of d implies that such w's cannot reach t in G_f and can therefore be deleted from the graph until the end of the first phase of the algorithm.

Layers facilitate implementation of the gap heuristic. We maintain the invariant that the sequence of non-empty layers (which must start with layer zero containing t) has no gaps. Note that only the relabeling operation moves vertices between layers. During relabeling, we check if a gap is created, i.e., if increasing distance label of v from its current value $d(v)$ makes both buckets in layer $d(v)$ empty. If this is the case, we delete v and all vertices at the higher layers from the graph, restoring the invariant. Note that deleting a vertex takes constant time, and the total cost of the gap heuristic can be amortized over the relabel operations.

Push and relabel operations are local. On some problem classes, the algorithm substantially benefits from the *global relabeling* operation. This operation performs backwards breadth-first search from the sink in G_f, computing exact distances to the sink and placing vertices into appropriate layer buckets. Vertices that cannot reach the sink are deleted from the graph until the end of the first phase. Global update places the remaining vertices in the appropriate buckets and resets their current arcs to the corresponding first arcs. HI-PR performs global updates after $\Omega(m)$ work has been done by the algorithm; this allows amortization of global updates.

HI-PR implements the highest-label algorithm, which runs in $O(n^2\sqrt{m})$ time. As the work of heuristics is amortized, HI-PR runs in the same time bound.

4   PAR Algorithm

First we describe a well-known *augment-relabel (AR)* variation of the push-relabel method.[2] The AR algorithm maintains a flow (not a preflow), and augments along the shortest augmenting path. However, instead of breadth-first search, it uses the relabel operation to find the paths. The method maintains a valid distance labeling. Any initial labeling can be used. To find the next augmenting path, the method starts at s and searches the admissible graph in the depth-first search manner. At a general step, the algorithm has an admissible path from s to the current vertex v and tries to extend it. If v has an admissible arc (v, w), the path is extended to w. (The admissible arcs can be efficiently found using the current arc data structure.) Otherwise the method shrinks the path, making the predecessor of v on the path the current vertex, and relabels v. An augmenting path is found if t becomes the current vertex. The algorithm augments the flow along the path and starts a new search. Note that the new search can start at s or at the last vertex of the augmenting path reachable from s in G_f after the augmentation.

We experimented with the AR algorithm and its preflow variation (which picks a vertex with excess, finds an admissible path to t, and pushes as much flow as possible on arcs of the path, possibly creating flow excesses at intermediate vertices). These algorithms performed very poorly. Next we discuss a related algorithm that performs well.

The partial augment-relabel (PAR) algorithm is a push-relabel algorithm that maintains a preflow and a distance labeling. The algorithm has a parameter k. At each step, the algorithm picks an active vertex v and attempts to find an admissible path of k arcs starting at v. If successful, the algorithm executes k push operations along the path, pushing as much flow as possible. Otherwise, the algorithm relabels v.

PAR looks for augmenting paths in the same way as AR. It maintains a current vertex x (initially v) with an admissible path from v to x. To extend the path, the algorithm uses the current arc data structure to find an admissible arc (x, y). If such an arc exists, the algorithm extends the path and makes y the current vertex. Otherwise the algorithm shrinks the path and relabels x. The

---

[2] [1] refers to this algorithm as the shortest augmenting path algorithm. However, this is only one of the methods that augment along the shortest paths. Methods of [14,15] are also shortest augmenting path algorithms.

search terminates if $x = t$, or the length of the path reaches k, or v is the current vertex and v has no outgoing admissible arcs.

As in the push-relabel method, we have the freedom to choose the next active vertex to process. We use the highest-label selection rule. One can show that, for $k = O(\sqrt{m})$, PAR has the same $O(n^2\sqrt{m})$ bound as HI-PR.

Implementation details. Our PAR implementation is similar to that of HI-PR. In particular, we use layers and highest-label selection. The gap heuristic is identical to that used in HI-PR. After experimenting with different values of k we used $k = 4$ in all of our experiments. The best value of k is problem-dependent, but we have seen only modest improvements compared to $k = 4$. Results for $3 \leq k \leq 6$ would have been similar. We concentrate on the differences in addition to the most obvious one, the use of partial augment strategy.

Note that HI-PR relabels only active vertices currently being processed, and as a side-effect we can maintain active vertices in a singly-linked list. PAR can relabel other vertices as well, and we may have to move an active vertex in the middle of a list into a higher-level list. Therefore PAR uses doubly-linked lists for active as well as inactive vertices. List manipulation becomes slower, but the overall effect is very minor. No additional space is required as the inactive list is doubly-linked in both implementations and a vertex is in at most one list at any time.

We also make improvements to global relabeling, which could also be applied to HI-PR. These include (i) incremental restart, (ii) early termination, and (iii) adaptive amortization.

Incremental restart takes advantage of the fact that if, since the previous global update, flows from vertices at distance D or less have not changed, we can start the update from layer D as lower layers are already in breadth-first order. This change can be implemented very efficiently as the only additional information we need is the value of D, which starts at n after each global update, and is updated to $min(d(w), D)$ each time we push flow to a vertex w. Incremental restart has little cost but can save substantial amount of work, especially in combination with the highest-label vertex selection.

The early termination heuristic stops breadth-first search when all vertices active immediately before the global update have been placed in their respective layers by the search. More precisely, let L be the highest distance label of an active vertex at this point. We stop breadth-first search after scanning all vertices in the new layer L. For vertices with distance labels of L and below that have not been scanned by breadth-first search, we set their distance labels to $L + 1$ and insert them into layer $L + 1$. Vertices with distance labels above $L + 1$ remain in their previous layers. In general, the early termination heuristic may stop before the breadth-first search is completed and make global updates less effective. However, in our experiments the work saved by early termination seem to outweigh the potential increase in other operations.

Note that global update with an incremental restart and early termination produces a valid distance labeling and the distance labels cannot decrease during an update. Thus the algorithm remains correct, and the running time bound does not get any worse.

With incremental restart and early termination, global updates sometimes cost substantially less than the time to do breadth-first search of the whole graph. We experimented with various amortization strategies based on a threshold, which is set based on the work done by the previous global update and the number n' of vertices left in the graph. When the work since the last global update exceeds the threshold, we do the next update. The code used in our experiments uses the number of relabel operation to measure the work and sets the threshold T as follows: $T = F\left(\frac{n}{100} + n'4^{S/n'}\right)$, where S is the number of vertices scanned during the last global update and F is the global update frequency parameter. The intuition is to do the next update earlier if the last one was cheap, but to limit the variation in the threshold value by a factor of 4.

Our experiments use a fixed value $F = 1.0$ and $k = 4$. One can improve performance by experimentally tuning these parameters to a a specific applications.

5   Experimental Results

We test code performance on DIMACS problem families [23] (see also [21]) and on problems from vision applications.[3] As we will see, many DIMACS problems are very simple and algorithm performance is sometimes sensitive to low-level details. To make sure that the performance is not affected by the order in which the input arcs are listed, we do the following. First, we re-number vertex IDs at random. Next, we sort arcs by the vertex IDs. The vision problems have been made available at http://vision.csd.uwo.ca/maxflow-data/ by the vision group at the University of Western Ontario, and include instances from stereo vision, image segmentation, and multiview reconstruction.

The main goal of our experiments is to compare PAR with HI-PR. We use the latest version, 3.6, of HI-PR and the current version, 0.23, of PAR. We also make a comparison to an implementation of Chandran and Hochbaum [7]. A paper describing this implementation is listed on authors' web sites as "submitted for publication" and no preprint is publicly available. The authors do make their code available, and gave several talks claiming that the code performs extremely well. These claims were about version 3.1 of their code, which we refer to as CH. Recently, an improved version, 3.21, replaced the old version on the web site. We compare to this version, denoted as CHn (n for new), as well. We are not aware of any public document that describes either of these codes.

Our experiments were conducted on an HP Evo D530 machine with 3.6 MGz Pentium 4 processor, 28 KB level 1 and 2 MB level 2 cache, and 2GB of RAM. The machine was running Fedora 7 Linux. C codes HI-PR, PAR, and CHn were compiled with the gcc version 4.1.2 compiler that came with the Fedora distribution using "-O4" optimization option. C++ code CH was compiled with the g++ version 4.1.2 compiler using "-O4" optimization.

For synthetic problems, we report averages over ten instances for each problem size. We give running time in seconds. In some tables we also give scan count

---

[3] Due to space restrictions we omit problem descriptions. See the references.

Table 1. RMF-Long (left) and RMF-Wide (right) problem families

	n	0.3 M	0.5 M	1.1 M	2.0 M	4.1 M	0.3 M	0.5 M	1.0 M	2.1 M	4.2 M
	m	1.3 M	2.6 M	5.1 M	10.2 M	20.3 M	1.3 M	2.6 M	5.2 M	10.3 M	20.7 M
HI-PR time		0.67	1.75	4.26	12.63	41.88	6.45	15.05	41.55	100.12	266.99
sd%		8.04	15.50	10.71	11.41	18.35	2.99	4.48	3.55	3.71	12.06
PAR time		0.32	0.65	1.35	2.79	5.89	3.76	9.29	21.67	50.90	128.61
sd%		5.88	8.69	7.18	7.12	8.78	5.88	8.69	7.18	7.13	8.78
HI-PR sc/n		8.16	11.25	13.25	20.04	33.97	52.93	60.90	76.55	88.64	102.43
PAR sc/n		4.99	5.02	5.05	5.16	5.26	47.16	54.64	62.06	70.24	80.63
CH time		0.74	1.79	4.68	9.21	24.67	8.53	17.30	72.61	476.50	1200.07
sd%		11.90	10.32	4.68	7.57	10.80	76.84	71.17	87.88	47.10	36.83
CHn time		0.59	1.36	3.28	7.43	16.73	2.49	6.31	13.56	85.05	430.42
sd%		18.92	15.34	12.51	14.17	8.69	9.56	18.65	17.88	113.28	90.64

Table 2. Wash-Wide problem family

	n	0.13 M	0.26 M	0.52 M	1.0 M	2.1 M	4.2 M	8.4 M
	m	0.4 M	0.8 M	1.6 M	3.1 M	6.3 M	12.5 M	25.0 M
HI-PR time		0.80	2.36	7.61	22.10	51.81	133.37	273.51
PAR time		0.47	1.53	4.33	12.71	29.48	77.40	160.17
HI-PR sc/n		16.20	19.99	25.51	30.46	32.32	39.92	39.22
PAR sc/n		9.01	12.26	14.21	18.55	19.66	25.86	25.27
CH time		0.39	1.29	3.23	8.20	18.91	47.05	118.41
CHn time		0.35	1.09	2.78	6.85	15.43	36.32	74.18

per vertex (sc/n), where the scan count (sc) is the sum of the number of relabel operations and the number of vertices scanned by the global update operations. This gives a machine-independent measure of performance. In the tables, $k = 10^3$ and $M = 10^6$. In Table 1, we also give standard deviation in percent $(sd\%)$.

Another experiment we ran, but omit due to the lack of space, measured how much improvement is due to the improved global updates. These usually improve performance, but by less than 20%. Most of the improvement compared to HI-PR is due to the PAR basic operation ordering.

5.1   Experiments with DIMACS Families

PAR vs. HI-PR. First we compare PAR to HI-PR on DIMACS families. On RMF-Long family (Table 1 left), the new code gives an asymptotic improvement, and its running time is almost linear: As the problem size increases by a factor of 16, the number of scans per vertex shows a minor increase from 4.99 to 5.26. On RMF-Wide family (Table 1 right), PAR is faster, by about a factor of two for larger problems.

On Washington problem families (Tables 2–3), PAR outperforms HI-PR, usually by a little less than a factor of two. Note that Wash-Long and Wash-Line problems are very easy, with larger problems requiring less then two scans per vertex.

Table 3. Wash-Long (left) and Wash-Line (right) problem families

n	0.5 M	1.0 M	2.1 M	4.2 M	8.4 M	41 K	66 K	104 K	165 K	262 K
m	1.6 M	3.1 M	6.3 M	12.6 M	25.2 M	2.1 M	4.2 M	8.4 M	16.8 M	33.5 M
HI-PR time	0.82	1.60	3.05	5.59	10.82	0.24	0.46	1.06	2.26	4.50
PAR time	0.51	0.98	1.81	3.46	6.66	0.15	0.28	0.64	1.40	3.02
HI-PR sc/n	3.98	3.62	3.26	2.68	2.55	2.07	2.06	2.05	2.05	2.04
PAR sc/n	2.49	2.19	1.83	1.66	1.56	1.13	1.11	1.10	1.09	1.07

Table 4. Acyclic-Dense problem family

n	2.0 K	2.9 K	4.1 K	5.8 K	8.2 K
m	2.1 M	4.2 M	8.4	16.8 M	33.6 M
HI-PR time	0.93	1.93	4.60	10.63	27.08
PAR time	0.13	0.25	0.51	1.02	2.05
HI-PR sc/n	8.81	9.12	10.50	11.25	12.39
PAR sc/n	1.87	1.81	1.93	1.91	1.93

The Acyclic-Dense problem family (Table 4) is also very easy for PAR, which performs asymptotically better than HI-PR. This problem family is very sensitive to initialization. A slightly different initial labeling can cause significant performance degradation.

The above experiments show that on DIMACS problem families, PAR outperforms HI-PR, asymptotically on RMF-Long and Acyclic-Dense families.

Comparison with CH. Next we compare HI-PR and PAR with CH and CHn. We exclude easy problem families where for large problem sizes PAR performs less than three scans per vertex. The data appear in Tables 1 and 2.

On RMF-Long and RMF-Wide families, PAR is asymptotically the fastest code. On the RMF-Wide problems, CH and CHn exhibit very high variance in the running time: Table 1 shows this for all sizes for CH and for the larger sizes for CHn. For the largest size, the ratio between the fastest and the slowest runs of CHn is 14.3, compared to 1.35 for PAR. This is an indication that CH and CHn are not robust. On Wash-Wide problems, CHn is the fastest code. PAR is slower by about a factor of two.

5.2 Vision Instances

Stereo vision problems (see Table 5) have several independent subproblems: tsukuba has 16, sawtooth – 20, venus – 22. The BVZ and KZ2 prefixes refer to different ways of defining the problem. As suggested in [5], we report the total time for each problem. Here CHn is the fastest code. PAR is the second fastest, losing by less than a factor of two. HI-PR loses to PAR by about a factor of two. CH performs poorly, losing by three orders of magnitude in some cases.

On multiview instances, (Table 6[4]) PAR is about a factor of two faster than HI-PR. CH crashes on these problems. CHn fails feasibility and optimality self-checks on the smaller problems and fails to allocate the memory it needs for the larger problems.

---

4   *dnf* stands for "did not finish."

Table 5. Stereo vision data

name	HI-PR	PAR	CH	CHn
BVZ–				
tsukuba	8.07	4.01	643.62	2.80
sawtooth	12.45	7.70	3,127.23	5.45
venus	23.65	11.79	2,707.32	7.23
KZ2–				
tsukuba	30.39	13.31	4,020.49	6.85
sawtooth	31.88	16.35	13,472.85	11.70
venus	61.64	24.68	12,898.89	15.84

Table 7. Segmentation data

name	HI-PR	PAR	CH	CHn
bone-xyzx-6-10	1.06	0.37	dnf	0.20
bone-xyzx-6-100	1.08	0.39	dnf	0.25
bone-xyz-6-10	2.41	0.86	dnf	0.50
bone-xyz-6-100	2.48	0.93	dnf	0.58
bone-xyzx-26-10	2.89	1.04	dnf	0.60
bone-xyzx-26-100	3.17	1.07	dnf	0.58
bone-xy-6-10	6.65	2.04	dnf	1.19
bone-xy-6-100	6.92	2.16	dnf	1.36
bone-xyz-26-10	6.38	2.25	dnf	1.20
bone-xyz-26-100	6.72	2.44	dnf	1.39
liver-6-10	34.59	16.90	dnf	14.18
liver-6-100	46.69	18.76	dnf	17.59
babyface-6-10	52.75	26.42	dnf	22.77
babyface-6-100	71.55	34.36	dnf	37.85

Table 6. Multiview data

name	HI-PR	PAR	CH	CHn
gargoyle-sml	4.37	2.68	dnf	dnf
camel-sml	8.54	4.56	dnf	dnf
gargoyle-med	125.20	53.04	dnf	dnf
camel-med	160.27	76.77	dnf	dnf

Data in Table 7 shows that on segmentation instances, CHn is the fastest for smaller problem sizes, but PAR loses by less than a factor of two. On larger problems, CHn and PAR perform similarly. HI-PR is two to three times slower than PAR. CH crashes on these problems.

6   Concluding Remarks

The push-relabel method allows endless variations. Over the years we tried many potentially promising ideas, but until now our attempts failed to produce an implementation more robust than HI-PR. Robustness is the main reason why HI-PR remained the benchmark for a long time. Our experiments give a strong evidence that PAR is a more robust code. It outperforms HI-PR on all problem families we used, and in some cases the improvement in performance is asymptotic. Simplicity is another reason for the popularity of HI-PR, and PAR is not much more complicated.

CH is not a very robust code. It is an order of magnitude slower that HI-PR on large RMF-Wide problems and over two orders of magnitude slower on stereo vision problems (the only vision problems it has not crashed on). Compared to PAR, CH is never significantly faster, and often significantly slower – by over three orders of magnitude on the KZ2-sawtooth instance, for example. Our experience with this code contradicts the claims made by its authors. CHn is more robust than CH. However it is noticeably slower on large RMF-Wide instances. Furthermore, it failed to run on the multiview instances due to higher memory overhead and insufficient precision. Fixing these problems will probably make CHn slower as it may require higher precision.

Graphs in vision problems are very regular and can be represented more compactly, as done in [5]. It would be interesting to implement PAR with such a representation of a graph. This would make PAR more efficient on the vision problems and would enable a direct comparison to the algorithm of [5]. The results of [5] also suggest that FIFO outperforms the highest-label selection on vision problems, so it would be interesting to study a FIFO version of PAR.

Our experiments indicate that the DIMACS data set is showing its age. Most problems are easy for PAR, requiring less than ten scans per vertex. Wash-Wide problems are somewhat harder. Only RMF-Wide problems show clear asymptotic increase in the number of scans per vertex, but even for these problems the rate of increase is small. The largest problems with millions of vertices are solved using under a hundred scans per vertex. Although some DIMACS problems are still useful, there is a need for other synthetic and real-life data sets. The vision problems made available by the UWO group at our request is a step in this direction.

Acknowledgments. I am grateful to the organizers of the 2008 IPAM Graph Cuts workshop: their invitation to speak motivated me to work on maximum flow algorithms once again. Many thanks to Yuri Boykov, Andrew Delong, Vladimir Kolmogorov, and Victor Lempitsky for providing problem instances form vision applications. In addition, I would like to thank Renato Werneck for stimulating discussions and many useful comments.

References

1. Ahuja, R.K., Magnanti, T.L., Orlin, J.B.: Network Flows: Theory, Algorithms, and Applications. Prentice-Hall, Englewood Cliffs (1993)
2. Anderson, R.J., Setubal, J.C.: Goldberg's Algorithm for the Maximum Flow in Perspective: a Computational Study. In: Johnson, D.S., McGeoch, C.C. (eds.) Network Flows and Matching: First DIMACS Implementation Challenge, pp. 1–18. AMS (1993)
3. Babenko, M.A., Goldberg, A.V.: Experimental Evaluation of a Parametric Flow Algorithm. Technical Report MSR-TR-2006-77, Microsoft Research (2006)
4. Badics, T., Boros, E.: Implementing a Maximum Flow Algorithm: Experiments with Dynamic Trees. In: Johnson, D.S., McGeoch, C.C. (eds.) Network Flows and Matching: First DIMACS Implementation Challenge, pp. 65–96. AMS (1993)
5. Boykov, Y., Kolmogorov, V.: An Experimental Comparison of Min-Cut/Max-Flow Algorithms for Energy Minimization in Vision. IEEE transactions on Pattern Analysis and Machine Intelligence 26(9), 1124–1137 (2004)
6. Boykov, Y., Veksler, O.: Graph Cuts in Vision and Graphics: Theories and Applications. In: Paragios, N., Chen, Y., Faugeras, O. (eds.) Handbook of Mathematical Models in Computer Vision, pp. 109–131. Springer, Heidelberg (2006)
7. Chandran, B., Hochbaum, D.: A computational study of the pseudoflow and push-relabel algorithms for the maximum flow problem (submitted, 2007)
8. Chekuri, C.S., Goldberg, A.V., Karger, D.R., Levine, M.S., Stein, C.: Experimental Study of Minimum Cut Algorithms. In: Proc. 8th ACM-SIAM Symposium on Discrete Algorithms, pp. 324–333 (1997)
9. Cheriyan, J., Maheshwari, S.N.: Analysis of Preflow Push Algorithms for Maximum Network Flow. SIAM J. Comput. 18, 1057–1086 (1989)

10. Cherkassky, B.V.: A Fast Algorithm for Computing Maximum Flow in a Network. In: Karzanov, A.V. (ed.) Collected Papers. Combinatorial Methods for Flow Problems, vol. 3, pp. 90–96. The Institute for Systems Studies, Moscow (1979) (in russian); English translation appears in AMS Trans., vol.158, pp. 23–30 (1994)

11. Cherkassky, B.V., Goldberg, A.V.: On Implementing Push-Relabel Method for the Maximum Flow Problem. Algorithmica 19, 390–410 (1997)

12. Dantzig, G.B.: Application of the Simplex Method to a Transportation Problem. In: Koopmans, T.C. (ed.) Activity Analysis and Production and Allocation, pp. 359–373. Wiley, New York (1951)

13. Derigs, U., Meier, W.: An Evaluation of Algorithmic Refinements and Proper Data-Structures for the Preflow-Push Approach for Maximum Flow. In: ASI Series on Computer and System Sciences vol. 8, pp. 209–223. NATO (1992)

14. Dinic, E.A.: Metod porazryadnogo sokrashcheniya nevyazok i transportnye zadachi. In: Issledovaniya po Diskretnoĭ Matematike, Nauka, Moskva (1973) (in russian); Title translation: Excess Scaling and Transportation Problems

15. Edmonds, J., Karp, R.M.: Theoretical Improvements in Algorithmic Efficiency for Network Flow Problems. J. Assoc. Comput. Mach. 19, 248–264 (1972)

16. Ford, L.R., Fulkerson, D.R.: Maximal Flow Through a Network. Canadian Journal of Math. 8, 399–404 (1956)

17. Goldberg, A.V.: Efficient Graph Algorithms for Sequential and Parallel Computers. PhD thesis, M.I.T., January 1987. Technical Report TR-374, Lab. for Computer Science, M.I.T (1987)

18. Goldberg, A.V.: An Efficient Implementation of a Scaling Minimum-Cost Flow Algorithm. J. Algorithms 22, 1–29 (1997)

19. Goldberg, A.V., Rao, S.: Beyond the Flow Decomposition Barrier. J. Assoc. Comput. Mach. 45, 753–782 (1998)

20. Goldberg, A.V., Tarjan, R.E.: A New Approach to the Maximum Flow Problem. J. Assoc. Comput. Mach. 35, 921–940 (1988)

21. Goldfarb, D., Grigoriadis, M.D.: A Computational Comparison of the Dinic and Network Simplex Methods for Maximum Flow. Annals of Oper. Res. 13, 83–123 (1988)

22. Hagerup, T., Sanders, P., Träff, J.L.: An implementation of the binary blocking flow algorithm. Algorithm Engineering, 143–154 (1998)

23. Johnson, D.S., McGeoch, C.C.: Network Flows and Matching: First DIMACS Implementation Challenge. In: AMS. Proceedings of the 1-st DIMACS Implementation Challenge (1993)

24. Karzanov, A.V.: Determining the Maximal Flow in a Network by the Method of Preflows. Soviet Math. Dok. 15, 434–437 (1974)

25. King, V., Rao, S., Tarjan, R.: A Faster Deterministic Maximum Flow Algorithm. J. Algorithms 17, 447–474 (1994)

26. Mehlhorn, K., Naher, S.: LEDA: A Platform for Combinatorial and Geometric Computing. Cambridge University Press, Cambridge (1999)

27. Nguyen, Q.C., Venkateswaran, V.: Implementations of Goldberg-Tarjan Maximum Flow Algorithm. In: Johnson, D.S., McGeoch, C.C. (eds.) Network Flows and Matching: First DIMACS Implementation Challenge, pp. 19–42. AMS (1993)

28. Ogielski, A.T.: Integer Optimization and Zero-Temperature Fixed Point in Ising Random-Field Systems. Phys. Rev. Lett. 57, 1251–1254 (1986)

29. Sleator, D.D., Tarjan, R.E.: A Data Structure for Dynamic Trees. J. Comput. System Sci. 26, 362–391 (1983)

30. Tuncel, L.: On the Complexity of Preflow-Push Algorithms for Maximum-Flow Problems. Algorithmica 11, 353–359 (1994)

An Optimal Dynamic Spanner for Doubling Metric Spaces

Lee-Ad Gottlieb[1,*] and Liam Roditty[2]

[1] Courant Institute, New York University, New York NY 10012
adi@cs.nyu.edu
[2] The Weizmann Institute of Science, Rehovot, 76100 Israel
liam.roditty@weizmann.ac.il

Abstract. A t-spanner is a graph on a set of points S with the following property: Between any pair of points there is a path in the spanner whose total length is at most t times the actual distance between the points. In this paper, we consider points residing in a metric space equipped with doubling dimension λ, and show how to construct a dynamic $(1 + \varepsilon)$-spanner with degree $\varepsilon^{-O(\lambda)}$ in $O(\frac{\log n}{\varepsilon^{O(\lambda)}})$ update time. When λ and ε are taken as constants, the degree and update times are optimal.

1 Introduction

A graph H is a t-spanner of G if $d_H(u, v) \leq t d_G(u, v)$, where $d_G(u, v)$ denotes the shortest path distance between u and v in G, and $d_H(u, v)$ denotes the shortest path distance between u and v in H. A spanner can also be defined for a set of points residing in Euclidean space: Let S be a set of points in $\Re^d$. The graph G is a complete graph whose vertices are the points of S, and the weight of every edge is the distance between its endpoints. A geometric t-spanner is then constructed on the graph G.

Geometric spanners have received a fair amount of attention in the past couple of decades. Various papers have dealt with the construction of geometric spanners with specific properties, such as linear number of edges, small weight (the weight of a spanner is the sum of the weights of its edges), small hop diameter and low degree. For points residing in low-dimensional Euclidean space, Vaidya [14], Salowe [12], Callahan and Kosaraju [4] and Soares [13] showed how to compute a geometric $(1+\varepsilon)$-spanner with $O(n/\varepsilon^d)$ edges in $O(n \log n + \varepsilon^d \log(1/\varepsilon)n)$ time. In the dynamic setting, where the problem is to *explicitly* maintain a set of edges that constitute a spanner of the point set, Arya *et al.* [2] obtained $O(\log^d n \log \log n)$ update time in the restricted model in which updates were assumed to be random: A point to be deleted is assumed to be selected at random from S, and a point to be inserted is assumed to be a random point of the new point set. Bose *et al.* [3] gave a semi-dynamic algorithm that supports insertions in $O(\log^{d-1} n)$ time. Gao *et al.* [6] considered both dynamic and kinetic spanners (a kinetic spanner supports movement of the points), and gave a

---

* Author's work partially supported by NSF grant IIS 0414763.

D. Halperin and K. Mehlhorn (Eds.): ESA 2008, LNCS 5193, pp. 478–489, 2008.
© Springer-Verlag Berlin Heidelberg 2008

spanner with update time and degree $O(\frac{\log \alpha}{\varepsilon^d})$, where α is the *aspect ratio* of the set, the ratio between the largest and smallest interpoint distances of the set. This result is of interest when α is small, which is often the case.

This paper is interested in the question of dynamic spanners for points that reside in a metric space equipped with a *doubling dimension*. Let the space within radius r of a point be called the ball centered at that point. A point set X has doubling dimension λ if all points of X that are covered by a ball of radius r can be covered by 2^λ balls of radius $\frac{r}{2}$. While a low Euclidean dimension implies a low doubling dimension (Euclidean metrics of dimension d have doubling dimension $\Theta(d)$ [8]), doubling dimension is more general than Euclidean dimension, so all results for low doubling dimension apply to low Euclidean dimension as well. In this setting Har-Peled and Mendel [9] showed how to construct a static constant degree spanner in $O(\frac{n \log n}{\varepsilon^{O(\lambda)}})$ time. Roditty [11] gave a dynamic spanner that supports insertions in $O(\frac{\log n}{\varepsilon^{O(\lambda)}})$ amortized time and deletions in $\tilde{O}(\frac{n^{1/3}}{\varepsilon^{O(\lambda)}})$ amortized time (where the notation $\tilde{O}$ is used to hide logarithmic factors). Very recently, these authors [7] gave a dynamic spanner that supports insertions in $O(\frac{\log^2 n}{\varepsilon^{O(\lambda)}})$ amortized time and deletions in $O(\frac{\log^3 n}{\varepsilon^{O(\lambda)}})$ amortized time.

In this paper, we improve on previous results by providing a $(1+\varepsilon)$-spanner of constant degree that supports updates in $O(\frac{\log n}{\varepsilon^{O(\lambda)}})$ worst case time. For insertions and constant ε, λ, $O(\log n)$ is in fact optimal. This follows from the fact that the task of inserting a point into a $(1 + \varepsilon)$-spanner subsumes within it the task of discovering a $(1 + \varepsilon)$-nearest neighbor of the new point. Since approximate nearest neighbor search is known to require logarithmic time in the algebraic decision tree model [1], insertions into a spanner must require logarithmic time as well. We make no claims on the optimality of deletions.

A further application of our spanner is dynamic maintenance of the closest pair of points in the set S. Note that in a $(2 - \epsilon)$-spanner ($\epsilon > 0$), the pair (or pairs) of closest points must have an edge between them, or else their spanner stretch would be greater than $2 - \epsilon$. By storing the edges in a heap based on weight, we can answer a closest pair query in $O(1)$ time.

Comparison to previous work. In [7] we showed how to obtain a spanner while building on the hierarchical partition introduced in [6] and [10]. These partitions had individual points appearing in as many as $O(\log \alpha)$ levels, and so in order to avoid a dependence on $\log \alpha$ in the update time of the hierarchy and the spanner, we introduced a complex process of point replacements that limited the number of times a single point appeared in the hierarchy. This gave us amortized $O(\frac{\log^3 n}{\varepsilon^{O(\lambda)}})$ update time, with degree $\Theta(\frac{\log n}{\varepsilon^{O(\lambda)}})$.

In this paper, we show that a much stronger result is possible if one is willing to make an additional assumption on the point set: We assume that even after a point is deleted from S, we can still query the distance between the deleted point and a point that remains in S, or the distance between two deleted points. Such an assumption is a rather common one and innocuous enough – it is clearly true of points in a well defined space such as Euclidean space – but one could devise instances in which it does not hold, such as when the points represent wireless users who are deleted when they log off the network.

Making this assumption is necessarily to allow us to use the hierarchy and nearest neighbor structure of [5], where such an assumption is made. The advantage in using this hierarchy is that it can be updated in $O(\frac{\log n}{\varepsilon^{O(\lambda)}})$ time as opposed to $O(\frac{\log \alpha}{\varepsilon^{O(\lambda)}})$ time, eliminating the central hurdle we faced in building upon the hierarchy of [6] and [10]. However, it introduces a quite different, yet similarly difficult problem: This hierarchy contains within it points that have been deleted from the point set, and these points are prohibited from appearing in the spanner. Using such a hierarchy to create a spanner is the central challenge addressed in this paper. We demonstrate a successful solution to this problem, resulting in a spanner with $O(\frac{\log n}{\varepsilon^{O(\lambda)}})$ update time and degree $\varepsilon^{-O(\lambda)}$.

We conclude the introduction with a comment concerning the doubling dimension.

Packing under the doubling dimension. It can be shown (via a repetitive application of the doubling property) that if set S has minimum inter-point distance a, then at most $(\frac{b}{a})^{O(\lambda)}$ points of S can be found within distance b of any $x \in S$.

The rest of this paper is organized as follows. In the next section we describe some data structure tools that are essential for our algorithm. In Section 2 we review previous work on maintaining hierarchies and relate it to spanner construction. In Section 3 we present our new spanner, in Section 4 we prove low degree. A discussion of how to maintain the spanner dynamically is deferred to the full version of this paper.

2   Hierarchical Partitions and Spanners

In this section we review previous work on hierarchical partitions of points that inhabit a doubling dimension, and show how to extend this work to maintain dynamic spanners in $O(\log \alpha)$ update time.

As described in [6,10], a subset of points $X \subseteq Y$ is an ϵ-discrete center set (ϵ-net in the terminology of [10]) of Y if it satisfies the following invariants:

(i) For every $x, y \in X$, $d(x, y) \geq \epsilon$.
(ii) Every point $y \in Y$ is within distance ϵ of some point $x \in X$.

We say that x *covers* y if $x \in X$, $y \in Y$ and $d(x, y) \leq \epsilon$. The previous conditions require that the points of X be spaced out, yet nevertheless cover all points of Y.

Let S be a set of points with doubling dimension λ, and let α be the aspect ratio of S, the ratio between the largest and smallest inter-point distance in S. (For ease of presentation, we assume that the minimum inter-point distance in S is 1.) The hierarchical partition is a hierarchy of discrete center sets. The bottom level of the hierarchy is the set $Y_{2^0=1} = S$, and the top level is the set $Y_{2^{\lceil \log \alpha \rceil}}$ that contains only a single point. Each level $i > 0$ of the hierarchy is a set Y_{2^i}, which is a 2^i-discrete center set of the set $Y_{2^{i-1}}$.

Extracting a spanner. The hierarchical partition described above can be used as a backbone for a geometric spanner. A few definitions are necessary. First recall that for a spanner H, $d_H(x, y)$ is the spanner distance between x and y. A point $x \in Y_{2^i}$ is a parent of $y \in Y_{2^{i-1}}$ if x covers y. If more than one point covers y then the closest one of these points is chosen to be the parent of y. A point x is an ancestor of y if there exists a series of points $\langle x, \ldots, y \rangle$ such that each point in the series is a parent of the subsequent one.

We use the hierarchical partition to decide which edges are included in the spanner. There are two types of edges. The first type consists of *parent-child edges* that connect each point in Y_{5^i} to its parent in $Y_{5^{i+1}}$. A point in $Y_{5^{i+1}}$ may have $2^{O(\lambda)}$ children, so this adds $2^{O(\lambda)}$ child-parent edges for each occurrence of a point in the hierarchy. The second type consists of *lateral edges* which connect points in the same level when the distance between them is below some threshold. Specifically, in level Y_{5^i} we add an edge between any two points that are within distance $c \cdot 2^i$ (for some constant $c > 16$ that will depend on the desired precision ε, as described below). A point in level Y_{5^i} may have $c^{O(\lambda)}$ points within distance $c \cdot 2^i$, so this adds $c^{O(\lambda)}$ lateral edges for each occurrence of a point in the hierarchy.

Let H be a spanner that contains the aforementioned parent-child and lateral edges. We can show that H has low stretch. Before proving this, we note a simple property of the hierarchy:

Property 1. Let $x' \in Y_{2^i}$ be an ancestor of $x \in Y_{2^j}$ $(i > j)$. Then $d_H(x) \leq \sum_{k=j+1}^{i} 2^k = 2 \cdot 2^i - 2^{j+1} < 2 \cdot 2^i$.

The main lemma of this section follows.

Lemma 1. *The stretch of H is less than $1 + \frac{1}{\frac{c}{16} - 1}$*

Proof. We must show that for any two points $x, y \in Y_1$, $\frac{d_H(x,y)}{d(x,y)} < 1 + \frac{1}{\frac{c}{16} - 1}$.

If $d(x, y) \leq c$ then x and y are connected by a lateral edge, so $d_H(x, y) = d(x, y)$ and we are done.

Otherwise, let $x', y' \in Y_{2^i}$ be the lowest ancestors of x and y (respectively) which are connected by a lateral edge. Since x' and y' are connected by a lateral edge $d_H(x', y') = d(x', y')$. Also note that by Property 1, $d_H(x, x')$ and $d_H(y, y')$ are both less than $2 \cdot 2^i$, from which it follows that $d(x, x')$ and $d(y, y')$ are also less than $2 \cdot 2^i$.

Now, the spanner distance from x to y is $d_H(x, y) \leq d_H(x, x') + d_H(x', y') + d(y', y) < 2 \cdot 2^i + d(x', y') + 2 \cdot 2^i = d(x', y') + 4 \cdot 2^i$. The true distance from x to y is $d(x, y) \geq d(x', y') - d(x', x) - d(y', y) > d(x', y') - 2 \cdot 2^i - 2 \cdot 2^i = d(x', y') - 4 \cdot 2^i$. It follows that the stretch of the spanner less than $\frac{d_H(x,y)}{d(x,y)} = \frac{d(x',y') + 4 \cdot 2^i}{d(x',y') - 4 \cdot 2^i} = 1 + \frac{8 \cdot 2^i}{d(x',y') - 4 \cdot 2^i}$. This term reaches its maximum when $d(x', y')$ reaches its minimum.

It remains only to place a lower bound on $d(x', y')$. By assumption, the children of x' and y' (in level $Y_{2^{i-1}}$) are not connected by a lateral edge, so the distance between them is greater than $c \cdot 2^{i-1}$. The distance from x' to its child (and the distance from y' to its child) is at most 2^i. It follows that $d(x', y') > c \cdot 2^{i-1} - 2 \cdot 2^i - 2 \cdot 2^i = c \cdot 2^{i-1} - 4 \cdot 2^i$.

The stretch of the spanner is less than $1 + \frac{8 \cdot 2^i}{d(x', y') - 4 \cdot 2^i} < 1 + \frac{8 \cdot 2^i}{c \cdot 2^{i-1} - 8 \cdot 2^i} = 1 + \frac{1}{\frac{c}{16} - 1}$. $\qquad\qquad\qquad\square$

Choosing $c = 16(\frac{1}{\varepsilon} + 1)$ yields a $(1 + \varepsilon)$-spanner. Since a point may appear in $O(\log \alpha)$ levels of the hierarchy, it may have $O(\frac{\log \alpha}{\varepsilon^{O(\lambda)}})$ lateral edges incident upon it in the spanner, and so the degree of the spanner is $O(\frac{\log \alpha}{\varepsilon^{O(\lambda)}})$.

To understand why the spanner construction guarantees low stretch, note that the path from two points $x, y \in Y_1$ consists of a set of parent-child edges, followed by a single lateral edge, followed by a second set of parent-child edges. Choosing a large value for c causes the length of the lateral edge to dwarf the lengths of the other edges, and this results in $d_H(x, y)$ being close to $d(x, y)$.

[10] showed how to dynamically maintain the above hierarchical partition in $O(\frac{\log \alpha}{\varepsilon^{O(\lambda)}})$ update time, and it is an easy matter to maintain the aforementioned spanner in the same time as well.

Modified hierarchical partition. Note that when $\alpha = n^{\omega(1)}$, then the update time of the above hierarchy (and spanner) becomes $\omega(\frac{\log n}{\varepsilon^{\Theta(\lambda)}})$. Improving on this, Cole and Gottlieb [5] modified the hierarchical partition to support insertions in $O(\frac{\log n}{\varepsilon^{O(\lambda)}})$ time. Achieving this update time requires the use of auxiliary data structures and is intricate, but for our purposes we need only to highlight the changes to the hierarchical partition.

The modified hierarchical partition is defined as follows. The bottom level is the set Y_1 and contains all the points, and the top level is the set Y_α that contains only a single point. Each level $i > 0$ of the hierarchy is represented by a set Y_{5^i} ($i > 0$) which is a 5^i-discrete center set of the set $Y_{5^{i-1}}$, where the definition of a discrete center set X of Y is slightly altered to satisfy the following invariants:

(i) For every $x, y \in X$, $d(x, y) \geq \frac{\epsilon}{5}$.
(ii) Every point $y \in Y$ is within distance $\frac{3}{5}\epsilon$ of some $x \in X$.

Notice that the second invariant, applied recursively, implies that every point of Y_{5^j} is within distance $\sum_{j+1}^{i}(\frac{3}{5})^i = 4 \cdot 5^{i-1} - 5^j$ of some point of Y_{5^i} ($i > j$). This is called the *close-containment* property. (The choice of the constant 5 to define the radius of each level of the hierarchy is due to considerations discussed in [5].) The previous definitions of covering and ancestral relationships are unchanged.

From the modified hierarchy a spanning tree T is extracted. The spanning tree directly corresponds to the hierarchy: Its nodes are arranged in levels, and it has one node for each point in the hierarchy. Two nodes in the tree are connected if and only if their corresponding points are a parent-child pair; by a consequence of the doubling dimension, a node may have at most $2^{O(\lambda)}$ children.

As previously noted, Steiner points (i.e., points that no longer belong to S) are present in the structure. While [5] showed that the presence of these Steiner points does not interfere in the execution of a nearest neighbor search, these points are not acceptable in the spanner. Our challenge then is to use a hierarchy that contains Steiner points as a tool for the extraction of a spanner that contains no Steiner points.

3   Spanner Construction

In this section, we build upon the hierarchy of [5] to create a $(1+\epsilon)$-spanner with degree $(1/\varepsilon)^{O(\lambda)}$. This spanner can be maintained dynamically in $O(\frac{\log n}{\varepsilon^{O(\lambda)}})$ time; we defer a discussion of dynamic updates to the full version of this paper. We assume that we have access to this hierarchy and its associated spanning tree T.

3.1   Motivation: An Incremental Spanner

Suppose for the moment that we wished to maintain a spanner under insertions alone, so that the hierarchy contained no deleted points. Then it would possible to maintain a dynamic spanner in $O(\frac{\log n}{\varepsilon^{O(\lambda)}})$ time using the hierarchy of [5] as a backbone. The spanner is created by assigning parent-child and lateral edges to all points.

This construction guarantees low stretch: As before, the path from two points x and y at the bottom of the hierarchy consists of a set of parent-child edges from x up to one of its ancestors, followed by a single lateral edge to an ancestor of y, follows by a second set of parent-child edges down to y. Choosing a large value for the size of lateral edges causes the length of the lateral edge to dwarf the lengths of the other edges, and this results in the spanner having low stretch for an appropriate value of c. (We omit the exact analysis, with is similar to what was shown in the previous section.)

The difficulty with this approach is that the hierarchy contains deleted points which cannot appear in the spanner. Further, since a point may appear in many levels of the hierarchy, and possess lateral edge for each level, the degree of the spanner may be very large. Below, we will use the spanning tree T to create a new hierarchy that addresses both of these problems: The new hierarchy contains no deleted points, and each point appears in the hierarchy at most twice (in the bottom level and possibly one additional level). We will use this new hierarchy to create a spanner that mimics the spanner described above.

Let the hierarchy, tree and spanner described above be called the *full* hierarchy, tree and spanner.

3.2   Step 1. Pruning the Spanning Tree

Recall that tree T corresponds to the full hierarchy. The first step in creating a new hierarchy involves pruning T in a straightforward manner, thereby creating a new spanning tree T_1.

Let *real* nodes (or leaves) in T be nodes that correspond to non-deleted points, and Steiner nodes (or leaves) be those nodes that correspond to deleted points. We create T_1 from T thus: First, we remove from T all Steiner leaves, as well as all nodes that have no real leaf descendant. Then we compress all single-child paths. (A single-child path is a maximal chain of nodes $v_1, v_2, \ldots, v_k$ in which v_i is the only child of v_{i-1} for every $i \in [2, k]$. Compressing the path means removing the nodes $v_2, \ldots, v_k$ and linking the children of v_k to v_1.) The resulting tree is T_1. By construction, parent-child relationships in T_1 may have been ancestor-descendant relationships in T. Also, all remaining internal nodes have at least two and at most $2^{O(\lambda)}$ children, and have real leaf node descendants. (For a node $v \in T$ that *survives* in T_1, we may refer both to $v \in T$ and to $v \in T_1$.)

3.3   Step 2. Creating a Better Hierarchy

The nodes of T correspond to points in the full hierarchy, so T_1 – whose nodes are a subset of T – represents a hierarchy which is a subset of the full hierarchy. We will call this the *intermediate* hierarchy. Because the construction of T_1 compressed single-child paths, the intermediate hierarchy obeys the packing property but not the covering property. However, the presence of parent-child connections between points in different levels of the hierarchy implies that it does obey a somewhat weaker covering property, where every point in level Y_{5^i} is within the radius of some point residing in a higher level (but not necessarily in level $Y_{5^{i+1}}$).

A slight modification to the intermediate hierarchy will yield the *final* hierarchy which has the properties we want: It contains no deleted points, and each point appears in at most two levels.

First recall that T_1 contains no Steiner leaves, but may contain other Steiner nodes. We introduce the following *assignment* scheme to associate each internal node with a unique leaf node: Assume an arbitrary left-right ordering on the children of internal nodes. Each internal node of T_1 has at least two children (since all single-child paths in T were compressed), which means that there are more leaf nodes than internal nodes. This allows us to assign to each internal node a single leaf descendant. For example, we assign to each internal node V the leftmost leaf descendant of v's rightmost child. This scheme assigns a leaf to at most one ancestor.

Since the assignment scheme assigns each internal node a unique leaf node, it in effect assigns to every point $x \in Y_{5^i}$ $(i > 0)$ a unique point $y \in Y_0$. The final hierarchy is created from the intermediate hierarchy by removing each point x from its level Y_{5^i} and adding the appropriate point y to Y_{5^i} in place of x. By the close-containment property, $d(x, y) \leq 4 \cdot 5^{i-1} - 1$; hence x and y are relatively 'close', and the final hierarchy can be viewed as a minor perturbation of the intermediate hierarchy. Crucially, the final hierarchy contains no deleted points, and each point appears in at most two levels.

Now that we have derived the final hierarchy, we can use it to extract a spanner. For presentation purposes, we will first give a spanner for the intermediate hierarchy (which contains Steiner points), since this spanner is more intuitive. The spanner for the final hierarchy is almost identical to the spanner of the intermediate hierarchy, only with the points of the intermediate hierarchy replaced by their assignment.

3.4   Step 3. A Spanner for the Intermediate Hierarchy

We wish to construct a spanner for the intermediate hierarchy; the new spanner should resemble the full spanner, and have the equivalent of parent-child edges and lateral edges. As before, the length of the lateral edges dwarf the lengths of parent-child edges, resulting in a spanner with low stretch.

Type I edges. The new spanner will have edges that mimic the behavior of parent-child edges in the full spanner.

Consider node v that survives in T_1. v has a parent node in T, and in the full spanner the points corresponding to these nodes have a parent-child edge connecting them. v's parent in T_1 was an ancestor of v in T, and their corresponding points are and an ancestor-descendant pair in T, but a parent-child pair in T_1. We add a spanner edge between these two points; this is a *parent-child edge* for the intermediate spanner.

We will need another type of edge to make up for the fact that the intermediate hierarchy obeys only a weak covering property (a point may be covered by another point at a much higher level). This new edge is similar to a parent-child edge: Let $x \in Y_{5^k}$ and $z \in Y_{5^i}$ $(k > i)$ be two points in the intermediate hierarchy that are an ancestor-descendant pair. Let $y \in Y_{5^j}$ $(j > i)$ be the lowest point in the hierarchy that covers z. If y is below x, then y becomes the step-parent of x. We add a spanner edge between x and y; this is a *step-parent edge.*

(We will see in Section 4 that step-parent edges are key to attaining low spanner degree. Note also that we did not specify how y can be located; we defer a description of this to the full paper.)

Type II edges. The new spanner will have edges that mimic the behavior of lateral edges in the full spanner.

Consider node v that survives in T_1. The point in the hierarchy corresponding to v, say $y \in Y_{5^i}$, is present in the intermediate hierarchy, and was also found in the full hierarchy. In the full spanner, y possessed a lateral edge to all level Y_{5^i} points within distance $c \cdot 5^i$ of y; call the set of these points R. For each point $x \in R$ that is present in the intermediate hierarchy at level Y_{5^i}, we add to the new spanner a lateral edge connecting x to y. Now, for each point $x \in R$ that is not present in the intermediate hierarchy, we must find an equivalent for the now missing lateral edge from x to y: Let x' be the highest descendant of x (in the full hierarchy) that is still present in the intermediate hierarchy. We add lateral edges from x' to all children of y in the intermediate hierarchy.

Let H be the spanner for the intermediate hierarchy described above (where $c \geq \frac{1}{5\varepsilon}$ and $c \geq \frac{133}{5}$). H is a spanner for S, but uses Steiner points.

Theorem 1. *H is a $(1 + \epsilon)$-spanner for S.*

Proof. To prove this, we define the notion of an *ancestral path* from a point $y \in Y_1$ in the intermediate hierarchy towards some level Y_{5^i}. The path begins at y, and at each step proceeds to y's step-parent. If y has no step-parent, then the path proceeds to y's parent in the intermediate hierarchy. The path terminates when the next candidate point is above level Y_{5^i}. The spanner distance (and true distance) from y to any other point on the path is less than $5^i \sum_{m=0}^{\infty} (\frac{1}{5})^m = \frac{5}{4} 5^i$.

Let $x, y \in Y_1$ be any two points at the bottom level of the hierarchy. We will show a spanner stretch of $(1 + \varepsilon)$ for $d_H(x, y)$. First choose j such that

$c \cdot 5^j \leq d(x, y) < c \cdot 5^{j+1}$. Let the last node in the ancestral path from x (y) towards level $j - 2$ be x' (y'). We will show below that x' and y' are connected by a lateral edge in the spanner; this implies a path from x to y which consists of the edges between points on the ancestral path from x to x', followed by a single lateral edge from x' to y', followed by the edges between points on the ancestral path from y' to y. As before, the length of the lateral edge dwarfs that of the other edges, resulting in low stretch.

More rigorously: We know that $d(x', y') \leq d(x, y) + d(x, y') + d(y, y') \leq d(x, y) + \frac{5}{4}5^{j-2} + \frac{5}{4}5^{j-2} \leq d(x, y) + \frac{5}{2}5^{j-2}$. It is also true that $d_H(x, y) \leq d_H(x', y') + d_H(x', x) + d_H(y', y) \leq d_H(x', y') + \frac{5}{4}5^{j-2} + \frac{5}{4}5^{j-2} = d_H(x', y') + \frac{5}{2}5^{j-2}$. We will show below that there is a lateral edge between points x' and y', so $d_H(x', y') = d(x', y')$. It follows immediately that $d_H(x, y) \leq d_H(x', y') + \frac{5}{2}5^{j-2} = d(x', y') + \frac{5}{2}5^{j-2} \leq d(x, y) + \frac{5}{2}5^{j-2} + \frac{5}{2}5^{j-2} \leq d(x, y) + 5 \cdot 5^{j-2}$. Therefore, the stretch of the spanner is $\frac{d_H(x, y)}{d(x, y)} < \frac{d(x, y) + 5 \cdot 5^{j-2}}{d(x, y)} = 1 + \frac{5 \cdot 5^{j-2}}{d(x, y)}$. This term is maximized when $d(x, y)$ assumes its minimum possible value, which is $c \cdot 5^j$. It follows that the spanner has stretch $1 + \frac{5 \cdot 5^{j-2}}{c \cdot 5^j} = 1 + \frac{1}{5c}$. Taking $c \geq \frac{1}{5\varepsilon}$ yields a $(1 + \varepsilon)$-spanner.

It remains only to demonstrate that x' and y' are indeed connected by a lateral edge in the spanner. Let x'' (y'') be the final (and unsuccessful) candidate for the ancestral path of x (y); x'' occupies level Y_{5^l} ($l \geq j - 1$), and without loss of generality we assume that y'' occupies the same or higher level than x''. We will show that the distance from x'' to the full hierarchy ancestor of y' in level Y_{5^l} is not greater than $c \cdot 2^l$; by construction, this implies the existence of a lateral edge between x' and y' in the spanner:

Now, the distance from x to x'', and also the distance from y to the ancestor of y' (in level Y_{b^l}), is less than $\frac{4}{5}5^l$. So the distance from x'' to the ancestor of y' is less than $d(x, y) + \frac{4}{5}5^l + \frac{4}{5}5^l = d(x, y) + \frac{8}{5}5^l < 5^{j+1} + \frac{8}{5}5^l \leq 5^{l+2} + \frac{8}{5}5^l = \frac{133}{5}5^l$. When $c \geq \frac{133}{5}$, x' and y' possess a lateral edge in the spanner.   □

3.5   Step 4. A Spanner for the Final Hierarchy

The spanner for the final hierarchy is similar to the one for the intermediate hierarchy, only with points of the intermediate hierarchy swapped with their assignment points. Recall that the distance from a point $x \in Y_{5^i}$ in the intermediate hierarchy to its assignment point is at most $\frac{3}{5}5^i$, so the swapping of points that creates the final hierarchy adds only a small perturbation. Therefore, the analysis of stretch for the final spanner is almost identical to that of the intermediate spanner. Modifying the proof above to incorporate this perturbation gives that the stretch of the spanner is $1 + \frac{5 \cdot (5^{j-2} + \frac{3}{5}5^{j-2})}{c \cdot (5^j - \frac{3}{5}5^j)} = 1 + \frac{4}{5c}$. Taking $c \geq \frac{4}{5\varepsilon}$ yields a $(1 + \varepsilon)$-spanner.

4   Analysis of Degree for the Final Spanner

In this section, we prove that the spanner for the final hierarchy has degree $(1/\varepsilon)^{O(\lambda)}$. In proving low degree for the spanner of the final hierarchy, it will be useful to refer back to the spanner of the intermediate hierarchy. Before beginning the proof, we will need an important structural lemma for the intermediate hierarchy.

4.1 Structural Lemma

Lemma 2. *Let $x \in Y_{5^i}$ and $z \in Y_{5^k}$ $(i > k)$, be a parent-child pair in in the intermediate hierarchy.*
(i) If z has a step-parent $y \in Y_{5^j}$ $(i > j > k)$ then there exist only $b^{O(\lambda)}$ points of the intermediate hierarchy in levels Y_{5^j} through $Y_{5^{k+1}}$ that contain z within b times their radius.
(ii) If z has no step-parent, then there exist only $b^{O(\lambda)}$ points of the intermediate hierarchy in levels Y_{5^i} through $Y_{5^{k+1}}$ that contain z within b times their radius.

Proof. For case (i) let $l = j - 1$, and for case (ii) let $l = i - 1$. Let B be the set of all level Y_{5^l} points in the full hierarchy that are within distance $b \cdot 5^i$ of z, $|B| = 2^{O(\lambda)}$. Note that, as a consequence of the close-containment property, any point of the full hierarchy in levels Y_{5^l} through $Y_{5^{k+1}}$ that contains z within b times its radius is a descendant of a point in B (or is itself in B). Consider in turn each point in B, but only if it survives in the intermediate hierarchy; if it does not survive, then consider instead its highest surviving descendant (assuming the descendant is in level $Y_{5^{k+1}}$ or higher). In total, $2^{O(\lambda)}$ points are to be considered.

Let the point under consideration be $w \in Y_{b^m}$ $(l > m > k)$. By assumption, w does not cover z; $d(w, z) > 5^m$. By the close-containment property, all descendants of w are within distance $\frac{4 \cdot 5^m}{5}$ of w, and therefore at distance greater than $5^m - \frac{4 \cdot 5^m}{5} = \frac{5^m}{5} = 5^{m-1}$ from z. Recall that all points at level $Y_{5^{m-1-\log_5 b}}$ have radius $\frac{5^{m-1}}{b}$. Hence, no descendants of w at level $Y_{5^{m-1-\log_5 b}}$ or lower contain z within b times their radius. Therefore, only descendants of w in levels higher than $Y_{5^{m-1-\log_5 b}}$ can contain z within a times their radius, and there are only $b^{O(\lambda)}$ such descendants.

Repeating the above analysis for each of $2^{O(\lambda)}$ points, we conclude that only $b^{O(\lambda)}$ points may contain z within b times their radius.   □

4.2 Proof of Low Degree

Now that we have the structural lemma, we can prove that the final spanner has degree $(1/\varepsilon)^{O(\lambda)}$. Recall that there are two types of edges incident on a point. Type I edges include parent-child and step-parent edges, and Type II edges include lateral edges. In proving low degree for the spanner of the final hierarchy, it will be again prove useful to refer back to the spanner of the intermediate hierarchy.

Type I edges. For each occurrence of a point y in the intermediate hierarchy, the point possesses $2^{O(\lambda)}$ parent-child edges. Similarly, for each occurrence of y, the point possesses a single step-parent (and an edge to this step-parent) and may also serve as a step-parent for at most $2^{O(\lambda)}$ other points which it covers:

To see that the occurrence serves as a step-parent for at most $2^{O(\lambda)}$ other points, note that each step-child of $y \in Y_{5^i}$ has a unique ancestor in level Y_{5^i} of the full hierarchy; this ancestor did not survive in the intermediate hierarchy. By close-containment, the distance from this step-child to its ancestor is less than $\frac{4 \cdot 5^i}{5}$, so the distance from the ancestor to y is less than $\frac{4 \cdot 5^i}{5} + 5^i = \frac{9 \cdot 5^i}{5}$. There are $2^{O(\lambda)}$ points in the full hierarchy that are this close to y, so $y \in Y_{5^i}$ can have only $2^{O(\lambda)}$ step-children.

Since a point in the final hierarchy corresponds to at most two occurrences of points in the intermediate hierarchy, each point has at most $2^{O(\lambda)}$ Type I edges incident upon it.

Type II edges. For each occurrence of point y in the hierarchy, say at level Y_{5^j}, y is given lateral edges for each point $z \in Y_{5^j}$ of the full hierarchy that satisfies $d(y, z) \leq c \cdot 5^j$: If z survived in the intermediate hierarchy, a lateral edge connects y and z. If z does not survive in the intermediate hierarchy, lateral edges connect the children of y to z's highest surviving descendant. This accounts for $c^{O(\lambda)}$ lateral edges incident on y.

However, the occurrence $y \in Y_{5^j}$ may in fact account for more lateral edges: The children of a point $x \in Y_{5^i}$ $(i > j)$ are given lateral edges to y if: (i) y is the highest surviving descendant of its ancestor in level Y_{5^i} of the full hierarchy, and this ancestor did not survive in the intermediate hierarchy; (ii) the distance from the ancestor to x is not greater than $c \cdot 5^i$; and (iii) the step-parent of y (if y has one) is above level Y_{5^i}. We can show that there are only $c^{O(\lambda)}$ points that satisfy these conditions: Conditions (i) and (iii) imply that the point $x \in Y_{5^i}$ is found at a lower level than the lowest point that contains $y \in Y_{5^j}$ within its radius (which is y's step-parent, or y's parent if y has no step-parent). Condition (ii), coupled with the close-containment property, implies that $d(x, y)$ is less than $5^j + \frac{4 \cdot 5^j}{5} = \frac{9 \cdot 5^j}{5}$. It follows from Lemma 2 that only $c^{O(\lambda)}$ points in the intermediate hierarchy may satisfy both these conditions. Hence, each occurrence of y may translate to $c^{O(\lambda)}$ lateral edges incident on y.

Since a point in the final hierarchy corresponds to at most two occurrences of points in the intermediate hierarchy, each point has at most $c^{O(\lambda)}$ Type II edges incident upon it. We may conclude:

Theorem 2. *The degree of the final spanner is* $c^{O(\lambda)} = (1/\varepsilon)^{O(\lambda)}$

References

1. Arya, S., Mount, D.M., Nathanyahu, S., Silverman, R., Yu, A.Y.: An optimal algorithm for approximate nearest neighbor searching in fixed dimension. Journal of the ACM 45(6), 891–923 (1998)
2. Arya, S., Mount, D.M., Smid, M.: Dynamic algorithms for geometric spanners of small diameter: Randomized solutions. Computational Geometry: Theory and Applications 13, 91–107 (1999)
3. Bose, P., Gudmundsson, J., Morin, P.: Ordered theta graphs. Computational Geometry: Theory and Applications 28, 11–18 (2004)

 4. Callahan, P.B., Kosaraju, S.R.: A decomposition of multidimensional point sets with applications to k-nearest-neighbors and n-body potential fields. J. ACM 42, 67–90 (1995)
 5. Cole, R., Gottlieb, L.: Searching dynamic point sets in spaces with bounded doubling dimension. In: ACM Symposium on Theory of Computing (2006)
 6. Gao, J., Guibas, L., Nguyen, A.: Deformable spanners and applications. In: ACM Symposium on Computational Geometry (2004)
 7. Gottlieb, L., Roditty, L.: Improved algorithms for fully dynamic geometric spanners and geometric routing. In: ACM Symposium on Discrete Algorithms (2008)
 8. Gupta, A., Krauthgamer, R., Lee, J.R.: Bounded geometries, fractals, and low-distortion embeddings. In (IEEE) Symposium on Foundations of Computer Science, pp. 534–543 (2003)
 9. Har-Peled, S., Mendel, M.: Fast construction of nets in low dimensional metrics, and their applications. SIAM J. Comput. 35(5), 1148–1184 (2006)
10. Krauthgamer, R., Lee, J.: Navigating nets: Simple algorithms for proximity search. In: ACM-SIAM Symposium on Discrete Algorithms (2004)
11. Roditty, L.: Fully dynamic geometric spanners. In: ACM Symposium on Computational Geometry (2007)
12. Salowe, J.S.: Constructing multidimensional spanner graphs. Int. J. Comput. Geometry Appl. 1(2), 99–107 (1991)
13. Soares, J.: Approximating euclidean distances by small degree graphs. Discrete & Computational Geometry 11, 213–233 (1994)
14. Vaidya, P.M.: A sparse graph almost as good as the complete graph on points in K dimensions. Discrete & Computational Geometry 6, 369–381 (1991)

RFQ: Redemptive Fair Queuing

Ajay Gulati[1] and Peter Varman[2]

[1] VMware Inc, Palo Alto, CA
[2] Department of ECE and Computer Science
Rice University, Houston TX 77005, USA
agulati@vmware.com, pjv@rice.edu

Abstract. Fair-queuing schedulers provide clients with bandwidth or latency guarantees provided they are well-behaved *i.e.* the requested service is always within strict predefined limits. Violation of the service bounds results in nullification of the performance guarantees of the misbehaving client.

In this paper we relax this notion of good behavior and present a generalized service model that takes the current system load into consideration. Consequently clients may opportunistically consume more than their contracted service without losing future performance guarantees, if doing so will not penalize well-behaved clients. We present a new algorithm RFQ (Redemptive Fair Queuing) along with a generalized traffic model called the Deficit Token Bucket (DTB). RFQ incorporates the notion of redemption, whereby a misbehaving client may be rejuvenated and regain its performance guarantees. We characterize the conditions for rejuvenating a client, and prove that RFQ meets its performance guarantees in the DTB model.

1 Introduction

The popularity of hosted application services, and benefits in cost, energy, and manageability of a shared infrastructure has spurred interest in server virtualization and storage consolidation technologies [1,2]. This has created the need for flexible and robust resource management strategies for client isolation and QoS provisioning in shared server systems [3]. *Resource scheduling* is used to provide each workload with the abstraction of having its own dedicated server, while flexibly sharing server capacity to handle bursts or low latency requests. A client's performance requirements are usually expressed by a combination of *throughput* and *latency* constraints. Throughput refers to the average rate of service completion, while latency or response time is the interval between the arrival time of a request and the time it completes service. A database workload, for instance, may have strict response time requirements for its transactions, whereas a back-up or other file transfer application might care more about overall throughput than the latency of individual requests.

The Service Level Agreement (SLA) of client c_i has three parameters $(\sigma_i, \rho_i, \delta_i)$: ρ_i is the *average* (long term) service demand of c_i, the *burst parameter* σ_i specifies the allowable instantaneous deviation from ρ_i (as made precise later), and δ_i is a bound on the *latency* of its requests. The scheduler aims to provide c_i a throughput of ρ_i and a response time guarantee of δ_i as long as c_i is well-behaved (*i.e.* honors its SLA as

D. Halperin and K. Mehlhorn (Eds.): ESA 2008, LNCS 5193, pp. 490–502, 2008.

defined precisely later). In current models [4, 5, 6] a client is considered *well-behaved* if in *every* time interval of size $T \geq 0$, the total amount of service requested is upper bounded by $U(T) = \sigma_i + \rho_i \times T$. Such an arrival model is also known as the token bucket model [7] with parameters σ_i and ρ_i. Well-behaved clients restrict the amount of service requested in any time interval (either voluntarily or by request dropping) in return for receiving guaranteed response times.

A major drawback of current QoS schedulers is their fragility with respect to errant client behavior. If a client violates its SLA by requesting more than $U(T)$ service in *any* interval T, the deadline guarantees for the client are effectively nullified. Unfortunately, this nullification is not restricted to just the offending requests but can persist indefinitely into the future. (See Example 1 in Section 2). In a practical setting this restriction is unacceptable. When the server has unused capacity (since not every client is sending at the maximum rate at all times), it is desirable to allow clients who can use the excess service to do so, without penalizing them in the future for their use of spare capacity. A robust model should distinguish between benign violations of input limits (as when a client merely utilizes spare capacity) from critical violations where the client should be penalized to prevent it from encroaching on the shares of other clients.

In this paper we make the following contributions: (*a*) we define a dynamic traffic model called the Deficit Token Bucket (DTB) model. DTB allows one to define a weaker notion of well-behaved clients that distinguishes between benign and critical arrival violations; (*b*) we present a new scheduling algorithm RFQ (Redemptive Fair Queuing) that provides performance guarantees under this weaker model of well-behaved clients, and includes mechanisms to accelerate the rehabilitation of a misbehaving client; (*c*) we provide an algorithm for proportionate bandwidth allocation by modifying certain parameters of RFQ. The resulting algorithm achieves the optimal worst case fairness index [8], an important measure of the quality of a fair-queuing scheduler. Note that RFQ meets its deadlines in all situations where the existing schedulers do, in addition to situations where the latter do not. We believe this is the first algorithm which can successfully distinguish between benign and critical use of spare capacity, that allows better server utilization and greater flexibility for the clients.

2   Relation to Previous Work

Formal work related to Fair Queuing algorithms for QoS-based resource allocation falls into two categories. First is a class of scheduling algorithms for proportionate bandwidth allocation such as PGPS [9], Virtual Clock [10], WFQ [11, 12], WF^2Q [8], SFQ [13], SCFQ [14], Leap Forward Virtual Clock [15], Latency-rate Servers [16], Greedy Fair Queuing [17], Elastic Round Robin [18], and Time Share Scheduling [19], which guarantee weight-proportional throughput to clients by dividing up the server bandwidth fairly between them. A fundamental limitation of these algorithms is the strong coupling between their throughput and response time guarantees. The latency of a client's requests is fixed by its bandwidth allocation, resulting in over-provisioning for clients with low throughput and low latency requirements. A corollary to this is the inability of these algorithms to handle bursts effectively. The algorithms do not distinguish a client that sends its requests at a uniform rate from a client sends the requests in periodic bursts, as long as the average request rates are the same. Both clients will receive the same bandwidth allocation, but the bursty client will incur large latencies. On the other hand, an algorithm with independent latency and throughput controls can schedule the requests to be sensitive to the latencies.

The second class of scheduling algorithms [4, 5, 20, 21, 6] are latency-sensitive in that both throughput and response time constraints may be independently specified provided certain capacity constraints are met. The fundamental result in this regard is the SCED [4, 5] algorithm to schedule workloads specified by a given set of service curves that meet the capacity constraints. However, this solution and its successors have the fundamental drawback that a client that uses spare capacity may get starved in the future when resource contention is high. We present a detailed example below to show the issue of starvation and the possibility for indefinite response time penalties in the SCED algorithm. In the example tag refers to the value assigned to a request that is used as a scheduling priority. Tags are spaced by the inverse of the throughput ρ_i when c_i is backlogged; the scheduler dispatches requests to the server in the order of these tags.

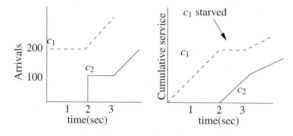

Fig. 1. c_1 is starved during [2,3] for using spare capacity during [1,2]

Example 1: Consider a system with two clients c_1 and c_2 with throughput requirements $\rho_1 = \rho_2 = 50$ req/s. Assume the system capacity is 100 req/s. Suppose that c_1 sends a burst of 200 requests at $t = 0$, and then sends requests at its desired rate of 50 req/s from $t = 2$ onwards. Suppose that c_2 is idle till $t = 2$, sends a burst of 100 requests at $t = 2$, and then sends requests at a steady rate of 50 req/s after $t = 3$. The input profiles are shown in Figure 1.

Now in the interval [0, 2], c_1 can utilizes the capacity unused by c_2 and will receives 100 req/s instead of its stipulated rate of 50 req/s. All these 200 requests will complete service by $t = 2$, but its tags (that are spaced apart by $1/\rho_i = 1/50$) will have reached a value of 200 x $1/50 = 4$ (much higher than the real time). Hence future requests of c_1 arriving after $t = 2$ will have tags beginning at 4 and increasing in increments of $1/50$. When c_2 becomes active at time $t = 2$, the 100 requests of c_2 will receive tags starting at 2 and spaced by $1/50$; all these tags are less than the tags of the pending requests of c_1. Hence, c_2 will get all the service, and complete its burst of 100 requests in 1 second at $t = 3$, starving c_1 of any service in this interval, After time $t = 3$ the requests of c_1 and c_2 are interleaved, since the tags of both c_1 and c_2 now begin at 4 and are separated by $1/50$. However, requests of c_1 have been pending since $t = 2$ and therefore these and all future requests of c_1 incur a latency of at least 1 second.

A better schedule can be constructed as follows. Serve the 200 requests of c_1 in the interval $[0,2]$ as before. From $t = 2$ onwards, give both c_1 and c_2 their guaranteed service rate of 50 req/s by interleaving the requests of c_1 and c_2. This ensures that neither c_1 nor c_2 will be starved of service, and that all requests of c_1 arriving after $t = 2$ will be served without delay. Note that c_2 missing its deadlines is justified since it is requesting more than its share during a period when there is no spare capacity in the system. In contrast, in the traditional fair scheduler c_1 misses deadlines indefinitely even though its only excess is to use unused service capacity between $[0,2]$. Our recent algorithm pClock [6] provided a solution to this problem, and showed empirically that it was able to avoid starvation in many cases. However, the formal conditions under which spare capacity can be safely used were no stronger than earlier results.

3   Model and Definitions

The system provides shared service to a set of m clients, $c_i, 1 \le i \le m$. Each request brings in a demand for a specified amount of service (e.g. IO requests, CPU time etc.). Clients' requests are held in private queues, and are dispatched to the server one at-a-time by the scheduler. The server capacity denoted by C is the rate at which it provides service. Time is represented by discrete time steps $t = 0, 1, 2, \cdots$. The SLA parameters of c_i are denoted by $(\sigma_i, \rho_i, \delta_i)$. The size of the request made by c_i at time t is denoted by $s_i(t), 0 \le s_i(t) \le \sigma_i$. The total amount of *service requested* by c_i in the interval $[a,b]$, is denoted by the *arrival function* $\mathscr{R}_i(a,b) = \sum_{t=a}^{b} s_i(t)$. The amount of *service provided* to c_i in the interval $[a,b]$ is denoted by $\mathscr{S}_i(a,b)$. A client is backlogged at some time instant if it has one or more requests pending in the queue or currently in service.

Definition 1. *The **backlog** $B_i(t)$ of a client c_i at time t is defined as $B_i(t) = \mathscr{R}_i(0,t) - \mathscr{S}_i(0,t)$. Client c_i is said to be **backlogged** at time t if $B_i(t) > 0$. A **system busy period** is a maximal-sized time interval during which at least one client is backlogged. The maximum size of any request is denoted by R_{max}. The **maximum service time** of a request is denoted by $\varepsilon = R_{max}/C$.*

Requests are classified as either *good* or *bad* based on two factors: (i) the total amount of service requested by the client relative to its SLA parameters, and (ii) the actual rate at which the client has received service. Good requests will be serviced within their stipulated response time, while bad requests cannot be guaranteed. This is the fundamental point of departure from previous schemes. In earlier models only the first factor is used to classify requests, while in our new model the load of the server is implicitly taken into account. If the server has sufficient capacity to absorb extra service without hurting the other clients, then future requests of this client are classified as good, and compete fairly with the other clients.

In order to classify requests we use a modified form of a token bucket algorithm [7]. For a client with arrival parameters σ and ρ we refer to it as (σ, ρ)-DTB (Deficit Token Bucket) model. Initially the bucket contains σ tokens. A request of size s will reduce the number of tokens in the bucket by s. If this results in the number of tokens becoming negative the request is classified as *bad*; else the request is *good*. The bucket is continually refilled with tokens at the constant rate of ρ but the maximum number of tokens is capped at σ. In addition, at a *synchronization point*, the number of tokens of a client c_i *with no current backlog* is increased to σ_i. Intuitively a synchronization point detects that there is unused server capacity and makes it available to clients. Clients that have a backlog are still paying the price for past misbehavior and therefore no tokens are added to their buckets.

Each client c_i is controlled by its own (σ_i, ρ_i)-DTB. Figure 2 shows the number of tokens as they change in DTB model. The solid line shows the total number of tokens accumulated and the dotted line shows the total service requested as a function of time. The difference between the two is the tokens available at that time instant. If the total service requested exceeds the cumulative tokens (*e.g.* beyond time a), the number of tokens will be negative. On the other hand, if a client gets idle the number of tokens will continue to increase at a rate ρ_i, but will be capped at σ_i.

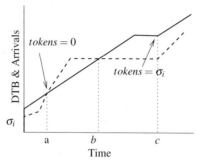

Fig. 2. DTB model for a client c_i

Definition 2. *A request from c_i of size s that arrives when the number of tokens in its bucket is at least s is* **good***; else the request is* **bad***. Client c_i is* **well-behaved** *in the interval $[a,b]$ if all its requests that arrive in the interval are good; else it is said to* **misbehave** *in that interval.*

Service guarantees can only be met if admission control ensures that the system has sufficient capacity to meet requirements of admitted clients. A *lower-bound* on the system capacity, referred to as the **System Capacity Constraint**, is stated below. This is derived by considering the situation in which all clients $c_i, 1 \le i \le m$, simultaneously send their maximum bursts (σ_i) at $t = 0$, followed by sending requests continuously at their designated throughput rates (ρ_i). If any of the inequalities in Definition 3 is violated, at least one request in the above arrival set will miss its deadline. The first constraint is needed to ensure that all c_i can receive throughput ρ_i. The second constraint follows by noting that for $k \le i$, c_k must complete $\sigma_k + \rho_k(\delta_i - \delta_k)$ amount of service by δ_i for it to meet its deadlines.

Definition 3. *Let the clients be arranged in order of non decreasing latencies, represented by $\delta_1 \le \delta_2 \le \cdots \le \delta_m$.*

The **System Capacity Constraint** *is defined by the following equations:*

$$\sum_{\forall i} \rho_i \le C \tag{1}$$

$$\forall \, i \, , \sum_{k=1}^{i} \sigma_k + \rho_k(\delta_i - \delta_k) \leq C \times \delta_i \qquad (2)$$

In Section 5, we show that these conditions are also *sufficient* to guarantee that no good requests are delayed.

4   Scheduling Algorithm RFQ

The algorithm *RFQ* is based on tagging requests to reflect their scheduling priority. Each request receives a *start tag* and a *finish tag*. The start tags determine eligibility of requests for scheduling; at any instant, only requests with start tags no more than the current time are eligible. Among eligible requests the one with the smallest finish tag is chosen and dispatched to the server. Pseudo code of algorithm is presented in Algorithm 1 below.

---

1 **Request Arrival:**
2 Let t_a be arrival time, of request r from c_i;
3 UpdateNumtokens( );
4 ComputeTags( );

1 **Request Completion:**
2 Let t_c be time the current request completes;
3 AdjustTags ( );
4 Dispatch( );

Algorithm 1. RFQ algorithm

There are two actions performed by the scheduler on a request arrival: *UpdateNumtokens* implements the DTB model by updating the number of available tokens for this client; *ComputeTags* assigns start and finish tags to the request to be used by the dispatcher. When a request completes service two actions are again required: *AdjustTags* is used for synchronizing tags with real time and rejuvenating clients as necessary, while routine *Dispatch* is used to select the next request to send to the server. These components are detailed in Algorithms 2 and 3.

UpdateNumtokens: For each client c_i, the routine maintains a variable *numtokens$_i$* that tracks the amount of tokens in its bucket at an arrival instant. The initial value of *numtokens$_i$* is set to σ_i at the start of a system busy period. The amount of tokens increases at the uniform rate of ρ_i. Hence in an interval of Δ seconds it will be incremented by $\Delta \times \rho_i$, but the total amount of tokens is capped at σ_i.

Compute Tags: This routine assigns *start* and *finish* tags (S_i^r and F_i^r respectively) to the request r arriving from c_i. The value assigned to the start tag S_i^r depends on whether the request is good or bad. Let the size of the request be s_i. If the request is good (*numtokens$_i$* $\geq s_i$), S_i^r is set to the current time t. The start tag of a bad request is set to a time in the future, specifically the earliest time at which the bucket would have accumulated s_i tokens if there are no further withdrawals. If there are $n \geq 0$ tokens currently in the bucket, the additional $(s_i - n)$ tokens required will be accumulated in a further $(s_i - n)/\rho_i$ time. The condition $n < 0$ signifies that there are pending requests with start tags beyond the current time; the request needs to earn s_i tokens and join the end of the queue of pending requests. This is done by setting is start tag to s_i/ρ_i beyond the largest start tag of c_i at this time. F_i^r is set to the sum of S_i^r and the latency bound δ_i. The count of tokens for the client is decremented by the service required (s_i), and the number of pending requests for the client is updated. The variables $MinS_i$ and $MaxS_i$ track the smallest and largest start tags of c_i respectively, and are updated as necessary.

UpdateNumtokens:
On arrival of request r of size s_i from client c_i at time t_a;
Let $\Delta = t_a$ − the arrival time of the previous request of c_i;
$numtokens_i \mathrel{+}= \Delta \times \rho_i$;
if $(numtokens_i > \sigma_i)$ **then**
$\qquad numtokens_i = \sigma_i$

ComputeTags:
On arrival of request r of size s_i from client c_i at time t_a;
if $(numtokens_i \geq s_i)$ **then**
$\qquad S_i^r = t_a$;
else
$\qquad$ **if** $(numtokens_i > 0)$ **then**
$\qquad\qquad S_i^r = t_a + (s_i - numtokens_i)/\rho_i$;
$\qquad$ **else**
$\qquad\qquad S_i^r = MaxS_i + s_i/\rho_i$

$MaxS_i = S_i^r$;
$F_i^r = S_i^r + \delta_i$;
$numtokens_i = numtokens_i - s_i$;
$backlog_i = backlog_i + 1$;
if $(backlog_i = 1)$ **then**
$\qquad MinS_i = S_i^r$

Algorithm 2. Components of RFQ algorithm at request arrival

AdjustTags: The routine checks for the condition where the start tags of all pending requests are greater than the current time t_c. We call this a *synchronization point*. Rather than allowing the tags to keep running ahead of real time (which is the fundamental cause for starvation; see Example 1 of Section 2), the algorithm synchronizes the backlogged clients and the idle clients. At a synchronization point, the algorithm shifts the tag values of all requests at the server by a fixed amount, so that the smallest start tag after the adjustment coincides with the current time t_c. The relative values of the tags are not changed: they just shift as a block by an offset equal to the difference between the smallest start tag in the system and the current time. Since new clients will begin their tags from the current time as well, all clients compete fairly from this point on, avoiding starvation. Note that an implementation just needs to maintain an offset value equal to the the shift amount, and does not need to explicitly alter each tag.

The occurrence of a synchronization point also indicates that there is spare server capacity that can be reallocated without risking future guarantees. Hence the routine also checks if there are any clients that can be rejuvenated. If client c_i at a synchronization point has a backlog of zero, then it can be rejuvenated and the number of tokens is changed to σ_i.

Note that this shift in tag values and infusion of tokens by rejuvenation raises the possibility that some clients may now miss their deadlines, since more requests are pushed into a given time interval. However, as we show in Theorem 1 the readjustment of tags does not result in any missed deadlines, since it exactly compensates for the spare capacity detected by the synchronization point.

Dispatch: This routine is invoked on the completion of each request. It selects a pending request to dispatch to the server. E is the set of *eligible requests* consisting of the requests whose start tags are less than or equal to the current time. Note that the *AdjustTags* routine guarantees that E is not empty as long as there is at least one request in the system, by forcing a synchronization if necessary. From the eligible requests, the one with the earliest finish tag is selected for service. The number of pending requests ($backlog_k$) and minimum start tag ($MinS_k$) of the selected client c_k are updated appropriately.

AdjustTags:
Let A be the set of currently backlogged clients at time t_c;
if $(\forall j \in A, MinS_j > t)$ **then**
    $mindrift = min_{j \in A} \{MinS_j - t_c\}$;
    $\forall j \in A$, Subtract $mindrift$ from $MinS_j$, $MaxS_j$ and all *start* and *finish* tags;
    $\forall j \notin A$, $numtokens_j = \sigma_j$;

Dispatch:
On completion of request from client c_i at time t_c;
Let E be the set of pending requests with start tags no more than t_c;
From E, select the request w with minimum finish tag and dispatch it to the server. Let the chosen request be from client c_k;
$backlog_k = backlog_k - 1$;
if $(backlog_k > 0)$ **then**
    Let the start tag of the next pending request of c_k be S_k^r;
    $MinS_k = S_k^r$;

Algorithm 3. Components of RFQ algorithm on request completion

5   Proof of Correctness

In this section we provide a proof of the scheduling guarantees of RFQ. We will show that if the system capacity satisfies the constraints noted in Definition 3, then every good request will meet its deadline. Note that the definition of good requests includes clients that may have misbehaved in the past, but have since been rejuvenated.

Definition 4. *A* **synchronization point** *is a departure instant t at which all start tags are greater than t. Immediately after the synchronization, the minimum start tag is t and every flow with zero backlog at t is rejuvenated so that it has σ_i tokens.*

Lemma 1. *If a good request completes service before the finish tag assigned to it by RFQ, then the request meets its latency bound.*

Proof. Consider a request r of c_i that arrives at some time instant t. Since the request is good, RFQ will set its start tag to the arrival time t and the finish tag to $t + \delta_i$. Hence if r finishes service by its finish tag, it meets its latency bound.

Lemma 2. *Consider an interval $[a, a + \tau]$ in which a is a synchronization point and there are no more synchronization points between a and $a + \tau$. For any c_i, the amount of its service that is assigned start tags in the interval $[a, a + \tau]$, is upper bounded by $\sigma_i + \tau \times \rho_i$.*

Proof. (Sketch) Within the interval there is no adjustment of tags or addition of tokens through rejuvenation. Recall that start tags are assigned so that a request has to pay for the service it requests by either getting the tokens from the bucket or delaying the start tag till it generates the required number of tokens, at the rate ρ_i. Since there are at most σ_i tokens initially in the bucket, the result follows.

Lemma 3. *For any time interval $[a, b]$ in which a is a synchronization point and there are no synchronization points between a and b, the total amount of service with start tags greater than or equal to a and finish tags less than or equal to b, is no more than $C \times (b - a)$.*

Proof. Without loss of generality, let the clients be indexed in non-decreasing order of their latencies so that for any two clients c_i and c_j, $1 \leq i < j \leq m$ implies that $\delta_i \leq \delta_j$. Let $n \leq m$ be the largest index such that $\delta_i \leq b - a$.

Consider a client $c_i, i \leq n$. Since there are no synchronization points in $(a, b]$, tags are not changed by AdjustTags at any time during this interval. Since a request of c_i with finish tag less than or equal to b must have its start tag no more than $b - \delta_i$, we must bound the amount of service of c_i with start tags in the interval $[a, b - \delta_i]$. From Lemma 2, the amount of service with start tags in the interval is upper bounded by $\sigma_i + (b - \delta_i - a)\rho_i$. For clients with index $j > n$, the amount of such service is 0.

Summing the bounds over all the clients, the amount of service is bounded by:

$$\sum_{i=1}^{n} (\sigma_i + \rho_i(b - a - \delta_i)) \tag{3}$$

Now from the Capacity Constraint equation 2 applied to the case $i = n$ we have:

$$\sum_{k=1}^{n} \sigma_k + \sum_{k=1}^{n} (\delta_n - \delta_k)\rho_k \leq C \times \delta_n \tag{4}$$

Applying equation 1 of the Capacity Constraint to the non-negative interval $b - a - \delta_n$
we have

$$\sum_{k=1}^{n} (b - a - \delta_n)\rho_k \leq C \times (b - a - \delta_n) \tag{5}$$

Combining equations 4 and 5 we get:

$$\sum_{k=1}^{n} \sigma_k + \sum_{k=1}^{n} (b - a - \delta_k)\rho_k \leq C \times (b - a) \tag{6}$$

Hence, the service required (Equation 3) is bounded by $C \times (b - a)$.

Theorem 1. *Consider the set of requests of c_i that arrive during an interval in which it is well behaved. The irrespective of the behavior of other clients, all these requests have a latency bounded by $\delta_i + \varepsilon$.*

Proof. We will prove the theorem by contradiction. Let Γ denote the set of requests of c_i that arrive in the interval. Since all requests in this interval are good the finish tag and the deadlines are the same. Assume to the contrary that a request in Γ with a finish tag t_d completes later than time $t_d + \varepsilon$.

Let t_0 be the start of the system busy period in which t_d occurs. Let t be the last time instant before t_d during which a request having finish tag greater than or equal to t_d begins service. If there is no such request it follows that all requests that are serviced in the interval $[t_0, t_d]$ have finish tags no more than t_d. Since the start tags of these requests are greater than or equal to t_0, from Lemma 3 we know that all these requests can be serviced in the interval $[t_0, t_d]$, which contradicts our assumption proving the theorem.

Otherwise $t_d > t \geq t_0$. Since a request with finish tag greater than or equal to t_d begins service at time t, it implies that there were no eligible requests with finish times less than t_d at t.

Partition the requests of Γ into two sets. Let **P** be the set of eligible requests at time t (*i,e* having a start tag less than or equal to t), and **Q** be the set of request with start tags greater than t. The request scheduled at t must be from **P** and since it has a finish tag greater than t_d, either this was the only request in **P** or all requests of **P** must have finish tags greater than t_d. In both these cases, no additional request of **P** can be scheduled before t_d. This is because in the first case there are no more requests, and in the second case it would contradict the definition of time t (*i.e.* the last instant before t_d when a request with deadline after t_d is scheduled). Hence the only requests scheduled between t and t_d are one request from **P** and requests from **Q**. Since the requests of **Q** have start tags greater than t the service required by the requests of **Q** with deadline t_d or less, is bounded by $C \times (t_d - t)$ by Lemma 3. The service required by the request of **P** that was scheduled at t is no more than $C \times \varepsilon$. Adding this to the service bound on **Q**, the total service required after t is no more than $C \times (t_d - t + \varepsilon)$. Hence all of these requests will finish by $t_d + \varepsilon$ – a contradiction.

5.1 RFQ as a Pure Bandwidth Allocator

We now show how to modify RFQ to act as a pure bandwidth allocator. We ignore σ_i and *numtokens$_i$* and assign $\delta_i = s_i/\rho_i$, where s_i is the size of the current request of client c_i. We simplify *ComputeTags* to ignore the different conditions based on *numto-kens*, and instead to always assign tags as follows: $S_i^r = max\{t_a, MaxS_i\}$, $F_i^r = S_i^r + \delta_i$ and $MaxS_i = S_i^r + s_i/\rho_i$. Similar as before, the scheduling is done using the minimum finish tag from the set of eligible requests.

In this case, the latency encountered by any request (referred to as the *intrinsic delay*) should ideally depend on the total service in its queue (including this request) and its guaranteed rate of service only, and not on the other clients [8]. We show below that RFQ meets these bounds.

Theorem 2. *The intrinsic delay of a request r from client c_i arriving at time τ is bounded by $\frac{Q_i(\tau)}{Cw_i} + \varepsilon_i$, where w_i is c_i's share of system capacity, i.e. $w_i = \rho_i/(\sum_{\forall j} \rho_j)$, $Q_i(\tau)$ is the amount of service pending in queue of c_i at time τ, and ε_i is a parameter independent of the other clients in the system.*

Proof. (Sketch) Let the total service of all pending requests of c_i including r be $Q_i(\tau)$. From the assignment it can be seen that r will get a finish tag no more than $\tau + Q_i(\tau)/\rho_i + s_i/\rho_i$, were s_i is the size of last completed request of c_i. We count the total amount of pending service from clients c_j, $j \neq i$, with finish tags no more than $\tau + Q_i(\tau)/\rho_i + s_i/\rho_i$. Now either all the start tags from other clients are higher than $\tau - R_{max}/C$ (which means that no one was eligible for scheduling) or the finish tags are $\geq \tau + s_i/\rho_i$. In the first case, the total service requested by client c_j with finish tags in the interval is bounded by $\rho_j \times (Q_i(\tau)/\rho_i + s_i/\rho_i + R_{max}/C)$. At most these requests will be serviced before r completes. The total amount of service from the tagged requests of all clients is bounded by $(((Q_i(\tau) + s_i)/\rho_i) + R_{max}/C)\Sigma_j\rho_j \leq (Q_i(\tau) + s_i)/w_i + R_{max}$. The time required to service this is bounded by: $(Q_i(\tau) + R_{max})/(Cw_i) + R_{max}/C$. Thus we get a bound for the maximum delay as: $Q_i(\tau)/(Cw_i) + \varepsilon_i$, where $\varepsilon_i = R_{max}/(Cw_i) + R_{max}/C$.

In second case we know that all the requests with finish tag $\leq \tau + s_i/\rho_i$ will be able to finish by the time $\tau + s_i/\rho_i$, because $C \geq \Sigma_{\forall k} \rho_k$. Thus the total amount of finish tags in the interval $[\tau + s_i/\rho_i, \tau + Q_i(\tau)/\rho_i + s_i/\rho_i]$ from all clients is again bounded by $(Q_i(\tau)\Sigma_{j \neq i}\rho_j$. The overall bound in this case would be $Q_i(\tau)/(Cw_i) + R_{max}/(Cw_i)$.

6   Conclusions

We presented a novel algorithm RFQ to provide independent bandwidth and latency guarantees to multiple clients sharing a server. Our algorithm improves upon previous schemes significantly by differentiating between benign and critical overuse of server resources. In doing so, we presented the DTB traffic model (deficit token bucket) and the RFQ scheduling algorithm, that provide a more relaxed characterization of client behavior. In this model a misbehaving client can be forgiven for exceeding its contracted limit on service requests, if the system determines that it will not affect the guarantees made to any well-behaved client. This flexibility allows clients to use spare capacity without fear of penalty, increasing system utilization and providing greater scheduling flexibility. We provided a formal model to characterize this behavior analytically. We also show its superior properties over existing schemes empirically in [6] and in the full version of this paper.

Acknowledgements

This research was done while the first author was a student at Rice University. The support of this research by the National Science Foundation under NSF Grant CNS-0541369 is gratefully acknowledged.

References

1. VMware, Inc.: Introduction to VMware Infrastructure (2007),
   http://www.vmware.com/support/pubs/
2. Barham, P., Dragovic, B., Fraser, K., Hand, S., Harris, T., Ho, A., Neugebauer, R., Pratt, I.,
   Warfield, A.: Xen and the art of virtualization. In: SOSP 2003: Proceedings of the nineteenth
   ACM symposium on Operating systems principles, pp. 164–177. ACM, New York (2003)
3. Waldspurger, C.: Memory resource management in vmware esx server (2002)
4. Sariowan, H., Cruz, R.L., Polyzos, G.C.: Scheduling for quality of service guarantees via service curves. In: Proceedings of the International Conference on Computer Communications
   and Networks, pp. 512–520 (1995)
5. Cruz, R.L.: Quality of service guarantees in virtual circuit switched networks. IEEE Journal
   on Selected Areas in Communications 13(6), 1048–1056 (1995)
6. Gulati, A., Merchant, A., Varman, P.: pClock: An arrival curve based approach for QoS guarantees in shared storage systems. In: Proceedings of the 2007 ACM SIGMETRICS International Conference on Measurement and Modeling of Computer Systems, pp. 13–24. ACM
   Press, New York (2007)
7. Evans, J., Filsfils, C.: Deploying IP and MPLS QoS for multiservice networks. Morgan Kaufmann, San Francisco (2007)
8. Bennett, J.C.R., Zhang, H.: WF^{2}Q: Worst-case fair weighted fair queueing. INFOCOM (1),
   120–128 (1996)
9. Parekh, A.K., Gallager, R.G.: A generalized processor sharing approach to flow control in
   integrated services networks: the single-node case. IEEE/ACM Trans. Netw. 1(3), 344–357
   (1993)
10. Zhang, L.: VirtualClock: A new traffic control algorithm for packet-switched networks. ACM
    Trans. Comput. Syst. 9(2), 101–124
11. Demers, A., Keshav, S., Shenker, S.: Analysis and simulation of a fair queuing algorithm.
    Journal of Internetworking Research and Experience 1(1), 3–26 (1990)
12. Greenberg, A.G., Madras, N.: How fair is fair queuing. J. ACM 39(3), 568–598 (1992)
13. Goyal, P., Vin, H.M., Cheng, H.: Start-time fair queuing: A scheduling algorithm for integrated services packet switching networks. Technical Report CS-TR-96-02, UT Austin (January 1996)
14. Golestani, S.: A self-clocked fair queueing scheme for broadband applications. In: INFOCOMM 1994, pp. 636–646 (April 1994)
15. Suri, S., Varghese, G., Chandramenon, G.: Leap forward virtual clock: A new fair queueing
    scheme with guaranteed delay and throughput fairness. In: INFOCOMM 1997 (April 1997)
16. Stiliadis, D., Varma, A.: Latency-rate servers: a general model for analysis of traffic scheduling algorithms. IEEE/ACM Transactions on Networking 6(5), 611–624 (1998)
17. Shi, H., Sethu, H.: Greedy fair queueing: A goal-oriented strategy for fair real-time packet
    scheduling. In: RTSS 2003: Proceedings of the 24th IEEE International Real-Time Systems
    Symposium, Washington, DC, USA, p. 345. IEEE Computer Society, Los Alamitos (2003)
18. Kanhere, S.S., Sethu, H., Parekh, A.B.: Fair and efficient packet scheduling using elastic
    round robin. IEEE Trans. Parallel Distrib. Syst. 13(3), 324–336 (2002)

19. Cobb, J.A., Gouda, M.G., El-Nahas, A.: Time-shift scheduling—fair scheduling of flows in high-speed networks. IEEE/ACM Trans. Netw. 6(3), 274–285 (1998)
20. Stoica, I., Zhang, H., Ng, T.S.E.: A hierarchical fair service curve algorithm for link-sharing, real-time, and priority services. IEEE/ACM Trans. Netw. 8(2), 185–199 (2000)
21. Ng, T.S.E., Stephens, D.C., Stoica, I., Zhang, H.: Supporting best-effort traffic with fair service curve. In: Measurement and Modeling of Computer Systems, pp. 218–219 (1999)

Range Medians

Sariel Har-Peled[1,*] and S. Muthukrishnan[2]

[1] Department of Computer Science, University of Illinois, 201 N. Goodwin Avenue,
Urbana, IL, 61801, USA
sariel@uiuc.edu
http://www.uiuc.edu/~sariel/
[2] Google Inc., 76 9th Av, 4th Fl., New York, NY, 10011
muthu@google.com

Abstract. We study a generalization of the classical median finding problem to batched query case: given an array of unsorted n items and k (not necessarily disjoint) intervals in the array, the goal is to determine the median in *each* of the intervals in the array. We give an algorithm that uses $O(n \log k + k \log k \log n)$ comparisons and show a lower bound of $\Omega(n \log k)$ comparisons for this problem. This is optimal for $k = O(n/\log n)$.

1 Introduction

The classical median finding problem is to find the *median* item, that is, the item of rank $\lceil n/2 \rceil$ in an unsorted array of size n. We focus on the comparison model, where items in the array can be compared only using comparisons, and we count the number of comparisons performed by any algorithm [1]. It is known since the 70's that this problem can be solved using $O(n)$ comparisons in the worst case [BFP+73]. Later research [BJ85, SPP76, DZ99, DZ01] showed that the number of comparisons needed for solving the median finding algorithm is between $(2 + \varepsilon)n$ and $2.95n$ in the worst case (in the deterministic case). Closing this gap for a deterministic algorithm is an open problem, but surprisingly, one can find the median using $1.5n + o(n)$ comparisons using a randomized algorithm [MR95].

We study the following generalization of the median problem.

The k-range-medians Problem. The input is an unsorted array $\mathcal{S}$ with n entries. A sequence of k queries $Q_1, \ldots, Q_k$ is provided. A query $Q_j = [l_j, r_j]$ is an *interval* of the array, and the output is $x_1, \ldots, x_k$, where

$$x_j = \text{median} \left\{ \mathcal{S}[l_j], \mathcal{S}[l_j + 1], \ldots, \mathcal{S}[r_j] \right\}$$

---

[*] Work on this paper was partially supported by a NSF CAREER award CCR-0132901.

[1] In the algorithms discussed in this paper, the computation performed beyond the comparisons will be linear in the number of comparisons.

D. Halperin and K. Mehlhorn (Eds.): ESA 2008, LNCS 5193, pp. 503–514, 2008.

for $j = 1, \ldots, k$. We refer to this as the *k-range-medians problem*. The problem is to build a data-structure for S such that it can answer this kind of queries quickly. Notice that the intervals are possibly overlapping.

This is the *interval* version of the classical median finding problem, and it is interesting on its own merit. In addition, there are many motivating scenarios where they arise.

Examples. A motivation arises in analyzing logs of internet advertisements (aka ads). We have the log of clicks on ads on the internet: each record gives the time of the click as well as the varying price paid by the advertiser for the click, and the log is arranged in time-indexed order. Then, $S[i]$ is the price for the ith click. Any given advertiser runs several ad campaigns simultaneously spread over different intervals of time. The advertiser then wishes to compare his cost to the general ad market during the period his campaigns ran, and a typical comparison is to the median price paid for clicks during those time intervals. This yields an instance of the *k-range-medians* problem, for possibly intersecting set of intervals.

As another example, consider IP networks where one collects what are known as SNMP logs: for each link that connects two routers, one collects the total bytes sent on that link in each fixed length duration like say 5 minutes [KMZ03]. Then, $S[i]$ is the number of bytes sent on that link in the ith time duration. A traffic analyst is interested in finding the median value of the traffic level within a *specific* time window such as a week, office hours, or weekends, or the median within *each* such time window. Equally, the analyst is sometimes interested in median traffic levels during specific external events such as the time duration when an attack happened or a new network routing strategy was tested.

There are other attributes in addition to time where applications may solve range median problems. For example, $S[i]$ may be the total value of real estate sold in postal zipcode area i arranged in sorted order, and an analyst may be interested in the median value for a borough or a city represented by a consecutive set of zipcodes.   □

One can ask similar interval versions of other problems too, for example, the median may be replaced by (say) the maximum, minimum, mode or even the sum.

- For sum, a trivial $O(n)$ preprocessing to compute all the prefix sums $P[j] = \sum_{i \leq j} S[i]$ suffices to answer any interval query $Q_j = [l_j, r_j]$ in optimal $O(1)$ time using $P[r_j] - P[l_j - 1]$.
- If the summation operator (i.e., $\sum$) is replaced by a semigroup operator (where the subtraction operator is absent), then S can be preprocessed in $O(nk)$ space and time and each query can be answered in $O(\alpha_k(n))$ where α_k is a slow growing function [Yao82], and this is optimal under general semigroup conditions [Yao85].
- For the special cases of the semigroup operator such as the maximum or minimum, a somewhat nontrivial algorithm is needed to get same optimal bounds as for the $\sum$ case (see for example [BFC04]).

The median operator is not a semigroup operator and presents a more difficult problem. The only prior results we know are obtained by using the various tradeoffs shown in [KMS05]. For the case when $k = 1$, the interesting tradeoffs for preprocessing time and query times are respectively, roughly, $O(n \log^2 n)$ and $O(\log n)$, or $O(n^2)$ and $O(1)$, or $O(n)$ and $O(n^\varepsilon)$ for constant fraction ε [KMS05]. These bounds for individual queries can be directly applied to each of the k interval queries in our problem, resulting in a multiplicative k factor in the query complexity. In particular, the work of Krizanc *et al.* [KMS05] implies an $O(n \log^2 n + k \log n)$ time algorithm for our problem.

Our main result is as follows.

Theorem 1. *There is a deterministic algorithm to solve the k-range-medians problem in $O(n \log k + k \log k \log n)$ time. Furthermore, in the comparison model, any algorithm that solves this problem requires $\Omega(n \log k)$ comparisons.*

The k-range-medians problem seems to be a fairly basic problem and it is worthwhile to have tight bounds for it. In particular, $\Theta(n \log k)$ may not be the bound one suspects at first glance to be tight for this problem. For $k = O(n/log n)$, our algorithm is optimal. It also improves [KMS05] for $k = O(n)$.

The lower bound holds even if the set of intervals is *hierarchical*, that is, for any two intervals in the set, either one of them is contained in the other, or they are disjoint. On the other hand, the upper bound holds even if the queries arrive online, in the amortized sense. Our algorithm uses *relaxed* sorting on pieces of the array, where only a subset of items in a piece is in their correct sorted location. Relaxed sorting like this has been used before for other problems, for example, see [AY89].

In the following, the kth element of a set S (or element of rank k) would refer to the kth smallest element in the set S. For simplicity, we assume the elements of S are all unique.

2 The Lower Bound

Recall that S is an unsorted array of n elements. Assume that n is a multiple of k. Let $\Psi(n, k) = \left\{ \frac{in}{k} \mid i = 1, \ldots, k \right\}$, for $n > k > 0$. We will say an element of S is the *ith element* of S if its rank in S is i.

Claim. Any algorithm **MedianAlg** that computes all the elements of rank in $\Psi(n, k)$ from S needs to perform $\Omega(n \log k)$ comparisons in the worst case.

Proof. Let $m_i = in/k$, for $i = 0, \ldots, k$. An element would be *labeled* i if it is larger than the m_{i-1}th element of S and smaller than the m_ith element of S (note, that the m_kth element of S is the largest element in S). An element would be *unlabeled* if its rank in S is in $\Psi(n, k)$.

Note, that the output of the algorithm is the indices of the k unlabeled elements. We will argue that just computing these k numbers requires $\Omega(n \log k)$ time.

Consider an execution of **MedianAlg** on $\mathcal{S}$. We consider the comparison tree model, where the input travels down the decision tree from the root, at any vertex a comparison is being made, the and the input is directed either to the right or left child depending on the result of the comparison.

A labelling (at a vertex v of the decision tree) is *consistent* with the comparisons seen so far by the algorithm if there is an input with this labelling, such that it agrees with all the comparisons seen so far and it reaches v during the execution. Let Z be the set of labellings of $\mathcal{S}$ consistent with the comparisons seen so far at this vertex v.

We claim that if $|\mathsf{Z}| > 1$ then the algorithm can not yet terminate. Indeed, in such a case there are at least two different labellings that are consistent with the comparisons seen so far. If not all the labellings of Z have the same set of k elements marked as unlabeled, then the algorithm has different output (i.e., the output is just the indices of the unlabeled elements), and as such the algorithm can not terminate.

So, let $\mathcal{S}[\alpha]$ be an element that has two different labels in two labellings of Z. There exists two distinct inputs $B = [b_1, \ldots, b_n]$ and $C = [c_1, \ldots, c_n]$ that realizes these two labellings. Now consider the input $D(t) = [d_1(t), \ldots, d_n(t)]$, where $d_i(t) = b_i(1 - t) + tc_i$, for $t \in [0, 1]$ and $i = 1, \ldots, n$. We can perturb the numbers $b_1, \ldots, b_n$ and $c_1, \ldots, c_n$ so that there is never a $t \in [0, 1]$ for which three entries of $D(\cdot)$ are equal to each other (this can be guaranteed by adding random infinitesimal noise to each number, and observing that the probability of this bad event has measure zero). Note that $D(0) = B$ and $D(1) = C$.

Furthermore, since for the inputs B and C our algorithm had reached the same node (i.e., v) in the decision tree, it holds that for all the comparisons the algorithm performed so far, it got exactly the same results for both inputs.

Now, assume without loss of generality, that the label for b_α in B is strictly smaller than the label for c_α in C. Clearly, for some value of t in this range, denoted by t^*, $d_\alpha(t)$ must be of rank in the set $\{m_1, \ldots, m_k\}$. Indeed, as t increases from 0 to 1, the rank of $d_\alpha(t)$ starts at the rank of b_α in B, and ends up with the rank of c_α in C. But $D(t^*)$ agrees with all the comparisons seen by the algorithm so far (since if $b_i < b_j$ and $c_i < c_j$ then $d_i(t) < d_j(t)$, for $t \in [0, 1]$). We conclude that the assignment that realizes $D(t^*)$ must leave $d_\alpha(t)$ unlabeled. Namely, the set Z has two labellings with different sets of k elements that are unlabeled, and as such the algorithm can not terminate and must perform SOME more comparisons if it reached v (i.e., v is not a leaf of the decision tree).

Thus, the algorithm can terminate only when $|\mathsf{Z}| = 1$. Let $\beta = n/k - 1$, and observe that in the beginning of **MedianAlg** execution, it has

$$M = \frac{n!}{k!(\beta!)^k}$$

possible labellings for the output. Indeed, a consistent labeling, is made out of k unlabeled elements, and then β elements are labeled by i, for $i = 1, \ldots, k$. Now, by Stirling's approximation, we have

$$M \geq \frac{(\beta k)!}{(\beta!)^k} \approx \frac{\sqrt{2\pi\beta k}\frac{(\beta k)^{\beta k}}{e^{\beta k}}}{\left(\sqrt{2\pi\beta}\frac{\beta^\beta}{e^\beta}\right)^k}\frac{(\beta k)!}{(\beta!)^k} = \frac{\sqrt{2\pi\beta k}(\beta k)^{\beta k}}{\left(\sqrt{2\pi\beta}\beta^\beta\right)^k} = k^{\beta k}\frac{\sqrt{2\pi\beta k}}{\left(\sqrt{2\pi\beta}\right)^k}.$$

Each comparison performed can only half this set of possible labellings, in the worst case. It follows, that in the worst case, the algorithms needs

$$\Omega(\log M) = \Omega\left(\beta k \log k - \frac{k}{2}\log(2\pi\beta)\right) = \Omega(\beta k \log k) = \Omega(n \log k)$$

comparisons, as claimed.

Lemma 1. *Solving the k-range-medians problem requires $\Omega(n \log k)$ comparisons.*

Proof. We will show that given an algorithm for the k-range-medians problem, one can reduce it, in linear time, to the problem of Claim 2. That would immediately imply the lower bound.

   Given an input array S of size n, construct a new array T of size $4n$ where the first n elements of T are $-\infty$, $T[n+1,\ldots,2n] = S$, and $T[j] = +\infty$, for $j = 2n+1,\ldots,4n$. Clearly, the ℓth element of S is the median of the range $[1, 2n + 2\ell - 1]$ in T. Thus, we can solve the problem of Claim 2 using k median range queries, implying the lower bound.

Observe that the lower bound holds even for the case when the intervals are hierarchical.

3   Our Algorithm

We first consider the case when all the query intervals are provided ahead of time. We will present a slow algorithm first, and later show how to make it faster to get our bounds. Our algorithm uses the following folklore result.

Theorem 2. *Given ℓ sorted arrays with total size n, there is a deterministic algorithm to determine median of the set formed by the union of these arrays using $O(\ell \log(n/\ell))$ comparisons.*

Since we were unable to find a reference to precisely this result beyond [KMS05] where a slightly weaker result is stated as a folklore claim, we describe this algorithm in Appendix A.

3.1   A Slow Algorithm

Here we show how to solve the k-range-medians problem.

   Let $I_1,\ldots,I_k$ be the given (not necessarily disjoint) k intervals in the array $S[1..n]$. We break S into (at most) $2k-1$ atomic disjoint intervals labeled in the sorted order $B_1,\ldots,B_m$, such that an atomic interval does not have an endpoint of any I_i inside it. Next, we sort each one of the B_i's, and build a balanced binary tree having $B_1, \ldots, B_m$ as the leaves in this order. In a bottom-up fashion we merge the sorted arrays sorted in the leaves, so that each node v stores a sorted array S_v of all the elements stored in its subtree. Let T denote this tree that has height $O(\log k)$.

Now, computing the median of an interval I_j, is done by extracting the $O(\log k)$ suitable nodes in T that cover I_j. Next, we apply Theorem 2, and using $O(\log n \log k)$ comparisons, we get the desired median. We now apply this to the k given intervals. Observe that sorting the atomic intervals takes $O(n \log n)$ comparisons and merging them in $O(\log k)$ levels takes $O(n \log k)$ comparisons in all. This gives:

Lemma 2. *The algorithm above uses $O(n \log n + k \log n \log k)$ comparisons.*

Note, that this algorithm is still mildly interesting. Indeed, if the intervals $I_1, \ldots, I_k$ are all "large", then the running time of the naive algorithm is $O(nk)$, and the above algorithm is faster for $k > \log n$.

3.2   Our Main Algorithm

The main bottleneck in the above solution was the presorting of the pieces of the array corresponding to atomic intervals. In the optimal algorithm below, we do not fully sort them.

Definition 3. *A subarray X is u-sorted if there is a sorted list $\mathcal{L}_X$ of at most (say) $20u$ elements of X such that these elements appear in this sorted order in X (not necessarily as consecutive elements). Furthermore, for an element α of $\mathcal{L}_X$, all the elements of X smaller than it appear before it in X and all the elements larger than α appear after α in X. Finally, we require that the distance between two consecutive elements of $\mathcal{L}_X$ in X is at most $|X|/u$, where $|X|$ denotes the size of X. We will refer to the elements of X between two consecutive elements of $\mathcal{L}_X$ as a segment.*

An array X of n elements that is n-sorted is just sorted, and a 0-sorted array is unsorted. Another way to look at it, is that the elements of $\mathcal{L}_X$ are in their final position in the sorted order, and the elements of the intervals are in an arbitrary ordering.

Lemma 3. *Given an unsorted array X, it can be u-sorted using $O(|X| \log u)$ comparisons, where $|X|$ denotes the number of elements of X.*

Proof. We just find the median of X, partition X into two equal size subarrays, and continue recursively on the two subarrays. The depth the recursion is $O(\log u)$, and the work at each level of the recursion is linear, which implies the claim.

Lemma 4. *Given a two u-sorted arrays X and Y, they can be merged into an u-sorted array using $O(|X| + |Y|)$ comparisons.*

Proof. Convert Y into a linked list. Insert the elements of $\mathcal{L}_X$ into Y. This can be done by scanning the list of Y until we arrive at the segment Y_i of Y that should contain an element b of $\mathcal{L}_X$ that we need to insert. We partition this segment using b into two intervals, add b to $\mathcal{L}_Y$, and continue in this fashion with each such b. This takes $O(|Y_i|) = O(|Y|/u)$ comparisons per b (ignoring the scanning cost which is $O(|Y|)$ overall). Let Z be the resulting u-sorted array, which contains all the elements of Y and all the elements of $\mathcal{L}_X$, and $\mathcal{L}_Z = \mathcal{L}_X \cup \mathcal{L}_Y$. Computing Z takes

$$O\left(|Y| + |\mathcal{L}_X|\frac{|Y|}{u}\right) = O(|Y|)$$

comparisons.

We now need to insert the elements of $X \setminus \mathcal{L}_X$ into Z. Clearly, if a segment X_i of X has α_i elements of $\mathcal{L}_Z$ in its range, then inserting the elements of X_i would take $O(|X_i| \log \alpha_i)$ comparisons. Thus, the total number of comparisons is

$$O\left(\sum_i |X_i| \log \alpha_i\right) = O\left(\sum_i \frac{|X|}{u} \log \alpha_i\right) = O\left(\frac{|X|}{u} \sum_i \alpha_i\right) = O(X),$$

since $|X_i| \le |X|/u$, $\log \alpha_i \le \alpha_i$ and $\sum_i \alpha_i = O(u)$.

The final step is to scan over Z, and merge consecutive intervals that are too small (removing the corresponding elements from $\mathcal{L}_Z$), such that each interval is of length at most $|Z|/u$. Clearly, this can be done in linear time. The resulting Z is u-sorted since its sorted list contains at most $2u + 1$ elements, and every interval is of length at most $|Z|/u$.

Note, that the final filtering stage in the above algorithm is need to guarantee that the resulting list $\mathcal{L}_Z$ size is not too large, if we were to use this merging step several times.

In the following, we need a modified version of Theorem 2 that works for u-sorted arrays.

Theorem 4. *Given ℓ u-sorted arrays $A_1, \dots, A_\ell$ with total size n and a rank k, there is a deterministic algorithm that returns ℓ subintervals $B_1, \dots, B_\ell$ of these arrays and a number k', such that the following properties hold.*

(i) *The k'th ranked element of $B_1 \cup \dots \cup B_\ell$ is the kth ranked element of $A_1 \cup \dots \cup A_\ell$.*
(ii) *The running time is $O(\ell \log(n/\ell))$ time.*
(iii) $\sum_{i=1}^{\ell} |B_i| = O(\ell \cdot (n/u))$.

Proof. For every element of $\mathcal{L}_{A_i}$ realizing the u-sorting of the array A_i, we assume we have its rank in A_i precomputed. Now, we execute the algorithm of Theorem 2 on these (representative) sorted arrays (taking into account their associated rank). (Note that the required modifications of the algorithm of Theorem 2 are tedious but straightforward, and we omit the details.) The main problem is that now the rank of an element is only estimated approximately up to an (additive) error of n/u. In the end of process of trimming down the representative arrays, we might still have active intervals of total length $2n/u$ in each one of these arrays, resulting in the bound on the size of the computed intervals.

Using the theorem above as well as two lemmas above, we get the following result, which is building up to the algorithmic part of Theorem 1.

Lemma 5. *There is a deterministic algorithm to solve the k-range-medians problem in $O(n \log k + k \log k \log n)$ time, when the k query intervals are provided in advance.*

Proof. We repeat the algorithm of Section 3.1 using u-sorting instead of sorting, for u to be specified shortly. Building the data-structure (i.e., the tree over the atomic intervals) takes $O(n \log u)$ comparisons. Indeed, we first u-sort the atomic intervals, and then we merge them as we go up the tree.

A query of finding the median of array elements in an interval is now equivalent to finding the median for $m = O(\log k)$ u-sorted arrays $A_1, \ldots, A_m$. Using the algorithm of Theorem 4 results in m intervals $B_1, \ldots, B_m$ that belong to $A_1, \ldots, A_m$, respectively, such that we need to find the k'th smallest element in $B_1 \cup \ldots \cup B_m$. The total length of the B_is is $O(mn/u)$. Now we can just use the brute force method. Merge $B_1, \ldots, B_m$ into a single array and find the k'th smallest element using the classical algorithm. This take $O(mn/u)$ comparisons. We have to repeat this k times, and the number of comparisons we need is

$$O\left(km\frac{n}{u} + km \log n\right) = O(n + k \log k \log n),$$

for $u = k^2$, since $m = O(\log k)$. Thus, in all, the number of comparisons using by the algorithm is $O(n \log k + k \log k \log n)$.

We can extend this bound to the case when the intervals are presented in an online manner, and we get amortized bounds.

Lemma 6 (When k is known in advance). *There is a deterministic algorithm to solve the k-range-medians problem in $O(n \log k + k \log k \log n)$ time, when the k query intervals are provided in an online fashion, but k is known in advance.*

Proof. The idea is to partition the array into u, $u \le k^2$ atomic intervals all of the same length, and build the data-structure of these atomic intervals. The above algorithm would work verbatim, except for every query interval I, there would be two "dangling" atomic intervals that are of size n/u that contain the two endpoints of I.

Specifically, to perform the query for I, we compute $m = O(\log k)$ u-sorted arrays using our data-structure. We also take these two atomic intervals, clip them into the query interval, u-sort them, and add them to the m u-sorted arrays we already have. Now, we need to perform the median query over these $O(\log k)$

u-sorted arrays, which we can do, as described above. Clearly, the resulting algorithm has running time

$$O\left(n \log u + k \log u \log n + k\frac{n}{u} \log u\right) = O(n \log k + k \log k \log n),$$

since $u = k^2$.

Lemma 7 (When k is *not* known in advance). *There is a deterministic algorithm to solve the k-range-medians problem in $O(n \log k + k \log k \log n)$ time, when the k query intervals are provided in an online fashion.*

Proof. We will use the algorithm of Lemma 6.

At each stage, we have a current guess to the number of queries to be performed. In the beginning this guess is a constant, say 10. When this number of queries is exceeded, we *square* our guess, rebuild our data-structure from scratch for this new guess, and continue. Let $k_1 = 10$ and $k_i = (k_{i-1})^2$ be the sequence of guesses, for $i = 1, \ldots, \beta$, where $\beta = O(\log \log k)$. We have that the total running time of the algorithm is

$$\sum_{i=1}^{\beta} O(n \log k_i + k_i \log k_i \log n) = O(n \log k + k \log k \log n),$$

since $\log k_{i-1} = (\log k_i)/2$, for all i.

Lemma 7 implies the algorithmic part of Theorem 1.

4   Concluding Remarks

The k-range-medians problem is a natural interval generalization of the classical median finding problem: unlike interval generalizations of other problems such as max, min or sum which can be solved in linear time, our problem (surprisingly) needs $\Omega(n \log k)$ comparisons, and we present an algorithm that solves this problem with running time (and number of comparisons) $O(n \log k + k \log k \log n)$. A number of technical problems remain and we list them below.

- Currently, our algorithm uses $O(n \log k)$ space. It would be interesting to reduce this to linear space.
- Say the elements are from an integer range $1, \ldots, U$. Can we design $o(n)$ time algorithms in that case using word operations? For the classical median finding problem, both comparison-based and word-based algorithms take $O(n)$ time. But given that the comparison-based algorithm needs $\Omega(n \log k)$ comparisons for our k-range-medians problem, it now becomes interesting if word-based algorithms can do better for integer alphabet.
- Say one wants to only answer median queries approximately for each interval (see [BKMT05] for some relevant results). Can one design $o(n \log k)$ algorithms?

Suppose the elements are integers in the range $1, \ldots, U$. We define an approximate version where the goal is to return an element within $(1 \pm \varepsilon)$ of the correct median in value, for some fixed ε, $0 < \varepsilon < 1$. Then we can keep an *exponential histogram* with each atomic interval of the number of elements in the range $[(1 + \varepsilon)^i, (1 + \varepsilon)^{i+1})$ for each i, and follow the algorithm outline here constructing them for all the suitably chosen intervals on the balanced binary tree atop these atomic intervals. For each interval in the query, one can easily merge the exponential histograms corresponding to and obtain an algorithm that takes time $O(n + k \log k \log U)$, since any two exponential histograms can be merged in $O(\log U)$ time. If the elements are not integers in the range $1, \ldots, U$ and one worked in the comparison model, similar results may be obtained using [GK01, GK04], or ε-nets. It is not clear if these bounds are optimal.

- We believe extending the problem to two (or more) dimensions is also of interest. There is prior work for range sum and minimums, but tight bounds for k range medians will be interesting.

Acknowledgements. The authors would like to thank the anonymous referees for their careful reading, useful comments and references. In particular, they identified mistakes in an earlier version of this paper.

References

[AY89]   Altman, T., Yoshihide, I.: Roughly sorting: Sequential and parallel approach. Journal of Information Processing 12(2), 154–158 (1989)

[BFC04]   Bender, M.A., Farach-Colton, M.: The level ancestor problem simplified. Theo. Comp. Sci. 321(1), 5–12 (2004)

[BFP+73]   Blum, M., Floyd, R.W., Pratt, V.R., Rivest, R.L., Tarjan, R.E.: Time bounds for selection. J. Comput. Sys. Sci. 7(4), 448–461 (1973)

[BJ85]   Bent, S.W., John, J.W.: Finding the median requires $2n$ comparisons. In: Proc. 17th Annu. ACM Sympos. Theory Comput., pp. 213–216 (1985)

[BKMT05]   Bose, P., Kranakis, E., Morin, P., Tang, Y.: Approximate range mode and range median queries. In: Proc. 22nd Internat. Sympos. Theoret. Asp. Comp. Sci., pp. 377–388 (2005)

[DZ99]   Dor, D., Zwick, U.: Selecting the median. SIAM J. Comput. 28(5), 1722–1758 (1999)

[DZ01]   Dor, D., Zwick, U.: Median selection requires $(2 + \epsilon)n$ comparisons. SIAM J. Discret. Math. 14(3), 312–325 (2001)

[GK01]   Greenwald, M., Khanna, S.: Space-efficient online computation of quantile summaries. In: Proc. 2001 ACM SIGOD Conf. Mang. Data, pp. 58–66 (2001)

[GK04]   Greenwald, M., Khanna, S.: Power-conserving computation of order-statistics over sensor networks. In: Proc. 23rd ACM Sympos. Principles Database Syst., pp. 275–285 (2004)

[KMS05]   Krizanc, D., Morin, P., Smid, M.: Range mode and range median queries on lists and trees. Nordic J. Comput. 12(1), 1–17 (2005)

[KMZ03]   Korn, F., Muthukrishnan, S., Zhu, Y.: Checks and balances: Monitoring data quality problems in network traffic databases. In: Proc. 29th Intl. Conf. Very Large Data Bases, pp. 536–547 (2003)

[MR95]   Motwani, R., Raghavan, P.: Randomized Algorithms. Cambridge University Press, New York (1995)

[SPP76]   Schönhage, A., Paterson, M., Pippenger, N.: Finding the median. J. Comput. Sys. Sci. 13(2), 184–199 (1976)

[Yao82]   Yao, A.C.: Space-time tradeoff for answering range queries. In: Proc. 14th Annu. ACM Sympos. Theory Comput., pp. 128–136 (1982)

[Yao85]   Yao, A.C.: On the complexity of maintaining partial sums. SIAM J. Comput. 14(2), 277–288 (1985)

A   Choosing Median from Sorted Arrays

In this section, we prove Theorem 2 by providing a fast deterministic algorithm for choosing the median element of ℓ sorted arrays. As we mentioned before, this result seems to be known, but we are unaware of a direct reference to it, and as such we provide a detailed algorithm.

A.1   The Algorithm

Let $A_1, \ldots, A_\ell$ be the given sorted arrays of total size n. We maintain ℓ active ranges $[l_i, r_i]$ of the array A_i where the required element (i.e., "median") lies, for $i = 1, \ldots, \ell$. Let k denote the rank of the required median. Let $n_{\mathrm{curr}} = \sum_i (r_i - l_i + 1)$ be the total number of currently active elements.

If $n_{\mathrm{curr}} \leq 32\ell$, then we find the median in linear time, using the standard deterministic algorithm. Otherwise, let $\Delta = \lfloor n_{\mathrm{curr}}/(32\ell) \rfloor$. Pick $u_i - 1$ equally spaced elements from the active range of A_i, where

$$u_i = 4 + \left\lceil \frac{r_i - l_i + 1}{\Delta} \right\rceil .$$

Let L_i be the resulting list of representatives, for $i = 1, \ldots, \ell$. Note that L_i breaks the active range of A_i into blocks of size

$$\nu_i \leq \left\lceil \frac{r_i - l_i + 1}{u_i} \right\rceil .$$

For each element of L_i we know exactly how many elements are smaller than it and larger than it in the ith array. Merge the lists $L_1, \ldots, L_\ell$ into one sorted list L. For an element x, let $\mathrm{rank}(x)$ denote the rank of x in the set $A_1 \cup \ldots \cup A_\ell$. Note, that now for every element x of L we can estimate its $\mathrm{rank}(x)$ to lie within an interval of length $T = \sum_{i=1}^{\ell} \nu_i$. Indeed, we know for an element of $x \in L$ between what two consecutive representatives it lies for all ℓ arrays. For element $x \in L$, let $R(x)$ denote this range where the rank of x might lie.

Now, given two consecutive representatives x and y in the ith array, if $k \notin R(x)$ and $k \notin R(y)$ then the required median cannot lie between x and y, and we can shrink the active range not to include this portion. In particular, the new active range spans all the blocks which might contain the median. The algorithm now updates the value of k and continues recursively on the new active ranges.

A.2   Analysis

The error estimate for the rank of a representative is bounded by

$$U = \sum_{i=1}^{\ell} \nu_i \le \ell + \sum_{i=1}^{\ell} \frac{r_i - l_i + 1}{u_i} \le \ell + \sum_{i=1}^{\ell} \frac{r_i - l_i + 1}{4 + \frac{r_i - l_i + 1}{\Delta}} = \ell + \Delta \sum_{i=1}^{\ell} \frac{r_i - l_i + 1}{4\Delta + r_i - l_i + 1}$$

$$\le \ell + \ell\Delta \le \frac{n_{\mathrm{curr}}}{32} + \ell \left\lfloor \frac{n_{\mathrm{curr}}}{32\ell} \right\rfloor \le \frac{n_{\mathrm{curr}}}{16},$$

since $\ell \le n_{\mathrm{curr}}/32$ and by the choice of Δ.

Consider the sorted merged array B of all the active elements. The length of B is n_{curr}, and assume, for the sake of simplicity of exposition, that the desired median is in the second half of B (the other case follows by a symmetric argument). Note, that any representative x that fall in the first quarter of B has a rank that lies in a range shorter than $T < n_{\mathrm{curr}}/4$, and as such it cannot include k. In particular, let t_i be the index in A_i of the first representative in the active range (of A_i) that does not falls in the first quarter of B. Observe that $\sum_i (t_i - l_i + 1) \ge n_{\mathrm{curr}}/4$. The total number of elements that are being eliminated by the algorithm (in the top of the recursion) is at least

$$\sum_i ((t_i - l_i + 1) - 2\nu_i) \ge \sum_i (t_i - l_i + 1) - 2 \sum_i \nu_i = \frac{n_{\mathrm{curr}}}{4} - 2U \ge \frac{n_{\mathrm{curr}}}{8}.$$

Namely, each recursive call continues on total length of all active ranges smaller by a factor of $(7/8)$ from the original array.

The total length of $L_1, \ldots L_\ell$ is $O(\ell)$, and as such the total work (ignoring the recursive call) is bounded by $O(\ell \log \ell)$. The running time is bounded by

$$T(n_{\mathrm{curr}}) = O(\ell \log \ell) + T((7/8)n_{\mathrm{curr}}),$$

where $T(\ell) = O(\ell \log \ell)$. Thus, the total running time is $O(\ell \log \ell \log(n_{\mathrm{curr}}/\ell))$.

A.3   Doing Even Better - A Faster Algorithm

Observe, that the bottleneck in the above algorithm is the merger of the representative lists $L_1, \ldots, L_\ell$. Instead of merging them, we will compute the median x of $L = L_1 \cup \ldots \cup L_\ell$. If $R(x)$ does not contain k, then we can throw away at least $n_{\mathrm{curr}}/4$ elements in the current active ranges and continue recursively. Otherwise, compute the element z of rank $n_{\mathrm{curr}}/4$ in L. Clearly, $k \notin R(z)$ and one can throw, as above, as constant fraction of the active ranges. The resulting running time (ignoring the recursive call) is $O(\ell)$ (instead of $O(\ell \log \ell)$). Thus, the running time of the resulting algorithm is $O(\ell \log(n_{\mathrm{curr}}/\ell))$.

Locality and Bounding-Box Quality of Two-Dimensional Space-Filling Curves

Herman Haverkort and Freek van Walderveen

Dept. of Computer Science, Eindhoven University of Technology, the Netherlands
cs.herman@haverkort.net, freek@vanwal.nl

Abstract. Space-filling curves can be used to organise points in the plane into bounding-box hierarchies (such as R-trees). We develop measures of the *bounding-box quality* of space-filling curves that express how effective different curves are for this purpose. We give general lower bounds on the bounding-box quality and on locality according to Gotsman and Lindenbaum for a large class of curves. We describe a generic algorithm to approximate these and similar quality measures for any given curve. Using our algorithm we find good approximations of the locality and bounding-box quality of several known and new space-filling curves. Surprisingly, some curves with bad locality by Gotsman and Lindenbaum's measure, have good bounding-box quality, while the curve with the best-known locality has relatively bad bounding-box quality.

1 Introduction

A space-filling curve is a continuous, surjective mapping from $\mathbb{R}$ to $\mathbb{R}^d$. Peano showed that such mappings exist for $d = 2$ and $d = 3$ [15]. Since then, quite a number of space-filling curves have appeared in the literature. Sagan wrote an extensive treatise [16], which discusses most curves included in our study. Space-filling curves are applied in areas as diverse as load balancing for grid computing, colour space dimension reduction, small antenna design, I/O-efficient computations on massive matrices, and the creation of spatial data indexes.

In this paper, we focus on the last application. We consider the following type of spatial data indexes for points in the plane. The data points are organised in blocks of at most B points, for some parameter B, such that each point is stored in one block. With each block we associate a bounding box, which is the smallest axis-aligned rectangle that contains all points stored in the block. The block bounding boxes are then organised in an index structure. Queries are answered as follows: to find all points intersecting a query window Q, we query the index for all bounding boxes that intersect Q; then we retrieve the corresponding blocks, and check the points stored in those blocks. To find the nearest neighbour to a query point q, one can use the index to search blocks in order of increasing distance from q. Thus one retrieves exactly the blocks whose bounding boxes intersect the largest empty circle around q.

An R-tree [12] is an example of the type of structure described above: the blocks constitute the leaves of the tree, and the higher levels of the tree act as

D. Halperin and K. Mehlhorn (Eds.): ESA 2008, LNCS 5193, pp. 515–527, 2008.

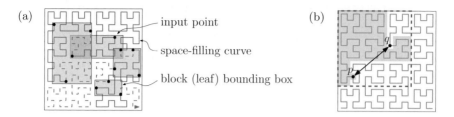

Fig. 1. (a) Leaves of an R-tree with $B = 3$. (b) L_2-locality ratio between p and $q =$ squared Euclidean distance between p and q, divided by the area covered by the curve section S between p and q: $(6^2 + 5^2)/87 \approx 0.70$. Bounding-box area ratio between p and $q =$ area of the bounding-box of the curve section S between p and q, divided by the area covered by S: $12 \cdot 12/87 \approx 1.66$. (WBA is the maximum over all pairs p and q).

an index structure for the block bounding boxes. In practice the query response time is mainly determined by the number of blocks that need to be retrieved: this is because the bounding box index structure can often be cached in main memory, while the blocks with data points are stored on slow external memory.

To build an R-tree one needs to organise the input points into blocks. One way of doing this is is by ordering the input points along a space-filling curve [9] and then putting each next group of B points together in a block (see Fig. 1(a)).

Since the number of blocks retrieved to answer a query is simply the number of bounding boxes intersected, it is important that the ordering induced by the space-filling curve makes us fill each block with points that lie close to each other and thus have a small bounding box. In fact, if the data and query points lie within a square of area 1, the average number of blocks retrieved for uniformly distributed point queries is simply the total area of the bounding boxes. For uniformly distributed line queries, the average number of blocks retrieved is proportional to the total perimeter of the bounding boxes. Therefore our goal is to have bounding boxes with small (total) area and small (total) perimeter.

Our results. We investigate which space-filling curves sort points into bounding boxes with small (total) area and small (total) perimeter most effectively. To this end we propose new quality measures of space-filling curves that express how effective different curves are. We also provide an algorithm to compute approximations of these and similar quality measures for any given curve. We give approximations of known measures of so-called curve-to-plane locality and of our new *bounding-box quality* measures for several well-known and new curves.

The known locality measures considered are the maximum, over all contiguous sections S of a space-filling curve, of the squared L_∞-, L_2- or L_1-distance between the endpoints of S divided by the area covered by S [6], see Fig. 1(b). Our first new measure is the maximum, over all contiguous sections S of a space-filling curve, of the area of the bounding box of S divided by the area covered by S. We call this measure the *worst-case bounding-box area ratio* (WBA, Fig. 1(b)). Our second new measure considers $1/16$ of the squared perimeter instead of the area, and we call it *worst-case bounding-box squared perimeter ratio* (WBP). We prove that WBA and WBP are at least 2 for a large class of space-filling curves. We also show that this class of curves has L_2-locality at least 4, thus complementing earlier results by Niedermeier et al. [13] who proved this for another class of space-filling curves. We present a new, *balanced* variation on Peano's space-filling curve with a WBA-value of 2.000 and a WBP-value of 2.155. This variation also performs very well on L_∞-, L_2- and L_1-locality.

Both WBA and WBP consider the worst case over all possible subsections of the curve. However, in the context of our application, it may be more relevant to study the total bounding box area and perimeter of a set of disjoint subsections of the curve that together cover the complete curve. Therefore we study the total bounding box area and perimeter of random subdivisions of the curve into subsections. Here we find that many curves perform roughly equally well, but those with particularly bad WBA- or WBP-values, such as the Sierpiński-Knopp curve [16] or H-order [13], are clearly suboptimal.

In the full paper [7], we also estimate the total diameter of the subsections in random subdivisions of the curve and present results for octagonal (instead of rectangular) bounding boxes.

2   Describing and Using Space-Filling Curves

Since we are concerned with the use of space-filling curves as a way to order points in the plane, we choose a method to describe space-filling curves that is based on defining how to order the space inside a (usually square) unit region.

We define an order (*scanning order*) $\prec$ of points in the plane as follows. We give a set of rules, each of which specifies (i) how to subdivide a region in the plane into subregions; (ii) what is the order of those subregions; and (iii) for each subregion, which rule is to be applied to establish the order within that subregion. We also specify a unit region of area 1 for each order (usually the unit square), and we indicate what rule is used to subdivide and order it. We assume that all data that should be ordered is scaled to lie within the unit region.

The definitions of the scanning orders discussed in this paper are shown in Fig. 2. Each rule is identified by a letter, and pictured by showing a region, its subdivision into subregions, the scanning order of the subregions (by numbers {0,1,2,...}), and the rules applied to the subregions (by letters). Variations of rules that consist of simply rotating or mirroring the order of and within subregions, are indicated by rotating or mirroring the letter identifying that rule. Variations that consist of reversing the order of and within the subregion are indicated by an overscore (Fig. 2(k,l,m))—making reversals explicit is the main difference between our notation and, for example, Asano et al. [2] or Wierum [17].

We can now see how we can implement a comparison operator that allows us to sort points according to a given scanning order. To decide whether p precedes q in the order, we determine in which subregions of the unit region p and q lie. If they are in different regions, p precedes q if and only if p lies in the lowest-numbered region of the two. If p and q lie in the same region, we compare them according to the rule for that subregion recursively.

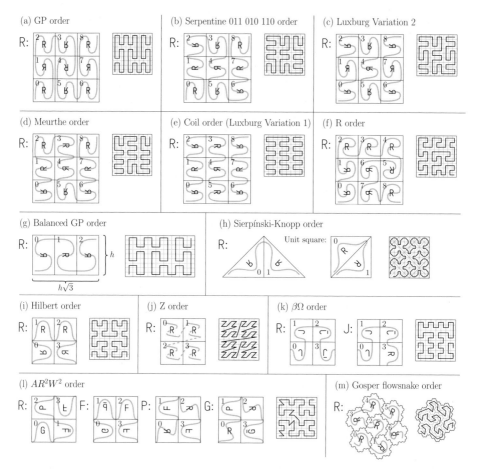

Fig. 2. Space-filling curve definitions and example approximating polylines

Each drawing in Fig. 2 includes a curve that roughly indicates the scanning order within the subdivisions. To obtain an arbitrarily fine approximation of a space-filling curve corresponding to a given scanning order, we may compute the subdivision of the unit region into subregions recursively to the desired depth of recursion, and connect the centre points of the resulting subregions by a polygonal curve in the order specified by the rules. Fig. 2 includes a small example for each scanning order. In the rest of this paper, whenever we write "space-filling curve", what we really mean is the scanning order that defines it.

The scanning orders considered in this paper are the following.

- *GP-order,* producing the curve described by G. Peano [15] (Fig. 2(a)). We call this order *GP-order* instead of *Peano order* to avoid confusion with other curves that have been referred to as the Peano curve by other authors.
- A number of variations following a scheme by Wunderlich [18] (Fig. 2(a–f)); some of these were also studied by Luxburg [11].

- A new variation of our own, obtained from GP-order by scaling the horizontal dimension by a factor $\sqrt{3}$. As we will see later, this *balanced GP-order* (Fig. 2(g)) has much better locality properties than the original GP-order.
- *Sierpiński-Knopp order,* producing the Sierpiński-Knopp curve [16]. It orders triangular regions, and can be used to order points as described above. Niedermeier et al. [13] describe a variation called H-order. For all purposes in our paper, Sierpiński-Knopp order and H-order are equivalent. (Fig. 2(h))
- *Hilbert order,* producing Hilbert's curve [8] (Fig. 2(i)).
- *Z-order,* which follows a space-filling curve by Lebesgue [10] (Fig. 2(j)).
- $\beta\Omega$-*order* (Fig. 2(k)), by Wierum [17].
- AR^2W^2-*order* (Fig. 2(l)), by Asano et al. [2].
- the *Gosper flowsnake order* (Fig. 2(m)) [5].

3   Quality Measures for Space-Filling Curves

Before we can discuss and analyse quality measures for space-filling curves in detail, we need to introduce some notation. For ease of writing, we assume that in any particular scanning order, each rule contains the same number of subregions.

A rule of a scanning order defines how to subdivide a unit region C of size (area) 1 into n subregions, numbered $0, ..., n - 1$. The scanning order inside subregion i is given by applying a transformation $\tau(i)$ to the unit region C. For any base-n number a we use a' to denote its first digit, and a'' to denote the remaining digits. We use $C(a)$ as a shorthand for $\tau(a')(C(a''))$, where $C(\emptyset) = C$. For example, $C(538)$ is subregion 8 of subregion 3 of subregion 5, and it is found by applying transformation $\tau(5)$ to $C(38)$. Similarly, we use $\tau(a)$ as a shorthand for $\tau(a') \circ \tau(a'')$, where $\tau(\emptyset)$ is the identity transformation.

By $|A|$ we denote the size of a region A. We have $0 < |C(i)| < 1$ for all $0 \le i < n$ (there are no empty subregions in the rules), and $\sum_{0 \le i < n} |C(i)| = |C| = 1$.

Let N_k denote the set of k-digit base-n numbers. We write $a \prec b$ if, in base-n notation, a and b have the same number of digits and $a < b$. By $C(\preceq b)$ we denote the union of subregion b and its predecessors, that is, $\bigcup_{i=0}^{b'-1} C(i) \cup \tau(b')(C(\preceq b''))$, where $C(\preceq \emptyset) = C$. Define $C(\prec b) := C(\preceq b) \setminus C(b)$, $C(\succeq a) := C \setminus C(\prec a)$, $C(\succ a) := C \setminus C(\preceq a)$, and $C(a, b) := C(\prec b) \setminus C(\prec a)$.

We may sometimes talk about the distance between two points along the curve. This may be a somewhat counter-intuitive concept for a curve that can be refined and therefore lengthened indefinitely. However, the distance between two points p and q along the curve is well-defined as the area filled by the section of the curve that runs from p to q, or more precisely, as:

$$|C(p,q)| := \lim_{k \to \infty} \min_{a,b \in N_k \text{ s.t. } p \in C(a), q \in C(b)} |C(a,b)|.$$

Pairwise locality measures We define locality with a generalised version of the definition by Gotsman and Lindenbaum [6]:

$$\text{WL}_r := \lim_{k \to \infty} \sup_{a,b \in N_k} \frac{d_r(C(a), C(b))^2}{|C(a,b)|},$$

where $d_r(S,T)$ is the L_r-distance between the centre point (S_x, S_y) of S and the centre point (T_x, T_y) of T. Thus $d_r(S,T) = (|S_x - T_x|^r + |S_y - T_y|^r)^{1/r}$ for $r \in \mathbb{N}$, and $d_\infty(S,T) = \max(|S_x - T_x|, |S_y - T_y|)$. We call this measure WL$_r$ for *Worst-case Locality*, as it indicates for points that lie close to each other on the curve how far from each other they might get in the plane.

Pairwise bounding box measures. One may expect a relation between locality and bounding box size. This is because points that lie close to each other along the curve are likely to be put together in a block. Then, if the distance between those points in the plane is small too, the block may have a small bounding box. However, we may also try to measure bounding box size directly. We define two measures to do so. The first is the *worst-case bounding box area ratio* (WBA):

$$\text{WBA} := \lim_{k \to \infty} \sup_{a,b \in N_k} \frac{|\text{bbox}(C(a,b))|}{|C(a,b)|},$$

where bbox(S) is the smallest axis-aligned rectangle that contains S. The second measure is the *worst-case bounding box square perimeter ratio* (WBP):

$$\text{WBP} := \frac{1}{16} \cdot \lim_{k \to \infty} \sup_{a,b \in N_k} \frac{\text{peri}(\text{bbox}(C(a,b)))^2}{|C(a,b)|},$$

where peri(S) is the perimeter of S in the L_2 metric. Taking the square of the perimeter is necessary, because otherwise WBP would be unbounded as k (the resolution of the "grid") goes to infinity. Since the rectangle of smallest perimeter that has any given area is a square, we have WBP $\geq \frac{1}{16}(4\sqrt{\text{WBA}})^2 = \text{WBA}$.

Total bounding box measures. For our application we argued that the average query response time is related to the total area and perimeter of the bounding boxes formed by grouping data points according to a given scanning order. When the points are sufficiently densely distributed in the unit region, the gap in the scanning order between the last point of a group and the first point in the next group will typically be small. Thus the grouping practically corresponds to subdividing the complete unit region into curve sections, of which we store the bounding boxes. Therefore we define the *average total bounding box area* (ABA):

$$\text{ABA} := \lim_{k \to \infty} \text{avg}_{a_1 \prec a_2 \prec \dots \prec a_{m-1} \in N_k} \left(\sum_{i=1}^{m} |\text{bbox}(C(a_{i-1}, a_i))| \right),$$

where a_0 is defined as 0, a_m is defined as $\emptyset$, and the average is taken over sets of $m-1$ cutting points $a_1, \dots, a_{m-1}$ uniformly chosen from the unit region, averaged over a range of values of m such that $\log m$ is uniformly distributed. For the *square average relative total bounding box perimeter* (ABP) we consider the total perimeter of m curve sections relative to $4\sqrt{m}$:

$$\text{ABP} := \lim_{k \to \infty} \left(\text{avg}_{a_1 \prec a_2 \prec \dots \prec a_{m-1} \in N_k} \frac{1}{4\sqrt{m}} \left(\sum_{i=1}^{m} \text{peri}(\text{bbox}(C(a_{i-1}, a_i))) \right) \right)^2$$

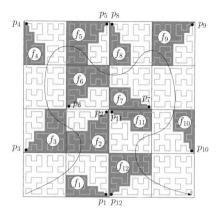

Fig. 3. Corner rectangles in a grid. The smooth curve illustrates the order of the rectangles along the curve. In each corner rectangle, we marked the outer corner and we shaded the front part.

4 Lower Bounds

Theorem 1. *Any scanning order that is based on recursively subdividing an axis-aligned rectangle into a regular grid of rectangles has* WBA ≥ 2.

Proof. Consider a subdivision of the unit rectangle into a regular grid of m rectangles, following the rules of the scanning order recursively to the depth where a grid of $\sqrt{m} \times \sqrt{m}$ rectangles is obtained. We distinguish two cases: either there is a pair of rectangles that are consecutive in the scanning order and do not share an edge, or all pairs of consecutive rectangles share an edge.

In the first case, the bounding box of such a pair contains at least four rectangles, and thus the curve section that covers that pair results in WBA ≥ 2.

In the second case, let $s_1, ... s_m$ be these rectangles in order along the space-filling curve. For each rectangle s_i $(1 < i \leq m)$, let the edge of entry be the edge shared with s_{i-1}, and for each rectangle s_i $(1 \leq i < m)$, let the edge of departure be the edge shared with s_{i+1}. Among rectangles $s_2, s_3, ..., s_{m-1}$, we distinguish two types of rectangles: straight rectangles and corner rectangles. A rectangle is *straight* if its edges of entry and departure are not adjacent. A *corner* rectangle is a rectangle s_i whose edges of entry and departure share a vertex—we call this vertex the inner corner, and the opposite vertex is the outer corner of s_i. The *front part* of s_i is the part of s_i that appears before the outer corner in the order.

Now we number the corner rectangles $t_1, t_2, ..., t_k$ in the order in which they appear on the curve, let $p_1, p_2, ..., p_k$ be their outer corners, and $f_1, f_2, ..., f_k$ be the areas of their front parts (Fig. 3). Note that any sequence of at least $\sqrt{m}$ rectangles must include a corner rectangle, so $k \geq \sqrt{m}$. Consider the curve section from p_i to p_{i+2}, for any $i = 1, 2, ..., k-2$. Let the width of this section (by number of rectangles) be w, let the height be h, and let $n \geq 3$ be the number of rectangles from t_i to t_{i+2} inclusive. Observe that because there is exactly one corner rectangle between t_i and t_{i+2}, namely t_{i+1}, we have $w \geq 2$, $h \geq 2$, and $w+h = n+1$ (the $+1$ is because t_{i+1} counts towards both w and h). Now the area of the curve section between p_i and p_{i+2} is $n - 1 + f_{i+2} - f_i$, and the area of its bounding box is $w \cdot h \geq 2(n-1)$. Hence we have WBA $\geq 2(n-1)/(n-1+f_{i+2}-f_i)$, or equivalently, $f_{i+2} - f_i \geq (2/\text{WBA} - 1)(n-1)$.

For the sake of contradiction, suppose WBA < 2. From the above we get $f_{2i+2} - f_{2i} \geq 2 \cdot (2/\text{WBA} - 1)$ for all $i \in \{1, 2, 3, ..., m'\}$, where m' is $\lfloor \frac{1}{2}\sqrt{m} \rfloor - 1$. Therefore $2/\text{WBA} - 1 \leq \frac{1}{2m'} \sum_{i=1}^{m'}(f_{2i+2} - f_{2i}) = \frac{1}{2m'}(f_{2m'+2} - f_2) < \frac{1}{2m'}$. This must be true for any grid of rectangles that is obtained by refining the subdivision recursively, following the rules of the scanning order. So we must have $\lim_{m \to \infty}(2/\text{WBA} - 1) = 0$ and thus $\lim_{m \to \infty} \text{WBA} = 2$.   □

Theorem 2 ([7]). *Any order with a rule that contains a triangle has* WBA ≥ 2.

Niedermeier et al. [13] prove WL$_2 \geq$ WL$_\infty \geq 3\frac{1}{2}$ for scanning orders that contain a section whose perimeter is an axis-aligned square. We found that their proof technique can also be applied to triangular curve sections, where we obtain WL$_2 \geq 4$. However, for scanning orders that contain rectangular (not square) sections this would not work. Using our proof technique of Theorem 1 we obtain:

Theorem 3. *Any scanning order that is based on recursively subdividing an axis-aligned rectangle into a regular grid of rectangles has* WL$_2 \geq$ WL$_\infty \geq 4$.

Niedermeier et al. also proved WL$_2 \geq$ WL$_\infty \geq 4$, but for another class of scanning orders, namely those that contain a cyclic section (its end touches its beginning) whose perimeter is an axis-aligned square.

5   Approximating the Worst-Case Measures

In this section we describe how we can obtain upper and lower bounds on the quality measures such as the worst-case locality and the worst-case bounding box quality measures defined in Section 3. For ease of description, we assume that the scanning order is defined by a single recursive rule without reversals.

Let μ be a mapping from regions to real numbers in a way that is invariant under all transformations $\tau(i)$ involved in the recursive definition of the scanning order. For example, $\mu(R)$ could be $|\text{bbox}(R)|/|R|$, or the square of the diameter of R divided by $|R|$. Our goal is to approximate $\mu^* = \lim_{k \to \infty} \sup_{i \prec j \in N_k} \mu(C(i,j))$. (We may also let μ depend on $C(i)$ or $C(j)$.) The mapping μ must be well-defined when $C(i,j)$ is not empty; when $|C(i,j)| = 0$ we may assume $\mu(C(i,j)) = \infty$.

We will compute the approximation of μ^* by exploring *probes*. A probe P is specified by three consecutive subsections of the order: a front section, a midsection, and a tail section. The probe P thus describes a set of contiguous subsections of the scanning order, namely all those subsections S that start

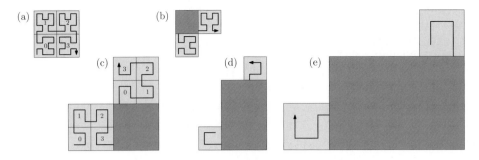

Fig. 4. (a) The Hilbert order.   (b) Base probe B_{02} of the Hilbert order. The dark area is the midsection.   (c) Canonical form $\mathcal{P}$ of B_{02}.   (d) Refinement $r_{32}(\mathcal{P})$ of $\mathcal{P}$. (e) The same refinement in canonical form: child $\mathcal{P}_{32}$ of $\mathcal{P}$.

somewhere in the front section of P and end somewhere in the tail section of P. For any probe P, let $\alpha(P)$ be the transformation that transforms C into the front section of P; let $M(P)$ be the midsection of P; and let $\omega(P)$ be the transformation that transforms C into the tail section of P. A section $P(i,j)$ of a probe P is the region $\alpha(P)C(\succeq i) \cup M(P) \cup \omega(P)C(\prec j)$. Let $\mu^*(P)$ be the maximum value of $\mu(S)$ over all subsections S covered by the probe, that is, $\mu^*(P) = \lim_{k\to\infty} \sup_{i,j\in N_k} \mu(P(i,j))$. A probe P may be rotated, mirrored, scaled and/or reversed: this does not affect the value of $\mu^*(P)$.

All subsections of the scanning order can be captured by a set of probes as follows. For $0 \le i < k < n$, let *base probe* B_{ik} be the probe with front transformation $\tau(i)$, midsection $\bigcup_{i<j<k} C(j)$, and tail transformation $\tau(k)$. For an example, see Fig. 4(a,b). We can prove $\mu^* = \max_{0\le i<k<n} \mu^*(B_{ik})$ [7]. Let *refinement* $r_{ij}(P)$ of probe P, with $i,j \in \{0,...,n-1\}$, be the probe with front transformation $\alpha(P) \circ \tau(i)$, tail transformation $\omega(P) \circ \tau(j)$, and midsection $\alpha(P)(C(\succ i)) \cup M(P) \cup \omega(P)(C(\prec j))$; see Fig. 4(c,d). Since $P = \bigcup r_{ij}(P)$, we have $\mu^*(P) = \max \mu^*(r_{ij}(P))$. We say a probe P is in canonical form if $\alpha(P)$ is the identity transformation. We can construct a canonical form $\mathcal{P}$ of any probe P by setting $\alpha(\mathcal{P})$ to the identity transformation, $M(\mathcal{P}) := \alpha(P)^{-1}(M(P))$, and $\omega(\mathcal{P}) := \alpha(P)^{-1} \circ \omega(P)$; see Fig. 4(c,e). Since μ is invariant under all transformations involved, we have $\mu^*(P) = \mu^*(\mathcal{P})$. Therefore it suffices to work only with probes in canonical form, where the *children* of a canonical probe $\mathcal{P}$ are the canonical forms of its refinements. Child $\mathcal{P}_{ij}$ is the canonical probe with midsection $M(\mathcal{P}_{ij}) := \tau(i)^{-1}(C(\succ i) \cup M(\mathcal{P}) \cup \omega(\mathcal{P})(C(\prec j)))$ and tail transformation $\omega(\mathcal{P}_{ij}) := \tau(i)^{-1} \circ \omega(\mathcal{P}) \circ \tau(j)$ (Fig. 4(e)).

Note that while computing $\mu^*(\mathcal{P})$ may be difficult, it may be easy to get a lower bound $\mu^-(\mathcal{P})$ and an upper bound $\mu^+(\mathcal{P})$ on $\mu^*(\mathcal{P})$. For example, if $\mu(A)$ is defined as $|\text{bbox}(A)|/|A|$, then $|\text{bbox}(M(\mathcal{P}))|/|C\cup M(\mathcal{P})\cup\omega(\mathcal{P})(C)|$ would be a lower bound on $\mu^*(\mathcal{P})$, and $|\text{bbox}(C\cup M(\mathcal{P})\cup\omega(\mathcal{P})(C))|/|M(\mathcal{P})|$ would be an upper bound on $\mu^*(\mathcal{P})$ (provided $|M(\mathcal{P})| > 0$, otherwise we define $\mu^*(\mathcal{P}) := \infty$).

Our algorithm to approximate μ^* is now as follows:

1 $Q \leftarrow$ an empty first-in-first-out queue
2 $R \leftarrow$ an empty dictionary
3 Insert the canonical forms of all base probes B_{ik} in Q and in R
4 $lowerBound \leftarrow \max_{\mathcal{P} \in Q} \mu^-(\mathcal{P})$

5   **while** we do not like the gap between $lowerBound$ and $\max_{\mathcal{P} \in Q} \mu^+(\mathcal{P})$
6   **do** Extract a probe $\mathcal{P}$ from the head of Q
7   **for** all canonical children $\mathcal{P}_{ij}$ of $\mathcal{P}$
8   **do if** $\mu^+(\mathcal{P}_{ij}) \geq lowerBound$ and R does not contain $\mathcal{P}_{ij}$
9   **then** Add $\mathcal{P}_{ij}$ to Q and R
10                        $lowerBound \leftarrow \max(lowerBound, \mu^-(\mathcal{P}_{ij}))$
11 Report that μ^* lies in the interval $[lowerBound, \max_{\mathcal{P} \in Q} \mu^+(\mathcal{P})]$.

The main idea of the algorithm is that we keep replacing probes by their refinements to get tighter lower and upper bounds on μ^*. In the full paper [7] we explain how the check if $\mathcal{P}_{ij}$ is contained in R on line 8 enables the algorithm to find good upper and lower bounds on μ^* relatively fast.

6   Computational Results

We implemented the approximation algorithm described above, specifically to compute the worst-case locality measures WL_∞, WL_2, and WL_1, and the worst-case bounding box quality measures WBA and WBP, for the curves mentioned in Section 2. We tested the 278 different orders that fit Wunderlich's scheme and are defined on a $k \times k$-grid, for $k \leq 4$. From these orders five curves $\mathcal{C}$ turned out to be "dominant" in the sense that there was no curve that was better than $\mathcal{C}$ on at least one measure and at least as good as $\mathcal{C}$ on the other measures. These five curves are Hilbert order, GP-order, Serpentine $011\,010\,110$, Luxburg's variation 2, and Meurthe order. We examined these curves further, together with coil order, balanced GP-order, $\beta\Omega$-order, AR^2W^2-order, Z-order and Sierpiński-Knopp order. For these curves we estimated the average total bounding box area and the square average relative total bounding box perimeter by random sampling: we generated 100 sets of numbers chosen uniformly between 0 and 1 that subdivide the curve, where the logarithm of the size of each set was chosen uniformly between $\log 500$ and $\log 18\,000$. We estimated the average total area (or relative perimeter) by taking the average over these 100 sample subdivisions.

The results of our computations are shown in Table 1. The exact worst-case locality was already known for Hilbert order [1,3,4,6,14], GP-order, coil order, and Luxburg 2 [11], and Sierpiński-Knopp order (or H-order) [13]. The other bounds have been computed by us. The bounds on the W-measures are the average of lower and upper bounds which have a gap of at most 0.0005. Only the bounds for the Gosper flowsnake are less precise (this order involves rotations by angles of $\arctan \frac{1}{5}\sqrt{3}$, which requires additional implementation effort and makes it more challenging to get bounds with high precision). The bounds on the A-measures result from our experiments with random subdivisions of curves.

Table 1. Bounds for different measures and curves. New curves printed in bold.

Order	WL_∞	WL_2	WL_1	WBA	ABA	WBP	ABP
Sierpiński-Knopp order	4	4	8	3.000	1.78	3.000	1.42
Balanced GP	4.619	4.619	8.619	2.000	1.44	2.155	1.19
GP	8	8	$10\,^2/_3$	2.000	1.44	2.722	1.28
Serpentine 011 010 110	5.625	6.250	10.000	2.500	1.44	2.500	1.20
Luxburg 2	$5\,^5/_8$	$6\,^1/_4$	10	2.500	1.49	2.500	1.24
Meurthe	5.333	5.667	10.667	2.500	1.41	2.667	1.17
Coil	$6\,^2/_3$	$6\,^2/_3$	$10\,^2/_3$	2.500	1.41	2.667	1.17
Hilbert	6	6	9	2.400	1.44	2.400	1.19
$\beta\Omega$	5.000	5.000	9.000	2.222	1.42	2.250	1.17
AR^2W^2	5.400	6.046	12.000	3.055	1.49	3.125	1.22
Z-order	∞	∞	∞	∞	2.92	∞	2.40
Gosper flowsnake	6.35	6.35	12.70	$\geq$3.18		$\geq$3.18	

7   Conclusions

Known locality measures of space-filling curves do not predict well how effective they are when grouping points into bounding boxes. Therefore we proposed new measures of bounding-box quality of space-filling curves. We presented new scanning orders that perform well on these measures, most notably the *balanced GP-order*, which has worst-case bounding box area ratio (WBA) 2.000, and worst-case bounding box square perimeter ratio (WBP) 2.155. On worst-case locality measures this curve also scores very well, much better than Peano's original curve, and beaten only by Sierpiński-Knopp order.

We conjecture that a WBA of 2 is in fact optimal and cannot be improved by any (recursively defined) space-filling curve. More provocatively we conjecture that the optimal WBP is also 2 (note that we have not actually found a curve with WBP less than 2.155). We add these conjectures to those by Niedermeier et al., who conjectured that the optimal WL_∞, WL_2, and WL_1 locality values are 4, 4, and 8, respectively (Niedermeier et al. posed this conjecture for curves filling a square, but we would like to drop this restriction). Niedermeier et al. proved that the conjectured lower bounds on the WL values are tight for a certain class of space-filling curves, but almost none of the curves in our study belongs to that class. For WL_2, WBA and WBP, we managed to prove the conjectured lower bounds for another class of curves, now including almost all curves mentioned in this paper. Still we have not been able to prove these lower bounds for *all* space-filling curves.

Our experiments on random points may give an impression of how effective the different curves would be in the application considered in this paper: a data structure for points in the plane, based on sorting the points into blocks of points that are consecutive along the curve. We see that it would be clearly suboptimal to use the order with the best WL_∞, WL_2 and WL_1 locality (Sierpiński-Knopp order) for this application. It seems to be better indeed to choose a curve based on WBA and WBP (balanced GP-order). Still the WBA and WBP measures do not predict performance on random points perfectly either: there are several curves with only moderate WBA and WBP values that seem to be as effective as the balanced GP-order (for example Hilbert order) or even slightly better (for example coil order or $\beta\Omega$-order) on random point data.

For what the WBA and WBP measures are worth, the conjectured near-optimality of the balanced GP-order suggests that there is little room for hope to find significantly more effective scanning orders in two dimensions. A first topic for further research is to determine the gap between our lower bound constructions and the performance of known space-filling curves when we consider generalisations to three dimensions. Chochia and Cole [4] and Niedermeier et al. [13] have some results on locality, but the gap is large and the field is still wide open, especially with respect to bounding box quality.

References

1. Alber, J., Niedermeier, R.: On multidimensional curves with Hilbert property. Theory of Computing Systems 33(4), 295–312 (2000)
2. Asano, T., Ranjan, D., Roos, T., Welzl, E., Widmayer, P.: Space-Filling Curves and Their Use in the Design of Geometric Data Structures. Theor. Comput. Sci. 181(1), 3–15 (1997)
3. Bauman, K.E.: The dilation factor of the Peano-Hilbert curve. Math. Notes 80(5), 609–620 (2006)
4. Chochia, G., Cole, M., Heywood, T.: Implementing the hierarchical PRAM on the 2D mesh: Analyses and experiments. In: Symp. on Parallel and Distributed Processing, pp. 587–595 (1995)
5. Gardner, M.: Mathematical Games—In which "monster" curves force redefinition of the word "curve". Scientific American 235(6), 124–133 (1976)
6. Gotsman, C., Lindenbaum, M.: On the metric properties of discrete space-filling curves. IEEE Trans. Image Processing 5(5), 794–797 (1996)
7. Haverkort, H., van Walderveen, F.: Locality and bounding-box quality of two-dimensional space-filling curves (manuscript, 2008) arXiv:0806.4787 [cs.CG]
8. Hilbert, D.: Über die stetige Abbildung einer Linie auf ein Flächenstück. Math. Ann. 38(3), 459–460 (1891)
9. Kamel, I., Faloutsos, C.: On packing R-trees. In: Conf. on Information and Knowledge Management, pp. 490–499 (1993)
10. Lebesgue, H.L.: Leçons sur l'intégration et la recherche des fonctions primitives, pp. 44–45. Gauthier-Villars (1904)
11. von Luxburg, U.: Lokalitätsmaße von Peanokurven. Student project report, Universität Tübingen, Wilhelm-Schickard-Institut für Informatik (1998)
12. Manolopoulos, Y., Nanopoulos, A., Papadopoulos, A.N., Theodoridis, Y.: R-trees: Theory and Applications. Springer, Heidelberg (2005)
13. Niedermeier, R., Reinhardt, K., Sanders, P.: Towards optimal locality in mesh-indexings. Discrete Applied Mathematics 117, 211–237 (2002)
14. Niedermeier, R., Sanders, P.: On the Manhattan-distance between points on space-filling mesh-indexings. Technical Report IB 18/96, Karlsruhe University, Dept. of Computer Science (1996)

15. Peano, G.: Sur une courbe, qui remplit toute une aire plane. Math. Ann. 36(1), 157–160 (1890)
16. Sagan, H.: Space-Filling Curves. Universitext series. Springer, Heidelberg (1994)
17. Wierum, J.-M.: Definition of a new circular space-filling curve: $\beta\Omega$-indexing. Technical Report TR-001-02, Paderborn Center for Parallel Computing (PC^2) (2002)
18. Wunderlich, W.: Über Peano-Kurven. Elemente der Mathematik 28(1), 1–10 (1973)

Probabilistic Analysis of Online Bin Coloring Algorithms Via Stochastic Comparison

Benjamin Hiller[1,*] and Tjark Vredeveld[2]

[1] Zuse Institute Berlin, Takustraße 7, D–14195 Berlin, Germany
hiller@zib.de
[2] Maastricht University, Department of Quantitative Economics, P.O. Box 616,
6200 MD Maastricht, The Netherlands
t.vredeveld@ke.unimaas.nl

Abstract. This paper proposes a new method for probabilistic analysis of online algorithms. It is based on the notion of stochastic dominance. We develop the method for the online bin coloring problem introduced in [15]. Using methods for the stochastic comparison of Markov chains we establish the result that the performance of the online algorithm GREEDYFIT is stochastically better than the performance of the algorithm ONEBIN for any number of items processed. This result gives a more realistic picture than competitive analysis and explains the behavior observed in simulations.

1 Introduction

We propose a new method for probabilistic analysis of online algorithms by using the concept of stochastic dominance. The traditional approach for analyzing online algorithms is competitive analysis [25,4], which characterizes an online algorithm by its competitive ratio, i.e., the worst-case ratio of the objective value achieved by the online algorithm to the optimal offline solution value. Online algorithms are then compared by comparing their competitive ratios, i.e., a smaller competitive ratio is better for a minimization problem. One drawback of competitive analysis is that it often provides rather pessimistic results due to its worst-case character. This is partly overcome by more elaborate variants like average-case competitive analysis [20] and smoothed competitive analysis [2].

In our approach, we suggest to compare the performance of algorithms on random input sequences directly using stochastic dominance. A random variable X is *stochastically dominated* by a random variable Y, written $X \leq_{\text{st}} Y$, if

$$\Pr[X \geq x] \leq \Pr[Y \geq x] \quad \text{for all } x \in \mathbb{R}. \tag{1}$$

Suppose we can describe the performance of two online algorithms $\mathcal{A}$ and $\mathcal{B}$ by random variables $\chi^{\mathcal{A}}$ and $\chi^{\mathcal{B}}$, respectively. We can then say that $\mathcal{A}$ is *stochastically better* than $\mathcal{B}$ (for a minimization problem), if $\chi^{\mathcal{A}} \leq_{\text{st}} \chi^{\mathcal{B}}$.

* Supported by the DFG research group "Algorithms, Structure, Randomness" (Grant number GR 883/10-3, GR 883/10-4) and a DAAD dissertation grant.

D. Halperin and K. Mehlhorn (Eds.): ESA 2008, LNCS 5193, pp. 528–539, 2008.

Stochastic comparison methods have been successfully applied in areas like queueing theory [23], finance, economics and in particular decision under risk [18]. In this paper we introduce these concepts to the study of online algorithms.

We use this approach to study algorithms for the online bin coloring problem introduced by Krumke et al. [15]. It has applications in commissioning [15], vehicle routing [8] and networking [16]. For the bin coloring problem, we are given a sequence of unit-size items, each of which has one of C colors. These items need to be packed sequentially into one of m initially empty bins of capacity B. As soon as a bin is *full,* i. e., has exactly B items, it is replaced by an empty one. The goal is to minimize the maximum number of different colors in one bin. We will refer to the number of different colors in a bin as its *colorfulness.* In the online version, the items arrive one by one and must be irrevocably assigned to a bin before the next item becomes known.

A natural algorithm for this problem is the algorithm GREEDYFIT [15]: it packs an item with an already present color in the bin with that color and otherwise chooses a bin which currently has the least number of different colors. Another simple algorithm, ONEBIN, packs all items in the same bin. Krumke et al. [15] analyzed these algorithms, showing the counterintuitive result that in terms of the competitive ratio, the trivial algorithm ONEBIN is better than the more sophisticated algorithm GREEDYFIT. The authors mentioned that the most challenging issue is to analyze the algorithms from an average-case point of view to explain the clear dominance of GREEDYFIT over ONEBIN observed in simulations. Such an average-case analysis is a consequence of our results.

Our Results. We propose a new probabilistic analysis of both deterministic and randomized online algorithms. As far as we know, this is the first use of stochastic dominance in the analysis of the quality of online and approximation algorithms.

Using this approach, we obtain results for the comparison of the GREEDYFIT and ONEBIN algorithms, which explain the superiority of GREEDYFIT over ONEBIN observed in simulations. For our analysis, we assume that the color sequences are generated by choosing the colors i. i. d. according to a color distribution γ. Note that in this model, all online algorithms eventually have to produce a bin with colorfulness B if the number of colors is sufficiently high, say $C \geq 2mB$. This implies that in this case, all online algorithms are asymptotically equally bad. Moreover, since eventually there will be a color subsequence of length $2mB$ with all colors different, the asymptotic competitive ratio is 1 with probability 1. Both issues indicate that asymptotic probabilistic analysis does not give meaningful results. We therefore show that GREEDYFIT is stochastically better than ONEBIN after n items, for any n. To be more precise, let the random variables χ_n^{GF} and χ_n^{OB} denote the maximum colorfulness attained after processing n items using GREEDYFIT and ONEBIN, respectively. We show that $\chi_n^{\mathrm{GF}} \leq_{\mathrm{st}} \chi_n^{\mathrm{OB}}$ for all n and distributions γ. We also obtain a similar result if the objective is the average colorfulness instead of the maximum colorfulness. Both results are based on an analysis of Markov chains related to the algorithms.

We emphasize several implications of this result. Stochastic dominance implies not only that the expected value of GREEDYFIT is bounded by that of ONEBIN, but also that the expected competitive ratio of GREEDYFIT is not more than that of ONEBIN. The expected competitive ratio [20] is defined as the expectation of the ratio between online algorithm and offline optimum. By considering the uniform color distribution, our result can be interpreted as a counting result stating that there are more instances for which GREEDYFIT manages to achieve a low maximum colorfulness than for ONEBIN. If the online bin coloring occurs as a subproblem and the overall performance depends in a non-decreasing way on the colorfulness achieved, than using GREEDYFIT is better in expectation than using ONEBIN w.r.t. to overall performance.

Related Work. Various alternatives to standard competitive analysis have been proposed, almost all of them are based on the idea of weakening the offline adversary. This can be done by considering randomized online algorithms [4] or by allowing the online algorithms to use more resources [11]. More related to our approach are concepts like the diffuse adversary [14], average-case competitive analysis [20] and smoothed competitive analysis [2], which are also based on random request sequences. Direct comparisons of online algorithms are done in comparative analysis [14] and the relative worst order ratio [6].

The bin coloring problem has been studied in [15,8,16]. It is shown in [8,16] that the offline version is NP-hard and that it cannot be approximated within a factor of $4/3$ unless $P = NP$. Lin et al. [16] provide an algorithm that finds a solution of cost $OPT + 1$ in the case that there are exactly mB items. For the online version, Krumke et al. [15] show that the competitive ratio of GREEDYFIT is at least $2m$, the competitive ratio of ONEBIN is at most $2m - 1$, and that the competitive ratio of any randomized algorithm is $\Omega(m)$ even if it is allowed to use more than m bins simultaneously. The bin coloring problem is also related to class-contrained knapsack problems [21,22]. In those versions of the knapsack problem, each item is characterized by a size and a color and each knapsack has an additional limit on the number of different colors that it can hold.

Although Markov chains are a natural tool for the study of online algorithms, they have not been used much so far in this context. One prominent example is the paging problem, where Karlin et al. [12] studied request sequences generated by a Markov chain. However, this work uses Markov chains to model the instances and not for analyzing algorithms, although the theory of Markov decision processes is used to derive lower bounds for all online algorithms. Initiated by Coffman et al. [7], online bin packing algorithms have been analyzed by modelling their behavior by Markov chains [13,1,19]. General methods for the analysis of Markov chains have then been used to prove results for online algorithms. In contrast to our approach these results are only asymptotic and expectation-based. Other uses of Markov chains in the analysis of algorithms are in the field of approximate sampling [24]. Some of the techniques used there are similar to ours since they are based on the concept of coupling, which is very useful to compare probability distributions.

There are many applications of the rich theory of stochastic comparison and stochastic dominance, see e.g., [23,18]. However, there are only few papers applying them to analyze or develop algorithms. The papers by Mitzenmacher [5,17] employ these methods to analyze routing algorithms.

Structure of the Paper. Section 2 defines the problem variants and introduces Markov chain models for the online algorithms, basic notation and technical preliminaries, including Theorem 1 which is the basis of our analysis. In Sections 3 and 4 we prove the result for minimizing the maximum and average colorfulness, respectively.

2   Problem Definition and Markov Chain Models

An instance of the bin coloring problem is described by the number of simultaneously open bins m, the bin capacity B and a sequence of n unit sized items, each of which has one of C colors. The items need to be packed in the open bins and whenever a bin has B items, it is closed and replaced by a new empty bin. The colorfulness of a bin is the number of different colors in this bin and the goal is to pack the items in the (open) bins such that the maximum colorfulness over all bins is minimized. A second objective is to pack the items in such a way that the sum of the colorfulnesses of all bins is minimized. When minimizing this second objective, we refer to the problem as *sum-BC*, whereas the first problem is refered to as *max-BC*. For probabilistic analysis, we still assume that the number of open bins m, the bin capacity B and the number of colors C is given deterministically. The color sequence, however, is generated by chosing each color independently according to a probability distribution function γ over the colors.

As mentioned before, asymptotic analysis does not give meaningful results. However, the algorithms GREEDYFIT and ONEBIN differ in *how long* they manage to produce bins of low colorfulness. We therefore will analyze the *transient* instead of the asymptotic behavior of the algorithms. Let the random variables χ_n^{GF} and χ_n^{OB} denote the maximum colorfulness attained after processing n items using GREEDYFIT and ONEBIN, respectively. We will show that GREEDYFIT is stochastically better than ONEBIN after n items, i. e., that $\chi_n^{\mathrm{GF}} \leq_{\mathrm{st}} \chi_n^{\mathrm{OB}}$. For the sum-BC problem, we show a similar result.

2.1   Markov Chain Models

Let us start with the max-BC and consider an arbitrary online bin coloring algorithm processing color sequences generated by our random model. The operation of any such algorithm can be described on a state space which encodes for every bin i its current number of items f_i and the set of colors in that bin C_i. Moreover, the state also keeps track of the maximal colorfulness attained so far. Formally, we have

$$\mathcal{S}_{\mathrm{max\text{-}BC}} := \mathcal{S}_{\mathrm{max\text{-}BC}}(m, B, C) = \big\{ (f_1, C_1, \ldots, f_m, C_m, \chi) \ \big| \ 0 \leq |C_i| \leq f_i \leq B,$$
$$|C_i| \leq \chi \leq \min\{B, C\} \big\}.$$

Note that the states reachable by the operation of an algorithm may be a subset of $\mathcal{S}_{\text{max-BC}}$. We will use $f_i(s)$, $C_i(s)$, and $\chi(s)$ to refer to the components of state s. Additionally, we define $c_i(s) := |C_i(s)|$. The state $(0, \emptyset, \ldots, 0, \emptyset, 0)$ is called the *initial empty state*.

Suppose an online bin coloring algorithm $\mathcal{A}$ is in state s and receives an item of color c. The algorithm then changes to state s' by putting this item in one of the bins, say bin i. There are two cases: Either color c is contained in $C_i(s)$, we say the color is *known (in bin i)*, or it is not, so the color is *new (in bin i)*. We will denote the successor state for the first case by $s^{\text{k}(i)}$ (the color c is not needed to determine the successor state), for the second by $s^{\text{n}(i,c)}$. It will be convenient not to consider the new color c, but to deal with the random state resulting from s if any new color distributed according to γ is seen. We will use the notation $s^{\text{n}(i)}$ for this random state.

The ONEBIN algorithm is then described by the transitions

$$s' = \begin{cases} s^{\text{k}(1)} & \text{with probability } \gamma(C_1(s)), \\ s^{\text{n}(1)} & \text{with probability } 1 - \gamma(C_1(s)), \end{cases} \qquad (2)$$

where we use the shortcut notation $\gamma(S) := \sum_{s \in S} \gamma(s)$. This defines a Markov chain which we denote by $\text{OB}(m, B, C, \gamma)$. Note that although ONEBIN uses only the first bin, we consider $\text{OB}(m, B, C, \gamma)$ as working on the whole state space with m bins.

Similarly, we can give a Markov chain $\text{GF}(m, B, C, \gamma)$ for GREEDYFIT. $\text{GF}(s)$ is the bin GREEDYFIT selects for an item with a new color in state s. Depending on the tie-breaking rule used by the specific variant of GREEDYFIT, $\text{GF}(s)$ may or may not be a random variable. We only need that $\text{GF}(s)$ is one of the bins having in state s the smallest number of colors.

$$s' = \begin{cases} s^{\text{k}(i)} & \text{with probability } \gamma(C_i(s)) \quad 1 \le i \le m, \\ s^{\text{n}(\text{GF}(s))} & \text{with probability } 1 - \gamma(\bigcup_i C_i(s)). \end{cases} \qquad (3)$$

The operation of online algorithms in the sum-BC problem can be captured by a similar Markov chain model. The main difference is that the χ-component is no longer the maximum of the colorfulness seen so far, but the sum. Note that the resulting Markov chains are infinite. Thus the state space $\mathcal{S}_{\text{sum-BC}}$ is basically the same as $\mathcal{S}_{\text{max-BC}}$, but with an unbounded χ-component. The χ-component increases each time a new color for a bin is encountered.

To avoid notational overhead, we will use the same notation for both problem variants. Therefore the sum-BC-Markov chains for ONEBIN and GREEDYFIT will be denoted by $\text{OB}(m, B, C, \gamma)$ and $\text{GF}(m, B, C, \gamma)$, too.

We use the notations $\text{OB}(m, B, C, \gamma)_n$ and $\text{GF}(m, B, C, \gamma)_n$ for the random state after n steps when ONEBIN and GREEDYFIT are started in the initial empty state. The goal of this paper is to show that, in both problem variants,

$$\chi\big(\text{GF}(m, B, C, \gamma)_n\big) \le_{\text{st}} \chi\big(\text{OB}(m, B, C, \gamma)_n\big) \quad \forall n$$

and for all parameters m, B, C and color distributions γ. This kind of result is known as *comparison result* for Markov chains in the probability theory literature, see e. g., [18].

2.2   A New Comparison Criterion

Unfortunately, the general comparison results for Markov chains based on stochastic monotonicity [18] are not sufficient to prove stochastic dominance between GREEDYFIT and ONEBIN. Doisy [9] developed a comparison criterion that is not based on stochastic monotonicity, however, this result is also too weak.

Our analysis is therefore based on the following criterion, which is an extension of a result in [3]. The criterion is based on *stopping times*. Given a Markov chain $X = (X_n)_{n \in \mathbb{N}_0}$ on state space $\mathcal{S}$ with valuation function $\chi \colon \mathcal{S} \to V, V \subseteq \mathbb{N}_0$, we denote by T_X^v the first time the Markov chain X reaches a state with valuation at least v.

Theorem 1. *Let $X = (X_n)_{n \in \mathbb{N}_0}$ and $Y = (Y_n)_{n \in \mathbb{N}_0}$ be Markov chains on state space $\mathcal{S}$ and let $\chi \colon \mathcal{S} \to V$ be a valuation function for some $V \subseteq \mathbb{N}_0$. Assume that the transitions of X and Y are such that the value of a state is nondecreasing in each step and that $\chi(X_0) = \chi(Y_0)$. Then the following are equivalent:*

1. $T_Y^v \leq_{\mathrm{st}} T_X^v \quad \forall v \in V.$
2. $\chi(X_n) \leq_{\mathrm{st}} \chi(Y_n) \quad \forall n \in \mathbb{N}_0.$

Proof. Let the Markov chain X be defined on the probability space $(\Omega, \mathcal{A}, \mathrm{prob})$. The stopping time T_X^v is then a random variable $T_X^v \colon \Omega \to \mathbb{N}_0$ that is defined by

$$T_X^v(\omega) := \min \left\{ n \mid \chi(X_n(\omega)) \geq v \right\}$$

for each $\omega \in \Omega$. Since $\chi(X_n(\omega)) \geq \chi(X_{n'}(\omega))$ whenever $n' \leq n$, we have the equivalence

$$T_X^v(\omega) \leq n \iff \chi(X_n(\omega)) \geq v,$$

which implies

$$\Pr\left[T_X^v \leq n\right] = \Pr\left[\chi(X_n) \geq v\right].$$

Of course, analogous statements hold for Y as well.

We now have the following chain of equivalences.

$$\chi(X_n) \leq_{\mathrm{st}} \chi(Y_n) \quad \forall n \in \mathbb{N}_0$$
$$\iff \Pr\left[\chi(X_n) \geq v\right] \leq \Pr\left[\chi(Y_n) \geq v\right] \quad \forall n \in \mathbb{N}_0, v \in V$$
$$\iff \Pr\left[T_X^v \leq n\right] \leq \Pr\left[T_Y^v \leq n\right] \quad \forall n \in \mathbb{N}_0, v \in V$$
$$\iff T_Y^v \leq_{\mathrm{st}} T_X^v \quad \forall v \in V.$$

$\square$

In the sequel, we denote by $T_X^v(s)$ the stopping time for reaching a state with valuation at least v when started deterministically in state in s.

How can we show $T_Y^v(s_0) \leq_{st} T_X^v(s_0)$? In order to apply a kind of induction technique we introduce a family of Markov chains $(X(n))_{n \in \mathbb{N}}$ derived from a Markov chain X as follows. The state space of $X(n)$ is $\mathcal{S} \times \{0, \ldots, n\}$ and the transitions are defined by

$$\Pr[X(n)_{i+1} = (s', i+1) \mid X(n)_i = (s, i)] := \Pr[X_{i+1} = s' \mid X_i = s] \quad \forall 0 \leq i < n,$$
$$\Pr[X(n)_{i+1} = (s, n) \mid X(n)_i = (s, n)] := 1 \qquad \forall i \geq n.$$

The Markov chain $X(n)$ can be thought of as an time-expanded, acyclic version of the chain X for the first n steps. Clearly, we have

$$\Pr[T_X^v(s) = i] = \Pr\left[T_{X(n)}^v((s, 0)) = i\right] \quad \forall 0 \leq i < n. \tag{4}$$

So in order to show $T_Y^v(s_0) \leq_{st} T_X^v(s_0)$, we can prove that

$$T_{Y(n)}^v((s_0, 0)) \leq_{st} T_{X(n)}^v((s_0, 0)) \quad \forall n \in \mathbb{N}.$$

To simplify notation, we will write $T_{X(n)}^v(s)$ for $T_{X(n)}^v((s, 0))$ from now on. We have the following simple result, the proof of which can be found in [10].

Lemma 1. *For any Markov chain $X = (X_n)_{n \in \mathbb{N}_0}$ on state space $\mathcal{S}$ with valuation function $\chi \colon \mathcal{S} \to V$, $V \subseteq \mathbb{N}_0$, the stochastic dominance relation*

$$T_{X(n+1)}^v(s) \leq_{st} T_{X(n)}^v(s)$$

holds for all states s, $n \in \mathbb{N}_0$, and $v \in V$.

2.3 Further Preliminaries

For two random variables X and Y, we will write $X = Y$ to mean that they have the same distribution function.

An important tool used frequently in this paper is the notion of mixture of random variables.

Definition 1. *Let $(X_m)_{m \in M}$ be a family of random variables and Θ be an M-valued random variable. The random variable Y defined by $Y := X_\Theta$, i.e., the X-variable to use is given by the realization of Θ, is called a mixture and denoted by $[(X_m)_{m \in M} \mid \Theta]$.*

The following results are well-known properties of $\leq_{st}$: closure under mixtures and equivalence to sample-path comparisons (see e.g., [18]).

Theorem 2 (Mixture Theorem). *Suppose $[(X_m)_{m \in M} \mid \Theta]$ and $[(Y_m)_{m \in M} \mid \Theta]$ are two mixtures controlled by the same random variable Θ satisfying $X_m \leq_{st} Y_m$ for all $m \in M$. Then we have $[(X_m)_{m \in M} \mid \Theta] \leq_{st} [(Y_m)_{m \in M} \mid \Theta]$.*

Theorem 3 (Strassen's Theorem). *For two random variables X and Y the following are equivalent:*

1. $X \leq_{\mathrm{st}} Y$
2. *There is a probability space $(\Omega, \mathcal{A}, P)$ with random variables $\tilde{X}, \tilde{Y} \colon \Omega \to \mathbb{R}$ such that*
   - $\tilde{X}$ *and* $\tilde{Y}$ *are distributed as X and Y, respectively, and*
   - $\Pr\left[\tilde{X} \leq \tilde{Y}\right] = 1.$

3   GREEDYFIT Is Better Than ONEBIN: max-BC

We will now apply the strategy described in Section 2.2 to the comparison of GREEDYFIT and ONEBIN. The main technique is to analyze a kind of stochastic recursion for $T^v_{X(n)}$ based on a mixture of random variables.

Let OB $=$ OB(m, B, C, γ) for fixed parameters m, B, C, γ. In a state $s \in \mathcal{S}_{\text{max-BC}}$ ONEBIN does the transitions to states

$$
\begin{cases}
s^{k(1)} & \text{with probability } \gamma(C_1(s)), \\
s^{n(1)} & \text{with probability } 1 - \gamma(C_1(s)).
\end{cases}
$$

Using the random variable $\Theta \colon \mathcal{S}_{\text{max-BC}} \to \mathbb{N}$ defined by

$$
\Theta(s) := \begin{cases}
1 & \text{the next color is known in bin 1,} \\
2 & \text{the next color is new in bin 1,}
\end{cases}
$$

we can come up with a recursive expression for $T^v_{\text{OB}(n)}(s)$, namely

$$
T^v_{\text{OB}(n)}(s) = \begin{cases}
0 & \chi(s) \geq v, \\
1 + \left[T^v_{\text{OB}(n-1)}\left(s^{k(1)}\right), T^v_{\text{OB}(n-1)}\left(s^{n(1)}\right) \, \middle| \, \Theta(s) \right] & \chi(s) < v.
\end{cases} \tag{5}
$$

This recursion and the Mixture Theorem are the most important ingredients for the proofs to come.

We call two states $s, s' \in \mathcal{S}_{\text{max-BC}}$ OB-*equivalent*, if the valuation, the number of items and the set of colors in bin 1 are the same in s and s', i.e., if $\chi(s) = \chi(s')$, $f_1(s) = f_1(s')$, and $C_1(s) = C_1(s')$. Note that ONEBIN behaves exactly the same in two OB-equivalent states and therefore the stopping times from two OB-equivalent states coincide. The following lemma gives some useful comparisons of stopping times from certain states in the OB(n) chains. The proof of this lemma can be found in [10].

Lemma 2. *Consider the ONEBIN Markov chain* OB $=$ OB(m, B, C, γ) *for parameters $m, B \geq 2$, C, and color distribution γ. We have for all states $s \in \mathcal{S}_{\text{max-BC}}$, $n \in \mathbb{N}$, and $v \in V$:*

1. $T^v_{\text{OB}(n)}\left(s^{n(1)}\right) \leq_{\mathrm{st}} T^v_{\text{OB}(n)}\left(s^{k(1)}\right)$, *and*
2. $T^v_{\text{OB}(n)}\left(s^{n(1)}\right) \leq_{\mathrm{st}} T^v_{\text{OB}(n)}(s')$ *for every state s' that is OB-equivalent to s.*

Theorem 4. *Let* OB *and* GF *be the* ONEBIN *and* GREEDYFIT *max-BC-Markov chains for fixed parameters* m, B, C *with* $B, m \geq 2$ *for some color distribution* γ. *We have for all states* $s \in \mathcal{S}_{\text{max-BC}}$, $n \in \mathbb{N}$, *and* $v \in V$:

$$T^v_{\text{OB}(n)}(s) \leq_{\text{st}} T^v_{\text{GF}(n)}(s).$$

Proof. The proof is by induction on n. Since GREEDYFIT is not worse than ONEBIN for a single step in each state s, we have $T^v_{\text{OB}(1)}(s) \leq_{\text{st}} T^v_{\text{GF}(1)}(s)$.

For the induction step, suppose we know that $T^v_{\text{OB}(n)}(s) \leq_{\text{st}} T^v_{\text{GF}(n)}(s)$ for all $s \in \mathcal{S}_{\text{max-BC}}$. Consider a state $s \in \mathcal{S}_{\text{max-BC}}$. Define the random variable $\Theta \colon \mathcal{S}_{\text{max-BC}} \to \{1, \ldots, m+1\}$ by

$$\Pr[\Theta(s) = i] = \begin{cases} \gamma(C_i(s)) & 1 \leq i \leq m, \\ 1 - \gamma(\bigcup_i C_i(s)) & i = m+1, \end{cases}$$

i.e., Θ in a sense "selects" the GREEDYFIT successor of state s. Using Θ, we can write the recursion for the stopping time of OB as

$$T^v_{\text{OB}(n+1)}(s)$$
$$= 1 + \left[T^v_{\text{OB}(n)}(s^{\text{k}(1)}), T^v_{\text{OB}(n)}(s^{\text{n}(1)}), \ldots, T^v_{\text{OB}(n)}(s^{\text{n}(1)}) \,\middle|\, \Theta(s) \right].$$

Observe that $s^{\text{k}(i)}$, $2 \leq i \leq m$, are OB-equivalent to s, $s^{\text{n}(\text{GF}(s))}$ is either OB-equivalent to s or equal to $s^{\text{n}(1)}$. We use Lemma 2 to bound this by

$$\leq_{\text{st}} 1 + \left[T^v_{\text{OB}(n)}(s^{\text{k}(1)}), \ldots, T^v_{\text{OB}(n)}(s^{\text{k}(m)}), T^v_{\text{OB}(n)}(s^{\text{n}(\text{GF}(s))}) \,\middle|\, \Theta(s) \right],$$

which by the induction hypothesis is bounded by

$$\leq_{\text{st}} 1 + \left[T^v_{\text{GF}(n)}(s^{\text{k}(1)}), \ldots, T^v_{\text{GF}(n)}(s^{\text{k}(m)}), T^v_{\text{GF}(n)}(s^{\text{n}(\text{GF}(s))}) \,\middle|\, \Theta(s) \right]$$
$$= T^v_{\text{GF}(n+1)}(s).$$

This concludes the induction step and the proof.   □

Corollary 1. *Let* OB *and* GF *be the* ONEBIN *and* GREEDYFIT *max-BC-Markov chains for fixed parameters* m, B, C *and color distribution* γ. *We have for all states* $s \in \mathcal{S}_{\text{max-BC}}$, *in particular the initial empty state, and for all* $n \in \mathbb{N}_0$ *that*

$$\chi(\text{GF}(s)_n) \leq_{\text{st}} \chi(\text{OB}(s)_n).$$

4   GREEDYFIT Is Better Than ONEBIN: sum-BC

The analysis of the sum-BC problem is very similar to the one of max-BC in the preceding section. Recall that the state space of the sum-BC only differs from the one of the max-BC in its interpretation of the χ-component: it now counts the sum of the colorfulnesses of all used bins instead of the maximum. Therefore, the χ-component increases with every transition due to a new color. Nevertheless, recursion (5) for the stopping times is also valid for the analysis of the sum-BC.

Note that the proof of Theorem 4 is based only on Lemma 2. The proof of item 2 of Lemma 2 only needs item 1 and OB-equivalence (see [10] for details). The notion of OB-equivalence introduced for the max-BC is also appropriate for the sum-BC. In particular, stopping times for two OB-equivalent states coincide also for the sum-BC-Markov chain of ONEBIN. Due to these observations, it is sufficient to prove an analogue of item 1 of Lemma 2 to establish stochastic dominance between GREEDYFIT and ONEBIN for the sum-BC. The proof uses the concept of a coupling Markov chain.

Definition 2. *Let $X = (X_n)_{n \in \mathbb{N}_0}$ and $Y = (Y_n)_{n \in \mathbb{N}_0}$ be Markov chains on state spaces $\mathcal{S}_X$ and $\mathcal{S}_Y$, respectively. A Markov chain $Z = (\tilde{X}, \tilde{Y})$ on state space $\mathcal{S}_X \times \mathcal{S}_Y$ is a coupling Markov chain if $\tilde{X}$ and $\tilde{Y}$ are distributed as X and Y, respectively. However, $\tilde{X}$ and $\tilde{Y}$ need not be independent.*

Lemma 3. *Consider the ONEBIN Markov chain $\text{OB} = \text{OB}(m, B, C, \gamma)$ for parameters $m, B \geq 2$, C, and color distribution γ for the sum-BC. We then have $T^v_{\text{OB}(n)}(s^{\text{n}(1)}) \leq_{\text{st}} T^v_{\text{OB}(n)}(s^{\text{k}(1)})$. for all states $s \in \mathcal{S}_{\text{sum-BC}}$, $n \in \mathbb{N}$, and $v \in V$.*

Proof. We will show the stronger $T^v_{\text{OB}}(s^{\text{n}(1,c)}) \leq_{\text{st}} T^v_{\text{OB}}(s^{\text{k}(1)})$ for all $c \notin C_1(s)$ by constructing a coupling Markov chain $Z = (X, Y)$ on a state space that is a subset of $\mathcal{S}_{\text{sum-BC}} \times \mathcal{S}_{\text{sum-BC}}$. The first component of Z behaves exactly as OB started in state $s^{\text{n}(1,c)}$ and the second component as OB started in $s^{\text{k}(1)}$.

A state $(s^{\text{n}}, s^{\text{k}})$ of Z that can be reached from the initial state $(s^{\text{n}(1,c)}, s^{\text{k}(1)})$ will always satisfy the invariant

- either $\chi(s^{\text{n}}) \geq \chi(s^{\text{k}})$, $f_1(s^{\text{n}}) = f_1(s^{\text{k}})$, and $C_1(s^{\text{n}}) = C_1(s^{\text{k}})$ or
- $\chi(s^{\text{n}}) = \chi(s^{\text{k}}) + 1$, $f_1(s^{\text{n}}) = f_1(s^{\text{k}})$, and $C_1(s^{\text{n}}) = C_1(s^{\text{k}}) \cup \{c\}$.

Since in both cases $\chi(s^{\text{n}}) \geq \chi(s^{\text{k}})$, the invariant implies

$$\Pr\left[T^v_X(s^{\text{n}(1,c)}) \leq T^v_Y(s^{\text{k}(1)})\right] = 1,$$

so by Strassen's Theorem the stochastic dominance is established.

It remains to describe Z. The initial state is $(s^{\text{n}(1,c)}, s^{\text{k}(1)})$, which obviously satisfies the invariant. Consider any state $(s^{\text{n}}, s^{\text{k}})$ satisfying the invariant. If s^{n} and s^{k} differ at most in the χ-component, then the transitions of Z are such that the same happens in both components, leading to further states satisfying the invariant.

Suppose s^{n} and s^{k} differ also in the C_1-component. The transitions are then determined by the next color c' drawn according to γ as follows:

$$\begin{cases} \left(s^{\text{n},\text{n}(1,c')}, s^{\text{k},\text{n}(1,c')}\right) & c' \notin C_1(s^{\text{n}}) = C_1(s^{\text{k}}) \cup \{c\}, \\ \left(s^{\text{n},\text{k}(1)}, s^{\text{k},\text{n}(1,c')}\right) & c' = c, \\ \left(s^{\text{n},\text{k}(1)}, s^{\text{k},\text{k}(1)}\right) & c' \in C_1(s^{\text{k}}). \end{cases}$$

Note that all the states satisfy the invariant and that the second kind of transition leads to states which differ at most in the χ-component (the other way of reaching such a state is when bin 1 is empty again). Finally, it can be verified that these transitions mirror the behavior of the OB chain in each component.   □

Remark 1. The above coupling argument can be generalized for any algorithm whose decisions do not depend on $\chi(s)$, both for sum-BC and max-BC.

Theorem 5. *Let* OB *and* GF *be the* ONEBIN *and* GREEDYFIT sum-BC-*Markov chains for fixed parameters* m, B, C *and color distribution* γ. *We have for all states* $s \in \mathcal{S}_{\text{sum-BC}}$, *in particular the initial empty state, and for all* $n \in \mathbb{N}_0$ *that*

$$\chi\big(\text{GF}(s)_n\big) \leq_{\text{st}} \chi\big(\text{OB}(s)_n\big).$$

5   Concluding Remarks

We introduced a new approach for the probabilistic analysis of online algorithms which is based on the concept of stochastic dominance. We applied this approach to the analysis of online algorithms for bin coloring problems. This analysis explains simulation results much better than the competitive analysis results existing so far and thus resolves an open problem posed in [15].

For the future it is interesting to see whether the method can be extended to analyze further bin coloring algorithms or more complicated probabilistic models, e. g., ones where the color sequence is generated by a Markov chain. As an example, consider the algorithm FIXEDCOLORS, which assigns the items to bins based on their colors and a fixed color-to-bin assignment. In simulations we observed that this algorithm is "in-between" ONEBIN and GREEDYFIT. We also observed that GREEDYFIT outperforms ONEBIN when operating on uniform color sequences, where ONEBIN has to cope with fewer colors than GREEDYFIT.

Similar techniques might also apply for other combinatorial online problems like bin packing or paging.

References

1. Albers, S., Mitzenmacher, M.: Average-case analyses of first fit and random fit bin packing. Random Structures Algorithms 16(3), 240–259 (2000)
2. Becchetti, L., Leonardi, S., Marchetti-Spaccamela, A., Schäfer, G., Vredeveld, T.: Average case and smoothed competitive analysis for the multi-level feedback algorithm. Math. Oper. Res. 31(1), 85–108 (2006)
3. ben Mamoun, M., Bušić, A., Fourneau, J.-M., Pekergin, N.: Increasing convex monotone Markov chains: Theory, algorithms, and applications. In: MAM 2006: Markov Anniversary Meeting, pp. 189–210. Boson Books, Raleigh (2006)
4. Borodin, A., El-Yaniv, R.: Online Computation and Competitive Analysis. Cambridge University Press, New York (1998)
5. Boyan, J., Mitzenmacher, M.: Improved results for route planning in stochastic transportation networks. In: Proc. 12th SODA, pp. 895–902 (2001)

6. Boyar, J., Favrholdt, L.M.: The relative worst order ratio for online algorithms. ACM Transactions on Algorithms 3(2) (2007)

7. Coffman Jr., E.G., Johnson, D.S., Shor, P.W., Weber, R.R.: Markov Chains, computer proofs, and average-case analysis of best fit bin packing. In: Proc. 25th STOC, pp. 412–421 (1993)

8. de Paepe, W.E.: Complexity Results and Competitive Analysis for Vehicle Routing Problems. Technische Universiteit Eindhoven, Ph.D. Thesis (2002)

9. Doisy, M.: A coupling technique for stochastic comparison of functions of Markov processes. Journal of Applied Mathematics & Decision Sciences 4(1), 39–64 (2000)

10. Hiller, B., Vredeveld, T.: Probabilistic analysis of online bin coloring algorithms via stochastic dominance. ZIB-Report 08-18, Zuse Institute Berlin (2008)

11. Kalyanasundaram, B., Pruhs, K.: Speed is as powerful as clairvoyance. J. ACM 47(4), 617–643 (2000)

12. Karlin, A.R., Phillips, S.J., Raghavan, P.: Markov paging. SIAM J. Comput. 30(2), 906–922 (2000)

13. Kenyon, C., Rabani, Y., Sinclair, A.: Biased random walks, Lyapunov functions, and stochastic analysis of best fit bin packing. J. Algorithms 27(2), 218–235 (1998)

14. Koutsoupias, E., Papadimitriou, C.H.: Beyond competitive analysis. SIAM J. Comput. 30(1), 300–317 (2000)

15. Krumke, S.O., de Paepe, W.E., Stougie, L., Rambau, J.: Online bin coloring. In: Meyer auf der Heide, F. (ed.) ESA 2001. LNCS, vol. 2161, pp. 74–84. Springer, Heidelberg (2001)

16. Lin, M., Lin, Z., Xu, J.: Almost optimal solutions for bin coloring problems. In: Deng, X., Du, D. (eds.) ISAAC 2005. LNCS, vol. 3827, pp. 82–91. Springer, Heidelberg (2005)

17. Mitzenmacher, M.: Bounds on the greedy routing algorithm for array networks. J. Comput. System Sci. 53, 317–327 (1996)

18. Müller, A., Stoyan, D.: Comparison Models for Stochastic Models and Risks. John Wiley & Sons, Chichester (2002)

19. Naaman, N., Rom, R.: Average case analysis of bounded space bin packing algorithms. Algorithmica 50, 72–97 (2008)

20. Scharbrodt, M., Schickinger, T., Steger, A.: A new average case analysis for completion time scheduling. J. ACM, 121–146 (2006)

21. Shachnai, H., Tamir, T.: On two class-constrained versions of the multiple knapsack problem. Algorithmica 29(3), 442–467 (2001)

22. Shachnai, H., Tamir, T.: Polynomial time approximation schemes for class-constrained packing problems. Journal of Scheduling 4(6), 313–338 (2001)

23. Shaked, M., Shanthikumar, J.G.: Stochastic Orders and their Applications. Academic Press, San Diego (1994)

24. Sinclair, A.: Algorithms for Random Generation and Counting: A Markov Chain Approach. Birkhäuser, Basel (1993)

25. Sleator, D.D., Tarjan, R.E.: Amortized efficiency of list update and paging rules. Comm. ACM 28(2), 202–208 (1985)

On the Complexity of Optimal Hotlink Assignment

Tobias Jacobs

Department of Computer Science, University of Freiburg

Abstract. The concept of *hotlink assignment* aims at reducing the navigation effort for users of a web directory or similar structure by inserting a limited number of additional hyperlinks called *hotlinks*. Given an access probability distribution of the leaves of the tree representing the web site, the goal of hotlink assignment algorithms is to minimize the expected path length between the root and the leaves.

We prove that this optimization problem is NP-hard, even if only one outgoing hotlink is allowed for each node. This answers a question that has been open since the first formulation of the problem in [3].

In this work we also investigate the model where hotlinks are only allowed to point at the leaves of the tree. We demonstrate that for this model optimal solutions can be computed in polynomial time. Our algorithm operates in a very general setting, where the maximum number of outgoing hotlinks is specified individually for each node. Experimental evaluation shows that the algorithm is applicable in practice.

1 Introduction

Due to the extensive growth of the Internet as a huge information source, the task of making an increasing amount of information accessible in a user-friendly way becomes increasingly important. The value of any information is closely related to its accessibility. Therefore, the effort spent by users searching for a specific piece of information, or trying to get an overview of some subset of the available information, should be minimized.

In this work we address the concept of improving the design of large web directories or similar structures by assigning additional hyperlinks called *hotlinks* to their pages. By taking access frequencies into account, hotlinks can especially reduce the access time of popular pages, while the site's original structure is preserved. A considerable amount of research has been spent on this approach, see e.g. [3,4,5,7,8,9,11,12,13,14,15,16,17]. The ideas can be applied in a number of additional scenarios, e.g. knowledge bases, file systems, menus of computer applications, and, as observed by Bose et. al. in [6], even in communication protocols.

Problem Definition: A hierarchical web site can be modeled as a *weighted tree* $T = (V, E, \omega)$ where (V, E) is a tree rooted at r. We assume that inner nodes represent navigation pages and the information is stored in the leaves. Let

D. Halperin and K. Mehlhorn (Eds.): ESA 2008, LNCS 5193, pp. 540–552, 2008.

$L \subseteq V$ be the set of those leaves. The weight function $\omega : L \rightarrow I\!R_0^+$ assigns a non-negative weight to each of them. These weights can be interpreted as access frequencies or, if normalized to sum up to 1, as access probabilities.

In order to access a leaf l, the user has to traverse the unique path from r to l. A *hotlink assignment (HLA)* is a set $A \subset V \times V$ of additional edges, providing shortcuts for the user. The elements of A are called *hotlinks*. For $(u, v) \in A$ we refer to v as u's *hotchild*. We further refer to u as v's *hotparent* and say that the hotlink *starts* in u and *ends* in v.

In this work we assume that the user only knows about the outgoing hotlinks of the nodes she has already visited and always takes any hotlink that leads her closer to her destination leaf. This is commonly referred to as the *greedy user model*. In contrast, in the *clairvoyant user model* users know their shortest path in $(V, E \cup A)$.

A straightforward consequence of the greedy user assumption is that for any hotlink (u, v) in a reasonable assignment, v is a descendant of u. Furthermore, there is no hotlink between an ancestor of u and a node on the path between u and v. Otherwise, (u, v) could be removed from the assignment without affecting the greedy user's path to any leaf.

The *path length* of a hotlink assignment A for T is defined as

$$p(A) = \sum_{l \in L} \omega(l) \operatorname{dist}^A(r, l) \ ,$$

where $\operatorname{dist}^A(u, v)$ denotes the number of edges and hotlinks a greedy user traverses when traveling from u to v.

Clearly, if there is no restriction concerning the assignment, then any reasonable hotlink will start in r. The usual restriction arises from the requirement that the number of hotlinks on a concise web page must be somehow limited. The *Hotlink Assignment Problem* denotes the task to compute a hotlink assignment for a given tree, achieving a minimum path length, where only one hotlink is allowed to start in each node.

Related Work: The concept of assigning hotlinks to web sites has been suggested by Perkowitz and Etzoni in [2]. Bose et. al. show in [3] that the problem is NP-hard when considering general DAGs instead of trees. The result applies to the clairvoyant user model. Note that it is not clear how to extend the greedy user model to DAGs, as in that kind of graphs shortest paths are not necessarily unique, and so the user's behaviour is not determined by the graph structure.

In [3], Bose et. al. also give a fundamental lower bound using coding theory: No hotlink assignment can result in a path length less than $H(\omega)/\log(\Delta + 1)$, where Δ is the degree of the tree and $H(\omega) = \sum_{l \in L} \omega(l) \log(\frac{1}{\omega(l)})$ is the *entropy* of the probability distribution of the leaves (assuming here that the weights sum up to 1). The bound holds for both user models.

In [6], Bose et. al. apply the close connection to coding theory proposing an asymmetric communication protocol based on hotlink assignment.

Gerstel et. al. [8] and Pessoa et. al. [12] have independently discovered an optimal HLA algorithm whose running time is exponential in the depth of the tree and thus polynomial for trees of logarithmic depth. The algorithm employs dynamic programming and is designed for the greedy user model, which has been introduced in those papers.

A considerable number of approximation algorithms for the problem have been proposed. Fast algorithms achieving a path length of $O(H(\omega))$ in both user models have been published in [5,14,15]. Dynamic maintenance of such HLAs has also been studied in [14]. These algorithms hold constant approximation ratios for trees of fixed degree. For the greedy user model, in [16] we present a 2-approximation for arbitrary trees.

An equivalent problem formulation is to maximize the *gain* $g(A) = p(\emptyset) - p(A)$. For the clairvoyant user model, Matichin and Peleg prove in [9] that the natural greedy strategy yields an approximation ratio of 2 in terms of the gain. We show in [16] that this ratio also holds in the greedy user model. In the same paper we also present a PTAS for the gain, which generalizes another 2-approximation given in [11].

Results from evaluating hotlink assignment algorithms experimentally have been published in [4,7,13] and most recently in [17].

Our Contribution: The main contribution of this work is to settle the complexity of the Hotlink Assignment Problem by showing that it is is NP-hard. Despite much previous work, the question whether there is hope to develop an efficient algorithm for computing optimal hotlink assignments has remained open since the first formulation of the problem in 2000.

In the second part of this paper we investigate a variant of the problem that arises from practice. In many applications where hotlinks are actually used, they only point directly to leaves. Examples are the product recommendations of amazon.com and similar sites, suggestions for completions to typed-in prefixes in web browsers, or suggestions for frequently used functions in menus of computer applications. The probable reason for this restriction is that users would find it confusing to end up on another navigation page after following a hotlink.

We present a polynomial time algorithm L-OPT that computes optimal HLAs $A \subset V \times L$ in a quite general model. In that model not only the tree and the weight function are part of the input, but also a function $\theta : V \to I\!N_0$ specifying the maximum number of outgoing hotlinks for each individual node. Our algorithm is based on a new dynamic programming approach. In the full paper, we discuss differences to other dynamic programming algorithms for hotlink assignment, and we propose an efficient implementation of L-OPT. Experimental evaluation shows that our implementation computes optimal HLAs for typical trees with up to 300,000 nodes within a few seconds on a standard PC.

Paper Organization: The proof of NP-hardness is presented in Sect. 2, while in Sect. 3 we investigate the model where hotlinks may only point to leaves. Section 4 concludes. Proofs abbreviated or omitted in this extended abstract appear in the full paper.

Further Notation: We denote the set of children, proper descendants and proper ancestors[1] of a node v by $\mathrm{ch}(v)$, $\mathrm{desc}(v)$ and $\mathrm{anc}(v)$, respectively.

For nodes v in T we write $v \in T$. We denote by T_v the maximal subtree of T rooted at v. For any set V' of nodes, let $T \setminus V'$ be the tree obtained from T by omitting all maximal subtrees rooted at a node in $V \cap V'$. Let further $T_{v,A} = T_v \setminus \{v' \in \mathrm{desc}(v) \mid \exists (u, v') \in A : u \in \mathrm{anc}(v)\}$ be the subtree rooted at v where the maximal subtrees rooted at the hotchildren of v's ancestors are omitted. Finally, for any subtree T' of T, we define $A|T' = \{(u, v) \in A \mid u, v \in T'\}$.

2 Proof of NP-Hardness

Consider the following decision problem: Given a weighted tree T and a real number α, is there a hotlink assignment A for T with $p(A) \leq \alpha$ and any node having at most one hotchild?

In this section we prove that the Hotlink Assigning Problem is NP-hard. We do this by a reduction from the *3-Set Cover* Problem, which is well-known to be NP-hard [1], to the above decision problem.

Instances of the 3-Set Cover Problem are given by a pair (C, D), where $C = \{c_1, \ldots, c_n\}$ is a set containing $n = 3k$ ($k \in \mathbb{N}$) elements, and $D = \{D_1, \ldots, D_m\}$ with $D_i = \{d_i^1, d_i^2, d_i^3\} \subseteq C$ and $|D_i| = 3$ for each $1 \leq i \leq m$ is a set containing subsets of C. The problem is to decide whether there exists a subset $D' = \{D_{i_1}, \ldots, D_{i_k}\}$ of D with $\bigcup_{j=1}^{k} D_{i_j} = C$ and $|D'| = k$.

We assume w. l. o. g. that the elements in the subsets are ordered, i.e. $x < y < z$ for any $D_i = \{d_i^1, d_i^2, d_i^3\}$ with $d_i^1 = c_x, d_i^2 = c_y, d_i^3 = c_z$. We further assume w. l. o. g. that there is at least one $d_i^x = c_j$ for any $c_j \in C$.

In the following we show how to construct an instance of the hotlink assignment decision problem corresponding to a given instance of 3-Set Cover.

Tree Structure: We first give the structure of the corresponding tree T. For each $D_i \in D$ we construct a subtree T^i of depth 1. The root of T^i is denoted as r_i and the eight leaves are $\pi_i, \bar{\pi}_i, \sigma_i^1, \bar{\sigma}_i^1, \sigma_i^2, \bar{\sigma}_i^2, \sigma_i^3$ and $\bar{\sigma}_i^3$. For $x \in \{1, 2, 3\}$, σ_i^x and $\bar{\sigma}_i^x$ will correspond to element $d_i^x \in D_i$.

Another part of T is the path P defined by the nodes $\{p_i \mid 1 \leq i \leq m\} \cup \{\bar{p}_i \mid 1 \leq i \leq m\}$ and the edges $\{(p_i, \bar{p}_i) \mid 1 \leq i \leq m)\} \cup \{(\bar{p}_i, p_{i-1}) \mid 2 \leq i \leq m)\}$. Additionally, for $1 \leq i \leq m$ there are nodes s_i, a_i and edges $(\bar{p}_i, s_i)$ and (s_i, a_i).

The rest of T is formed by the path Q. Nodes in Q are $\{q_j \mid 1 \leq j \leq n\} \cup \{\bar{q}_j \mid 1 \leq j \leq n\} \cup \{t_j \mid 1 \leq j \leq n\} \cup \{b_j \mid 1 \leq j \leq n\}$. The edges are $\{(q_j, \bar{q}_j) \mid 1 \leq j \leq n\} \cup \{(\bar{q}_j, q_{j-1}) \mid 2 \leq j \leq n\} \cup \{(\bar{q}_j, t_j) \mid 1 \leq j \leq n\} \cup \{(t_j, b_j) \mid 1 \leq j \leq n\}$.

The construction of T is completed by connecting P and Q by the edge $(\bar{p}_1, q_n)$ and by appending T^i to Q via $(\bar{q}_1, r_i)$ for $1 \leq i \leq m$. A figure visualizing the tree structure is included in the full paper.

---

[1] All descendants/ancestors of a node v, not including v itself, are proper descendants/ancestors of v.

Notation and General Idea: For $1 \leq i \leq m$, the set $\{p_i, \bar{p}_i\}$ is denoted by P_i. Respectively, $\{q_j, \bar{q}_j\} = Q_j$ for $1 \leq j \leq n$.

Intuitively, the idea of the reduction is the following: By the weights of π_i, $\bar{\pi}_i$ and a_i, it will be enforced that, in an optimal assignment, each T^i has one or two hotparents in P_i. Additionally, each T^i has three pairs of "natural" hotparents $q_j, \bar{q}_j$ in Q, which will be determined by the weights of the σ_i^xs and $\bar{\sigma}_i^x$s. Achieving the threshold path length α will be possible if and only if there is an assignment where, for a collection of k subtrees $T^{i_1}, \ldots, T^{i_k}$, each of these subtrees contains all hotchildren of its natural hotparents.

Fix any T^i and let $d_i^1 = c_{j_1}, d_i^2 = c_{j_2}$ and $d_i^3 = c_{j_3}$ in the 3-Set Cover instance. We say that T^i is *undeveloped*, if there are hotlinks (p_i, r_i) and $(\bar{p}_i, a_i)$ (Fig. 1a). From the status of being undeveloped, T^i is *developed to j_3* by replacing (p_i, r_i) and $(\bar{p}_i, a_i)$ with (p_i, π_i), $(\bar{p}_i, \bar{\pi}_i)$, (q_{j_3}, r_i) and $(\bar{q}_{j_3}, b_{j_3})$ (Fig. 1b). For $x \in \{2, 3\}$, from the status of being developed to j_x, T^i is developed to j_{x-1} by replacing (q_{j_x}, r_i) and $(\bar{q}_{j_x}, b_{j_x})$ with (q_{j_x}, σ_i^x), $(\bar{q}_{j_x}, \bar{\sigma}_i^x)$, $(q_{j_{x-1}}, r_i)$ and $(\bar{q}_{j_{x-1}}, b_{j_{x-1}})$. From the status of being developed to j_1, T^i becomes *fully developed* by replacing (q_{j_1}, r_i) and $(\bar{q}_{j_1}, b_{j_1})$ with (q_{j_1}, σ_i^1) and $(\bar{q}_{j_1}, \bar{\sigma}_i^1)$ (Fig. 1c).

Observe that, if T^i is fully developed, then it contains all hotchildren of P_i, Q_{j_1}, Q_{j_2} and Q_{j_3}. Therefore, there is a solution to an instance of the 3-Set Cover problem if and only if there is a hotlink assignment for the corresponding tree T where exactly k subtrees $T^{i_1}, \ldots, T^{i_k}$ are fully developed.

Weight Assignment: Let $h = 2(n + m) + 1$ be the depth of T. We begin by setting the weight of b_1 to h and by assigning $\omega(\sigma_i^x) = \omega(\bar{\sigma}_i^x) = h + 1$ for each $d_i^x = c_1$ in the instance of the 3-Set Cover Problem.

For a fixed j, $2 \leq j \leq n$, assume that the weights of all $b_{j'}$ and all σ_i^x and $\bar{\sigma}_i^x$ with $d_i^x = c_{j'}$ are given for any $j' < j$. We denote the set of those leaves as L_{j-1}. The weight of b_j is set to

$$\omega(b_j) = 2h \sum_{v \in L_{j-1}} \omega(v) + 1 . \tag{1}$$

In the consequence, b_j's weight is more than twice the total weighted path length to all leaves lighter than b_j.

Then, for any $d_i^x = c_j$, we assign $\omega(\bar{\sigma}_i^x) = \omega(b_j) + 1$. Furthermore, $\omega(\sigma_i^x) = \omega(b_j) + w_i^{x-1}$, where w_i^{x-1} is chosen as follows:

In case of $x \in \{2, 3\}$, let $d_i^{x-1} = c_{j'}$. We choose w_i^{x-1} such that the reward (i.e. decrease in path length) for developing T^i to j' is $3\omega(b_{j'})$. When developing T^i to j', the length of the path to b_j increases by one, while the path length to σ_i^x decreases by one. The length of the path to $\bar{\sigma}_i^x$ does not change, and the path length to all σ_i^y and $\bar{\sigma}_i^y$ with $y < x$ is increased by $\text{dist}(q_j, q_{j'})$. Finally, the new hotlink $(\bar{q}_{j'}, b_{j'})$ causes the path length to $b_{j'}$ to decrease by one. Thus, the overall weighted path length decreases by

$$w_i^{x-1} - \text{dist}(q_j, q_{j'}) \cdot \sum_{1 \leq y < x} \left(\omega(\sigma_i^y) + \omega(\bar{\sigma}_i^y) \right) + \omega(b_{j'}) .$$

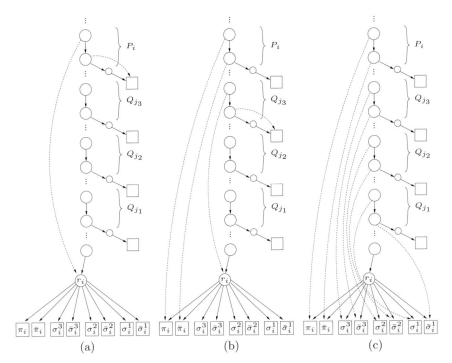

Fig. 1. Subtree T^i representing the subset $\{c_{j_1}, c_{j_2}, c_{j_3}\} = D_i \in D$, as it is (a) undeveloped, (b) developed to j_3, and (c) fully developed

So, in order to provide the desired reward, we choose

$$w_i^{x-1} = \text{dist}(q_j, q_{j'}) \cdot \sum_{1 \leq y < x} \left(\omega(\sigma_i^y) + \omega(\bar{\sigma}_i^y) \right) + 2\omega(b_{j'}) \ .$$

In case of $x = 1$, we choose $w_i^{x-1} = 1$ so that fully developing T^i achieves an extra reward of 1, which can be shown by a similar calculation.

As we have assumed that in 3-Set Cover the subsets are ordered, the values of $\omega(\sigma_i^y)$ and $\omega(\bar{\sigma}_i^y)$ have already been assigned for $y < x, d_i^x = c_j$, so our weight-assignment is well-defined.

It remains to specify the weights of $\pi_i, \bar{\pi}_i$ and a_i for $1 \leq i \leq m$, which is done with respect to similar objectives: a_i must be heavier than two times the weighted path length to all leaves lighter then a_i, and the reward for developing T^i to j' (with $d_i^3 = c_{j'}$ in the 3-Set Cover instance) must be $3\omega(b_{j'})$. For a fixed i, let the weight of any $\pi_{i'}, \bar{\pi}_{i'}, a_{i'}$ for $1 \leq i' < i$ be already given. We assign

$$\omega(a_i) = 2h \cdot \left(\sum_{v \in L_n} \omega(v) + \sum_{i'=1}^{i-1} \left(\omega(\pi_{i'}) + \omega(\bar{\pi}_{i'}) + \omega(a_{i'}) \right) \right) + 1 \ , \qquad (2)$$

$\omega(\bar{\pi}_i) = \omega(a_i) + 1$ and $\omega(\pi_i) = \omega(a_i) + w_i^3$. Let $d_i^3 = c_{j'}$. Then, due to the same argumentation as above, we choose

$$w_i^3 = \text{dist}(p_i, q_{j'}) \cdot \sum_{1 \leq x \leq 3} \left(\omega(\sigma_i^x) + \omega(\bar{\sigma}_i^x) \right) + 2\omega(b_{j'}) \ .$$

Concerning the problem size, it is not hard to observe that the number of bits required to encode the weights of the leaves is polynomial in the size of the 3-Set Cover instance. The analysis can be found in the full paper.

Proof of Equivalence: We call $B = \{(p_i, r_i) \mid 1 \leq i \leq m\} \cup \{(\bar{p}_i, a_i) \mid 1 \leq i \leq m\}$ the *basic assignment* for T. Observe that all T^is are undeveloped in B. The *surplus* of an assignment A for T is defined as $p(B) - p(A)$.

Instead of explicitly specifying a threshold path length α for the decision problem, we consider a surplus value $\beta = p(B) - \alpha$. We are going to prove that a surplus of at least β can be achieved if and only if there is a solution to the instance of 3 Set-Cover. Namely, we consider

$$\beta = 3 \sum_{j=1}^{n} \omega(b_j) + k \ .$$

Lemma 1. *Given an instance I of the 3-Set Cover Problem, if I has a solution, then there is a HLA for the corresponding tree achieving a surplus of β.*

Proof. Starting with B, we can develop T^is such that we achieve an assignment where exactly k subtrees $T^{i_1}, \ldots, T^{i_k}$ are fully developed and the others remain undeveloped. For $1 \leq j \leq n$ there is some T^i that is developed to j during that procedure and thus gains a reward of $3\omega(b_j)$. Furthermore, for the step to full development of each $T^{i_1}, \ldots, T^{i_k}$ a reward of 1 is achieved.   □

Before we prove that the inverse direction of Lemma 1 holds as well, we introduce some additional concepts. For a given hotlink assignment A, we say that P_i is *closed* if $(p_i, r_i), (\bar{p}_i, a_i) \in A$. Let $d_i^3 = c_j$. We say that P_i is *open subject to j* if $(p_i, \pi_i), (\bar{p}_i, \bar{\pi}_i) \in A$.

Respectively, we say that Q_j is *closed*, if $(q_j, r_i), (\bar{q}_j, b_j) \in A$ for some T^i with $d_i^x = c_j$ and $x \in \{1, 2, 3\}$. We say that Q_j is *open*, if $(q_j, \sigma_i^x), (\bar{q}_j, \bar{\sigma}_i^x) \in A$ for some T^i with $d_i^x = c_j$ and $x \in \{1, 2, 3\}$. In case of $x \in \{2, 3\}$ and $d_i^{x-1} = c_{j'}$, we say that Q_j is *open subject to j'*.

Lemma 2. *Let A^* be an optimal HLA for a tree T corresponding to an instance of 3-Set Cover. Then P_i is either open or closed for each $i = 1, \ldots, m$.*

Proof (sketch). For any fixed i we assume that the lemma already holds[2] for $i' > i$. We infer from (2) that the path length between p_i and any leaf lighter than a_{i+1} is at most $6.5\omega(a_i) + 2w_i^3 + 2$ if P_i is closed or open. By systematically considering all other hotlink configurations, we conclude that any of them is either obviously sub-optimal or results in a path length of at least $7\omega(a_i)$.

Lemma 3. *Given an instance I of the 3-Set Cover Problem, if I has no solution, then no HLA for the corresponding tree achieves a surplus of at least β.*

---

[2] The argumentation naturally includes the base case $i = m$.

Proof (sketch). Let T be the tree corresponding to an instance of 3-Set Cover having no solution. Let A^* be an optimal hotlink assignment for T. Throughout the proof we assume that A^* achieves a surplus of at least β.

From Lemma 2 we know that, for $1 \leq i \leq m$, P_i is either closed or open. Assume that for $1 \leq j \leq n$, (a) also Q_j is either closed or open and (b) there is either exactly one $Q_{j'}$ or exactly one P_i that is open subject to j.

Then we know that A^* can be obtained from B by developing subtrees: For $j = n, \ldots, 1$ consider the unique P_i or $Q_{j'}$ that is open subject to j in A^* and develop T^i to j, where T^i is the subtree containing the hotchildren of P_i or $Q_{j'}$ in A^*. Note that T^i also is the tree containing hotchildren of Q_j in A^*, because otherwise either property (a) or (b) would be violated. If Q_j is open in A^* and the hotchild of q_j in A^* is σ_i^1, then fully develop T^i. If Q_j is open subject to some j'' in A^*, then Q_j will be made open in a later step of development.

Due to this construction, the surplus of A^* is at least $3 \sum_{j=1}^{n} \omega(b_j)$. On the other hand, as the corresponding 3-Set Cover instance has no solution, it is not possible that k subtrees are fully developed in A^*, so the surplus is strictly less than $3 \sum_{j=1}^{n} \omega(b_j) + k = \beta$, which contradicts the initial assumption.

To show that properties (a) and (b) indeed hold for $1 \leq j \leq n$, we fix a j and assume that they have already been proven for $j' > j$. There is *at least* one P_i or $Q_{j'}$ open subject to j, because otherwise we can show that a surplus of β cannot be achieved. Furthermore, by a careful case analysis it can be proved that property (a) holds and there is *at most* one P_i or $Q_{j'}$ open subject to j. □

Theorem 1. *The Hotlink Assignment Problem for trees is NP-hard.*   □

3   Hotlink Assignment to Leaves

In this section we consider the model where only leaves are allowed to be hotchildren, i.e. $A \subset V \times L$, and the maximum number of hotchildren of each node is arbitrarily specified by a function $\theta : V \to I\!N_0$. Hence, problem instances are given by a pair (T, θ). We assume w. l. o. g. that $\theta(v) \leq |L|$ for any $v \in V$. To our best knowledge, that variant of the Hotlink Assignment Problem has not been addressed yet. In the following, we show that in this model optimal solutions can be computed in polynomial time by a dynamic programming algorithm.

Algorithm L-OPT: On the top level, our algorithm can be described as follows: (1) If T has a depth of less than 2, return $\emptyset$. (2) Recursively compute an optimal hotlink assignment for each $(T_v, \theta), v \in \text{ch}(r)$. (3) *Merge* these hotlink assignments to obtain an optimal assignment for (T, θ).

Given a problem instance (T, θ) and a node $v \in T$, we denote by θ_{+v}/θ_{-v} the function obtained from θ by increasing/decreasing the image of v by 1.

Assume that there is an efficient method for transforming an optimal HLA A for (T, θ) into an optimal assignment A^+ for (T, θ_{+r}). Then step (3) in the the above algorithm can be computed efficiently: Apply that method $\theta(r)$ times to the assignment resulting from step (2), which is clearly optimal for (T, θ'), where θ' is obtained from θ by setting the image of r to 0. So the main algorithmic challenge in this section is the development of such a transformation method.

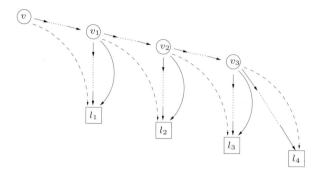

Fig. 2. When applying the transformation sequence (l_1, l_2, l_3, l_4), the solid hotlinks are replaced with the dashed ones. Dotted lines represent tree paths.

Lemma 4. *Let A be an optimal hotlink assignment for a weighted tree T. If $(v_1, l_1), (v_2, l_2) \in A$, $v_2 \in \mathrm{desc}(v_1)$ and $l_1 \in \mathrm{desc}(v_2)$, then $\omega(l_1) \geq \omega(l_2)$.* $\square$

Lemma 5. *Let A be optimal for (T, θ) and let $(v, l) \in A$. Then $A \setminus \{(v, l)\}$ is optimal for $(T \setminus \{l\}, \theta_{-v})$.* $\square$

Let A be a hotlink assignment for (T, θ). A *transformation sequence for A into* θ_{+v} is a sequence of leaves $(l_1, \ldots, l_k), k \geq 0$, where l_i has a hotparent $v_i \in \mathrm{anc}(l_{i+1})$ in A for $1 \leq i \leq k-1$. Such a sequence represents the modification of A where all hotlinks pointing to $l_1, \ldots, l_k$ are replaced with (v, l_1) and (v_i, l_{i+1}) for $1 \leq i \leq k-1$ (see Fig. 2). In case of $k = 0$, the *empty* transformation sequence represents the identity. A transformation sequence is *optimal* if the resulting hotlink assignment is optimal for (T, θ_{+v}).

Lemma 6. *Let A be an optimal hotlink assignment for (T, θ), and let $v \in T$. There exists an optimal transformation sequence for A into θ_{+v}.*

Proof (sketch). Consider an optimal assignment A^+ for (T, θ_{+v}). The additional hotchild l_1 of v in A^+ becomes the first element of our transformation sequence. If l_1 already has a hotparent v_1 in A, we use Lemma 5 and induction to apply the lemma to $(T \setminus \{l\}, \theta_{-v_1})$ and $A \setminus \{(v_1, l_1)\}$. $\square$

Let $(l_1, \ldots, l_k)$ be a transformation sequence for A into θ_{+v}. Let $v_0 = v$ and let v_i be the hotparent of l_i for $1 \leq i \leq k-1$. We say that the sequence is *ordered*, if $v_i \in \mathrm{desc}(v_{i-1})$ for $1 \leq i \leq k-1$ and, in case of l_k having a hotparent v_k in A, $v_k \in \mathrm{desc}(v_{k-1})$. Fig. 2 is an example of an ordered transformation sequence.

Lemma 7. *Let A be an optimal hotlink assignment for (T, θ). There is an optimal ordered transformation sequence for A into θ_{+r}.*

Proof (sketch). We show that any optimal transformation sequence for A into θ_{+r} can be modified such that it is ordered and still optimal. We do this by induction over the length of the sequence. For the basic case, the empty sequence, there is nothing to show. For the induction step, consider an optimal sequence of length 1 or larger that is not ordered. Using Lemma 4, we can show that the first component that violates the specification of ordered transformation sequences can be removed without increasing the path length of the resulting assignment. □

Theorem 2. *Given an optimal hotlink assignment for (T, θ), an optimal assignment for (T, θ_{+r}) can be computed in polynomial time.*

Proof. Let A be optimal for (T, θ). From Lemma 7 follows that it suffices to find an optimal ordered transformation sequence for A into θ_{+r}. We describe the algorithm for solving that task in a recursive manner. Assumed that (T, θ) and A are fixed, the algorithm takes a node $v \in T$ as the input, and computes an optimal transformation sequence for $A|T_{v,A}$ into θ_{+v}.

If $T_{v,A}$ contains no leaves, this is the empty sequence. Otherwise, for each leaf l in $T_{v,A}$, L-OPT computes a best ordered transformation sequence that starts with l. If l has no hotparent in A, then that sequence is (l). Else, if $(v', l) \in A$, the algorithm recursively computes an optimal transformation sequence for $A|T_{v',A}$ into $\theta_{+v'}$ and appends that sequence to l. For each leaf l, the algorithm calculates the benefit (decrease in path length) $s(v.l)$ caused by the corresponding best sequence and returns the sequence maximizing that benefit. Formally,

$$s(v) = \begin{cases} \max\limits_{l \text{ is a leaf in } T_{v,A}} s(v, l) & \text{if } T_{v,A} \text{ contains a leaf} \\ 0 & \text{otherwise ,} \end{cases} \tag{3}$$

$$s(v, l) = \begin{cases} \big(\mathrm{dist}(l, v) - 1\big)\, \omega(l) & \text{if } l \text{ has no hotparent in } A \\ \mathrm{dist}(v', v)\, \omega(l) + s(v') & \text{if } l \text{ has a hotparent } v' \text{ in } A \text{ .} \end{cases} \tag{4}$$

As (T, θ) and A are fixed, a table containing all possible values of $s(v)$ and the corresponding transformation sequences has linear size. At most $|V|$ different possibilities have to be compared during the computation of any table entry, so the table can be built in quadratic time.

The formal correctness proof of the algorithm appears in the full paper. □

Corollary 1. *An optimal hotlink assignment for any problem instance (T, θ) can be computed in polynomial time.* □

Experimental Evaluation: Our test set consists of 40 trees representing the structure of Brazilian and German university web sites. They contain up to 300,000 nodes, and several subtrees have a depth larger than 100. Subsets of these instances have been applied for experiments presented in [13,17]. Like done in all experimental studies on hotlink assignment published so far (cf. [4,7,13,17]), we randomly assign weights using Zipf distribution, i.e. the ith heaviest leaf is assigned a weight of $\frac{1}{iH_m}$, where H_m is the mth harmonic number and m is the number of leaves in the tree. We consider constant functions of $\theta = 1, \ldots, 15$.

The runtime of our L-OPT implementation is depicted in Fig. 3. It is not completely monotonic in the tree size, other factors seem to influence it as well.

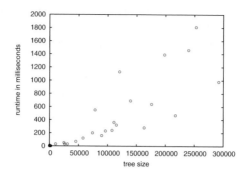

Fig. 3. Runtime of L-OPT with $\theta = 1$ on tree instances of different sizes

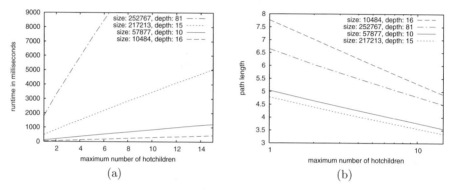

Fig. 4. Development of (a) runtime and (b) weighted path length for varying values of θ. In subfigure (b) the horizontal axis is scaled logarithmically.

However, the typical runtime is only slightly superlinear in the number of nodes. On all instances the algorithm terminates within a few seconds or less.

Fig. 4a and 4b exemplarily show the development of runtime and path length on four selected instances for $\theta = 1, \ldots, 15$. While the runtime grows linearly with θ, the path length improves only logarithmically. As a larger number of hotlinks also reduces the clarity of web pages, only small values of θ are advisable in practice.

4   Conclusion

We have proven that the Hotlink Assignment Problem for trees is NP-hard. This holds in the general case where hotlink are allowed to start *and* end in *any* node.

When hotlinks are allowed to start in the root only, then it is known that the problem is solvable in polynomial time (cf. [10]). We have shown in this paper that there also is an efficient algorithm when hotlinks may start in any node, but may only end in leaves.

The latter model constitutes a maximally general scenario that is computationally tractable and has a practical application. We note that for the problem to become intractable it suffices that hotlinks may additionally end in inner nodes having only leaf children. This becomes clear reconsidering the solutions to the class of "difficult" tree instances given in Sect. 2.

Acknowledgement. The author wishes to thank an anonymous referee for an extensive list of helpful comments.

References

1. Karpf, R.M.: Reducibility among combinatorial problems. In: Complexity of Computer Computations, pp. 85–103. Plenum Press, New York (1972)
2. Perkowitz, M., Etzioni, O.: Towards adaptive web sites: Conceptual framework and case study. Computer Networks 31(11-16), 1245–1258 (1999)
3. Bose, P., Czyzowicz, J., Gasienicz, L., Kranakis, E., Krizanc, D., Pelc, A., Vargas Martin, M.: Strategies for hotlink assignments. In: Lee, D.T., Teng, S.-H. (eds.) ISAAC 2000. LNCS, vol. 1969. Springer, Heidelberg (2000)
4. Czyzowicz, J., Kranakis, E., Krizanc, D., Pelc, A., Vargas Martin, M.: Evaluation of hotlink assignment heuristics for improving web access. In: Proceedings of the 2nd International Conference on Internet Computing (ICOMP) (2001)
5. Kranakis, E., Krizanc, D., Shende, S.: Approximate hotlink assignment. In: Eades, P., Takaoka, T. (eds.) ISAAC 2001. LNCS, vol. 2223. Springer, Heidelberg (2001)
6. Bose, P., Krizanc, D., Langerman, S., Morin, P.: Asymmetric communication protocols via hotlink assignments. In: Proceeding of the 9th Colloquium on Structural Information and Communication Complexity (SIROCCO) (2002)
7. Czyzowicz, J., Kranakis, E., Krizanc, D., Pelc, A., Vargas Martin, M.: Enhancing hyperlink structure for improving web performance. Journal of Web Engineering 1(2), 93–127 (2003)
8. Gerstel, O., Kutten, S., Matichin, R., Peleg, D.: Hotlink enhancement algorithms for web directories. In: Ibaraki, T., Katoh, N., Ono, H. (eds.) ISAAC 2003. LNCS, vol. 2906, pp. 68–77. Springer, Heidelberg (2003)
9. Matichin, R., Peleg, D.: Approximation algorithm for hotlink assignments in web directories. In: Dehne, F., Sack, J.-R., Smid, M. (eds.) WADS 2003. LNCS, vol. 2748, pp. 271–280. Springer, Heidelberg (2003)
10. Li, K., Shen, H.: Optimal placement of web proxies for tree networks. In: IEEE International Conference on e-Technology, e-Commerce and e-Service (EEE 2004) (2004)
11. Matichin, R., Peleg, D.: Approximation algorithm for hotlink assignment in the greedy model. In: Kralovic, R., Sýkora, O. (eds.) SIROCCO 2004. LNCS, vol. 3104, pp. 233–244. Springer, Heidelberg (2004)
12. Pessoa, A., Laber, E., de Souza, C.: Efficient algorithms for the hotlink assignment problem: The worst case search. In: Fleischer, R., Trippen, G. (eds.) ISAAC 2004. LNCS, vol. 3341, pp. 778–792. Springer, Heidelberg (2004)
13. Pessoa, A., Laber, E., de Souza, C.: Efficient implementation of a hotlink assignment algorithm for Web sites. In: Proceedings of the 6th Workshop on Algorithm Engineering and Experiments (ALENEX) and the First Workshop on Analytic Algorithmics and Combinatorics (ANALCO) (2004)

14. Douïeb, K., Langerman, S.: Dynamic hotlinks. In: Dehne, F., López-Ortiz, A., Sack, J.-R. (eds.) WADS 2005. LNCS, vol. 3608, pp. 182–194. Springer, Heidelberg (2005)
15. Douïeb, K., Langerman, S.: Near-entropy hotlink assignments. In: Azar, Y., Erlebach, T. (eds.) ESA 2006. LNCS, vol. 4168, pp. 292–303. Springer, Heidelberg (2006)
16. Jacobs, T.: Constant factor approximations for the hotlink assignment problem. In: Dehne, F., Sack, J.-R., Zeh, N. (eds.) WADS 2007. LNCS, vol. 4619, pp. 188–200. Springer, Heidelberg (2007)
17. Jacobs, T.: An experimental study of recent hotlink assignment algorithms. In: Proc. of the Workshop on Algorithm Engineering and Experiments (ALENEX) and the First Workshop on Analytic Algorithmics and Combinatorics (ANALCO) (2008)

Oblivious Randomized Direct Search
for Real-Parameter Optimization

Jens Jägersküpper[*]

Technische Universität Dortmund, Informatik 2, 44221 Dortmund, Germany
JJ@Ls2.cs.uni-dortmund.de

Abstract. The focus is on black-box optimization of a function $f\colon \mathbb{R}^N \to \mathbb{R}$ given as a black box, i.e. an oracle for f-evaluations. This is commonly called direct search, and in fact, most methods for direct search are heuristics. Theoretical results on the performance/behavior of such heuristics are still rare. One reason: Like classical optimization algorithms, also direct-search methods face the challenge of step-size control, and usually, the more sophisticated the step-size control, the harder the analysis. Obviously, when we want the search to actually converge to a stationary point (i.e., the distance from this point tends to zero) at a nearly constant rate, then step sizes must be adapted. In practice, however, obtaining an ε-approximation for a given $\varepsilon > 0$ is often sufficient, and usually all N parameters are bounded, so that the maximum distance from the optimum is bounded. Thus, in such cases reasonable step sizes lie in a predetermined bounded interval. Considering the minimization of the distance from a fixed point as the objective, we address the question, for randomized heuristics that use isotropic sampling to generate new candidate solutions, whether we might get rid of step-size control – namely of the problems connected to it, like so-called premature convergence – by choosing step sizes randomly according to some properly predefined distribution over this interval. As this choice of step sizes is oblivious to the course of the optimization, we gain robustness against a loss of step-size control. Naturally, the question is: What is the price w.r.t. local convergence speed? As we shall see, merely a factor of order $\ln(d/\varepsilon)$, where d is the diameter of the the decision space, an N-dimensional interval region.

1 Introduction

Here optimization in high-dimensional Euclidean space $\mathbb{R}^N$ is considered, and the crucial aspect is how the optimization time scales with N, the dimensionality of the search space. Furthermore, the optimization time depends on the *approximation error* ε – here defined as the Euclidean distance from the optimum point in $\mathbb{R}^N$– of the approximate solution to be found. That is, we consider the optimization time as a function of N as well as of ε. Unless stated differently, asymptotics (essentially O and Ω) are w.r.t. $N \to \infty$, though.

The scenario we consider is black-box optimization, i.e., the function f to optimized is given by a black box, namely an oracle for f-evaluations. In practice, in particular in

---

[*] Supported by the German Research Foundation (DFG) through the collaborative research center "Computational Intelligence" (SFB 531).

D. Halperin and K. Mehlhorn (Eds.): ESA 2008, LNCS 5193, pp. 553–564, 2008.

various engineering disciplines, this is a very common situation: f is given by simulations or even by real-world experiments. In such situations – unless simulations allow for algorithmic/automatic differentiation, which is rarely the case – there is no information about the gradient or the Hessian, so that classical optimization methods cannot be applied. In the beginning of black-box optimization, in order to make use of established first-order methods, usually gradient approximation by finite forward/symmetric differences was used, which costs N (or $2N$) f-evaluations per iteration. Nowadays, the focus lies on optimization methods that abandon gradient approximation, but try to find good solutions directly. Such methods are commonly called direct-search methods, and in fact, most of these are heuristics. Theoretical results on the performance and the behavior of such heuristics are still rare, cf. [1]. Among the first and most prominent direct-search heuristics are the pattern search by Hooke/Jeeves and the (downhill) simplex method by Nelder/Mead, cf. [2] for a comprehensive review. Surprisingly, also already in the 1960s randomized direct-search methods were proposed, one is the so-called *evolution strategy* by Rechenberg [3] and Schwefel. In this algorithm, in each iteration i a new candidate solution is generated by adding a so-called *Gaussian mutation vector* $m \in \mathbb{R}^N$ to the current candidate solution $x^{[i-1]}$. Each component of m is i. i. d. according to a zero-mean normal distribution with variance σ^2. If the so-called *mutant* $y := x^{[i-1]} + m$ improves upon $x^{[i-1]}$, then $x^{[i]} := y$, otherwise $x^{[i]} := x^{[i-1]}$. Rechenberg and Schwefel focused on how to update σ adaptively to the course of the optimization, and they proposed different mechanisms how to adapt σ such that close-to-optimal (local) performance is achieved on the simple quadratic form $x \mapsto \sum_{k=1}^{N} x_k^2$, which is commonly called SPHERE in the field of (meta)heuristics; for some $x^* \in \mathbb{R}^N$ let $\text{SPHERE}_{x^*}(x) := \text{SPHERE}(x - x^*)$. The simple heuristic just described is a so-called (1+1) Evolution Strategy. It fits the general framework of iterative methods considered in the following:

For a given initial candidate solution $x^{[0]} \in \mathbb{R}^N$ and $i := 1$ DO

1. generate the displacement $m^{[i]} \in \mathbb{R}^N$ according to some distribution $D^{[i]}$ over $\mathbb{R}^N$
2. evaluate f at the sample $y^{[i]} := x^{[i-1]} + m^{[i]} \in \mathbb{R}^N$
3. decide whether to accept the new sample; if so, $x^{[i]} := y^{[i]}$, else $x^{[i]} := x^{[i-1]}$
4. $i := i + 1$ and GOTO 1 (unless stopping criterion met)

In many (meta)heuristics, the randomly chosen displacement vector m follows a (multivariate) normal distribution. Actually, sampling in each iteration i a predefined number of search points each i. i. d. according to a (multivariate) normal distribution with mean $x^{[i-1]}$ was already proposed 1958 in [4]—without being specific about how to choose/adapt the variance, though. Since then randomized direct-search heuristics have become more and more popular, cf. [5].

The probably most apparent rule to decide (in Instruction 3) whether the sample y is to be accepted to become the next candidate solution is so-called *elitist selection,* namely, in the case of minimization, $x^{[i]} := y^{[i]}$ if and only if $f(y^{[i]}) \leq f(x^{[i-1]})$. This rule is commonly used, and it might be one reason why SPHERE is so attractive as a starting point for a theoretical analysis: In this scenario the approximation error in the search space (namely the Euclidean distance from the optimum) is reduced if and only if there is an improvement w. r. t. the f-value. Apparently, this makes the reasoning easier. (We focus on the approximation error in the search space here.) More-over, when considering a fixed distribution D in Instruction 1 for the sampling, elitist selection in combination with $f := $ SPHERE results in maximum expected reduction of the approximation error because negative gains (i. e., y is further away from the op-timum) are zeroed out, whereas positives gains (i. e., y is closer to the optimum) are accepted. Thus, this combination can somewhat be considered a best-case scenario.

One reason for choosing the normal distribution to generate new search points seems to be that this distribution has maximum (differential) entropy. Another reason is the fol-lowing invariance property: An N-dimensional Gaussian mutation (the N components are i. i. d. according to a zero-mean normal distribution with variance σ^2) is *isotropi-cally distributed* over $\mathbb{R}^N$, i. e., its distribution is spherically symmetric, more precisely, invariant w. r. t. orthonormal transformations. The nice property of an isotropically dis-tributed vector is that its (possibly) random length is independent of its random direction and that the direction is uniformly random:

Proposition 1. *Let the vector u be uniformly distributed over the unit hyper-sphere $\{y \in \mathbb{R}^N \mid |y| = 1\}$. A vector x is isotropically distributed over $\mathbb{R}^N$ if and only if there exists a non-negative random variable ℓ (independent of u) such that the distribution of x equals the one of $\ell \cdot u$.*

A formal proof can be found in [6, Sec. 2.1] for instance. The random length of a Gaussian mutation (a vector that is distributed according to an isotropic multivariate normal distribution) follows a scaled χ-distribution.

In black-box optimization, when we do not know anything about f, using isotropic distributions (centered at the current iterate) to sample new candidate solutions seems reasonable because of the invariance properties. When we restrict the class of algo-rithms covered by our framework given above by requiring (in each iteration i) the distributions $D^{[i]}$ in Instruction 1 to be isotropic, then we can ask for an upper bound on the expected reduction of the approximation error in one step. Therefore, one may think of the best-case scenario in which SPHERE is minimized and elitist selection is used (in which positive gains (reduction of the distance from the optimum) are ac-cepted, whereas negative gains are zeroed out). Let $x^* \in \mathbb{R}^N$ denote the optimum and let $d^{[i]}$ be defined as the distance of $x^{[i]}$ from the optimum after the ith iteration. Fur-thermore, for a given distance $d^{[i-1]}$, let $\Delta^{[i]} : \mathbb{R}^N \to \mathbb{R}$ denote the random variable defined as $\text{dist}(x^{[i-1]} + m^{[i]}, x^*) - d^{[i-1]}$ which is induced by the distribution $D^{[i]}$ used to sample $m^{[i]}$ in the ith iteration. For SPHERE$_{x^*}$, elitist selection corresponds to the indicator variable $\mathbb{1}_{\{\Delta^{[i]} \geq 0\}}$ (which resolves to "1" if $\Delta^{[i]} \geq 0$, otherwise to "0"), so that the random variable $\Delta_+^{[i]} := \Delta^{[i]} \cdot \mathbb{1}_{\{\Delta^{[i]} \geq 0\}}$ corresponds to the spatial gain towards the optimum x^* in the ith iteration. Note that the distribution of $\Delta_+^{[i]}$ has an atom at zero with a weight equal to the probability that $y^{[i]} = x^{[i-1]} + m^{[i]}$ is such that it is discarded in Instruction 3.

As shown in [7], for any isotropic distribution $D^{[i]}$ over $\mathbb{R}^N$ the expected spatial gain towards a predefined point (for instance x^*) is bounded above by

$$\mathsf{E}\left[\Delta_+^{[i]}\right] < d^{[i-1]} \cdot 0.52/(N-1) \quad \text{for} \quad N \geq 4. \tag{1}$$

Thus, if in each iteration i the isotropic distribution $D^{[i]}$ was the best possible, then we would observe linear convergence (w. r. t. the distance from the optimum) at an expected rate larger (i. e. worse) than $1 - 0.52/(N - 1)$. By substituting $(N - 1)/0.52$ for n in the well-known inequality $(1 - 1/n)^{n-1} > 1/e$, we easily get that the total expected gain after (the first) k iterations is less than halve the initial approximation error unless $k > \ln 2/(0.52/(N - 1.52)) > 1.33N - 2.03$. (Due to the best-case assumption on the $D^{[i]}$, the factors by which the approximation error is reduced in k sequent steps are in fact i. i. d., so that we can indeed take the expectation of the one-step factor to the kth power to obtain the expectation of the factor which corresponds to the total reduction in the k steps.) Yet this does not tell us much anyway: The randomness is in the total gain rather than in the number of iterations. Instead, we would like to know a lower bound on the expected number of steps necessary to actually halve the approximation error. The local/one-step result from Equation (1) can indeed be transformed into the following lower-bound result on the runtime [8, Thm. 13]:

Theorem 2. *For any heuristic that fits our framework: When the $D^{[i]}$ are isotropic distributions, then the expected number of iterations necessary to halve the approximation error (defined as the distance from a fixed point in $\mathbb{R}^N$) is bounded from below by $0.5/(0.52/(N-1)) > 0.96N - 1 = \Omega(N)$.*

Note that this theorem holds for *any* adaptation mechanisms which determines for each iteration i according to what isotropic distribution $D^{[i]}$ to sample $m^{[i]}$. Interestingly, as shown in [9], even if in each iteration i the point $x^{[i]}$ was magically chosen from the line $\{x^{[i-1]} + \alpha \cdot m^{[i]} \mid \alpha \in \mathbb{R}\}$ such that the distance of $x^{[i]}$ from the optimum is minimum (a "perfect" line search along a uniformly random direction), we would observe linear convergence at an expected rate larger (i. e. worse) than $1 - 1/N$.

Now, talking about linear convergence at an expected rate makes sense only if the steps resemble each other up to a rescaling of the situation, which is in fact the case when assuming that in each iteration $D^{[i]}$ was chosen as the best isotropic distribution, namely the one that maximizes the expected gain. When considering a concrete heuristic, namely a concrete adaptation mechanism to determine the $D^{[i]}$, then – because of the black-box scenario – it seems that the $D^{[i]}$ just cannot be chosen such that a steady convergence is observed. Rather the expected reduction of the approximation error will vary from step to step. This is particularly true for step-size adaptations that aim at maximizing the local convergence speed, i. e., they try to choose in each iteration i the distribution $D^{[i]}$ such that expected one-step gain is maximum. To get around this non-steadiness – and to preclude detrimental effects of a possible loss of step-size control like premature convergence – one may ask the following

> **Question:** Is there a distribution D^* over $\mathbb{R}^N$ such that using $D^{[i]} := D^*$ in each iteration i results in a virtually steady convergence (i. e. at a virtually constant expected rate) to the optimum x^* when minimizing SPHERE$_{x^*}$?

It is quite easy to see that such a distribution cannot exist if the approximation error is supposed to become arbitrarily small. Such a D^* might exist, however, when we merely aim at an ε-approximation and know an upper bound $d_{\max}$ on the approximation errors that can occur.

In fact, we shall see in Section 3 that for the latter situation there is an isotropic distribution such that the algorithm in our framework that uses this distribution in each iteration and elitist selection converges linearly at an expected rate smaller (i. e. better) than $1 - 1/O(N \cdot \ln(d_{max}/\varepsilon))$. This algorithm will be called *oblivious randomized direct search (ORDS)*. As we shall moreover see, as long as the approximation error, namely the distance from the optimum x^* of SPHERE$_{x^*}$, is in the interval $[2\varepsilon, d_{max}]$, the expected number of iterations that ORDS needs to halve the approximation error is bounded above by $O(N \cdot \ln(d_{max}/\varepsilon))$. This is off from the general lower bound for isotropic sampling (Theorem 2) merely by a factor of order $\ln(d_{max}/\varepsilon)$. This is a remarkable property – especially when considered together with the results of related work to be discussed in the next section.

2   Related Work

A question similar to the one posed above has already been investigated in [10] (although with a different motivation). The scenario investigated therein is the minimization of a unimodal one-dimensional function over the interval $(-1, 1]$. The search wraps around when the interval is left; e. g., when the point $x = 1.5$ is sampled, $f(-0.5)$ is computed. In this scenario, the approximation error is bounded above by 1. The authors propose using the following distribution with the density $f_{RH} : \mathbb{R} \to \mathbb{R}_{\geq 0}$ defined by $f_{RH}(m) := 1/|2 \cdot p \cdot m|$ for $m \in [\varepsilon, 1] \cup [-1, -\varepsilon]$ and $f_{RH}(m) := 0$ otherwise, where $p := \ln(1/\varepsilon)$ for normalization and $\varepsilon \in (0, 1)$ is the predefined smallest step length. Note that $\int_{d/2}^{d} f_{RH}(m)\, dm = (\ln(d) - \ln(d/2))/(2p) = \ln(2)/(2p)$, which is independent of d. Thus, the probability to halve the distance from the optimum is at least $\ln(2)/(2p)$ in a step – independently of the distance d from the optimum. Obviously, $\varepsilon \leq d/2$ is required for actual independence of d. Concerning the expected number of steps to halve the approximation error, the authors conclude that "the expected waiting time (and this is clearly an upper bound) is thus $2p/\ln 2$. The number of steps required to get within δ of the optimum is therefore $O(p \cdot \ln(1/\delta))$." Apparently, $\delta \geq 2\varepsilon$ seems to be assumed there. As long as the approximation error is at least $\delta + \varepsilon$, the expected factor by which the distance from the optimum is reduced equals $1 - \alpha/\ln(1/\varepsilon)$ for some $\alpha > 0$ almost constant. Obviously, the smaller the minimum step length ε, the larger (i. e. worse) the expected convergence rate. Taking the minor technical issue discussed above into account, for $\delta = 2\varepsilon$ we obtain a bound of $O(\ln^2(1/\varepsilon))$ to find an 2ε-approximation when using a minimal step length of ε. Compared to binary search, this is off by a factor of order $\ln(1/\varepsilon)$. Dietzfelbinger/Rowe/Wegener/Woelfel [11] focus on whether this $\ln(1/\varepsilon)$-factor is inherent to the usage of a fixed distribution, i. e., whether any fixed distribution according to which the samples are drawn needs $\Omega(\ln^2(1/\varepsilon))$ iterations (in expectation) to obtain an ε-approximation. Actually, they consider a discrete version of the problem, where a *blind search* on the integers $0, \ldots, n$ is performed using a fixed distribution μ over $\{1, \ldots, n\}$ for the sampling. Namely, the search starts at a (uniformly) random position in $\{0, \ldots, n\}$. In each iteration the new position is given by the current position minus a number chosen according to μ – given that this new position is non-negative; otherwise the search stays at its position. Dietzfelbinger et al. prove that for the distribution defined by $\mu(m) := 1/(m \cdot H_n)$

for $m \in \{1, \ldots, n\}$ and $\mu(m) := 0$ otherwise (where $H_n = \sum_{i=1}^{n} 1/n$ is the nth Harmonic number; for normalization) the expected number of iterations to reach position zero is $O(\ln^2 n)$. Their main result is, however, that the expected number of steps is $\Omega(\ln^2 n)$ for *any* distribution μ, i.e., losing a factor of order $\ln n$ compared to binary search is inherent to blind search on the integers using a fixed distribution.

3   "Oblivious Randomized Direct Search" and its Analysis

In the present paper, we focus on direct search in N-dimensional Euclidean space. Namely, we consider the minimization of $\text{SPHERE}_{\boldsymbol{x}^*}$, i.e., the minimization of the (squared) distance from the unique optimum $\boldsymbol{x}^* \in \mathbb{R}^N$. Note the following obvious, but important observation: As $\boldsymbol{x}^*$ is not known, any candidate for the distribution D^* that might satisfy the property we ask for in the question at the end of Section 1 must necessarily be isotropic! Since any isotropic distribution can be decomposed according to Proposition 1, we are actually looking for some length distribution L^* such that the distribution $D^* \sim L^* \cdot U$ over $\mathbb{R}^N$ has the desired property, where U is uniformly distributed upon the unit hyper-sphere (uniformly random direction, independent of L^*). And since we consider isotropic distributions, we can restrict ourselves to the distance from the optimum $\boldsymbol{x}^*$. Now, assume that the current candidate solution $\boldsymbol{x}$ is located at distance d from $\boldsymbol{x}^*$. Then $p_{d,\ell,\alpha} := \mathrm{P}\{\mathrm{dist}(\boldsymbol{x} + \ell \cdot U, \boldsymbol{x}^*) \leq \alpha \cdot d\}$ equals the probability that adding an isotropically distributed vector with a fixed length ℓ to $\boldsymbol{x}$ generates a point such that the approximation error is reduced by (at least) the factor $\alpha \in (0,1)$. Note that $p_{d',\ell',\alpha} = p_{d,\ell,\alpha}$ whenever $\ell'/d' = \ell/d$ because of scale invariance. Now assume that the length ℓ is not fixed, but independently chosen according to some probability distribution with density μ. Then the probability to reduce the approximation error by at least the factor $\alpha \in (0,1)$ equals

$$p_{d,\mu,\alpha} := \int_{(1-\alpha)d}^{(1+\alpha)d} p_{d,\ell,\alpha} \cdot \mu(\ell) \, \mathrm{d}\ell.$$

The integral limits are due to the following fact: For the hyper-sphere with radius ℓ centered at $\boldsymbol{x}$ to intersect with the hyper-ball with radius $\alpha \cdot d$ centered at $\boldsymbol{x}^*$, the radius ℓ must be in the interval $[d - \alpha d, d + \alpha d]$. If ℓ is smaller than $d - \alpha d$ or larger than $d + \alpha d$, the sphere and the ball do not intersect. By substituting $d \cdot x$ for ℓ and using $p_{d,d\cdot x,\alpha} = p_{1,x,\alpha}$, we obtain

$$p_{d,\mu,\alpha} = \int_{(1-\alpha)}^{(1+\alpha)} p_{1,x,\alpha} \cdot \mu(x \cdot d) \cdot d \, \mathrm{d}x.$$

Thus, if μ was such that $\mu(x \cdot d) \cdot d$ is independent of d, i.e., $\mu(x \cdot d) \cdot d = \mu(x \cdot d') \cdot d'$, then $p_{d,\mu,\alpha}$ would indeed be independent of d. As a consequence, we choose $\mu(\ell)$ as β/ℓ for some constant $\beta > 0$. Then $\mu(x \cdot d) \cdot d = \beta/x$, so that

$$p_{d,\mu,\alpha} = \beta \cdot \int_{(1-\alpha)}^{(1+\alpha)} \frac{p_{1,x,\alpha}}{x} \, \mathrm{d}x,$$

which seems independent of d. However, as already pointed out in the discussion of related work in Section 2, $p_{d,\mu,\alpha}$ is actually independent of d only if the support of μ covers $[d - \alpha d, d + \alpha d]$. Note that μ must have bounded support $[a, b]$ with $0 < a < b$ in our case since neither $\int_0^a 1/x\,dx$ nor $\int_b^\infty 1/x\,dx$ are finite. Actually, when we choose $[a, b]$ as the support for μ, then $1/\beta$ equals $\int_a^b 1/x\,dx = \ln b - \ln a = \ln(b/a)$ for normalization. Later we will focus on how to choose the support $[a, b] \subset \mathbb{R}_{>0}$ of

$$\mu\colon \mathbb{R} \to \mathbb{R} \text{ with } \mu(\ell) := \begin{cases} \frac{1}{\ell \cdot \ln(b/a)} & \text{for } \ell \in [a, b] \\ 0 & \text{for } \ell \notin [a, b]. \end{cases} \tag{2}$$

Note the similarity between μ and the distributions in the two related papers discussed in Section 2. In the remainder, we focus on the following iterative method:

ORDS$_{[a,b]}$ (Oblivious Randomized Direct Search) is the method in our framework that uses elitist selection in Instruction 3 and in each iteration the isotropic distribution $D^* \sim \mu \cdot U$ in Instruction 1, where U is uniformly distributed upon the unit hypersphere and μ as in Equation (2) with support $[a, b]$.

Unfortunately, for the analysis of ORDS the reciprocal of the probability to halve the approximation error in a single step does not result in a reasonable upper bound on the expected waiting time until the approximation error is halved. The reason is that, for $N \geq 4$, the probability to halve the approximation error in an iteration i is exponentially small in N, namely smaller than $2^{-N} \cdot 0.43\sqrt{N-1}$ for any isotropic distribution $D^{[i]}$ [12, Lemma 3]. Instead, we will explicitly calculate a lower bound on the expected one-step gain in the following – and with it an upper bound on the expected convergence rate. For a start, we follow [12, p. 329]:

"Consider the hyper-plane H that contains the current candidate solution x ($\neq x^*$) and is orthogonal to the line passing through x and x^*. Assume that the isotropically distributed vector m happens to have the length $\ell > 0$. Then $y = x + m$ is uniformly distributed upon the hyper-sphere centered at x with radius ℓ. The random variable

$$G_\ell(y) := \begin{cases} \text{dist}(y, H) & \text{if } y \text{ lies in the half-space w.r.t. } H \text{ containing } x^* \\ -\text{dist}(y, H) & \text{otherwise} \end{cases}$$

corresponds to the *signed distance* of the sample $x + m$ from the hyper-plane H (under the condition that $|m| = \ell$). Obviously, the support of G_ℓ is $[-\ell, \ell]$. For $N \geq 4$ the density of G_ℓ at some $g \in [-\ell, \ell]$ equals $(1 - (g/\ell)^2)^{(N-3)/2}/(\ell \cdot \Psi)$, where $\Psi := \int_{-1}^1 (1 - x^2)^{(N-3)/2}\,dx$ (for normalization); cf. [8]. Actually, for a given distance of $d = \text{dist}(x, x^*)$ from the optimum we are interested in the random variable

$$\Delta_{d,\ell}(y) := d - \text{dist}(y, x^*)$$

which corresponds to the spatial gain towards the optimum x^* (under the condition $|m| = \ell$). The support of the random variable $\Delta_{d,\ell}$ is $[-\ell, \min\{\ell, 2d - \ell\}]$. The interrelation between $\Delta_{d,\ell}$ and G_ℓ is depicted in Figure 1. Simple geometry reveals (for any y with distance ℓ from x^*) the interrelation

$$G_\ell(y) = \Delta_{d,\ell}(y) + \frac{\ell^2 - (\Delta_{d,\ell}(y))^2}{2d}. \text{"}$$

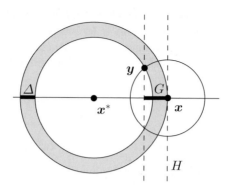

Fig. 1. Interrelation of the random variables G_ℓ and $\Delta_{d,\ell}$

As a consequence for the present situation, $G_\ell(\boldsymbol{y}) \geq \Delta_{d,\ell}(\boldsymbol{y}) \geq G_\ell(\boldsymbol{y}) - \ell^2/(2d)$, where $\boldsymbol{y}$ is a point from the hyper-sphere with radius ℓ centered at $\boldsymbol{x}$. In particular, $\Delta_{d,\ell}(\boldsymbol{y}) = 0$ corresponds to $G_\ell(\boldsymbol{y}) = \ell^2/(2d)$, so that

$$\mathsf{E}\big[\Delta_{d,\ell}^+\big] := \mathsf{E}[\Delta_{d,\ell} \cdot \mathbb{1}_{\{\Delta_{d,\ell} \geq 0\}}] \geq \mathsf{E}[G_\ell \cdot \mathbb{1}_{\{G_\ell \geq \ell^2/(2d)\}}] - \ell^2/(2d). \tag{3}$$

Note that $\mathsf{E}[\Delta_{d,\ell}^+]$ is the expected one-step gain towards the optimum $\boldsymbol{x}^*$ at distance d, given that the length of the isotropic distribution happens to be ℓ, when minimizing $\textsc{Sphere}_{\boldsymbol{x}^*}$ using elitist selection (a best-case scenario). As the integral behind $\mathsf{E}[\Delta_{d,\ell}^+]$ seems to not have an algebraically closed form, we will use the lower bound $\mathsf{E}[G_\ell \cdot \mathbb{1}_{\{G_\ell \geq \ell^2/(2d)\}}] - \ell^2/(2d)$, which can be easily calculated. Therefore recall that the density of G_ℓ at $g \in [-\ell, \ell]$ equals $(1 - (g/\ell)^2)^{(N-3)/2}/(\ell \cdot \Psi)$. Utilizing that $(1 - x^2)^{(N-1)/2}/(1 - N)$ is an anti-derivative of the function $x \cdot (1 - x^2)^{(N-3)/2}$, for $g \in [-\ell, \ell]$ and $N \geq 4$

$$\begin{aligned}
\mathsf{E}[G_\ell \cdot \mathbb{1}_{\{G_\ell \geq g\}}] &= \frac{1}{\Psi \cdot \ell} \cdot \int_g^\ell x \cdot (1 - (x/\ell)^2)^{(N-1)/2} \, \mathrm{d}x \\
&= \frac{\ell^2}{\Psi \cdot \ell} \cdot \left[\frac{-1}{N-1} \cdot (1 - (x/\ell)^2)^{(N-1)/2} \right]_g^\ell \\
&= \frac{\ell}{\Psi \cdot (N-1)} \cdot (1 - (g/\ell)^2)^{(N-1)/2}.
\end{aligned}$$

As $\Psi = \sqrt{\pi} \cdot \Gamma((N-1)/2)/\Gamma(N/2)$, here Γ denotes the well-known gamma function,

$$\frac{1}{\Psi \cdot (N-1)} \geq \sqrt{(N-2)/2\pi}/(N-1) \geq 1/\sqrt{2\pi(N+1)} > 0.3989/\sqrt{N+1}$$

where we use $\sqrt{N-2}/(N-1) \geq 1/\sqrt{N+1}$ for $N \geq 3$. Thus, for $g := \ell^2/(2d)$

$$\mathsf{E}[G_\ell \cdot \mathbb{1}_{\{G_\ell \geq \ell^2/(2d)\}}] > (1 - (\ell/(2d))^2)^{(N-1)/2} \cdot \ell \cdot 0.3989/\sqrt{N+1}.$$

For $\ell \leq d/\sqrt{N}$, we have $(1 - (\ell/(2d))^2)^{(N-1)/2} \geq (1 - 0.25/N)^{(N-1)/2} \geq \mathrm{e}^{-1/8} > 0.8824$, so that (using $0.8824 \cdot 0.3989 > 0.35$)

$$\mathsf{E}[G_\ell \cdot \mathbb{1}_{\{G_\ell \geq \ell^2/(2d)\}}] > 0.35 \, \ell/\sqrt{N+1} \quad \text{for} \quad \ell \leq d/\sqrt{N} \text{ and } N \geq 4. \tag{4}$$

Together with Equation (3), we thus obtain the following lower bound on the expected spatial gain towards the optimum in the search space:

$$E\left[\Delta_{d,\ell}^{+}\right] > \frac{0.35\,\ell}{\sqrt{N+1}} - \frac{\ell^2}{2d} \quad \text{for } \ell \le d/\sqrt{N} \text{ and } N \ge 4. \tag{5}$$

(In particular, for a length ℓ of $0.35d/\sqrt{N+1}$ this lower bound on the expected gain resolves to $0.06125d/(N+1) = \Omega(d/N)$, which is off from the general upper bound in Equation (1) by a factor of less than $8.5 + 17/(N-1)$ only. As a consequence, using the lower bound from Equation (5) is safe – in particular when we focus on the asymptotic order of the gain as N grows.)

Now, recall from Equation (2) the distribution μ with support $[a, b]$ according to which the length ℓ of the isotropically distributed vector is chosen. Then, given that $a \le 0.1d/\sqrt{N+1}$ and $b \ge 0.7d/\sqrt{N+1}$, we obtain (for $N \ge 4$)

$$E\left[\Delta_{d,\mu}^{+}\right] = \int_0^\infty E\left[\Delta_{d,\ell}^{+}\right] \cdot \mu(\ell)\,\mathrm{d}\ell$$

$$> \int_{0.1d/\sqrt{N+1}}^{0.7d/\sqrt{N+1}} \left(\frac{0.35\,\ell}{\sqrt{N+1}} - \frac{\ell^2}{2d}\right) \cdot \frac{1}{\ell \cdot \ln(b/a)}\,\mathrm{d}\ell$$

$$= \frac{0.09d}{(N+1) \cdot \ln(b/a)},$$

where we use that $\Delta_{d,\ell}^{+}$ (and thus its expectation) is non-negative anyway, so that integration limits can be chosen, and the bound from Equation (5). Note that this lower bound on the expected one-step gain is off from the general upper bound in Equation (1) by a factor of less than $\ln(b/a) \cdot 5.8 \cdot (N+1)/(N-1) = O(\ln(b/a))$. All in all, we have just proved the following.

Lemma 3. *Let $ORDS_{[a,b]}$ minimize SPHERE_{x^*} in $\mathbb{R}^N$, $N \ge 4$. If the approximation error d (distance from the optimum x^*) and a and b are such that $a \le 0.1d/\sqrt{N+1}$ as well as $b \ge 0.7d/\sqrt{N+1}$, then the expected factor by which the approximation error is reduced in a step is smaller (i. e. better) than $1 - \frac{0.09}{(N+1)\cdot\ln(b/a)}$.*

When we aim at an ε-approximation, then $a := 0.1\varepsilon/\sqrt{N+1}$ must be chosen for the preceding lemma to apply. (Actually, $a := \varepsilon/\sqrt{N}$ should work; the factor 0.1 is due to the application of the bound in Equation (5) and the rough estimation of the integral's value.) For the choice of b recall the discussion that led to the definition of μ in Equation (2). Hence, we choose b as twice the maximum possible approximation error. In the SPHERE scenario, this is twice the initial approximation error. If the initial approximation error is not known – like in the following setting – an upper bound can be used. (The length of a diagonal in the N-dimensional interval region $[0,1]^N$ is $\sqrt{N}$.)

Theorem 4. *Let $ORDS_{[a,b]}$ minimize SPHERE_{x^*} in $\mathbb{R}^N$, $N \ge 4$. Assume that the optimum point x^* as well as the initial search point lie in the set $[0,1]^N$. Then choosing $a := 0.1\varepsilon/\sqrt{N+1}$ and $b := 2\sqrt{N+1}$ ensures linear convergence at an expected rate smaller (i. e. better) than $1 - \frac{0.09}{(N+1)\cdot\ln(20(N+1)/\varepsilon)} = 1 - 1/O(N\ln(N/\varepsilon))$ until the approximation error drops below $\varepsilon + a < \varepsilon \cdot (1 + 0.1/\sqrt{N})$.*

Now that we know an upper bound on the expected factor by which the approximation error is reduced in each step (unless the approximation error drops below $\varepsilon + a$) we would like to turn this into an upper bound on the expected number of steps to reduce the approximation error by a predefined amount. The following lemma, which can be found in [8] including a full proof, will enable us to do so.

Lemma 5. *Let* $X_1, X_2, \ldots$ *denote random variables with bounded support and* S *the random variable defined by* $S := \min\{ t \mid X_1 + \cdots + X_t \geq g \}$ *for a predefined* $g > 0$. *Given that* S *is a stopping time, i. e., the event* $\{S = k\}$ *depends solely on* $X_1, \ldots, X_k$, *if* $\mathsf{E}[S] < \infty$ *and* $\mathsf{E}[X_i \mid S \geq i] \geq \phi > 0$ *for all* i, *then* $\mathsf{E}[S] \leq \mathsf{E}[X_1 + \cdots + X_S]/\phi$.

Proof. Note that the X_i need not be independent and that, since the X_i are bounded, the precondition $\mathsf{E}[S] < \infty$ implies $\mathsf{E}[X_1 + \cdots + X_S] < \infty$. Then

$$\mathsf{E}[X_1 + \cdots + X_S] = \sum_{i=1}^{\infty} \mathsf{P}\{S \geq i\} \cdot \mathsf{E}[X_i \mid S \geq i] \geq \sum_{i=1}^{\infty} \mathsf{P}\{S \geq i\} \cdot \phi = \mathsf{E}[S] \cdot \phi$$

where the first equation is the major part of the proof of Wald's equation.   □

We concentrate on the expected number of steps to halve the approximation error, and thus, for the application of Lemma 5 we let X_i denote the spatial gain towards the optimum in the ith iteration and choose $g := d^{[0]}/2$ and $\ell := \frac{0.09}{(N+1)\cdot\ln(20(N+1)/\varepsilon)} d^{[0]}/2$, where we use that $0 \leq X_i \leq d^{[0]}$ in our scenario, and that the condition $\{S \geq i\}$ merely means that the approximation error has not been halved within the first $i - 1$ iterations, i. e., $d^{[i-1]} > d^{[0]}/2$. Finally, we use the trivial bound $\mathsf{E}[X_1 + \cdots + X_S] \leq d^{[0]}$ (which actually costs us a factor of nearly 2) and note that $\mathsf{E}[S] < \infty$ since in each iteration the success/stopping region is hit with positive probability. All in all, the application of the previous lemma yields the following upper bound on the expected number of steps to halve the approximation error.

Corollary 6. *Consider the settings from Theorem 4. Then, unless the approximation error is smaller than* $2(\varepsilon + a) < 2\varepsilon(1 + 0.1/\sqrt{N})$, *the expected number of steps to halve the approximation error is at most* $d^{[0]}/\frac{0.09 \cdot d^{[0]}/2}{(N+1)\cdot\ln(20(N+1)/\varepsilon)}$, *which is smaller than* $22.3 \cdot (N + 1) \cdot (\ln(N + 1) + 3 - \ln \varepsilon) = O(N \cdot \ln(N/\varepsilon))$.

This upper bound is off from the general lower bound when using isotropic samples (Theorem 2) – which covers perfect adaptation – by less than a factor of $23.2 \ln(N/\varepsilon)$ for large N. As the location of the optimum $\boldsymbol{x}^* \in [0, 1]^N$ is not known, random initialization is the most appropriate choice, finally yielding the main result:

Theorem 7. *Let* $ORDS_{[a,b]}$ *minimize* $SPHERE_{\boldsymbol{x}^*}$ *in* $\mathbb{R}^N$, $N \geq 4$, *for some* $\boldsymbol{x}^* \in [0, 1]^N$, *where* $a := 0.1\varepsilon/\sqrt{N + 1}$ *and* $b := 2\sqrt{N + 1}$. *Then, unless the approximation error is smaller than* $\varepsilon' := \varepsilon + a < \varepsilon \cdot (1 + 0.1/\sqrt{N})$, *the search converges linearly at an expected rate smaller than* $1 - \frac{0.09}{(N+1)\cdot\ln(20(N+1)/\varepsilon)}$, *and moreover, when the initial candidate solution is sampled uniformly at random from* $[0, 1]^N$, *the expected number of steps to obtain an* ε'-*approximation is* $O(N \cdot \ln^2(N/\varepsilon))$.

Proof. Obviously, the (expected) initial approximation error is bounded above by $\sqrt{N}$. As a consequence, the approximation error must be halved at most $\ln(\sqrt{N}/\varepsilon)/\ln 2$ times in expectation (w.r.t. the initialization) to obtain an ε-approximation. As the random initialization and the sampling of μ are independent, we can multiply by the expected number of steps to halve the approximation error to obtain an upper bound on the expected runtime of $22.3 \cdot (N{+}1) \cdot \ln(20(N{+}1)/\varepsilon) \cdot \ln(\sqrt{N}/\varepsilon)/\ln 2$, which is bounded above by $32.2 \cdot (N{+}1) \cdot \ln^2((N{+}1)/\varepsilon) + O(N \cdot \ln(N/\varepsilon))$. $\qquad \square$

4   Discussion and Conclusion

The choice of the unit hyper-cube $[0,1]^N$ as the decision space was somewhat arbitrary, of course. For any bounded N-dimensional interval region we can choose b as twice its diameter d. Then the expected number of steps to halve the approximation error on SPHERE is $O(N \cdot \ln(d/\varepsilon))$, which is larger than the general lower bound (when using isotropic sampling to generate candidate solutions) by a factor of order $\ln(d/\varepsilon)$. Actually, this is the factor that ORDS loses in the best-case scenario. In practice, the optimization scenario is often not best-case, but the function to be optimized may be multi-modal for instance. Then (usual) step-size controls result in the convergence to the stationary point that is closest to the (random) staring point. On the one hand, they (usually) accelerate the convergence to the nearest local optimum, but on the other hand, the step sizes rapidly become too small to escape the local optimum region. This is bad in particular when there are many local optima, so that a large number of restarts is necessary to initialize within one of the "good" local-optimum regions. Also ORDS may converge to the nearest local optimum, but as it does so without favoring smaller and smaller step-sizes, and because of the heavy tailed distribution of the step-lengths, ORDS simultaneously searches more globally, i.e., the chance of escaping the local optimum region is preserved. This can also be considered as an implicit mechanism for automated restarts. In particular, after such a "restart", i.e., after a long step that made the search leave the current local optimum region into another one, the step-sizes need *not* be re-adjusted in ORDS as it would be necessary for (usual) step-size controls. Preliminary experimental investigations of ORDS support this hypothesis on its behavior, and also the simulations presented in [10] (the first work discussed in Section 2) indicate that the concept behind ORDS can work well. (The authors consider a bunch of multi-modal test functions, but also "a difficult real-world application, from medical image interpretation.")

Thus, besides the interesting theoretical aspects of ORDS and its runtime analysis presented here, the distribution used in ORDS to sample new candidate solutions may indeed be used in more complex algorithms. For instance, it could be used within the CMA-ES (Covariance Matrix Adaptation Evolution Strategy, cf. [13]) instead of multivariate normal distributions. This would supersede the complex and expensive step-size adaptation (by the so-called cumulative step-size adaptation (CSA)), but the learning and the continuous adaptation of the inverse Hessian (similar to a quasi-Newton approach) would be retained, which particularly helps with the optimization of ill-conditioned problems. An experimental investigation of such an algorithm with a (statistical) comparison to other direct-search heuristics shall help us assess the potential for practical optimization.

Acknowledgment. The author thanks Ingo Wegener (for posing the underlying question and giving some initial thoughts about the subject of this paper) and the reviewers who provided detailed and helpful comments.

References

1. Wegener, I.: Towards a theory of randomized search heuristics. In: Rovan, B., Vojtáš, P. (eds.) MFCS 2003. LNCS, vol. 2747, pp. 125–141. Springer, Heidelberg (2003)
2. Kolda, T.G., Lewis, R.M., Torczon, V.: Optimization by direct search: New perspectives on some classical and modern methods. SIAM Review 45(3), 385–482 (2004)
3. Rechenberg, I.: Cybernetic solution path of an experimental problem. Royal Aircraft Establishment (1965)
4. Brooks, S.H.: A discussion of random methods for seeking maxima. Operations Research 6(2), 244–251 (1958)
5. Wegener, I.: Randomized search heuristics as an alternative to exact optimization. In: Lenski, W. (ed.) Logic versus Approximation. LNCS, vol. 3075, pp. 138–149. Springer, Heidelberg (2004)
6. Fang, K.T., Kotz, S., Ng, K.W.: Symmetric multivariate and related distributions. Monographs on statistics and applied probability, vol. 36. Chapman & Hall, London (1990)
7. Jägersküpper, J.: Analysis of a simple evolutionary algorithm for minimization in Euclidean spaces. In: Baeten, J.C.M., Lenstra, J.K., Parrow, J., Woeginger, G.J. (eds.) ICALP 2003. LNCS, vol. 2719, pp. 1068–1079. Springer, Heidelberg (2003)
8. Jägersküpper, J.: Algorithmic analysis of a basic evolutionary algorithm for continuous optimization. Theoretical Computer Science 379(3), 329–347 (2007)
9. Jägersküpper, J.: Lower bounds for hit-and-run direct search. In: Hromkovič, J., Královič, R., Nunkesser, M., Widmayer, P. (eds.) SAGA 2007. LNCS, vol. 4665, pp. 118–129. Springer, Heidelberg (2007)
10. Rowe, J.E., Hidovic, D.: An evolution strategy using a continuous version of the Gray-code neighbourhood distribution. In: Deb, K., et al. (eds.) GECCO 2004. LNCS, vol. 3102, pp. 725–736. Springer, Heidelberg (2004)
11. Dietzfelbinger, M., Rowe, J.E., Wegener, I., Woelfel, P.: Tight bounds for blind search on the integers. In: Proc. 25th Annual Symposium on Theoretical Aspects of Computer Science (STACS), IBFI Schloss Dagstuhl, Germany. Dagstuhl Seminar Proceedings, vol. 8001, pp. 241–252 (2008)
12. Jägersküpper, J.: Lower bounds for randomized direct search with isotropic sampling. Operations Research Letters 36(3), 327–332 (2008)
13. Hansen, N., Ostermeier, A.: Completely derandomized self-adaptation in evolution strategies. Evolutionary Computation 9(2), 159–195 (2001)

Path Minima in Incremental Unrooted Trees[*]

Haim Kaplan and Nira Shafrir

School of Computer Science, Tel Aviv University, Tel Aviv 69978, Israel
{haimk,shafrirn}@post.tau.ac.il

Abstract. Consider a dynamic forest of unrooted trees over a set of n vertices which we update by *link* operations: Each link operation adds a new edge adjacent to vertices in two different trees. Every edge in the forest has a weight associated with it, and at any time we want to be able to answer a *path-min* query which returns that edge of minimum weight along the path between two given vertices.

For the case where the weights are integers we give an algorithm that performs $n-1$ link operations and m pathmin queries in $O(n+m\alpha(m,n))$ time. This extends well known results of Tarjan [11] and Yao [12] to a more general dynamic setting at the cost of restricting the weights to be integers. We also suggest a simpler data structures for the case where trees are rooted and the link operation always adds an edge between the root of one tree and an arbitrary vertex of another tree.

1   Introduction

The *incremental path minima problem in rooted trees* is defined as follows. Let F be a forest of rooted trees with n vertices. Each edge e has an integer weight $w(e)$. We have to support the following operations on the forest.

- make-tree(v): Create a new tree consisting of the singleton node v.
- link(u,v,c). We assume that $u \in T^1$, $v \in T^2$, v is the root of T^2, and $T^1 \neq T^2$. Replace the trees T^1 and T^2, by the tree that is created by adding the edge $e = (u,v)$ with $w(e) = c$.
- path-min(u,v): If u and v belong to the same tree, return the edge of minimum weight on the unique path between u and v. Otherwise, return null.

We give an algorithm that supports $n - 1$ link operations and m path-min queries in $O(n + m\alpha(m,n))$ time where $\alpha(m,n)$ is the inverse of Ackermann's function. Alstrup and Holm [2] claimed this result without describing the data structure.

The *incremental path minima problem in unrooted trees* is defined analogously as follows. Let F be a forest of unrooted trees. Each edge e has an integer weight $w(e)$. The operations make-tree and path-min are defined as for rooted trees. We change the link(u,v,c) operation and remove the requirement that u is a

---

[*] This work is partially supported by United States - Israel Binational Science Foundation, project number 2006204.

D. Halperin and K. Mehlhorn (Eds.): ESA 2008, LNCS 5193, pp. 565–576, 2008.

root. That is we only require that $u \in T^1$, $v \in T^2$, and $T^1 \neq T^2$. The operation replaces the trees T^1 and T^2 by the tree that is created by adding the edge $e = (u, v)$ with $w(e) = c$. This data type is more general in the sense that it allows link between any two vertices that are not in the same tree. Our main result is a data structure with the same time bounds for this unrooted version of the problem.

Our data structures are based on two main components. The first component is *incremental trees*. Incremental trees support add-leaf and add-root operations and path-min queries in $O(1)$ time. They are based on a similar structure of Alstrup and Holm [2] for the level ancestor problem. We restrict the weights to be integers so we can use q-heaps [4] to construct incremental trees. We assume the RAM model of computation with word size b so that a weight of an edge fits into a single word. We also make sure that $b \geq \log n$ where n is the number of vertices in our forest.

The second component is a recursive decomposition of trees suggested by Gabow [6]. Gabow used this scheme to answer m nearest common ancestor (nca) queries on rooted trees while allowing links in $O(n + m\alpha(m, n))$ time. This recursive structure supports all links in $O(n + m)$ time and each query in $O(\alpha(m, n))$ time. Gabow also used a similar technique to solve the list splitting problem [5]. (See also [10] for a similar recursive structure.)

The recursive scheme at high level is as follows. A tree T is partitioned into clusters each of which is a subtree of T. Each cluster is represented as an incremental tree. We then contract each cluster and represent the resulting tree recursively. The depth of the recursion is $O(\alpha(m, n))$.

These two components alone are not sufficient. Even for the rooted problem subtle issues arise as of how to organize the information so that we only spend a constant time per level of the recursion when we answer a query. In the rooted version of the problem there is a natural root for each cluster and we maintain information on paths to this root. When such a root does not exist it is not clear anymore on which path to maintain information.

Our application for the incremental path minima problem in unrooted trees is an optimal algorithm for a restricted version of the mergeable trees problem [8] which arises in computational topology. The mergeable trees problem is defined as follows. Let F be a forest of rooted trees. Each node v has a unique weight $w(v)$. Each $S \in F$ is a heap ordered tree so that $w(v) \geq w(p(v))$. The data structure supports the following operations.

- merge(u, v). Let $u \in S^1$, $v \in S^2$, (S^1 may be equal to S^2.) Create a new tree S in which the path from u to the root of S^1 is merged with the path of v to the root of S^2, in a way that preserves heap order. In case $S^1 \neq S^2$ we call the merge an *external-merge* and otherwise we call it an *internal-merge*.
- nca(u, v): If u and v belong to the same tree return the nearest common ancestor of u and v. Otherwise, returns null.

Recently, Georgiadis *et al* [7] showed a reduction from the mergeable trees problem without internal merges to the *incremental* path minima problem in unrooted trees. A merge operation translates to a link and an nca query translates to a path-min operation. Thus we get a data structure that supports $n - 1$ external merges and m nca queries (where the weights are integers), in $O(n + m\alpha(m, n))$ time. This is particularly interesting since it matches the lower bound for the problem, see [8]. For more on the connection between these problems see [7].

Related results. Yao [12] and Alon and Schieber [1] (See also [3]) solved the following static problem. Let T be a tree with n nodes each associated with an element of a semigroup $(S, \circ)$. We want to preprocess the tree to answer queries of the form: Given two vertices u and v what is the product ($\circ$) of the element of S associated with the vertices on the path from u to v. Yao and Alon and Schieber show how to preprocess the tree in linear time so that we can answer each query in $O(\alpha(n))$ (where $\alpha(n)$ is yet another version of an inverse to Ackermann's function). As a special case we can use their data structure for a static version of our problem in which there is a single tree given in advance which we want to preprocess for path-min queries.

Tarjan [11] in his seminal paper used path compression to solve a restricted version of the problem on rooted trees. In Tarjan's version link(v,w,c) is defined only if both v and w are roots of their trees, and path-min queries are restricted to paths from a given vertex to the root. Tarjan also considered an arbitrary semigroup. This special case has numerous applications, one of which is to verify that a given tree is a minimum spanning tree.

Both algorithms mentioned above, when applied to computing path minima queries, work in the comparison model and need not assume that keys are integers.

The outline of the rest of the paper. To fully grasp our new ideas one has to go into a quite deep technical discussion. To help the reader we try to expose some of these ideas through a somewhat less formal discussion in Section 2, focusing on the difference between the rooted and the unrooted problems. In Section 3 we define incremental trees perform add-leaf and add-root and min query in $O(1)$ time (but no link). In Section 4 we describe the data structure for incremental path minima in rooted trees problem. In Section 5 we give a simple but not optimal data structure for incremental path minima in unrooted trees problem that supports $n - 1$ link m pathmin queries in $O(n + m\alpha^2(m, n))$ time. In the full version of this paper [9] we describe how to improve this running time to $O(n + m\alpha(m, n))$.

2 Highlights of the Data Structure

In this section we try to give a high level intuition of the differences between the rooted problem and the unrooted problem. This shows where the difficulties are, and the ideas that we introduce to cope with them. We focus on the query operation.

We avoid formal definitions at this point but recall that each of our trees is partitioned into clusters. Each cluster is a connected subtree which we represent as an incremental tree. The clusters are contracted, and the contracted tree is again partitioned into clusters that are represented as incremental trees, and so on. See Figure 1(A).

For a vertex $x \in T$, we denote by $C_k(x)$ the cluster of level k that contains it. Levels of clusters decrease with our recursion so the nodes of a cluster of level k are clusters of level $k + 1$. In particular if $C_k(x)$ is not a top-level cluster then $C_{k+1}(x)$ is one of its nodes, and if C_k contains the vertices x and y of T then $C_k(x) = C_k(y) = C_k$.

Let (x, y), $x, y \in T$, be the edge of T that connects between the clusters $C_{k+1}(x)$ and $C_{k+1}(y)$ in a cluster C_k. What would be the weight of this edge when we consider it as an edge of C_k ? To define this weight we must root C_k as a subtree of T even if the original tree is unrooted. Then if say $C_{k+1}(x)$ is the parent of $C_{k+1}(y)$ the weight of (x, y) is the minimum weight of an edge on the path from y to the root of $C_{k+1}(x)$ that is induced by the orientation of C_k.

When T is rooted then the root of each cluster is naturally defined. See Figure 1(A). In unrooted trees we can designate an arbitrary vertex to be a root. But to maintain such a root we will have to change directions of many edges during a link. On the other hand we still want the clusters to be rooted so that we can define the weight of each edge in a cluster. A key idea is to exploit the freedom that we have, and allow each cluster to be independently oriented, see Figure 1(B).

The query pathmin(x, y) for both rooted and unrooted trees works roughly as follows. We find the highest level k such that $C_k(x) = C_k(y)$. Let $C_k = C_k(x) = C_k(y)$. (For an illustration see vertices x and y in Figure 1(A) and Figure 1(B). In these figures we assume that $k + 2 = \ell$, and all the clusters of level $k + 1$ in are in the same cluster of level k). By the definition of C_k we have that the clusters $C_{k+1}(x)$ and $C_{k+1}(y)$ are different nodes in C_k. Let C_{k+1} be the nearest common ancestor of $C_{k+1}(x)$ and $C_{k+1}(y)$ in C_k, $(C_{k+1} = C_{k+1}(a)$ in the Figures). For simplicity assume that $C_{k+1} \neq C_{k+1}(y)$, and $C_{k+1} \neq C_{k+1}(x)$.

Let (x_r, x''), $x_r, x'' \in T$, be the edge between $C_{k+1}(x)$ to its parent cluster in C_k where $x_r \in C_{k+1}(x)$. Similarly, let (y_r, y''), $y_r, y'' \in T$, be the edge between $C_{k+1}(y)$ to its parent cluster in C_k. Let $C_{k+1}(x_1)$ be the cluster that precedes C_{k+1} on the path from $C_{k+1}(x)$ to C_{k+1} and let $(x_1, \hat{x})$ be the edge between cluster $C_{k+1}(x_1)$ to C_{k+1}. Similarly, let $C_{k+1}(y_1)$ be the cluster that precedes C_{k+1} on the path from $C_{k+1}(y)$ to C_{k+1} and let $(y_1, \hat{y})$ be the edge between cluster $C_{k+1}(y_1)$ to C_{k+1}. The query path consists of the following parts. (1) from x to x_r in $C_{k+1}(x)$; (2) from x_r to x_1; (3) the edge $(x_1, \hat{x})$; (4) from $\hat{x}$ to $\hat{y}$ in C_{k+1}; (5) The edge $(\hat{y}, y_1)$; (6) from y_1 to y_r; and (7) from y_r to y.

We find the minimum on part (2) and part (6) by a query to the incremental tree of the cluster C_k. We find the minimum on part (4) recursively. Since $C_{k+1}(\hat{x}) = C_{k+1}(\hat{y}) = C_{k+1}$ the depth of this recursion is $O(\alpha(m, n))$.

The way we find the minimum on parts (1) and (7) is different in the rooted and the unrooted data structures. In the rooted structure we use the fact that x_r is the root vertex of the cluster $C_{k+1}(x)$. This special case of finding the minimum from a vertex to the root of a cluster is easier and takes $O(\alpha(m, n))$ time.

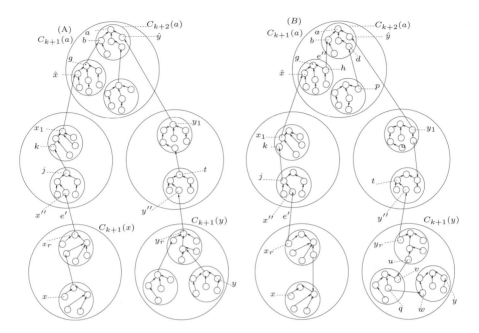

Fig. 1. In both figures we assume here that $k + 2 = \ell$, and that the small circles are the vertices of T. (A) The recursive structure for a rooted tree. Medium circles are clusters of T_{k+2}. Large circles are clusters of T_{k+1}. Edges of level $k + 2$ are contained inside clusters of level $k + 2$, (edges such as (a, b) $(\hat{x}, g)$ and so on). The edges (b, g) and (k, j) are of level $k + 1$. The edges (x_r, x''), (y_r, y''), $(x_1, \hat{x})$ and $(y_1, \hat{y})$ are of level k. Let $e' = (x_r, x'')$. The weight of the edge $e'(k)$ is the minimum weight of an edge on the path from x_r to x_1. (B) The recursive structure in unrooted trees. Each cluster is oriented independently. We have that $r(C_{k+2}(a)) = t(C_{k+2}(a)) = a$, $r(C_{k+2}(g)) = g$, and $t(C_{k+2}(g)) = h$. Let $e' = (x_r, x'')$. The weight of $e'(k)$ is the minimum weight of an edge on the path from x_r to x_1. The weight of $e'(k + 1)$ is the minimum weight of an edge on the path from x_r to j. Let $e'' = (h, b)$. The weight of $e''(k + 1)$ is the minimum weight of an edge on the path from h to a in T.

If the trees are unrooted, (see Figure 1(B)), then x_r is not necessarily the root vertex of the cluster $C_{k+1}(x)$ and y_r is not necessarily the root vertex of the cluster $C_{k+1}(y)$. This makes the query slightly more difficult. We suggest two solutions. In the simple data structure of Section 5, we find the minimum on parts (1) and (7) again using recursion. This additional recursion degrades the running time of a query to $O(\alpha(m, n)^2)$.

In the full version of the paper we show how to reduce the query time in unrooted trees to $O(\alpha(m, n))$ by storing more information. For each edge (u, v) such that $C_{k+1}(v) \neq C_{k+1}(u)$, we maintain the edge of minimum weight on the path from u to each cluster of level $k + 2$ in $C_{k+1}(u)$. Using this information we find the edge of minimum weight on the path between y and y_r in $O(\alpha(m, n))$ time. To save this additional information we had to restrict the size of a cluster from above, and to change the implementation of both link and query.

3   Incremental Trees and Partial Incremental Trees

Our building blocks are *incremental trees*. An incremental tree is a data structure to maintain a rooted tree T, with an integer weight on each vertex, such that the following operations are supported in $O(1)$ time.

add-leaf(v,w,c): Add a new leaf v with parent w to T. The weight of the edge (v, w) is c.

add-root(v,c): Add a new root v to T. The old root of T, say r, becomes a child of v and the weight of the edge (r, v) is c.

min(v,w): Returns the edge of minimum weight on the path from v to w.

change-weight(v,c): v is a leaf or v's parent is the root of T. Changes the weight of the edge between v and its parent to c.

Our incremental trees also support nearest common ancestor (nca) queries in constant time. If the data structure does not support the add root operation then we call it a *partial incremental tree*. A detailed implementation of partial incremental trees and incremental trees appears in the complete version of this paper.

4   A Data Structure for Rooted Trees

We use the following definition of Ackermann's function

$$
\begin{aligned}
A(i, 1) &= 2 & i &\geq 1 \\
A(1, j) &= 2^j & j &\geq 1 \\
A(i, j) &= A(i - 1, A(i, j - 1)) & i, j &\geq 2
\end{aligned}
$$

and the inverse functions

$$
\begin{aligned}
a(i, n) &= \min\{j \mid A(i, j) \geq n\} \\
\alpha(m, n) &= \min\{i \mid A(i, \lceil m/n \rceil) \geq n\} \quad m, n \geq 1 \ .
\end{aligned}
$$

Assume for now that we know the number of operations m ahead of time[1] and let $\ell = \alpha(m, n)$. We denote a tree in our forest of rooted trees by T. We denote by $p(v)$ the parent of a node v, and by $|T|$ the number of vertices in T.

Our forest is represented using a recursive family of data structures. At the top level each tree T in the forest is a member of the data structure D_ℓ. Each tree in D_ℓ is classified to a *universe*. There are $a(\ell, n)$ universes $0, \cdots, a(\ell, n) - 1$ in D_ℓ. The size of the tree T determines its universe as follows. If $|T| < 4$ then T is in universe 0. Otherwise, if $2A(\ell, i) \leq |T| < 2A(\ell, i + 1)$ then T is in universe i. (Note that $2A(\ell, 1) = 4$.)

Let T be in universe $i > 0$. The vertices of T are partitioned into *clusters*. Each cluster is a subtree of T that contains at least $2A(\ell, i)$ vertices. Let T' be the tree obtained from T by contracting each cluster into a single node. The tree

---

[1] If m is not known ahead of time then we can globally rebuild the structure when $m = 2n$, and subsequently every time m is doubled. This does not affect the time bounds.

T' is represented using the data structure $D_{\ell-1}$ which is defined analogously. The last data structure in this recurrence is D_1. In D_1 each tree consists of a single cluster (so the tree with this cluster contracted is a singleton which is not represented using a recursive structure).

In the data structure D_j we have $a(j, n)$ universes $0, \cdots, a(j, n) - 1$. Let H be a tree in D_j. If $|H| < 4$ then H is in universe 0 and otherwise if $2A(j, i) \leq |H| < 2A(j, i+1)$ then H is in universe i. If H is in universe $i > 0$ then the vertices of H are partitioned into *clusters*. Each cluster is a subtree of H that contains at least $2A(j, i)$ vertices. The tree H' obtained by contracting each cluster, is represented using the data structure D_{j-1}.

Consider a tree T in our forest. The tree T is a member of D_ℓ. If $|T| \geq 4$ then a tree T', obtained from T by contracting its clusters, is in $D_{\ell-1}$. Similarly, if $|T'| \geq 4$ then a tree T'' obtained by contracting clusters of T', is a member of $D_{\ell-2}$ and so on. We can also think of T'' as obtained from T by contracting even larger subtrees (each such subtree is a cluster of T' which is a cluster of clusters of T). When thinking of T as a member of D_ℓ we denote it by T_ℓ. We denote by $T_{\ell-1}$, the tree T' corresponding to T in $D_{\ell-1}$. In general we denote by T_j the tree corresponding to T in D_j. For $j < \ell$, the tree T_j contains all the edges of T that connect two clusters of T_{j+1}. See Figure 1(A).

We also use the following definitions. Let v be a vertex in T. We define $C_{\ell+1}(v) = v$. We denote by $C_\ell(v)$ the cluster in T_ℓ that contains v. The cluster $C_\ell(v)$ is a subtree of T. We define recursively $C_j(v)$ for $j < \ell$ to be the cluster of T_j that contains $C_{j+1}(v)$.

One can think of $C_j(v)$ as a subtree of T by substituting the subtrees of T corresponding to all clusters $C_{j+1}(w)$ contained in $C_j(v)$. We also refer to $C_j(v)$ as a node of T_{j-1}.

For $j \leq \ell + 1$, we define $r(C_j(v))$ to be the root of the subtree of T that $C_j(v)$ represents. Let $e = (x, y) \in T = T_\ell$ and let j be the smallest level such that $C_{j+1}(x) \neq C_{j+1}(y)$. We define the *level* of e to be j and denote it by $\text{level}(e) = j$. A copy of the edge e appears in each T_i, for $j \leq i \leq \ell$. We denote by $e(i)$ the copy of e that appears in T_i. The edge e is contracted into the cluster $C_j(x) = C_j(y)$ in T_j, and therefore does not exist in T_i, for any $i < j$. We sometimes use e when in fact we refer to $e(j)$; the context will make clear which edge we refer to. Since $|T_j| < \frac{1}{2}|T_{j+1}|$ for any $j < \ell$, it is clear that $\sum_{j=1}^{\ell} |T_j| = O(|T|)$.

For each tree T in our forest and for every level j such that T_j exists, we maintain T_j. In addition, the node representing the cluster C_j has a pointer to $r(C_j)$, a pointer to the cluster of level $j+1$ which is the root of C_j, and a pointer to the cluster of level $j - 1$ containing C_j, if it exists. The edge representing a copy $e(j)$ of the edge e, has a pointer to e.

Let $e = (u, v) \in T$ such that $\text{level}(e) = j$ and assume $v = p(u)$. We store with e a list $L(e)$ of size $\ell - j + 1$. Entry ℓ of $L(e)$ contains e. For level $j \leq k < \ell$ entry k of $L(e)$ contains the edge f of minimum weight on the path from u to $r(C_{k+1}(v))$ in T. We represent $L(e)$ as a doubly linked list with pointers to its first and last entry.

Consider a copy $e(k)$ of e in T_k for some $j \leq k \leq \ell$. Let f be the edge stored in entry k of $L(e)$. The *weight* of $e(k)$, denoted by $w(e(k))$, is equal to the weight of f. Since $\sum_{j=1}^{\ell} |T_j| = O(|T|)$, the total space used to store the lists $L(e)$ is linear. Figure 1(A) illustrates this recursive structure.

Let C_j, $j \leq \ell$, be a cluster of T_j. We represent C_j as an incremental tree whose nodes are clusters of T_{j+1}. We keep a pointer from C_j to the incremental tree that represents it. We also sometimes refer to C_j as the incremental tree itself. Let $e = (u, v)$ be an edge of level j. Then, $e(j)$ is contained in a cluster $C_j(u) = C_j(v)$, and in the incremental tree representing it. The weight of $e(j)$ in this incremental tree is $w(e(j))$. If T is in universe 0, $(|T| < 4)$, we think of T as a single cluster C and represent C as an incremental tree.

In this abstract we describe only the path-min query. The link is similar to the link of unrooted trees described in the next section.

Assume that x and y are two vertices in the same tree T and let P_{xy} be the path from x to y in T. We want to find the edge of minimum weight on P_{xy}. Let k be the largest level for which $C_k(y) = C_k(x)$.[2] We define a recursive procedure $pathmin_k(x, y, e_x, e_y)$, where either e_x or e_y may be null. If $e_x = (x', x)$ is not null, then e_x is an edge incident to x which is of level $< k$ and we have a pointer to the entry k in $L(e_x)$. Moreover, x is the parent of x'. Similarly, if $e_y = (y', y)$ is not null, then e_y is an edge incident to y which is of level $< k$ and we have a pointer to entry k in $L(e_y)$ and y is the parent of y'. If e_x is not null, let $a = x'$ otherwise let $a = x$. Similarly, if e_y is not null, let $b = y'$, otherwise let $b = y$. The procedure $pathmin_k(x, y, e_x, e_y)$ finds the edge of minimum weight on P_{ab}.

We first assume that both $e_x = (x', x)$ and $e_y = (y', y)$ exist. We will relax these assumption later. The procedure $pathmin_k(x, y, e_x, e_y)$ works as follows. The base case is when $k = \ell$. In this case we perform $\min_{C_\ell(x)}(x, y)$ and get the edge f of minimum weight on P_{xy}. We return the edge of minimum weight among $\{e_x, e_y, f\}$. So assume now that $k < \ell$. If $C_{k+1}(x) = C_{k+1}(y)$ then we advance in $L(e_x)$ and in $L(e_y)$ one step to entry $k + 1$, and return the answer of $pathmin_{k+1}(x, y, e_x, e_y)$. If $C_{k+1}(x) \neq C_{k+1}(y)$ then we find $C_{k+1}(z) = nca_{C_k(x)}(C_{k+1}(x), C_{k+1}(y))$ and perform one of the following cases.

Case 1: $C_{k+1}(z) \neq C_{k+1}(x)$ **and** $C_{k+1}(z) \neq C_{k+1}(y)$. Let $C_{k+1}(x_1)$ be the node in $C_k(x)$ on the path from $C_{k+1}(x)$ to $C_{k+1}(z)$ that precedes $C_{k+1}(z)$, and assume that $x_1 = r(C_{k+1}(x_1))$. Let $C_{k+1}(y_1)$ be the node in $C_k(x)$ on the path from $C_{k+1}(y)$ to $C_{k+1}(z)$ that precedes $C_{k+1}(z)$, and assume that $y_1 = r(C_{k+1}(y_1))$. Let $\hat{x}$ be the parent of x_1 in T. Note that $\hat{x} \in C_{k+1}(z)$ and the edge $(x_1, \hat{x})$ is of level k. Similarly, let $\hat{y}$ be the parent of y_1 in T. Note that $\hat{y} \in C_{k+1}(z)$ and the edge $(y_1, \hat{y})$ is of level k. The path $P_{x'y'}$ splits into five disjoint parts: (a) from x' to $r(C_{k+1}(x))$, (b) from $r(C_{k+1}(x))$, to x_1, (c) from x_1 to y_1, (d) from y_1 to $r(C_{k+1}(y))$, (e) from $r(C_{k+1}(y))$ to y'.

The minimum edge on part (a) is stored with entry k of $L(e_x)$. We find the minimum edge on part (b) by a $\min_{C_k(x)}(C_{k+1}(x), C_{k+1}(x_1))$ query. We find

---

[2] The level k always exists, since there exists a level j such that T_j is in universe 0. The tree T_j consists of a single cluster $C_j = C_j(x) = C_j(y)$.

the minimum edges on parts (d) and (e) symmetrically. To find the minimum edge on part (c) we recursively perform $pathmin_{k+1}(\hat{x}, \hat{y}, (x_1, \hat{x}), (y_1, \hat{y}))$. Since $(x_1, \hat{x})$ is of level k, entry $k + 1$ is the next to last entry in $L((x_1, \hat{x}))$ and we can access it in $O(1)$ time. The situation with respect to $(y_1, \hat{y})$ is analogous. We return the edge of smallest weight among the minimum weight edges in each of the five parts.

Case 2: $C_{k+1}(z) = C_{k+1}(x)$ **and** $C_{k+1}(z) \neq C_{k+1}(y)$. Let $C_{k+1}(y_1)$ be the node in $C_k(x)$ on the path from $C_{k+1}(y)$ to $C_{k+1}(z)$ that precedes $C_{k+1}(z)$, and assume that $y_1 = r(C_{k+1}(y_1))$. Let $\hat{y} = p(y_1)$. Here we split $P_{x'y'}$ into three parts: (a) from x' to y_1, (b) from y_1 to $r(C_{k+1}(y))$, (c) from $r(C_{k+1}(y))$ to y'.

We find the minimum edge on parts (b) and (c) as we did in the previous case. We advance one step in $L(e_x)$ to entry $k + 1$, and we find the minimum edge on part (a) by performing $pathmin_{k+1}(x, \hat{y}, e_x, (y_1, \hat{y}))$. As in the previous case entry $k + 1$ in $L((y_1, \hat{y}))$ is next to last and we access it in $O(1)$ time. We return the edge of smallest weight among the minimum weight edges in each of the three parts.

Case 3: $C_{k+1}(z) = C_{k+1}(y)$, **and** $C_{k+1}(z) \neq C_{k+1}(x)$. This case is symmetric to the previous case.

If e_x is null and we perform Case 1 or Case 3, then we compute the minimum on the path from x to $r(C_{k+1}(x))$ by another procedure which we call *min-root*.

The procedure *min-root*(x, k) finds the edge of minimum weight on the path between a vertex x and $r(C_k(x))$ as follows. Let $b = r(C_k(x))$. If $k = \ell$ return the result of the query $\min_{C_k(x)}(x, b)$. If $C_{k+1}(x) = C_{k+1}(b)$ perform *min-root*$(x, k + 1)$. Otherwise, $C_{k+1}(x) \neq C_{k+1}(b)$, and we perform $\min_{C_k(x)}(C_{k+1}(x), C_{k+1}(b))$, and get in $O(1)$ time the edge f_1 of minimum weight on the path between $r(C_{k+1}(x))$ to b. We also perform *min-root*$(x, k + 1)$ to find the edge f_2 of minimum weight on the path between x and $r(C_{k+1}(x))$. We return the edge of smaller weight among f_1 and f_2.

We answer the *pathmin* query by finding the maximum level k such that $C_k(x) = C_k(y)$ and calling $pathmin_k(x, y, null, null)$.

It is clear that *min-root* runs in $O(\ell-k)$ time. Notice that if e_x is not null when we call $pathmin_k(x, y, e_x, e_y)$, then it would not be null also in the recursive call invoked by this *pathmin*. It follows that while performing $pathmin_k(x, y, null, null)$, we call twice to *min-root* with level at least $k + 1$, and other than these two calls it takes $O(1)$ time per level between k and ℓ. So *pathmin* at level k also takes $O(\ell - k)$ time.

5   An $O(n + m\alpha(m, n)^2)$ Structure for Unrooted Trees

We use the recursive decomposition of Gabow [6] as in the previous algorithm together with incremental trees. Here the incremental trees do not need to support the add-root operation. Each tree is partitioned into clusters as before and we keep the notation where $C_j(v)$ is the cluster which contains v in T_j. The tree with its clusters contracted is represented recursively. Each cluster C_k of a tree

T_k is rooted at a certain node C_{k+1} (which is a cluster of level $k+1$). The cluster C_{k+1} in turn is rooted at some cluster C_{k+2} etc. If we unravel this recursion all the way to its bottom we obtain a vertex v of T_ℓ which is the root of the cluster C_k when thinking of it as a subtree of T. We denote this vertex by $r(C_k)$. The cluster C_k as a rooted subtree of T_k is represented by an incremental tree.

Let C_{j+1} be a node of the cluster C_j. Assume C_{j+1} is not the root of C_j and let C'_{j+1} be the parent of C_{j+1} in C_j. Let $e = (v, w)$ be the edge (of level j) such that $e(j)$ connects C_{j+1} to C'_{j+1} in C_j, so $C_{j+1} = C_{j+1}(v)$ and $C'_{j+1} = C_{j+1}(w)$. We define the j-root of C_{j+1} to be the vertex v, and denote it by $t(C_{j+1})$. This is the "root" of C_{j+1} when considering it as a subtree of C_j. Notice that $t(C_{j+1})$ need not be equal to $r(C_{j+1})$. If C_{j+1} is the root of C_j then we define $t(C_{j+1})$ to be $r(C_{j+1})$.

As in Section 3 a node representing the cluster C_j has a pointer to the root of its subtree in T, to the cluster C_{j+1} which is the root of C_j and to the cluster C_{j-1} containing C_j if such a cluster exists. Let $e = (u, v) \in T$ be an edge of level j such that $C_{j+1}(v)$ is the parent of $C_{j+1}(u)$ in the incremental tree $C_j(v)$ $(= C_j(u))$. We store with e two lists $L_e(v)$ and $L_e(u)$. The list $L_e(v)$ is of length exactly $\ell - j + 1$. Entry ℓ of $L_e(v)$ contains e. For level $j \le k < \ell$ entry k of $L_e(v)$ contains the edge f of minimum weight on the path from u to $t(C_{k+1}(v))$ in T. The *weight* of $e(k)$, $w(e(k))$, is equal to the weight of f. If level$(e) = j$ then $e(j)$ is contained in a cluster C_j. The weight $w(e(j))$ is also maintained by the incremental tree representing C_j. Similarly, entry ℓ of $L_e(u)$ contains e, and for level $j \le k < \ell$, entry k contains the edge of minimum weight on the path from v to $t(C_{k+1}(u))$ in T. Notice that since $C_{j+1}(v)$ is the parent of $C_{j+1}(u)$, then $u = t(C_{j+1}(u))$ and e is the value of entry j in $L_e(u)$. Each list is represented as a doubly linked list with pointers to its first and last entry. Since $\sum_{j=1}^{\ell} |T_j| = O(|T|)$ the total space used to store these lists is linear. Figure 1(B) illustrates the data structure, and the weights of the edges in different levels.

Our query algorithm is similar to the query algorithm of Section 4. Let P_{xy} be the path from x to y. We define a recursive procedure $pathmin_k(x, y, e_x, e_y)$ as in Section 4. We first assume that both e_x and e_y exist. Let $e_x = (x', x)$ and let $e_y = (y', y)$.

The procedure $pathmin_k(x, y, e_x, e_y)$ finds the minimum on $P_{x'y'}$ under the assumptions that: (1) $C_k(y) = C_k(x)$, (2) the edge e_x is of level $< k$ (that is $x' \notin C_k(x)$), and we have a pointer to the entry in $L_{e_x}(x)$ associated with level k, and (3) the edge e_y is of level $< k$ (that is $y' \notin C_k(y)$), and we have a pointer to the entry associated with level k in $L_{e_y}(y)$.

The implementation of $pathmin_k(x, y, e_x, e_y)$ is the same as described in Section 4. The main difference of our algorithm here and the algorithm of Section 4 is when e_x or e_y are not available.

Let $d = t(C_{k+1}(x))$. In Section 4 we used the min-root algorithm to find the edge of minimum weight on the path from x to d. Here we cannot use the min-root procedure since $t(C_{k+1}(x))$ may not be the root of $C_{k+1}(x)$ (recall that here each cluster is rooted independently of the higher level clusters containing it).

Instead, if e_x does not exist, we find the edge of minimum weight on the path from x to d as follows. There exists an edge $e' = (d, q)$ of level k, between

$C_{k+1}(x)$ ($= C_{k+1}(d)$) and $C_{k+1}(q)$ in $C_k(x)$, where q in on P_{xy}. We locate the entry in $L_{e'}(d)$ associated with level $k+1$ and recursively perform $pathmin_{k+1}$ $(x, d, null, e')$.[3] If e_y does not exist and we have to find the minimum from y to $t(C_{k+1}(y))$, then we do it similarly.

The complexity of $pathmin_k$ is dominated by the number of recursive calls to $pathmin$. To bound this number observe that: (1) Each call to $pathmin$ in which e_x (e_y) does not exist makes at most a single call to $pathmin$ in which both edges exist and a single call to $pathmin$ in which e_x (e_y) does not exist. (2) A call to $pathmin$ in which both e_x and e_y exist makes at most a single recursive call to $pathmin$ in which e_x and e_y exist.

From the first observation follows that there are $O(\ell - k)$ recursive calls to $pathmin$ in which e_x does not exist, and at most $O(\ell - k)$ recursive calls to $pathmin$ in which e_y does not exist. This together with the second observation imply that the total number of recursive calls initiated by $pathmin_k$ is $O((\ell - k)^2)$.

The implementation of link. Let x be a vertex in a tree T_ℓ^1 and let y be a vertex of T_ℓ^2. The operation $link_\ell(x, y)$ combines T_ℓ^1 and T_ℓ^2 by adding the edge $e = (x, y)$. When combining T_ℓ^1 and T_ℓ^2 we also have to combine $T_{\ell-1}^1$ and $T_{\ell-1}^2$ etc. Therefore the implementation of link is recursive. We define the recursive operation $link_j(C_{j+1}(x), C_{j+1}(y))$ where $C_{j+1}(x)$ is a node in T_j^1 and $C_{j+1}(y)$ is a node in T_j^2. The operation $link_j(C_{j+1}(x), C_{j+1}(y))$ combines T_j^1 and T_j^2 by adding the edge (x, y) to the resulting tree T_j. Let q_1 be the universe of T_j^1 and let q_2 be the universe of T_j^2. To perform $link_j(C_{j+1}(x), C_{j+1}(y))$ we perform the appropriate of the following four cases.

Case 1: $|T_j^1| + |T_j^2| \geq 2A(j, \max\{q_1, q_2\} + 1)$. Create a new tree T_j in universe $\max\{q_1, q_2\} + 1$ containing a single, initially empty, cluster C. Traverse T_j^1 top down and insert all nodes of T_j^1 to C by performing add-leaf operations. Then insert $C_{j+1}(y)$ as a child of $C_{j+1}(x)$ into C by another add-leaf operation which adds $e(j)$ to the new cluster. Finally insert all the nodes of T_j^2 into C, top-down by performing add-leaf operations.

To insert $C_{j+1}(y)$ as a child of $C_{j+1}(x)$ we have to compute the edges of $L_e(x)$ and $L_e(y)$ associated with level j. The weight of the edge associated with level j in $L_e(x)$ is the weight of $e(j)$ in the incremental tree representing the new cluster.

Notice that the edge of level j in $L_e(y)$ is e. We now show how to update the edge of level j of $L_e(x)$. If $j = \ell$, then the edge of level ℓ of $L_e(x)$ is e. Otherwise, if $j < \ell$, we have to find the edge of minimum weight in T on the path from y to $t(C_{j+1}(x))$. Let $b = t(C_{j+1}(x))$. We do that by a $pathmin_{j+1}(x, b, null, null)$ query in T^1. Let f be the edge returned by this query. The edge of level j of $L_e(x)$ is the edge of minimum weight among (x, y) and f.

Each edge $f = (v, w)$ such that $f(j)$ is either in T_j^1 or in T_j^2 becomes an edge of T_j. The level of f becomes j and we discard any element of $L_f(v)$ and $L_f(w)$ of level $< j$. Let $f = (v, w)$ be an edge such that $f(j) \in T_j^2$. We have to update the edges of level j of $L_f(v)$ and $L_f(w)$ since $t(C_{j+1}(v))$ and $t(C_{j+1}(w))$

---

[3] Notice that $pathmin_{k+1}(x, d, null, e')$ actually finds the edge of minimum weight on P_{xq}. The result remains correct since $q \in P_{xy}$.

may have changed in C. Assume $C_{j+1}(v)$ is the parent of $C_{j+1}(w)$ in C. Then clearly $w = t(C_{j+1}(w))$ and therefore the edge of level j of $L_f(w)$ is f. Let $b = t(C_{j+1}(v))$. The edge of level j of $L_f(v)$ should be the edge of minimum weight on the path from w to b in $C_{j+1}(v)$. We find this edge by performing $pathmin_{j+1}(w, b, null, null)$ on T^2. We perform these updates to all edges of T_j^2 while traversing it top-down.

Case 2: $q_1 > q_2$. We traverse the clusters of T_j^2 top down starting from $C_{j+1}(y)$ inserting them one by one into $C_j(x)$ by performing add-leaf operations to $C_j(x)$. We start by inserting $C_{j+1}(y)$ as a child of $C_{j+1}(x)$. The edge connecting these two clusters is $e(j)$. We compute its weight and update $L_e(x)$ and $L_e(y)$ exactly as in Case 1. The partition of T_j^2 into clusters of levels $\leq j$ is discarded. Let $f = (v, w)$ be an edge such that $f(j) \in T_j^2$. The level of f becomes j. We discard any elements of $L_f(v)$ and $L_f(w)$ of levels smaller than j, and update the edge of level j in these lists exactly as in case 1.

Case 3: $q_1 < q_2$. This case is analogous to Case 2.

Case 4: $q_1 = q_2$. Create T_j by adding $e(j)$. Recursively perform $link_{j-1}(C_j(x), C_j(y))$ combining T_{j-1}^1 and T_{j-1}^2. We update the edges of level j of $L_e(x)$ and $L_e(y)$ as in Case 1.

References

1. Alon, N., Schieber, B.: Optimal preprocessing for answering on-line product queries. Technical report Tech. Report 71/87, Tel Aviv University
2. Alstrup, S., Holm, J.: Improved algorithms for finding level ancestors in dynamic trees. In: Welzl, E., Montanari, U., Rolim, J. (eds.) ICALP 2000. LNCS, vol. 1853, pp. 73–84. Springer, Heidelberg (2000)
3. Chazelle, B., Rosenberg, B.: The complexity of computing partial sums off-line. Int. J. Comput. Geometry Appl. 1(1), 33–45 (1991)
4. Fredman, M.L., Willard, D.E.: Trans-dichotomous algorithms for minimum spanning trees and shortest paths. J. Comput. Syst. Sci. 48(3), 533–551 (1994)
5. Gabow, H.N.: A scaling algorithm for weighted matching on general graphs. In: FOCS, pp. 90–100 (1985)
6. Gabow, H.N.: Data structures for weighted matching and nearest common ancestors with linking. In: SODA, pp. 434–443 (1990)
7. Georgiadis, L., Kaplan, H., Shafrir, N., Tarjan, R.E., Werneck, R.F.: Data structures for mergeable trees (2007), http://arxiv.org/abs/0711.1682v1
8. Georgiadis, L., Tarjan, R.E., Werneck, R.F.: Design of data structures for mergeable trees. In: SODA, pp. 394–403 (2006)
9. Kaplan, H., Shafrir, N.: Finding path minima in incremental unrooted trees. Technical report, http://www.cs.tau.ac.il/~haimk/papers/pathmin.pdf
10. La Poutre, J.A.: New techniques for the union-find problem. In: SODA, pp. 54–63 (1990)
11. Tarjan, R.E.: Applications of path compression on balanced trees. J. ACM 26(4), 690–715 (1979)
12. Yao, A.C.: Space-time tradeoff for answering range queries (extended abstract). In: STOC, pp. 128–136 (1982)

Improved Competitive Performance Bounds for CIOQ Switches

Alex Kesselman[1], Kirill Kogan[2], and Michael Segal[3]

[1] Google, Inc.
alx@google.com
[2] Cisco Systems, South Netanya, Israel
and
Communication Systems Engineering Dept., Ben Gurion University, Beer-Sheva,
Israel
kkogan@cisco.com
[3] Communication Systems Engineering Dept., Ben Gurion University, Beer-Sheva,
Israel
segal@cse.bgu.ac.il

Abstract. Combined input and output queued (CIOQ) architectures with a moderate fabric *speedup* $S > 1$ have come to play a major role in the design of high performance switches. In this paper we study CIOQ switches with First-In-First-Out (FIFO) buffers providing Quality of Service (QoS) guarantees. The goal of the switch policy is to maximize the total value of packets sent out of the switch. We analyze the performance of a switch policy by means of competitive analysis, where a uniform performance guarantee is provided for all traffic patterns. Azar and Richter [8] proposed an algorithm β-*PG* (Preemptive Greedy with a preemption factor of β) that is 8-competitive for an arbitrary speedup value when $\beta = 3$. We improve upon their result by showing that this algorithm achieves a competitive ratio of 7.5 and 7.47 for $\beta = 3$ and $\beta = 2.8$, respectively. Basically, we demonstrate that β-*PG* is at most $\frac{\beta^2+2\beta}{\beta-1}$ and at least $\frac{\beta^2-\beta+1}{\beta-1}$-competitive.

1 Introduction

The main tasks of a router are to receive a packet from the input port, to find its destination port using a routing table, to transfer the packet to that output port, and finally to transmit it on the output link. If a burst of packets destined to the same output port arrives, it is impossible to transmit all the packets immediately, and some of them must be buffered inside the switch (or dropped).

A critical aspect of the switch architecture is the placement of buffers. In the output queuing (OQ) architecture, packets arriving from the input lines immediately cross the switching fabric, and join a queue at the switch output port. Thus, the OQ architecture allows one to maximize the throughput, and permits the accurate control of packet latency. However, in order to avoid contention, the internal speed of an OQ switch must be equal to the sum of all the input line

D. Halperin and K. Mehlhorn (Eds.): ESA 2008, LNCS 5193, pp. 577–588, 2008.

rates. The recent developments in networking technology produced a dramatic growth in line rates, and have made the internal speedup requirements of OQ switches difficult to meet. This has in turn generated great interest in the input queuing (IQ) switch architecture, where packets arriving from the input lines are queued at the input ports. The packets are then extracted from the input queues to cross the switching fabric and to be forwarded to the output ports.

It is well-known that the IQ architecture can lead to low throughput, and it does not allow the control of latency through the switch. The main problem of the IQ architecture is head-of-line (HOL) blocking, which occurs when packets at the head of various input queues contend on a specific output port of the switch. To alleviate the problem of HOL blocking, one can maintain at each input a separate queue for each output. This technique is known as virtual output queuing (VOQ).

Another method to get the delay guarantees of an IQ switch closer to that of an OQ switch is to increase the *speedup* S of the switching fabric. A switch is said to have a speedup S, if the switching fabric runs S times faster than each of the input or the output lines. Hence, an OQ switch has a speedup of N (where N is the number of input/output lines), while an IQ switch has a speedup of 1. For values of S between 1 and N, packets need to be buffered at the inputs before switching as well as at the outputs after switching. This architecture is called a combined input and output queued (CIOQ) architecture. CIOQ switches with a moderate speedup S have recently received increasing attention in the literature, see e.g. [11,12].

In the present paper we consider CIOQ switches with First-In-First-Out (FIFO) buffers. We study the case of traffic with packets of variable values where the value of a packet represents its priority. This corresponds to the DiffServ (Differentiated Services) model [9]. The goal of the switch policy is to maximize the total value of the packets sent out of the switch.

Given a CIOQ switch, the switch policy consists of a buffer management policy controlling the usage of the buffers, a scheduling policy controlling the switch fabric, and a transmission policy controlling the output buffers. The buffer management policy decides for any packet that arrives to a buffer, whether to accept or reject it (in the latter case the packet is lost). If preemption is allowed, the buffer management policy can drop from the buffer a packet previously accepted to make room for a new packet. The scheduling policy is responsible for selecting packets to be transferred from the input queues to the output queues. This has to be done in a way that prevents contention, i.e., at any given time at most one packet can be removed from any CIOQ input port, and at most one packet can be added to any CIOQ output port. The transmission policy selects the packet to be sent on the output link.

Since Internet traffic is difficult to model and it does not seem to follow the more traditional Poisson arrival model [23,25], we do not assume any specific traffic model. We rather analyze our policies against arbitrary traffic and provide a uniform throughput guarantee for all traffic patterns, using competitive analysis [24,10]. In competitive analysis, the online policy is compared to the optimal offline policy OPT, which knows the entire input sequence in advance. The competitive ratio of a policy A is the maximum, over all sequences of packet arrivals σ, of the ratio between the value of packets sent by OPT out of σ, and the value of packets sent by A out of σ.

Our results. We consider a CIOQ switch with FIFO buffers of limited capacity. We assume that each packet has an intrinsic value designating its priority. We analyze the β-Preemtive Greedy policy (β-PG) that was shown to be 8-competitive by Azar and Richter [8] for $\beta = 3$. We improve upon their result by establishing that β-PG is 7.47-competitve for $\beta = 2.8$. Basically, we demonstrate that the β-PG policy achieves a competitive ratio of $\frac{\beta^2 + 2\beta}{\beta - 1}$ (for $\beta > 1$). In particular, our result implies that for the value $\beta = 3$ used by Azar and Richter [8] the competitive ration of β-PG is at most 7.5. Our proof technique, unlike that of [8], does not make use of dummy packets. In addition, we show a first lower bound of $\frac{\beta^2 - \beta + 1}{\beta - 1}$ on the performance of β-PG for sufficiently large S. Thus, β-PG is at least 3.5 and 3.36-competitive for $\beta = 3$ and $\beta = 2.8$, respectively.

Related work. A large number of scheduling algorithms have been proposed in the literature for the IQ switch architecture: these are PIM [4], iSLIP [22], Batch [14] to name a few. These algorithms achieve high throughput when the traffic pattern is admissible (uniform), i.e. the aggregate arrival rate to an input or output port is less than 1. However, their performance typically degrades when traffic is non-uniform [21]. Most of the above works on the control of IQ and CIOQ switches assume that there is always enough buffer space to store the packets when and where needed. Thus, all packets arriving to the switch eventually cross it. However, contrary to this setting it is observed empirically in the Internet that packets are routinely dropped in switches. In the present work we address the question of the design of control policies for switches, when buffer space is limited, and thus packet drop may occur.

The problem of throughput maximization in the context of a single buffer has been explored extensively in recent years (see [15] for a good survey). Competitive analysis of preemptive and non-preemptive scheduling policies for shared memory OQ switches was given by Hahne et al. [16] and Kesselman and Mansour[18], respectively. Aiello et al. [1] consider the throughput of various protocols in a setting of a network of OQ switches with limited buffer space. Kesselman et al. [17] study the throughput of local buffer management policies in a system of merge buffers.

Azar and Richter [7] presented a 4-competitive algorithm for a weighted multi-queue switch problem with FIFO buffers. An improved 3-competitive algorithm was given by Azar and Richter [6]. Albers and Schmidt [3] proposed a deterministic 1.89-competitive algorithm for the case of unit-value packets. Azar and Litichevskey [5] derived a 1.58-competitive algorithm for switches with large buffers. Albers and Jacobs [2] gave an experimental study of new and known online packet buffering algorithms.

Kesselman and Rosén [19] study CIOQ switches with FIFO buffers. For the case of packets with unit values, they present a switch policy that is 3-competitive for any speedup. For the case of packets with variable values, they propose two switch policies achieving a competitive ratio of $4S$ and $8\min(n, 2\log\alpha)$, where n is the number of distinct packet values and α is the ratio between the largest and the smallest value. Azar and Richter [8] obtained a 8-competitive algorithm for CIOQ switches with FIFO buffers, which is the first algorithm that achieves a constant competitive ratio for the general case of arbitrary speedup and packet values. Kesselman and Rosén [20] considered the case of CIOQ switches with Priority Queuing (PQ) buffers and proposed a policy that is 6-competitive for any speedup.

Organization. The rest of the paper is organized as follows. The model description appears in Section 2. The switch policy is presented and analyzed in Section 3 and Section 4, respectively. We mention some conclusions in Section 5.

2   Model Description

In this section we describe our model. We consider an $N \times N$ CIOQ switch with a speedup S (see Figure 1). Packets, of equal size, arrive at input ports. Each packet is labeled with the output port on which it has to leave the switch and is placed in the input queue corresponding to its output port. When a packet crosses the switch fabric, it is placed in the output queue and resides here until it is sent on the output link. For a packet p, we denote by $V(p)$ its value.

Each input i maintains for each output j a separate queue $VOQ_{i,j}$ of capacity $BI_{i,j}$ (Virtual Output Queuing) and each output j maintains a queue OQ_j of capacity BO_j.

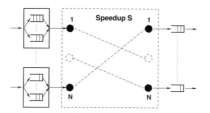

Fig. 1. An example of a CIOQ switch

We divide time into discrete steps, where a step is the time interval between arrivals of two consecutive packets at an input line. During each time step one or more packets can arrive on each input port, and one packet can be forwarded from each output port.

We divide each time step into three phases. The first phase is the *transmission* phase during which a packet from each non-empty output queue can be sent on the output link. The second phase is the *arrival* phase. In the arrival phase one or more packets arrive at each input port. The third phase is the *scheduling* *phase* when packets are transferred from the input buffers to the output buffers. In a switch with a speedup of S, up to S packets can be removed from any input and up to S packets can be added to each output. This is done in (up to) S cycles, where in each cycle we compute a matching between the inputs and the outputs and transfer the packets accordingly. We denote the s-th scheduling cycle $(1 \leq s \leq S)$ at time step t by t_s.[1]

Suppose that the switch is managed by a policy A. By $VOQ_{i,j}^A$ we denote $VOQ_{i,j}$ as managed by A, and by OQ_j^A we denote OQ_j as managed by A. By $X_{i,j}^A(t_s)$ we denote a variable indicating whether A has scheduled a packet from input i to output j in scheduling cycle t_s ($X_{i,j}^A(t_s) = 1$ if some packet has been scheduled from input i to output j and $X_{i,j}^A(t_s) = 0$ otherwise). By $P_{i,j}^A(t_s)$ we denote the packet itself in case $X_{i,j}^A(t_s) = 1$, or a dummy packet with zero value otherwise.

We represent the state of a switch as an $N \times N$ bipartite multi-graph with the set of nodes V_{N_I, N_O} representing the input and the output ports. Each packet p in $VOQ_{i,j}$ creates an edge (i, j) whose weight equals $V(p)$.

The switch has FIFO buffers. That is, packets leave a queue in the order of their arrivals.

The switch policy is composed of three main components, namely, a transmission policy, a buffer management policy and a scheduling policy.

Transmission Policy. The transmission policy at each time step decides which packet is transmitted out of each output buffer.

Buffer Management Policy. The buffer management policy controls the admission of packets into the buffers. More specifically, when a packet arrives to a buffer, the buffer management policy decides whether to *accept* or *reject* it. An accepted packet can be later *preempted* (dropped).

Scheduling Policy. At every scheduling cycle, the scheduling policy first decides which packets are eligible for scheduling. Then it specifies which packets are transferred from the inputs to the outputs. This is done by computing a matching in the bipartite graph representing the switch state and including only the edges corresponding to the eligible packets.

The aim of the switch policy is that of maximizing the total value of packets sent from the output ports. Let σ be a sequence of packets arriving at the inputs of the switch. Let $V^A(\sigma)$ and $V^{OPT}(\sigma)$ be the total value of packets transmitted out of the sequence σ, by an online switch policy A and an optimal offline policy OPT, respectively. The competitive ratio of a switch policy is defined as follows.

Definition 1. *An online switch policy A is said to be c-competitive if for every input sequence of packets σ, $V^{OPT}(\sigma) \leq c \cdot V^A(\sigma) + d$, where d is a constant independent of σ.*

3 β-Preemptive Greedy Switch Policy

In this section we describe the switch policy that was first introduced by Azar and Richter [8]. We treat each virtual input or output queue as a separate buffer

---

[1] With slight abuse of notation we say that $t_0 = (t-1)_S$, $t_{S+1} = (t+1)_1$ and $t = t_1$.

with *independent* buffer management policy. The β-preemptive greedy (β-PG) policy appearing in Figure 2 uses a natural preemptive greedy buffer management policy and a scheduling policy based on maximum weight matching. The value of the parameter β will be determined later. Observe that a packet p is not scheduled to an output buffer if it will be dropped or if it will preempt another packet p' such that $V(p') > V(p)/\beta$. In what follows when we say "first packet", or "last packet", we mean the first or last packet according to FIFO order in the relevant set.

- **Transmission:** Transmit the first packet from each non-empty output queue.
- **Buffer Management of Input and Output Buffers (greedy):** Accept an arriving packet p if there is free space in the buffer. Drop p if the buffer is full and $V(p)$ is less than the minimal value among the packets currently in the buffer. Otherwise, drop from the buffer a packet p' with the minimal value and accept p (we say that p *preempts* p').
- **Scheduling:** For each buffer $VOQ_{i,j}$, consider the first packet in $VOQ_{i,j}$ and denote this value by w. Mark this packet as *eligible*, if OQ_j is not full or if the minimal value among the packets in OQ_j is at most w/β.
  Compute a *maximum weight* matching.

Fig. 2. The β-Preemptive Greedy Switch Policy (β-PG)

4   Analysis

We will show that β-PG achieves a competitive ratio of $\frac{\beta^2+2\beta}{\beta-1}$ for any speedup S assuming that $\beta > 1$. We also derive a lower bound of $\frac{\beta^2-\beta+1}{\beta-1}$ on the performance of β-PG for sufficiently large S. Our analysis proceeds along the lines of the work in [20], which studies Priority Queuing (PQ) buffers. However, extension from PQ to FIFO buffers is technically challenging.

In what follows we fix an input sequence σ. To prove the competitive ratio of β-PG we will assign value to the packets sent by β-PG so that no packet is assigned more than $\frac{\beta^2+2\beta}{\beta-1}$ times its value and then show that the value assigned is indeed at least $V^{OPT}(\sigma)$.

For the analysis, we assume that OPT maintains FIFO order and never preempts packets. Notice that any schedule of OPT can be transformed into a non-preemptive FIFO schedule without affecting its value. The following lemma is due to [19].

Lemma 1. *For any finite input sequence σ, the value of OPT in the model without FIFO restriction equals the value of OPT in the FIFO model.*

The assignment routine presented in Figure 3 specifies how to assign value to the packets sent by β-PG (we will show that it is feasible).

Observe that the assignment routine assigns some value only to packets that are scheduled out of the input queues. Furthermore, if a packet is preempted at

- **Step 1:** Assign to each packet scheduled by β-PG at time t_s its own value.
- Let p' be the packet scheduled by OPT at time t_s from $VOQ_{i,j}^{OPT}$, if any. Let p be the first packet in $VOQ_{i,j}^{PG}$ at time t_s if any or a dummy packet with zero value otherwise.
- **Step 2:** If p is *not eligible* for transmission and either (i) $V(p') \leq V(p)$ or (ii) $V(p') > V(p)$, p' is present in $VOQ_{i,j}^{PG}$ and p' has been previously assigned some value by Step 4, then proceed as follows: Let p'' be the packet that will be sent from OQ_j^{PG} at the same time at which OPT will send p' from OQ_j^{OPT} (we will later show that p'' exists and its value is at least $V(p)/\beta$). If (i), assign the value of p' to p''. If (ii), re-assign to p'' the value that was previously assigned to p' by Step 4.
- **Step 3:** If $V(p') > V(p)$ then proceed as follows:
  - **Sub-Step** 3.1: If p' was scheduled by β-PG prior to time t_s, then assign the value of $V(p')$ to p'.
  - **Sub-Step** 3.2: Else if p' is not present in $VOQ_{i,j}^{PG}$, consider the set of packets with value at least $V(p')$ that are scheduled by β-PG from $VOQ_{i,j}^{PG}$ prior to time t_s. Assign the value of $V(p')$ to a packet in this set that is not in $VOQ_{i,j}^{OPT}$ at the beginning of t_s, and has not previously been assigned a value by either Sub-Step 3.1 or Sub-Step 3.2 (we will later show that such a packet exists).
  - **Sub-Step** 3.3: Else (p' is present in $VOQ_{i,j}^{PG}$), remove the value assigned to p' by Step 4 and assign the value of $V(p')$ to p' (we will later show that the removed value is re-assigned by Step 1).
- **Step 4:** If a packet q preempts a packet q' at an *input* or *output* queue of β-PG, re-assign to q the value that has been previously assigned to q'.

Fig. 3. Assignment Routine – executed at the end of scheduling cycle t_s

an output queue then the total value assigned to it is re-assigned to the packet that preempts it. The following observation follows from the finiteness of the input sequence.

Observation 1. *When the assignment routine finishes, only packets that are eventually sent by β-PG are assigned some value.*

The following claim bounds the total value that can be assigned to a β-PG packet before it leaves a virtual output queue.

Claim. The weight assigned to a *beta-PG* packet before it leaves a virtual output queue is at most its own value.

Proof. Initially, a β-PG packet q' in a virtual output queue can be assigned its own value by Sub-Step 3.3. If q' is later preempted by a packet q, then q is re-assigned the value that was assigned to q by Step 4. Obviously, q is assigned at most its own value as $V(q) > V(q')$. Note that if q will be assigned its own value by Sub-Step 3.3, then the value assigned to q by Step 4 is either re-assigned by the case (ii) of Step 2 or removed by Step 4 and re-assigned by Step 1. The claim follows.

In the next claim we show that when the case (ii) of Step 2 re-assigns the value assigned to a β-PG packet located at a virtual output queue, the value of the first packet in this queue is at least the value that needs to be re-assigned.

Claim. If the case (ii) of Step 2 applies and we re-assign the value assigned to the packet p' in $VOQ_{i,j}^{PG}$ by Step 4, then we have that $V(p)$ is at least the value to be re-assigned, where p is the first packet in $VOQ_{i,j}^{PG}$.

Proof. Consider the time step at which p' has arrived and was accepted by both β-PG and OPT. If the case (ii) of Step 2 applies, p' should have preempted another packet q' in $VOQ_{i,j}^{PG}$ and was re-assigned the value that had been previously assigned to q' by Step 4. Since β-PG always preempts the least valuable packet from a queue, all packets in $VOQ_{i,j}^{PG}$ preceding p', and p in particular, must have a value of at least $V(q')$. Moreover, according to Claim 4, q' had been assigned at most its own value. That establishes the claim.

Now we show that the assignment routine is feasible and establish an upper bound on the value assigned to a single packet.

Lemma 2. *The assignment routine is feasible and no packet is assigned more than $\frac{\beta^2 + 2\beta}{\beta - 1}$ times its own value.*

Proof. First we show that the assignment as defined is feasible. Step 1, Sub-Step 3.1, Sub-Step 3.3 and Step 4 are clearly feasible. We therefore consider Steps 2 and 3.2.

First we consider Step 2. Let p be the first packet in $VOQ_{i,j}^{PG}$. Assume that p is not eligible for transmission. Then, by the definition of β-PG, the minimal value among the packets in OQ_j is at least $V(p)/\beta$ and OQ_j is full. Thus, during the following BO_j time steps, β-PG will send packets with value of at least $V(p)/\beta$ out of OQ_j. The packet p' scheduled by OPT from $VOQ_{i,j}^{OPT}$ at time t_s will be sent from OQ_j^{OPT} in one of these time steps (recall that by our assumption OPT maintains FIFO order). Since $V(p') \leq V(p)$ we have that the packet as specified in Step 2 indeed exists, and its value is at least $V(p)/\beta$.

Next we consider Sub-Step 3.2. First note that if this case applies, then the packet p' (scheduled by OPT from $VOQ_{i,j}^{OPT}$ at time t_s) is dropped by β-PG from $VOQ_{i,j}^{PG}$ at some time $t_q < t_s$.

Let $t_r \geq t_q$ be the last time before t_s at which a packet of value at least $V(p')$ is dropped from $VOQ_{i,j}^{PG}$. Since the greedy buffer management policy is applied to $VOQ_{i,j}^{PG}$, $VOQ_{i,j}^{PG}$ contains $BI_{i,j}$ packets with value of at least $V(p')$ at this time. Let P be the set of these packets. Note that $p' \notin P$ because it has already been dropped by β-PG at this time. We have that in $[t_r, t_s)$, β-PG has actually scheduled all packets from P, since in $[t_r, t_s)$ no packet of value at least $V(p')$ has been dropped, and at time t_s all packets in $VOQ_{i,j}^{PG}$ have value less than $V(p')$. We show that at least one packet from P is *available* for assignment at time t_s, i.e., it has not been assigned any value by Step 3 and is not currently present in $VOQ_{i,j}^{OPT}$. Let x be the number of packets from P that are currently present in $VOQ_{i,j}^{OPT}$. By the construction, these x packets are unavailable. From the rest of the packets in P, a packet is considered available unless it has been already assigned a value by Step 3. Observe that a packet from P can be assigned a value by Step 3 only during $[t_r, t_s)$ (when it is scheduled).

We now argue that OPT has scheduled at most $BI_{i,j} - 1 - x$ packets out of $VOQ_{i,j}$ in $[t_r, t_s)$, and thus P contains at least one available packet. To see this observe that the x packets from P that are present in $VOQ_{i,j}^{OPT}$ at time t_s, were already present in $VOQ_{i,j}^{OPT}$ at time t_r. The same applies to packet p' (recall that $p' \notin P$). Since OPT maintains FIFO order, all the packets that OPT scheduled out of $VOQ_{i,j}^{OPT}$ in $[t_r, t_s)$ where also present in $VOQ_{i,j}^{OPT}$ at time t_r. Therefore, the number of such packets is at most $BI_{i,j} - 1 - x$ (recall that the capacity of $VOQ_{i,j}$ is $BI_{i,j}$). We obtain that at least one packet from P is available for assignment at Sub-Step 3.2 since $|P| = BI_{i,j}$, x packets are unavailable because they are present in $VOQ_{i,j}^{OPT}$ and at most $BI_{i,j} - 1 - x$ packets are unavailable because they have been already assigned a value by Step 3.

Next we demonstrate that no packet is assigned more than $\frac{\beta^2 + 2\beta}{\beta - 1}$ times its own value. Consider a packet p sent by β-PG. Claim 4 implies that p can be assigned at most once its own value by Sub-Step 3.3 and Step 4, before it leaves the virtual output queue. In addition, p is assigned its own value by Step 1.

By the specification of Sub-Step 3.2, this step does not assign any value to p if it is assigned a value by either Sub-Step 3.1 or Sub-Step 3.2. We also show that Sub-Step 3.1 does not assign any value to p if it is assigned a value by either Sub-Step 3.1 or Sub-Step 3.2. That is due to the fact that by the specification of Sub-Step 3.2, if p is assigned a value by Sub-Step 3.2 at time t_s, then p is not in the input buffer of OPT at this time. Therefore, Sub-Step 3.1 cannot be later applied to it. We obtain that p can be assigned at most its own value by Sub-Step 3.1 and Sub-Step 3.2 after it leaves the virtual output queue.

Now let us consider Step 2. Observe that cases (i) and (ii) are mutually exclusive. Furthermore, if case (ii) apples, then by Claim 4 the value of the first packet in the β-PG queue is at least the value that needs to be re-assigned. We obtain that p can be assigned at most β times its own value by Step 2 of the assignment routine.

Finally, we bound the value assigned to a packet by Step 4 in the output queue. Note that this assignment is done only to packets that are actually transmitted out of the switch (i.e. they are not preempted). In addition, p can preempt another packet p' such that $V(p') \leq V(p)/\beta$. We say that p *transitively* preempts a packet p'' if either p directly preempts p'' or p preempts a packet p' that transitively preempts p''. Observe that any preempted packet in an output queue can be assigned at most three times its own value by Step 1, Step 3 and Step 4 due to preemption in the virtual output queue. Hence, the total value that can be assigned to p by Step 4 due to transitively preempted packets in the output queue is bounded by $\frac{3}{\beta - 1}$ times its own value.

We have that in total no packet is assigned more than $3 + \beta + \frac{3}{\beta - 1} = \frac{\beta^2 + 2\beta}{\beta - 1}$ times its own value.

Let $W^{OPT}(\sigma, t_s)$ be the total value of packets *scheduled* out of the input buffers of OPT by time t_s and let $M^{PG}(\sigma, t_s)$ be the total value assigned to packets in β-PG by time t_s, on input sequence σ. We demonstrate that the value gained by OPT is bounded by the value assigned by the assignment routine.

Lemma 3. *For any time t_s the following holds: $W^{OPT}(\sigma, t_s) \leq M^{PG}(\sigma, t_s)$.*

At this point we are ready to prove the main theorem.

Theorem 2. *The competitive ratio of the β-PG policy is at most $\frac{\beta^2 + 2\beta}{\beta - 1}$ for any speedup.*

Proof. Suppose that OPT sends the last packet in σ out of an output buffer at time t^*. By Lemma 3,

$$W^{OPT}(\sigma, t^*) \leq M^{PG}(\sigma, t^*).$$

Lemma 2 and Observation 1 imply that

$$M^{PG}(\sigma, t^*) \leq \frac{\beta^2 + 2\beta}{\beta - 1} V^{PG}(\sigma).$$

It follows that

$$V^{OPT}(\sigma) \leq \frac{\beta^2 + 2\beta}{\beta - 1} V^{PG}(\sigma),$$

since $W^{OPT}(\sigma, t^*) = V^{OPT}(\sigma)$ (recall that by our assumption OPT does not preempt packets).

Finally, we establish a lower bound on the performance of β-PG.

Theorem 3. *The β-PG algorithm is at least $\frac{\beta^2 - \beta + 1}{\beta - 1}$-competitive for sufficiently large S.*

Proof. Consider the following scenario. All packet arrivals are destined to output port 1 with queue OQ_1 of capacity S^2. The capacity of virtual output queues $VOQ_{i,1}$ for $1 \leq i \leq S^2$ is S and the capacity of virtual output queues $VOQ_{j,1}$ for $S^2 + 1 \leq j \leq S^2 + S$ is one.

During time slots $t = 0, \ldots, S^2 - 1$ each of the input ports $1, \ldots, S^2$ receives one packet of value β^i $(i = 0, \ldots, S^2 - 1)$. Note that by definition of β-PG, it will always preempt old packets from OQ_1 and transfer there the newly arrived packets since they are more valuable by a factor of β than the previously arrived packets.

During time slots $t = S^2, \ldots, S^2 + S - 1$ each of the input ports $S^2 + 1, \ldots, S^2 + S$ receives one packet of value $\beta^{S^2} - \epsilon$. The β-PG algorithm will drop all but $2S$ of these packets since no packets in OQ_1 will be preempted and by time $t = S^2 + S - 1$ only $2S$ of these packets can be buffered in virtual output queues $VOQ_{j,1}$ for $S^2 + 1 \leq j \leq S^2 + S$ and in OQ_1.

On the other hand, OPT will first buffer all packets that arrived at input ports $1, \ldots, S^2$ during time slots $t = 0, \ldots, S^2 - 1$ without transferring them to OQ_1. Then OPT will transfer all packets that arrived at input ports $S^2 + 1, \ldots, S^2 + S$ to OQ_1 and send them on the output link. Having done with these packets, OPT will deliver all packets buffered at input ports $1, \ldots, S^2$. In this way, the value obtained by OPT is $V_{OPT} = S^2(\beta^{S^2 - 1} - 1)/(\beta - 1) + S^2(\beta^{S^2} - \epsilon)$. At the same time, the value obtained by β-PG is $V_{PG} = (\beta^{S^2-2} - 1)/(\beta - 1) + S^2\beta^{S^2-1} + 2S(\beta^{S^2} - \epsilon)$.

For sufficiently large S, which is a function of N, and a constant value of β, V_{PG} is dominated by $S^2\beta^{S^2-1}$. Therefore, V_{OPT}/V_{PG} tends to $1/(\beta - 1) + \beta$.

5   Conclusions

A major problem addressed today in networking research is the need for a fast switch architecture supporting guaranteed QoS. In this paper we study CIOQ switches with FIFO queues. We consider switch policies that maximize the switch throughput for any traffic pattern and use competitive analysis to evaluate their performance. Our main results are an improved upper bound and the first lower bound on the competitive ratio of the switch policy proposed by Azar and Richter [8]. An interesting future research direction is to close the gap between the upper and lower bounds, which still remains rather substantial.

References

1. Aiello, W., Kushilevitz, E., Ostrovsky, R., Rosén, A.: Dynamic Routing on Networks with Fixed-Size Buffers. In: Proceedings of SODA 2003, pp. 771–780 (2003)
2. Albers, S., Jacobs, T.: An experimental study of new and known online packet buffering algorithms. In: Arge, L., Hoffmann, M., Welzl, E. (eds.) ESA 2007. LNCS, vol. 4698, pp. 63–74. Springer, Heidelberg (2007)
3. Albers, S., Schmidt, M.: 'On the Performance of Greedy Algorithms in Packet Buffering. SIAM Journal on Computing 35(2), 278–304 (2005)
4. Anderson, T., Owicki, S., Saxe, J., Thacker, C.: High speed switch scheduling for local area networks. In: ACM Trans. on Computer Systems, pp. 319–352 (November 1993)
5. Azar, Y., Litichevskey, M.: Maximizing throughput in multi-queue switches. Algorithmica 45(1), 69–90 (2006)
6. Azar, Y., Richter, Y.: The zero-one principle for switching networks. In: Proceedings of STOC 2004, pp. 64–71 (2004)
7. Azar, Y., Richter, Y.: Management of Multi-Queue Switches in QoS Networks. Algorithmica 43(1-2), 81–96 (2005)
8. Azar, Y., Richter, Y.: An improved algorithm for CIOQ switches. ACM Transactions on Algorithms 2(2), 282–295 (2006)
9. Black, D., Blake, S., Carlson, M., Davies, E., Wang, Z., Weiss, W.: An Architecture for Differentiated Services. In: Internet RFC , vol. 2475 (1998)
10. Borodin, A., El-Yaniv, R.: Online Computation and Competitive Analysis. Cambridge University Press, Cambridge (1998)
11. Chuang, S.T., Goel, A., McKeown, N., Prabhakar, B.: Matching Output Queueing with a Combined Input Output Queued Switch. IEEE Journal on Selected Areas in Communications 17, 1030–1039 (1999)
12. Dai, J.G., Prabhakar, B.: The Throughput of Data Switches with and without Speedup. In: Proceedings of INFOCOM 2000, pp. 556–564 (2000)
13. Datta, S., Sitaraman, R.K.: The Performance of Simple Routing Algorithms That Drop Packets. In: Proceedings of SPAA 1997, pp. 159–169 (1997)

14. Dolev, S., Kesselman, A.: Bounded Latency Scheduling Scheme for ATM Cells. Journal of Computer Networks 32(3), 325–331 (2000)
15. Epstein, L., Van Stee, R.: SIGACT news online algorithms. Chrobak, M. (ed.), vol. 35(3), pp. 58–66 (2004)
16. Hahne, E.L., Kesselman, A., Mansour, Y.: Competitive Buffer Management for Shared-Memory Switches. In: Proceedings of SPAA 2001, pp. 53–58 (2001)
17. Kesselmanm, A., Lotker, Z., Mansour, Y., Patt-Shamir, B.: Buffer Overflows of Merging Streams. In: Di Battista, G., Zwick, U. (eds.) ESA 2003. LNCS, vol. 2832, pp. 349–360. Springer, Heidelberg (2003)
18. Kesselman, A., Mansour, Y.: Harmonic Buffer Management Policy for Shared Memory Switches. Theoretical Computer Science, Special Issue on Online Algorithms. In: Memoriam: Steve Seiden, vol. 324, pp. 161-182 (2004)
19. Kesselman, A., Rosén, A.: Scheduling Policies for CIOQ Switches. Journal of Algorithms 60(1), 60–83 (2006)
20. Kesselman, A., Rosén, A.: Controlling CIOQ Switches with Priority Queuing and in Multistage Interconnection Networks. Journal of Interconnection Networks (to appear)
21. Marsan, M.A., Bianco, A., Filippi, E., Giaccone, P., Leonardi, E., Neri, F.: A Comparison of Input Queuing Cell Switch Architectures. In: Proceedings of 3rd International Workshop on Broadband Switching Systems, Kingston, Canada (June 1999)
22. McKeown, N.: Scheduling Algorithms for Input-Queued Cell Switches. Ph. D. Thesis, University of California at Berkeley (1995)
23. Paxson, V., Floyd, S.: Wide Area Traffic: The Failure of Poisson Modeling. IEEE/ACM Transactions on Networking 3, 226–244 (1995)
24. Sleator, D., Tarjan, R.: Amortized Efficiency of List Update and Paging Rules. CACM 28, 202–208 (1985)
25. Veres, A., Boda, M.: The Chaotic Nature of TCP Congestion Control. In: Proceedings of INFOCOM 2000, pp. 1715–1723 (March 2000)

Two-Stage Robust Network Design with Exponential Scenarios

Rohit Khandekar[1], Guy Kortsarz[2,*], Vahab Mirrokni[3,**],
and Mohammad R. Salavatipour[4,***]

[1] IBM T.J.Watson research center
rkhandekar@gmail.com
[2] Department of Computer Science, Rutgers University-Camden. Currently visiting IBM
Research at Yorktown Heights
guyk@crab.rutgers.edu
[3] Google Research, New York, NY, USA
mirrokni@theory.csail.mit.edu
[4] Dept. of Computing Science, University of Alberta, Edmonton, Alberta T6G 2E8, Canada
mreza@cs.ualberta.ca

Abstract. We study two-stage *robust* variants of combinatorial optimization problems like Steiner tree, Steiner forest, and uncapacitated facility location. The robust optimization problems, previously studied by Dhamdhere et al. [1], Golovin et al. [6], and Feige et al. [4], are two-stage planning problems in which the requirements are revealed after some decisions are taken in stage one. One has to then complete the solution, at a higher cost, to meet the given requirements. In the robust Steiner tree problem, for example, one buys some edges in stage one after which some terminals are revealed. In the second stage, one has to buy more edges, at a higher cost, to complete the stage one solution to build a Steiner tree on these terminals. The objective is to minimize the total cost under the worst-case scenario. In this paper, we focus on the case of *exponentially many* scenarios given implicitly. A scenario consists of any subset of k terminals (for Steiner tree), or any subset of k terminal-pairs (for Steiner forest), or any subset of k clients (for facility location). We present the first constant-factor approximation algorithms for the robust Steiner tree and robust uncapacitated facility location problems. For the robust Steiner forest problem with uniform inflation, we present an $O(\log n)$-approximation and show that the problem with two inflation factors is impossible to approximate within $O(\log^{1/2-\epsilon} n)$ factor, for any constant $\epsilon > 0$, unless NP has randomized quasi-polynomial time algorithms. Finally, we show APX-hardness of the robust min-cut problem (even with singleton-set scenarios), resolving an open question by [1] and [6].

1 Introduction

In a classical optimization problem, we are usually given a system with some known parameters and constraints and the goal is to find a feasible solution of minimum cost

* Partially supported by NSF Award Grant number 072887.
** Part of this work was done when the author was at Microsoft Research.
*** Supported by NSERC and an Alberta Ingenuity New Faculty award.

D. Halperin and K. Mehlhorn (Eds.): ESA 2008, LNCS 5193, pp. 589–600, 2008.

(or maximum profit) with respect to the constraints. These parameters and constraints, which heavily influence the optimum solution, are assumed to be precisely known. However, in reality, often it is very costly (or maybe impossible) to have an accurate picture about the values of the parameters or even the constraints of the optimization problem at hand at the time of planning. Two of the common approaches studied in the literature to address this uncertainty about future are referred to as *robust optimization* and *stochastic optimization*.

Robust and Stochastic optimization. Robust optimization has been studied in both decision theory [10] and Mathematical Programming [2] and deals with the uncertainty in data. In a typical data-robust model, we have a finite set of scenarios that can materialize and each scenario contains one possible set of data values. The goal is to find a solution that is good with respect to all or most scenarios. One example in this category is min-max regret, in which the goal is to minimize the maximum regret over all possible scenarios, where the regret of a scenario is defined as the difference between the cost of the solution in that scenario with respect to optimal solution for that scenario.

In Stochastic optimization, we are provided with a probability distribution on the possible scenarios and the goal is then to find a solution that minimizes the expected cost over this distribution. This approach is useful if we have a good idea about the probability distribution (which may be a strong requirement), and we have a repeated decision making framework. One particular version of stochastic optimization, that has attracted much attention in the last decade, is two-stage (or multi-stage) stochastic optimization, where the solution is built in two stages: in the first stage we have to decide to build a partial solution based on the probability distribution of possible scenarios. In stage two, once the actual scenario is revealed, we have to complete our partial solution to a feasible solution for the given scenario. There has been considerable amount of research focused on two-stage (or multi-stage) stochastic version of classical optimization problems such as set-cover, Steiner tree, vertex cover, facility location, cut problems, and other network design problems [11,13,7,8] and efficient approximation algorithms have been developed for many of these problem. In some cases, the set of possible scenarios and the corresponding probabilities are given explicitly [11,8], and some papers study a more general model in which the sets of possible scenarios are given implicitly as the product of a set of independent trials, or by an oracle [1,7,9,13].

Demand-robust optimization. More recently, a new notion of robustness has been introduced by Dhamdhere et al. [1] which can be viewed as the worst-case analogue of the (two-stage) stochastic optimization problem. This model, called *demand-robust optimization* (and we simply call robust optimization in the rest of the paper), deals with both uncertainty in data as well as constraints of the problem. In a two-stage robust optimization problem, similar to a two-stage stochastic optimization, we are given a set of possible scenarios (which can be explicit or implicit) and the goal is to compute a solution in two stages while minimizing the maximum cost over all possible scenarios. The major difference of this model w.r.t. data-robust model is that each possible scenario might have a different set of constraints to be satisfied. For example, in the robust Steiner tree problem, we are given a graph $G = (V, E)$ with a cost function $c : E \to \mathbb{R}^+$ on the edges. In the second stage one of m possible scenarios materializes; scenario i consists of a set $S_i \subseteq V$ of terminals that need to be connected to each other. We also have an inflation factor λ_i for edge costs. Each edge e costs c_e in the first stage and $\lambda_i \cdot c_e$ in the second stage if scenario i materializes. Our goal is to select a subset of edges $E_1 \subseteq E$ in the first stage, and a set $E_2(i) \subseteq E$ in the second stage if scenario i is revealed, so that $E_1 \cup E_2(i)$ is a feasible solution for the Steiner tree problem with terminal set S_i; the overall cost paid in scenario i is $c(E_1) + \lambda_i \cdot c(E_2(i))$. The objective function is to minimize this cost over all possible scenarios, i.e., to minimize $c(E_1) + \max_i \lambda_i \cdot c(E_2(i))$. Since in this model of robustness, each scenario has a different requirement, it allows one to handle uncertainty in the set of constraints. It also provides a worst-case guarantee unlike only the expected-cost guarantee as in the two-stage stochastic optimization model. In a very recent work [4] authors consider a more general model of (two-stage) robust optimization in which scenarios are given implicitly, and therefore, one can have an exponentially large set of possible scenarios.

1.1   Previous Work

We are aware of only three other papers [1,6,4] which have studied (demand) robust optimization. In [1,6], authors consider the robust problems with polynomially-many explicitly given scenarios. They present constant factor approximation algorithms for robust versions of Steiner tree, vertex cover, and Facility location problems. They also give polylogarithmic approximation for robust min-cut and multi-cut. In the problem of robust min-cut, we are given a edge-weighted graph $G = (V, E)$, a source $s \in V$, and inflation factor $\lambda_i(e)$; scenario i consist of a terminal $t_i \in V$. The goal is to find a subset $E_1 \subseteq E$ for stage one and $E_2(i) \subseteq E$ for stage two (if scenario i arrives) so that $E_1 \cup E_2(i)$ is a s, t_i-cut. In [1], the authors present an $O(\log m)$-approximation where m is the number of scenarios. This was improved to a $(1 + \sqrt{2})$-approximation in [6]. In the robust multi-cut, each scenario consists of a set of pairs of nodes that form a multi-cut problem. For this problem [1] present an $O(\log rm \cdot \log \log rm)$ where m is the number of scenarios and r is the maximum number of pairs in any scenario.

Feige et al. [4] consider covering problems (such as set cover) where the set of possible scenarios is given implicitly, and therefore can be exponentially large. For example, in the robust set cover problem, we are given a universe of elements $U = \{e_1, \ldots, e_m\}$ and a collection of sets $\mathcal{S} = \{S_1, \ldots, S_m\}$, where $S_i \subseteq U$ and has cost $c(S_i)$, an inflation factor λ, and an integer k. Each scenario is a subset $U' \subset U$ of size k that needs to be covered. We have to purchase a collection of sets $\mathcal{S}_1 \subseteq \mathcal{S}$ in stage one. Once a set U' of elements is given in stage two, we have to purchase some (possibly none) other sets $\mathcal{S}_2(U') \subset \mathcal{S}$ where the cost of each set now is inflated by λ, so that $\mathcal{S}_1 \cup \mathcal{S}_2(U')$ is a set cover for the given set U'. The goal is to minimize the maximum total cost over all possible scenarios. Using an LP rounding method, they give a general framework for designing approximation algorithms for a class of robust covering problems using competitive algorithms for online variants of the problems. However, this framework does not apply to robust network design problems like robust Steiner tree, and gives logarithmic approximation for robust uncapacitated metric facility location problem.

1.2   Our Results

The model we study in this paper is the (demand) robust optimization model with (possibly) implicit sets of scenarios (which can be exponentially many). We study Steiner tree, Steiner forest, uncapacitated facility location, and min-cut problems under this model and present some approximation algorithms and hardness results.

Specifically, we provide the first constant factor approximation algorithms for the (exponential scenarios) robust Steiner tree and robust facility location problems. Our algorithms are combinatorial in nature and are based on nice structural properties of the stage one solution of a near-optimum algorithm.

Theorem 1. *There exists a polynomial-time 5.55-approximation algorithm for two-stage robust Steiner tree problem with a uniform inflation factor. Here a scenario consists of any k terminals out of given terminals.*

Theorem 2. *There exists a polynomial-time 10-approximation algorithm for robust uncapacitated facility location problem in which the inflation factor may depend on the facility. Here a scenario consists of any k clients (perhaps co-located) out of given clients.*

We then present a logarithmic approximation for robust Steiner forest problem. This algorithm first approximates the given (shortest-path) metric by a tree metric (thereby, losing a logarithmic factor) and solves the problem on trees within a constant factor. For the problem on trees, we first solve a standard LP relaxation using a dynamic-programming based separation oracle and then round it to a near-optimum integral solution.

Theorem 3. *There exists a polynomial-time $O(\log n)$-approximation algorithm for two-stage robust Steiner forest problem on n-vertex graph with a uniform inflation factor. Here a scenario consists of any k terminal-pairs out of given terminal-pairs.*

We complement this result by showing that the robust Steiner forest problem with two inflation factors is impossible to approximate within a factor of $O(\log^{\frac{1}{2}-\epsilon} n)$, for any constant $\epsilon > 0$, unless NP has randomized quasi-polynomial time algorithms. We emphasize that our $O(\log n)$-approximation algorithm of Theorem 3 holds for exponentially many scenarios (i.e., k source-sink pairs need to be connected in stage 2), and our hardness result holds for even polynomially many scenarios, in which we have to connect only *one source-sink pair* in the second stage. However in the hardness result, we allow two possible values for the inflation factors on the edge-costs.

Theorem 4. *For any constant $\epsilon > 0$, there is no $O(\log^{\frac{1}{2}-\epsilon} n)$-approximation for robust Steiner forest in which only one pair arrives in stage two, we have only two (distinct) edge costs and two (distinct) inflation factors, unless NP has randomized quasi-polynomial time algorithms.*

Finally, we resolve an open question posed by Dhamdhere et al. [1] and Golovin et al. [6] about the hardness of the two-stage robust min-cut problem by proving the following theorem.

Theorem 5. *The two-stage robust min-cut problem is APX-hard even with a uniform inflation factor and which consists of a single source and three sinks.*

Organization. The remainder of the paper is organized as follows. In the next section, we present our 5.55-approximation algorithm for robust Steiner tree and then the $O(\log n)$-approximation for Steiner forest. Finally we present the proof of Theorem 5. Due to space limit, we postpone the proofs of Theorems 2 and 4 to the full version of our paper.

2   A Constant Approximation for Robust Steiner Tree Problem

In this section we prove Theorem 1. Recall that the input to the Steiner tree problem is an undirected graph $G = (V, E)$, a cost function $c : E \to \mathbb{R}^+$, and a subset $T \subseteq V$ called "terminals". The objective is to find a connected subgraph H that includes all the terminals T and has minimum cost $c(H) := \sum_{e \in H} c_e$.

In the robust version of the Steiner tree problem, the input also contains an integer k and a real number $\lambda \geq 1$. There are two stages. In the first stage the algorithm has to identify a subset $E_1 \subseteq E$ of edges to buy. In the second stage, the cost of each edge in $E \setminus E_1$ increases by a factor of λ and a subset $T' \subseteq T$ of at most k terminals is revealed. We refer to T' as a "scenario". The algorithm, in the second stage, has to augment the solution E_1 by buying edges $E_2(T')$ so that the resulting graph $E_1 \cup E_2(T')$ includes a Steiner tree on terminals T'. The choice of edges $E_2(T')$ is allowed to depend on the subset T'. The overall cost of this solution is thus $\sum_{e \in E_1} c_e + \lambda \cdot \sum_{e \in E_2(T')} c_e$. The objective is to minimize the maximum overall cost over all scenarios, i.e., to minimize

$$\sum_{e \in E_1} c_e + \max_{T' \subseteq T, |T'| \leq k} \lambda \cdot \sum_{e \in E_2(T')} c_e.$$

The edge-costs c_e induce a shortest-path metric on the vertices V: for any two vertices $u, v \in V$, we use $d_G(u, v)$ to denote the length of the shortest path between u and v, under costs c_e in graph G.

2.1   The Algorithm

Let E_1^* and $E_2^*(T')$ be the set of edges the optimum buys in the first stage and the second stage for scenario T' respectively. Let $\text{OPT} = \text{OPT}_1 + \lambda \cdot \text{OPT}_2$ be the overall cost of the optimum, where $\text{OPT}_1 = \sum_{e \in E_1^*} c_e$ is its cost in the first stage and $\text{OPT}_2 = \max_{T' \subseteq T, |T'| \leq k} \sum_{e \in E_2^*(T')} c_e$ is the maximum cost in the second stage divided by λ.

First stage. Our algorithm, in the first stage, guesses (an upper bound on) the value of OPT_2.[1] It then computes a subset of terminals $\mathcal{C} = \{c_1, c_2, \ldots, c_p\} \subseteq T$ called "centers" and an assignment $\pi : T \to \mathcal{C}$ that satisfy:

---

[1] The algorithm in fact tries all guesses of OPT_2 that are powers of $(1 + \epsilon)$, for a small constant $\epsilon > 0$, and takes the cheapest solution for any of these guesses. We also point out that we can, in polynomial time, estimate the cost of our solution for a given guess on OPT_2. That is, in polynomial-time, we can find a scenario that maximizes the cost of the solution (or its upper bound proved). To simplify the presentation, we assume that the guess on OPT_2 is exact.

- The centers are far apart: $d_G(c_i, c_j) > \frac{r \cdot OPT_2}{k}$ for all $i \neq j$, and
- Each terminal is close to its assigned center: $d_G(t, \pi(t)) \leq \frac{r \cdot OPT_2}{k}$ for all $t \in T$,

where $r > 1$ is a constant to be determined later. Such a clustering can be computed as follows. Pick any terminal and name it c_1. Assign all terminals within a distance of $\frac{r \cdot OPT_2}{k}$ from c_1 to c_1 and remove these terminals. Pick any one of the remaining terminals and name it c_2, and so on.

The algorithm then computes an approximate minimum-cost Steiner tree $\mathcal{T}$ in G on the centers $\mathcal{C}$ under the costs c_e. Currently, the best known polynomial-time algorithm for the Steiner tree problem is γ-approximate, where $\gamma < 1.55$ [12]. The algorithm buys the edges in the Steiner tree in the first stage.

Second stage. In the second stage, a subset T' of at most k terminals is revealed. The algorithm, in the second stage, buys the shortest path from each terminal $t \in T'$ to its assigned center $\pi(t)$. It is easy to see that the algorithm computes a feasible solution to the problem.

2.2   The Analysis

We first introduce the notion of a "ball" of certain radius around a vertex in a graph. Consider the graph $G = (V, E)$ with edge-costs c_e. We think of each edge e as a continuous interval of length c_e. For a vertex v and a radius $R > 0$, let $B_G(v, R)$ denote, intuitively speaking, the "moat" of radius R around v. More precisely, $B(v, R)$ contains

- all the vertices u such that $d_G(u, v) \leq R$,
- all edges $e = (u, w)$ such that $d_G(u, v) \leq R$ and $d_G(w, v) \leq R$, and
- for the edges $e = (u, w)$ such that $d_G(u, v) \leq R$ and $d_G(w, v) > R$, the sub-interval of edge e of length $R - d_G(u, v)$ adjacent to vertex u.

Note that since $d_G(c_i, c_j) > \frac{r \cdot OPT_2}{k}$ for any two distinct centers in $\mathcal{C}$, the balls $B_G(c_i, \frac{r \cdot OPT_2}{2k})$ and $B_G(c_j, \frac{r \cdot OPT_2}{2k})$ are disjoint. It is easy to see that the algorithm pays at most $\lambda \cdot r \cdot OPT_2$ in the second stage. This holds since the distance of any terminal to its assigned center is at most $\frac{r \cdot OPT_2}{k}$. Since at most k terminals need to be connected to their centers, the total cost of these connections is at most $\lambda \cdot k \cdot \frac{r \cdot OPT_2}{k}$. We now bound the cost of the algorithm in stage one using the following lemma.

Lemma 1. *Assuming $r > 4$, there exists a Steiner tree on centers $\mathcal{C}$ in G that has cost at most $\frac{r}{r-4} \cdot OPT_1 + OPT_2$.*

Proof. Recall that E_1^* is the set of edges optimum buys in stage one and $OPT_1 = \sum_{e \in E_1^*} c_e$. Let H be a graph obtained from G by shrinking the edges in E_1^*. We now perform another clustering of the centers $\mathcal{C}$ in the shortest-path metric on $\mathcal{C}$ induced by the graph H. For centers $c_i, c_j \in \mathcal{C}$, let $d_H(c_i, c_j)$ denote the shortest-path length under lengths c_e in H. We identify a subset of centers $\mathcal{L} = \{l_1, l_2, \ldots, l_t\}$ called "leaders" and a mapping $\phi : \mathcal{C} \to \mathcal{L}$ such that

- The leaders are far apart: $d_H(l_i, l_j) > 2OPT_2/k$ for all $i \neq j$, and
- Each center is close to its mapped leader: $d_H(c, \phi(c)) \leq 2OPT_2/k$ for all centers $c \in \mathcal{C}$.

Such a clustering can be computed as follows. Pick any center and name it l_1. For all centers $c \in \mathcal{C}$ with $d_H(c, l_1) \le 2\text{OPT}_2/k$, define $\phi(c) = l_1$. Remove all such centers from $\mathcal{C}$ and repeat.

Analogous to $B_G(v, R)$, we use $B_H(v, R)$ to denote the ball of radius R centered at v in the graph H with length c_e for $e \in H$. Note that the balls of radii $\frac{\text{OPT}_2}{k}$ around the leaders in $\mathcal{L}$ are disjoint in H.

Claim. The following inequality holds: $|\mathcal{L}| \le k$.

Proof. Assume on the contrary that $|\mathcal{L}| > k$ and let $T' \subseteq \mathcal{L}$ be any subset of size $k + 1$. Consider the scenario T'. Since even after shrinking the edges in E_1^* that optimum bought in the first stage, the balls of radii $\frac{\text{OPT}_2}{k}$ centered at the centers in T' in the graph H are disjoint. Therefore the minimum Steiner tree on T' in H has cost more than OPT_2. This is a contradiction since the optimum pays at most $\lambda \cdot \text{OPT}_2$ in the second phase to connect all the centers in T' after shrinking the edges in E_1^*. Thus the claim holds.

Since $|\mathcal{L}| \le k$, we now consider scenario $\mathcal{L}$. There exists a Steiner tree $E_{\mathcal{L}}^*$ on $\mathcal{L}$ in H with cost at most OPT_2. Thus $E_1^* \cup E_{\mathcal{L}}^*$ has cost at most $\text{OPT}_1 + \text{OPT}_2$ and contains a Steiner tree on $\mathcal{L}$ in G. We now show how to extend this into a subgraph with low cost and which contains a Steiner tree on $\mathcal{C}$ in G.

Now recall that the balls of radii $\frac{r \cdot \text{OPT}_2}{2k}$ around the centers $\mathcal{C}$ are disjoint in G. Note however that $d_H(c, \phi(c)) \le \frac{2\text{OPT}_2}{k}$ for all centers $c \in \mathcal{C}$. Thus at least $\frac{r \cdot \text{OPT}_2}{2k} - \frac{2\text{OPT}_2}{k} = \left(\frac{r}{2} - 2\right) \cdot \frac{\text{OPT}_2}{k}$ cost of E_1^* must lie inside the ball of radius $\frac{r \cdot \text{OPT}_2}{2k}$ around each center $c \in \mathcal{C}$. We can thus extend the subgraph $E_1^* \cup E_{\mathcal{L}}^*$ by adding shortest paths from each c to $\phi(c)$ in H and charge this additional cost to the contribution of E_1^* in the respective balls around centers $c \in \mathcal{C}$. The resulting subgraph clearly contains a Steiner tree on $\mathcal{C}$ in G. The overall cost of this subgraph is thus at most $\text{OPT}_1 + \text{OPT}_2 + \frac{2}{\frac{r}{2}-2} \cdot \text{OPT}_1 = \frac{r}{r-4} \cdot \text{OPT}_1 + \text{OPT}_2$. We remind the reader thet OPT_2 is the cost of computing a Steiner tree on the leaders. Hence the proof.

Since we use a γ-approximation algorithm to compute a Steiner tree in stage one, the overall cost of stage one is at most $\frac{\gamma \cdot r}{r-4} \cdot \text{OPT}_1 + \gamma \cdot \text{OPT}_2$. Combining this with the second stage cost, the overall cost of our solution is:

$$\frac{\gamma \cdot r}{r - 4} \cdot \text{OPT}_1 + (\gamma + \lambda r) \cdot \text{OPT}_2. \qquad (1)$$

A trivial strategy for solving the robust Steiner tree is to select nothing in stage 1 and make all the selections in stage 2. Given that every edge is inflated by λ and we use a γ-approximation for Steiner tree, this strategy will have an approximation factor of $\lambda \cdot \gamma$. Using the best known approximation algorithm for Steiner tree [12], which has approximation 1.55, we get a 1.55λ-approximation. For values of $\lambda \le 3.51$ we use this trivial strategy which gives an approximation factor of 5.45. For values of $\lambda > 3.51$ we use the above algorithm with parameter r defined below.

Let $r = r^*$ to be the solution of: $\frac{\gamma \cdot r}{r-4} = \frac{\gamma}{\lambda} + r$. Then the two factors in front of OPT_1 and OPT_2 in the ratio of our algorithm calculated in Equation (1) become equal at

$r = r^* = \frac{\gamma\lambda - \gamma + 4\lambda + \sqrt{\gamma^2\lambda^2 - 2\gamma^2\lambda + 8\gamma\lambda^2 + \gamma^2 + 8\gamma\lambda + 16\lambda^2}}{2\lambda}$. Therefore, for $r = r^*$ and with $\gamma = 1.55$, the ratio of our algorithm becomes: $\frac{5.55\lambda - 1.55 + \sqrt{30.8025\lambda^2 + 7.595\lambda + 2.4025}}{2\lambda}$. It can be verified that this expression is upper bounded by 5.55 (it has a limit of 5.55). Thus, for values of $\lambda > 3.51$, by choosing $r = r^*$, the ratio of our algorithm presented will be at most 5.55 and for smaller values of λ we use the trivial strategy which has ratio at most 5.55 as well. This completes the proof of Theorem 1.

3 A Logarithmic Approximation for Robust Steiner Forest Problem

In this section, we prove Theorem 3. The input to the Steiner forest problem is an undirected graph $G = (V, E)$ with non-negative edge-costs c_e. We are also given a set of terminal-pairs $T \subseteq V \times V$. Similar to the robust Steiner tree problem, the input also has an integer k and a real number $\lambda \geq 1$. There are two stages. In the first stage the algorithm has to identify a subset $E_1 \subseteq E$ of edges to buy. In the second stage, the cost of each edge in $E \setminus E_1$ increases by a factor of λ and a subset $T' \subseteq T$ of at most k terminal-pairs is revealed. We refer to T' as a "scenario". The algorithm, in the second stage, has to augment the solution E_1 by buying edges $E_2(T')$ so that the resulting graph $E_1 \cup E_2(T')$ includes a Steiner forest on terminal-pairs T', i.e., $E_1 \cup E_2(T')$ contains a path between each terminal-pair in T'. The objective is to minimize the maximum overall cost over all scenarios, i.e., to minimize $\sum_{e \in E_1} c_e + \max_{T' \subseteq T, |T'| \leq k} \lambda \cdot \sum_{e \in E_2(T')} c_e$.

3.1 Reduction to the Tree Metric

We use the standard technique of reducing the problem to the tree metric while incurring a logarithmic approximation. More formally, let $d_G(u, v)$ denote the shortest-path distance between vertices u and v in G under the edge-costs c_e. We use the following theorem of Fakcharoenphol et al. [3].

Lemma 2 (Fakcharoenphol et al. [3]). *Any metric $d(\cdot, \cdot)$ over n points V can be $O(\log n)$-probabilistically approximated by metrics defined by hierarchically well-separated trees. That is, there exists a distribution on tree metrics d_T on V such that*

- $d_T(u, v) \geq d(u, v)$ *for all $u, v \in V$ and all T, and*
- $E_T[d_T(u, v)] \leq O(\log n) \cdot d(u, v)$ *for all $u, v \in V$.*

In the remainder of the section, we obtain a constant-approximation for the robust Steiner forest problem on a metric d_T given by a tree T with edge-costs c_e, i.e., in which $d_T(u, v)$ denotes the length of the unique path between u and v in T.

For a scenario $T' \subseteq T$ of at most k terminal pairs, let $E(T')$ denote the union of the unique paths between the terminal-pairs in T'. We now consider the following integer linear programming formulation of our problem. Let $x_e \in \{0, 1\}$ denote an integer variable that takes value 1 if edge e is picked in stage one, and 0 otherwise. Note that any edge $e \in E(T')$ is picked in stage two for scenario T' if and only if $x_e = 0$. Thus the stage two cost for scenario T' is $\lambda \cdot \sum_{e \in E(T')} c_e \cdot (1 - x_e)$. It is now easy to see that the following integer program is identical to our problem.

$$
\begin{aligned}
\min \quad & \sum_e c_e \cdot x_e + \lambda \cdot C_2 \\
\text{s.t.} \quad & \sum_{e \in E(T')} c_e \cdot (1 - x_e) \leq C_2 \quad \forall \text{ scenarios } T' \\
& x_e \in \{0, 1\} \qquad \forall \text{ edges } e \\
& C_2 \geq 0
\end{aligned} \tag{2}
$$

A linear relaxation of the above integer program is obtained by replacing the integrality constraints $x_e \in \{0, 1\}$ by $0 \leq x_e \leq 1$ for each edge e. This linear program has polynomially many variables and exponentially many constraints. We now give an approximate separation oracle for this program and solve it using the ellipsoid algorithm.

The separation oracle: The separation oracle for the above linear program needs to solve the following problem: given $x_e \in [0, 1]$ for each edge e, find a scenario T' such that $\sum_{e \in E(T')} y_e$ is maximized, where $y_e = c_e \cdot (1 - x_e)$. Recall that a scenario T' consists of at most k terminal pairs from T and $E(T')$ denotes the union of the paths between the terminal-pairs in T'. Thus the separation oracle can be viewed as the following problem. Given a set of paths T on a tree $\mathcal{T}$ with edge-profits $y_e \geq 0$, find a subset of at most k paths that maximizes the total profit in the union of the paths.

We now give a dynamic programming based 2-approximation algorithm for the above problem. Pick any vertex $r \in \mathcal{T}$ in the tree to be the "root" and imagine that $\mathcal{T}$ is hung from r. Thus we get a natural ancestor-descendant relation between the vertices of $\mathcal{T}$: vertex u is called an ancestor of vertex v if u lies on the unique path between v and root r; and vertex v is called a descendant of vertex u if u is an ancestor of v.

Now any path $p \in T$ can be expressed as a disjoint union of two paths p_1 and p_2 such that the end-points of both p_1 and p_2 satisfy the ancestor-descendant relation. We call such paths "up-paths". We now solve our profit maximization problem on this collection of up-paths. It is easy to see that the maximum profit of at most k up-paths obtained in a manner given above is at least *half* of the maximum profit of at most k paths in the original problem.

The maximum profit collection of k up-paths can be computed by dynamic programming as follows. In what follows, we say that a path p "covers" an edge e if $e \in p$. For every vertex $v \in \mathcal{T}$, let $\mathcal{T}_v$ be the subtree rooted at v. For each $v \in \mathcal{T}$, for each of its ancestors $u \in \mathcal{T}$, and for each integer $0 \leq l \leq k$, let $\mathrm{p}(v, u, l)$ denote the maximum profit that can be accrued in the subtree $\mathcal{T}_v$ by at most l paths that together cover each edge on the path between v and u in $\mathcal{T}$. We compute the values of p from leaves up. Below, we only consider triplets (v, u, l) where u is an ancestor of v (possibly, $u = v$) and l is an integer (possibly $l < 0$ to simplify the description). We first initialize the values of $\mathrm{p}(v, u, l)$ to $-\infty$.

To simplify the exposition, we assume that each vertex has at most two children. This assumption can be made without loss of generality as described below. Consider a vertex v with $c > 2$ children $v_1, \ldots, v_c$. We expand v into a binary tree with c leaves corresponding to its c children. The profit of any new edge on this binary tree is set to zero. The original paths can be extended naturally. It is easy to see that the maximum achievable profit in the new instance is same as that in the original instance.

Now for the base case of the dynamic program, we set $p(v, u, l)$ where v is a leaf and $l \geq 0$ to 0. Now consider any internal vertex $v \in \mathcal{T}$ and assume that we have already computed (and stored) the values of $p(v', u, l)$ for all children v' of v.

We first explain how to compute $p(v, u, l)$ when v has only one child v_1. Let $e = (v, v_1)$. If $u = v$, we set $p(v, v, l) = \max\{p(v_1, v_1, l), p(v_1, v, l) + y_e, p(v_1, v_1, l-1) + y_e\}$. For $u \neq v$, we let $p(v, u, l) = \max\{p(v_1, u, l) + y_e, \max_{u'} p(v_1, u', l-1) + y_e\}$ where the maximum is taken over vertices u' on the path between v_1 and u such that there is a path between u' and one of its ancestor that covers the path between u' and u.

Now we explain how to compute $p(v, u, l)$ when v has exactly two children v_1 and v_2. First consider the case when $u = v$. Let $e_1 = (v, v_1)$ and $e_2 = (v, v_2)$. We set $p(v, v, l)$ to be the maximum of the following different ways of accruing a profit. Below the maximum is taken over l' where $0 \leq l' \leq l$. The maximum profit without covering edges e_1 and e_2 is $\max_{l'}(p(v_1, v_1, l') + p(v_2, v_2, l - l'))$. The maximum profit covering e_1 but not e_2 is $\max_{l'}(\max\{p(v_1, v, l'), p(v_1, v_1, l' - 1)\} + y_{e_1} + p(v_2, v_2, l - l'))$. Similarly, the maximum profit covering e_2 but not e_1 is maximum of $\max_{l'}(\max\{p(v_2, v, l'), p(v_2, v_2, l' - 1)\} + y_{e_2} + p(v_1, v_1, l - l'))$. Similarly, the maximum profit covering both e_1 and e_2 is $\max_{l'}(\max\{p(v_1, v, l'), p(v_1, v_1, l'-1)\} + y_{e_1} + \max\{p(v_2, v, l - l'), p(v_2, v_2, l - l' - 1)\} + y_{e_2})$.

Now consider the case when $u \neq v$. Again let $e_1 = (v, v_1)$ and $e_2 = (v, v_2)$. We set $p(v, u, l)$ to be the maximum of the following different ways of accruing a profit. Below the maximum is taken over l' where $0 \leq l' \leq l$. The maximum profit without covering edges e_1 and e_2 is $\max_{l'}(p(v_1, v_1, l') + p(v_2, v_2, (l - l'') - l'))$ if l'' is the minimum number of paths needed to cover the edges on path between v and u. The maximum profit covering e_1 but not e_2 is $\max_{l'}(p(v_1, u, l') + y_{e_1} + p(v_2, v_2, l - l'))$. Similarly, the maximum profit covering e_2 but not e_1 is maximum of $\max_{l'}(p(v_2, u, l') + y_{e_2} + p(v_1, v_1, l-l'))$. Similarly, the maximum profit covering both e_1 and e_2 is the maximum of $\max_{l'}(p(v_1, u, l') + y_{e_1} + p(v_2, v, l - l') + y_{e_2})$ and $\max_{l'}(p(v_2, u, l') + y_{e_2} + p(v_1, v, l - l') + y_{e_1})$.

The Rounding: Since there is a 2-approximation to the separation oracle, we can compute, using the ellipsoid algorithm, a feasible solution $(\{x_e^*\}, C_2^*)$ to (2) such that $\sum_e c_e \cdot x_e^* + \lambda \cdot \frac{C_2^*}{2} \leq \text{OPT}^* \leq \sum_e c_e \cdot x_e^* + \lambda \cdot C_2^*$ where OPT^* denotes the cost of the optimum fractional solution to (2). We round this solution to an integral feasible solution to the Steiner forest problem on trees as follows: pick $e \in E$ in stage one if and only if $x_e^* \geq \frac{1}{3}$. In stage two, given a scenario T', pick the remaining edges in $E(T')$ to form a feasible solution.

The cost of the stage one of our solution is $\sum_{e: x_e^* \geq 1/3} c_e \leq 3 \sum_e c_e \cdot x_e^*$. The stage two cost of scenario T' is $\lambda \cdot \sum_{e: x_e^* < 1/3} c_e \leq \frac{3}{2} \lambda \cdot \sum_{e: x_e^* < 1/3} c_e \cdot (1 - x_e^*) \leq \frac{3}{2} \lambda \cdot C_2^*$. Thus the overall cost of our solution is at most $3 \sum_e c_e \cdot x_e^* + \frac{3}{2} \lambda \cdot C_2^* \leq 3 \cdot \text{OPT}^*$. Since OPT^* is at most the optimum integral solution, our algorithm is a 3-approximation.

4   APX-Hardness of the Robust Min-Cut Problem

In this section, we prove Theorem 5. In the robust min-cut problem we are given an undirected graph $G = (V, E)$ with edge-costs $c_e \geq 0$, a source $s \in V$, a collection of sinks $T \subseteq V$, and a inflation factor $\lambda_i \geq 1$ for every $t_i \in T$. There are two stages in the algorithm. The algorithm has to choose edges $E_0 \subseteq E$ in the first stage. We are then given a *single* sink $t_i \in T$. We call t_i a "scenario". In such a scenario, the cost of each edge $e \in E \setminus E_0$ becomes $\lambda_i \cdot c_e$. The algorithm, then, has to pick edges $E_1(t_i) \subseteq E \setminus E_0$ such that s and t_i are not connected in the graph $(V, E \setminus \{E_0 \cup E_1(t_i)\})$. The objective is to minimize the maximum cost of the solution under any scenario: $c(E_0) + \max_{t_i \in T} \lambda_i \cdot c(E_1(t_i))$, where $c(X) = \sum_{e \in X} c_e$ for $X \subseteq E$.

In [11], the authors give $(1 + \sqrt{2})$-approximation algorithm for this problem and pose as an open question to determine if this problem is NP-hard. We show that the special case, in which there are only *three* sinks and all inflation factors λ_i are equal, is already APX-hard. We reduce the APX-hard problem of finding *multi-way cut* to our problem. The input to the multi-way cut problem is an undirected graph $G = (V, E)$ with edge-costs $c_e \geq 0$ and a collection $T \subseteq V$ of terminals. The problem is to find a subset $E' \subseteq E$ of minimum total cost $c(E')$ such that all terminals in T lie in different connected components in $(V, E \setminus E')$. In [5] the following theorem is proved.

Theorem 6. [5] *There exists a universal constant $\alpha > 0$, value of which is known, such that given an instance of the multi-way cut problem on 3 terminals, it is NP-hard to distinguish between the following cases: (i)"yes-instance": there exists a multi-way cut of cost at most 1, or (ii)"no-instance": all multi-way cuts have cost at least $1 + \alpha$.*

Given an instance of the multi-way cut problem $\mathcal{I} = \{G = (V, E), \{c_e\}, T = \{t_1, t_2, t_3\}\}$, we construct a new graph G' from G by adding a new vertex s and edges $e_1 = (s, t_1), e_2 = (s, t_2), e_3 = (s, t_3)$. We let $\lambda = 2$. In the instance for the robust min-cut problem, s serves as a source, T serves as a collection of terminals, and the edge-costs as given by c_e for $e \in E$ and $c_{e_1} = c_{e_2} = c_{e_3} = 1 + \alpha$, where α is the constant from Theorem 6. Let $\beta = 1 + \alpha$.

Lemma 3. *If $\mathcal{I}$ is a yes-instance then the optimum cost of the robust min-cut is at most $1 + 2\beta$.*

Proof. Let E^* be the minimum multi-way cut in G. We pick E^* in stage one. Then given any terminal $t_i \in T$ as a scenario, we pick the edge e_i in stage two. This clearly forms a feasible solution with cost $c(E^*) + \lambda \cdot \beta \leq 1 + 2\beta$.

Lemma 4. *If $\mathcal{I}$ is a no-instance then the optimum cost of the robust min-cut is at least $\min\{3\beta, 1 + 2\beta + \alpha\}$.*

Proof. Fix an optimum algorithm, say OPT. We consider four cases depending upon whether OPT picks zero, one, two, or three of the edges e_1, e_2, e_3 in stage one. If OPT picks exactly one edge, say e_1, in stage one, we consider scenario t_2. Since OPT has to pick e_2 in stage two for this scenario, the overall cost is at least $c_{e_1} + \lambda \cdot c_{e_2} = \beta + 2\beta = 3\beta$. If OPT picks exactly two edges, say $\{e_1, e_2\}$, in stage one, we consider scenario t_3. Since OPT has to pick e_3 in stage two for this scenario, the overall cost is at least $2\beta + \lambda \cdot \beta = 4\beta$. Similarly, if OPT picks three edges in stage one, its cost is at least 3β.

Now consider the case where OPT does not pick any edge out of e_1, e_2, e_3 in stage one. Let E_0 be the set of edges OPT picks in stage one. Let $H = (V, E \setminus E_0)$. Let $E_{123} \subseteq E \setminus E_0$ the minimum multi-way cut separating t_1, t_2, t_3 in H. Note that

$c(E_0) + c(E_{123}) \geq 1 + \alpha$ and hence $c(E_{123}) \geq 1 + \alpha - c(E_0)$. For $i = 1, 2, 3$, let E_i denote the minimum cut separating t_i from the other two terminals in H. Note that each of $E_1 \cup E_2$, $E_2 \cup E_3$, and $E_3 \cup E_1$ form a multi-way cut separating the terminals in H. Therefore, $c(E_1) + c(E_2) \geq c(E_{123})$, $c(E_2) + c(E_3) \geq c(E_{123})$, and $c(E_3) + c(E_1) \geq c(E_{123})$. Thus $c(E_1) + c(E_2) + c(E_3) \geq \frac{3}{2} \cdot c(E_{123})$ and hence $\max_i c(E_i) \geq c(E_{123})/2 \geq (1 + \alpha - c(E_0))/2$.

Without loss of generality, let $c(E_1) = \max_i c(E_i)$. Now consider scenario t_1. In stage two, OPT must pick edge e_1. Moreover OPT either picks a cut separating t_1 from the other terminals in H or picks at least one edge out of e_2, e_3. If OPT picks a cut, its overall cost is at least $c(E_0) + \lambda \cdot c_{e_1} + \lambda c(E_1) \geq c(E_0) + 2\beta + 2 \cdot (1 + \alpha - c(E_0))/2 = 2\beta + 1 + \alpha$. In the other case, the overall cost of OPT is at least $c(E_0) + \lambda \cdot c_{e_1} + \lambda \min\{c_{e_2}, c_{e_3}\} \geq 4\beta$. This completes the proof.

Since $\beta = 1 + \alpha$, we get that the ratio of costs of the robust min-cuts in a yes-instance and a no-instance is at least $\frac{3+3\alpha}{3+2\alpha}$. This completes the proof of Theorem 5.

References

1. Dhamdhere, K., Goyal, V., Ravi, R., Singh, M.: How to pay, come what may: Approximation Algorithms for Demand-Robust Covering Problems. In: Proc. of 46th IEEE FOCS (2005)
2. Dantzig, G.B.: Linear programming under uncertainty. Management Sci. 1, 197–206 (1955)
3. Fakcharoenphol, J., Rao, S., Talwar, K.: A tight bound on approximating arbitrary metrics by tree metrics. J. Comput. Syst. Sci. 69(3), 485–497 (2004)
4. Feige, U., Jain, K., Mahdian, M., Mirrokni, V.: Robust Combinatorial Optimization with Exponential Scenarios. In: Fischetti, M., Williamson, D.P. (eds.) IPCO 2007. LNCS, vol. 4513, pp. 439–453. Springer, Heidelberg (2007)
5. Dahlhaus, E., Johnson, D., Papadimitriou, C., Seymour, P., Yannakakis, M.: The Complexity of Multiterminal Cuts. SIAM J. Comput. 23(4), 864–894 (1994)
6. Golovin, D., Goyal, V., Ravi, R.: Pay Today for a Rainy Day: Improved Approximation Algorithms for Demand-Robust Min-Cut and Shortest Path Problems. In: Proc. of STACS, pp. 206–217 (2006)
7. Gupta, A., Pál, M., Ravi, R., Sinha, A.: Boosted sampling: approximation algorithms for stochastic optimization. In: Proc. of 36th ACM STOC (2004)
8. Gupta, A., Ravi, R., Sinha, A.: An edge in time Saves nine: LP Rounding Approximation Algorithms for Stochastic Network Design. In: Proc. of 45th IEEE FOCS (2004)
9. Immorlica, N., Karger, D., Minkoff, M., Mirrokni, V.: On the costs and benefits of procrastination: approximation algorithms for stochastic combinatorial optimization problems. In: Proc. of SODA 2004 (2004)
10. Milnor, J.W.: Games against nature. In: Thrall, R.M., Coomb, C.H., Davis, R.L. (eds.) Decision Processes. Wiley, Chichester
11. Ravi, R., Sinha, A.: Hedging uncertainty: Approximation algorithms for stochastic optimization problems. In: Bienstock, D., Nemhauser, G.L. (eds.) IPCO 2004. LNCS, vol. 3064, pp. 101–115. Springer, Heidelberg (2004)
12. Robins, G., Zelikovsky, A.: Improved Steiner tree approximation in graphs. In: Proc. of SODA 2000, pp. 770–779 (2000)
13. Shmoys, D., Swamy, C.: Stochastic optimization is (almost) as easy as deterministic optimization. In: Proc. of 45th IEEE FOCS 2004 (2004)

An Optimal Incremental Algorithm for Minimizing Lateness with Rejection

Samir Khuller[1],[*] and Julián Mestre[2],[**]

[1] University of Maryland, College Park, MD 20742, USA
[2] Max-Planck-Institut für Informatik, 66123 Saarbrücken, Germany

Abstract. This paper re-examines the classical problem of minimizing maximum lateness which is defined as follows: given a collection of n jobs with processing times and due dates, in what order should they be processed on a single machine to minimize maximum lateness? The lateness of a job is defined as its completion time minus its due date. This problem can be solved easily by ordering the jobs in non-decreasing due date order. We now consider the following question: which subset of k jobs should we reject to reduce the maximum lateness by the largest amount? While this problem can be solved optimally in polynomial time, we show the following surprising result: there is a fixed permutation of the jobs, such that for all k, if we reject the first k jobs from this permutation, we derive an optimal solution for the problem in which we are allowed to reject k jobs. This allows for an incremental solution in which we can keep incrementally rejecting jobs if we need a solution with lower maximum lateness value. Moreover, we also develop an optimal $O(n \log n)$ time algorithm to find this permutation.

1 Introduction

Scheduling problems arise in many contexts in computer science and operations research. Let us begin by defining the problem of *scheduling jobs to minimize maximum lateness*. Given a set of jobs A, each having a processing time and a due date, we want to schedule the jobs on a single machine. A job is considered to be *late* if it finishes after its due date, in which case its *lateness* is the difference between its finishing time and its due date; if a job finishes on time, its lateness is 0. Our objective is to find a schedule on a single machine minimizing the maximum lateness among all jobs.

More formally, let $A = \{1, \ldots, n\}$ be a set of jobs and let p_i and d_i denote the processing time and due date of job i. Without loss of generality, we can assume that in an optimal solution the machine is never idle and that the schedule is non-preemptive. Thus a schedule is specified with a permutation σ on n elements,

---

[*] Research supported by NSF grant CCF 0728839.
[**] Research supported by an Alexander von Humboldt Fellowship.

D. Halperin and K. Mehlhorn (Eds.): ESA 2008, LNCS 5193, pp. 601–610, 2008.

where $\sigma(j)$ denotes position of job $j \in A$ in our schedule. Then the lateness of the ith job can be defined as

$$L_i = \sum_{j:\sigma(j)\leq\sigma(i)} p_j - d_i. \tag{1}$$

Our objective is to find a permutation σ minimizing $\max_i L_i$. It is well-known [6] that scheduling the jobs in non-decreasing due date order yields an optimal solution.

For the problem of *scheduling jobs to minimize maximum lateness with rejection*, in addition to the n jobs, we are given a budget k. Our objective is to identify a set of k jobs to reject, so as to minimize the maximum lateness of the remaining jobs. An incremental solution for the problem is a list of the jobs such that for any k, the first k jobs in the list form an optimal solution for minimizing lateness with k rejections. Our main contribution is to show that such a list always exists and that it can be computed in $O(n \log n)$ time. Not only does the incremental approach let us develop a faster algorithm, it also uncovers some surprising structural properties of the underlying problem. Moreover, if all due dates are identical then we need to order the jobs in non-increasing processing time order, since this is an optimal rejection order, so the problem is at least as hard as sorting.

Previous Work: Scheduling to minimize maximum lateness with rejection was studied by Sengupta [11]. In fact, he considered a more general formulation where each job j has a rejection penalty of e_j, and there is a bound on the total penalty of rejected jobs. In this case Sengupta shows that the problem is actually *NP-complete*. However, he also gives a simple dynamic programming solution that runs in time $O(nk + n \log n)$ when all $e_j = 1$, and there is a budget k on the number of jobs we can reject. This algorithm computes the optimal set of k jobs to reject, to get the maximum possible reduction in the maximum lateness. Of course, it may happen that the optimal set of k jobs to reject chosen by the algorithm is not a subset of the optimal set of $k + 1$ jobs to reject chosen by the algorithm.

Other scheduling problems with rejection have been considered as well, both in the offline setting [3,7,10,1] and in the online setting [4,1]). To the best of our knowledge, none of these works have considered incremental solutions for scheduling with rejection.

Related Work on Incremental Algorithms: Perhaps the earliest example of an incremental algorithm is Gonzalez's algorithm for the K-center problem [5], which yields a 2 approximation. Mettu and Plaxton [9] defined the online median problem and showed that there is a way to choose centers incrementally, such that selecting the first K centers, gives a constant factor approximation to the K-median problem. Even though several constant factor approximations were developed for the basic K-median problem, there is no mechanism to enforce that the solution using K medians would be a subset of the solution using K' medians when $K' > K$. Mettu and Plaxton's work then led to several subsequent improvements and simpler proofs [8,2].

For the problem of minimizing maximum lateness with rejection, we develop an optimal solution for the rejection problem and moreover prove that the optimal solution can be computed incrementally. As a consequence it follows that there is an optimal rejection set of i jobs, that is a subset of the an optimal rejection set of $(i+1)$ jobs. However, in choosing an optimal rejection set of size i one has to be extremely careful, since there are many optimal solutions and not all of them have the incremental property.

2   Alternative Problem Formulation and Notation

Before presenting the algorithms, it is convenient to modify the problem formulation slightly. The fact that a job's lateness (1) is allowed to be negative can make the analysis cumbersome. A standard way [6] to avoid this issue is to add a sufficiently large constant to the right hand side of (1) so that the lateness of every job is always positive.

$$M_i = \sum_{j:\sigma(j)\leq\sigma(i)} p_j + \left(\max_{h\in A} d_h - d_i\right). \tag{2}$$

There is a natural interpretation of measure (2): After the machine finishes processing job i, the job must be *delivered*; only once the job is delivered we considered the job to be completed. The *delivery time* of the ith job is given by $s_i = \max_{h\in A} d_h - d_i$. Although our single machine can process only one job at a time, any number of jobs can be delivered in parallel (see Figure 1.) The objective is to minimize the makespan of the schedule, that is, the maximum completion time over all jobs. The two formulations are equivalent since a schedule with makespan $\max_{h\in A} d_h + \delta$ under (2) has lateness δ under (1), and vice versa.

Another way to deal with negative lateness is to minimize tardiness, which is defined as $T_i = \max\{0, L_i\}$. Clearly, if we have an optimal algorithm for minimizing lateness with rejection, we immediately get an algorithm for minimizing tardiness with rejection: Once the lateness becomes negative we can stop rejecting jobs for the tardiness objective.

Notation: When talking about a set A, we use $A-j$ and $A+i$ to denote $A\setminus\{j\}$ and $A\cup\{i\}$ respectively. We use $p(A)$ as a shorthand for $\sum_{j\in A} p_j$. When talking about a sequence ℓ, we use $\ell(1)$ and $\ell(|\ell|)$ to denote the first and last elements of ℓ respectively.

For simplicity, from now on we assume that the jobs are given in non-increasing order of delivery time; that is, we assume that $s_1 \geq s_2 \geq \ldots \geq s_n$. Thus, for any set of jobs $X \subseteq A$, we can denote the completion time of job $i \in X$ in an optimal schedule for X with

$$M_i^X = p(\{j \in X \mid j \leq i\}) + s_i.$$

And the makespan of X with

$$M(X) = \max_{i\in X} M_i^X.$$

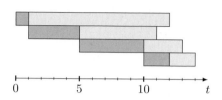

i	p_i	s_i
1	1	11
2	4	6
3	5	3
4	2	2

Fig. 1. Dark rectangles denote processing times and light rectangles denote delivery times. Why a greedy choice is not enough: The third job is a greedy choice, but the only optimal solution when $k = 2$ is to reject the first and the second jobs.

3   An Incremental Solution

Our goal is to produce an optimal incremental solution for scheduling with rejections to minimize lateness. In other words, we want to construct a list of jobs $x_1, x_2, \ldots, x_n$ such that for any k, the set $\{x_1, \ldots, x_k\}$ is an optimal solution for minimizing lateness with k rejections. Clearly, the only way to produce such a solution is to repeatedly remove the job that decreases the lateness of the remaining jobs the most, we call this a *greedy choice*.

Definition 1. *A job $i \in A$ is said to be a* greedy choice *for a set of jobs A if $M(A - i) \le M(A - j)$ for all $j \in A$.*

Interestingly, repeatedly selecting a greedy choice may not lead to an optimal incremental solution. Consider the example in Figure 1. The third job is a greedy choice, but for $k = 2$ the unique optimal solution is to reject the first and the second jobs. There is still hope, however, since the instance does allow an optimal incremental solution, namely $\langle 2, 1, 3, 4 \rangle$. To get around this pitfall we need a notion stronger than greedy choice.

Definition 2. *Let $A = \{1, \ldots, n\}$ be a set of jobs. A job $i \in A$ is said to be a* strongly greedy choice *for A if i is a greedy choice for $\{j, \ldots, n\}$ for all $j \le i$.*

Our algorithm, whose pseudo-code is given below, repeatedly identifies a strongly greedy choice for A, adds it to the list, and removes it from A. It is worth noting here that the existence of a strongly greedy choice is not obvious. Indeed, in the next section we show that such a job always exists.

```
INCREMENTAL(A)
1   ℓ ← ⟨⟩
2   while A ≠ ∅ do
3       i ← strongly greedy choice for A
4       insert i at the end of ℓ
5       A ← A − i
6   return ℓ
```

4   Analysis

In this section we prove that INCREMENTAL always finds an optimal incremental solution for minimizing lateness with rejections. To that end we introduce two lemmas, whose proofs make use of the following property.

Property 1. Let $A = \{1, \ldots, n\}$ and $A' = \{2, \ldots, n\}$. For any set $X \subseteq A'$ we have $M(A \setminus X) = \max\{p_1 + s_1, M(A' \setminus X) + p_1\}$.

Lemma 1 will establish that Line 3 in our algorithm is well defined, and Lemma 2 will show that the choice made there is the right one.

Lemma 1. *Every set A of jobs admits a strongly greedy choice.*

Proof. By induction on the size of $A = \{1, \ldots, n\}$. The base case $(n = 1)$ is trivial. For the inductive step $(n > 1)$, if 1 is a greedy choice then we are done since 1 is trivially a strongly greedy choice, so let us assume otherwise.

Let $A' = \{2, \ldots, n\}$. By induction, there exists a strongly greedy choice i for A'; thus, we only need to show that i is a greedy choice for A. Since i is a greedy choice for A', we have $M(A' - i) \leq M(A' - j)$ for any $j > 1$. By Property 1, it follows that $M(A - i) \leq M(A - j)$ for any $j > 1$. Furthermore, since 1 is not a greedy choice for A, we have $M(A - 1) > M(A - j)$ for some $j > 1$; thus, $M(A - i) < M(A - 1)$ and we are done. $\square$

Lemma 2. *Let i be a strongly greedy choice for A. For any set $S \subseteq A - i$ there exists $j \in S$ such that $M(A \setminus (S - j + i)) \leq M(A \setminus S)$.*

Proof. By induction on the size of A and $k = |S|$. For the base case $(k = 1)$ we note that i is a greedy choice for A so the lemma holds. For the inductive step $(k > 1)$ let $A = \{1, \ldots, n\}$ and $A' = \{2, \ldots, n\}$. There are a few cases to consider depending on whether $1 \in S$ or $1 = i$.

First, consider the case $1 \notin S$ and $i \neq 1$. By Definition 2, i is a strongly greedy choice for A'. By induction, there exists $j \in S$ such that $M(A' \setminus (S - j + i)) \leq M(A' \setminus S)$. It follows, by Property 1, that $M(A \setminus (S - j + i)) \leq M(A \setminus S)$.

Second, consider the case $1 \in S$ and $i \neq 1$. Let $S' = S - 1$. Notice that $M(A \setminus S) = M(A' \setminus S')$. Again, i is a strongly greedy choice for A'. By inductive hypothesis on A and S' there is a job $j \in S'$ such that $M(A' \setminus (S' - j + i)) \leq M(A' \setminus S')$. Thus, it follows that $M(A \setminus (S - j + i)) \leq M(A \setminus S)$.

Third, consider the case $i = 1$. Let j be the smallest job in S. We will argue that $M(A \setminus (S - j + 1)) \leq M(A \setminus S)$. Let t be the leftmost job attaining the makespan of $M(A - j)$. If $t < j$ then $M(A - j) = M_t^A$ and $M(A \setminus S) = M_t^A$; furthermore, since 1 is a greedy choice, we have $M(A - 1) \leq M(A - j) = M(A \setminus S)$. Otherwise, if $t > j$, we have $M(A - j) = M_t^A - p_j$. Since $M(A - 1) \geq M_t^A - p_1$, this implies $p_1 \geq p_j$. Clearly, the finishing time of all jobs other than j cannot increase since $p_1 \geq p_j$. We only need to show that the finishing time of j is at most $M(A \setminus S)$. Let $X = \{2, \ldots, j - 1\}$ be the set of jobs scheduled before j.

$$M_j^{A \setminus (S - j + 1)} = p(X) + p_j + s_j \leq p(X) + p_1 + s_{j-1} = M_{j-1}^{A \setminus S} \leq M(A \setminus S).$$

We have exhausted all possible cases, so the lemma follows. $\square$

Theorem 1. *The procedure* INCREMENTAL *outputs an optimal incremental solution.*

Proof. First we note that the algorithm actually outputs a solution since, by Lemma 1, Line 3 is well defined. Let $A = \{1, \ldots, n\}$ be the input of INCREMENTAL and $\langle x_1, \ldots, x_n \rangle$ be its output. We prove that $\{x_1, \ldots, x_k\}$ is an optimal solution with k rejections by induction on k and n. The base case, where $k = 1$ and $n \in Z^+$, is trivial since x_1 is a greedy choice for A.

For the inductive step, let S be an optimal solution with k rejections for A. By Lemma 2, we can assume without loss of generality that $x_1 \in S$. Therefore, $S - x_1$ is an optimal solution with $k - 1$ rejections for $A - x_1$. We can think of $x_2, \ldots x_n$ as the output of INCREMENT$(A - x_1)$. Thus, by induction, $\langle x_2, \ldots, x_k \rangle$ is an optimal solution with $k - 1$ rejections for $A - x_1$. It follows that $x_1, \ldots, x_k$ is an optimal solution with k rejections for A. $\qquad\square$

5 Implementation

So far we have focused on the correctness of INCREMENTAL and have not discussed its running time. Although it is not difficult implement INCREMENTAL to run in $O(n^3)$ time, in this section we outline two variations of it that lead to faster running times. The first algorithm is based on divide and conquer and runs in $O(n^2)$ time. The second algorithm resembles insertion sort and runs in $O(n \log n)$ time. The reason for including the description of the slower algorithm is two-fold: First, its implementation details are more straightforward than the faster algorithm; second, its quadratic running time is a worst-case bound and it should perform better in practice.

In each case, to prove that the algorithms produce an optimal incremental solution we argue that their output coincides with INCREMENTAL. It should be noted right away that INCREMENTAL is underspecified, since there could be many strongly greedy choices to select from in Line 3. However, *every* possible execution produces a valid incremental solution. From now on, when we say "the output of algorithm X is the same as INCREMENTAL" we mean there exists an execution of INCREMENTAL whose output is the same as that of algorithm X.

5.1 Divide and Conquer

Consider the following divide and conquer algorithm. Let $A = \{1, \ldots, n\}$ be our input instance. First, we find the smallest greedy choice for A, denote this job by i. Second, we identify the smallest job j attaining the maximum lateness in $A - i$. If $j > i$ then i is a strongly greedy choice (this will be proven later) in which case, i must come first followed by an incremental solution for $A - i$. Otherwise $j < i$, in this case we make two recursive calls on $\{1, \ldots, j\}$ and $\{j + 1, \ldots, n\}$. To merge the solutions returned by the two calls, take the leading job from the second solution, followed by the jobs from the first solution (in order), followed by the remaining jobs from the second sequence (also in order). The pseudo-code for this procedure is given below.

```
DIVIDE-AND-CONQUER(A = {1, ..., n})
  1   i ← min{p | p is a greedy choice of A}
  2   j ← min{p | p has maximum lateness in A − i}
  3   if j > i
  4       ℓ ← DIVIDE-AND-CONQUER(A − i)
  5       insert i to the front of ℓ
  6   else
  7       ℓ ← DIVIDE-AND-CONQUER({j + 1, ..., n})
  8       ℓ′ ← DIVIDE-AND-CONQUER({1, ..., j})
  9       insert ℓ′ after the first element of ℓ
 10   return ℓ
```

Theorem 2. *The procedure* DIVIDE-AND-CONQUER *can be implemented to run in $O(n^2)$ time and returns an optimal incremental solution for minimizing lateness with rejections.*

Proof. Let $T(n)$ be the running time of the algorithm on an instance with n jobs. It can be shown that finding the leftmost greedy choice, splitting the instance for the recursive calls, and the merging can be done in $O(n)$ time. Therefore, the running time obeys the recursion $T(n) = T(n_1) + T(n_2) + O(n)$ for some $n_1 + n_2 = n$. If we had control over how the instance is split we could choose $n_1 = n_2 = \frac{n}{2}$ to get a running time of $O(n \log n)$. Of course, we do not have control over this and in the worst case we have $n_1 = 1$ and $n_2 = n - 1$, which yields a running time of $T(n) = O(n^2)$.

To prove the correctness of the algorithm, let us show by induction on n that the output of DIVIDE-AND-CONQUER is the same as INCREMENTAL. The base case $(n = 1)$ is obvious. For the inductive step $(n > 1)$, if $j > i$ then we claim that i is strongly greedy, in which case both algorithms place i first and then process $A - i$, which by inductive hypothesis we can assume to be the same. Let i^* be the leftmost strongly greedy choice for A and assume, for the sake of contradiction, that $i < i^*$. This means that there exists $h < i$ such that for $A' = \{h, \ldots n\}$ we have $M(A' - i^*) < M(A' - i)$. Note, however, that

$$M(A - i^*) = \max\left\{M(A \setminus A'),\ p(A \setminus A') + M(A' - i^*)\right\}$$

equals

$$M(A - i) = \max\left\{M(A \setminus A'),\ p(A \setminus A') + M(A' - i)\right\}.$$

This mean that $M(A \setminus A') = M(A - i)$ contradicting the fact that j is the leftmost job with maximum lateness in $A - i$.

Consider the case when $j < i$. Let i^* be a strongly greedy choice for A. Clearly the makespan of $A - i^*$ is attained by j and $i^* \geq i > j$. Now consider what happens in the execution of INCREMENTAL(A) after processing i^*. For all $h > j$ in $A - i^*$ we have $M_h^{A-i^*} \leq M_j^{A-i^*}$. Since the finishing time of j in $A - i^*$ is larger than that of jobs $h > j$, the next job to be removed by INCREMENTAL must be less or equal than j. This is true until all jobs in $\{1, \ldots, j\}$ are removed:

Suppose the algorithm has removed so far the jobs $X \subset \{1, \ldots, j\}$ and let j' be the largest indexed job in $\{1, \ldots, j\} \setminus X$, then

$$M_{j'}^{(A-i^*)\setminus X} = M_j^{A-i^*} - p(X) - s_j + s_{j'} \geq M_h^{A-i^*} - p(X) = M_h^{(A-i^*)\setminus X}$$

This mean that after removing i^*, INCREMENTAL removes all jobs in $\{1, \ldots, j\}$ before removing any jobs from $\{j+1, \ldots, n\} - i^*$. By inductive hypothesis the recursive calls in Lines 7 and 8 find the optimal orderings for $\{1, \ldots, j\}$ and $\{j+1, \ldots, n\}$ respectively, which are then combined accordingly in Line 9.   □

5.2   Fast Incremental

In order to further improve the running time, we introduce an interesting property about the structure of incremental solutions.

Lemma 3. *Let $A = \{1, \ldots, n\}$ be a set of jobs and $B = \{j, \ldots, n\}$ be any suffix of A. Then the order induced on B by the solution output by* INCREMENTAL(A) *and the order of the solution output by* INCREMENTAL(B) *are the same.*

Proof. As we already mentioned at the beginning of the section, the lemma statement does not imply that every execution of INCREMENTAL(A) and INCREMENTAL(B) will coincide; rather, we mean that for every execution of the former, there is an execution of the latter in which the orderings coincide, and vice versa.

By induction on n. Suppose that i is chosen by INCREMENTAL(A) as a strongly greedy choice for A. If $i \in A \setminus B$ then it does not affect INCREMENTAL(B), and by inductive hypothesis on $A - i$ and B their output is the same. Otherwise, i must also be a strongly greedy choice for B, so both algorithms agree on their first decision and by inductive hypothesis on $A - i$ and $B - i$ the rest of the output also coincides. Conversely, suppose i is chosen by INCREMENTAL(B) as strongly greedy choice for B. Let i^* be the leftmost greedy choice of A. If $i^* \in A \setminus B$, we let INCREMENTAL(A) use this job, by inductive hypothesis on $A - i^*$ and B the rest of the output coincides. Otherwise, $i^* \in B$ for A, in which case we claim that i is also a strongly greedy choice for A and by inductive hypothesis the lemma follows. Consider any suffix A' of A, by definition i^* is a greedy choice for A', furthermore

$$M(A' - i^*) = \max \{M(A' \setminus B), \ p(A' \setminus B) + M(B - i^*)\}.$$

Similarly,

$$M(A' - i) = \max \{M(A' \setminus B), \ p(A' \setminus B) + M(B - i)\}$$

However, since i is a (strongly) greedy choice for B we have $M(B - i) \leq M(B - i^*)$. Thus, it follows that i is a greedy choice for A'; that is, $M(A' - i) \leq M(A' - i^*)$.   □

It is worth noting that a similar statement about the prefixes of A is not true, and it is ultimately the reason why we cannot modify DIVIDE-AND-CONQUER to run in $O(n \log n)$ time. Nevertheless, a scheme similar to insertion sort does achieve this running time. The underlying idea is very simple: Process jobs from right to left, maintaining an incremental solution for the jobs processed thus far.

FAST-INCREMENTAL($A = \{1, \ldots, n\}$)
1 $\ell \leftarrow \langle \rangle$
2 **for** $i \leftarrow n$ **down to** 1 **do**
3   let $j \in \{1, \ldots, |\ell| + 1\}$ be the smallest index such that i
        is a greedy choice for $\{i, \ell(j), \ldots, \ell(|\ell|)\}$
4   insert i to the left of the jth position in ℓ
5 **return** ℓ

Theorem 3. *The procedure* FAST-INCREMENTAL *can be implemented to run in* $O(n \log n)$ *time and outputs an optimal incremental solution.*

Proof. Let us first argue the correctness of FAST-INCREMENTAL and then discuss the details behind its implementation. Consider the $k + 1$st iteration of FAST-INCREMENTAL where we are trying to insert $i = n - k$ into ℓ and $|\ell| = k$, and denote by ℓ' the ordering after i is inserted. Let us show by induction on k that ℓ' is an incremental solution for $\{i, \ldots, n\}$. For the base case ($k = 0$) there is nothing to show. For the inductive step ($k > 0$), by Lemma 3 it suffices to prove that i is inserted in ℓ to the left of the jth element (or at the end if $j = k+1$) where j is the smallest index such that i is a strongly greedy choice for $\{i, \ell(j), \ldots, \ell(k)\}$, which happens if and only if i is a greedy choice for that set.

To argue the $O(n \log n)$ running time we show that Line 3 of the $k + 1$st iteration can be carried out in $O(\log k)$ time. As a warm-up we first discuss a slower $O(k)$ time implementation. For the given sequence ℓ, define μ_j to be the makespan of $\{\ell(j), \ldots, \ell(k)\}$, that is, $\mu_j = M(\{\ell(j), \ldots, \ell(k)\})$ and $\mu_{k+1} = \mu_{k+2} = 0$. The following easy-to-prove property is the basis for our implementation of Line 3.

Property 2. Job i is a greedy choice for the set $\{i, \ell(j), \ldots, \ell(k)\}$ if and only if $\mu_j \leq \max\{\mu_{j+1}, s_i\} + p_i$.

Thus, provided with the μ-values we can find the correct position where to insert i in $O(k)$ time. Although computing the μ-values from scratch could take as much as $O(k^2)$ time, we can update the values from the previous iteration in just $O(k)$ time: If i is to be inserted to the left of the jth position in the sequence then we set $\mu'_h = \max\{s_i, \mu_h\} + p_i = \mu_h + p_i$ for $1 \leq h < j$, $\mu'_j = \max\{s_i, \mu_j\} + p_i$, and $\mu'_{h+1} = \mu_h$ for $j \leq h \leq k$.

To improve upon this, we need to keep track of the differences of the μ-values instead of the μ-values themselves. Let $\delta_j = \mu_j - \mu_{j+1}$ for $1 \leq j \leq k$, where μ_{k+1} is taken to be 0. To find out where to insert i first we identify the smallest j' such that $\mu_{j'} < s_i$. Observe that j' fulfills the condition of Property 2; thus, we only need to check whether there exists $j'' < j'$ for which the same condition holds.

For $j'' = j' - 1$ we can check directly. For $j'' \leq j' - 2$, since $\mu_{j''+1} \geq \mu_{j'-1} \geq s_i$, the condition of Property 2 is the equivalent to $\mu_{j''} - \mu_{j''+1} \leq p_i$, in which case j'' is the smallest index such that $\delta_{j''} \leq p_i$ and $j'' \leq j' - 2$, if there is any.

All these tests can be performed in $O(\log k)$ time if we maintain an augmented balanced binary tree whose leaves are the values $\delta_1, \ldots, \delta_k$, where each internal node keeps track of the sum of the δ-values, and the minimum δ-value in its subtree. When inserting i to the left of the jth position, the effect of setting $\mu'_h = \mu_h + p_i$ for all $1 \leq h < j$, $\mu'_j = \max\{s_i, \mu_{j+1}\} + p_i$, and $\mu'_{h+1} = \mu'_h$ for all $j \leq h \leq k$ can be easily achieved by inserting a new value $\delta'_j = \mu'_j - \mu'_{j+1}$ and setting $\delta'_{j-1} = \mu'_{j-1} - \mu'_j$. The remaining values are left unchanged since $\delta'_h = \mu'_h - \mu'_{h+1} = \mu_h + p_i - \mu_h - p_i = \delta_h$ for $h \leq j - 2$ and $\delta'_h = \mu'_h - \mu'_{h+1} = \mu_{h-1} - \mu_{h-2} = \delta_{h-1}$ for $h > j$. Thus, in each iteration, the tree can be updated in $O(\log k)$ time as well. $\qquad\square$

Acknowledgements. We would like to thank the anonymous referees for helpful suggestions.

References

1. Bartal, Y., Leonardi, S., Marchetti-Spaccamela, A., Sgall, J., Stougie, L.: Multiprocessor scheduling with rejection. SIAM J. Discrete Math. 13(1), 64–78 (2000)
2. Chrobak, M., Kenyon, C., Noga, J., Young, N.E.: Oblivious medians via online bidding. In: Proceedings of the 13th Latin American Symposium on Theoretical Informatics, pp. 311–322 (2006)
3. Engels, D.W., Karger, D.R., Kolliopoulos, S.G., Sengupta, S., Uma, R.N., Wein, J.: Techniques for scheduling with rejection. J. Algorithms 49(1), 175–191 (2003)
4. Epstein, L., Noga, J., Woeginger, G.J.: On-line scheduling of unit time jobs with rejection: minimizing the total completion time. Operations Research Letters 30(6), 415–420 (2002)
5. Gonzalez, T.F.: Clustering to minimize the maximum intercluster distance. Theoretical Computer Science 38, 293–306 (1985)
6. Hall, L.A.: Approximation Algorithms for NP-Hard Problems, ch. 2. PWS Publishing Company (1997)
7. Hoogeveen, H., Skutella, M., Woeginger, G.J.: Preemptive scheduling with rejection. Mathematical Programming 94(2-3), 361–374 (2003)
8. Lin, G., Nagarajan, C., Rajaraman, R., Williamson, D.P.: A general approach for incremental approximation and hierarchical clustering. In: Proceedings of the 17th Annual ACM-SIAM Symposium on Discrete Algorithms, pp. 1147–1156 (2006)
9. Mettu, R.R., Plaxton, C.G.: The online median problem. SIAM Journal on Computing 32(3), 816–832 (2003)
10. Seiden, S.S.: Preemptive multiprocessor scheduling with rejection. Theor. Comput. Sci. 262(1), 437–458 (2001)
11. Sengupta, S.: Algorithms and approximation schemes for minimum lateness/tardiness scheduling with rejection. In: Proceedings of the 15th International Workshop on Algorithms and Data Structures, pp. 79–90 (2003)

More Robust Hashing:
Cuckoo Hashing with a Stash

Adam Kirsch[1,*], Michael Mitzenmacher[1,*], and Udi Wieder[2]

[1] Harvard University
{kirsch,michaelm}@eecs.harvard.edu
[2] Microsoft Research Silicon Valley
uwieder@microsoft.com

Abstract. Cuckoo hashing holds great potential as a high-performance hashing scheme for real applications. Up to this point, the greatest drawback of cuckoo hashing appears to be that there is a polynomially small but practically significant probability that a failure occurs during the insertion of an item, requiring an expensive rehashing of all items in the table. In this paper, we show that this failure probability can be dramatically reduced by the addition of a very small constant-sized *stash*. We demonstrate both analytically and through simulations that stashes of size equivalent to only three or four items yield tremendous improvements, enhancing cuckoo hashing's practical viability in both hardware and software. Our analysis naturally extends previous analyses of multiple cuckoo hashing variants, and the approach may prove useful in further related schemes.

1 Introduction

In a multiple choice hashing scheme, each item can reside in one of d possible locations in a hash table. Such schemes allow for simple $O(1)$ lookups, since there are only a small number of places where an item can be stored. *Cuckoo hashing* refers to a particular class of multiple choice hashing schemes, where one can resolve collisions among items in the hash table by moving items as needed, as long as each item resides in one of its corresponding locations. Collisions, however, remain the bane of cuckoo hashing schemes and multiple choice hashing schemes in general: there is always some chance that on the insertion of a new item, none of the d choices are or can easily be made empty to hold it, causing a failure. In the theory literature, the standard response to this difficulty is to perform a full rehash if this rare event occurs. Since a failure in such schemes generally occurs with low probability (e.g., $O(n^{-c})$ for some constant $c \geq 1$), these rehashings have very little impact on the average performance of the scheme, but they make for less than ideal probabilistic worst case guarantees. Moreover, for many schemes, the constant c in the $O(n^{-c})$ failure probability bound is smaller than one actually desires in practice; values of $c \leq 3$ arguably

* Supported in part by NSF grant CNS-0721491 and a grant from Cisco Systems.

D. Halperin and K. Mehlhorn (Eds.): ESA 2008, LNCS 5193, pp. 611–622, 2008.

lead to failures at too high a rate for commercial applications (assuming that the hidden constants are not too small). In particular, in many applications, such as indexing, elements are inserted and deleted from the hash table over a long period of time, increasing the probability of failure at some point throughout the life of the table. Furthermore, if the hash table is required to be *history independent* then a failure may trigger a long series of rehashings. See [10] for details.

In this paper, we demonstrate that with standard cuckoo hashing variants, one can construct much more robust hashing schemes by utilizing very small amounts of memory outside the main table. Specifically, by storing a *constant* number of items outside the table in an area we call the *stash*, we can dramatically reduce the frequency with which full rehashing operations are necessary. A constant-sized stash is quite natural in most application settings. In software, one could use one or more cache lines for quick access to a small amount of such data; in hardware, one could effectively use content-addressable memories (CAMs), which are too expensive to store large tables but are cost-effective at smaller sizes. The intuition behind our approach is quite natural. If the items cause failures essentially independently, we should expect the number of items S that cause errors to satisfy $\mathbf{Pr}(S \geq s) = O(n^{-cs})$ for some constant $c > 0$ and every constant $s \geq 1$. In this case, if we can identify problematic items during the insertion procedure and store them in the stash, then we can dramatically reduce the failure probability bound.

Of course, failures do not happen independently, and formalizing our results requires revisiting and modifying the various analyses for the different variants of cuckoo hashing. We summarize our general approach. For many hashing schemes, it is natural to think of the hash functions as encoding a sample of a random graph G from some distribution. One can often show that the insertion procedure is guaranteed to be successful as long as G satisfies certain structural properties (e.g., expansion properties). The failure probability of the hashing scheme is then bounded by the probability that G does not satisfy these requirements. In this context, allowing a stash of constant size lessens these requirements, often dramatically reducing the corresponding failure probability. For example, if the properties of interest are expansion properties, then a stash effectively exempts sets of constant size from the expansion requirements. When such sets are the bottleneck in determining the failure probability, the stash allows dramatic improvements. Our work demonstrates that the technique of utilizing only a constant-sized stash is applicable to a number of interesting hashing schemes, and that one can often determine whether the technique is applicable by a careful examination of the original analysis. Furthermore, when the technique is applicable, the original analysis can often be modified in a fairly straightforward way.

Specifically, we first consider a variant of the cuckoo hashing scheme introduced by Pagh and Rodler [11], which uses two choices. We then consider a variation proposed by Fotakis et al. [4], which utilizes more than two choices. In this version of the paper, we omit many of the more technical details of the analysis due to space constraints; a full version of this work is given in [7]. (In the full version [7], we also consider a variation of cuckoo hashing due to Dietzfelbinger and Weidling [2], which allows buckets to hold more than one item.) Finally, we verify the potential for this approach in practice via some simple simulations that demonstrate the power of a small stash.

Before continuing, we note that the idea of using a small amount of additional memory to store items that cannot easily be accommodated in the main hash table is not new to this work. For instance, Kirsch and Mitzenmacher [5, 6] examine hash table constructions designed for high-performance routers where a small number of items can be efficiently stored in a CAM of modest size. (In particular, [6] specifically considers improving the performance of cuckoo hashing variants by reordering hash table operations.) However, the constructions in [5] technically require a linear amount of CAM storage (although the hidden constant is very small), and the schemes in [6] are not formally analyzed. Our new constructions are superior in that they only require a small constant amount of additional memory and have provably good performance.

2   Standard Cuckoo Hashing

We start by examining the standard cuckoo hashing scheme proposed by Pagh and Rodler in [11]. Here we attempt to insert n items into a data structure consisting of two tables, T_1 and T_2, each with $m = (1 + \epsilon)n$ buckets and one hash function (h_1 for T_1 and h_2 for T_2), where $\epsilon > 0$ is some fixed constant. Each bucket can store at most one item. To insert an item x, we place it in $T_1[h_1(x)]$ if that bucket is empty. Otherwise, we *evict* the item y in $T_1[h_1(x)]$, replace it with x, and attempt to insert y into $T_2[h_2(y)]$. If that location is free, then we are done, and if not, we evict the item z in that location and attempt to insert it into $T_1[h_1(z)]$, etc. Of course, this is just one variant of the insertion procedure; we could, in principle, attempt to place x in either of $T_1[h_1(x)]$ or $T_2[h_2(x)]$ before performing an eviction, or place an upper bound on the number of evictions that the insertion procedure can tolerate without generating some sort of failure. We find this variant simplest to handle.

Pagh and Rodler [11] show that if the hash functions are chosen independently from an appropriate universal hash family, then with probability $1 - O(1/n)$, the insertion procedure successfully places all n items with at most $\alpha \log n$ evictions for the insertion of any particular item, for some sufficiently large constant α. Furthermore, they show that if the insertion procedure is modified so that, if inserting a particular item requires more than $\alpha \log n$ evictions, the hash functions are resampled and all items in the table are reinserted, then the expected time required to place all n items into the table is $O(n)$.

Devroye and Morin [1] show that the success of the cuckoo hashing insertion procedure can be interpreted in terms of a simple property of a random multigraph that encodes the hash functions[1]. In particular, Kutzelnigg [8] uses this approach to show that, if the hash functions are (heuristically) assumed to be

---

[1] Some of the details in the proofs in [1] are not accurate and are corrected in part in this paper, as well as by Kutzelnigg [8].

independent and fully random, then the probability that the hash functions admit *any* injective mapping of the items to the hash buckets such that every item x is either in $T_1[h_1(x)]$ or $T_2[h_2(x)]$ is $1 - \Theta(1/n)$. (In fact, [8] identifies the exact constant hidden in the Theta notation.)

In this section, we use the approach of Devroye and Morin [1] to show that if the hash functions are independent and fully random and items that are not successfully placed in $\alpha \log n$ evictions result in some (easily found) item being placed in the stash, then the size S of the stash after all items have been inserted satisfies $\mathbf{Pr}(S \geq s) = O(n^{-s})$ for every integer $s \geq 1$. Equivalently, the use of a stash of constant size allows us to drive down the failure probability of standard cuckoo hashing exponentially.

We now proceed with the technical details. We view the hash functions h_1 and h_2 as defining a bipartite multi-graph with m vertices on each side, with the left and right vertices corresponding to the buckets in T_1 and T_2, respectively. For each of n items x, the hash values $h_1(x)$ and $h_2(x)$ are encoded as an instance of the edge $(h_1(x), h_2(x))$. Following [1], we call this multi-graph the *cuckoo graph*.

The key observation in [1] is that the standard cuckoo hashing insertion procedure successfully places all n items if and only if no connected component in the cuckoo graph has more than one cycle. In this case, the number of evictions required to place any item can be essentially bounded by the size of the largest connected component, which can be bounded with high probability using standard techniques for analyzing random graphs.

We modify the insertion algorithm in the following way: whenever an insertion of element x fails, so the component of the cuckoo graph with the edge $(h_1(x), h_2(x))$ has more than one cycle, we put an item in the stash whose corresponding edge belongs to a cycle, effectively removing at least one cycle from the component. There are various ways of implementing an insertion algorithm with this property. One way is to observe that in a successful insertion, at most one vertex of the cuckoo graph is visited more than once, and no vertex is visited more than twice. Thus, if during an insertion we keep track of which memory slots we have already evicted items from, we can identify the slot that was evicted twice and thus put in the stash an element whose corresponding edge belongs to a cycle. This cycle detection mechanism requires us to remember how many times each slot was evicted. In practice, it may be better to set a limit of $\alpha \log n$ on the number of possible evictions. If $\alpha \log n$ evictions do not suffice then we 'roll back' to the original configuration (which we can do by remembering the last item evicted) and try to insert the element a second time, this time with a 'cycle detection' mechanism.

Of course, the most natural insertion algorithm is to impose an a-priori bound of $\alpha \log n$ on the number of evictions, and if after $\alpha \log n$ evictions an empty slot had not been found, put the current element in the stash. Unfortunately, this insertion algorithm does not guarantee that the element put in the stash corresponds to a cycle edge, a property essential for the analysis. Nevertheless, simulations given in Section 4 suggest that the same qualitative results hold for both cases.

The following theorem is the main result of this section.

Theorem 1. *For every constant integer $s \geq 1$, for a sufficiently large constant α, the size S of the stash after all items have been inserted satisfies $\mathbf{Pr}(S \geq s) = O(n^{-s})$.*

The rest of this section is devoted to the proof of Theorem 1. We start with the following observation, which is almost the same as one in [1].

Lemma 1. *Consider a walk W in the cuckoo graph corresponding to an insertion, and suppose that this walk takes place in a connected component of size k. Then the number of vertices visited during the walk (with multiplicity) is at most $k + 1$.*

Proof. From the definition of our insertion algorithm, W either contains no repeated vertices, or exactly one repeated vertex that occurs exactly twice. Since there are only k vertices in the connected component containing W, it is not possible for W to visit more than $k + 1$ vertices.

The following observation allows us to quantify the relationship between the items that we put in the stash and the connected components in the cuckoo graph with at least two cycles. For the proof, see [7].

Lemma 2. *Let G be a connected multi-graph with v vertices and $v + k$ edges, for some $k \geq 0$. Suppose that we execute the following procedure to completion: while G contains at least two cycles, we delete some edge in some cycle in G. Then the number of edges that we delete from G is exactly k.*

We are now ready to delve into the main technical details of the proof of Theorem 1. For a distribution D, let $\mathcal{G}(m, m, D)$ denote the distribution over bipartite graphs with m nodes on each side, obtained by sampling $\ell \sim D$ and throwing ℓ edges independently at random (that is, each edge is put in the graph by uniformly and independently sampling its left node and its right node). Note that the cuckoo graph has distribution $\mathcal{G}(m, m, D)$ when D is concentrated at n. Now we fix some arbitrary vertex v of the $2m$ vertices. For any bipartite multi-graph G with m vertices on each side, we let $C_v(G)$ denote the connected component containing v. We then order the edges of G in some arbitrary way, and imagine that they are inserted into an initially empty graph in that order. We say that an edge is *bad* if at the time that it is inserted it closes a cycle (possibly of length 2). Note that while the set of bad edges depends on the ordering of the edges, the number of bad edges in each connected component of G is the same for all orderings. Thus, we may define $B_v(G)$ to be the number of bad edges in $C_v(G)$, and $f(G)$ to be the total number of bad edges in G. We also let $T(G)$ denote the number of connected components in G with at least one cycle.

Lemma 2 now tells us that S has the same distribution as $f(\mathcal{G}(m, m, n)) - T(\mathcal{G}(m, m, n))$. Thus, we have reduced the problem of bounding the size of the stash to the problem of analyzing the bad edges in the cuckoo graph. To that end we use stochastic dominance techniques.

Definition 1. *For two graphs G and G' with the same vertex set V, we say that $G \geq G'$ if the set of edges of G contains the set of edges of G'. Similarly, for two tuples of graphs $(G_1, \ldots, G_t)$ and $(G'_1, \ldots, G'_t)$ with vertex set V, we say that $(G_1, \ldots, G_t) \geq (G'_1, \ldots, G'_t)$ if $G_i \geq G'_i$ for $i = 1, \ldots, t$. Let g be a function from t-tuples of graphs on V to reals. We say g is* non-decreasing *if $g(x) \geq g(y)$ whenever $x \geq y$.*

Definition 2. *Let μ and ν be two probability measures over t-tuples graphs with some common vertex set V. We say that μ stochastically dominates ν, written $\mu \succeq \nu$, if for every non-decreasing function g, we have $\mathbf{E}_\mu[g(G)] \geq \mathbf{E}_\nu[g(G)]$.*

Since S has the same distribution as $f(\mathcal{G}(m, m, n)) - T(\mathcal{G}(m, m, n))$, and the function $f(G) - T(G)$ is increasing, it suffices to consider some distribution over graphs that stochastically dominates $\mathcal{G}(m, m, n)$. To this end, we let $\mathrm{Po}(\lambda)$ denote the Poisson distribution with parameter λ, or, where the context is clear, we slightly abuse notation by letting $\mathrm{Po}(\lambda)$ represent a random variable with this distribution. We now give the following stochastic dominance result.

Lemma 3. *Fix any $\lambda > 0$. For any $G \sim \mathcal{G}(m, m, \mathrm{Po}(\lambda))$, the conditional distribution of G given that G has at least n edges stochastically dominates $\mathcal{G}(m, m, n)$.*

Proof. For a left vertex u and a right vertex v, let $X(u, v)$ denote the multiplicity of the edge (u, v) in $\mathcal{G}(m, m, \mathrm{Po}(\lambda))$. By a standard property of Poisson random variables, the $X(u, v)$'s are independent with common distribution $\mathrm{Po}(\lambda/m^2)$. Thus, for any $k \geq 0$, the conditional distribution of G given that G has exactly k edges is exactly the same as $\mathcal{G}(m, m, k)$ (see, e.g., [9, Theorem 5.6]). Since $\mathcal{G}(m, m, k_1) \succeq \mathcal{G}(m, m, k_2)$ for any $k_1 \geq k_2$, the result follows.

The key advantage of introducing $\mathcal{G}(m, m, \mathrm{Po}(\lambda))$ is the "splitting" property of Poisson distributions used in the proof of Lemma 3: if $\mathrm{Po}(\lambda)$ balls are thrown randomly into k bins, the joint distribution of the number of balls in the bins is the same as k independent $\mathrm{Po}(\lambda/k)$ random variables. This property simplifies our analysis. First, however, we must show that we can choose λ so that $\mathcal{G}(m, m, \mathrm{Po}(\lambda))$ has at least n edges with overwhelming probability for an appropriate choice of λ. This follows easily from a standard tail bound on Poisson random variables. Indeed, setting $\lambda = (1 + \epsilon')n$ for any constant $\epsilon' > 0$ gives

$$\mathbf{Pr}(\mathrm{Po}(\lambda) < n) \leq e^{-\lambda} \left(\frac{e\lambda}{n} \right)^n = e^{-n[\epsilon' - \ln(1 + \epsilon')]} = e^{-\Omega(n)},$$

where we have used [9, Theorem 5.4] and the fact that $\epsilon' > \ln(1 + \epsilon')$, which follows from the standard inequality $1 + \epsilon' < e^{\epsilon'}$ for $\epsilon' > 0$. Therefore, by Lemmas 1 and 3,

$$\mathbf{Pr}(S \geq s) \leq \mathbf{Pr}(\max_v |C_v(\mathcal{G}(m, m, \mathrm{Po}(\lambda)))| > \alpha \log n)$$

$$+ \mathbf{Pr}(f(\mathcal{G}(m, m, \mathrm{Po}(\lambda))) - T(\mathcal{G}(m, m, \mathrm{Po}(\lambda))) \geq s) + e^{-\Omega(n)}$$

and so it suffices to show that for a sufficiently large constant α,

$$\mathbf{Pr}(\max_v |C_v(\mathcal{G}(m, m, \mathrm{Po}(\lambda)))| > \alpha \log n) = O(n^{-s}) \quad \text{and} \quad (1)$$

$$\mathbf{Pr}(f(\mathcal{G}(m, m, \mathrm{Po}(\lambda))) - T(\mathcal{G}(m, m, \mathrm{Po}(\lambda)) \geq s)) = O(n^{-s}). \quad (2)$$

Since we work with the probability space $\mathcal{G}(m, m, \mathrm{Po}(\lambda))$ from this point on, we slightly abuse notation and, for all vertices v, let $C_v = C_v(\mathcal{G}(m, m, \mathrm{Po}(\lambda)))$ denote the connected component containing v in $\mathcal{G}(m, m, \mathrm{Po}(\lambda))$, and let $B_v = B_v(\mathcal{G}(m, m, \mathrm{Po}(\lambda)))$ denote the number of bad edges in C_v. To establish (1), we first introduce a bound on $|C_v|$. The proof technique is essentially the same as in [1, Lemma 1]. For details, see [7].

Lemma 4. *There exists some constant $\beta \in (0, 1)$ such that for any fixed vertex v and integer $k \geq 0$, we have $\mathbf{Pr}(|C_v| \geq k) \leq \beta^k$.*

Clearly, Lemma 4 establishes (1) for a sufficiently large constant α. Turning our attention to (2), we first bound the number of bad edges in a single connected component of $\mathcal{G}(m, m, \mathrm{Po}(\lambda))$, and then use a stochastic dominance argument to obtain a result that holds for all connected components. Then we have the following key technical lemma.

Lemma 5. *For every vertex v and $t, k, n \geq 1$, $\mathbf{Pr}(B_v \geq t \mid |C_v| = k] \leq \left(\frac{3e^5 k^3}{m}\right)^t$.*

Proof. We reveal the edges in C_v following a breadth-first search starting at v. That is, we first reveal all of the edges adjacent to v, then we reveal all of the edges of the form (u, w) where u is a neighbor of v, and so on, until all of C_v is revealed. Suppose that during this process, we discover that some node u is at distance i from v. Define $B(u)$ to be the number of edges that connect u to nodes at distance $i - 1$ from v. In other words, $B(u)$ is the number of edges that connect u to the connected component containing v at the time that u is discovered by the breadth-first search. It is easy to see that $B_v = \sum_u \max\{0, B(u) - 1\}$. We bound B_v by bounding $B(u)$ for each u. The result now follows from a combination of stochastic dominance arguments and tail bound calculations; for details, see [7].

Combining Lemmas 5 and 4 now tells us that for any vertex v and constant $t \geq 1$,

$$\mathbf{Pr}(B_v \geq t) \leq \sum_{k=1}^{\infty} \mathbf{Pr}(B_v \geq t \mid |C_v| = k) \cdot \mathbf{Pr}(|C_v| \geq k) \leq \sum_{k=1}^{\infty} \left(\frac{3e^5 k^3}{m}\right)^t \cdot \beta^k$$

$$= O(n^{-t}) \quad \text{as } n \to \infty. \quad (3)$$

Equation (3) gives a bound for the number of bad edges in a single connected component of $G(m, m, \mathrm{Po}(\lambda))$. We now extend this result to all connected components in order to show (2), which will complete the proof. The key idea is the following stochastic dominance result, which can be proven using a straightforward coupling; for details, see [7].

Lemma 6. *Fix some ordering $v_1, \ldots, v_{2m}$ of the vertices. For $i = 1, \ldots, 2m$, let $C'_{v_i} = C_{v_i}$ if v_i is the first vertex in the ordering to appear in C_v, and let C'_{v_i} be the empty graph on the $2m$ vertices otherwise. Let $C''_{v_1}, \ldots, C''_{v_m}$ be independent random variables such that each C''_{v_i} is distributed as C_{v_i}. Then $(C''_{v_1}, \ldots, C''_{v_{2m}})$ stochastically dominates $(C'_{v_i}, \ldots, C'_{2m})$.*

Now let B denote the common distribution of the B_v's, and let $B'_1, \ldots, B'_{2m}$ be independent samples from B. By Lemma 6, we have that $f(\mathcal{G}(m, m, \mathrm{Po}(\lambda))) - T(\mathcal{G}(m, m, \mathrm{Po}(\lambda)))$ is stochastically dominated by $\sum_{i=1}^{2m} B'_i - |\{i : B'_i \geq 1\}|$. Applying (3) now implies that there exists a constant $c \geq 1$ such that for sufficiently large n,

$$\mathbf{Pr}(f(\mathcal{G}(m, m, \mathrm{Po}(\lambda))) - T(\mathcal{G}(m, m, \mathrm{Po}(\lambda))) \geq s)$$

$$\leq \mathbf{Pr}\left(\sum_{i=1}^{2m} B'_i \geq s + |\{i : B'_i \geq 1\}|\right) = O(n^{-s}),$$

where we have omitted several steps of the calculation; for details, see [7]. We have now established (2), completing the proof of Theorem 1.

3   Generalized Cuckoo Hashing

We now turn our attention to the generalized cuckoo hashing scheme proposed by Fotakis et al. [4]. Here, we attempt to insert n items into a table with $(1+\epsilon)n$ buckets and d hash functions (assumed to be independent and fully random), for some constant $\epsilon > 0$. We think of the hash functions as defining a bipartite random multi-graph model $\mathcal{G}(n, \epsilon, d)$, which is sampled by creating n left vertices, representing items, each with d incident edges, and $(1 + \epsilon)n$ right vertices, representing hash locations. The right endpoints of the edges are chosen independently and uniformly at random from the vertices on the right. We think of a partial placement of the items into the hash locations as a matching in $\mathcal{G}(n, \epsilon, d)$. For a graph G in the support of $\mathcal{G}(n, \epsilon, d)$ and a matching M in G, we let G_M denote the directed version of G where an edge e is oriented from right to left if $e \in M$, and e is oriented from left to right if $e \notin M$.

   To perform an insertion of one of the n items, we think of the current placement of items into hash locations as defining a matching M on a sample G from $\mathcal{G}(n, \epsilon, d)$, and then we simulate a breadth-first search of depth at most $2t + 1$ on G_M starting from the left vertex u corresponding to the new item, for some $t \geq 0$ to be specified later. If we encounter an unmatched right vertex v during this process, then we move the items in the hash table accordingly to simulate augmenting M using the discovered path from u to v. If not, then we declare the insertion procedure to be a failure.

   Fotakis et al. [4] show the following three results, which we extend to a variant of the insertion procedure that uses a stash.

Proposition 1. *For any constant $\epsilon \in (0, 1)$ and $d \geq 2(1 + \epsilon) \ln(e/\epsilon)$, a sample G from $\mathcal{G}(n, \epsilon, d)$ contains a left-perfect matching with probability $1 - O(n^{4-2d})$.*

Proposition 2. *For any* $d < (1+\epsilon)\ln(1/\epsilon)$, *the probability that a sample* G *from* $\mathcal{G}(n,\epsilon,d)$ *contains a left-perfect matching is* $2^{-\Omega(n)}$.

Theorem 2. *It is possible to choose* $t = O(\ln(1/\epsilon))$ *such that for any constants* $\epsilon \in (0,0.2)$ *and* $d \geq 5+3\ln(1/\epsilon)$, *the probability that the insertion of the* n *items completes without generating a failure is* $O(n^{4-d})$ *as* $n \to \infty$.

Proposition 1 is essentially a feasibility result, in that it tells us that it is highly likely that the hash functions admit a valid placing of the items into the table, for an appropriate choice of $d = \Omega(\ln(1/\epsilon))$. Proposition 2 tells us that this lower bound on d is asymptotically tight. Theorem 2 then tells us that for appropriate ϵ and d, not only do the hash functions admit a valid placing of the items into the table with high probability, but the insertion algorithm successfully finds such a placement by using a breadth-first search of depth $O(\ln(1/\epsilon))$.

Finally, we note that the emphasis of [4] is slightly different from ours. That work also shows that, with high probability, no insertion operation requires the examination of more than $o(n)$ right vertices with high probability. It also shows that, if, whenever a failure occurs, the hash functions are resampled and all items in the table are reinserted, then the expected time to insert a single item is $O(\ln(1/\epsilon))$. While these are significant results, they follow fairly easily from the analysis used to prove Theorem 2, and the exact same arguments apply to the counterpart to Theorem 2 that we prove later in this section, which considers a variation of the insertion procedure that allows for items to be placed in a stash. Thus, for our purposes, Theorem 2 is the most significant result in [4], and so we use it as our benchmark for comparison.

It is important to recall that, in practice, one would not expect to use a breadth first search for placement, but instead use a random walk approach, replacing a random one of the choices for the item to be placed at each step [4]. Analyzing this scheme (even without a stash) remains an important open problem.

Having reviewed the results of [4], we are now ready to describe a way to use a stash in the insertion procedure. The modification is very simple: whenever an insertion operation for an item x would generate a failure during the original procedure, we attempt to reinsert every item currently in the stash into the table, and then we add x into the stash. Alternatively, if there is some maximum size s of the stash, then if inserting an item x into the table using the original procedure would result in a failure, we simply place x in the stash if the stash has fewer than s items, and otherwise we attempt to reinsert every item in the stash into the table, until (hopefully) one of those insertions succeeds. In that case, we can place x in the stash, and otherwise we declare a failure. This variant is probably better suited to practice, since it only requires us to attempt to reinsert all items in the stash when the stash is full. However, the first method is easier to work with (since it never generates a failure), so we use it in the following discussion, although our results can be applied to the second method as well.

Let S denote the maximum size of the stash as the n items are inserted. We show the following three results, which should be viewed as counterparts to Proposition 1, Proposition 2, and Theorem 2, respectively.

Proposition 3. *For any constants $c, \epsilon > 0$, for sufficiently large constant d, for every integer constant $s \geq 0$, the probability that a sample G from $\mathcal{G}(n, \epsilon, d)$ does not have a matching of size at least $n - s$ is $O(n^{1-c(s+1)})$ as $n \to \infty$. Furthermore, the minimum value of d necessary for this result to hold is at most $d = (2 + o(1)) \ln(1/\epsilon)$, where here the asymptotics are taken as $\epsilon \to 0$ with c held constant.*

Proposition 4. *For every constant $\epsilon > 0$, $s \geq 0$, and $d \leq (1 + \epsilon) \ln \left(\frac{1+\epsilon}{2(\epsilon + s/n)} \right)$, the probability that a sample G from $\mathcal{G}(n, \epsilon, d)$ contains a matching of size $n - s$ is $2^{-\Omega(n)}$.*

Theorem 3. *For every constants $c > 0$ and $\epsilon \in (0, 0.2)$, for sufficiently large constant d, for every integer constant $s \geq 1$, we have $\mathbf{Pr}(S \geq s) = O(n^{1-cs})$ as $n \to \infty$. Furthermore, the minimum value of d necessary for this result to hold is at most $3 \ln(1/\epsilon) + O(1)$, where here the asymptotics are taken as $\epsilon \to 0$ with c held constant.*

Like Proposition 1, Proposition 3 tells us that for an appropriate choice of $d = \Omega(\ln(1/\epsilon))$, it is likely that the hash functions admit a placing of at least $n - s$ items into the table and at most s items into the stash. Proposition 4 then tells us that this lower bound on d is asymptotically tight. Finally, Theorem 3 tells us that with a stash of bounded, constant size, our modified insertion algorithm gives a dramatically improved upper bound on the failure probability for inserting the items when compared to Theorem 2 for the original insertion algorithm, for the same number of hash functions. The proofs of these results are conceptually straightforward modifications to the analysis in [4], but unfortunately they seem to require a lot of technical detail, and so we omit them. For details, see [7].

4   Some Simple Experiments

In order to demonstrate the potential importance of our results in practical settings, we present some simple experiments. We emphasize that these experiments are not intended as a rigorous empirical study; they are intended only to be suggestive of the practical relevance of the general stash technique. First, we consider using a cuckoo hash table with $d = 2$ choices, consisting of two sub-tables of size 1200. We insert 1000 items, allowing up to 100 evictions before declaring a failure and putting some item into the stash. In this experiment we allow the stash to hold as many items as needed; the number of failures gives the size the stash would need to be to avoid rehashing or a similar failure mode. In our experiments, we use the standard Java pseudorandom number generator to obtain hash values. We consider both standard cuckoo hashing, where after 100 evictions the last item evicted is moved to the stash, and the slightly modified version considered in Section 2, where if an item is not placed after 100 evictions, we reverse the insertion operation and redo it, this time looking for a "bad edge" in the cuckoo graph to place in the stash. Recall that this removal process was important to our analysis.

The results from one million trials are presented in Table 2a. As expected, in most cases, in fact over 99% of the time, no stash is needed. The simple expedient of including a stash that can hold just 4 items, however, appears to reduce the probability for a need to rehash to below 10^{-6}. A slightly larger stash would be sufficient for most industrial strength applications, requiring much less memory than expanding the hash table to achieve similar failure rates. It is worth noting that there appears to be little difference between standard hashing and the modified version. It would be useful in the future to prove this formally.

Table 1. For $d = 2$, failures measured over 10^6 trials for 1000 items, requiring a maximum stash size of four (a), and failures measured over 10^7 trials, requiring a maximum stash size of three (b)

Stash Size	Standard	Modified
0	992812	992919
1	6834	6755
2	338	307
3	17	15
4	1	2

(a) 1000 items

Stash Size	Standard	Modified
0	9989861	9989571
1	10040	10350
2	97	78
3	2	1
4	0	0

(b) 10000 items

We show similar results for placing 10000 items using $d = 2$ choices with two sub-tables of size 12000 in Table 2b. Here we use 10^7 trials in order to obtain a meaningful comparison. The overall message is the same: a very small stash greatly reduces the probability that some item cannot be placed effectively. In the full version of this work [7], we also consider the case where $d = 3$ using the *random walk* variant introduced in [4]. The results are similarly encouraging.

5   Conclusion

We have shown how to greatly improve the failure probability bounds for a large class of cuckoo hashing variants by using only a constant amount of additional space. Furthermore, our proof techniques naturally extend the analysis of the original schemes in a straightforward way, strongly suggesting that our techniques will continue to be broadly applicable for future hashing schemes. Finally, we have also presented some simple experiments demonstrating that our improvements have real practical potential.

There remain several open questions. As a technical question, it would be useful to extend our analysis to work with the original cuckoo hashing variants, in place of the modified variants we have described. More importantly, the analysis of random-walk variants when $d > 2$, in place of breadth-first-search variants, remains open both with and without a stash. A major open question is proving the above bounds for *explicit* hash families that can be represented, sampled, and evaluated efficiently. Such explicit constructions are provided for standard cuckoo hashing in [11] and [3]. It would be interesting to improve upon those constructions and extend them to the case of a stash.

Acknowledgment

The authors are grateful to Thomas Holenstein for useful discussions.

References

1. Devroye, L., Morin, P.: Cuckoo Hashing: Further Analysis. Information Processing Letters 86(4), 215–219 (2003)
2. Dietzfelbinger, M., Weidling, C.: Balanced Allocation and Dictionaries with Tightly Packed Constant Size Bins. Theoretical Computer Science 380(1-2), 47–68 (2007)
3. Dietzfelbinger, M., Woelfel, P.: Almost Random Graphs with Simple Hash Functions. In: Proceedings of the Thirty-Fifth Annual ACM Symposium on Theory of Computing (STOC), pp. 629–638 (2003)
4. Fotakis, D., Pagh, R., Sanders, P., Spirakis, P.: Space Efficient Hash Tables With Worst Case Constant Access Time. Theory of Computing Systems 38(2), 229–248 (2005)
5. Kirsch, A., Mitzenmacher, M.: The Power of One Move: Hashing Schemes for Hardware. In: Proceedings of the 27th IEEE International Conference on Computer Communications (INFOCOM) (2008)
6. Kirsch, A., Mitzenmacher, M.: Using a Queue to De-amortize Cuckoo Hashing in Hardware. In: Proceedings of the Forty-Fifth Annual Allerton Conference on Communication, Control, and Computing (2007)
7. Kirsch, A., Mitzenmacher, M., Wieder, U.: More Robust Hashing: Cuckoo Hashing with a Stash (manuscript, Temporary version),
   http://www.eecs.harvard.edu/~kirsch/pubs/
8. Kutzelnigg, R.: Bipartite Random Graphs and Cuckoo Hashing. In: Proceedings of the Fourth Colloquium on Mathematics and Computer Science (2006)
9. Mitzenmacher, M., Upfal, E.: Probability and Computing: Randomized Algorithms and Probabilistic Analysis. Cambridge University Press, Cambridge (2005)
10. Naor, M., Segev, G., Wieder, U.: History Independent Cuckoo Hashing. In: Proceedings of the 35th International Colloquium on Automata, Languages and Programming (ICALP) (to appear, 2008)
11. Pagh, R., Rodler, F.: Cuckoo Hashing. Journal of Algorithms 51(2), 122–144 (2004)

Better and Simpler Approximation Algorithms for the Stable Marriage Problem

Zoltán Király*

Department of Computer Science and Communication Networks Laboratory, Eötvös University, Pázmány Péter sétány 1/C Budapest, Hungary H-1117
kiraly@cs.elte.hu

Abstract. We first consider the problem of finding a maximum stable matching if incomplete lists and ties are both allowed, but ties only for one gender. For this problem we give a simple, linear time 3/2-approximation algorithm, improving on the best known approximation factor 5/3 of Irving and Manlove [5]. Next, we show how this extends to the Hospitals/Residents problem with the same ratio if the residents have strict orders. We also give a simple linear time algorithm for the general problem with approximation factor 5/3, improving the best known 15/8-approximation algorithm of Iwama, Miyazaki and Yamauchi [7]. For the cases considered in this paper it is NP-hard to approximate within a factor of 21/19 by the result of Halldórsson et al. [3].

Our algorithms not only give better approximation ratios than the cited ones, but are much simpler and run significantly faster. Also we may drop a restriction used in [5] and the analysis is substantially more moderate.

Keywords: stable matching, Hospitals/Residents problem, approximation algorithms.

1 Introduction

An instance of the stable marriage problem consists of a set U of N men, a set V of N women, and a preference list for each person, that is a weak linear order (ties are allowed) on some members of the opposite gender. A pair ($m \in U$, $w \in V$) is called acceptable if m is on the list of w and w is on the list of m. We model acceptable pairs with a bipartite graph $G = (U, V, E)$, (where E is the set of acceptable pairs; we may assume that if w is not on the list of m then m is also missing from the list of w). A matching in this graph consists of mutually disjoint acceptable pairs. A matching M is *stable* if there is no blocking pair, where an acceptable pair is *blocking* if they strictly prefer each other to their current partners (the exact definition is given below). It is well-known that a stable matching always exists and can be found in linear time. An interesting problem, motivated by applications, is to find a stable matching of

* Research is supported by EGRES group (MTA-ELTE), OTKA grants NK 67867, K 60802 and T 046234, and by Hungarian National Office for Research and Technology programme NKFP072-TUDORKA7.

D. Halperin and K. Mehlhorn (Eds.): ESA 2008, LNCS 5193, pp. 623–634, 2008.

maximum size. This problem is known to be NP-hard for even very restricted cases [6,8]. Moreover, it is APX-hard [2] and cannot be approximated within a factor of $21/19 - \delta$, even if ties occur only in the preference lists of one gender, furthermore if every list is either totally ordered or consists of a single tied pair [3]. As the applications of this problem are important, researchers started to develop good approximation algorithms in the last decade. We say that an algorithm is approximating with factor r if it gives a stable matching M with size $|M| \geq (1/r) \cdot |M_{\text{opt}}|$ where M_{opt} is a stable matching of maximum size. It is easy to give a 2-approximating algorithm, as any stable matching is maximal. The first non-trivial approximation algorithm was given by Halldórsson et al. [3] and was recently improved by Iwama, Miyazaki and Yamauchi [7] to a 15/8-approximation. This was later improved for the special case, where ties are allowed for only one gender and only at the ends of the lists, by Irving and Manlove [5]. (We must emphasize that the second restriction is not needed for our results.) They gave a 5/3-approximating algorithm for this special case. Their algorithm also applies for the Hospitals/Residents problem (see later) if residents have strictly ordered lists. If, moreover, ties are of size 2, Halldórsson et al. [3] gave an 8/5-approximation and in [4] they described a randomized algorithm for this special case with expected factor of 10/7. The paper of Irving and Manlove [5] also gives a detailed list of known and possible applications that motivate investigating approximation algorithms.

We store the lists as priorities. For an acceptable pair (m, w) let $\text{pri}(m, w)$ be an integer from 1 up to N representing the priority of w for m. We say that $m \in U$ strictly prefers $w \in V$ to $w' \in V$ if $\text{pri}(m, w) > \text{pri}(m, w')$. Ties are represented by the same number, e.g., if m equally prefers w_1, w_2 and w_3 then $\text{pri}(m, w_1) = \text{pri}(m, w_2) = \text{pri}(m, w_3)$. Of course, $\text{pri}(m, w)$ is not related to $\text{pri}(w, m)$. We represent these priorities by writing $\text{pri}(m, w)$ and $\text{pri}(w, m)$ close to the corresponding end of edge mw.

Let M be a matching. If m is *matched* in M, or in other words m is not *single*, we denote m's partner by $M(m)$. Similarly we use $M(w)$ for the partner of woman w. A pair (m, w) is *blocking* if $mw \in E \setminus M$ (they are an acceptable pair and they are not matched) and

- m is either single or $\text{pri}(m, w) > \text{pri}(m, M(m))$, and
- w is either single or $\text{pri}(w, m) > \text{pri}(w, M(w))$.

The famous algorithm of Gale and Shapley [1] for finding a stable matching is the following. Initially every man is active and makes any strict order of acceptable women according to the priorities (higher priority comes before lower).

Each active man m proposes to the next woman w on his strict list if w exists, otherwise (if he has processed the whole list) m inactivates himself. If the proposal was (temporarily) accepted then m inactivates himself, otherwise, if m was rejected, m keeps on proposing to the next woman from his list.

Each woman w who got some proposals keeps the best man as a partner and rejects all other men. More precisely, the first man m who proposed to w will be her first partner ($M(w) := m$). Later if w gets a new proposal from another man m', she rejects m' if $\text{pri}(w, m') \leq \text{pri}(w, M(w))$; otherwise w rejects $M(w)$, then

$M(w)$ is re-activated, and finally w keeps $M(w) := m'$ as a new partner. The algorithm finishes if every man is inactive (either has a partner or has searched over his strict list). This algorithm runs in $O(|E|)$ time if G is given by edge-lists and sorting is done by bucket sort (we may suppose that every person has a non-empty list).

Theorem 1 (Gale-Shapley). *Algorithm GS defined above always ends in a stable matching M.*

Proof. Let $mw \in E \setminus M$. If m never made a proposal to w then in the end he has a partner w' who precedes w on m's strict list, consequently $\mathrm{pri}(m, w') \geq \mathrm{pri}(m, w)$. Otherwise, w rejected m at some point, when w had a partner m' not worse than m. Observe that after w received a proposal, she will always have a partner. Moreover, when w changes partner, she always chooses a (strictly) better one. Thus in the end $\mathrm{pri}(w, M(w)) \geq \mathrm{pri}(w, m') \geq \mathrm{pri}(w, m)$, so mw is not blocking.

In what follows, we will use not only the statement of this theorem (as most of the previous results do), but the Algorithm GS itself with some modifications/extensions.

In the *Hospitals/Residents* problem the roles of women are played by hospitals and the roles of men are played by residents. Moreover, each hospital w has a positive integer capacity $c(w)$ (the number of free positions). Instead of matchings we consider *assignments*, that is a subgraph F of G, such that all residents have degree at most one in F, and each hospital w has degree at most $c(w)$ in F. For a resident m who is assigned, $F(m)$ denotes the corresponding hospital. For a hospital w, $F(w)$ denotes the set of residents assigned to it. We say that hospital w is *full* if $|F(w)| = c(w)$ and otherwise *under-subscribed*. Here a pair (m, w) is *blocking* if $mw \in E \setminus F$ (they are an acceptable pair and they are not assigned to each other) and

- m is either single or $\mathrm{pri}(m, w) > \mathrm{pri}(m, F(m))$, and
- w is either under-subscribed or $\mathrm{pri}(w, m) > \mathrm{pri}(w, m')$ for at least one resident $m' \in F(w)$.

An assignment is *stable* if there is no blocking pair. It is easy to modify Algorithm GS to give a stable assignment for the Hospitals/Residents problem. Each hospital w manages to keep a set of buckets indexed by integers up to N, containing each assigned resident m in the bucket indexed by $\mathrm{pri}(w, m)$; and w also stores the number of assigned residents and a pointer to the first non-empty bucket. If hospital w gets a new proposal from resident m then it accepts him either if w is under-subscribed or if $\mathrm{pri}(w, m) > \mathrm{pri}(w, m')$ for the worst assigned resident m'. Apart from this, the algorithm is the same. It clearly gives a stable assignment, and it is easy to see that also runs in $O(|E|)$ time (rejections can be decided in constant time as well as updating the data when accepting). We call this modified GS algorithm HRGS. As before, we are interested in giving a maximum size assignment, i.e., a stable assignment F with maximum number of edges (that is a maximum number of assigned residents).

In the next section we consider the special case of the maximum stable marriage problem, where each man's list is strictly ordered. We allow arbitrary number of arbitrarily long ties for each woman. We give a simple algorithm running in time $O(|E|)$. First we run Algorithm GS, then we give extra scores to single men, that raise their priorities. These men are re-activated and start making proposals from the beginning of their lists. A simple proof shows that this slightly modified algorithm gives a 3/2-approximation to the maximum stable marriage problem.

In Section 3 we show that this algorithm applies to the Hospitals/Residents problem as well in the (practically plausible) case when residents have strictly ordered lists, also giving 3/2-approximation for the maximum assignment in time $O(|E|)$.

Section 4 contains a slightly more complicated algorithm for the general case. First we run the algorithm of Section 2, then change the roles of men and women. In the second phase women get extra scores and make proposals to men. This algorithm still runs in linear-time, and gives a 5/3-approximation. Finally we propose some open problems.

2   Men Have Strictly Ordered Lists

In this section we suppose that the lists of men are strictly ordered. We are going to define extra scores, $\pi(m)$ for every man with the following properties. Initially $\pi(m) = 0$ and at any time $0 \leq \pi(m) < 1$ for each man. We also define adjusted priorities: $\mathrm{pri}'(m, w) := \mathrm{pri}(m, w)$ and $\mathrm{pri}'(w, m) := \mathrm{pri}(w, m) + \pi(m)$ for each acceptable pair (m, w). It is straightforward to see that if M is stable with respect to pri' then it is also stable with respect to pri.

We define a modification of Algorithm GS, that is called rmGS (reduced men-proposal GS), as follows. This algorithm starts with a stable matching, given extra scores and a set of active men. Run the original GS algorithm (active men make proposals; at the beginning of the algorithm they start from the beginning of their strict lists), where women use pri' to decide rejections. Stop when every man is inactive.

If some men with zero extra score remained single, we increase the score of those men to ε and re-activate them. In the next round they start making proposals from the beginning of their strict list. At any time let SM denote the set of single men, and $\Pi_0 := \{m \in U : \pi(m) = 0\}$. We fix $\varepsilon = 1/2$.

Our approximation algorithm is as follows:

ALGORITHM GSA1
run GS
FOR $m \in U$ $\pi(m) := 0$
WHILE $SM \cap \Pi_0 \neq \emptyset$
      FOR $m \in SM \cap \Pi_0$
          $\pi(m) := \varepsilon$
          re-activate m
     run rmGS

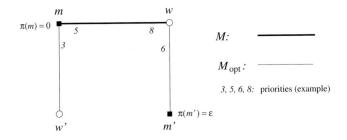

Fig. 1. A path of length three in $M \cup M_{\mathrm{opt}}$

This simple algorithm runs in $O(|E|)$ time, as there are at most $2|E|$ proposals altogether. It is easy to see that Algorithm GSA1 gives a stable matching M with respect to the adjusted priority, hence M is stable for the original problem as well.

Let M_{opt} denote any maximum size stable matching (stable for the original priorities).

Theorem 2. *If men have strictly ordered preference lists, M is the output of Algorithm GSA1 and M_{opt} is a maximum size stable matching then*

$$|M_{\mathrm{opt}}| \leq \frac{3}{2} \cdot |M|.$$

Proof. We use an idea of Iwama, Miyazaki and Yamauchi [7]. Take the union of M and M_{opt}. We consider common edges as a two-cycle. Each component of $M \cup M_{\mathrm{opt}}$ is either an alternating cycle (of even length) or an alternating path. It is enough to prove that in each component there are at most $3/2$ times as many M_{opt}-edges as M-edges. This is clearly true for each component except for alternating paths of length three with the M-edge mw in the middle (see Figure 1).

We claim that such a component cannot exist. Suppose that $M(m) = w$, $M_{\mathrm{opt}}(m) = w' \neq w$, $M_{\mathrm{opt}}(w) = m' \neq m$ and that m' and w' are single in M. Observe first that w' never got a proposal during Algorithm GSA1. Consequently $\pi(m) = 0$ at the end, as otherwise he would have proposed to each acceptable woman. We may also conclude that $\mathrm{pri}(m, w) > \mathrm{pri}(m, w')$ because there are no ties in the men's lists. When the algorithm finishes, $\pi(m') = \varepsilon$, and m' proposed to every acceptable woman with this extra score, but w rejected him. This means that $\mathrm{pri}(w, m) = \mathrm{pri}'(w, m) \geq \mathrm{pri}'(w, m') = \mathrm{pri}(w, m') + \varepsilon$ consequently $\mathrm{pri}(w, m) > \mathrm{pri}(w, m')$. However, in this case edge mw blocks M_{opt}, a contradiction.

We have an example (see Figure 2) showing that for our algorithm this bound is tight (a possible order of proposals and extra score increases is the following: $mw, m'w, m'w'', m''w'', \pi(m'') = \varepsilon, m''w''$).

Note: for open questions please see the section "Open Problems".

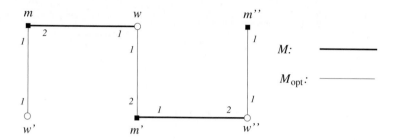

Fig. 2. An example where GSA1 gives $|M| = (2/3) \cdot |M_{\text{opt}}|$

3   Hospitals/Residents with Strictly Ordered Residents' Lists

We consider the Hospitals/Residents problem with the restriction that residents have strict orders on acceptable hospitals. Note, that for real-life applications of this scheme, this assumption is realistic. Here, as appropriate, residents get extra scores. The adjusted priorities are defined as in Section 2.

For a reader familiar with this topic it is straightforward that after "cloning" of hospitals the previous algorithm runs with the same approximation ratio. However, we describe an algorithm for this problem in some detail for not only to newcomers, but for three more reasons: (i) the cloning is not well defined in the literature, (ii) we give a linear time algorithm, and (iii) for showing an example and a theorem at the end of this section.

We modify GSA1 by replacing GS by HRGS and define rmHRGS as a modification of HRGS analogously to the derivation of rmGS from GS. Here SM denotes the set of unassigned residents and again $\Pi_0 := \{m \in U : \pi(m) = 0\}$.

ALGORITHM HRGSA1
run HRGS
FOR $m \in U$ $\pi(m) := 0$
WHILE $SM \cap \Pi_0 \neq \emptyset$
        FOR $m \in SM \cap \Pi_0$
            $\pi(m) := \varepsilon$
            re-activate m
        run rmHRGS

Algorithm HRGSA1 also runs in time $O(|E|)$ (hospitals need to have $2N$ buckets), and gives a stable assignment F.

Theorem 3. *If residents have strictly ordered preference lists, F is the output of Algorithm HRGSA1 and F_{opt} is any maximum size stable assignment then*

$$|F_{\text{opt}}| \leq \frac{3}{2} \cdot |F|.$$

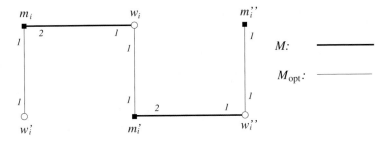

Fig. 3. A building block of the example where HRGSA1 gives $|F| = (2/3) \cdot |F_{\mathrm{opt}}|$

Proof. We suppose that positions at hospital w are numbered by $1 \ldots c(w)$. For the proof we make an auxiliary bipartite graph $G' = (U, V', E')$ and new preference lists as follows. The set U of residents remains unchanged. The set V' consists of the positions, i.e., $V' = \{w^i : w \in V, \, 1 \leq i \leq c(w)\}$. An edge connects resident m and position w^i if (m, w) was an acceptable pair (if hospital w was acceptable to m then all positions at w are acceptable to m). Each position w^i inherits the preference list of hospital w. For resident m we have to make a new (and also strict) preference list. Take the original list, and replace each w by $w^1 < w^2 < \ldots < w^{c(w)}$ (thus if w_1 was preferred by m to w_2 then all positions of w_1 will be preferred to all positions of w_2). If F is an assignment in G then it defines a matching M in G' by distributing edges of F incident to a hospital w to distinct positions $w^1, w^2, \ldots, w^{d_F(w)}$. And, conversely, any matching M of G' defines an assignment in G. The crucial observation is that if assignment F is stable in G then the associated matching M is stable in G', and if matching M is stable in G then the associated assignment F is stable in G. Moreover, if we imagine running Algorithm GSA1 on G', the resulting matching M corresponds to the assignment F given by Algorithm HRGSA1. Using these observations Theorem 2 implies this theorem.

We note that the example on Figure 2 can be easily modified to show that this algorithm cannot achieve better approximation ratio than $3/2$, not even if all hospitals have large capacities and if each hospital has an absolutely unordered list (i.e., $\mathrm{pri}(w, m) = 1$ for every acceptable resident m).

We make c copies of the example shown in Figure 3, one for each $i = 1 \ldots c$. Then glue together the c copies of w_i, the c copies of w'_i and the c copies of w''_i. Assign capacity c to each hospital (w, w' and w''). The following is a possible run of Algorithm HRGSA1 yielding an assignment F with $|F| = 2c$, while $|F_{\mathrm{opt}}| = 3c$. First every resident m''_i proposes to hospital w''. Next, every resident m_i proposes to hospital w; now hospitals w and w'' are full. Then every resident m'_i proposes first to w'' and then to w, but they are always rejected. So every resident m'_i gets an extra score. They propose again to hospital w'' and they succeed. Now every resident m''_i gets an extra score, and proposes again to w'' but they are rejected.

However, with a different type of restriction we are able to prove a stronger theorem. For a hospital w let $\tau(w)$ denote the length of the longest tie for w, and let $\lambda := \max_{w \in V} \tau(w)/(2c(w))$.

Theorem 4. *Algorithm HRGSA1 gives approximation ratio not worse than*

$$\frac{3}{2} - \frac{1}{6} \cdot \frac{1-\lambda}{1+\lambda}$$

Proof. The proof is very technical, so we only sketch the idea of it. Every component of $M \cup M_{\text{opt}}$ (in G') that is a 5-path has a middle hospital-position w^i such that hospital w is full. Each such hospital has at most $\tau(w)/2$ positions in such a bad component and $c(w) - \tau(w)/2 \geq \frac{1-\lambda}{2\lambda}\tau(w)$ other positions lying in a good component (where the ratio of F-edges against the F_{opt}-edges is at least $3/4$). In the "worst case" this component is a 7-path that can contain at most 3 such hospital-positions.

4   General Stable Marriage

Now we consider the general maximum stable marriage problem. First we run the algorithm of Section 2, then change the roles of men and women. In the second phase women get extra scores and propose to men.

Accordingly, we also use extra scores $\pi(w)$ for women: initially $\pi(w) = 0$ and at any time $0 \leq \pi(w) < 1$ for each woman w. We also re-define adjusted priorities: $\text{pri}'(m, w) := \text{pri}(m, w) + \pi(w)$ and $\text{pri}'(w, m) := \text{pri}(w, m) + \pi(m)$ for each acceptable pair (m, w). It is straightforward to see that if M is stable with respect to pri' then it is also stable with respect to pri.

In the first phase we run Algorithm GSA1, women do not get extra scores in this phase. Next, in the second phase we change the roles of men and women, in this phase we increase extra scores of women only. At the beginning of the second phase each woman makes any strict order of acceptable men according to the adjusted priorities (higher priority comes before lower).

We define Algorithm rwGS (reduced woman-proposal GS) similarly to Algorithm rmGS. The algorithm starts with a stable matching, given extra scores and a set of active women. Run the original GS algorithm with interchanged roles: active women make proposals, and men use pri' to decide rejections. But here we have a major difference. If a woman w with $\pi(w) = 0$ is rejected by her actual partner at any time during the process then she gets $\pi(w) := \varepsilon/2$ extra scores, activates herself, and starts making proposals *from the beginning of her strict list*. Stop when every woman is inactive.

If some women with less than ε extra score remained single, we increase the score of those women to ε and re-activate them. In the next round they start making proposals from the beginning of their strict list. At any time let SW denote the set of single women and $\Pi := \{w \in V : \pi(w) \leq \varepsilon/2\}$. We also use $\varepsilon = 1/2$.

Our approximation algorithm is as follows.

ALGORITHM GSA2
Phase 1
run GSA1
Phase 2
FOR $w \in V$ $\pi(w) := 0$
WHILE $SW \cap \Pi \neq \emptyset$
      FOR $w \in SW \cap \Pi$
          $\pi(w) := \varepsilon$
          re-activate w
      run rwGS

First we claim that the algorithm runs in time $O(|E|)$. To see this we must consider two things. In Phase 2, every woman processes her strict list at most twice, so there are at most $2|E|$ proposals in the second phase. The strict lists of women can be calculated in $O(|E|)$ time altogether using bucket sort with $2N$ buckets.

Lemma 1. *The matching M given by Algorithm GSA2 is stable with respect to* pri$'$ *consequently it is stable with respect to* pri.

Proof. We use the facts that in Phase 1 the positions of women do not decline, while during Phase 2 the positions of men do not decline. Let mw be any edge in $E \setminus M$. First suppose that at the end $\pi(w) > 0$. After woman w got her final extra score, she started to propose to men: either w did not propose to m, in this case pri$'(w, m) \leq$ pri$'(w, M(w))$; or else w proposed to m but m rejected her, in this case pri$'(m, w) \leq$ pri$'(m, M(m))$. In both cases we get that the edge mw is not blocking. Now suppose that at the end $\pi(w) = 0$. In this case w is matched in M, and also matched in M', where M' denotes the matching at the end of Phase 1. Moreover $M(w) = M'(w) = m' \neq m$. In Phase 1, after man m got his final score, either m did not propose to w, in this case pri$'(m, M(m)) \geq$ pri$((m, M(m)) \geq$ pri$(m, M'(m)) \geq$ pri$(m, w) =$ pri$'(m, w)$; or else m proposed to w but w rejected him, in this case pri$'(w, M(w)) =$ pri$'(w, M'(w)) \geq$ pri$'(w, m)$. In both cases we get again that the edge mw is not blocking.

Theorem 5. *If M is the output of Algorithm GSA2 and M_{opt} is any maximum size stable matching then*
$$|M_{\mathrm{opt}}| \leq \frac{5}{3} \cdot |M|.$$

Proof. First we need a technical lemma. Let M' denote the matching given at the end of Phase 1. Consider components of $M \cup M_{\mathrm{opt}}$ as before.

Lemma 2. *Suppose $M \cup M_{\mathrm{opt}}$ has a component that is an alternating path of length three, with the M-edge mw in the middle. Then $w' = M_{\mathrm{opt}}(m)$ is matched in M'.*

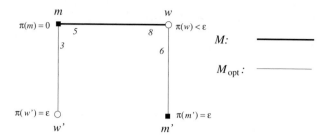

Fig. 4. A path of length three in $M \cup M_{\mathrm{opt}}$

Proof. Let $m' = M_{\mathrm{opt}}(w)$ (see Figure 4) and suppose w' was single at the end of Phase 1 (i.e., w' is single in M'). As this is a component of $M \cup M_{\mathrm{opt}}$, clearly both m' and w' are single in M, and moreover, as matched men never become single in Phase 2, m' is also single in M'.

First we observe that as w' is single in M', m did not propose to her during Phase 1, so $\pi(m) = 0$ (as $\pi(m)$ could only be positive after m searched over his strict list). However m' remained single, so $\pi(m') = \varepsilon$ at the end of the algorithm.

In Phase 2, w did not propose to m' (m' remained single, thus he did not receive any proposals), so $\pi(w) \leq \varepsilon/2$. Next we use $M(w) = m$, and we consider two cases. If $M'(w) = m$ then in Phase 1, when w rejected m' the last time, she had $\mathrm{pri}'(w, m) \geq \mathrm{pri}'(w, m') = \mathrm{pri}(w, m') + \varepsilon$, so that in this case $\mathrm{pri}(w, m) > \mathrm{pri}(w, m')$. Otherwise, if $M'(w) \neq m$ then in Phase 2 w started to make proposals from the beginning of her strict list (that was made with respect to pri' after Phase 1), but she did not propose to m', so $\mathrm{pri}'(w, m) \geq \mathrm{pri}'(w, m')$ also implying $\mathrm{pri}(w, m) > \mathrm{pri}(w, m')$.

At the beginning of Phase 2, $\pi(w')$ was set to ε, and w' remained single. This means that w' proposed to m and m rejected her. Consequently $\mathrm{pri}'(m, w) \geq \mathrm{pri}'(m, w')$, thus $\mathrm{pri}(m, w) > \mathrm{pri}(m, w')$. These arguments show that mw is blocking for M_{opt}, a contradiction.

We continue the proof of the theorem. Let SM denote the set of single men at the end of the algorithm. First note, that men in SM were also single after Phase 1, since in Phase 2 men's positions do not decline. Let $\widehat{SM} \subseteq SM$ denote the set of those single men who are matched in M_{opt}. Observe that for each man $m \in \widehat{SM}$, woman $M_{\mathrm{opt}}(m)$ exists and is matched in both M' and M (at the end of any Phase at least one person in any acceptable pair is matched). We further partition $\widehat{SM}$ as follows. Let SM_1 consist of each man $m \in \widehat{SM}$, for whom man $M(M_{\mathrm{opt}}(m))$ is matched in M_{opt}; and $SM_2 := \widehat{SM} \setminus SM_1$. Let $SM_1^1 := \{m \in SM_1 : M_{\mathrm{opt}}(M(M_{\mathrm{opt}}(m)))$ is matched in $M\}$ and $SM_1^2 := SM_1 \setminus SM_1^1$. By Lemma 2, for every man m in SM_1^2, woman $M_{\mathrm{opt}}(M(M_{\mathrm{opt}}(m)))$ is matched in M' (i.e., at the end of Phase 1). The next lemma plays a crucial role in the proof of the theorem.

Lemma 3
$$|SM_1| \leq \frac{2}{3} \cdot |M|$$

Proof. *Case 1* $|SM_1^1| \geq |SM_1|/2$.

We form clubs, every club is led by a man in SM_1 and has one or two other men who are matched in M. For every man $m \in SM_1$ the second member of his club is $M(M_{\text{opt}}(m))$. For each man $m \in SM_1^1$, his club contains a third member: $M(M_{\text{opt}}(M(M_{\text{opt}}(m))))$. We claim that these clubs are pairwise disjoint.

We formed one club for each man in SM_1 so it is enough to prove that any man m' who is matched in M belongs to at most one club. If $M(m')$ is single in M_{opt} then m' is not a member of any club. If $m = M_{\text{opt}}(M(m')) \in SM$, then either $m \in SM_1$ and m' belongs to m's club or otherwise m' has no club at all. In the other case ($m \notin SM$), m' belongs to the club of $m^* = M_{\text{opt}}(M(M_{\text{opt}}(M(m'))))$ as a third member if m^* exists and $m^* \in SM_1^1$; and m' has no club otherwise.

Let MM denote the set of men who are matched in M. We have

$$|M| = |MM| \geq |SM_1| + |SM_1^1| \geq \frac{3}{2} \cdot |SM_1|.$$

Case 2 $|SM_1^2| > |SM_1|/2$.

In this case we form different clubs, here the non-leader members will be men matched in M'. For every man $m \in SM_1$ the second member of his club is $M'(M_{\text{opt}}(m))$. For each man $m \in SM_1^2$, his club contains a third member: $M'(M_{\text{opt}}(M(M_{\text{opt}}(m))))$. We claim that these clubs are also pairwise disjoint.

If $M'(m')$ is single in M_{opt} then m' is not a member of any club. If $m = M_{\text{opt}}(M'(m')) \in SM$, then either $m \in SM_1$ and m' belongs to m's club or otherwise m' has no club at all. Otherwise, m' belongs to the club of $m^* = M_{\text{opt}}(M(M_{\text{opt}}(M'(m'))))$ as a third member if m^* exists and $m^* \in SM_1^2$; and m' has no club otherwise.

Let MM' denote the set of men who are matched in M'. As men matched after Phase 1 remain matched till the end, we have

$$|M| = |MM| \geq |MM'| \geq |SM_1| + |SM_1^2| \geq \frac{3}{2} \cdot |SM_1|.$$

We are ready to finish the proof of the theorem. Let MM_{opt} denote the set of men who are matched in M_{opt}. We claim that $|MM \cap MM_{\text{opt}}| \leq |MM| - |SM_2|$. This is true because $|SM_2|$ is the number of components of $M \cup M_{\text{opt}}$ isomorphic to a path with two edges and with a woman in the middle; and for each such path the M-matched man is single in M_{opt}.

$$|M_{\text{opt}}| = |MM_{\text{opt}}| = |MM \cap MM_{\text{opt}}| + |SM \cap MM_{\text{opt}}| \leq$$

$$\leq (|MM| - |SM_2|) + (|SM_1| + |SM_2|) \leq |M| + \frac{2}{3} \cdot |M| = \frac{5}{3} \cdot |M|.$$

5 Open Problems

Open Problem 1. *Is it possible to improve the performance of GSA1 if we use smaller ε, increase extra scores more than once, and give extra scores to not only single men, but also to partners of each woman who is a neighbor of a single man?*

Open Problem 2. *Is it possible to improve the performance of GSA1 if we use the method of Irving and Manlove [5] after GSA1?*

Open Problem 3. *Is it possible to improve the performance of GSA2 if we use smaller ε, increase extra scores more than once, alternately for men and women? (For example with $\varepsilon < 1/N$ repeat the algorithm N times, in the ith repetition increasing the extra scores of singles to $i\varepsilon$).*

Open Problem 4. *Is it possible to improve the performance of GSA2 if we use the method of Halldórsson et al. [3], or the method of Iwama, Miyazaki and Yamauchi [7] after GSA2?*

Acknowledgement

I am grateful to Tamás Fleiner for his invaluable advice. I am also indebted to the referees of ESA'08.

References

1. Gale, D., Shapley, L.S.: College admissions and the stability of marriage. Amer. Math. Monthly 69, 9–15 (1962)
2. Halldórsson, M.M., Irving, R.W., Iwama, K., Manlove, D.F., Miyazaki, S., Morita, Y., Scott, S.: Approximability results for stable marriage problems with ties. Theor. Comput. Sci. 306, 431–447 (2003)
3. Halldórsson, M.M., Iwama, K., Miyazaki, S., Yanagisawa, H.: Improved approximation results for the stable marriage problem. ACM Trans. Algorithms, Article 30 3(3) (2007)
4. Halldórsson, M.M., Iwama, K., Miyazaki, S., Yanagisawa, H.: Randomized approximation of the stable marriage problem. Theor. Comput. Sci. 325, 439–465 (2004)
5. Irving, R.W., Manlove, D.F.: Approximation algorithms for hard variants of the stable marriage and hospitals/residents problems. Journal of Combinatorial Optimization (2007), doi:10.1007/s10878-007-9133-x
6. Iwama, K., Manlove, D.F., Miyazaki, S., Morita, Y.: Stable marriage with incomplete lists and ties. In: Wiedermann, J., Van Emde Boas, P., Nielsen, M. (eds.) ICALP 1999. LNCS, vol. 1644, pp. 443–452. Springer, Heidelberg (1999)
7. Iwama, K., Miyazaki, S., Yamauchi, N.: A 1.875-approximation algorithm for the stable marriage problem. In: SODA 2007: Proceedings of the eighteenth annual ACM-SIAM symposium on Discrete algorithms, pp. 288–297 (2007)
8. Manlove, D.F., Irving, R.W., Iwama, K., Miyazaki, S., Morita, Y.: Hard variants of stable marriage. Theor. Comput. Sci. 276, 261–279 (2002)

Edit Distances and Factorisations of Even Permutations

Anthony Labarre*

Université libre de Bruxelles (U.L.B.),
Département de Mathématique, CP 216
Service de Géométrie, Combinatoire et Théorie des Groupes
Boulevard du Triomphe, B-1050 Bruxelles, Belgium
alabarre@ulb.ac.be

Abstract. A number of fields, including genome rearrangements and interconnection network design, are concerned with sorting permutations in "as few moves as possible", using a given set of allowed operations. These often act on just one or two segments of the permutation, e.g. by reversing one segment or exchanging two segments. The *cycle graph* of the permutation to sort is a fundamental tool in the theory of genome rearrangements. In this paper, we present an algebraic reinterpretation of the cycle graph as an even permutation, and show how to reformulate our sorting problems in terms of particular factorisations of the latter permutation. Using our framework, we recover known results in a simple and unified way, and obtain a new lower bound on the *prefix transposition distance* (where a *prefix transposition* displaces the initial segment of a permutation), which is shown to outperform previous results. Moreover, we use our approach to improve the best known lower bound on the *prefix transposition diameter* from $2n/3$ to $\left\lfloor \frac{3n+1}{4} \right\rfloor$.

1 Introduction

We study the problem of computing *edit distances* between permutations, i.e. the minimum number of operations needed to transform a permutation into another, using a given set of allowed operations. Those operations satisfy the property that the induced edit distance between any two permutations π and σ of the same set equals the distance between $\sigma^{-1} \circ \pi$ and the *identity permutation* $\iota = \langle 1 \ 2 \ \cdots \ n \rangle$, thereby allowing us to restrict our attention to *sorting permutations* using a minimum number of allowed operations. Two areas in which these problems have applications are the fields of *genome rearrangements* and *interconnection network design*, which we briefly review below.

In genome rearrangements (recently surveyed in [1]), the permutation to sort represents an ordering of genes in a given genome, and the allowed operations model *mutations* that are known to actually occur in evolution. Rearrangements

---

* Funded by the "Fonds pour la Formation à la Recherche dans l'Industrie et dans l'Agriculture" (F.R.I.A.). Research supported by "Communauté française de Belgique - Actions de Recherche Concertées".

D. Halperin and K. Mehlhorn (Eds.): ESA 2008, LNCS 5193, pp. 635–646, 2008.

studied in that context include *reversals* [2], which reverse a segment of the permutation, *block-interchanges* [3], which exchange two not necessarily contiguous segments, and *transpositions* [4], which displace a block of contiguous elements. While the complexity of the sorting and distance computation problems is known for the first two operations (NP-hard for reversals [5] and polynomial for block-interchanges [3]), it is open for transpositions, and the best polynomial time approximation algorithm to date has ratio 11/8 [6].

In interconnection network design (see [7] for a thorough survey), permutations stand e.g. for processors and form the vertex set of a graph whose edges correspond to physical connections between two devices. One wants to build a graph with small degree and small *diameter*, among other desirable properties, and this is often done by choosing a set of allowed operations on permutations, then connecting two permutations if there is an allowed operation that transforms one into the other [8]. In that setting, sorting algorithms for permutations correspond to *routing algorithms* for the corresponding networks. Two kinds of operations that received much attention in that context are *prefix reversals* [9], which reverse the initial segment of the permutation, and *prefix exchanges* [10], which swap the first element of the permutation with another element. Those operations gave birth to the *pancake network* and *star graph* topologies, respectively, which are extensively studied models in that field. We also mention *prefix transpositions* [11], which displace the initial segment of the permutation; they bear little relevance with biological problems, but they are hoped to shed light and give insight on the seemingly challenging problem of sorting by transpositions.

The *cycle graph* is a ubiquitous structure in the field of genome rearrangements. In this paper, we present a way of encoding the cycle graph as an even permutation, inspired by a previous work of ours [12], and show how to reformulate *any* sorting problem of the form described above in terms of particular factorisations of the latter permutation. We first illustrate the power of our framework by recovering known lower bounds on the block-interchange and transposition distances, and then use it to prove a new lower bound on the prefix transposition distance. We prove that our lower bound always outperforms the one proved in [11], and show experimentally that it is a significant improvement over both that result and the only other known lower bound [13]. Finally, we use this new result to improve the previously best known lower bound on the maximal value of the prefix transposition distance from $2n/3$ to $\left\lfloor \frac{3n+1}{4} \right\rfloor$.

2   Notation and Definitions

2.1   Basic Permutation Group Theory

Let us start with a quick reminder of basic notions on permutations (for details, see e.g. [14]). The *symmetric group* S_n is the set of all permutations of $\{1, 2, \ldots, n\}$, together with the usual function composition $\circ$, applied from right to left. Permutations are denoted by lower case Greek letters, typically $\pi = \langle \pi_1 \ \pi_2 \ \cdots \ \pi_n \rangle$, with $\pi_i = \pi(i)$. The usual *graph* $\Gamma(\pi)$ of the permutation π contains an arc (i, j) whenever $\pi_i = j$, and decomposes in a single way into disjoint cycles, leading to another notation for π based on its *disjoint cycle decomposition*. For instance, when $\pi = \langle 4\ 1\ 6\ 2\ 5\ 7\ 3 \rangle$, the disjoint cycle notation is $\pi = (1, 4, 2)(3, 6, 7)(5)$ (notice the parentheses and the commas). As in [15], we order the vertices of $\Gamma(\pi)$ by positions. The number of cycles in $\Gamma(\pi)$ is denoted by $c(\Gamma(\pi))$, and the *length* of a cycle is the number of elements it contains. It is common to drop the 1-cycles from that representation, and to call the permutation a *k-cycle* if the resulting decomposition consists of a single cycle of length $k > 1$. A permutation π is *even* if the number of even cycles in $\Gamma(\pi)$ is even or, equivalently, if it can be expressed as a product of an even number of 2-cycles. The *alternating group* A_n is the set of all even permutations in S_n. Finally, the *conjugate* of a permutation π by a permutation σ, both in S_n, is the permutation $\pi^\sigma = \sigma \circ \pi \circ \sigma^{-1}$. It has the same disjoint cycle decomposition as π, and can be obtained, if $\pi = (c_{1,1}, c_{1,2}, \ldots, c_{1,\ell_1}) \cdots (c_{m,1}, c_{m,2}, \ldots, c_{m,\ell_m})$, by replacing each element in each cycle of π with the element onto which it is mapped by σ, i.e. $\pi^\sigma = (\sigma_{c_{1,1}}, \sigma_{c_{1,2}}, \ldots, \sigma_{c_{1,\ell_1}}) \cdots (\sigma_{c_{m,1}}, \sigma_{c_{m,2}}, \ldots, \sigma_{c_{m,\ell_m}})$. All permutations that have the same disjoint cycle decomposition form a *conjugacy class* (of S_n).

2.2   Genome Rearrangements and Prefix Operations

We recall a number of operations on permutations, starting with the most general one, introduced in [3]. For any π in S_n, the *block-interchange* $\beta(i, j, k, l)$ with $1 \le i < j \le k < l \le n+1$ applied to π exchanges the closed intervals determined respectively by i and $j-1$ and by k and $l-1$. It transforms π into $\pi \circ \beta(i, j, k, l)$, where $\beta(i, j, k, l)$ is the following permutation:

$$\begin{pmatrix} 1 \cdots i-1 & \boxed{i \cdots j-1} & j\ j+1 \cdots k-1 & \boxed{k \cdots l-1} & l\ l+1 \cdots n \\ 1 \cdots i-1 & \boxed{k \cdots l-1} & j\ j+1 \cdots k-1 & \boxed{i \cdots j-1} & l\ l+1 \cdots n \end{pmatrix}.$$

Two particular cases of block-interchanges are of interest: when $j = k$, the resulting operation exchanges two adjacent intervals, and is called a *transposition*, denoted by $\tau(i, j, l)$; when $j = i+1$ and $l = k+1$, the resulting operation swaps two not necessarily adjacent elements in respective positions i and k, and is called an *exchange*, denoted by $\varepsilon(i, k)$. Two generic problems are studied in connection to these operations: the problem of finding a sequence of transformations that sorts a permutation π and is of the shortest possible length, and the related problem of merely computing the length of such a sequence, called the *distance* of π (with respect to the given operation). It is easily seen that the sorting problem on π is equivalent to factorising π into the product of permutations that are allowed transformations, provided that the inverse of an edit operation is still an allowed edit operation (which is easily shown to be the case for all operations considered in this paper). Indeed, any sorting sequence for π, i.e. $\pi \circ x_1 \circ x_2 \circ \cdots \circ x_t = \iota$, where x_i belongs to the set S of allowed operations for $1 \le i \le t$, immediately yields the factorisation $\pi = x_t^{-1} \circ x_{t-1}^{-1} \circ \cdots \circ x_1^{-1}$, and vice versa. We denote $bid(\pi)$, $td(\pi)$ and $exc(\pi)$ the block-interchange distance, transposition distance and exchange distance of π, respectively. Moreover, the *diameter* of S_n with respect to a given set of edit operations is the maximal value that the corresponding edit distance can reach.

The following traditional tool introduced by Bafna and Pevzner [4] has proved most useful in the study of genome rearrangements. The *cycle graph* of π in S_n is the bicoloured directed graph $G(\pi)$, whose vertex set $(\pi_0 = 0, \pi_1, \ldots, \pi_n, \pi_{n+1} = n+1)$ is ordered by positions, and whose arc set consists of:

- *black* arcs (π_i, π_{i-1}) for $1 \leq i \leq n+1$;
- *grey* arcs $(\pi_i, \pi_i + 1)$ for $0 \leq i \leq n$.

The set of black and grey arcs decomposes in a single way into *alternating cycles*, i.e. cycles which alternate black and grey arcs, and we note the number of such cycles $c(G(\pi))$. The *length* of an alternating cycle in $G(\pi)$ is the number of black arcs it contains, and a *k-cycle* in $G(\pi)$ is an alternating cycle of length k. Fig. 1 shows an example of a cycle graph, together with its decomposition into a 4-cycle and a 2-cycle.

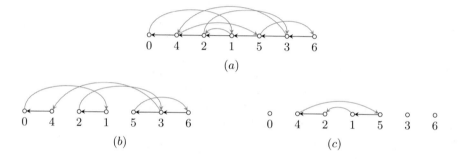

(a)

(b)   (c)

Fig. 1. (*a*) The cycle graph of $\langle 4\ 2\ 1\ 5\ 3 \rangle$, (*b*) and (*c*) the two cycles in its decomposition

Setting $i = 1$ in the rearrangement operations presented above turns them into "prefix rearrangements". The corresponding "prefix distances" are defined as before, and we denote $ptd(\pi)$ and $pexc(\pi)$ the *prefix transposition distance* and *prefix exchange distance* of π, respectively. While the computational complexity of sorting by transpositions or by prefix transpositions is unknown, a polynomial time algorithm for sorting by prefix exchanges is known [10], as well as a formula for computing the associated distance.

Theorem 1. *[10] For any π in S_n, we have*

$$pexc(\pi) = n + c(\Gamma(\pi)) - 2c_1(\Gamma(\pi)) - \begin{cases} 0 \text{ if } \pi_1 = 1, \\ 2 \text{ otherwise,} \end{cases}$$

where $c_1(\Gamma(\pi))$ denotes the number of 1-cycles in $\Gamma(\pi)$, or equivalently the number of fixed points of π.

Dias and Meidanis [11] initiated the study of sorting by prefix transpositions, and derived a lower bound on the corresponding distance using the following concepts. Given a permutation π in S_n, build the permutation $\widetilde{\pi} = \langle 0\ \pi_1\ \cdots\ \pi_n\ n+1 \rangle$; a pair $(\widetilde{\pi}_i, \widetilde{\pi}_{i+1})$ with $0 \leq i \leq n$ is a *prefix transposition breakpoint* if $\widetilde{\pi}_{i+1} \neq \widetilde{\pi}_i + 1$ or if $i = 0$, and an *adjacency* otherwise. The number of prefix transposition breakpoints of π is denoted by $ptb(\pi)$. Noting that a prefix transposition can create at most two adjacencies and that ι is the only permutation with one prefix transposition breakpoint, they obtained the following lower bound.

Lemma 1. *[11] For any π in S_n:*

$$ptd(\pi) \geq \left\lceil \frac{ptb(\pi) - 1}{2} \right\rceil . \tag{1}$$

Finally, Chitturi and Sudborough [13] recently obtained new bounds on the prefix transposition distance. They used the following concepts, based on permutations of $\{0, 1, 2, \ldots, n-1\}$ rather than $\{1, 2, \ldots, n\}$. For a permutation π, an ordered pair (π_i, π_{i+1}) is an *anti-adjacency* if $\pi_{i+1} = \pi_i - 1 \pmod{n}$. A *strip* in a permutation π is a maximal interval of π that contains only adjacencies, and a *clan* is a maximal interval of π that contains only *anti*-adjacencies. They prove the following lower bound.

Lemma 2. *[13] For any π in S_n, let $\Upsilon(\pi)$ denote the set of all clans of π of length at least 3, and $s(\pi)$ denote the number of strips of π. Then*

$$ptd(\pi) \geq \frac{s(\pi) + \frac{\sum_{C \in \Upsilon(\pi)}(|C|-2)}{3}}{2} . \tag{2}$$

Using Lemma 2, Chitturi and Sudborough prove a lower bound of $2n/3$ on the prefix transposition distance of the reverse permutation $\langle n\ n-1\ \cdots\ 2\ 1 \rangle$, and therefore on the prefix transposition diameter. They also prove an upper bound on the prefix transposition diameter.

Theorem 2. *[13] For all π in S_n, we have $ptd(\pi) \leq n - \log_8 n$.*

3   A General Lower Bounding Technique

In a previous paper [12], we introduced the following mapping:

$$f : S_n \rightarrow A_{n+1} : \pi \mapsto \overline{\pi} = (0, \pi_n, \pi_{n-1}, \ldots, \pi_1) \circ (0, 1, 2, \ldots, n) , \tag{3}$$

which in particular maps ι onto $\overline{\iota} = \langle 0\ 1\ 2\ \cdots\ n \rangle$. That mapping allowed us to encode a cycle graph $G(\pi)$ using an even permutation $\overline{\pi}$, as illustrated by the following example: let $\pi = \langle 4\ 2\ 1\ 5\ 3 \rangle$, whose cycle graph is depicted in Fig. 1. Then

$$\overline{\pi} = (0, 3, 5, 1, 2, 4) \circ (0, 1, 2, 3, 4, 5) = (0, 2, 5, 3)(1, 4) ,$$

and the two disjoint cycles of $\overline{\pi}$ correspond to the two alternating cycles of $G(\pi)$, whose elements they list in the order they are encountered; indeed:

1. the first cycle of $G(\pi)$ (Fig. 1(b)) starts with 0, then visits 2 after following a grey-black path (i.e. a grey arc followed by a black arc), then visits 5 after following a grey-black path, and in the same way visits 3 after following a grey-black path before finally going back to 0, which corresponds to the first cycle of $\overline{\pi}$;
2. the second cycle of $G(\pi)$ (Fig. 1(c)) starts with 4, then visits 1 after following a grey-black path, which corresponds to the second cycle of $\overline{\pi}$.

Consequently, speaking about cycles of $\overline{\pi}$, of $\Gamma(\overline{\pi})$ or of $G(\pi)$ is equivalent. We will now demonstrate how f can be used to obtain bounds on sorting problems. The following result expresses how the action of *any* rearrangement operation σ on π is translated on $\overline{\pi}$. In the following, we identify permutations in S_n with their extended versions in S_{n+1} (i.e. we identify π with $\langle 0\ \pi_1\ \pi_2\ \cdots\ \pi_n \rangle$).

Lemma 3. *For all π, σ in S_n, we have $\overline{\pi \circ \sigma} = \overline{\sigma}^{\pi} \circ \overline{\pi}$.*

Proof. The following relation will be useful:

$$\pi = (0, \pi_n, \pi_{n-1}, \ldots, \pi_1) \circ \pi \circ (0, 1, \ldots, n) . \tag{4}$$

By definition, we have:

$$\begin{aligned}
\overline{\pi \circ \sigma} &= (0, (\pi \circ \sigma)_n, (\pi \circ \sigma)_{n-1}, \ldots, (\pi \circ \sigma)_1) \circ (0, 1, \ldots, n) \\
&= (0, \pi_{\sigma_n}, \pi_{\sigma_{n-1}}, \ldots, \pi_{\sigma_1}) \circ (0, 1, \ldots, n) \\
&= \pi \circ (0, \sigma_n, \sigma_{n-1}, \ldots, \sigma_1) \circ \pi^{-1} \circ (0, 1, \ldots, n) \\
&= \pi \circ (0, \sigma_n, \sigma_{n-1}, \ldots, \sigma_1) \circ (0, 1, \ldots, n) \circ (0, 1, \ldots, n)^{-1} \circ \pi^{-1} \\
&\quad \circ (0, 1, \ldots, n) \\
&= \pi \circ \overline{\sigma} \circ (\pi \circ (0, 1, \ldots, n))^{-1} \circ (0, 1, \ldots, n) \\
&= \pi \circ \overline{\sigma} \circ ((0, \pi_n, \ldots, \pi_1)^{-1} \circ \pi)^{-1} \circ (0, 1, \ldots, n) \qquad \text{(using (4))} \\
&= \pi \circ \overline{\sigma} \circ \pi^{-1} \circ (0, \pi_n, \ldots, \pi_1) \circ (0, 1, \ldots, n) \\
&= \pi \circ \overline{\sigma} \circ \pi^{-1} \circ \overline{\pi} . \qquad\qquad\qquad\qquad\qquad\qquad \square
\end{aligned}$$

We are now ready to prove our main result.

Theorem 3. *Let X be a subset of S_n whose elements are mapped by f onto $X' \subseteq A_{n+1}$. Moreover, let $\mathscr{C}$ be the union of the conjugacy classes (of S_{n+1}) that intersect with X'; then for any π in S_n, any factorisation of π into t elements of X yields a factorisation of $\overline{\pi}$ into t elements of $\mathscr{C}$.*

Proof. Induction on t. The base case is $\pi \in X$, and clearly $\overline{\pi} \in X' \subseteq \mathscr{C}$. For the induction, let $\pi = g_t \circ g_{t-1} \circ \cdots \circ g_1$, where $g_i \in X$ for $1 \le i \le t$, and let $\sigma = g_{t-1} \circ \cdots \circ g_2 \circ g_1$; by Lemma 3, we have:

$$\overline{\pi} = \overline{g_t \circ g_{t-1} \circ \cdots \circ g_2 \circ g_1} = \overline{g_t \circ \sigma} = g_t \circ \overline{\sigma} \circ g_t^{-1} \circ \overline{g_t} .$$

By induction, $\bar{\sigma} = g'_{t-1} \circ g'_{t-2} \circ \cdots \circ g'_1$, where $g'_i \in \mathscr{C}$ for $1 \leq i \leq t$; therefore:

$$
\begin{aligned}
g_t \circ \bar{\sigma} \circ g_t^{-1} &= g_t \circ g'_{t-1} \circ g'_{t-2} \circ \cdots \circ g'_1 \circ g_t^{-1} \\
&= \underbrace{g_t \circ g'_{t-1} \circ g_t^{-1}}_{h_t} \circ \underbrace{g_t \circ g'_{t-2} \circ g_t^{-1}}_{h_{t-1}} \circ g_t \circ \cdots \circ g_t^{-1} \circ \underbrace{g_t \circ g'_1 \circ g_t^{-1}}_{h_1} ,
\end{aligned}
$$

and $h_1, \ldots, h_{t-1} \in \mathscr{C}$, which completes the proof. $\square$

As we briefly explain before applying our method in the next section, Theorem 3 allows us to prove lower bounds on our sorting problems: indeed, as we explained in Section 2.2, any sorting sequence of length t for π made of elements of X yields a factorisation of π into the product of t elements (of X, provided X contains both the transformations and their inverses, which is easily shown to be the case for all operations considered in this paper), which can in turn be converted, as in the proof of Theorem 3, into a factorisation of $\bar{\pi}$ into the product of t elements of $\mathscr{C}$. Therefore, the length of a shortest such factorisation of $\bar{\pi}$ into the product of elements of $\mathscr{C}$ is a lower bound on the length of a factorisation of π into the product of elements of X.

4   Recovering Previous Results

We illustrate how to use Theorem 3 to recover two previously known results on bid and td. First, we need to characterise the image of a block-interchange by our mapping.

Lemma 4. *For any block-interchange $\beta(i, j, k, l)$, we have*

$$
\overline{\beta(i, j, k, l)} = (j - 1, l - 1) \circ (i - 1, k - 1) .
$$

Proof. Using (3) and the definition of a block-interchange, we have

$$
\begin{aligned}
&(0, n, n - 1, \ldots, l, j - 1, j - 2, \ldots, i, k - 1, k - 2, \ldots, j, l - 1, l - 2, \ldots, \\
&\quad k, i - 1, i - 2, \ldots, 1) \circ (0, 1, 2, \ldots, n) \\
&= (0)(1) \cdots (i - 2)(i - 1, k - 1)(i)(i + 1) \cdots (j - 2)(j - 1, l - 1)(j) \\
&\quad (j + 1) \cdots (k - 2)(k)(k + 1) \cdots (l - 2)(l)(l + 1) \cdots (n) \\
&= (j - 1, l - 1) \circ (i - 1, k - 1) .
\end{aligned}
$$
$\square$

Note that $(j-1, l-1)$ and $(i-1, k-1)$ might not be disjoint, since by definition of $\beta(i, j, k, l)$ we may have $j = k$ (hence the use of $\circ$ in the expression of $\overline{\beta(i, j, k, l)}$). We can now recover a known lower bound on the block-interchange distance, which is actually the exact distance [3].

Theorem 4. *[3] For all π in S_n, we have $bid(\pi) \geq \frac{n+1-c(\Gamma(\bar{\pi}))}{2}$.*

Proof. By Theorem 3 and Lemma 4, a lower bound on $bid(\pi)$ is given by the length of a minimum factorisation of $\bar{\pi}$ into pairs of exchanges. Since this length equals $(n + 1 - c(\Gamma(\bar{\pi})))/2$ (see e.g. [16]), the proof follows. $\square$

Let us now characterise the image of a transposition by our mapping.

Lemma 5. *For any transposition* $\tau(i,j,l)$*, we have*

$$\overline{\tau(i,j,l)} = (i-1, l-1, j-1) \ .$$

Proof. As noted in Section 2.2, we have $\tau(i,j,l) = \beta(i,j,j,l)$; Lemma 4 yields:

$$\overline{\tau(i,j,l)} = \overline{\beta(i,j,j,l)} = (j-1, l-1) \circ (i-1, j-1) = (i-1, l-1, j-1) \ . \quad \square$$

We recover the following known lower bound on the transposition distance, where $c_{odd}(\Gamma(\overline{\pi}))$ denotes the number of odd cycles in $\Gamma(\overline{\pi})$.

Theorem 5. *[4] For all* π *in* S_n*, we have* $td(\pi) \geq \frac{n+1-c_{odd}(\Gamma(\overline{\pi}))}{2}$.

Proof. By Theorem 3 and Lemma 5, a lower bound on $td(\pi)$ is given by the length of a minimum factorisation of $\overline{\pi}$ into 3-cycles. Since this length equals $(n+1-c_{odd}(\Gamma(\overline{\pi})))/2$ (see e.g. [16]), the proof follows. $\quad \square$

5   An Improved Lower Bound on the Prefix Transposition Distance

Using our theory, we prove a *new* lower bound on $ptd(\pi)$ and show that it always outperforms (1). We will find it convenient to express $ptb(\pi)$ (defined after Theorem 1 page 638) as follows.

Lemma 6. *For any* π *in* S_n*, we have*

$$ptb(\pi) = n + 1 - c_1(\Gamma(\overline{\pi})) + \begin{cases} 1 \text{ if } \pi_1 = 1, \\ 0 \text{ otherwise.} \end{cases}$$

Proof. The formula results from the observation that, among the $n+1$ pairs of adjacent elements in $\overline{\pi}$, each adjacency in $\overline{\pi}$ gives rise to a 1-cycle in $\Gamma(\overline{\pi})$, and from the fact that if $\pi_1 = 1$, then we counted the 1-cycle that corresponds to $(0,1)$ as an adjacency, which we correct by adding 1. $\quad \square$

Let $d_3^1(\pi)$ denote the length of a minimum factorisation of π in S_n into a product of 3-cycles, where each 3-cycle in the factorisation is further required to contain the first element.

Proposition 1. *For any* π *in* S_n*, we have* $ptd(\pi) \geq d_3^1(\overline{\pi})$.

Proof. Replace i with 1 in Lemma 5, and mimic the proof of Theorem 5. $\quad \square$

Next, we show how to compute $d_3^1(\pi)$ for π in A_n. The following simple observation will be useful.

Observation 1. *For any* π *in* A_n*, we have* $n \equiv c(\Gamma(\pi)) \pmod 2$.

Lemma 7. *For any* π *in* A_n*, we have*

$$d_3^1(\pi) = \frac{n + c(\Gamma(\pi))}{2} - c_1(\Gamma(\pi)) - \begin{cases} 0 \text{ if } \pi_1 = 1, \\ 1 \text{ otherwise.} \end{cases}$$

Proof. Given a minimum factorisation of length ℓ of an even permutation π into prefix exchanges, we can construct a sequence of $\ell/2$ 3-cycles by noting that $(1,j) \circ (1,i) = (1,i,j)$. Therefore $d_3^1(\pi) \leq \ell/2$. On the other hand, assume there exists a shorter sequence of 3-cycles acting on the first element whose product is π; then one can split each of these 3-cycles into two prefix exchanges using the relation above and find a shorter expression for π as a product of prefix exchanges, a contradiction. The result follows from Theorem 1. $\qquad\square$

As a corollary, we obtain the following lower bound on the prefix transposition distance:

Theorem 6. *For any π in S_n, we have*

$$ptd(\pi) \geq \frac{n+1+c(\Gamma(\overline{\pi}))}{2} - c_1(\Gamma(\overline{\pi})) - \begin{cases} 0 \ \textit{if } \pi_1 = 1, \\ 1 \ \textit{otherwise.} \end{cases} \qquad (5)$$

Proof. Follows from Proposition 1 and Lemma 7. $\qquad\square$

We conclude this section by proving that our lower bound always outperforms Dias and Meidanis' (Lemma 1).

Theorem 7. *Lower bound (5) is always at least as large as lower bound (1).*

Proof. Assume $\pi \neq \iota$ (otherwise the result trivially holds); this implies that $\Gamma(\overline{\pi})$ has at least one cycle of length at least 2, which means that $c(\Gamma(\overline{\pi})) - c_1(\Gamma(\overline{\pi})) \geq 1$. There are two cases to prove: if $\pi_1 = 1$, then lower bound (1) becomes

$$\left\lceil \frac{(n+1-c_1(\Gamma(\overline{\pi}))+1)-1}{2} \right\rceil = \left\lceil \frac{n+1-c_1(\Gamma(\overline{\pi}))}{2} \right\rceil ,$$

and lower bound (5) satisfies

$$\frac{n+1+c(\Gamma(\overline{\pi}))-2c_1(\Gamma(\overline{\pi}))}{2} \geq \frac{n+2-c_1(\Gamma(\overline{\pi}))}{2} \geq \left\lceil \frac{n+1-c_1(\Gamma(\overline{\pi}))}{2} \right\rceil .$$

On the other hand, if $\pi_1 \neq 1$, then lower bound (1) becomes

$$\left\lceil \frac{(n+1-c_1(\Gamma(\overline{\pi})))-1}{2} \right\rceil = \left\lceil \frac{n-c_1(\Gamma(\overline{\pi}))}{2} \right\rceil ,$$

and by Observation 1, lower bound (5) becomes

$$\frac{n+1+c(\Gamma(\overline{\pi}))}{2} - c_1(\Gamma(\overline{\pi})) - 1 = \left\lceil \frac{n+1+c(\Gamma(\overline{\pi}))-2c_1(\Gamma(\overline{\pi}))-2}{2} \right\rceil$$

$$\geq \left\lceil \frac{n-c_1(\Gamma(\overline{\pi}))}{2} \right\rceil . \qquad\square$$

6   A Tighter Lower Bound on the Prefix Transposition Diameter

Dias and Meidanis [11] observed that the prefix transposition diameter lies between $n/2$ and $n - 1$, and conjectured that it is equal to $n - \lfloor \frac{n}{4} \rfloor$. Recently, Chitturi and Sudborough [13] improved those bounds to $2n/3$ and $n - \log_8 n$, respectively. Using our new lower bound on the prefix transposition distance, we further improve the lower bound on the prefix transposition diameter.

Theorem 8. *For $n \geq 2$, the prefix transposition diameter of S_n is at least* $\lfloor \frac{3n+1}{4} \rfloor$.

Proof. We construct a family of permutations whose prefix transposition distance is at least $\lfloor \frac{3n+1}{4} \rfloor$. Let $\pi = \langle 3\ 2\ 1\ 4\ 7\ 6\ 5\ \cdots\ n - 4\ n\ n - 2\ n - 3 \rangle$, or any other 2-*permutation*, i.e. a permutation such that $\Gamma(\overline{\pi})$ contains only cycles of length 2 (this requires that $n \equiv 3 \pmod 4$). There are four cases to examine, each of which relies on Theorem 6:

1. if $n \equiv 3 \pmod 4$, we have $ptd(\pi) \geq (n + 1 + (n + 1)/2)/2 - 0 - 1 = \frac{3n-1}{4}$.
2. if $n \equiv 0 \pmod 4$, let σ be a permutation such that $\Gamma(\overline{\sigma})$ is obtained by inserting a fixed point at the beginning of $\Gamma(\overline{\pi})$; since $\overline{\sigma}$ fixes 0 and has $n/2$ 2-cycles, we have $ptd(\sigma) \geq (n + 1 + n/2 + 1)/2 - 1 - 0 = \frac{3n}{4}$.
3. if $n \equiv 1 \pmod 4$, let σ' be a permutation such that $\Gamma(\overline{\sigma'})$ is obtained by inserting a fixed point anywhere in $\Gamma(\overline{\sigma})$; we have $ptd(\sigma') \geq (n + 1 + \frac{n-2+1}{2} + 2)/2 - 2 = \frac{3n+1}{4}$.
4. if $n \equiv 2 \pmod 4$, let σ'' be a permutation such that $\Gamma(\overline{\sigma''})$ is obtained by inserting a 3-cycle (a, c, b) with $a < b < c$ anywhere in $\Gamma(\overline{\pi})$. Since σ'' has $(n + 1 - 3)/2 + 1$ cycles of length at least 2, we have $ptd(\sigma'') \geq (n + 1 + \frac{n+1-3}{2} + 1)/2 - 0 - 1 = \frac{3n-2}{4}$.   □

7   Experimental Results

We generated all permutations in S_n, for $1 \leq n \leq 10$, along with their prefix transposition distance, and compared lower bounds (1), (2) and (5) to the actual distance. Table 1 shows the results. It can be observed that many more permutations are tight with respect to our lower bound (column 5) than with respect to Dias and Meidanis' (column 3) or Chitturi and Sudborough's (column 4).

   We also examined how large the gap between our lower bound and the actual prefix transposition distance can get. The remaining columns of Table 1 list the number of permutations whose prefix transposition distance equals our lower bound plus Δ. We note that, for $n \leq 9$, all permutations have a prefix transposition distance that is at most our lower bound plus 2 (plus 3 for $n = 10$).

Table 1. Experimental results; column 3 lists the number of cases where (1) is tight [17], column 4 lists the number of cases where (2) is tight, and columns 5 to 8 list the number of cases where (5) underestimates $ptd(\pi)$ by Δ

n	$n!$	tight w.r.t. (1)	tight w.r.t. (2)	$\Delta = 0$	$\Delta = 1$	$\Delta = 2$	$\Delta = 3$
1	1	1	1	1	0	0	0
2	2	2	2	2	0	0	0
3	6	4	4	6	0	0	0
4	24	13	15	22	2	0	0
5	120	41	48	106	14	0	0
6	720	196	255	574	143	3	0
7	5 040	862	1 144	3 782	1 234	24	0
8	40 320	5 489	7 737	27 471	12 310	539	0
9	362 880	31 033	44 187	229 167	128 576	5 137	0
10	3 628 800	247 006	369 979	2 103 510	1 427 966	97 321	3

8 Conclusions

We presented a new framework for reformulating any edit distance problem on permutations as a minimum-length factorisation problem on a related even permutation, under the implicit assumption that the edit operations are revertible. This approach is based on a new representation of a structure known as the *cycle graph*, which pervades the field of genome rearrangements in several different forms; it previously allowed us to enumerate permutations whose cycle graph decomposes into a given number of alternating cycles [12], and allowed us in this work to recover two previously known results in a simple and unified way. Moreover, we used our approach to derive a new lower bound on the prefix transposition distance that, as we showed both theoretically and experimentally, is a significant improvement over previous results. From that result, we deduced an improved lower bound on the prefix transposition diameter of the symmetric group, whose exact value is still unknown.

Future research will need to focus on computational complexity issues, since the complexity of sorting permutations by transpositions or by any prefix operation (except prefix exchanges) is still open, as well as on finding improved approximations and upper bounds on the corresponding distances. We hope that our framework will provide further insight on various issues related to those edit distance problems and their variants, and will allow us to characterise polynomial time solvable cases, if the general problems indeed prove to be difficult.

References

1. Li, Z., Wang, L., Zhang, K.: Algorithmic approaches for genome rearrangement: a review. IEEE Transactions on Systems, Man and Cybernetics, Part C 36(5), 636–648 (2006)
2. Kececioglu, J., Sankoff, D.: Exact and approximation algorithms for sorting by reversals, with application to genome rearrangement. Algorithmica 13(1-2), 180–210 (1995)

3. Christie, D.A.: Sorting permutations by block-interchanges. Information Processing Letters 60(4), 165–169 (1996)
4. Bafna, V., Pevzner, P.A.: Sorting by transpositions. SIAM Journal on Discrete Mathematics 11(2), 224–240 (1998)
5. Caprara, A.: Sorting permutations by reversals and eulerian cycle decompositions. SIAM Journal on Discrete Mathematics 12(1), 91–110 (1999)
6. Elias, I., Hartman, T.: A 1.375-approximation algorithm for sorting by transpositions. IEEE/ACM Transactions on Computational Biology and Bioinformatics 3(4), 369–379 (2006)
7. Lakshmivarahan, S., Jwo, J.S., Dhall, S.K.: Symmetry in interconnection networks based on Cayley graphs of permutation groups: A survey. Parallel Computing 19(4), 361–407 (1993)
8. Akers, S.B., Krishnamurthy, B.: A group-theoretic model for symmetric interconnection networks. IEEE Transactions on Computers 38(4), 555–566 (1989)
9. Gates, W.H., Papadimitriou, C.H.: Bounds for sorting by prefix reversal. Discrete Mathematics 27(1), 47–57 (1979)
10. Akers, S.B., Krishnamurthy, B., Harel, D.: The star graph: An attractive alternative to the n-cube. In: Proceedings of the Fourth International Conference on Parallel Processing, August 1987, pp. 393–400. Pennsylvania State University Press (1987)
11. Dias, Z., Meidanis, J.: Sorting by prefix transpositions. In: Laender, A.H.F., Oliveira, A.L. (eds.) SPIRE 2002. LNCS, vol. 2476, pp. 65–76. Springer, Heidelberg (2002)
12. Doignon, J.P., Labarre, A.: On Hultman numbers. Journal of Integer Sequences 10(6), Article 07.6.2, 13 pages (2007)
13. Chitturi, B., Sudborough, I.H.: Bounding prefix transposition distance for strings and permutations. In: Proceedings of the Forty-First Annual Hawaii International Conference on System Sciences, January 2008, p. 468. IEEE Computer Society Press, Los Alamitos (2008)
14. Wielandt, H.: Finite permutation groups. Translated from German by R. Bercov. Academic Press, New York (1964)
15. Labarre, A.: New bounds and tractable instances for the transposition distance. IEEE/ACM Transactions on Computational Biology and Bioinformatics 3(4), 380–394 (2006)
16. Jerrum, M.R.: The complexity of finding minimum-length generator sequences. Theoretical Computer Science 36(2-3), 265–289 (1985)
17. Fortuna, V.J.: Distâncias de transposição entre genomas. Master's thesis, Universidade Estadual de Campinas, São Paulo, Brazil (March 2005)

Speed Scaling Functions for Flow Time Scheduling Based on Active Job Count

Tak-Wah Lam[1], Lap-Kei Lee[1], Isaac K.K. To[2], and Prudence W.H. Wong[2]

[1] Department of Computer Science, University of Hong Kong
{twlam,lklee}@cs.hku.hk
[2] Department of Computer Science, University of Liverpool
{isaacto,pwong}@liverpool.ac.uk

Abstract. We study online scheduling to minimize flow time plus energy usage in the dynamic speed scaling model. We devise new speed scaling functions that depend on the number of active jobs, replacing the existing speed scaling functions in the literature that depend on the remaining work of active jobs. The new speed functions are more stable and also more efficient. They can support better job selection strategies to improve the competitive ratios of existing algorithms [8,5], and, more importantly, to remove the requirement of extra speed. These functions further distinguish themselves from others as they can readily be used in the non-clairvoyant model (where the size of a job is only known when the job finishes). As a first step, we study the scheduling of batched jobs (i.e., jobs with the same release time) in the non-clairvoyant model and present the first competitive algorithm for minimizing flow time plus energy (as well as for weighted flow time plus energy); the performance is close to optimal.

1 Introduction

Energy usage is an important concern in recent research on online scheduling. A popular approach to reducing energy usage is *dynamic speed scaling* (see e.g., [10,13]), which allows a processor to vary its speed dynamically. A processor incurs an energy of s^α per unit time when running at speed s, where $\alpha \geq 2$ (typically 2 or 3 [10,20]). Running a job slower saves energy, yet it takes longer and may affect performance. A lot of effort has been devoted to revisiting classical scheduling problems with dynamic speed scaling and energy concern taken into consideration (see [14] for a survey). The challenge arises from the conflicting objectives of providing good "quality of service" (QoS) and conserving energy. These studies first focused on the *infinite speed model* [24] where any speed may be used, and have recently shifted to the more realistic *bounded speed model* [12], which imposes a bound T on the maximum allowable speed.

One commonly used QoS measure for job scheduling is the total flow time. Here, jobs with arbitrary size are released at unpredictable times and the flow

---

* This research is partly supported by Hong Kong RGC Grant HKU/7140/06E and EPSRC Grant EP/E028276/1.

D. Halperin and K. Mehlhorn (Eds.): ESA 2008, LNCS 5193, pp. 647–659, 2008.

time of a job is the time elapsed since it arrives until it is completed. Preemption is allowed without penalty. When energy is not a concern, the objective is simply to minimize the total flow time of all jobs, and the online algorithm SRPT (shortest remaining processing time) is optimal [3]. If jobs carry weights, another online algorithm HDF (highest density first) has been shown to be $(1 + 1/\epsilon)$-competitive for weighted flow time, when using $(1 + \epsilon)$ times faster processor [9]; in fact, no online algorithm can be $O(1)$-competitive without extra speed [4].

The above results assume clairvoyance, i.e., the size of a job is known at release time. In some applications like operating systems, job size is only known when the job finishes. This is referred to as the non-clairvoyant model. The earlier work focused on batched jobs (i.e., all jobs have the same release time), and Motwani et al. [19] have shown that the online algorithm Round Robin is 2-competitive for flow time. There is a matching lower bound of 2 when the number of jobs is large. Kim and Chwa [17] further showed that a weighted version of Round Robin is also 2-competitive for weighted flow time. For jobs with arbitrary release times, Kalyanasundaram and Pruhs [16] showed that SETF (shortest elapsed time first) is $(1 + \epsilon)$-speed $(1 + 1/\epsilon)$-competitive for flow time. The result has also been generalized to weighted flow time with the same performance [6, 17].

Flow time and energy. To understand the tradeoff between flow time and energy, Albers and Fujiwara [1] proposed combining the dual objectives into a single objective of minimizing the sum of total flow time and energy. The intuition is that, from an economic viewpoint, users are willing to pay a certain (say, x) units of energy to reduce one unit of flow time. By changing the units of time and energy, one can further assume that $x = 1$ and thus would like to optimize total flow time plus energy. Albers and Fujiwara focused on the clairvoyant model and their work has been improved by Bansal et al. [8, 5]. As far as we know, there is no previous work on the non-clairvoyant model.

In the infinite speed model, Bansal et al. [8] gave an $O(1)$-competitive online algorithm for minimizing flow time plus energy; precisely, the competitive ratio is $\mu_\epsilon \gamma_1$, where ϵ is any positive constant, $\mu_\epsilon = \max\{(1 + 1/\epsilon), (1 + \epsilon)^\alpha\}$ and $\gamma_1 = \max\{2, \frac{2(\alpha-1)}{\alpha-(\alpha-1)^{1-1/(\alpha-1)}}\}$. E.g., if $\alpha = 2$, the competitive ratio is 5.236. Very recently, Bansal et al. [5] adapted this result to the bounded speed model. Assuming that the online algorithm can have a higher maximum speed of $(1+\epsilon)T$ for any $\epsilon > 0$, the competitive ratio in this case increases slightly to $\mu_\epsilon \gamma_2$, where $\gamma_2 = 2\alpha/(\alpha - (\alpha - 1)^{1-1/(\alpha-1)}) = (2 + o(1))\alpha/\ln\alpha$. Table 1 shows the competitive ratios for some fixed α. Both results also hold for weighted flow time plus energy.

Follow-up questions. The speed function of the algorithms by Bansal et al. [8, 5] depends on the *remaining work* of "active" jobs (i.e., jobs that have not been completed). There are several questions related to such a speed function.

- In the non-clairvoyant model, work-based speed functions are not applicable since job size, and hence remaining work, is not known to the online algorithm. Can one devise a speed function for the non-clairvoyant model?

Table 1. Results on clairvoyant scheduling for minimizing flow time plus energy. Note that the new results in this paper do not demand extra speed.

	$\alpha = 2$	$\alpha = 3$
Infinite speed model ($T = \infty$)	5.236 [8] **2.667** [this paper]	7.940 [8] **3.252** [this paper]
Bounded speed model	10.472 with max speed $1.618T$ [5] **3.6** with max speed T [this paper]	11.910 with max speed $1.466T$ [5] **4** with max speed T [this paper]

- Work-based speed functions would demand the processor speed to change continuously which is undesirable practically. Can one design a more stable speed function that changes in a discrete manner?
- The algorithms in [8,5] require extra speed even in the unweighted setting. In contrast, the classic result on flow-time scheduling does not need extra speed [3]. This is perhaps due to the inefficiency of the work-based speed functions; specifically, they are sometimes slower than a critical threshold ($(\frac{n}{\alpha-1})^{1/\alpha}$ where n is the number of active jobs). When this happens, we can decrease the flow time plus energy by increasing the speed. It is natural to ask whether a speed function that never goes below this threshold can work without extra speed and gives a better competitive ratio.

Our contribution. In this paper, we answer affirmatively the above questions by introducing new speed functions that depend on the number of active jobs. They are more stable, changing only at job arrival or completion. Using these functions leads to improvements in the clairvoyant model and provides the first competitive results on non-clairvoyant scheduling of batched jobs.

- **Clairvoyant scheduling:** Define the speed function AJC to be $n^{1/\alpha}$, where n is the number of active jobs. We use SRPT (instead of SJF (shortest job first) in [8,5]) to select jobs. Our algorithm is more competitive for minimizing flow time plus energy and does not need extra speed: for the infinite and bounded speed model, the competitive ratios are respectively $\beta_1 = 2/(1 - \frac{\alpha-1}{\alpha^{\alpha/(\alpha-1)}})$ and $\beta_2 = 2(\alpha+1)/(\alpha - \frac{\alpha-1}{(\alpha+1)^{1/(\alpha-1)}})$. Table 1 compares these ratios with those in [8,5]. The improvement is more significant for large α, as β_1 and β_2 tend to $2\alpha/\ln\alpha$, while $\mu_\epsilon\gamma_1$ and $\mu_\epsilon\gamma_2$ [8,5] tend to $2(\alpha/\ln\alpha)^2$.
- **Non-clairvoyant scheduling:** We focus on batched jobs, i.e., when all jobs are released at time 0. For scheduling unweighted jobs, we use the speed function $\text{AJC}^* = (\frac{n}{\alpha-1})^{1/\alpha}$, where n is the total number of active jobs. Coupling with Round Robin, we give an algorithm that is $(2-\frac{1}{\alpha})$-competitive in the infinite speed model and 2-competitive in the bounded speed model. The latter inherits a lower bound of 2 from flow-time scheduling [19]. We can further generalize this algorithm for minimizing weighted flow time plus energy, and the corresponding ratios become $(2 - \frac{1}{\alpha})^2$ and 4, respectively.

Technically speaking, the analysis of existing clairvoyant algorithms requires indirect comparison via a notion called fractional flow. In contrast, we divide the time into "stable intervals", and directly compare the flow time of the on-line algorithm against an optimal offline algorithm in each interval. This makes the analysis tighter. For the non-clairvoyant algorithms, we first prove that the performance of our algorithm is close to that of a clairvoyant algorithm based on SJF (shortest job first) plus AJC*. Then we show that SJF-AJC* is optimal against any offline algorithm for minimizing flow time plus energy.

Remarks. The theoretical study of energy-efficient scheduling was initiated by Yao, Demers and Shenker [24]. They considered deadline scheduling in the infinite speed model. Their result was improved by Bansal et al. [7], and extended to the bounded speed model by Chan et al. [12] and Bansal et al. [5]. Irani et al. [15] considered a setting where the processor has a sleep state. Pruhs et al. [21] also studied offline scheduling for minimizing the total flow time on a processor with a given amount of energy. The offline problem of minimizing the makespan subject to a fixed amount of energy has been studied in [11,22]. Recently, multiprocessor setting has received attention, with interesting offline [11,22] and online results [2,18]. As some of these multiprocessor algorithms (in particular, [18]) are based on the single-processor algorithms in [8,5], our new result on clairvoyant scheduling immediately leads to an improvement.

2   Definitions and Notations

We consider a job set $\mathcal{J}$ to be scheduled on a processor whose speed can be varied between 0 and T, the speed bound. In the infinite speed model, $T = \infty$, so any speed is allowed. When running at speed s, the processor processes s units of work and consumes s^α units of energy in each unit of time, where $\alpha \geq 2$. Preemption is allowed; a preempted job can resume at the point of preemption. We use r_i and p_i to denote the release time and work requirement (or *size*) of a job J_i in $\mathcal{J}$, respectively. If $r_i = 0$ for all jobs, we call $\mathcal{J}$ *batched jobs*.

Consider a particular time t in a schedule of $\mathcal{J}$. For any job J_i in $\mathcal{J}$, we let q_i denote its remaining work at t, and say it is *active* if $r_i \leq t$ and $q_i > 0$. The *flow time* F_i of J_i is the time elapsed since it arrives until it is completed. The *total flow time* is given by $F = \sum_i F_i$. Note that $F = \int_0^\infty n(t)\, dt$, where $n(t)$ denotes the number of active jobs at time t, and the energy consumption is $E = \int_0^\infty s(t)^\alpha\, dt$, where $s(t)$ is the speed of the processor at time t. Our aim is to minimize the total flow time plus energy, $G = F + E$. We observe that each of E, F and G is the integration over all time from 0 to ∞. We call the integration over a period of time to be the *contribution* to their respective value during that period. E.g., the contribution to G from t_1 to t_2 is $\int_{t_1}^{t_2}(n(t) + s(t)^\alpha)\, dt$.

3   Clairvoyant Scheduling with Arbitrary Release Times

In this section, we study the case where a job arrives at arbitrary time and its size is known upon arrival. Define the speed function AJC (active job count) to be $\min\{T, n^{1/\alpha}\}$, where n is the number of active jobs and T is maximum speed.

Coupling with SRPT, we have the algorithm **SRPT-AJC**. We first explain that SRPT gives the best job selection (Lemma 1). In the next two subsections, we analyze SRPT-AJC in the infinite speed and bounded speed models.

Lemma 1. *Consider a job sequence $\mathcal{J}$. Suppose a schedule S for $\mathcal{J}$ uses speed function f. Then, among all schedules of $\mathcal{J}$ using the speed function f, the one selecting jobs in accordance with SRPT incurs the least total flow time.*

Proof. We modify S in multiple steps to a SRPT schedule. In each step the new schedule S' has total flow time reduced. Then the lemma follows.

Let t be the first time when S does not follow SRPT, running J_i instead of the shortest remaining work job J_j. S' differs from S during the time intervals since t when S runs either job: J_j is run to completion before J_i, using the same speed function. J_j thus completes in S' earlier than J_i does in S. So the sum of their completion time, and thus the total flow time, is less in S' than in S.   □

3.1   Analysis of SRPT-AJC for the Infinite Speed Model

We analyze SRPT-AJC for the infinite speed model, comparing it against an optimal offline schedule OPT. By Lemma 1, OPT uses the SRPT policy as well.

Overview. Consider any time t. Let $G_a(t)$ and $G_o(t)$ be the flow time plus energy incurred up to t by SRPT-AJC and OPT, respectively. We drop the parameter t when it refers to the current time. Our analysis exploits amortization and potential functions (e.g., [8, 12]): if there is a potential function $\Phi(t)$ and a value β such that the followings hold, then SRPT-AJC is β-competitive.

- *Boundary condition: Φ is initially 0 and finally non-negative.*
- *Arrival condition:* When a job is released, Φ does not increase.
- *Running condition:* At any other time, the rate of change of G_a plus that of Φ is no more than β times the rate of change of G_o, i.e., $\frac{dG_a}{dt} + \frac{d\Phi}{dt} \leq \beta \frac{dG_o}{dt}$.

We first show such a potential function Φ, whose design is motivated by the work in [8, 5]. We will choose β to be $2/(1 - \frac{\alpha-1}{\alpha^{\alpha/(\alpha-1)}})$. Then we show that the above conditions hold, and thus can conclude the competitiveness of SRPT-AJC.

Theorem 1. *SRPT-AJC is β_1-competitive for flow time plus energy in the infinite speed model, where $\beta_1 = 2/(1 - \frac{\alpha-1}{\alpha^{\alpha/(\alpha-1)}})$.*

Potential function $\Phi(t)$. Consider any time t. For any $q \geq 0$, let $n_a(q)$ denote the current number of active jobs with remaining work at least q in SRPT-AJC, and similarly $n_o(q)$ for OPT. So $n_a(0)$ and $n_o(0)$ are the total number of active jobs in the schedules, which we abbreviate as n_a and n_o, respectively. It is useful to consider $n_a(q)$ and $n_o(q)$ as functions of q which change when a job arrives or runs for a while (see Fig. 3.1). We define the potential function as

$$\Phi(t) = \eta \int_0^\infty \phi(q)\, dq \ , \text{ where } \phi(q) = \left(\sum_{i=1}^{n_a(q)} i^{1-1/\alpha} \right) - n_a(q)^{1-1/\alpha} n_o(q) \ ,$$

and $\eta = 2/(1 - \frac{\alpha-1}{\alpha^{\alpha/(\alpha-1)}})$. (In bounded speed model, $\eta = 2/(1 - \frac{1-1/\alpha}{(\alpha+1)^{1/(\alpha-1)}})$.)

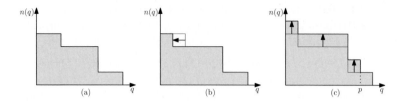

Fig. 1. (a) At any time, $n_a(q)$ or $n_o(q)$ (denoted by $n(q)$ above) is a step function containing unit height stripes, the area under $n(q)$ is the total remaining work. (b) If we run a job selected with SRPT at speed s for a period of time Δ, the top stripe shrinks by $s\Delta$. (c) When a job of size p is released, $n(q)$ increases by 1 for all $q \leq p$.

At $t = 0$ or ∞, no job remains, so $\Phi = 0$. The integration of the first term of $\phi(q)$ is proportional to the total flow time plus energy of SRPT-AJC after t if no more job arrives (which is $2 \int_0^\infty \sum_{i=1}^{n_a(q)} i^{1-1/\alpha}\, dq$), paying the cost once OPT completes all jobs. The second term of $\phi(q)$ makes the arrival condition hold.

Lemma 2. *When a job arrives, the change of Φ is non-positive.*

Proof. Suppose a job J_j arrives. For $q > p_j$, $n_a(q)$ and $n_o(q)$, and hence $\phi(q)$, are unchanged. For $q \leq p_j$, both $n_a(q)$ and $n_o(q)$ increase by 1 (see Fig. 3.1(c)). So the first term of $\phi(q)$ increases by $(n_a(q) + 1)^{1-1/\alpha}$. The increase of the term $n_a(q)^{1-1/\alpha}n_o(q)$ is interpreted in two-steps: (i) increase to $(n_a(q)+1)^{1-1/\alpha}n_o(q)$, and (ii) increase to $(n_a(q)+1)^{1-1/\alpha}(n_o(q)+1)$. The increase in step (ii), $(n_a(q)+1)^{1-1/\alpha}$, covers the increase in the first term of $\phi(q)$, so $\phi(q)$ cannot increase. $\square$

Running condition. The rest of this section proves the following lemma.

Lemma 3. *When no job arrives, $\frac{dG_a}{dt} + \frac{d\Phi}{dt} \leq \beta_1 \frac{dG_o}{dt}$ where $\beta_1 = 2/(1 - \frac{\alpha-1}{\alpha^{\alpha/(\alpha-1)}})$.*

Consider any time t. Let s_a and s_o be the speed of SRPT-AJC and OPT, respectively, and q_a and q_o be the remaining work of the job they run. We divide the time line into *stable intervals* by breaking it when the following events occur.

- A job arrives, or is completed by either SRPT-AJC or OPT.
- The speed s_a or the job chosen by SRPT-AJC changes.
- The speed s_o or the job chosen by OPT changes.
- Either $n_o(q_a)$ or $n_a(q_o)$ changes.

Φ does not increase on job arrival (Lemma 2), and is unchanged on other events above ($\phi(q)$ changes for single q). So we focus on its change in a stable interval.

We first bound $\frac{d\Phi}{dt}$. Consider a stable interval of length dt. We analyze $d\Phi$ as if $\phi(q)$ is modified in two steps: (i) $n_a(q)$ decreases due to the execution of SRPT-AJC. (ii) $n_o(q)$ decreases due to the execution of OPT. We denote these changes by $d\Phi_1$ and $d\Phi_2$, respectively. Then $d\Phi = d\Phi_1 + d\Phi_2$.

Lemma 4. *Consider a stable interval of length dt. (i) $d\Phi_1 \leq \eta(n_o - n_a)dt$; (ii) $d\Phi_2 \leq \eta n_a^{1-1/\alpha} s_o dt$.*

Proof. (i) Consider SRPT-AJC. $n_a(q)$ decreases from n_a to $n_a - 1$ for all $q \in [q_a - s_a dt, q_a]$ (see Fig. 3.1(b)). For any $q \in [q_a - s_a dt, q_a]$, $\phi(q)$ is changed by:

$$\left(\sum_{i=1}^{n_a-1} i^{1-1/\alpha}\right) - (n_a - 1)^{1-1/\alpha} n_o(q) - \left(\sum_{i=1}^{n_a} i^{1-1/\alpha}\right) + n_a^{1-1/\alpha} n_o(q)$$

$$\leq -n_a^{1-1/\alpha} + n_a^{-1/\alpha} n_o(q) \leq -n_a^{1-1/\alpha} + n_a^{-1/\alpha} n_o \ .$$

(The first inequality is due to $n^{1-1/\alpha} - (n-1)^{1-1/\alpha} \leq n^{-1/\alpha}$ for any $n \geq 1$. The second holds since $n_o(q) \leq n_o$.) Recall that $s_a = n_a^{1/\alpha}$. Integrating over all q,

$$d\Phi_1 \leq \eta(-n_a^{1-1/\alpha} + n_a^{-1/\alpha} n_o)(n_a^{1/\alpha} dt) = \eta(n_o - n_a)dt \ .$$

(ii) Consider OPT. As in (i), $\phi(q)$ is changed only for $q \in [q_o - s_o dt, q_o]$. Note that $n_a(q) \leq n_a$ for all q. Then for any $q \in [q_o - s_o dt, q_o]$, $\phi(q)$ is changed by

$$-n_a(q)^{1-1/\alpha}(n_o(q) - 1) + n_a(q)^{1-1/\alpha} n_o(q) = n_a(q)^{1-1/\alpha} \leq n_a^{1-1/\alpha} \ .$$

Integrating over all q, we have $d\Phi_2 \leq \eta n_a^{1-1/\alpha} s_o dt$. $\qquad\square$

Proof (Lemma 3). We introduce a constant $\mu > 0$ into Lemma 4 (ii) using the Young's Inequality (see Corollary 9 of [8]), leading to $d\Phi_2 \leq \eta n_a^{1-1/\alpha} s_o dt \leq \left(\eta(1 - \frac{1}{\alpha})\mu^{\alpha/(\alpha-1)} n_a + \frac{\eta s_o^\alpha}{\alpha \mu^\alpha}\right)dt$. Since $s_a = n_a^{1/\alpha}$, $\frac{dG_a}{dt} = n_a + s_a^\alpha = 2n_a$. Also, $\frac{dG_o}{dt} = n_o + s_o^\alpha$. Since $d\Phi = d\Phi_1 + d\Phi_2$, by Lemma 4 (i), we have

$$\frac{dG_a}{dt} + \frac{d\Phi}{dt} \leq 2n_a + \eta\left(n_o - n_a + \left(1 - \frac{1}{\alpha}\right)\mu^{\alpha/(\alpha-1)} n_a + \frac{s_o^\alpha}{\alpha\mu^\alpha}\right) . \qquad (1)$$

Lemma 3 follows with $\beta_1 = \eta = 2/(1 - \frac{\alpha-1}{\alpha^{\alpha/(\alpha-1)}})$ and $\mu = \alpha^{-1/\alpha}$. $\qquad\square$

3.2 Analysis of SRPT-AJC for the Bounded Speed Model

We now turn to the bounded speed model. We use the same potential function while setting $\eta = 2/(1 - \frac{1-1/\alpha}{(\alpha+1)^{1/(\alpha-1)}})$. Most of the analysis in Sect. 3.1 still holds, except Lemma 4 (i). As the speed used might be T instead of $n^{1/\alpha}$ if n is large, the decrease in Φ_1 is not sufficient to guarantee the original competitive ratio. We observe that the difference $(n_a - n_o)$ is upper bounded by T^α (Lemma 5). Then the competitiveness is only slightly worse (Theorem 2).

Lemma 5. *At any time, the number of active jobs in SRPT-AJC and OPT satisfy $n_a - n_o \leq T^\alpha$.*

Proof. This is trivial if $n_a < T^\alpha$. Suppose $n_a \geq T^\alpha$ at time t. Let t_0 be the last moment before t when n_a changes from less than T^α to at least T^α. Consider the interval $[t_0, t)$, where SRPT-AJC runs at full speed. Suppose k jobs arrive, and OPT completes x of them, so $n_o \geq k - x$. Since SRPT maximizes the number of jobs completed at any time [23], SRPT-AJC also completes at least x jobs. So n_a increases by at most $k - x \leq n_o$ since t_0, and the lemma follows. $\qquad\square$

Theorem 2. *SRPT-AJC is β_2-competitive for flow time plus energy in the bounded speed model, where $\beta_2 = 2(\alpha+1)/(\alpha - \frac{\alpha-1}{(\alpha+1)^{1/(\alpha-1)}})$.*

Proof. The boundary and arrival conditions still hold. It remains to establish the running condition. Its analysis is split into two cases.

Case 1: $n_a \leq T^\alpha$. The arguments in Sect. 3.1 still hold, leading to (1). Set $\mu = (\alpha+1)^{-1/\alpha}$ and recall that $\eta = 2/(1 - \frac{1-1/\alpha}{(\alpha+1)^{1/(\alpha-1)}})$, (1) implies $\frac{dG_a}{dt} + \frac{d\Phi}{dt} \leq \eta n_o + (1 + 1/\alpha)\eta s_o^\alpha \leq \beta_2 \frac{dG_o}{dt}$.

Case 2: $n_a > T^\alpha$. The arguments in Sect. 3.1 hold, except Lemma 4 (i). We still have $\frac{dG_o}{dt} = n_o + s_o^\alpha$ and $\frac{dG_a}{dt} = n_a + T^\alpha < 2n_a$. For $d\Phi_1$,

$$d\Phi_1 \leq \eta(-n_a^{1-1/\alpha} + n_a^{-1/\alpha}n_o)T dt = \eta(n_o - n_a)\left(\frac{T^\alpha}{n_a}\right)^{1/\alpha} dt \ .$$

If $n_o \geq n_a$, $d\Phi_1 \leq \eta(n_o - n_a)dt$ as before (since $T^\alpha/n_a \leq 1$), leading to (1), so the arguments in Case 1 apply. If $n_o < n_a$, Lemma 5 implies

$$d\Phi_1 \leq -\eta(n_a - n_o)\left(\frac{T^\alpha}{n_a}\right)^{1/\alpha} dt \leq \frac{-\eta(n_a - n_o)^{1+1/\alpha}}{n_a^{1/\alpha}} dt \ .$$

Note that $f(n_a - n_o) \geq f(n_a) - f'(n_a) n_o$ for the convex function $f(x) = x^{1+1/\alpha}$, which is equivalent to $(n_a - n_o)^{1+1/\alpha} \geq n_a^{1+1/\alpha} - (1+1/\alpha)n_a^{1/\alpha}n_o$. We thus have

$$d\Phi_1 \leq -\eta((n_a^{1+1/\alpha} - (1+1/\alpha)n_a^{1/\alpha}n_o)/n_a^{1/\alpha})dt = \eta((1+1/\alpha)n_o - n_a)dt \ ,$$

and $\frac{dG_a}{dt} + \frac{d\Phi}{dt} \leq 2n_a + \eta\left((1 + \frac{1}{\alpha})n_o - n_a + (1 - \frac{1}{\alpha})\mu^{\alpha/(\alpha-1)}n_a + \frac{s_o^\alpha}{\alpha\mu^\alpha}\right)$.

Setting $\mu = (\alpha+1)^{-1/\alpha}$, this implies $\frac{dG_a}{dt} + \frac{d\Phi}{dt} \leq (1+\frac{1}{\alpha})\eta(n_o + s_o^\alpha) = \beta_2 \frac{dG_o}{dt}$. $\square$

4   Non-clairvoyant Scheduling of Batched Jobs

In this section, we study non-clairvoyant scheduling of batched jobs. Recall that the online algorithm knows the size of a job only when the job finishes.

AJC* and RR-AJC*. For batched jobs, we use a more energy-conservative speed function AJC*, defined as $\min\{T, (\frac{n(t)}{\alpha-1})^{1/\alpha}\}$, where $n(t)$ is the number of active jobs at t. To cope with unknown job sizes, RR-AJC* uses AJC* with RR: split the processor equally among all active jobs.

To analyze RR-AJC*, we consider a clairvoyant algorithm SJF-AJC* (shortest job first plus AJC*). In Sect. 4.1, we show an interesting relation that the flow time plus energy incurred by RR-AJC* is close to that of SJF-AJC*. In Sect. 4.2 we complete the analysis by showing SJF-AJC* is optimal.

In some applications, jobs may carry weights to reflect their importance. We use w_i to denote the weight of a job J_i, and define its *density* ρ_i to be w_i/p_i. The weighted flow time of a job is simply its flow time multiplied by its weight. The above result can be generalized for weighted flow time plus energy as follows.

AJW* and WRR-AJW*. The speed function AJW* (active job weight) is defined as $\min\{T, (\frac{w(t)}{\alpha-1})^{1/\alpha}\}$ where $w(t)$ is the total weight of active jobs at t. The algorithm WRR-AJW* uses AJW* with the WRR policy: split the processor among all active jobs in the ratio of their weights. We define the *normalized work* of a job as its work divided by its weight. Every active job has the same normalized processed work at any time.

To analyze WRR-AJW*, we consider a clairvoyant algorithm HDF-AJW* (highest density first plus AJW*). The relation between WRR-AJW* and HDF-AJW* is the same as before (Sect. 4.1). However, HDF-AJW* is not optimal. Yet we show that HDF-AJW* is competitive in Sect. 4.3.

We use the weighted setting as a common platform, where RR-AJC* (resp. SJF-AJC*) is WRR-AJW* (resp. HDF-AJW*) with job weights all equal to one. Without loss of generality, we assume the input $\mathcal{J} = \{J_1, J_2, \ldots, J_n\}$ is in increasing job density order, i.e., $\rho_1 \leq \rho_2 \leq \cdots \leq \rho_n$ (ties are broken by job IDs).

4.1   Comparing WRR-AJW* against HDF-AJW*

As jobs are batched, WRR implies that jobs complete in the order of normalized work, from J_n to J_1. Thus $w(t) = \sum_{j=1}^{i} w_j$ if J_i is the smallest normalized work job at t. We can thus compare WRR-AJW* against HDF-AJW* easily.

Lemma 6. *For scheduling batched jobs, the weighted flow time plus energy of WRR-AJW* is (i) at most $(2 - 1/\alpha)$ times of HDF-AJW* in the infinite speed model, and (ii) at most 2 times of HDF-AJW* in the bounded speed model.*

To prove Lemma 6, we focus on the contributions to weighted flow time and energy during the time when a particular job J_i is the job with the smallest normalized work in WRR-AJW*. Due to the WRR policy, each of the remaining jobs J_j with $1 \leq j \leq i$ is run for the same amount of normalized work. We thus evaluate the weighted flow time and energy incurred by WRR-AJW* during this period, denoted as $F_w(J_i)$ and $E_w(J_i)$. They are compared against the weighted flow time and energy incurred by HDF-AJW* to process that same amount of normalized work for each of these jobs, denoted as $F_h(J_i)$ and $E_h(J_i)$. We show that both $F_w(J_i)/F_h(J_i)$ and $E_w(J_i)/E_h(J_i)$ are no greater than $(2 - 1/\alpha)$ for $T = \infty$, and 2 for general T. Summing over all J_i leads to Lemma 6.

Lemma 7. *If $T = \infty$, $F_w(J_i) \leq (2-1/\alpha)F_h(J_i)$ and $E_w(J_i) \leq (2-1/\alpha)E_h(J_i)$.*

Proof. Due to the rules in the speed function AJW*, when $T = \infty$ we have $F_w(J_i) = (\alpha - 1)E_w(J_i)$ and $F_h(J_i) = (\alpha - 1)E_h(J_i)$. So it suffices to show $F_w(J_i) \leq (2 - 1/\alpha)F_h(J_i)$.

Let us first consider WRR-AJW*. Let Δh be the normalized work processed for each job $J_1, \ldots, J_i$. We have seen that $w(t) = \sum_{k=1}^{i} w_k$, $s = (\frac{w(t)}{\alpha-1})^{1/\alpha}$. The amount of work processed for J_j $(1 \leq j \leq i)$ is $w_j \Delta h$, so the total weighted flow time incurred $F_w(J_i) = \sum_{j=1}^{i} w_j \Delta h \sum_{k=1}^{i} w_k/s = (\alpha-1)^{1/\alpha}(\sum_{j=1}^{i} w_j)^{2-1/\alpha} \Delta h$.

In contrast, HDF-AJW* runs only the highest density (i.e., least normalized work) job. At time t when processing J_j, $w(t) = \sum_{k=1}^{j} w_k$, $s = (\frac{w(t)}{\alpha-1})^{1/\alpha}$. The weighted flow time incurred for processing an amount of work $w_j \Delta h$ for J_j is thus $w_j \Delta h (\sum_{k=1}^{j} w_k)/s = (\alpha-1)^{1/\alpha} \Delta h (\sum_{k=1}^{j} w_k)^{1-1/\alpha} w_j$. We thus have

$$F_{\mathrm{h}}(J_i) = (\alpha-1)^{1/\alpha} \Delta h \sum_{j=1}^{i} \left(\sum_{k=1}^{j} w_k \right)^{1-1/\alpha} w_j .$$

To approximate $\sum_{j=1}^{i} \left(\sum_{k=1}^{j} w_k \right)^{1-1/\alpha} w_j$, we use the staircase-like function

$$f(x) = \left(\sum_{k=1}^{j} w_k \right)^{1-1/\alpha} \quad \text{if } x \in [\sum_{k=1}^{j-1} w_k, \sum_{k=1}^{j} w_k) \text{ where } 1 \le j \le i .$$

Note that $\sum_{j=1}^{i} (\sum_{k=1}^{j} w_k)^{1-1/\alpha} w_j$ is exactly $\int_0^{\sum_{j=1}^{i} w_j} f(x)\, \mathrm{d}x$. On the other hand, $f(x) \ge x^{1-1/\alpha}$ for all $x \in [0, \sum_{j=1}^{i} w_j)$. We thus have

$$\sum_{j=1}^{i} \left(\sum_{k=1}^{j} w_k \right)^{1-1/\alpha} w_j \ge \int_0^{\sum_{j=1}^{i} w_j} x^{1-1/\alpha}\, \mathrm{d}x = \frac{(\sum_{j=1}^{i} w_j)^{2-1/\alpha}}{2-1/\alpha} ,$$

and $F_{\mathrm{h}}(J_i) \ge (\alpha-1)^{1/\alpha} \Delta h \left(\sum_{j=1}^{i} w_j \right)^{2-1/\alpha} / (2 - \frac{1}{\alpha}) = F_{\mathrm{w}}(J_i)/(2 - \frac{1}{\alpha})$. □

Proof (Lemma 6). We obtain (i) $(T = \infty)$ by summing the relations about F_{h} and F_{w} and those about E_{h} and E_{w} in Lemma 7 over all J_i.

For (ii) $(T < \infty)$, suppose WRR-AJW* processes Δh normalized work for each of $J_1, \ldots, J_i$. We first focus on $E_{\mathrm{w}}(J_i)$ and $E_{\mathrm{h}}(J_i)$. If $(\sum_{j=1}^{i} w_j/(\alpha-1))^{1/\alpha} \le T$, Lemma 7 applies, so $E_{\mathrm{w}}(J_i) \le (2 - 1/\alpha)E_{\mathrm{h}}(J_i)$. Otherwise, we try to find a $k \in \{1, \ldots, i\}$ such that $\sum_{j=1}^{k} w_j$ is exactly $(\alpha-1)T^{\alpha}$ (so that the speed bound is just not exceeded). If no such k exists, for the sake of analysis we split some job J_u into two jobs J_{u1} and J_{u2} with the same density and total weight, so that $w_{u1} + \sum_{j=1}^{u-1} w_j = (\alpha-1)T^{\alpha}$. We set $k = u1$. This job splitting does not affect the speed function, and thus the energy consumption, of either WRR-AJW* and HDF-AJW* (speed used for J_{u1}, J_{u2} and J_u are all T). We now notice that both WRR-AJW* and HDF-AJW* run $J_{k+1}, \ldots, J_i$ at speed T, consuming the same energy E_0. The other jobs are run as if $T = \infty$, so Lemma 7 leads to $E_{\mathrm{w}}(J_i) - E_0 \le (2 - 1/\alpha)(E_{\mathrm{h}}(J_i) - E_0)$. This implies $E_{\mathrm{w}}(J_i) \le (2 - 1/\alpha)E_{\mathrm{h}}(J_i)$.

We now compare $F_{\mathrm{w}}(J_i)$ and $F_{\mathrm{h}}(J_i)$. Again the interesting case is when $(\sum_{j=1}^{i} w_j/(\alpha-1))^{1/\alpha} > T$, otherwise $F_{\mathrm{w}}(J_i) \le (2-1/\alpha)F_{\mathrm{h}}(J_i)$ by Lemma 7. For WRR-AJW*, the processor uses speed T, so the time needed is $\sum_{j=1}^{i} w_j \Delta h/T$, and $F_{\mathrm{w}}(J_i) = (\sum_{j=1}^{i} w_j)^2 \Delta h/T$. For HDF-AJW*, the time needed to run J_j for $w_j \Delta h$ units of work is at least $w_j \Delta h/T$ (since the speed used cannot be faster than T), incurring weighted flow time of at least $\sum_{k=1}^{j} w_k w_j \Delta h/T$. We thus have $F_{\mathrm{h}}(J_i) \ge \sum_{j=1}^{i} \sum_{k=1}^{j} w_k w_j \Delta h/T > (\sum_{j=1}^{i} w_j)^2 \Delta h/2T = F_{\mathrm{w}}(J_i)/2$.

Summing these relations over all J_i gives the desired ratio in Lemma 6. □

4.2 Analysis of SJF-AJC*

We show that the speed function AJC* minimizes the flow time plus energy for scheduling batched jobs using SJF (equivalently, SRPT) (Lemma 8), implying the optimality of SJF-AJC* for flow time plus energy. Combining with Lemma 6, we obtain the competitive ratio of RR-AJC* (Theorem 3).

Lemma 8. *Consider a set of batched jobs $\mathcal{J}$. Among all schedules of $\mathcal{J}$ using SJF for job selection, the schedule that incurs the minimum flow time plus energy sets the speed at any time t as $\min\{T, (\frac{n(t)}{\alpha-1})^{1/\alpha}\}$, where $n(t)$ is the number of active jobs at t.*

Proof. Consider a particular job J_i in the optimal schedule. We only need to consider cases where its speed is constant, otherwise we can average the speed to reduce energy usage without affecting flow time. Note that $n(t)$ is unchanged when J_i is run. Suppose J_i runs at speed s. Then its contribution to flow time plus energy is $n(t)p_i/s + s^{\alpha-1}p_i$, which is minimized when $s = (\frac{n(t)}{\alpha-1})^{1/\alpha}$. □

Theorem 3. *For scheduling batched jobs to minimize flow time plus energy, the algorithm RR-AJC* is (i) $(2 - 1/\alpha)$-competitive in the infinite speed model, and (ii) 2-competitive in the bounded speed model.*

Proof. Since every other schedule can be modified to the SJF-AJC* schedule by Lemma 1 and then Lemma 8 while reducing total flow time plus energy, SJF-AJC* is optimal for total flow time plus energy. The theorem thus follows naturally from Lemma 6. □

4.3 Analysis of HDF-AJW*

When jobs are weighted, the clairvoyant algorithm HDF-AJW* is not optimal for weighted flow time plus energy. Instead we analyze HDF-AJW* via a variant concerning fractional flow. Due to space limitation, we only sketch the ideas.

Consider a schedule of $\mathcal{J}$. At any time t, the *fractional weight* $\widehat{w}_i$ of J_i is defined to be $w_i(q_i/p_i)$ (recall that q_i is the remaining work of J_i). We define $\widehat{w}(t) = \sum_{J_i \text{ is active}} \widehat{w}_i$. The *fractional flow* is defined as $\widehat{F} = \int_0^\infty \widehat{w}(t)\,dt$. We now define our variant of HDF-AJW*.

Algorithm HDF-FW. It differs from HDF-AJW* only in the speed function, which uses the speed function FW defined as $(\frac{\widehat{w}(t)}{\alpha-1})^{1/\alpha}$ at any time t.

We follow the framework in Sect. 4.2 to show the optimality of HDF-FW: Firstly, HDF minimizes fractional flow for a fixed speed function. Secondly, FW minimizes the fractional flow plus energy for scheduling batched jobs using HDF.

Lemma 9. *Consider a set of weighted batched jobs. The algorithm HDF-FW is optimal for minimizing the fractional flow plus energy of the schedule.*

By comparing the contribution to the weighted flow time plus energy of HDF-AJW* against that to the fractional flow plus energy of HDF-FW when each job J_i is running, we can show the following lemma.

Lemma 10. *Consider a set of batched jobs. Let $\widehat{G}_{\mathrm{hf}}$ be the fractional flow plus energy with HDF-FW. Then the weighted flow time plus energy with HDF-AJW* is (i) $G_{\mathrm{h}} \leq (2 - 1/\alpha)\widehat{G}_{\mathrm{hf}}$ in the infinite speed model, and (ii) $G_{\mathrm{h}} \leq 2\widehat{G}_{\mathrm{hf}}$ in the bounded speed model.*

We note that for any schedule, the fractional flow is at most the weighted flow time. Thus HDF-AJW* is $(2 - 1/\alpha)$-competitive for weighted flow time plus energy. Together with Lemma 6, we obtain the competitive ratio of WRR-AJW*.

Theorem 4. *Consider a set of weighted batched jobs. The algorithm WRR-AJW* is (i) $(2 - 1/\alpha)^2$-competitive in the infinite speed model, and (ii) 4-competitive in the bounded speed model.*

References

1. Albers, S., Fujiwara, H.: Energy-efficient algorithms for flow time minimization. ACM Trans. Alg. 3(4), 49 (2007)
2. Albers, S., Muller, F., Schmelzer, S.: Speed scaling on parallel processors. In: Proc. SPAA, pp. 289–298 (2007)
3. Baker, K.R.: Introduction to Sequencing and Scheduling. Wiley, New York (1974)
4. Bansal, N., Chan, H.L.: Weighted flow time does not have O(1) competitive algorithms (manuscript)
5. Bansal, N., Chan, H.L., Lam, T.W., Lee, L.K.: Scheduling for speed bounded processors. In: Proc. ICALP (to appear, 2008)
6. Bansal, N., Dhamdhere, K.: Minimizing weighted flow time. ACM Trans. Alg. 3(4), 39 (2007)
7. Bansal, N., Kimbrel, T., Pruhs, K.: Speed scaling to manage energy and temperature. J. ACM 54(1) (2007)
8. Bansal, N., Pruhs, K., Stein, C.: Speed scaling for weighted flow time. In: Proc. SODA, pp. 805–813 (2007)
9. Becchetti, L., Leonardi, S., Marchetti-Spaccamela, A., Pruhs, K.: Online weighted flow time and deadline scheduling. J. Discrete Algorithms 4(3), 339–352 (2006)
10. Brooks, D., Bose, P., Schuster, S., Jacobson, H.M., Kudva, P., Buyuktosunoglu, A., Wellman, J.-D., Zyuban, V.V., Gupta, M., Cook, P.W.: Power-aware microarchitecture: Design and modeling challenges for next-generation microprocessors. IEEE Micro. 20(6), 26–44 (2000)
11. Bunde, D.P.: Power-aware scheduling for makespan and flow. In: Proc. SPAA, pp. 190–196 (2006)
12. Chan, H.L., Chan, W.T., Lam, T.W., Lee, L.K., Mak, K.S., Wong, P.W.H.: Energy efficient online deadline scheduling. In: Proc. SODA (2007)
13. Grunwald, D., Levis, P., Morrey, C.B., Neufeld, M.: Policies for dynamic clock scheduling. In: Proc. OSDI, pp. 73–86 (2000)
14. Irani, S., Pruhs, K.: Algorithmic problems in power management. SIGACT News 32(2), 63–76 (2005)
15. Irani, S., Shukla, S., Gupta, R.: Algorithms for power savings. ACM Trans. Alg. 3(4), 41 (2007)
16. Kalyanasundaram, B., Pruhs, K.: Speed is as powerful as clairvoyance. J. ACM 47(4), 617–643 (2000)

17. Kim, J.-H., Chwa, K.-Y.: Non-clairvoyant scheduling for weighted flow time. IPL 87(1), 31–37 (2003)
18. Lam, T.W., Lee, L.K., To, I.K.K., Wong, P.W.H.: Competitive non-migratory scheduling for flow time and energy. In: Proc. SPAA, pp. 256–264 (2008)
19. Motwani, R., Phillips, S., Torng, E.: Nonclairvoyant scheduling. Theoretical Computer Science 130(1), 17–47 (1994)
20. Mudge, T.N.: Power: A first-class architectural design constraint. IEEE Comp. 34(4), 52–58 (2001)
21. Pruhs, K., Uthaisombut, P., Woeginger, G.: Getting the best response for your erg. In: Proc. SWAT, pp. 14–25 (2004)
22. Pruhs, K., van Stee, R., Uthaisombut, P.: Speed scaling of tasks with precedence constraints. In: Proc. WAOA, pp. 307–319 (2005)
23. Schrage, L.: A proof of the optimality of the shortest remaining processing time discipline. Operations Research 16(3), 687–690 (1968)
24. Yao, F., Demers, A.J., Shenker, S.: A scheduling model for reduced CPU energy. In: Proc. FOCS, pp. 374–382 (1995)

Facility Location in Dynamic Geometric Data Streams*

Christiane Lammersen and Christian Sohler

Computer Science Department I,
University of Bonn, 53117 Bonn, Germany
{cl,sohler}@informatik.uni-bonn.de

Abstract. We present a randomized algorithm that maintains a constant factor approximation for the cost of the facility location problem in the dynamic geometric data stream model. In this model, the input is a sequence of insert and delete operations of points from a discrete space $\{1 \ldots \Delta\}^d$, where d is a constant. The algorithm needs $\log^{\mathcal{O}(1)} \Delta$ time to process an insertion or deletion of a point, uses $\log^{\mathcal{O}(1)} \Delta$ bits of storage, and has a failure probability of $1/\Delta^{\Theta(1)}$.

Keywords: facility location, dynamic data streams, approximation.

1 Introduction

The problem of processing large streams of geometric data arises in many applications such as mobile networks, sensor networks, astronomy, etc. In some of these applications data is continuously changing. For example, in mobile networks the position of network nodes may change over time and in sensor networks the measured data changes. New positions or measurements are typically communicated via wireless communication in form of a stream of update operations. Such an update may, for example, specify the 'name' of the network node, its 'old position' and its 'new position'. Thus we can also think of it as a deletion of the old data value followed by an insertion of the new value. The model of dynamic geometric data stream addresses such a scenario. We are given a stream of insert and delete operations of points from the discrete space $\{1, ..., \Delta\}^d$ and our goal is to maintain certain statistics about the current data. The difficulty is that the size of the processed data prevents us from storing it completely. This restriction is modelled by allowing only space polylogarithmic in Δ and the length of the stream.

In this paper, we study a facility location problem for dynamic geometric data streams. In this problem, we are given a set of clients that have to be served by a set of facilities. It is possible to open a facility at any client for a given cost of f. The cost of serving a client is proportional to its distance to the nearest facility. This problem models many applications where we have to allocate resources to satisfy some requirement as good as possible while at the

---

* Supported by DFG grant So 514/1-1.

D. Halperin and K. Mehlhorn (Eds.): ESA 2008, LNCS 5193, pp. 660–671, 2008.

same time we have to pay for the used resources. For example, we may organize a wireless network hierarchically, i.e. some nodes (cluster heads) are responsible for a certain subset of nodes (cluster). Clearly, a cluster head has a certain overhead in communication, storage space, and processing time required for additional communication, etc. This overhead corresponds to the cost to open/maintain a facility. The distance to the facility corresponds to the connection cost.

Since in the facility location problem the number of open facilities can be as large as the considered point set (and this can be as large as Δ^d), we cannot compute a solution in the streaming model. Instead, we focus on approximating the cost of a solution. We remark that approximating the cost can be very useful in resource allocation problems to monitor the cost of an existing solution.

Our Contribution. We develop a constant factor approximation algorithm for the cost of the facility location problem over dynamic data streams in d-dimensional space, where d is a constant. The best previous result was an $\mathcal{O}(\log^2 \Delta)$-approximation algorithm [13].

Our Techniques. The main difficulty is to define a solution, whose cost a) is a constant factor approximation and b) can be efficiently approximated within a constant factor in the streaming model. Our starting point is the work of Indyk [13], which defines a partition of the space into cubic cells and a set of cells such that the number of these cells gives an $\mathcal{O}(\log \Delta)$-approximation [13]. During the approximation process to estimate the number of these cells, the algorithm of [13] looses another $\mathcal{O}(\log \Delta)$ factor.

In our work, we use a similar partition of the space into nested grids, and we show that opening a subset of the cells defined in [13] gives a constant factor approximation. In detail, we call a cell heavy, if the product of the side length of the cell and number of points inside the cell is at least f. Our subset essentially consists of all heavy cells such that neither the cell itself nor any of its neighbors include a (smaller) heavy cell.

The main difficulty is now to give a streaming algorithm that approximates the number of these cells sufficiently well and so the algorithm to do this is our main technical contribution. We approximate the number of these cells in each grid level with additive error by taking random samples and computing certain set differences of cells and finally applying known algorithms to approximate the number of distinct items (cells). We then show that the additive error can be charged to obtain a small multiplicative error.

Related Work. The model of dynamic geometric data streams has been introduced in [13] where the author studied different geometric problems including minimum spanning tree, minimum matching and minimum bichromatic matching, facility location, and k-median. For both matching problems and the minimum spanning tree problem $\mathcal{O}(\log \Delta)$-approximation algorithms for the cost of the optimal solution have been obtained. For the facility location problem an $\mathcal{O}(\log^2 \Delta)$-approximation algorithm for the cost of the optimal solution has been proposed. For the k-median problem also a $(1+\varepsilon)$-approximation algorithm with prohibitively high running time for the extraction of an optimal solution has been given. The result for the minimum spanning tree problem has subsequently been improved by a $(1+\varepsilon)$-approximation algorithm [7]. In the same paper, the authors also considered the computation of a random almost uniformly distributed sample in a dynamic data stream. A similar method for random sampling in dynamic data streams has been obtained independently in [4]. Furthermore, a more efficient $(1+\varepsilon)$-algorithm for the k-median problem has been developed in [8], where similar results have also been obtained for the k-means problem, the Euclidean MaxCut, and a few other problems.

A large number of geometric data streaming algorithms have been developed in the insertion-only model. We will focus our summary about the known results in this field on the facility location problem and two clustering problems, namely the k-median and the k-means problem, which are closely related to the facility location problem. One important technique in the development of streaming algorithms is the construction of coresets. Here the goal is to reduce the complexity of a huge point set to a weighted point set of small size (called coreset), such that the small coreset approximates the whole point set with respect to the given problem. Several coreset constructions are known for clustering problems [3,5,6,8,11,12]. The metric facility location problem that maintains a set of facilities approximating the optimal facility configuration within a constant factor has been considered in [9]. Unfortunately, the space requirement for this approach is dependent on the number of opened facilities which can be linear in the input size. Another algorithm for a metric facility location problem has been developed in the multi-pass streaming model [2]. The algorithm computes an $\mathcal{O}(\ell)$-approximation of the optimal solution by using $\mathcal{O}(\ell)$ passes and a memory space of $\tilde{\mathcal{O}}(kn^{2/\ell})$, where k is the number of opened facilities and n is the number of input points.

Because sublinear time algorithms are closely related to streaming algorithms, we also mention one work in this model. Bădoiu et al. [1] presented a constant factor approximation algorithm for the uniform metric facility location problem that uses $\mathcal{O}(n\log^2 n)$ time. Despite the relation of streaming and sublinear time algorithms, their techniques cannot be transferred to the other model. Furthermore, Meyerson [14] proposed an online algorithm with a polylogarithmic competitive ratio that maintains a set of facilities for a sequence of demand points.

2   Preliminaries

In the model of dynamic data streams, we are given a stream of insert and delete operations of points from a discrete space $\{1, ..., \Delta\}^d$, where d is a constant. We assume that the stream is consistent, i.e. no point is deleted that is not present in the data structure and no point is inserted multiple times (without being deleted before). Insert and delete operation both get the coordinates of the point. We use $P = \{p_1, \ldots, p_n\}$ to denote a set of n points in the discrete space $\{1 \ldots \Delta\}^d$. In the streaming context, P will refer to the current set, i.e. the set obtained after applying an input sequence of insertions and deletions. Let $d(p,q)$ denote the Euclidean distance between p and q. In the minimum facility location problem, for a parameter f, we try to find a set $F \subseteq P$ of points that minimizes the objective $f \cdot |F| + \sum_{p \in P} d(p, F)$, where $d(p, F) = \min_{q \in F}\{d(p, q)\}$. We call the first part of the objective the opening cost and second part the connection cost.

To compute the cost of the minimum facility location problem, we impose $\log(\Delta) + 1$ nested squared grids over the point space $\mathcal{G}(0), \mathcal{G}(1), \ldots, \mathcal{G}(\log \Delta)$, shifted by a vector chosen uniformly at random from $[0, \Delta]^d$. The side length of each cell in grid $\mathcal{G}(i)$ is 2^i. We say that the grid cells in $\mathcal{G}(i)$ are in level i. The *parent cell* of a cell $\mathcal{C} \in \mathcal{G}(i)$ is the cell in $\mathcal{G}(i + 1)$ that contains $\mathcal{C}$. The set of neighbors $\Gamma(\mathcal{C})$ of a cell $\mathcal{C}$ in grid $\mathcal{G}(i)$ is the set of $3^d - 1$ cells in grid $\mathcal{G}(i)$ that share some part of the boundary. In grid $\mathcal{G}(i)$ a cell is called *heavy*, if it contains more than $f/2^i$ points.

Definition 1. *We call a cell of grid $\mathcal{G}(i)$ heavy, if it contains at least $T(i) = \frac{f}{2^i}$ points of P. A grid cell that is not heavy is* light.

3 Construction of a Good Estimator

Our first step will be to define a certain partition of the input space and to relate this partition to the cost of the facility location problem. In particular, if we assign to each cell in this partition a weight that corresponds to the number of points inside the cell times the side length of the cell, the sum of these weights will be a constant factor approximation for the cost of the facility location problem. We need the following definition.

Definition 2. *A cell of grid $\mathcal{G}(i)$ is called* useful, *if it neither contains a heavy subcell nor any of the $3^d - 1$ neighboring cells $\Gamma(\mathcal{C})$ in grid $\mathcal{G}(i)$ contains a heavy subcell. A grid cell that is not useful is* useless.

Our space partition consists of all *maximal*-useful cells, i.e. all cells that are useful, but their parent cell is useless. We define $\mathcal{SP}(i)$ to be the set of all maximal-useful cells in grid $\mathcal{G}(i)$ and $\mathcal{SP} = \bigcup_i \mathcal{SP}(i)$ the set of all maximal-useful cells. The cells in $\mathcal{SP}$ form a partition of the input space, because we can simply construct $\mathcal{SP}$ in a process similar to that of building a quadtree and splitting recursively every useless cell. The idea is now to place a facility in each heavy cell in $\mathcal{SP}$. We remark that this strategy of choosing the set of facilities is a refinement of the one proposed in [13]. More precisely, the facilities in [13] are chosen from all heavy cells in $\bigcup_i \mathcal{G}(i)$, whereas we choose the facilities from a subset of those cells.

Our next step is to define a value $E(P)$ that is a constant factor approximation for the cost of the optimal solution of the facility location problem. Let $n_P(\mathcal{C})$ be the number of points in set P falling into cell $\mathcal{C}$. Then the estimator for the facility location cost is defined as

$$E(P) = \sum_{i=0}^{\log \Delta} \sum_{\mathcal{C} \in \mathcal{SP}(i)} n_P(\mathcal{C}) \cdot 2^i. \tag{1}$$

Properties of the Partition. Before we prove that $E(P)$ is indeed an $\mathcal{O}(1)$-approximation of the cost of the facility location problem, we discuss some properties of the space partition that are needed in the analysis. We say that two cells in a space partition are neighbors, if they share at least one point of their boundary. Furthermore, the distance between two cells is defined as the minimum distance between two points, such that one point lies on the boundary of one cell and the other point on the boundary of the other cell. Now, we prove that the space partition that consists of all maximal-useful cells has the following properties.

Lemma 1. *The set SP of all maximal-useful cells has the following four properties:*

  i) *The side length of each cell in SP differs from the side length of each of its neighbors by a factor of at most 2, i.e. the space partition is balanced.*
 ii) *Let i be any level and let C be any useless cell in $\mathcal{G}(i)$. Then there is a heavy cell in SP that has distance at most $\sqrt{d} \cdot 2^{i+1}$ from C.*
iii) *Let i be any level and let C be any light cell in $SP(i)$. Then there exists a heavy cell in SP in a distance of at most $5 \cdot \sqrt{d} \cdot 2^i$ from C.*
 iv) *Let i be any level and let C be any heavy cell in $SP(i)$. Then we have $\frac{f}{2^i} \leq n_P(C) < 2^{d+1} \cdot \frac{f}{2^i}$.*

Proof.

  i) The proof is by contradiction. Assume that C_{big} is a cell in $SP(i)$ that has a neighbor cell C_{small} in $SP(j)$, $j \leq i - 2$, i.e. C_{small} has side length $2^j \leq 2^{i-2}$. This situation is illustrated in Figure 1. Let C'_{small} be the parent cell of C_{small}. Since C_{small} is maximal-useful, its parent C'_{small} is useless. Hence, C_{small} or at least one neighboring cell in $\Gamma(C'_{\text{small}})$ has a heavy subcell. This subcell is either contained in C_{big} or one of its neighboring cells $\Gamma(C_{\text{big}})$ (see also Figure 1). Hence, C_{big} is also a useless cell and cannot be a cell in $SP(i)$, which is a contradiction.

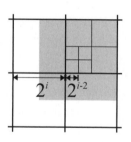

Fig. 1. Arrangement of cells that leads to the desired contradiction

 ii) We proceed by induction. Let ℓ be the minimum value such that $SP(\ell)$ is not empty. Let C be a useless cell in grid $\mathcal{G}(\ell + 1)$. Since C is useless, either C or one of its neighbors contains a heavy subcell $\mathcal{H}$. By the choice of ℓ, we know that $\mathcal{H}$ is useful, which proves the base case. Now, let C be a useless cell in grid $\mathcal{G}(i)$. By definition, C either contains a heavy subcell or one of its neighboring cells contains a heavy subcell. Let $\mathcal{H}$ be such a subcell. $\mathcal{H}$ has distance at most $\sqrt{d} \cdot 2^{i-1}$ from C. If $\mathcal{H}$ is useful, it is maximal-useful and is in SP and we are done. Otherwise, $\mathcal{H}$ is useless and in grid $\mathcal{G}(j)$, $j < i$. By induction hypothesis, we have a heavy cell $\mathcal{H}'$ in SP with distance at most $\sqrt{d} \cdot 2^j \leq \sqrt{d} \cdot 2^i$ from $\mathcal{H}$. Since $\mathcal{H}$ has a diagonal of length $\sqrt{d} \cdot 2^{i-1}$, we get that the distance from C to $\mathcal{H}'$ is at most $2 \cdot \sqrt{d} \cdot 2^{i-1} + \sqrt{d} \cdot 2^i = \sqrt{d} \cdot 2^{i+1}$.

iii) Let $\mathcal{C}$ be a light cell in $\mathcal{SP}(i)$. Let $\mathcal{C}'$ be the parent cells of $\mathcal{C}$. By ii), there is a heavy cell within a distance of $\sqrt{d} \cdot 2^{i+2}$ from $\mathcal{C}'$. Hence, the distance from $\mathcal{C}$ is at most $5 \cdot \sqrt{d} \cdot 2^i$.

iv) The cell $\mathcal{C}$ contains at least $\frac{f}{2^i}$ points, because it is a heavy cell. The number of points in $\mathcal{C}$ is less than $2^{d+1} \cdot \frac{f}{2^i}$, because each of the 2^d subcells of $\mathcal{C}$ is light, so that there are less than $\frac{f}{2^{i-1}}$ points inside of them. $\qquad\square$

Analysis of the estimator $E(P)$. Let $\mathrm{OPT}(P)$ be the facility location cost for the point set P that arises for an optimal algorithm. Then we can give an appropriate lower and upper bound for the estimator $E(P)$ depending on the value $\mathrm{OPT}(P)$.

Lemma 2. $E(P) = \Omega(\mathrm{OPT}(P))$.

Proof. Our goal is to define a set of open facilities whose cost is $\mathcal{O}(E(P))$. This proves $E(P) = \Omega(\mathrm{OPT}(P))$. We will show that it suffices to open one facility in each heavy cell in $\mathcal{SP}$.

We give an upper bound for the contribution of the points in each cell in $\mathcal{SP}$. Every heavy cell $\mathcal{C} \in \mathcal{SP}(i)$ contributes at most $f + n_P(\mathcal{C}) \cdot \sqrt{d} \cdot 2^i$, because we open one facility in $\mathcal{C}$ and connect the points in $\mathcal{C}$ to it. Since $\mathcal{C}$ is heavy, it contains at least $f/2^i$ points. Thus, we have $f + n_P(\mathcal{C}) \cdot \sqrt{d} \cdot 2^i = \mathcal{O}(n_P(\mathcal{C}) \cdot 2^i)$. The points in each light cell $\mathcal{C}$ in $\mathcal{SP}$ will be connected to the nearest open facility. Due to Lemma 1, the distance from any light cell $\mathcal{C} \in \mathcal{SP}(i)$ to the nearest heavy cell $\mathcal{C}_h$ in $\mathcal{SP}$ is at most $5 \cdot \sqrt{d} \cdot 2^i$. The distance between $\mathcal{C}$ and $\mathcal{C}_h$ achieves its maximum in the case that we have a chain of light cells between $\mathcal{C}$ and $\mathcal{C}_h$ such that the side length of the light cells is non-increasing in direction $\mathcal{C}_h$ and the side length of $\mathcal{C}_h$ is 2^0. Thus, the connection cost for the points in $\mathcal{C}$ is at most $n_P(\mathcal{C}) \cdot \sqrt{d} \cdot (2^i + 5 \cdot 2^i + 2^0) = \mathcal{O}(n_P(\mathcal{C}) \cdot 2^i)$. Summing up over all cells gives that the cost of the defined solution is $\mathcal{O}(E(P))$. $\qquad\square$

Lemma 3. $E(P) = \mathcal{O}(\mathrm{OPT}(P))$.

Proof. Let F_{OPT} be a set of optimal facilities. We partition the set $\mathcal{SP}(i)$ into two subsets $\mathcal{SP}_{\mathrm{near}}(i)$ and $\mathcal{SP}_{\mathrm{dist}}(i)$. $\mathcal{SP}_{\mathrm{near}}(i)$ contains all cells $\mathcal{C}$ whose distance $\min_{q \in F_{\mathrm{OPT}}} d(q, \mathcal{C})$ to the nearest facility from F_{OPT} is less than 2^{i-1}, i.e.

$$\mathcal{SP}_{\mathrm{near}}(i) = \left\{ \mathcal{C} \in \mathcal{SP}(i) \mid \min_{q \in F_{\mathrm{OPT}}} d(q, \mathcal{C}) < 2^{i-1} \right\}.$$

$\mathcal{SP}_{\mathrm{dist}}(i)$ contains all other cells from $\mathcal{SP}(i)$, i.e. $\mathcal{SP}_{\mathrm{dist}}(i) = \mathcal{SP}(i) \backslash \mathcal{SP}_{\mathrm{near}}(i)$. For each cell $\mathcal{C} \in \bigcup_{i=0}^{\log \Delta} \mathcal{SP}_{\mathrm{dist}}(i)$, the cost to connect the points inside $\mathcal{C}$ to the nearest facility in F_{OPT} is at least $n_P(\mathcal{C}) \cdot 2^{i-1}$. This is exactly half of the cost we charge for the cell $\mathcal{C}$ in the definition of $E(P)$. Thus, the cost that we charge for the set $\bigcup_{i=0}^{\log \Delta} \mathcal{SP}_{\mathrm{dist}}(i)$ is upper bounded by two times the connection cost in F_{OPT}.

The side length of each cell in $\mathcal{SP}_{\mathrm{near}}(i)$ is 2^i. By Lemma 1, the side length of any cell in $\mathcal{SP}$ differs from the side length of each of its neighbors by a factor of at most 2. Thus, for every facility in F_{OPT}, there cannot be more than 3^d cells in $\bigcup_{i=0}^{\log \Delta} \mathcal{SP}_{\text{near}}(i)$. Furthermore, for each cell in $\mathcal{SP}$, in the definition of $E(P)$ we charge a cost $\mathcal{O}(f)$. This follows due to the fact that a cell in $\mathcal{SP}(i)$ contains at most $2^{d+1} \cdot \frac{f}{2^i}$ points, so that we charge at most $2^{d+1} \cdot f = \mathcal{O}(f)$. Thus, the cost that arises for all cells in $\bigcup_{i=0}^{\log \Delta} \mathcal{SP}_{\text{near}}(i)$ is at most a constant factor larger than the optimal cost. □

4   Randomized Algorithm

In this section, we describe how our randomized algorithm implements the ideas of Section 3. The idea of the algorithm is closely related to our partition into maximal-useful cells. We try to identify heavy cells in grid $\mathcal{G}(i)$ by taking each point with probability $1/T(i)$ into a random sample. Recall that a cell in grid $\mathcal{G}(i)$ is heavy, if it contains at least $T(i) = f/2^i$ points. Thus, in expectation we will see at least one point in every heavy cell of grid $\mathcal{G}(i)$ (however, some sample points will also end up in light cells). We call a cell in grid $\mathcal{G}(i)$ marked, if it contains a sample point. We open one facility in every marked cell C in grid $\mathcal{G}(i)$ such that a) no subcell of C is marked and b) no smaller cell within a distance of less than 2^{i-1} is marked.

The output value $E_{\text{rand}}(P)$ of the algorithm is $E_{\text{rand}}(P) := f \cdot |\mathcal{F}|$, where $\mathcal{F}$ denotes the set of cells, where we open a facility. The idea of condition b) is that in our space decomposition $\mathcal{SP}$ the size of neighboring cells differs only by a factor of 2. Hence, a marked cell from $\mathcal{SP}$ prevents at most a constant number of other cells from $\mathcal{SP}$ to open a facility.

The random sampling of points is done via fully random hash functions. For each level i, it uses a random hash function $h_i : \{1 \ldots \Delta\}^d \to \{1, \ldots, \lceil T(i) \rceil\}$, such that each point is mapped independently to a random value from the set $\{1, \ldots, \lceil T(i) \rceil\}$. We put a point p into the sample set of level i, if the hash value $h_i(p)$ is equal to 1. The reason why we use hash functions is that we must be able to handle delete operations on our sample set. The issue of full randomness is discussed later.

Analysis. We show that our randomized algorithm computes facility location cost that is an $\mathcal{O}(1)$-approximation of the estimator $E(P)$. Let $\mathcal{F}(i)$ be the set of marked cells in $\mathcal{G}(i)$ that do not have a marked subcell and that do not have a smaller marked cell within distance less than 2^{i-1}. The cells in the set $\bigcup_{i=0}^{\log \Delta} \mathcal{F}(i)$ are exactly the cells in which the algorithm opens its facilities, i.e. $\mathcal{F} = \bigcup_{i=0}^{\log \Delta} \mathcal{F}(i)$. Thus, the estimator of the randomized algorithm is given by

$$E_{\text{rand}}(P) = \sum_{i=0}^{\log \Delta} f \cdot |\mathcal{F}(i)| . \tag{2}$$

We consider the partition $\mathcal{SP}$ of the input space. We are interested in the number of marked cells from $\mathcal{SP}$. However, f times the number of marked cells does not immediately give a lower bound on $E_{\text{rand}}(P)$, because we do not open a facility in a marked cell in $\mathcal{SP}(i)$, if there is a smaller cell within distance less than 2^{i-1} that is marked. Since neighboring cells in $\mathcal{SP}$ differ by at most a factor of 2 in their size, a cell in $\mathcal{SP}$ can only be blocked if one of its neighboring cells contains a marked subcell. Hence, every marked cell in $\mathcal{SP}$ can prevent at most a constant number of other facilities in cells from $\mathcal{SP}$ being opened. Thus, if we can show that the expected number of marked cells is $\Omega(E(P)/f)$, we are done.

We say that a point $p \in \mathcal{SP}(i)$ is marked, if it is marked in grid $\mathcal{G}(i)$. Let X_p denote the indicator random variable for the event that p is marked. We get that $\mathbf{E}[\sum_{p \in \mathcal{C}} X_p] = n_P(\mathcal{C})/T(i) = n_P(\mathcal{C}) \cdot 2^i/f$. From Lemma 1, it follows for every cell $\mathcal{C} \in \mathcal{SP}$ that $\mathbf{E}[\sum_{p \in \mathcal{C}} X_p] \leq 2^{d+1}$. Hence, we can group cells into sets $\mathcal{S}_1, \ldots, \mathcal{S}_\ell$ such that for each set $\mathcal{S}_i$, $1 \leq i \leq \ell-1$, we have $12 \leq \sum_{\mathcal{C} \in \mathcal{S}_i} \sum_{p \in \mathcal{C}} \mathbf{E}[X_p] \leq 12+2^{d+1}$ and $\sum_{\mathcal{C} \in \mathcal{S}_\ell} \sum_{p \in \mathcal{C}} \mathbf{E}[X_p] \leq 12+2^{d+1}$ for the set $\mathcal{S}_\ell$. We use Y_i to denote the random variable $\sum_{\mathcal{C} \in \mathcal{S}_i} \sum_{p \in \mathcal{C}} X_p$. Now, we can apply Chernoff bounds to get that $\mathbf{Pr}[Y_i \leq \frac{1}{2}\mathbf{E}[Y_i]] \leq e^{-\frac{1}{12}\mathbf{E}[Y_i]}$. This implies that $\mathbf{Pr}[Y_i \leq 6] \leq 1/e$ for $1 \leq i < \ell$. Hence, with probability at least $1/e$ at least one of the cells in $\mathcal{S}_i$ is marked. Let Z_i denote the random variable for the event that at least one cell in $\mathcal{S}_i$ is marked. By Chernoff bounds, we get that with probability at least $3/4$ the number of marked cells is $\Omega(E(P)/f)$. For $\ell = 1$ the optimal cost is $\Theta(f)$ and in case that no cell is marked we can always safely output f.

Lemma 4. $E_{rand}(P) = \Omega(E(P))$ *with probability at least $3/4$.*

To prove the upper bound, we first observe that every cell $\mathcal{C}$ is either contained in $\mathcal{SP}$ or it can be partitioned into cells from $\mathcal{SP}$ ($\mathcal{C}$ lies above $\mathcal{SP}$) or it is a subcell of a cell of $\mathcal{SP}$ ($\mathcal{C}$ lies below $\mathcal{SP}$). We will first show that the overall expected number of sample points from cells that do not lie 'far above' $\mathcal{SP}$ is $\mathcal{O}(E(P)/f)$. Hence, the overall cost created by these cells is $\mathcal{O}(E(P))$. Then we prove that the expected contribution of cells 'far above' $\mathcal{SP}$ is also $\mathcal{O}(E(P))$. The latter follows, because every such cell $\mathcal{C}$ in grid $\mathcal{G}(i)$ has a (smaller) heavy cell from $\mathcal{SP}$ within distance 2^{i-1}. These heavy cells will be typically marked and so the expected contribution of $\mathcal{C}$ is small.

Definition 3. *We say that a cell $\mathcal{C}$ in grid $\mathcal{G}(i)$ has* height k*, if the smallest cell of $\mathcal{SP}$ that is contained in $\mathcal{C}$ has side length 2^{i-k}. If no cell of $\mathcal{SP}$ is contained in $\mathcal{C}$ then we define its height to be $-\infty$.*

Let X_p denote the indicator random variable for the event $h_i(p) = 1$. Furthermore, for a cell $\mathcal{C}$ in grid $\mathcal{G}(i)$, let $X_{\mathcal{C}} = \sum_{p \in P \cap \mathcal{C}} X_p$ denote the random variable for the number of sample points in cell $\mathcal{C}$. With this definition, it follows that, for every cell $\mathcal{C}$ in grid $\mathcal{G}(i)$, we have $\mathbf{E}[X_{\mathcal{C}}] = n_P(\mathcal{C})/T(i) = n_P(\mathcal{C}) \cdot 2^i/f$. Moreover, the expected number of sample points (from different grids) in a cell $\mathcal{C}$ and its subcells is $\mathbf{E}[\sum_{\mathcal{C}' \subseteq \mathcal{C}} X_{\mathcal{C}'}] \leq 2 \cdot n_P(\mathcal{C}) \cdot 2^i/f$. Let us now consider an arbitrary cell $\mathcal{C}$ in grid $\mathcal{G}(i)$ with height $k \geq 0$. $\mathcal{C}$ can be partitioned into cells $\mathcal{C}_1, \ldots, \mathcal{C}_\ell$ from $\mathcal{SP}$ that differ in size by at most 2^k. Hence, $\mathbf{E}[X_{\mathcal{C}}] \leq 2^k \cdot \mathbf{E}[\sum_{1 \leq i \leq \ell} X_{\mathcal{C}_i}]$. The set of cells of height k do not overlap in their interior, so the expected number of sample points in cells of height k^* or of hight smaller than k^*, for k^* being a constant greater than $\log(10\sqrt{d})$, is $\mathcal{O}(E(P)/f)$. Thus, by Markov inequality with probability at least $7/8$ the opening cost for facilities in these cells is $\mathcal{O}(E(P))$.

Now, let us consider an arbitrary cell $\mathcal{C}$ in grid $\mathcal{G}(i)$ with height bigger than k^*. This cell contains a subcell from $\mathcal{SP}$ of size at most $2^{i-k^*} < 2^i \cdot \frac{1}{10\sqrt{d}}$ by the definition of height and the value of k^*. By Lemma 1, we know that every cell in $\mathcal{SP}(j)$ has a heavy cell in $\mathcal{SP}$ within distance at most $5\sqrt{d} \cdot 2^j$. We conclude that there is a heavy cell in $\mathcal{SP}$ within distance less than 2^{i-1} from $\mathcal{C}$. Every parent cell of a heavy cell is heavy and contains the cell, hence there is a cell in grid $\mathcal{G}(i-1)$ within distance less than 2^{i-1} of $\mathcal{C}$ that is heavy, i.e. $\mathcal{C}$ or a neighbor of $\mathcal{C}$ is heavy. In other words, every cell in grid $\mathcal{G}(i)$ with height at least k^* is heavy and contains a heavy cell in $\mathcal{SP}$ or has a neighbor in grid $\mathcal{G}(i-1)$ that is heavy and contains a heavy cell in $\mathcal{SP}$. We will now proceed as follows. For each heavy cell $\mathcal{H}_i$ in $\mathcal{SP}(i)$, we consider all cells that contain it. For each such cell $\mathcal{H}_j$, $j > i$, in grid $\mathcal{G}(j)$, we assume that its constant number of neighbors in grid $\mathcal{G}(j+1)$ all contain a facility, if and only if $\mathcal{H}_j$ is not marked. Thus, every heavy cell contributes at most $f + \mathcal{O}(f) \cdot \sum_{j \geq i} \mathbf{Pr}[\mathcal{H}_j$ is not marked$]$. We have $\mathbf{Pr}[\mathcal{H}_i$ is not marked$] = (1 - 1/T(i))^{n_P(\mathcal{H}_i)} \leq \left(\frac{1}{e}\right)^{n_P(\mathcal{H}_i)/(2T(i))}$. It follows that $\mathbf{Pr}[\mathcal{H}_j$ is not marked$] \leq e^{-j} \cdot \mathbf{Pr}[\mathcal{H}_i$ is not marked$]$. This implies $\sum_{j \geq i} \mathbf{Pr}[\mathcal{H}_j$ is not marked$] = \mathcal{O}(1)$. Hence, the expected contribution from cells with height greater than k^* is at most $\mathcal{O}(f)$ times the number of heavy cells in $\mathcal{SP}$. However, the number of heavy cells in $\mathcal{SP}$ is at most $E(P)/f$. Thus, the overall contribution of the cells with height greater than k^* is at most $E(P)$. Using Markov inequality we get the following lemma.

Lemma 5. $E_{rand}(P) = \mathcal{O}(E(P))$ *with probability at least* $3/4$.

5   Streaming Algorithm

In this section, we describe how our randomized algorithm can be transferred to a streaming algorithm that maintains a constant factor approximation for the facility location cost under insertions and deletions. Let $\mathcal{M}(i)$ be the subset of marked cells in $\mathcal{G}(i)$ and let $\mathcal{U}(i)$ be the subset of cells in $\mathcal{G}(i)$ that have a cell contained in the set $\bigcup_{j=0}^{i-1} \mathcal{M}(j)$ within a distance of less than 2^{i-1}. Thus, we have $E_{rand}(P) = \bigcup_{i=0}^{\log \Delta} f \cdot |\mathcal{M}(i) \backslash \mathcal{U}(i)|$. Now, the difficulty is to maintain for each level i a good estimator for the value $|\mathcal{M}(i) \backslash \mathcal{U}(i)|$ in the streaming model.

We use a similar technique as described in [13] to solve this problem. In particular, we use two data structures that both maintain the number of distinct elements in a stream, under insertions and deletions. The first data structure called $DE_1(i)$ is supposed to maintain a good estimator for the value $|\mathcal{M}(i) \cup \mathcal{U}(i)|$ and the second data structure called $DE_2(i)$ is supposed to maintain a good estimator for the value $|\mathcal{U}(i)|$. Then, the difference of both estimators is a good estimator for the desired value $|\mathcal{M}(i) \backslash \mathcal{U}(i)|$. Let $C_p(i)$ be the cell in level i that contains the point p and let $h_i : \{1 \ldots \Delta\}^d \to \{1, \ldots, \lceil T(i) \rceil\}$ be the random hash function introduced in Section 4. Then our implementation is as follows:

- INSERT(i, p): if $h_i(p) = 1$ insert $C_p(i)$ in $DE_1(i)$ and, for each $j > i$, insert $C_p(j)$ and all cells in $\mathcal{G}(j)$ such that $C_p(i)$ is within a distance of less than 2^{j-1} in both $DE_1(j)$ and $DE_2(j)$

- DELETE(i, p): if $h_i(p) = 1$ delete $\mathcal{C}_p(i)$ from $DE_1(i)$ and, for each $j > i$, delete $\mathcal{C}_p(j)$ and all cells in $\mathcal{G}(j)$ such that $\mathcal{C}_p(i)$ is within a distance of less than 2^{j-1} from both $DE_1(j)$ and $DE_2(j)$
- Estimator for the cost of level i: invoke $DE_1(i)$ and $DE_2(i)$ and output their difference as an estimator for the cost of level i

Analysis. We show that our streaming algorithm outputs a constant factor approximation of the optimal facility location cost, has polylogarithmic update time, and uses polylogarithmic memory space. For that purpose, we analyze the quality and complexity of the random hash functions and the distinct elements data structures.

We use the technique introduced in [7] to overcome the assumption of totally random hash functions. For that purpose, we replace each fully random hash function h_i by a hash function h'_i that maps each point $p \in \{1 \ldots \Delta\}^d$ independently and almost uniformly at random to a value from $\{1, \ldots, \lceil T(i) \rceil\}$. More precisely, for a user-defined value $\alpha < 1$, the hash value $h'_i(p)$ is equal to 1 with probability greater than $1/\lceil T(i) \rceil - \alpha$ and less than $1/\lceil T(i) \rceil + \alpha$. We refer the reader to [7] for more details about the construction of h'_i. However, its space requirement is only $\mathcal{O}(\log^2(\Delta/\alpha))$ bits. Thus, for $\alpha = 1/\Delta^d$, the hash function h'_i is sufficiently close to a fully random hash function and needs $\mathcal{O}(\log^2 \Delta)$ bits of storage.

From the analysis in Sections 3 and 4, it follows that $E_{\text{rand}}(P) = \Omega(\text{OPT}(P))$ and $E_{\text{rand}}(P) = \mathcal{O}(\text{OPT}(P))$ is true with probability at least 9/16. Thus, with probability at least 9/16 we have that $1/c \cdot \text{OPT}(P) \le E_{\text{rand}}(P) \le c \cdot \text{OPT}(P)$ for an appropriate chosen constant c. If we use the technique presented in [10], our data structures to maintain the number of distinct elements under insertions and deletions have the following properties.

Lemma 6 ([10]). *There is a data structure that maintains a $(1+\varepsilon)$-approximation of the number of distinct elements in a data stream under insertions and deletions with probability $1 - \delta$. The update time of an element is $\mathcal{O}(\log \frac{1}{\varepsilon} \cdot \log \frac{1}{\delta})$ and the storage requirement is $\mathcal{O}(\frac{1}{\varepsilon^2} \cdot (\log \Delta + \log m) \cdot \log \Delta \cdot \log \frac{1}{\delta})$ bits, where Δ^d is the size of the domain of the elements and m is the sum of frequencies of the elements in the stream.*

We will show that the error of the facility location cost that occurs by using those DE data structures is dependent on the value $\sum_{i=0}^{\log \Delta} f \cdot |\mathcal{M}(i)|$. Hence, we give an appropriate upper bound of this value to be able to restrict the error.

Lemma 7. *If $E_{rand}(P) \le c \cdot \text{OPT}(P)$ then we have $\sum_{i=0}^{\log \Delta} f \cdot |\mathcal{M}(i)| \le c \cdot 3^d \cdot (\log(\Delta) + 1) \cdot \text{OPT}(P)$.*

Proof. We open in each marked cell in $\mathcal{G}(0)$ one facility. Thus, $f \cdot |\mathcal{M}(0)| = f \cdot |\mathcal{F}(0)| \le c \cdot \text{OPT}(P)$. For any level $i > 0$, we open a facility in each cell $\mathcal{C} \in \mathcal{M}(i)$ such that no subcell of $\mathcal{C}$ is marked and no smaller cell within a distance of less than 2^{i-1} is marked. Hence, for at most 3^d cells in $\mathcal{M}(i)$ there exists at least one cell in $\bigcup_{j=0}^{i} \mathcal{F}(j)$. As a consequence, $f \cdot |\mathcal{M}(i)| \le 3^d \cdot \bigcup_{j=0}^{i} |\mathcal{F}(j)| \le 3^d \cdot c \cdot \text{OPT}(P)$

is true for any level i. Now, the lemma follows simply by the fact that there are $\log(\Delta) + 1$ levels. $\square$

We can show that the error of the facility location cost that occurs by using DE data structures to maintain the number of distinct elements in data streams can be reduced to $1/(2c) \cdot \text{OPT}(P)$.

Lemma 8. *If $E_{rand}(P) \leq c \cdot \text{OPT}(P)$ and if we run each DE data structure to maintain a $(1 + \varepsilon)$-approximation of distinct elements in data streams under insertions and deletions with an error parameter $\varepsilon \leq 1/(4c^2 \cdot 3^{2d} \cdot (\log(\Delta) + 1)^2)$ and a failure probability $\delta < (1 - \sqrt{8/9})/(2(\log(\Delta) + 1))$, then the error of the estimator for the value $\sum_{i=0}^{\log \Delta} f \cdot |\mathcal{M}(i) \backslash \mathcal{U}(i)|$ that occurs by using DE data structures and that is dependent on the number of cells in $\bigcup_{i=0}^{\log \Delta} \mathcal{U}(i)$ is at most $1/(4c) \cdot \text{OPT}(P)$ with probability greater than $\sqrt{8/9}$.*

Proof. By union bound, the probability that each of the $2(\log(\Delta) + 1)$ DE data structure maintains a $(1 + \varepsilon)$-approximation is greater than $\sqrt{8/9}$.

For any level i and each cell $\mathcal{C}$ in $\mathcal{U}(i)$, either $\mathcal{C}$ has a subcell that is contained in $\bigcup_{j=0}^{i-1} \mathcal{M}(j)$ or at least one cell in $\Gamma(\mathcal{C})$ in grid $\mathcal{G}(i)$ has a subcell that is contained in $\bigcup_{j=0}^{i-1} \mathcal{M}(j)$. Thus, for at most 3^d cells in $\mathcal{U}(i)$, there exists at least one cell in $\bigcup_{j=0}^{i-1} \mathcal{M}(j)$. Hence, we have $|\mathcal{U}(i)| \leq 3^d \cdot \sum_{i=0}^{\log \Delta} |\mathcal{M}(i)|$. Summation over all levels results in $\bigcup_{i=0}^{\log \Delta} |\mathcal{U}(i)| \leq 3^d \cdot (\log(\Delta) + 1) \cdot \sum_{i=0}^{\log \Delta} |\mathcal{M}(i)|$. Thus, we can upper bound the error that occurs by using DE data structures and that is dependent on the number of cells in $\bigcup_{i=0}^{\log \Delta} \mathcal{U}(i)$ by at most $\varepsilon \cdot f \cdot \sum_{i=0}^{\log \Delta} |\mathcal{U}(i)| \leq \varepsilon \cdot f \cdot 3^d \cdot (\log(\Delta) + 1) \cdot \sum_{i=0}^{\log \Delta} |\mathcal{M}(i)|$ with probability greater than $\sqrt{8/9}$. Now, the correctness follows due to Lemma 7. $\square$

In a similar way, we can prove the following lemma.

Lemma 9. *If $E_{rand}(P) \leq c \cdot \text{OPT}(P)$ and if we run each DE data structure to maintain a $(1 + \varepsilon)$-approximation of distinct elements in data streams under insertions and deletions with an error parameter $\varepsilon \leq 1/(4c^2 \cdot 3^d \cdot (\log(\Delta) + 1))$ and a failure probability $\delta < (1 - \sqrt{8/9})/(2(\log(\Delta) + 1))$, then the error of the estimator for the value $\sum_{i=0}^{\log \Delta} f \cdot |\mathcal{M}(i) \backslash \mathcal{U}(i)|$ that occurs by using DE data structures and that is dependent on the number of marked cells is at most $1/(4c) \cdot \text{OPT}(P)$ with probability greater than $\sqrt{8/9}$.*

If $1/c \cdot \text{OPT}(P) \leq E_{rand}(P) \leq c \cdot \text{OPT}(P)$ and if we run each DE data structure with an error parameter $\varepsilon \leq 1/(4c^2 \cdot 3^{2d} \cdot (\log(\Delta) + 1)^2)$ and a failure probability $\delta < (1 - \sqrt{8/9})/(2(\log(\Delta) + 1))$, the total error of the DE data structures is at most $1/(2c) \cdot \text{OPT}(P)$ with probability greater than $8/9$. Thus, we have $\frac{1}{2c} \cdot \text{OPT}(P) \leq E_{rand}(P) \leq \frac{2c^2+1}{2c} \cdot \text{OPT}(P)$ with probability greater than $1/2$. Following standard amplification techniques, we can run $\Theta(r)$ copies of our streaming algorithm in parallel to reduce the failure probability to $1/2^r$.

Theorem 1. *There is a randomized algorithm that maintains with probability $1 - \delta$ a constant factor approximation of the minimum facility location cost for a* *stream of points in the discrete space* $\{1 \dots \Delta\}^d$ *under insertions and deletions, where* d *is a constant. The algorithm needs* $\mathcal{O}(\log(1/\delta) \cdot \log^2 \Delta \cdot (\log \log \Delta)^2)$ *time to process an insertion or deletion of a point and uses* $\mathcal{O}(\log(1/\delta) \cdot \log^7 \Delta \cdot \log \log \Delta)$ *bits of storage.*

Proof. We only give a sketch of the proof. To get a failure probability of δ, we run $\Theta(\log(1/\delta))$ copies of our algorithm. For each copy we set the error parameter and the failure probability as defined in Lemma 8. Now, the update time follows due to Lemma 6 and the fact that we have at most $\mathcal{O}(\log^2 \Delta)$ update operations on DE data structures caused by a point. We can create one random hash function by using $\mathcal{O}(\log^2 \Delta)$ bits [7]. Now, the space requirement follows due to Lemma 6 and the fact that, for each insertion of a point, our algorithm adds a constant number of cells to each DE data structure, so that the sum of frequencies m of elements in each DE data structure is $\mathcal{O}(n) = \mathcal{O}(\Delta^d)$. □

References

1. Bădoiu, M., Czumaj, A., Indyk, P., Sohler, C.: Facility location in sublinear time. In: Caires, L., Italiano, G.F., Monteiro, L., Palamidessi, C., Yung, M. (eds.) ICALP 2005. LNCS, vol. 3580, pp. 866–877. Springer, Heidelberg (2005)
2. Chang, K.L.: Pass-Efficient Algorithms for Facility Location. Technical Report YALEU/DCS/TR-1337 (2005)
3. Chen, K.: On k-Median clustering in high dimensions. In: Proc. 17th ACM-SIAM Sympos. Discrete Algorithms, pp. 1177–1185 (2006)
4. Cormode, G., Muthukrishnan, S., Rozenbaum, I.: Summarizing and Mining Inverse Distributions on Data Streams via Dynamic Sampling. DIMACS Technical Report 2005-11 (2005)
5. Feldman, D., Fiat, A., Sharir, M.: Coresets for Weighted Facilities and Their Applications. In: Proc. 47th FOCS, pp. 315–324 (2006)
6. Feldman, D., Monemizahdeh, M., Sohler, C.: A PTAS for k-means clustering based on weak coresets. In: Proc. 23rd SoCG, pp. 11–18 (2007)
7. Frahling, G., Indyk, P., Sohler, C.: Sampling in dynamic data streams and applications. In: Proc. 21st SoCG, pp. 142–149 (2005)
8. Frahling, G., Sohler, C.: Coresets in Dynamic Geometric Data Streams. In: Proc. 37th STOC, pp. 209–217 (2005)
9. Fotakis, D.: Memoryless facility location in one pass. In: STACS, pp. 608–620 (2006)
10. Ganguly, S.: Counting distinct items over update streams. Theoretical Computer Science 378(3), 211–222 (2007)
11. Har-Peled, S., Kushal, A.: Smaller coresets for k-median and k-means clustering. In: Proc. 21st SoCG, pp. 126–134 (2005)
12. Har-Peled, S., Mazumdar, S.: On coresets for k-means and k-median clustering. In: Proc. 36th STOC, pp. 291–300 (2004)
13. Indyk, P.: Algorithms for dynamic geometric problems over data streams. In: Proc. 36th STOC, pp. 373–380 (2004)
14. Meyerson, A.: Online Facility Location. In: Proc. 32nd FOCS, pp. 426–431 (2001)

The Effects of Local Randomness in the Adversarial Queueing Model⋆

Yann Lorion and Maik Weinard

Institute of Computer Science
Johann Wolfgang Goethe-Universität Frankfurt am Main
Robert-Mayer-Straße 11-15
60054 Frankfurt am Main, Germany
lorion@tm.cs.uni-frankfurt.de, weinard@thi.cs.uni-frankfurt.de

Abstract. We study the effect of randomness in the adversarial queueing model. All proofs of instability for deterministic queueing strategies exploit a finespun strategy of insertions by an adversary. If the local queueing decisions in the network are subject to randomness, it is far from obvious, that an adversary can still trick the network into instability. We show that uniform queueing is unstable even against an oblivious adversary. Consequently, randomizing the queueing decisions made to operate a network is not in itself a suitable fix for poor network performances due to packet pileups.

1 Introduction

We work in the adversarial queueing model (see [1]) that has provided a useful framework for the worst case analysis of queueing policies as well as network topologies. Many papers have been published in the adversarial queueing setup throughout the last decade, for a resume see [2].

Graphs are the natural model of communication networks. The vertices represent the routers and the directed edges indicate the established connections. We assume the data that is to be transported is organized in blocks of roughly equal size. We will call these blocks packets and assume that every edge can transport one packet per time step. Apart from the routing policies, that assign the paths the packets take, the queueing decisions are crucial for a networks performance. Queueing policies decide whenever an edge e is contested which packet seeking to traverse edge e may proceed immediately and which ones have to wait. FIFO for example is the most prominent queueing policy.

The adversarial queueing model was designed to allow a worst case analysis of queueing policies in given networks: the insertions of packets are done by an adversary who also decides which path the packet is supposed to follow on its way to the destination. Clearly it would be easy for an adversary to create arbitrary large delays by simply introducing more packets, that *need* a specific edge e, than e can handle. Therefore the only restriction of the adversary is to not straightforwardly overload an edge.

⋆ Partially supported by DFG project SCHN 503/4-1.

D. Halperin and K. Mehlhorn (Eds.): ESA 2008, LNCS 5193, pp. 672–683, 2008.

Definition 1. *A sequence of insertions is legal for an (r, b)-Adversary, if for every time interval I and every edge $e \in E$ the number of packets inserted during I and requiring edge e is bounded by $r|I| + b$. We call $r \leq 1$ the rate and b the burstiness of the adversary.*

Hence if the insertions are performed by an (r, b)-adversary there is no obvious capacity reason for the network to fail. However it has been shown that queueing policies like FIFO allow arbitrary pileups of packets even if r is chosen arbitrarily small (see [3]). On the other hand strategies like LIS (Longest-In-System, giving priority to the *oldest* packet) avoid arbitrary pileups and arbitrary transportation times in every given network. We refer to this ability to keep packet numbers and transportation times bounded as *stability*.

Definition 2. *A network G is stable under a queueing strategy P against a (r, b)-adversary, if, starting with an empty initial configuration, the number of packets in the system is upper bounded by some $B(r, b, G)$ that depends on the network topology and the parameters of the adversary but not on the time that the network is exposed to the adversary.*

We investigate uniform queueing: the packet traversing edge e is drawn randomly from the set of packets ready to traverse edge e. Each packet is drawn with the same probability $\frac{1}{|Q(e)|}$ with $Q(e)$ being the set of packets waiting before edge e. This set is usually referred to as the queue of edge e. The term queue in this context does not imply a first-in-first-out handling of objects.

We assume, the adversary is oblivious and needs to present his entire sequence of insertions in advance. He is not allowed to change that sequence later on and cannot adapt it to the result of the random queueing choices in the network. We choose this weakest form of an adversary as we seek a negative result about uniform queueing.

Of course, as the queueing is based on random choices, the network could accidentally mimic a universally stable strategy like Nearest-To-Source. Hence we need to slightly relax our term of instability. We are able to show, that uniform queueing is not stable *with high probability*.

Definition 3. *A network G is* highly probably instable *if for every given constant c a sequence of insertions exists such that the number of packets in the system after the insertions is at least c with arbitrarily high probability. Through the entire paper the term 'highly probable' will be used as 'with probability $1 - \exp(-\Theta(n))$', n being the size of the initial set of packets (see Section 2).*

Our result contrasts a result by [4]. They developed a stable queueing policy based on randomization: A random priority is determined for every newly inserted packet. Every router along the path of the packet advances packets based on this priority. Hence a router must trust the priority tag on the packet and every sender must honestly put low priorities on his packets with the appropriate probability. We feel that realistically a router should be restricted to use only locally reproducible information. Uniform queueing is the simplest possible

strategy that utilizes local randomness. As more sophisticated strategies that do
not advance all packets with the same probability are easier to predict for the
adversary, our result suggests, that access to local randomness does not help in
ensuring stability for a system.

2   Proof of Instability

Most instability proofs in the adversarial queueing setup use the baseball graph
of Andrews e.a. (see Figure 1) or a variation of it. It was first used [4] to show the
instability of FIFO for rates greater than 0.85. Even though simulation suggests
that the baseball graph is also unstable for uniform queueing it appears that
this only holds for very high rates above 0.99. In order to keep the proof simpler,
we use an extension of the baseball graph (see Figure 1), in which one of each
double edges is split into k edges. This will allow us to prove highly probable
instability for the rate 0.95. The value of k will be discussed later.

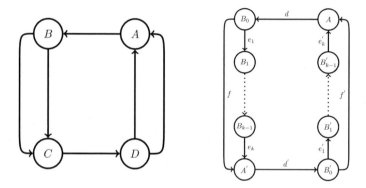

Fig. 1. Baseball graph and extended baseball graph

Next we need to describe the insertions of an (r, b)-adversary with $r = 0.95$. As
usual in adversarial queueing the insertions are described in rounds. It is assumed
a certain number of packets that still need to traverse a certain remaining path
are in the system. Based on this assumption insertions are performed, such that
afterwards a higher number of packets with the same properties as the initial
set is in the system. As arbitrarily many rounds can be executed, the number of
packets in the system eventually rises beyond any bound. A sufficiently large set
of packets to get the hole process started can always be achieved using burstiness
or separate insertion paths (see [4]).

In the case of randomized queueing that we are interested in, the issue of
stringing together rounds is more sophisticated as the starting set of packets of
later rounds is not fixed but subject to a random distribution. We will address
these specific difficulties in section 2.4.

One round of the adversary is divided into three parts called phases. At the
beginning of a round we assume n packets with the target B_0 being in the queue

of d. We will call this set of packets $\mathcal{W}$ and refer to these packets as $\mathcal{W}$-packets. Similar notation will be used for further sets.

The complete injection scheme is given in Table 1. Namely the following insertions are performed: During the first phase the adversary injects $\mathcal{X}$-packets with the path $\{d, e_1, \ldots, e_k, d'\}$. Since only one packet can cross edge d per time step, these packets collide with the $\mathcal{W}$-packets and some of the $\mathcal{X}$-packets will still be stuck in the queue of d at the end of phase 1.

In the second phase the adversary continues to inject packets into the queue of edge d, these $\mathcal{Y}$-packets have the path $\{d, f, d'\}$ assigned to them. Again, there is a collision in d and some of the $\mathcal{Y}$-packets remain in the queue of edge d. Furthermore the adversary simultaneously injects packets in every queue of the edges e_i each with only that one edge to cross. These packets collide with $\mathcal{X}$-packets, slow these down and keep some of them from reaching their goal before phase 2 is over.

During the last phase the adversary tries to collect as many packets as possible with destination B'_0 in the queue of edge d'. For this purpose he injects packets with path $\{d'\}$ wich collide with packets injecten in the first two phases. The goal after the third phase is that the number of packets in the queue of edge d' is larger than the size of the initial set $\mathcal{W}$.

In the following sections we need to carefully analyze how the flows of packets interact and we establish lower bounds on numbers of packets of the given types.

Table 1. Packet injection scheme of the first round

Phase	Time steps	# packets	Name	Path
At the beginning		n	$\mathcal{W}$	$\{d\}$
1	$2.9n$	$2.755n$	$\mathcal{X}$	$\{d, e_1, \ldots, e_k, d'\}$
2	$2n$	$1.9n$	$\mathcal{Y}$	$\{d, f, d'\}$
		$\forall i : 1.9n$	$\forall i : \mathcal{Y}'_i$	$\forall i : \{e_i\}$
3	$4.6n$	$4.37n$	$\mathcal{Z}$	$\{d'\}$

2.1   First Phase

During the first phase the adversary injects packets with the path $\{d, e_1, \ldots, e_k, d'\}$ into the system. We will call this set of packets $\mathcal{X}$.

In the queue Q_d the $\mathcal{X}$-packets collide with the initial set. The length t of the first phase is chosen to maximize the number of $\mathcal{X}$-packets in Q_d. Observe that at most rt $\mathcal{X}$-packets can be inserted in time t and some of them might be picked by the queuing policy, traverse d and get lost for our purposes. On the other hand the total number of packets in Q_d decreases with rate $(1 - r)$. Hence care must be taken when choosing the parameter t.

We can compute the optimal value for t by switching to a model of continuous packets allowing us to use differential equations. (see [5]). The results obtained by using the continuous model do not fully match the expectation values of a discrete model, but become more accurate for increasing n. Being able to choose an arbitrarily large value for n, the results satisfy our requirements.

It turns out that the maximum number of $\mathcal{X}$-packets in Q_d in the continuous model is reached after $nr(1-r)^{\frac{1-r}{r}} \approx 2.9n$ time steps, hence we let the running time t of the first phase be $2.9n$. During this $2.9n$ time steps the rate forbids the adversary to inject more than $r \cdot 2.9n = 2.755n$ $\mathcal{X}$-packets. Hence in $0.145n$ time steps the adversary does not insert any packets.

We need a highly probable lower bound of $\mathcal{X}$-packets in Q_d after the first phase. We thus consider a worst case for the adversary in which he makes all his injections at the beginning of the phase, leaving the last $0.145n$ time steps without injections. That way the probability of $\mathcal{X}$-packets being chosen to traverse d and getting lost is the highest. Any lower bound on the number of $\mathcal{X}$-packets in Q_d at the end of the phase will hold as well for every legal distribution of the insertions in the $2.9n$ steps. For the analysis of this exchange process during the first $2.755n$ time steps in Q_d the following theorem [6] comes in handy.

Theorem 1. *Let Z be the number of nonempty bins when M balls are placed randomly into N bins. The expectation of Z is given by*

$$\mu = E[Z] = N - N\left(1 - \frac{1}{N}\right)^M \geq N\left(1 - e^{-\frac{M}{N}}\right).$$

The probability of a linear deviation by a factor ϵ can be bounded by

$$P[|Z - \mu| \geq \epsilon\mu] \leq 2\exp\left(-\frac{\epsilon^2\mu^2(N - 1/2)}{N^2 - \mu^2}\right) = e^{-\Theta(\epsilon^2 N)} \qquad , \text{ for } M < 2N.$$

In our setup, the bins correspond to the positions in the queue of d. A ball being thrown into a bin corresponds to the packet in the position being chosen to traverse d and being replaced by the new $\mathcal{X}$-packet. Initially all the positions in the queue are taken by $\mathcal{W}$-Packets. If a position is chosen for the first time, this $\mathcal{W}$-packet is replaced with an $\mathcal{X}$-packet. If the same position is picked again, one $\mathcal{X}$-packet is replaced with a similar packet leaving the numbers unchanged. Hence the number of bins, that have been hit by at least one ball is the number of $\mathcal{X}$-packets in the queue at the end of Phase 1.

Setting $N = n$ and $M = 2.755n$ we get an expected number of $\mathcal{X}$-packets in Q_d after the first $2.755n$ time steps of $n\left(1 - e^{-2.755}\right) > 0.935n$. Any linear deviation from the expected number is highly improbable.

For the remaining $0.145n$ time steps of phase 1 we assume (worst case) that a $\mathcal{X}$-packet is chosen to traverse d in every step. Hence we expect at least $0.79n$ $\mathcal{X}$-packets in Q_d at the end of phase 1. Furthermore for every $\epsilon_1 > 0$ it is highly improbable to eventually have less than $(0.79 - \epsilon_1)n$ $\mathcal{X}$-packets in Q_d. The total number of packets in Q_d at the end of the first phase is exactly $n - 2.9n \cdot (1 - r) = 0.855n$.

2.2   Second Phase

During the second phase the adversary inserts two distinct sets of packets simultaneously. He injects $\mathcal{Y}$-packets with the path $\{d, f, d'\}$ and for every i with

$(1 \leq i \leq k)$ he injects $\mathcal{Y}'_i$-packets with the path $\{e_i\}$. Observe that these insertions may legally be done simultaneously, as the assigned paths of the sets are edge disjoint. The $\mathcal{Y}$-packets collide with a set of exactly $0.855n$ packets in Q_d consisting of mostly $\mathcal{X}$-packets and some remaining $\mathcal{W}$-packets.

The adversary's intent is to maximize the number of $\mathcal{Y}$-Packets in Q_d, and at the same time keep as many $\mathcal{X}$-packets as possible in the queues $Q_{e_1}, ..., Q_{e_k}$.

The optimal running time for maximizing the number of $\mathcal{Y}$-packets in Q_d can be shown to be about $2.5n$ time steps. Observe that the replacement of $\mathcal{W}$- and $\mathcal{X}$-packets in Q_d by $\mathcal{Y}$-packets is essentially the same setup as the replacement of the $\mathcal{W}$-packets with the $\mathcal{X}$-packets in the first phase.

However, letting the second phase run for $2.5n$ time steps gives the $\mathcal{X}$-packets to much time to traverse all the e_i, reach B'_0 and vanish. The adversary needs a large number of $\mathcal{X}$-packets still *stuck in the network* at the end of the phase. Simulations have shown that a running time of $2n$ is a good compromise and we now prove a lower bound for the number of $\mathcal{X}$- and $\mathcal{Y}$-packets still in the system at the end of the phase that will be met with high probability.

At first we concentrate on the Queue Q_d. In $2n$ steps the adversary may insert $1.9n$ $\mathcal{Y}$-packets. As soon as a $\mathcal{Y}$-packet is inserted into Q_d it has a chance to be chosen to traverse d and be lost for our purposes. We thus analyze the setup with the adversary inserting his $1.9n$ packets in the first $1.9n$ steps and remaining inactive for the last $0.1n$ steps.

Using Theorem 1 with $N = 0.855n$ and $M = 1.9n$ we obtain an expected number of $\mathcal{Y}$-packets in Q_d after the first $1.9n$ time steps of phase 2 of $0.855n \left(1 - \exp(-\frac{20}{9})\right) > 0.72n$. Any linear deviation from the expected number is highly improbable.

For the remaining $0.1n$ time steps of phase 2 we assume (worst case) that a $\mathcal{Y}$-packet is chosen to traverse d in every step. Hence we expect at least $0.62n$ $\mathcal{Y}$-packets in Q_d at the end of phase 2. Furthermore for every $\epsilon_2 > 0$ it is highly improbable to eventually have less than $(0.62 - \epsilon_2)n$ $\mathcal{Y}$-packets in Q_d.

Secondly we examine the course of the $\mathcal{X}$-packets in phase 2. We need to guarantee that a certain number of $\mathcal{X}$-packets is still *stuck in the network* at the end of phase 2. We know that we start phase 2 with at least $(0.79 - \epsilon_1)n$ $\mathcal{X}$-packets with high probability. Thus we seek an highly probable upper bound on the number of $\mathcal{X}$-packets that reach B' and leave the system during phase 2.

We can model the random processes of phase 2 in an idealized manner exploiting the following lemma:

Lemma 1. *Given an initially empty bin a round consists of putting a red and a blue ball into the bin and removing one ball at random afterwards. The total number of balls in the bin after N rounds is N, the expected number of red balls is $\frac{1}{2}N$ and the probability that at least $N\left(\frac{1}{2} + \epsilon\right)$ of the balls are red is smaller than $(1 - \epsilon)^{\epsilon N}$.*

Proof. The first two claims are obvious. To calculate the deviation of the expected value we build a Markov chain with a state for every possible constellation of balls in the bin. Each state has a label $[r, b]$ describing the number of red and blue balls. At the beginning the bin is empty, hence we label the first state

$[0, 0]$. Every state $[r, b]$ has two transitions, $[r, b] \to [r + 1, b]$ with probability $\frac{b+1}{r+b+2}$ and $[r, b] \to [r, b + 1]$ with probability $\frac{r+1}{r+b+2}$.

Starting in $[0, 0]$, after N transitions the Markov chain reaches a state $[r, b]$ with $r + b = N$. What is the probability to reach a *distorted state* (i.e.: a state $[r, (N - r)]$ with $r \geq N(1/2 + \epsilon)$)? We calculate an upper bound by multiplying the number of paths ending in a distorted state with the highest probability of such a path.

There are $N(1/2 - \epsilon)$ distorted states and no state is reached by more paths than the state $[N(1/2 + \epsilon), N(1/2 - \epsilon)]$. Hence

$$R := N \left(\frac{1}{2} - \epsilon \right) \cdot \binom{N}{\frac{N}{2} - \epsilon N}$$

is an upper bound for the number of paths to any distorted state.

Now we need to find the path to a distorted state with the highest probability. The most probable path ends in $[N(1/2 + \epsilon), N(1/2 - \epsilon)]$ and its run is depicted in figure 2. Namely it stays in balanced states for as long as possible. We call a state $[r, b]$ balanced if $r - 1 \leq b \leq r + 1$. The last ϵn transitions have to increase the number of red balls.

Along the path with the highest probability the denominator of the transition probabilities increases each step by one. In between balanced states the numerator of the transition probability increases every two steps by one and for the last ϵn transitions stays constant, giving a total probability of

$$T := \frac{1}{(N + 1)!} \cdot \left[\left(\frac{N - \epsilon N}{2} \right)! \right]^2 \left(\frac{N - \epsilon N}{2} \right)^{\epsilon N}.$$

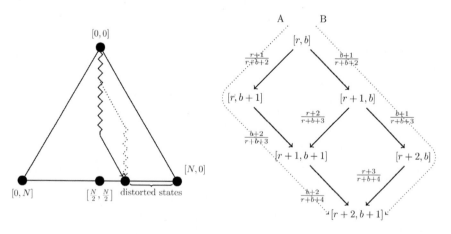

Fig. 2. The first figure shows the most probable path to a distorted state. The alternative path (dotted) is less probable, which is shown with a local argument in the second figure. For $r \geq b$ the probability for path A is higher than for path B.

$$\frac{(r+1)(b+2)(b+2)}{(r+b+2)(r+b+3)(r+b+4)} > \frac{(b+1)(b+1)(r+3)}{(r+b+2)(r+b+3)(r+b+4)} \Leftrightarrow 2rb + 3r + 1 > 2b^2 + 2b$$

Hence $R \cdot T \leq (1 - \epsilon)^{\epsilon N}$ is an upper bound of the probability to reach a distorted state (See [5] for the arithmetics).   □

We need an upper bound on the number of $\mathcal{X}$-packets traversing every e_i during phase 2. We obtain that by showing that the ratio of $\mathcal{X}$-packets that reach a certain Q_{e_i} approaches 0 as i increases. Hence by choosing k large enough we can assure that an arbitrary high percentage of $\mathcal{X}$ packets remains in the system.

For the analysis we assume (worst case) that an $\mathcal{X}$-packet traverses d in every time step of phase 2 maximizing the number of $\mathcal{X}$ packets that have a chance to reach their destination.

Furthermore for every i we assume that the $\mathcal{X}$-packets that do reach Q_{e_i} during phase 2 arrive consecutively during the first steps of phase 2. Again this is a worst case assumption as it gives packets most time to traverse the edge.

Finally, for the sake of the argument we assume, that the adversary may insert $\mathcal{Y}'$-packets at rate 1. We will then show how this assumption can be lifted.

Let $q_i n$ be a highly probable upper bound on the number of $\mathcal{X}$ packets that reach e_i. We proceed by induction over i. For $i = 1$ we set $q_1 = 2$ as we assume a $\mathcal{X}$ packet traverses d in every step of phase 2.

For the first $q_i n$ steps of phase 2 a $\mathcal{X}$-packet and a $\mathcal{Y}_i$-packet arrives in Q_{e_i}. Lemma 1 guarantees, that with high probability at most $q_i(\frac{1}{2} + \epsilon)n$ packets traverse e_i during this phase.

For the last $(2 - q_i)n$ steps of phase 2, there are no $\mathcal{X}$-packets arriving in Q_{e_i}, we are hence in the *replacement setup* discussed in Theorem 1 with $N = q_i\left(\frac{1}{2} - \epsilon\right)n$ and $M = (2 - q_i)n$. We neglect $\mathcal{Y}'$-packets that might be in Q_{e_i} after $q_i n$ steps, as they can only slow down $\mathcal{X}$-packets. We get from Theorem 1 that with high probability at most

$$n\left[q_i\left(\frac{1}{2} - \epsilon\right)\left(1 - e^{-\frac{2-q_i}{q_i(1/2-\epsilon)}}\right) + \epsilon'\right] \geq q_i n\left(\frac{1}{2} - \epsilon^*\right)\left(1 - e^{-\frac{2-q_i}{q_i(1/2-\epsilon^*)}}\right)$$

$\mathcal{X}$-packets cross the edge e_{i+1} at the end of phase 2 (for an adequate ϵ^*). Hence a high probable higher bound of $\mathcal{X}$-packets, that reach $Q_{e_{i+1}}$, is given by

$$q_{i+1} \leq q_i n\left(1/2 + \epsilon^*\right) + q_i n\left(1/2 - \epsilon^*\right)\left(1 - e^{-\frac{2-q_i}{q_i(1/2-\epsilon^*)}}\right)$$

$$= q_i n\left(1 - (1/2 - \epsilon^*)e^{-\frac{2-q_i}{q_i(1/2-\epsilon^*)}}\right) \leq q_i\left(1 - \frac{e^{\frac{6}{q_i}-3}}{3}\right) \quad \text{for } \epsilon^* \leq 1/6.$$

Because $0 < e^{\frac{6}{q_i}-3}/3 < 1$, the sequence is strictly monotonically decreasing and approaches 0 (see [5]). Hence every given ratio of $\mathcal{X}$-packets can be held in $Q_{e_1}, \ldots, Q_{e_k}$ with high probability if we choose k sufficiently large:

Theorem 2. *We assume that in every time step of the second phase one $\mathcal{X}$-packet arrives in Q_{e_1} and that the adversary injects one $\mathcal{Y}'$-packet for every edge $e_1, \ldots, e_k$. Let $q_i n$ for $1 \leq i \leq k$ be the number of $\mathcal{X}$-packets reaching Q_{e_i} during the second phase, then $\forall \epsilon \in]0, 1[\; \exists k \in \mathbb{N} : P(q_k n \geq \epsilon n) \leq e^{-\Theta(n)}$.*

To simplify matters we choose concrete numbers. We assume that the value of k is large enough, so that 99% of the $\mathcal{X}$-packets are held in $Q_{e_1}, \ldots, Q_{e_k}$ with high probability[1]. Hence during the $2n$ time steps of the second phase only $0.02n$ $\mathcal{X}$-packets pass Q_{e_k}. As in our setup at most $(0.79 - \epsilon_1)n$ $\mathcal{X}$-packets pass d during the second phase, the likelihood of such a high amount of packages passing Q_{e_k} is even lower.

In order to comply to the rate of 0.95 the adversary must restrain from inserting packets for $0.1n$ time steps. Hence he cannot insert $\mathcal{Y}_i'$-packets in every time step like we assumed. However, even if in each of these $0.1n$ steps a $\mathcal{X}$-packet is chosen in each Q_{e_i} at most $0.1n$ $\mathcal{X}$-packets slip through, while the composition of packets in each queue stays the same.

So with high probability after the second phase the queues $Q_d, Q_{e_1}, \ldots, Q_{e_k}$ contain at least $(0.79 - \epsilon_1)n - 0.02n - 0.1n = (0.67 - \epsilon_1)n$ $\mathcal{X}$-packets.

2.3   Third Phase

During the third phase the adversary wants to collect packets with destination B_0' in $Q_{d'}$. He injects only $\mathcal{Z}$-packets with the path $\{d'\}$, so that all other queues are emptied. The total number of packets with destination B_0' – all $\mathcal{X}$- and $\mathcal{Y}$-packets – is at the beginning of the third phase with high probability at least $(0.67 - \epsilon_1)n + (0.62 - \epsilon_2)n = (1.29 - \epsilon_3)n$.

We let the running time of the third phase be $4.6n$. At the beginning of the first phase there were n packets in Q_d, hence after the second phase Q_d contains $n - 4.9(1 - r)n = 0.755n$ packets. These packets cross the edge d during the first $0.755n$ time steps of phase 3. Every $\mathcal{Y}$-packets that arrives in Q_f is one time step later in $Q_{d'}$. No queue Q_{e_i} contains more than $1.9n$ packets, so every $\mathcal{X}$-packet in Q_{e_i} reach $Q_{d'}$ after at most $1.9n + k + 1$ time steps. For $n >> k$, a running time of $4.6n$ is more than sufficient.

Theorem 3. *With high probability at least $(1.29 - \epsilon_3)n + 4.6n \cdot 0.95 = (5.66 - \epsilon_3)n$ packets reach the queue of d' during phase 3 but only $4.6n$ can traverse d'. Hence with high probability the queue $Q_{d'}$ contains at least $(1.06 - \epsilon_3)n$ packets with destination B_0' after the third phase (i.e. $\mathcal{W}$-packets of the next round).*

We had started with a queue Q_d containing n packets with destination B_0 and have now arrived at a queue $Q_{d'}$ containing at least $(1.06 - \epsilon_3)n$ packets with destination B_0' for every arbitrarily small ϵ_3.

To obtain an arbitrarily large number of packets, we need to repeat the three phases. At this point we need the symmetry of the graph. The adversary can repeat all three phases – henceforth called a round – only this time starting in A' and ending in A etc.

---

[1] In fact we have shown that q_{i+1} has a certain maximal value with high probability, provided q_i is of a certain maximum value. As we are only interested in a constant number k of iterations, the bound for the total number holds with high probability as well.

2.4   Repeating the Three Phases

Repeating rounds is not as trivial as it seems at first glance. The adversary has to determine his strategy before even one packet has crossed an edge. For the first round he knows the number of packets waiting in Q_d and is able to calculate optimal running times for all three phases. For every further round he has to guess the number of packets and thus the running times.

From Theorem 3 we know, that if the adversary expects the growth rate to be arbitrarily close to 1.06, the real growth rate will be higher with high probability. Hence all running times will be based on an underestimated number of packets, motivating the following theorem.

Theorem 4. *Let n_{re}^i be the real number and n_{est}^i be the estimated number of W-packets at the beginning of the i-th round. If $n_{re}^i = n_{est}^i(1+\delta)$ for $\delta > 0$, then the expected value of $n_{re}^{i+1} = n_{est}^{i+1}(1+\gamma)$ with $0 < \gamma < \delta$, hence the real number of packets rises regardless of an adversary underestimating the number of packets.*

Proof. For this proof we look more precisely into the results of the differential equations mentioned in Section 2.1. Let n_{est} be the estimated number of W-packets at the beginning of an arbitrary round. The running time of the first phase chosen by the adversary depends only on his estimation.

$$n_{est}\left(\frac{(1-r)^{\left(\frac{1-r}{r}\right)}-1}{r-1}\right).$$

The expected[2] number of $\mathcal{X}$-packets in Q_d after the first phase however depends on the real number of packets initially in Q_d.

$$E_{\mathcal{X}}(t) = -\left(\frac{n_{re}{}^r}{tr-t+n_{re}}\right)^{\left(\frac{1}{r-1}\right)} + tr - t + n_{re}$$

Let $t = t_1$ be the value maximizing $E_{\mathcal{X}}(t)$. Let $n_{re} := (1+\delta)n_{est}$ for $\delta \geq 0$, hence

$$E_{\mathcal{X}}(t_1) = -\left((1-r)^{\left(\frac{1-r}{r}\right)}+\delta\right)^{\left(\frac{1}{1-r}\right)} \cdot n_{est}^{\left(\frac{1}{1-r}\right)} \cdot (n_{est}+n_{est}\delta)^{\left(\frac{r}{r-1}\right)}$$

$$+ n_{est}(1-r)^{\left(\frac{1-r}{r}\right)} + n_{est}\delta$$

$$= n_{est}\left[-\left((1-r)^{\left(\frac{1-r}{r}\right)}+\delta\right)^{\left(\frac{1}{1-r}\right)} \cdot (1-\delta)^{\left(\frac{r}{r-1}\right)} + (1-r)^{\left(\frac{1-r}{r}\right)}+\delta\right].$$

The difference between the expected number of $\mathcal{X}$-packets after a first phase based on the real and one based on an underestimated number of packets is

$$E_{\mathcal{X}}(t_1)-E_{\mathcal{X}}^{real}(t_1^{real}) = n_{est}\left[-\left((1-r)^{\left(\frac{1-r}{r}\right)}+\delta\right)^{\left(\frac{1}{1-r}\right)} \cdot (1-\delta)^{\left(\frac{r}{r-1}\right)}+(1-r)^{\frac{1}{r}}+\delta\right]$$

and $0 \leq E_{\mathcal{X}}(t_1) - E_{\mathcal{X}}^{real}(t_1^{real}) \leq \delta \cdot E_{\mathcal{X}}^{real}(t_1^{real})$ holds for $0 \leq \delta < 1$.

---

[2] As already mentioned the results of the differential equations do not fully match, but converges to the expected value from the discrete system. As we are able to choose an arbitrarily large value for n, this suffices.

If a round starts with an underestimated number of packets, after the first phase the expected value of $\mathcal{X}$-packets will still be higher than estimated, but the factor of the underestimation will decrease – a self correcting process.

Example 1. If the adversary starts the first phase *knowing* the real number of packets ($n_{est} = n_{re}$), the rate $r = 0.95$ leads to an optimal running time $t_1 \approx 2.9 n_{est} = 2.9 n_{re}$ for the first phase and an expected number of $E_{\mathcal{X}} \approx 0.81 n_{est} = 0.81 n_{re}$ $\mathcal{X}$-packets. An adversary underestimating the number of packets by the factor two ($n_{re} = 2 n_{est}$) calculates an optimal running time of $t_1 \approx 2.9 n_{est} \approx 1.5 n_{re}$. In this case $E_{\mathcal{X}} \approx 0.7 n_{re} \approx 1.4 n_{est}$ holds, so the expected value of $\mathcal{X}$-packets has grown from $0.81 n_{est}$ to $1.4 n_{est}$ by a factor lower than two.

Since at the beginning of the second phase there are still more packets in Q_d than the adversary assumes we have the same effect on the expectation value as just shown for the first phase.

For $Q_{e_1}, \ldots, Q_{e_k}$ we assumed a worst case that holds even if $n_{re} > n_{est}$. In our assumption one $\mathcal{X}$-packet per time step tried to cross $Q_{e_1}, \ldots, Q_{e_k}$. No matter how wrong the adversary estimated the number of $\mathcal{X}$-packets, this assumption will always hold.

The bound of deviation in Theorem 1 is even better if $n_{est} < n_{re}$. The more packets there are, the less probable it is to pick a newly injected packet to leave the queue. The same holds for Q_d in the second phase.

The third phase could be a problem, if its running time was not sufficient for all packets to reach $Q_{d'}$, as remaining packets from previous rounds might interfere with packets of following rounds. However the following lemma indicates that this problem cannot arise if the running time is chosen to be $4.6 n_{est}$ time steps.

Lemma 2. *The real number of packets n_{re} cannot be higher than $4.6 n_{est}$.*

Proof. At the beginning of the first round $n_{re}^1 = n_{est}^1$. If n_{re}^j is higher than $4.6 n_{est}^j$, a first point in time i exists, so that $n_{re}^i \leq 4.6 n_{est}^i$ and $n_{re}^{i+1} > 4.6 n_{est}^{i+1}$. The adversary estimates a growth rate of 1.06, hence $4.6 n_{est}^{i+1}$ equals $1.06 \cdot 4.6 n_{est}^i = 4.87 n_{est}^i$ at the end of round i. To have at least $4.87 n_{est}^i$ packets at the end of the third phase turning into $\mathcal{W}$-packets of the $(i+1)$-th round, at the beginning of the third phase there were at least $4.6 n_{est}^i \cdot (1 - r) + 4.87 n_{est}^i = 5.1 n_{est}^i$ $\mathcal{X}$- and $\mathcal{Y}$-packets waiting in queues. During the first two phases less than $2.9 n_{est}^i$ $\mathcal{X}$- and $2 n_{est}^i$ $\mathcal{Y}$-packets were injected, hence this is impossible. □

We conclude, that at the beginning of every round only packets with the path d (d') exist. The number of packets in the system rises even with the adversary underestimating the number of packets:

Theorem 5. *Uniform queueing is highly probably instable at rate 0.95 on the extended baseball graph.*

Simulations show that on the other hand overestimating the number of packets can lead to a total loss of all packets (see [5]).

3   Conclusion

We have shown that uniform queueing is unstable with high probability. We have assumed an oblivious adversary who may not react to the random queueing decisions, which makes the construction of an insertion sequence resulting in a packet pileup considerably more involved.

In online setups quite often introducing randomness into a process makes the construction of a malicious input impossible. Randomized quicksort outperforms deterministic quicksort, randomized paging algorithms do better than deterministic ones. Our result shows that uniform queueing, which can be seen as a form of randomized FIFO, is unstable just as well as FIFO. The simulations however show, that it appears to be superior to FIFO in terms of absolute numbers of packets.

Uniform queueing is the randomized queueing strategy with the least foreseeable behaviour. Hence our result appears to suggesting that local randomness in general is insufficient to enforce stability.

References

[1] Borodin, A., Kleinberg, J., Raghavan, P., Sudan, M., Williamson, D.P.: Adversarial queuing theory. J. ACM 48(1), 13–38 (2001)
[2] Cholvi, V., Echagüe, J.: Stability of fifo networks under adversarial models: State of the art. Comput. Networks 51(15), 4460–4474 (2007)
[3] Bhattacharjee, R., Goel, A., Lotker, Z.: Instability of fifo at arbitrarily low rates in the adversarial queueing model. SIAM Journal on Computing 34(2), 318–332 (2005)
[4] Andrews, A., Fernandez, L., Liu, K.: Universal-stability results and performance bounds for greedy contention-resolution protocols. J. ACM: Journal of the ACM 48 (2001)
[5] Lorion, Y., Weinard, M.: The effects of local randomness in the adversarial queueing model. Technical Report 2008/01, Frankfurter Informatik Berichte (2008) ISSN 1616-9107
[6] Kamath, A.P., Motwani, R., Palem, K., Spirakis, P.: Tail bounds for occupancy and the satisfiability threshold conjecture. Random Structures and Algorithms 7, 59–80 (1995)

Parallel Imaging Problem

Thành Nguyen[*] and Éva Tardos[**]

Cornell University
{thanh,eva}@cs.cornell.edu

Abstract. Metric Labeling problems have been introduced as a model for understanding noisy data with pair-wise relations between the data points. One application of labeling problems with pair-wise relations is image understanding, where the underlying assumption is that physically close pixels are likely to belong to the same object.

In this paper we consider a variant of this problem, we will call Parallel Imaging, where instead of directly observing the noisy data, the data undergoes a simple linear transformation first, such as adding different images. This class of problems arises in a wide range of imaging problems. Our study has been motivated by the Parallel Imaging problem in Magnetic Resonance Image (MRI) reconstruction. We give a constant factor approximation algorithm for the case of speedup of two with the truncated linear metric, motivated by the MRI reconstruction problem. Our method uses local search and graph cut techniques.

1   Introduction

In this paper we propose a problem, we will call Parallel Imaging, that combines features of the Metric Labeling problem with linear algebra. Metric Labeling problems have been studied extensively [8,2,5,6] with one of the primary applications for image processing. In the image processing application the data observed is associated with each pixel of an image (such as intensity, depth, etc). Given noisy data about the image we want to recover the most likely original data. Motivated by a model of images via Markov Random Field [9] this imaging problem is often solved via an energy minimization approach called the Metric Labeling problem that combines features of the assignment and graph partitioning problems. In this paper, we consider a variant of this problem where there are multiple independent data values associated with each node of the graph, and we are observing different linear combinations of the associated data at each node.

Our original motivation for studying this problem came from Magnetic Resonance Imaging (MRI), an important medical technology widely used for both clinical and research applications. For many medical applications its essential to reduce scan time mainly due to reducing motion artifacts. To speed up the

[*] Supported in part by ONR grant N00014-98-1-0589 and ITR grant CCR-0325453.
[**] Supported in part by ITR grant CCR-0325453, ONR grant N00014-98-1-0589 and NSF grant CCR-0729006.

D. Halperin and K. Mehlhorn (Eds.): ESA 2008, LNCS 5193, pp. 684–695, 2008.

image acquisition MRI technology uses multiple parallel scans. Raj, Singh and Zabih [10] show how this parallel MRI imaging problem gives rise to the kind of the labeling problem discussed in this paper where the number of observations associated with each node is the speedup factor used in the process. Our main result is a constant factor approximation algorithm for the case of this problem speeding up image acquisition by a factor of two.

The Metric Labeling Problem. The Metric Labeling problem is defined as follows. We are given a graph G and a label set L. Our goal is to associate a label value $f(v) \in L$ with each node v of the graph G. There are two competing factors in defining the most appropriate label for a node. First, the label $f(v)$ should be identical, or at least similar to an observed data value $o(v)$. Second, neighboring nodes in the graph should obtain similar labels. These goals are expressed by an "energy" function of the form: Assignment Cost + Separation Cost =

$$\sum_{v \in V} A_v(f(v), o(v)) + \sum_{e=(u,v) \in E} w_e d(f(v), f(u)).$$

Here $A_v(\alpha, o(v))$, or sometimes we only write $A_v(\alpha)$, is an assignment cost of assigning label α to a node v with observed label $o(v)$. The assignment cost is trying to encourage a labeling that is close to the observation. The goal of the second term is to encourage neighboring nodes to have the same or similar labels. The function $d(\alpha, \beta)$ is the distance between labels, and we will assume that this distance is a metric, and the value w_e for an edge $e = (u, v)$ expresses the strength of the connection between u and v, the strength of the penalty for assigning u and v (very) different labels.

Image Reconstruction Problem. In imaging problems, an image is modeled as a graph whose vertices are the pixels of the image, and the neighbors of a vertex are either 4 or 8 pixels around. Labels can represent a variety of properties of the associated object, such as color, intensity (darkness), or distance from the camera. In this paper we consider black-and-white imaging problems, such as the images obtained by the MRI technology, and will use integers (intensity or darkness) as labels. For such problems, the most commonly used term for the assignment penalty function $A_v(.,.)$ is the square norm $(f(v) - o(v))^2$, where assignment cost is then

$$\sum_{v \in V} A_v(f(v), o(v)) = ||f - o||_2^2.$$

This assignment cost is motivated via the probabilistic roots of the labeling problem. If the observed labeling $o(v)$ is generated from a labeling $f(v)$ by adding Gaussian random noise, then the above assignment cost is proportional to the probability that $f(v)$ is the original labeling, assuming we see observation $o(v)$.

The separation term expresses the goal that most pairs of neighboring nodes should have same or similar labels. In the context of imagining, this is a reasonable expectation as most useful images have only a few objects (e.g., the organ that is subject of the MRI, and some of the neighboring organs), and pixels belonging to the same object or same body part typically have the same or similar labels. One simple option is to use the linear metric $d(u, v) = |f(v) - f(u)|$. However, a more robust metric is the *truncated linear metric* $d(\alpha, \beta) = \min(M, |\alpha - \beta|)$ where M is a parameter of the problem. Here, small changes in labeling come with a small penalty, as small change in label can reflect gradual changes in the object, but the bigger the change is, the more likely that we have an object boundary. However, once the difference of the assigned labels is large enough, it does suggest an object boundary independent of the actual size of the difference. Our goal is to only have few object boundaries. This suggests that after some difference, the penalty should remain constant and not grow further with the difference in labels. This robustness of the truncated linear metric helps in obtaining sharp object boundaries of the resulting images.

Our problem: Parallel Imaging Problem. In MRI, when an image is scanned with double speed, instead of getting the data on each pixel, we obtain a linear transform of the image. In particular, a receiver is observing an image whose width is equal to half of the the width of the original image, obtained by adding these two strips of the original image with some positive coefficients depending on the position of the receiver. See [10] for more details. Hence, in order to reconstruct an image, we need data on more than one receiver. Assume we have k receivers with the corresponding linear transform $H_1, .., H_k$ and the observed data vectors $o_1, .., o_k$.

Now, we model an image as two *identical* copies G_1, G_2 corresponding to the strips of the image. And we use the following convention if v_1 is a node in G_1 then v_2 is its copy in G_2 and vice versa. Let $f : V_1 \cup V_2 \to L$ be a labeling. Without noise, the linear transform H_j at receiver j adds the labeling of v_1 and v_2 with some positive coefficients h_{jv_1} and h_{jv_2} for all pairs of vertices to get $o_j(v) = h_{jv_1} f(v_1) + h_{jv_2} f(v_2)$.

Similar to the traditional Metric Labeling problem, our goal now is to find a labeling f to minimize the sum of assignment cost and separation cost. The assignment cost is : $\sum_j \|H_j f - o_j\|^2$. And the separation cost is the sum of the separation cost of f in G_1 and G_2 as discussed above. More precisely, we need to find a labeling to minimize

$$\sum_j \|H_j f - o_j\|^2 + \sum_{uv \in G_1 \cup G_2} w_{uv} d(f(v), f(v)).$$

We call this problem *Parallel Metric Labeling* if d is an arbitrary metric, and *Parallel Imaging* if d is a linear truncated metric. The main result of this paper is a constant approximation for the Parallel Imaging problem.

Note. We simplify the problem a bit by considering each "strip" of the original image as a separate graph G_i, that are not related to each other. This simplification ignores the edges connecting the strips, but only a very small fraction of the edges are ignored, so the method should still lead to good image quality.

Related works. In this paper, we consider a class of applications where data is observed via a linear transformation. Traditional reconstruction models for such data do not use priors. Given the data f, the observation is through a linear transformation Hf, where H is a non-negative matrix. The traditional reconstruction uses a least squares application to reconstruct the data: Given observed data o, the method looks for the labeling f that minimizes $||o - Hf||_2^2$. We consider a problem, which adds priors to the above least squares image reconstruction. This problem combines the combinatorial problem of Metric Labeling with added linear algebraic features. The problem was introduced by Raj, Singh and Zabih [10]. In this work they developed practical heuristics for this problem based on ideas from Metric Labeling.

The Metric Labeling problem was introduced in [8], and studied extensively [2,5,6,8]. The problem is $\mathcal{NP}$-hard for general metric. The best known approximation algorithm for the problem is an $O(\log |L|)$ [8] and has no $\Omega(\sqrt{\log n})$ approximation unless $\mathcal{NP}$ has quasi-polynomial time algorithms [2]. Many special cases of the Metric Labeling problem have been considered: [3,7,4,6], among which [3] and [6] are the closest to ours.

Boykov, O. Veksler, and R. Zabih [3] were the first to develop a local search technique, called α-extension, for the Metric Labeling problem. For linear truncated metrics, Gupta and Tardos [6] extend the "α-extension" local move to "interval" local move to obtain a constant approximation. These techniques are discussed in details in section 4. Our result is a nontrivial extension of [6]: our assignment cost depends on *pairs of nodes*. As will be shown, there is a method to reduce our problem to the traditional Metric Labeling on a different metric. However, this metric does not have an embedding with a constant distortion to tree metric as in the case of truncated one and therefore, one cannot get a constant approximation using this approach. In order to give a constant approximation, we need to develop a new graph construction for the new assignment cost, and extend the interval-local move introduced in [6].

Organization. The rest of our paper is organized as follows: In section 2 we show that our problem can be reduced to the traditional Metric Labeling, but this only gives a logarithmic approximation. In section 3, we give a graph construction for our new assignment cost. This is a basic step for us to develop a local search algorithm in section 4.

2   The Parallel Metric Labeling Problem

In this section, we show that the Parallel Metric Labeling problem can be thought of as a traditional labeling problem with a larger label set and a different metric. Viewing the Parallel Metric Labeling as a traditional labeling problem on a bigger label set immediately implies that known techniques for Metric Labeling to give a logarithmic approximation for the problem. However, using the larger label set does not allow us to take advantage of the special structure of the linear truncated metric needed for a constant factor approximation, but this way of thinking about the Parallel Labeling problem will still be useful in the subsequent sections on defining our combinatorial algorithm (based on graph cuts and local search).

Now, if instead of considering a labeling as a function on the vertices of G_1 and G_2, we consider it as a mapping from the vertices of a *single* copy to pairs of labels. The new set of labels is now the set of pairs of numbers. The assignment cost depending on these two numbers is now a function of a new label. Given two vertices u an v with the labeling (α_1, β_1) and (α_2, β_2), the separation cost is

$$d_2((\alpha_1, \alpha_2), (\beta_1, \beta_2)) = d(\alpha_1, \beta_1) + d(\alpha_2, \beta_2).$$

Now, if d is a metric on L then d_2 defined as above is also a metric on L^2. Therefore, given a Parallel Metric Labeling problem with a metric d, we can understand the problem as an instance of a traditional Metric Labeling problem with the metric d_2 on a larger set of labels. Using the approximation algorithm for the Metric Labeling problem in [8], we have the following result:

Theorem 1. *There is a $O(\log |L|)$ approximation for the Parallel Metric Labeling problem with any metric d. When d is a truncated linear metric, which is the Parallel Imaging problem, we get a $O(\log M)$ approximation, where M is the truncation parameter.*

Proof. Due to [8], there exists an algorithm for the Metric Labeling problem that approximates the best solution up to a factor of $O(distort)$, where $distort$ is the distortion of a probabilistic embedding of the metric in to random trees.

Any metric on K vertices can be probabilistically embedded into to random trees with distortion $\log K$. This gives the $O(\log |L|^2) = O(\log |L|)$ approximation. It is not hard to see that the 2 dimensional truncated linear metric can be embedded into random trees with distortion of $O(\log M)$, which proves the theorem.   □

3   The Problem with Linear Metric Is Solvable

We now consider the Parallel Metric Labeling problem where the metric is the linear metric, i.e., $d(\alpha, \beta) = |\alpha - \beta|$. We will give a graph cut construction that allows us to get the optimal labeling.

Ideas of using graph cut to find a best labeling have been used in Boykov et al. [3], Ishikawa and Geiger [7], and Gupta and Tardos [6] for the traditional labeling problem. These approaches use the following basic construction:

The basic construction. The basic idea is to build a chain for each vertex as follows. For each vertex v, build a chain $v^1, v^2, ..., v^L$ of length L representing the possible labels that the vertex can be assigned to. We also add a super source s and a super sink t to the network as shown in Figure 1(a). Consider the following correspondence between (s, t)-cuts and labelings:

A labeling $f : V \to L$ assigns v to α, $(f(v) = \alpha)$ if and only if the edge $v^\alpha v^{\alpha+1}$ is in the corresponding cut. Here we use the notation that $v^{L+1} = t$ for all nodes *v*. To make sure that the mapping between the labelings and the graph cuts is well defined, we need to guarantee that for every node v there is exactly one edge of its corresponding chain in the cut. To do this, we add the edges $v^{\alpha+1}v^{\alpha}$ with infinite capacity. Further, we do not want to cut edge (s, v^1), so we also assign an infinite capacity to this edge in both directions. Now we have a one-to-one mapping between *finite* cuts and all the possible labelings.

New assignment cost. In the traditional Metric Labeling problem, assignment cost is a function of the label of one vertex: $A_v(\alpha)$. This can be captured easily by assigning a capacity of $A_v(\alpha)$ to the edges $(v^{\alpha}, v^{\alpha+1})$ [3,7]. Now, recall from section 2, our new assignment cost is a function on *pairs* of labels: If v_1 is labeled α; v_2 is labeled β, i.e., $f(v) = (\alpha, \beta)$, then the assignment cost is

$$A_v(f(v)) = \sum_{j=1}^{k} ||H_j f(v) - o_j(v)||^2 = \sum_{j=1}^{k}(h_{jv_1}\alpha + h_{jv_2}\beta - o_j(v))^2. \quad (1)$$

This assignment cost cannot be separated into terms that depends on α and β separately, as there is the term $2\sum_{j=1}^{k} h_{jv_1} h_{jv_2}\alpha\beta = c_v\alpha\beta$. Note that $c_v > 0$ by the assumption that all the matrices H_j are nonnegative.

The new observation is that we can modify the chain construction above to capture this assignment cost: For node $v_1 \in G_1$ we connect the chain of nodes $v_1^1, \ldots v_1^L$ as described by the above construction. However, for node $v_2 \in G_2$ we connect the chain backwards, reversing the rolls of s and t in the construction for the copy G_2 as shown in Figure 1(b). If a cut separates nodes v_i^{α} and $v_i^{\alpha+1}$, then the corresponding labeling assigns v_i to label α. Note that the chain for v_2 starts its numbering from the t side, and increases towards the s side, and we are using the notation that $v_1^{L+1} = t$ and $v_2^{L+1} = s$ for all nodes v. To model the assignment cost, we now add a complete graph between the chains of v_1 and v_2 with capacity $c_v/2$ on each edge. The cut corresponding to labeling $f(v_1) = \alpha$ and $f(v_2) = \beta$ cuts $\alpha\beta + (L-\alpha)(L-\beta)$ of these edges, so these edges contribute a total of $\frac{c_v}{2}(2\alpha\beta - L\alpha - L\beta + L^2)$ to the capacity of the cut.

After adding the above edges between the pairs of chains, the remaining terms in the assignment cost can be written as the sum of two functions depending on α and β separately. Any such assignment cost can be captured exactly via the capacity of the edges in the two chains. However, these costs may now be negative. Consider a chain, say corresponding to node v_i that has some of the resulting edge capacity negative. To make all capacities nonnegative, we will add the same positive number to every edge on the chain. This change adds a constant to the capacity of all cuts, as each finite cut uses exactly one edge in every chain.

Separation cost. As shown in [3,7], the technique of building chains can also help us to capture some classes of separation cost function. For simplicity we consider the case of linear separation cost $d(\alpha, \beta) = |\alpha - \beta|$. In this case, consider an edge of the original graph $e = (u, v)$, we know that the chains corresponding to u, v are in the same order, because they are both in the same graph G_1 or G_2. We add edges $u^{\alpha}v^{\alpha}$, $\forall \alpha \in L$ with the capacity of w_e. Note that if a cut uses $u^{\alpha}u^{\alpha+1}$ and

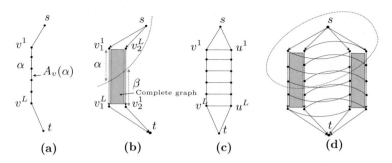

Fig. 1. Constructions for the problem with linear metric

$v^\beta v^{\beta+1}$, then these edges contribute to the cut a total capacity of $w_e|\alpha - \beta|$, which is exactly the separation cost of the corresponding labeling. See Figure 1(c).

We combine the constructions described above as shown on Figure 1(d). We use the construction for new assignment cost and the construction of for separation cost to get the following theorem:

Theorem 2. *The Parallel Metric Labeling problem with linear metric and can be solved in polynomial time via a graph construction such that the minimum cut of this graph is equal to the minimum cost of the labeling plus a constant.*   □

4   Constant Approximation Via Local Search

In the previous section, we give a new graph construction whose minimum cut gives the optimal solution of the Parallel Metric Labeling problem with linear metric. The problem is, however, $\mathcal{NP}$ hard for the truncated linear metric. Local search has been proved to be a successful method for this type of problems. Our algorithm also uses this approach. First let us explain some of previous works that use the local search method for the traditional Metric Labeling problem.

Local Search. For uniform metric d, $(d(i,j) = 1$ iff $i \neq j)$, Boykov et al [3] give a local search algorithm that tries to relabel some vertices to a label α. Such best local move can be found via graph cut algorithm. The graph construction is shown in Figure 2 (a): For each edge (u, v) we build a node p_{uv} and connect it with u, v and the super sink s. The weight of $sp_{uv}, up_{uv}, vp_{uv}$ are $d(f(u), f(v)), d(f(v), \alpha), d(f(u), \alpha)$ respectively, where $f(u), f(v)$ are the current labeling of u and v. The edges su, sv have weights of the current assignment cost of u and v, while tu, tv have weights of the assignment cost of u and v if assigned to the new label α. Given a cut X such that $s \in X$, in its corresponding relabeling, a vertex u is relabeled iff $u \in X$. The main observation is the following: Because d is a metric, the weights of $sp_{uv}, up_{uv}, vp_{uv}$ satisfy the triangle inequality. Thus, any minimum cut separating s and t would cut at most 1 edge among these three edges. And therefore a minimum cut captures exactly the cost of the corresponding relabeling. As a result, a best local move can be found by a single minimum cut algorithm.

For truncated metric with the truncated parameter M, Gupta and Tardos [6] extended the local move above to an "interval" local move, where at every step they pick a random interval I of length M and try to reduce the cost of a current labeling by changing some vertices to labels in I. They construct a graph to find a local move. See Figure 2 (b). It is shown that although a best labeling could not be found, approximate optimal local moves are enough for a constant approximation. The idea of the analysis is analogous to that of Boykov et. al. For a locally optimal labeling, consider a random interval I and use the fact that relabeling all nodes that have labels $\alpha \in I$ in the optimum, does not yield a cut with improved cost. The main new observation is that for a random interval, the probability that there is an error in the term associated with an edge $e = uv$ in the cut construction is $1/M$ times the distance $d(f^*(u), f^*(v))$ between the labels assigned to its nodes in the optimum. This fact is used to show that the expected error is proportional to the optimal separation cost.

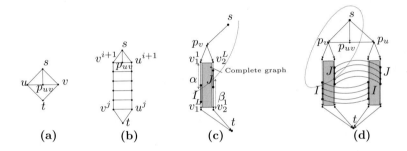

Fig. 2. Constructions for the local search technique

Our Local Move and the Construction for a Local Move

Our approach is similar to these results. There are, however, some difficulties that we need to overcome. First, our assignment cost depends on pairs of nodes. To solve this we use the idea developed in the previous section to construct a new graph whose cuts approximately capture the cost of relabeling. Second, we need to modify the "interval" local move in [6] for our problem. To see why a naive extension of the interval local move does not work, consider a local move that picks a random interval I from $1, .., L$ and finds an approximately good relabeling to this interval, i.e., changing some labels to labels in I. This will not give us a provable approximation algorithm. For example, when reassigning a node in Metric Labeling, we capture the assignment cost exactly, while here a node v in G needs two labels: one of v_1 and one for v_2, and maybe only one of the two is in the interval I. To capture the two different labels for a node v, we do the following:

> Pick two random intervals I, J of length at most M each. We will allow in one local move to relabel pairs of vertices (v_1, v_2) where v_1, v_2 are copies of vertex v in the original graph G, to a new pair of labels $(\alpha, \beta) \in I \times J$.

To describe the construction let us fix intervals I, J. Our main goal is to give a construction where local moves correspond to cuts and the capacity of each cut has only a small additive error compared to the corresponding local move. The construction is shown on Figures 2 (c) and (d). For vertex v, we add two chains $\{v_1^1, .., v_1^L\}$ and $\{v_2^L, .., v_2^1\}$, as shown on Figure 2(c), to the graph $G_{I \times J}$. We also add vertex p_v connecting to v_1^1 and v_2^1. Connect the super source s to p_v with the capacity $A_v(f(v))$, where $f(v)$ is the label currently assigned to vertex v, and $A_v(f(v))$ is the corresponding assignment cost. Connect v_1^L and v_2^1 to the super sink t. We use the notation: $v_1^{L+1} = t$, $v_2^{L+1} = p_v$.

We would like to have the following one-to-one correspondence between cuts and labelings. The cut C uses the edge sp_v if and only if v retains its label $f(v)$ and uses some pair of edges $v_1^\alpha v_1^{\alpha+1}$ and $v_2^{\beta+1} v_2^\beta$, where $(\alpha, \beta) \in I \times J$, if v_1 and v_2 is reassigned to labels (α, β) in the corresponding relabeling. To make sure exactly one of the conditions above occurs, we need to assign infinite capacity to some other edges. This step is similar to the constructions above. We now need to add more edges to capture the assignment cost and separation cost.

Assignment cost. This construction is similar to the construction of the linear case in the previous section. We want to capture the assignment cost of v as given in the formula (1): We add a complete bipartite graph between $\{v_1^1, .., v_1^L\}$ and $\{v_2^L, .., v_2^1\}$ as shown on Figure 2(c). The edges go both ways between v_1^α and v_2^β with capacity $\frac{c_v}{2}$. The contribution of these edges to the cut corresponding to the relabeling to (α, β) is $\frac{c_v}{2}(\alpha\beta + (L-\alpha)(L-\beta)) = c_v\alpha\beta + \frac{c_v}{2}(L^2 - L\alpha - L\beta)$. The remaining terms in the assignment cost depend on α and β separately, so we can use the edges of the chain to capture the assignment cost. To make sure all capacities are nonnegative, we may have to add a constant to the cost.

Separation cost. For each edge in the original graph $e = (u, v)$ let us consider the following construction shown on Figure 2(d): Add edges between the chains of u and v: $u_1^\alpha v_1^\alpha$, $u_2^\beta v_2^\beta$ for all $\alpha \in I$, $\beta \in J$. These edges are bidirectional and have a capacity of w_e. We also add one more vertex p_{uv}, and connect p_{uv} with p_u, p_v and s in both directions. The capacity of the edge sp_{uv} is $w_e d_2(f(u), f(v))$, (that is f's separation cost on the edge e); of $p_{uv}p_v$ $p_{uv}p_u$ are $2Mw_e$. These three numbers satisfy the triangle inequality. Therefore, at most one of the three edges adjacent to p_{uv} is cut. This implies that for a minimum cut C and for each edge (u, v) one of the followings could happen.

- All of p_{uv}, p_u and p_v are on the s side of the cut. In the corresponding relabeling both u and v get new labels. In this case, the cut perfectly captures the separation cost.
- s is on one side and p_u, p_v, p_{uv} are on the other side. In the corresponding relabeling the label of u and v do not change, and the capacity of the edge sp_{uv} captures exactly the separation cost.
- p_{uv} is on the s side, and so is exactly one of p_u or p_v, say p_v. See Figure 2(d). In the corresponding relabeling, u keeps its original label, while v gets a new label. For this case, the cut does not capture exactly the separation

cost. However, it is not hard to see that the capacity exceeds the separation cost, and the total corresponding capacity is $2w_e M$ from edge (p_{uv}, p_u) and at most $w_e(2M)$ from the edges between the chains, while the cost of the corresponding labeling is $w_e d(f'(v), f(u))$, where $f'(v)$ is the new label that v gets.

We have seen that the construction above does not capture exactly the cost of a local move. For an edge $e = (u, v)$, when one of the nodes (say u) retains its label and v is labeled with some element $f'(v) \in I \times J$. In this case the separation cost is always greater or equal than the real separation cost of e. And this value is at most $4Mw_e$. We summarize this in the following theorem:

Theorem 3. *Given a labeling f, and $I \times J \subset L^2$ where I and J are of size at most M, then there exists a network $G_{I \times J}$ and a constant $CONST$ with the following properties. All labelings g that can be reached by relabeling to $I \times J$ correspond to cuts in $G_{I \times J}$ with capacity at least the $Q(g) + CONST$. If g is a labeling obtained by a local move, then the capacity of the corresponding cut over-estimates $Q(g) + CONST$ by replacing the separation cost of $w_e d(f'(u), f'(v))$ for edges $e = (u, v)$ where exactly one end receives a label in $I \times J$ by a possibly larger term which is at most $4w_e M$. And finally, the minimum $s-t$ cut in $G_{I \times J}$ corresponds to a labeling.* □

The Algorithm and Its Analysis

We use the above construction in a local search algorithm. At each step we pick two intervals I, J randomly according to Definition 1 below and find the minimum cut in the graph $G_{I \times J}$. If the corresponding labeling has a lower cost, then change the labeling to this new one. The algorithm stops if we cannot find an improving move.

Definition 1. *Given a parameter D, a random partitioning process of the grid L^2 into smaller grids according to D is defined as follow. Pick $r = (\alpha, \beta) \in \{1, .., D\}^2$ uniform-randomly, for each $k \equiv \alpha \pmod{D}$, and $l \equiv \beta \pmod{D}$, delete all edges in the row k, and column l of the grid. The L^2 grid now is partitioned into smaller parts, each of them is a grid of the form $I \times J$ for some intervals I, J. We call this set of small grids $Partition(r)$. A random rectangle is understood as a random grid taken uniformly from a random $Partition(r)$.*

We prove the following main theorem:

Theorem 4. *Any local optima f of the local search algorithm above with $D = M$ has cost $Q(f)$ that is at most constant times the optimal cost: $9Q(f^*)$. For any constant $\epsilon > 0$, a solution with cost at most $(9 + \epsilon)Q(f^*)$ can be reached in polynomial time.*

Proof sketch. We first need the following notation. For any subset $X \subset V$, let $A^*(X)$ and $A(X)$ be the optimum and the current labeling assignment cost of the vertices in X. For any subset of edges $Y \subset E$, let $S^*(Y), S(Y)$ be the separation cost for those edges paid by the optimum and the current labeling respectively. Clearly, $Q(f) = A(V) + S(E), Q(f^*) = A^*(V) + S^*(E)$. Consider the case where the algorithm chooses a random rectangle $I \times J$. Let V_{IJ} be the set of nodes in G to which f^* assigns labels from $I \times J$. Let E_{IJ} be the set of edges in G such that both ends are assigned to $I \times J$ in f^*. Let σ_{IJ} be the set of edge in G such that exactly one end is assigned to $I \times J$ in f^*. For a random partition r, let σ_r be the edges in E_{IJ} for all rectangles $I \times J$ in $Partition(r)$, we have: $\sigma_r = \frac{1}{2} \sum_{IJ \in Partition(r)} \sigma_{IJ}$.

Given two intervals I, J, define the following local move.

$$f'(v) = \begin{cases} f^*(v) & \text{if } f^*(v) \in I \times J \\ f(v) & \text{otherwise.} \end{cases}$$

The 9-approximation guarantee follows from comparing $Q(f)$ and $Q(f')$ for every I, J. If we could find a minimum local move exactly then the local optimality of f would imply the inequality : $Q(f) \leq Q(f')$ for every I, J. However, the graph cut construction only gives us an approximate minimum local move (Theorem 3). As a result, we only have a weaker inequality. For every I, J the cost $Q(f)$ is no more than the cost of the labeling corresponding to the minimum cut in $G_{I \times J}$. The cost of all cuts corresponding to local moves have the same additive constant. In addition, the cost $Q(f')$ of the local move f' can have an additive cost at most $4M \sum_{e \in \sigma_{IJ}} w_e - S'(\sigma_{IJ})$, where $S'(\sigma_{IJ})$ denotes the separation cost of f' on the set of edges σ_{IJ}. The labeling f is locally optimal, and hence with this additive cost the local move f' does not correspond to a smaller capacity cut. This gives us the following inequality

$$Q(f) \leq Q(f') + 4M \sum_{e \in \sigma_{IJ}} w_e - S'(\sigma_{IJ}).$$

Expressing the terms contributing to $Q(f)$ and $Q(f')$, and deleting terms that contribute to both we get the following:

$$A(V_{IJ}) + S(E_{IJ}) + S(\sigma_{IJ}) \leq A^*(V_{IJ}) + S^*(E_{IJ}) + 4M \sum_{e \in \sigma_{IJ}} w_e.$$

Summing this inequality over all the rectangles in $Partition(r)$, we get the following, as the edges in σ_{IJ} each contribute to two interval pairs.

$$Q(f) + S(\sigma_r) \leq A^*(V) + S^*(E - \sigma_r) + 8M \sum_{e \in \sigma_r} w_e.$$

$$\Rightarrow Q(f) + S(\sigma_r) \leq A^*(V) + S^*(E) + 8M \sum_{e \in \sigma_r} w_e.$$

Now, we need to bound the error term $8M \sum_{e \in \sigma_r} w_e$. This value depends on the partition. Recall that we picked $r \in \{1, .., M\}^2$ at random. We will bound the expected value of this term. What is the probability that an edge $e = (u, v)$ is in σ_r? This probability depends on how far the coordinates of $f^*(u), f^*(v)$

are from each other. More precisely, if $f^*(u) = (\alpha_1, \beta_1), f^*(v) = (\alpha_2, \beta_2)$, then $(u, v) \in \sigma(r)$ if either α_1, α_2 or β_1, β_2 are separated by a random border as described in Definition 1. The probability of this event is at most:

$$\frac{\min\{M, |\alpha_1 - \alpha_2|\}}{M} + \frac{\min\{M, |\beta_1 - \beta_2|\}}{M} = \frac{d(f^*(u), f^*(v))}{M} = \frac{d_e}{M}.$$

Thus, one has the expected value of $8M \sum_{e \in \sigma_r} w_e$ is at most $8S^*(E) = 8 \sum_{e \in \sigma_r} w_e d_e$. Taking the expected value of the inequality above we have:

$$Q(f) \leq Q(f) + S(\sigma_r) \leq A^*(V) + S^*(E) + 8S^*(E) \leq 9Q(f^*),$$

which proves that a local optimum is a 9-approximate solution.

Taking only big enough improvements, the algorithm will find in polynomial time a solution that is within an $9 + \epsilon$ factor to the optimum value. $\square$

Acknowledgments. We thank Ramin Zabih for introducing this problem, and Gurmeet Singh and Ashish Goel for numerous discussions.

References

1. Archer, A., Fakcharoenphol, J., Harrelson, C., Krauthgamer, R., Talvar, K., Tardos, E.: Approximate Classification via Earthmover Metrics. In: Proc. SODA 2004 (2004)
2. Chuzhoy, J., Naor, S.: The Hardness of Metric Labeling. In: Proc. FOCS 2004 (2004)
3. Boykov, Y., Veksler, O., Zabih, R.: Markov Random Fields with efficient approximations. In: Proc. CVPR 1998 (1998)
4. Boykov, Y., Veksler, O., Zabih, R.: Fast approximate energy minimization via graph cuts. In: Proc. ICCV 1999 (1999)
5. Chekuri, C., Khanna, S., Naor, S., Zosin, L.: A Linear Programming Formulation and Approximation Algorithms for the Metric Labeling Problem. SIAM J. on Discrete Mathematics, 606–635 (2004)
6. Gupta, A., Tardos, E.: A Constant Factor Approximation Algorithm for a Class of Classification Problems. In: Proc. STOC 2000 (2000)
7. Ishikawa, H., Geiger, D.: Segmentation by grouping junctions. In: Proc. CVPR 1998 (1998)
8. Kleinberg, J., Tardos, E.: Approximation Algorithms for Classification Problems with Pairwise Relationships: Metric Partitioning and Markov Random Fields. J. ACM 49(5), 616–639 (2002)
9. Li, S.: Makrov Random Field modeling in Computer Vision. Springer, Heidelberg (1995)
10. Raj, A., Singh, G., Zabih, R.: MRF's for MRI's: Bayesian Reconstruction of MR Images via Graph Cuts. In: Proc. CVPR 2006 (2006)

An Online Algorithm for Finding the Longest Previous Factors

Daisuke Okanohara[1] and Kunihiko Sadakane[2]

[1] Department of Computer Science, University of Tokyo.
Hongo 7-3-1, Bunkyo-ku, Tokyo 113-0013, Japan
hillbig@is.s.u-tokyo.ac.jp
[2] Department of Computer Science and Communication Engineering, Kyushu
University. Motooka 744, Nishi-ku, Fukuoka 819-0395, Japan
sada@csce.kyushu-u.ac.jp

Abstract. We present a novel algorithm for finding the longest factors
in a text, for which the working space is proportional to the history text
size. Moreover, our algorithm is online and exact; in that, unlike the
previous batch algorithms [4, 5, 6, 7, 14], which needs to read the entire input beforehand, our algorithm reports the longest match just after
reading each character. This algorithm can be directly used for data compression, pattern analysis, and data mining. Our algorithm also supports
the window buffer, in that we can bound the working space by discarding the history from the oldest character. Using the dynamic rank/select
dictionary [17], our algorithm requires $n \log \sigma + o(n \log \sigma) + O(n)$ bits of
working space, and $O(\log^3 n)$ time per character, $O(n \log^3 n)$ total time,
n is the length of the history, and σ is the alphabet size. We implemented
our algorithm and compared it with the recent algorithms [4, 5, 14] in
terms of speed and the working space. We found that our algorithm can
work with a smaller working space, less than 1/2 of those for the previous
methods in real-world data, and with a reasonable decline in speed.

1 Introduction

The problem in searching for the longest previous factor is as follows: given a
history $T[0, i-1]$, and a next character $T[i] = c$, find the longest substring (or
factor) that occurs in the history: $T[j, \ldots, j+l-1] = T[i-l+1, \ldots, i]$, and
report (j, l), the position, and the length of the matched substring.

This problem is fundamental in many applications, including data compression and pattern analysis. For example, we can directly use this algorithm for
the LZ77 compression methods [27]; we compress the data by replacing a substring of a text with a pointer to its longest previous occurrence in the input.
Our algorithm also solves the LZ-factorization problem, which has become interesting, because it can be used for succinct indexing, and for finding the runs
in the string [5].

A straightforward solution to this problem is to search the history on the
fly by using the sequential search. However, this requires $O(n)$ time for each

D. Halperin and K. Mehlhorn (Eds.): ESA 2008, LNCS 5193, pp. 696–707, 2008.
© Springer-Verlag Berlin Heidelberg 2008

character, where n is the length of the history, and thus the total complexity becomes $O(n^2)$, which would be prohibitive for a large n.

Therefore, many previous studies used the indexing method, wherein the index is constructed for the history, and then search is performed in less than $O(n)$ time. In particular, previous studies for this problem [4, 5, 6, 7, 14, 15] take the batch approach; first, we read the whole input beforehand, and then construct the index such as suffix arrays (SA) or suffix trees. Then, we report the match information at last. The time complexity of their algorithm is linear in the text size. For example, in the most recent study [4], they proposed to search the factors using SA; they first build SA. Then, at each position, they perform binary search on SA to find the longest match substring, and check whether these matched factors appeared previously by checking the range minimum queries on corresponding SAs. A working space is about 6 times of the original text size.

However, this batch method has several drawbacks. If the data is larger than the available resource, we need to divide the data into small pieces, and would lose some information. Another problem is that if we do not know the length of the input text beforehand, such as is the case in the data streaming problem, these algorithms cannot work.

We instead take the online approach, and we also maintain an index to make the search faster. The problem here is that it would require a very large working space if we apply the usual data structure (e.g. trie, hash) to this problem. In this paper, we will find the actual longest match. We therefore employ the recent compressed full-text indexing methods [22]. Compressed full-text indexing methods are data structures that support various string processing efficiently, by using a space proportional to that of the text itself.

In particular, we use the succinct version of the enhanced suffix arrays (ESA) [1], in which the sizes are linear in the text size. ESA supports almost the same operations of suffix trees, and can solve various string problems, which cannot be supported by the original suffix arrays. Note that, in the previous study [1], the longest matching problem is solved by using ESA; however, their method is the batch algorithm. On the other hand, our new method reports the longest matching information online.

Moreover, we propose a method to simulate the sliding window, to limit the working space by discarding the history from the oldest character.

With recent dynamic rank/select dictionary [17], our algorithm requires $n \log \sigma + o(n \log \sigma) + O(n)$ bits of working space, and $O(\log^3 n)$ time per character, where n is the length of history, and σ is the alphabet size. Since our algorithm employs well-studied succinct data structures: **rank/select** and range minimum queries (**rmq**), it is easy to implement.

To measure the practical performance, we implemented our algorithm with simpler data structures, and compared it with previous methods. We found that our algorithm requires less than $1/2$ of the working space of the previous methods in real-word data, and is about 4 times slower than the previous method [4, 5, 14].

2   Preliminaries

For the computation model, we use the word RAM, with word-length $\Theta(\log n)$, where any arithmetic operation for $\Theta(\log n)$-bit numbers and $\Theta(\log n)$-bit memory I/Os are achieved in constant time.

Let Σ be a finite ordered alphabet, and $\sigma = |\Sigma|$. Let $T[0 \ldots n-1]$ be an input text of length n, drawn from Σ. In this paper, we adopt for technical convenience the assumption that T is preceded by $\$ $ ($T[-1] = \$$), which is a character from Σ that is lexicographically smaller than all other characters, and appearing nowhere else in T. Note that, although in conventional suffix arrays, it is assumed that T is followed by $T[n] = \$$, we append the special character at the beginning of T, because we will construct the *prefix* arrays instead of the suffix arrays.

2.1   Rank and Select

Let us define $\mathbf{rank}_c(T, i)$ as the number of occurrences of a character c in $T[0, i]$, and $\mathbf{select}_c(T, j)$ as the position of $(j + 1)$-th occurrence of c in T. We also define $\mathbf{pred}_c(T, i)$ as the largest position of the occurrence of c before i in T, and $\mathbf{succ}_c(T, i)$ as the smallest position of the occurrence of c after i in T. These **pred** and **succ** can be supported by using a constant number of **rank** and **select** operations. That is, $\mathbf{pred}_c(T, i) = \mathbf{select}_c(T, \mathbf{rank}_c(T, i-1) - 1)$, and $\mathbf{succ}_c(T, i) = \mathbf{select}_c(T, \mathbf{rank}_c(T, i))$. Here, we define $\mathbf{select}_c(T, -1) = -1$, and $\mathbf{select}_c(T, k) = n$ when $k + 1$ is larger than the number of c in T.

For the dynamic-case, let us define the operation $\mathbf{insert}(T, c, p)$ as the insertion of a character c at $T[p]$, and also define the operation $\mathbf{delete}(T, p)$ as the deletion of a character at $T[p]$.

To achieve these operations, we can use the data structure in [17] that supports **rank** and **select** in $O((1 + \frac{\log \sigma}{\log \log n}) \log n)$ time, and **insert** and **delete** in $O((1 + \frac{\log \sigma}{\log \log n}) \log n)$ amortized time in $n \log \sigma + o(n \log \sigma)$ bits. If $\sigma < \log n$, the operation time is $O(\log n)$ time.

2.2   Range Minimum Query

The range minimum query (RMQ) problem is as follows: given an array $E[0, n-1]$ of elements from a totally ordered set, $\mathbf{rmq}_E(l, r)$ returns the index of the smallest element in $E[l, r]$, i.e., $\mathbf{rmq}_E(l, r) = \arg \min_{k \in \{l, \ldots, r\}} \{E[k]\}$, or the leftmost such element in the case of a tie.

The most simple but naive algorithm for this problem searches the array from l to r each time a query is presented, and in the worst case results in a $\Theta(n)$ query time. In the static case, we can build index for RMQ [9, 10], which supports RMQ in constant time using $2n + o(n)$ bits. In this paper, we will use the dynamic version of RMQ index.

2.3   Suffix Arrays, BWT, FM-Index

Let $T_i := T[i, \ldots, n]$ be a suffix of T. A suffix array [12, 19] of T is a permutation of all the suffixes of input text T so that the suffixes are lexicographically sorted. Formally, the suffix arrays of T is an array $A[0 \ldots n]$ containing a permutation of the interval $[0 \ldots n]$, such that $T_{A[i]} < T_{A[i+1]}$, for all $0 \le i < n$, where "$<$" between strings is the lexicographical order.

The burrows-wheeler transform (BWT) [2] is a reversible transformation from a string to a string. Given a string $T[0 \ldots n]$ and its suffix array $A[0 \ldots n]$, its BWT, $B[0 \ldots n]$, is defined as $B[i] := T[A[i] - 1]$, except when $A[i] = 0$, where $B[i] = T[n] = \$$.

By using B (BWT of T), we can simulate functions of suffix arrays, called FM-index. FM-index [8] is a compressed full-text index that supports various operations, including exact string matching, and operations in compressed suffix arrays. FM-index consists of B and **rank** operations on it. FM-index uses LF operations to perform several operations such as exact matching. The operation $LF(i)$ is defined as $LF(i) = j$ such that $A[j] = A[i] - 1$. The relation between LF and BWT can be shown as $LF(i) = \mathbf{rank}_{c'}(T_B, i) + C(c')$ [22]; where $c' = B[i]$ and $C(c')$ gives the number of characters smaller than c' in $T[0 \ldots n]$. FM-index also supports the operation $SA_{lookup}(i)$, which returns the i-th value of suffix arrays [8, 22]. We sampled every $d = \log_\sigma n \log \log n$ SAs, which are stored in $o(n \log \sigma)$ bits of space. Then, one SA_{lookup} operation requires d LF operations. Since one LF operation requires $O((1 + \frac{\log \sigma}{\log \log n}) \log n)$ time (**rank** operation), the total time for SA_{lookup} operation is $O(\log^2 n)$ time [17]. Note that while we consider the dynamic case here, these operations can be $O(\log n)$ time faster in the static case.

We consider *prefix* arrays instead of *suffix* arrays, and we apply the above discussion to the *prefix* arrays similarly. We define the BWT of text for prefix arrays as $B[i] := T[A[i] + 1]$, where $A[i]$ is the prefix array that is a permutation of all the prefixes of input text T, so that the prefixes are reverse-lexicographically sorted. The left table in the figure 1 shows the example of prefix arrays for the text $T = abaababa$.

2.4   Hgt Array

The Hgt array $H[0, n - 1]$ for T is defined as $H[i] = lcp(T_{A[i]}, T_{A[i+1]})$, where $lcp(T_{A[i]}, T_{A[i+1]})$ is the length of the longest common prefix between $T_{A[i]}$ and $T_{A[i+1]}$. That is, H contains the lengths of the longest common prefixes of T's suffixes that are consecutive in lexicographic order. If we store H explicitly, we need $O(n \log n)$ bits of space. Sadakane [23] gave the data structure to store H efficiently in only $2n$ bits of space. For this, we use the fact that $H[i] \ge H[LF(i)] - 1$. Let $L[i]$ be a bit array of $2n$ bits such that $L[i] = 1$ if $i = H[LF^k[p]] + 2n - k$ and $L[i] = 0$ otherwise, where $p = A^{-1}[n]$, and $LF^k[p] = LF^{k-1}[LF[p]]$ for $k > 1$ and $LF^1[p] = LF[p]$. Then, $H[i]$ is calculated by $\mathbf{select}_1(L, k) - 2k$, where $k = SA[i]$ [23].

In this paper, we consider the Hgt array defined on the *prefix* array. Therefore, $H[i]$ is the length of the longest common suffix between $T_{A[i]}$ and $T_{A[i+1]}$. The

T = $abaababa
s = 4, t = 0

i	prefix	B	H
0	$	a	0
1	$a	b	1
2	$abaa	b	1
3	$aba	a	3
4	$abaababa	$	3
5	$abaaba	b	0
6	$ab	a	2
7	$abaab	a	2
8	$abaabab	a	0

Insertion of a (Prefix = $abaababaa)
s = 3, t = 0

i	prefix	B	H
0	$	a	0
1	$a	b	1
2	$abaa	b	4
3	$abaababaa	$	1
4	$aba	a	3
5	$abaababa	a	3
6	$abaaba	b	0
7	$ab	a	2
8	$abaab	a	2
9	$abaabab	a	0

Deletion of a (T[0])
s = 2, t = 0

i	prefix	B	H
0	$a	b	1
1	$abaa	b	4
2	$abaababaa	$	1
3	$aba	a	3
4	$abaababa	a	3
5	$abaaba	b	0
6	$ab	a	2
7	$abaab	a	2
8	$abaabab	a	0

Fig. 1. Example of one step in our algorithm

example of Hgt is shown in the right column of figure 1. In this figure we store H explicitly for explanation, while we keep H in compressed form in our algorithm.

3   Algorithm

We propose a novel algorithm for searching for the longest factors in a text. The problem is formally defined as follows; given a history $T = [0, \ldots, n-1]$, and the next character $c = T[n]$, we find the longest substring that matches the current suffix: $T[j, \ldots, j + l - 1] = T[i - l + 1, \ldots, i]$, and report the position and the length of the matched substring. We perform this process for all $i \in [0, \ldots, n-1]$.

Our algorithm relies on the incremental construction of Enhanced Suffix Arrays (ESA) [1] in a similar way to Weiner's suffix tree construction algorithm [26]. In this algorithm suffixes are inserted from the shortest one to the longest one. This is because the addition of a single symbol to the end of text in a suffix array may cause $\Omega(n)$ changes, whereas in reverse order construction, this is never the case.

However, our algorithm processes from the beginning to the end of the string, and actually builds the *prefix* arrays; we insert prefixes from the shortest one to the longest one, and at the i-th step, our algorithm builds a complete ESA for $T[0, \ldots, i]$. For example, if the input text is $x_1 x_2 x_3 x_4$, we insert the prefixes in order x_1, $x_1 x_2$, $x_1 x_2 x_3$, and $x_1 x_2 x_3 x_4$.

In each step, our algorithm keeps two arrays, the BWT of T (B), and the Hgt arrays H. Note that these data structures are stored in compressed form. We also store the auxiliary data structures to support **rank/select** operations on B, and **rmq** operations on H. Figure 1 is the example of B and H for the text $T = abaababa$.

Besides these data structures, we also keep the following variables:

- s: The position for the new prefix in the prefix array.
- l_p, l_s: The length of the longest common prefix between previous/successor prefix and the new prefix.

Note that s corresponds to the position where $B[s] = \$$. While the update for B is the same as for the previous studies for the incremental construction of compressed suffix arrays [3, 18], others are new.

Algorithm 1 shows the pseudo code of our entire algorithm. After reading each character, this reports the position and the length of the longest match. Figure 1 shows the example of one step in our algorithm. The tables to the left and the center of the figure show B and H for the text $T = abaababa$, and those for the text after the insertion of a. The table to the right of the figure shows B and H for the text after deleting the oldest history $a = T[0]$.

3.1   B Update

Although we use the same algorithm for updating B (The BWT of T) described in [3, 18], we explain it here again for the sake of clarity. We again note that we construct prefix arrays instead of suffix arrays and we therefore process from the beginning of the text to the end of the text, unlike the previous studies [3, 18] wherein suffix arrays were built from the end of the text to the beginning of the text.

We initialized s as 0. At the i-th step, we insert $c = T[i]$ into s-th position in B (**insert**(B, s, c)). Then, we update s as

$$s = LF(s) = \mathbf{rank}_c(B, s) + C(c) \tag{1}$$

where $C(c)$ returns the number of characters smaller than c in the current B. We define the operation **inc**(C, c) that increments $C(c')$ such that $c' < c$ by one and **dec**(C, c) that decrements $C(c')$ such that $c' < c$ by one. We keep C using a data structure proposed in [20], that supports **inc**(C, c), **dec**(C, c) and the lookup $C(c)$ in $O(\log \sigma)$ time. If we allow for the sorting of the symbols by its frequency in T, the look up and update time for the s-th frequent character is $O(\log(s))$ time [20].

3.2   H Update

We now explain how to update H arrays. First, l_p and l_s are initialized as 0. Let $h(s_1, s_2)$ be the length of the longest common prefix (Here, we consider the common prefix, not the common suffix, because we build the prefix arrays) between the substring s_1 and s_2. At the i-th step we insert the new prefix $s_{new} = T[0, \ldots, i]$ to the current prefix arrays. Then, we need to update the corresponding Hgt values, $H[s - 1]$ and $H[s]$. Let s_{pre} be the previous prefix, and s_{suc} be the successor prefix. Then, $H[s - 1] = h(s_{pre}, s_{new})$, and $H[s] = h(s_{new}, s_{suc})$.

First, we consider the case $l_p = h(s_{pre}, s_{new})$. Let $c = T[i]$ be the current character. If the first character of s_{pre} is not c, $l_p = 0$. Otherwise, first characters of s_{pre} and s_{new} are c; let us denote $s_{pre} = cs'_{pre}$ and $s_{new} = cs'_{new}$. The value $h(s'_{pre}, s'_{new})$ is the range minimum query of H between p'_{pre} and p'_{new}, where p'_{pre} is the position of s'_{pre}, and p'_{new} is the position of s'_{new}. Then, $l_p = 1 + h(s'_{pre}, s'_{new})$. The position p'_{pre} can be calculated as $\mathbf{pred}_c(B, s'_{new})$ and s'_{new} is the value of s in the previous step. We can calculate l_s similarly.

Algorithm 1. The overall algorithm for searching the longest match. After reading each character, it reports the position and the length of the matched substring.

Input: A text $T[0, \ldots, n-1]$
$s := 0$ // The position in B for the next character
$l_p, l_s \leftarrow 0$ // The lcp between previous/successor prefix and the new prefix
B // The BWT of T
H // The hgt Array
for $i = 0$ **to** $n - 1$ **do**
   $c \leftarrow T[i]$
   insert(B, c, s)
   if $l_p \geq l_s$ **then**
      Report: $(l_p + 1, SA_{lookup}(p))$
      insert$(H, l_p + 1, p)$
   else
      Report: $(l_s + 1, SA_{lookup}(p + 1))$
      insert$(H, l_s + 1, p + 1)$
   end if
   $l_p \leftarrow \mathbf{rmq}(H, \mathbf{pred}_c(B, s), s)$
   $l_s \leftarrow \mathbf{rmq}(H, s, \mathbf{succ}_c(B, s))$
   $s \leftarrow \mathbf{rank}_c(B, p) + C(c)$
   inc(C, c)
end for

If the H are stored in the compressed form (Section 2.4), we need one SA_{lookup} operation for one character.

Figure 1 shows the examples of updating H. In the left table, $s = 4$ and a new character "a" will be inserted to $B[4]$. The s'_{pre}, and s'_{suc} are "\$aba" and "\$ab" (The both of values of B are a). Then $l_p = 1 + \mathbf{rmq}(H, 3, 3) = 4$ and $l_s = 1 + \mathbf{rmq}(H, 4, 5) = 1$. The new s is 3, and we update $H[2] = 4$, and $H[3] = 1$.

To support **rmq** operations on H, we store a balanced search tree for RMQs of blocks of length $\log n$ taking $O(n)$ bits. This requires $O(\log n)$ accesses to H, each of which requires $O(\log^2 n)$ time. Therefore, the total time for **rmq** over H is $O(\log^3 n)$.

3.3   Simulating the Window Buffer

If the working space is limited, say 1 MB, we often discard the history from the oldest one, and search the longest match from only the previous 1 MB. This is usually called the sliding window buffer, which is used for many LZ77 compression implementations.

Larsson [15, 16] proposed to simulate the sliding window with suffix trees. On the contrary, our algorithm simulates the sliding window buffer for suffix arrays with Hgt arrays.

Here, we need to update the data structure in accordance with discarding the history from the oldest one. This can be supported in a very similar way to the insertion operation.

To achieve this operation, we keep another variable t, which denotes the position for the oldest character in B. We initialized t as 0 (the position of the first character in B is 0, because it is preceded by \$). If we apply the delete operation to the current data structure, and let $c = B[t]$. Then, we update t as,

$$t = \mathbf{select}_c(B, t - C(c)). \tag{2}$$

We simultaneously perform $\mathbf{dec}(C, c)$, and decrease s by 1 if $t < s$. For the update of H we set $H[t-1] = \min(H[t-1], H[t])$, and delete $H[t]$. We can also update $t = \Psi[t]$ similar to the lookup with samples of SAs, which requires additional space.

Note that this operation does not actually delete the oldest character but just ignores it. Therefore, the order of prefix arrays is not changed after the deletion. If it actually deletes the character, it may cause $\Omega(n)$ changes in B and H. For example, given a text $T = \$zaaaaa$, if the oldest character (z) is deleted, then the orders of prefixes are totally reversed.

On the other hand, our algorithm preserves the order, and therefore all operations can be done in $O(\log^2 n)$ time. The longest common suffix information larger than the window size (w) should be upper bounded by w. In detail, the code in Algorithm 1 is changed as $\mathbf{insert}(H, \min(l_p + 1, w), p)$, and $\mathbf{insert}(H, \min(l_s + 1, w), p + 1)$ where w is the window size.

3.4   Output LZ-Factorization

The LZ factorization of T is a factorization into chunks $T = w_1 w_2 \ldots w_k$ such that each w_j, $j \in 1 \ldots k$ is (1) a letter that does not occur in previous history or otherwise (2) the longest substring that occurs at least twice in w_1, w_2, ..., w_j. For example, when $T = abaababa$, $w_1 = a, w_2 = b, w_3 = a, w_4 = aba, w_5 = ba$. The LZ factorization is used for many applications, such as including data compression, pattern analysis, and finding the runs in the text [5].

The difference between LZ-factorization and our method is that the former reports the repetition information at the left of the phrase, while the latter reports all the repetition at each position. The modification of our algorithm to output LZ-factorization is straight forward; when the matched length is not increasing, it is the separation of the LZ-factorization, and reports the occurrence of the longest match at that position. Figure 2 shows the algorithm to report LZ-factorization in an online-manner using our algorithm. We specify the factorization by a pair of a position of previous occurrence and its length.

4   Overall Analysis

The update of the position s is achieved by using one $\mathbf{rank}$ and one $\mathbf{inc}(C, i)$ operations. A $\mathbf{rank}$ operation requires $O((1 + \frac{\log \sigma}{\log \log n}) \log n)$ time [17], and a

---

Algorithm 2. This algorithm outputs the LZ-factorization of a text $T = T[0, \ldots, n-1]$. This algorithm employs the result of our algorithm.

Input: Text $T[0, \ldots, n-1]$
$i_{prev} = 0$ // The position of the beginning of the next phrase.
$(len_{prev}, pos_{prev}) = (0, 0)$
for $i = 0$ **to** $n - 1$ **do**
   $(len, pos) = process(T[i])$ // Result of the algorithm 1.
   if $len \leq len_{prev}$ **then**
      $len = min(len, i - i_{prev})$
      Report $w_t = (len, pos_{prev} - len), \quad t = t + 1$
      $i_{prev} = i$
   end if
   $pos_{prev} = pos$
end for
Output: $w_1, \ldots, w_t$

$inc(C, i)$ operation requires $O(\log \sigma)$ time. The two **rmq** operations are required in H, which requires $O(\log^3 n)$ time. The insertion of a new character into $T[p]$ requires $O((1 + \frac{\log \sigma}{\log \log n}) \log n)$. The update of the Hgt arrays requires $O(\log^2 n)$ time. Therefore, the bottleneck of our algorithm is the **rmq** operation on H arrays. Note that this can be improved to $O(\log^2 n)$ time if we keep the balanced parentheses sequence representing the topology of the suffix tree [24]. Due to the space limitation, we defer a discussion of the details to the full paper.

For the space analysis, T can be kept in $n \log \sigma + o(n \log \sigma)$ bits of space [17], and The Hgt arrays can be kept in $O(n)$ bits of space. By summarizing the above result, we obtain the following theorem.

Theorem 1. *Let T be an input text of original length n drawn from Σ and $\sigma = |\Sigma|$. We can solve the online longest previous factor problem using $n \log \sigma + O(n) + o(n \log \sigma)$ bits of space in $O(n \log^3 n)$ time.*

5   Experiments

In the experiments, we used simpler data structures. We store B and H by a balanced binary tree. Each leaf in the tree has the buffer of the fixed size to store the portion of the B and H. After the insertion, we check whether the leaf is full or not. If the leaf is full, we split the leaf into two leaves as children of the original leaf. To reduce the space requirement further, if the leaf is full, we first check whether the preceding node or succeeding node is full or not. If one of them is not full (say r), we move the buffer in the full leaf to the leaf r. We do not use the succinct representation for H, because this representation requires SA lookup operation, which is very slow in practice. We instead used the direct representation, and set the smallest bit width for each node, so that all values of H in the node can be represented correctly.

Table 1. Description of the data used in experiments

String	Size (bytes)	Σ	Description
fib35	9227465	2	The 35th Fibonacci string
fib36	14930352	2	The 36th Fibonacci string
fss9	2851443	2	The 9th run rich string of [11]
fss10	12078908	2	The 10th run rich string of [11]
rnd2	8388608	2	Random string, small alphabet
rnd21	8388608	21	Random string, larger alphabet
ecoli	4638690	4	E.Coli Genome
chr22	34553758	4	Human Chromosome 22
bible	4047392	62	King James Bible
howto	39422105	197	Linux Howto files
chr19	63811651	4	Human Chromosome 19

Table 2. Peak memory usage in bytes per input symbol

String	OS	CPSa	CPSd	kk-LZ	CPS6n
fib35	6.85	17.00	11.50	19.92	5.75
fib36	6.85	17.00	11.50	20.76	5.75
fss9	6.84	17.00	11.10	21.27	5.73
fss10	6.86	17.00	11.10	22.47	5.50
rnd2	3.14	17.00	9.00	11.83	5.75
fnd21	3.29	17.00	9.00	-	5.75
ecoli	4.13	17.00	9.00	11.11	5.79
chr22	4.28	17.00	9.00	11.03	5.78
bible	3.40	17.00	9.00	-	5.72
howto	4.63	17.00	9.00	-	5.78
chr19	3.78	17.00	9.00	11.07	5.78

Table 3. Runtime in milliseconds for searching the longest previous factors

String	OS	CPSa	kk-LZ	CPS6n
fib35	22446	5093	9225	4068
fib36	41629	8728	15822	7273
fss9	4623	1261	1853	629
fss10	31855	7020	9280	5538
rnd2	15821	3929	5206	10186
fnd21	21787	4360	-	17605
ecoli	7975	1953	1028	6448
chr22	119056	18800	12855	79861
bible	7098	1558	-	3309
howto	156715	19000	-	60568
chr19	256483	38336	29193	166939

We denote our algorithm implemented in the above way **os**. We also implemented the other SA-based LZ-factorization, the **cps** of [5]. The implementation **kk-lz** of Kolpakov and Kucherov's algorithm was obtained from [14], and **cps6n** [4] was written by its author. Note that while **os** reports the matching result online, others report the matching results last. All programs were written in C or C++. All running times given are the average of two runs, and do not include the time spent reading input files. There are no large variances between the two trials. Memory usage was recorded with the memusage command. Times were recorded with the standard C getrusage function. All experiments were conducted on a 3.0 GHz Xeon processor with 32GB main memory. The operation system is the Linux version 2.6.9. The compiler was g++ (gcc version 4.0.3) executed with the -O3 option.

Times for the **cps**, and **cps6n** implementations include the time required for SA and LCP array construction. We used libdivsufsort [21] for SA construction, and the linear-time algorithm [13] for LCP construction. The implementation of kk-lz is only suitable for strings on small alphabets ($\sigma \leq 4$), so the times are only given for some files.

Table 1 shows the list of the test data. All data are taken from [25].

Table 2 shows the result of the peak memory usage of each program. The values in the column of CPSd is taken from [5]. These results indicate that our algorithm requires a smaller memory than other programs, especially when the values in H are small. This is because **os** dynamically set the bit width for H in each node, so that all values of H in the node can be represented.

Table 3 shows the result of the runtime of each program. Almost all the runtimes of **os** are about 4 times that of **cps**.

6   Conclusion

In this paper, we presented a novel algorithm for searching the longest match using a small working space. Our algorithm is online, which can process very large text data, and streaming data. The proposed method is based on the construction of enhanced prefix arrays. Our method is based on the well-studies **rank**, **select**, and **rmq** operations, and is therefore easy to implement. Our general approach can be adapted to simulate a sliding window buffer, by efficiently updating the index by discarding the history from the oldest one.

The experimental results show that our method requires about 1/2 or 1/4 the working space of those for the previous methods [5, 14] for real world data, with a reasonable decline in the speed

Since the compressed suffix trees (CST) can be simulated by adding the balanced parenthesis tree (BP) to ESA [24], we can extend our algorithm to build the CST incrementally. Due to space limitations, we defer a discussion of the details to the full paper.

As for our next step, we would like to further reduce the working space and time. In particular, the data structures for the Hgt array is the bottleneck of our algorithm, and it is expected to propose a new succinct representation for Hgt array with faster operation.

Acknowledgements. The authors would like to thank Simon J. Puglisi, who provided the code and helpful comments. The work is supported in part by the Grant-in-Aid of the Ministry of Education, Science, Sports and Culture of Japan.

References

1. Abouelhoda, M.I., Kurtz, S., Ohlebusch, E.: Replacing suffix trees with enhanced suffix arrays. Journal of Discrete Algorithms 2(1), 53–86 (2004)
2. Burrows, M., Wheeler, D.: A block sorting lossless data compression algorithm. Technical Report 124, Digital Equipment Corporation (1994)
3. Chan, H., Hon, W.K., Lam, T.W., Sadakane, K.: Compressed indexes for dynamic text collections. ACM Transactions on Algorithms 3(2), 21 (2007)
4. Chen, G., Puglisi, S.J., Smyth, W.F.: LZ factorization in less time and space. Mathematics in Computer Science (MCS) Special Issue on Combinatorial Algorithms (2008)

5. Chen, G., Puglisi, S.J., Smyth, W.: Fast and practical algorithms for computing all the runs in a string. In: Ma, B., Zhang, K. (eds.) CPM 2007. LNCS, vol. 4580, pp. 307–315. Springer, Heidelberg (2007)
6. Crochemore, M., Ilie, L.: LZ factorization in less time and space. Information Processing Letters 106, 75–80 (2008)
7. Crochemore, M., Ilie, L., Smyth, W.F.: A simple algorithm for computing the Lempel–Ziv factorization. In: DCC, pp. 482–488 (2008)
8. Ferragina, P., Manzini, G.: Opportunistic data structures with applications. In: Proc. of FOCS (2000)
9. Fischer, J., Heun, V.: Theoretical and practical improvements on the RMQ-problem, with applications to LCA and LCE. In: Lewenstein, M., Valiente, G. (eds.) CPM 2006. LNCS, vol. 4009, pp. 36–48. Springer, Heidelberg (2006)
10. Fischer, J., Heun, V.: A new succinct representation of rmq-information and improvements in the enhanced suffix array. In: Chen, B., Paterson, M., Zhang, G. (eds.) ESCAPE 2007. LNCS, vol. 4614. Springer, Heidelberg (2007)
11. Franek, F., Simpson, R.J., Smyth, W.F.: The maximum number of runs in a string. In: AWOCA, pp. 26–35 (2003)
12. Gonnet, G.H., Baeza-Yates, R., Snider, T.: New indices for text: PAT trees and PAT arrays. Information Retrieval: Algorithms and Data Structures, 66–82 (1992)
13. Kasai, T., Lee, G., Arimura, H., Arikawa, S., Park, K.: Linear-time longest-common-prefix computation in suffix arrays and its applications. In: Amir, A., Landau, G.M. (eds.) CPM 2001. LNCS, vol. 2089, pp. 181–192. Springer, Heidelberg (2001)
14. Kolpakov, R., Kucherov, G.: Mreps, http://bioinfo.lifl.fr/mreps/
15. Larsson, J.: Extended application of suffix trees to data compression. In: Proc. of DCC, pp. 190–199 (1996)
16. Larsson, J.: Structures of String Matching and Data Compression. PhD thesis, Lund University (1999)
17. Lee, S., Park, K.: Dynamic rank-select structures with applications to run-length encoded texts. In: Ma, B., Zhang, K. (eds.) CPM 2007. LNCS, vol. 4580, pp. 95–106. Springer, Heidelberg (2007)
18. Lippert, R., Mobarry, C., Walenz, B.: A space-efficient construction of the burrows wheeler transform for genomic data. Journal of Computational Biology (2005)
19. Manber, U., Myers, E.W.: Suffix arrays: A new method for on-line string searches. SIAM J. Comput. 22(5), 935–948 (1993)
20. Moffat, A.: An improved data structure for cumulative probability tables. Software: Practice and Experience 29, 647–659 (1999)
21. Mori, Y.: libdivsufsort, http://code.google.com/p/libdivsufsort/
22. Navarro, G., Mäkinen, V.: Compressed full-text indexes. ACM Computing Surveys 39(1) (2007)
23. Sadakane, K.: Succinct representations of LCP information and improvements in the compressed suffi arrays. In: ACM-SIAM SODA, pp. 225–232 (2002)
24. Sadakane, K.: Compressed suffix trees with full functionality. J. Theory of Computing Systems (2007)
25. Smyth, W.F.: http://www.cas.mcmaster.ca/~bill/strbings/
26. Weiner, P.: Linear pattern matching algorihms. In: Proceedings of the 14th IEEE Symposium on Switching and Automata Theory, pp. 1–11 (1973)
27. Ziv, J., Lempel, A.: A universal algorithm for sequential data compression. IEEE Transactions on Information Theory 23(3), 337–343 (1977)

Collusion-Resistant Mechanisms with Verification Yielding Optimal Solutions[*]

Paolo Penna[1] and Carmine Ventre[2],[**]

[1] Dipartimento di Informatica ed Applicazioni, Università di Salerno, Italy
penna@dia.unisa.it
[2] Computer Science Department, University of Liverpool, UK
Carmine.Ventre@liverpool.ac.uk

Abstract. A *truthful mechanism* consists of an algorithm augmented with a suitable payment function which guarantees that "players" cannot improve their utilities by "cheating". Mechanism design approaches are particularly appealing for designing "protocols" that cannot be manipulated by rational players.

We present new constructions of so called mechanisms *with verification* introduced by Nisan and Ronen [STOC 1999]. We first show how to obtain mechanisms that, for single-parameter domains, are resistant to *coalitions* of colluding agents even in the case in which compensation among members of the coalition is allowed (i.e., *n-truthful* mechanisms). Based on this technique we derive a class of *exact* truthful mechanisms with verification for *arbitrary* bounded domains. This class of problems includes most of the problems studied in the algorithmic mechanism design literature and for which exact solutions cannot be obtained with truthful mechanisms *without verification*. This result improves over all known previous constructions of exact mechanisms with verification.

1 Introduction

A large body of the literature studies ways to incorporate economic and game-theoretic considerations in the design of algorithms and protocols. One of the most studied and acknowledged paradigms is *mechanism design* (see, e.g., [1, 4, 7, 12, 13, 16]). Distributed computations over the Internet often involve self-interested parties (referred to as *selfish agents*) which may manipulate the protocol by misreporting a fundamental piece of information they hold (their own *type*). The protocol runs some algorithm which, because of the misreported information, is no longer guaranteed to return a "globally optimal" solution (optimality is naturally expressed as a function of agents' types) [13, 16]. Since agents can manipulate the algorithm by misreporting their types, one augments the algorithms with carefully designed payment functions which make it disadvantageous for an agent to do so. A *mechanism* consists of an algorithm (also termed social choice function) and a payment rule which associates a payment to every agent. Each agent derives a *utility* which depends on the solution computed by the algorithm, on

---

[*] Research funded by the European Union through IST FET Integrated Project AEOLUS (IST-015964).

[**] The author is also supported by DFG grant Kr 2332/1-2 within Emmy Noether Program.

D. Halperin and K. Mehlhorn (Eds.): ESA 2008, LNCS 5193, pp. 708–719, 2008.

the type of the agent, and on the payment that the agent receives from the mechanism (the solution and the payment depend on the *reported* types). A mechanism is *truthful* if truthtelling is a *dominant strategy* for all agents. That is, the utility of any agent is maximized when this agent reports her type truthfully, no matter which strategy the other agents follow. An even stronger solution concept is that of *c-truthful* mechanism [9] which requires that no *coalition* of up to c agents can increase the utility of its members even when compensations (or side payments) among them occur.

The construction of a truthful mechanism is a challenging problem since the mechanism must fix the "rules" in advance without knowing the types of the agents. The only available information is that each agent's type belongs to some *domain* which depends on the problem and agents can only report types in that domain. Intuitively speaking, constructing truthful mechanisms for richer domains is more difficult because there are more ways in which an agent can cheat the mechanism.

In their seminal work on algorithmic game theory, Nisan and Ronen [13] suggested a rather innovative paradigm called *mechanisms with verification*. They showed that these mechanisms can overcome the main limitations of the "classical" approach which cannot guarantee exact (or even approximate solutions) for some interesting problems. Intuitively speaking, these mechanisms can optimize only certain global cost functions. Suppose that each agent i has a type t^i which, for every feasible solution x, specifies a cost $t^i(x)$ associated to this solution. The only known general technique for designing truthful mechanisms are the classical Vickrey-Clarke-Groves (VCG) mechanisms [5, 10, 23]; these mechanisms optimize only *utilitarian* problems, that is, global cost functions of the form

$$\sum_i \alpha_i \cdot t^i(x) \tag{1}$$

where each α_i is some nonnegative constant. Moreover, the celebrated Robert's Theorem [20] states that these are the only global cost functions that can be optimized, i.e., for which there exists an exact truthful mechanism, when agents' domains are unrestricted. Furthermore, no positive result on the construction of "classical" c-truthful mechanisms is known, even for simple domains.

This work presents new constructions of mechanisms with verification which guarantee c-truthful mechanisms for certain domains or exact solutions for a much more general class of global cost functions. Before discussing these and prior results in detail, we describe informally the main idea of mechanisms with verification:

Mechanisms with verification. Nisan and Ronen [13] introduced mechanisms with verification for a task scheduling problem in which each agent corresponds to a machine of type t^i. Tasks needs to be allocated to the machines, and each task allocation x results in a completion time $t^i(x)$ for a machine of type t^i. The key observation, made by Nisan and Ronen [13], is that machine i cannot release its tasks before $t^i(x)$ time steps. Therefore, if agent i reports a type b^i and a solution x is implemented, the mechanism is able to detect that b^i is *not* the true type of machine i if $b^i(x) < t^i(x)$.

Mechanisms *with verification* are based on this idea and apply to the following general framework (see Section 1.2 for a formal definition). For every feasible solution x, an agent of type t^i has a cost $t^i(x)$ associated to this solution. This cost is the time that this agent must spend for implementing solution x (artificial delays can be introduced at no cost since an agent can use the idle time for other purposes).[1] Agent i is caught lying if her reported type b^i and the computed solution x are such that $b^i(x) < t^i(x)$. Agents who are caught lying receive no payment.

In contrast, the classical approach in mechanism design is to provide always each agent with a payment that depends only on the reported types. In order to distinguish these mechanisms from mechanisms with verification, in the sequel we use the term mechanisms *without verification*.

1.1   Our Contribution and Related Work

We study the existence of truthful (or even c-truthful) mechanisms with verification that guarantee *exact* solutions for problems in which the objective is to minimize some global cost function of interest. Intuitively speaking, our basic question is whether one can augment an optimal algorithm with a suitable payment function in order to guarantee that no agent (or even coalitions of colluding agents) can benefit from misreporting their types (i.e., part of the input of the algorithm). We consider a rather general class of objective functions in which the global cost of a solution depends on the various costs that the agents associate to that solution; Naturally, the overall cost cannot decrease if the cost of one agent increases (see Section 2 for a formal definition). The contribution of this work is twofold:

- We provide a sufficient condition for which an algorithm can be turned into a c-*truthful* mechanism with verification, for any $c \geq 1$. This result applies to the class of *single-parameter* bounded domains (see Section 3 for a formal definition).
- We then show how to obtain optimal truthful mechanisms with verification for the much more general case of *arbitrary* bounded domains, i.e., the mechanism needs only an upper bound on the agents' costs (see Section 1.2). Despite the fact that these domains are extremely rich, we provide *exact* truthful mechanisms with verification for *every* problem in which the global cost function is of the form

$$\text{Cost}(t^1(x), \dots, t^n(x)) \qquad (2)$$

where $t^i(x)$ is the cost that agent i associates to solution x and the above function is naturally nondecreasing in its arguments.

The conditions for obtaining these mechanisms are stated in terms of *algorithmic properties* so that the design of the entire mechanism reduces to the design of an algorithm that fulfills these conditions. All our mechanisms satisfy also the *voluntary participation* condition saying that truthful agents have always a nonnegative utility.

The result on single-parameter bounded domains is the first technique for obtaining c-truthful mechanisms, for $c > 1$, without restricting to a particular class of global cost functions and it might be of some independent interest. For instance, certain non-utilitarian graph problems studied in [19] have single-parameter domains and thus are

---

[1] Nisan and Ronen [13] considered the case in which an agent introducing an artificial delay to her computations will pay *this* augmented cost. This is one of the differences between mechanisms with verification we consider and those in [13]. See [18] for a discussion.

the right candidate for studying exact n-truthful mechanisms based on our constructions (namely Theorems 4 and 5). Interestingly enough, the only way to guarantee c-truthfulness without verification, for $c \geq 2$, is to run a (useless) mechanism which returns always the same *fixed* solution [9, 21].

The result on arbitrary bounded domains improves significantly over the best known constructions of mechanisms with verification. In particular, [22] shows exact mechanisms for cost functions like (2) in the case of *finite* domains, i.e., there is a finite set of possible types that each agent can report to the mechanism. Exact n-truthful mechanisms with verification for a *subclass* of the cost functions in (2) are presented in [18]: For instance, it cannot give exact mechanisms for global cost functions of the form of the form $\max_i t^i(x)$. These so called min-max problems received a lot of attention in the algorithmic mechanism design literature [4, 8, 11, 12, 13]. These works prove that there is no exact or even r-approximate mechanism without verification, for some $r > 1$; results apply also to finite domains and to mechanisms without verification that run in exponential time and/or use randomization [12].

We instead show exact mechanisms with verification for any global cost function of the form (2) without assuming finite domains like in [22] (see Definition 2 and Theorem 6). Indeed, we only need to consider an (arbitrarily large) upper bound on the agents' costs, which turns out to be reasonable in practice. These arbitrary bounded domains are, in general, infinite because there are infinitely many types that an agent can report. Since the "cycle-monotonicity" approach adopted in all recent constructions [2, 3, 22] cannot deal with infinite domains, we use a totally different idea which is to turn c-truthful mechanisms for single-parameter domains into truthful mechanisms for arbitrary domains (see Section 4). The result of Theorem 6 is "tight" in the sense that one cannot relax any of the assumptions without introducing additional conditions (see Theorems 7 and 8). Finally, an explicit formula for the payments guarantees that the entire mechanism runs in polynomial-time if the algorithm is polynomial-time and the domain is finite (Corollary 1).

In this work we do not consider frugality issues, that is, how much the mechanism pays the agents. The optimality of the payments is an important issue *in general* since even truthful mechanisms must have large payments for rather simple problems [6]. Our positive results pose another interesting question that is to design *computationally-efficient* algorithms satisfying the conditions required by our methods.

Roadmap. Preliminary definitions are given in Section 1.2. In Section 2 we introduce the class of optimal algorithms leading to (c-)truthful mechanisms. Mechanisms for single-parameter domains are given in Section 3, while those for arbitrary domains are presented in Section 4. Due to lack of space some of the proofs are sketched or missing. The interested reader may refer to the full version of the paper [17].

1.2   Preliminaries

We have a finite set $\mathcal{O}$ of feasible alternative *solutions* (or *outcomes*). Without loss of generality, we assume that $\mathcal{O} = \{1, \ldots, a\}$, where $a = |\mathcal{O}|$, and sometimes write $x \leq y$

to denote the fact that outcome x precedes outcome y in this fixed order. There are n selfish agents, each of them having a so called *type*

$$t^i : \mathcal{O} \to \mathbb{R}^+$$

which associates a monetary *cost* to every feasible outcome. If an agent i receives a payment equal to r^i and an outcome x is selected, then her *utility* is equal to

$$r^i - t^i(x). \tag{3}$$

Each type t^i belongs to a so called *domain* D^i which consists of all admissible types, that is, a subset of all functions $u : \mathcal{O} \to \mathbb{R}$. The type t^i is *private knowledge*, that is, it is known to agent i only. Everything else, including each domain D^i, is *public knowledge*. Hence, each agent i can *misreport* her type to *any* other element b^i in the domain D^i. We sometimes call such b^i the *bid* or *reported type* of agent i. We let D being the cross product of all agents domains, that is, D contains all bid vectors $\mathbf{b} = (b^1, \ldots, b^n)$ with b^i in D^i. An *algorithm* A is a function

$$A : D \to \mathcal{O}$$

which maps all agents (reported) types $\mathbf{b}$ into a feasible outcome $x = A(\mathbf{b})$.[2] A *mechanism* is a pair (A, p), where A is an algorithm and $p = (p^1, \ldots, p^n)$ is a vector of suitable *payment functions*, one for each agent, where each payment function

$$p^i : D \to \mathbb{R}$$

associates some amount of money to agent i. We say that D is a *bounded domain* if there exists ℓ such that $b^i(x)$ belongs to the interval $[0, \ell]$, for all outcomes x, for all b^i in D^i, and for all agents i. Unless we make further assumptions on the domain D, we have (algorithms over) *arbitrary bounded domains*. Throughout the paper we consider only type vectors $\mathbf{t}$ in the domain D and we denote by t^i the type corresponding to agent i.

We say that an agent i is *truthtelling* if she reports her type, that is, the bid b^i coincides with her type t^i. Given an algorithm A and bids $\mathbf{b} = (b^1, \ldots, b^i, \ldots, b^n)$, we say that agent i is *caught lying by the verification* if the following inequality holds:

$$t^i(A(\mathbf{b})) > b^i(A(\mathbf{b})).$$

A mechanism (A, p) is a *mechanism with verification* if, on input bids $\mathbf{b}$, every agent that is caught lying does not receive any payment, while every other agent i receives her associated payment $p^i(\mathbf{b})$. Hence, the utility of an agent i whose type is t^i is equal to

$$\text{Utility}^i(\mathbf{b}) := \begin{cases} p^i(\mathbf{b}) - t^i(A(\mathbf{b})) & \text{if } i \text{ is not caught lying,} \\ 0 - t^i(A(\mathbf{b})) & \text{otherwise.} \end{cases}$$

On the contrary, we say that (A, p) is a *mechanism without verification* if every agent receives *always* her associated payment $p^i(\mathbf{b})$.

---

[2] In the game theory literature A is often referred to as *social choice function*.

For any two type vectors $\mathbf{t}$ and $\mathbf{b}$, we say that a coalition C *can misreport* $\mathbf{t}$ *to* $\mathbf{b}$ if the vector $\mathbf{b}$ is obtained by changing the type of some of the agents in C, i.e., $t^i = b^i$ for every agent i *not* in the coalition C. For any two type vectors $\mathbf{t}$ and $\mathbf{b}$, we say that *verification does not catch* $\mathbf{t}$ *misreported to* $\mathbf{b}$ if $t^i(A(\mathbf{b})) \leq b^i(A(\mathbf{b}))$ for every agent i. Conversely, we say that *verification catches* $\mathbf{t}$ *misreported to* $\mathbf{b}$ if $t^i(A(\mathbf{b})) > b^i(A(\mathbf{b}))$ for some agent i.

Mechanisms (with verification) which are resistant to coalitions of $c \geq 1$ colluding agents that can exchange side payments satisfy the following definition.

Definition 1 (c-truthfulness [9]). *A mechanism (with verification) is c-truthful if, for any coalition of size at most c and any bid of agents not in the coalition, the sum of the utilities of the agents in the coalition is maximized when all agents in the coalition are truthtelling.*

Mechanisms (with verification) satisfying the definition above only for $c = 1$ are called *truthful* mechanisms (with verification).

Since the above condition must hold for *all* possible bids of agents outside the coalition under consideration, one can restrict the analysis to the case in which these agents are actually truthtelling. Thus the following known fact holds:

Fact 1. *A mechanism (with verification) is c-truthful if and only if, for any coalition C of size at most c and for any two type vectors $\mathbf{t}$ and $\mathbf{b}$ such that C can misreport $\mathbf{t}$ to $\mathbf{b}$, the corresponding agents' utilities satisfy*

$$\sum_{i \in C} \text{Utility}^i(\mathbf{t}) \geq \sum_{i \in C} \text{Utility}^i(\mathbf{b}). \tag{4}$$

Throughout the paper we make use of the following standard notation. Given a type vector $\mathbf{v} = (v^1, \ldots, v^n)$, we let $\mathbf{v}^{-i}$ being the vector of length $n - 1$ obtained by removing v^i from $\mathbf{v}$, i.e., the vector $(v^1, \ldots, v^{i-1}, v^{i+1}, \ldots, v^n)$. We also let $(w, \mathbf{v}^{-i})$ be the vector $(v^1, \ldots, v^{i-1}, w, v^{i+1}, \ldots, v^n)$, which is obtained by replacing the i-th entry of $\mathbf{v}$ with w.

2 A Class of Optimal Algorithms

We focus on algorithms which minimize some global cost function of interest. Our ultimate goal is to derive a general technique to augment these algorithms with a suitable payment function so that the resulting mechanism with verification is truthful or even n-truthful (i.e., resistant to any coalition of colluding agents).

Towards this end, we consider algorithms that satisfy the following:

Definition 2 (exact algorithm with fixed tie breaking rule). *Let* $\text{Cost} : \mathcal{O} \times D \to \mathbb{R}$ *be a function of the form*

$$\text{Cost}(x, \mathbf{t}) = \text{Cost}(t^1(x), \ldots, t^n(x)),$$

which is monotone non-decreasing in each $t^i(x)$. We say that an algorithm A is an exact *algorithm if there exists $\mathcal{O}' \subseteq \mathcal{O}$ such that, for all type vectors $\mathbf{t}$, it holds that*

$$A(\mathbf{t}) \in \arg\min_{x \in \mathcal{O}'} \{\text{Cost}(x, \mathbf{t})\}.$$

Further, we say that A uses a fixed tie breaking rule if, for any two type vectors **t** *and* **b**, $\text{Cost}(A(\mathbf{t}), \mathbf{t}) = \text{Cost}(A(\mathbf{b}), \mathbf{t})$ *implies that the outcomes* $A(\mathbf{t})$ *and* $A(\mathbf{b})$ *in the outcome set* $\mathcal{O}$ *satisfy:* $A(\mathbf{t}) \leq A(\mathbf{b})$.[3] *We say that A is an* exact algorithm with fixed tie breaking rule *if it is an exact algorithm and it uses a fixed tie breaking rule.*

Note that the definition of exact algorithm requires only the algorithm being optimal with respect to an arbitrarily fixed subset of solutions. Of course all positive results apply to algorithms that are optimal with respect to all solutions, i.e., the case $\mathcal{O}' = \mathcal{O}$. Observe also that the class of exact algorithm with fixed tie breaking rules strictly generalizes the class of algorithms that admit VCG-based truthful mechanisms (without verification) [15] and that optimizes *utilitarian* cost functions, that is, functions of the form (1).

3   Collusion-Resistant Mechanisms for Single-Parameter Agents

In this section we consider the case of *single-parameter* agents (see e.g. [9]). Here, each outcome partitions the agents into two sets: those that are *selected* and those that are *not selected*. The value $t^i(x)$ depends *uniquely* on the fact that i is selected in x or not and it is completely specified by a *parameter* t_i, which is a real number such that

$$t^i(x) = \begin{cases} t_i & \text{if } i \text{ is selected in } x, \\ 0 & \text{if } i \text{ is not selected in } x. \end{cases} \tag{5}$$

Whether i is selected in x is publicly known, for every outcome x, and thus each agent can only specify (and misreport) the parameter t_i. We assume *single-parameter bounded domains*, that is, each parameter t_i belongs to the interval $[0, \ell]$.

In the sequel we will provide sufficient conditions for the existence of c-truthful mechanisms, for any given $c \leq n$.

3.1   Sufficient Conditions for c-Truthfulness

We begin with a *necessary* condition. Observe that in order to have truthful mechanisms for single-parameter agents (even when using verification [2]) the algorithm must select agents "monotonically":

Definition 3 (monotone). *We say that algorithm A is* monotone *if the following holds. Having fixed the bids of all agents but i, agent i is selected if bidding a cost less than a threshold value $b_i^{\oplus}$, and is not selected if bidding a cost more than a threshold value $b_i^{\oplus}$. In particular, for every* **b** $\in D$ *and for every i, there exists a value $b_i^{\oplus}$ which depends only on $\mathbf{b}^{-i}$ and such that (i) i is selected in $A(b^i, \mathbf{b}^{-i})$ for $b^i < b_i^{\oplus}$ and (ii) i is not selected in $A(b^i, \mathbf{b}^{-i})$ for $b^i > b_i^{\oplus}$.*

From Definition 3 we can easily obtain the following:

Fact 2. *If algorithm A is monotone and i is selected in $A(\mathbf{b})$, then $b_i \leq b_i^{\oplus}$. Moreover, if i is not selected in $A(\mathbf{b})$ then $b_i \geq b_i^{\oplus}$. Hence, for bounded domains the threshold values of Definition 3 are in the interval $[0, \ell]$.*

---

[3] Recall that we identify solutions with integers and thus fix an arbitrary order of them.

From (5) we immediately get the following:

Fact 3. *For single-parameter agents, it holds that verification does not catch* $\mathbf{t}$ *misreported to* $\mathbf{b}$ *if and only if* $t_i \leq b_i$ *for all* i *that is selected in* $A(\mathbf{b})$.

We next give a rather technical *sufficient* condition for c-truthfulness on single-parameter bounded domains. Below we show that, in the case of exact algorithms, this leads to a simpler condition for n-truthfulness on these domains.

Definition 4 (c-resistant). *We say that* $\mathbf{b}$ *is* c-*different from* $\mathbf{t}$ *if these two type vectors differ for at most* c *agents' types. A monotone algorithm* A *is* c-*resistant if, for every* $\mathbf{b}$ *which is* c-*different from* $\mathbf{t}$ *and such that verification does not catch* $\mathbf{t}$ *misreported to* $\mathbf{b}$, *it holds that* $t_i^{\oplus} \leq b_i^{\oplus}$ *for all* i *that is not selected in* $A(\mathbf{b})$.

Theorem 4. *Every c-resistant algorithm* A *admits a c-truthful mechanism with verification for single-parameter bounded domains.*

Proof. We define the payment functions as follows:

$$p^i(\mathbf{b}) := \begin{cases} \hbar - b_i^{\oplus} & \text{if } i \text{ is not selected in } A(\mathbf{b}) \\ \hbar & \text{otherwise} \end{cases} \tag{6}$$

where $\hbar := c \cdot \ell$.

Let us consider an arbitrary coalition C of size at most c and any two type vectors $\mathbf{t}$ and $\mathbf{b}$ such that C can misreport $\mathbf{t}$ to $\mathbf{b}$. Because of Fact 1, it suffices to prove (4). Either verification does not catch $\mathbf{t}$ misreported to $\mathbf{b}$ or verification catches $\mathbf{t}$ misreported to $\mathbf{b}$. We consider the two cases separately.

If verification catches $\mathbf{t}$ misreported to $\mathbf{b}$, then we have at least one agent $j \in C$ which does not receive any payment for $\mathbf{b}$. Moreover, the payment received by every other agent i in the coalition is at most $\hbar$. Hence, we have

$$\sum_{i \in C} \text{Utility}^i(\mathbf{b}) \leq (c-1)\hbar = c\hbar - \hbar.$$

We next show that the utility of every truthtelling agent is at least $\hbar - \ell$. Indeed, the definition of $p^i()$ implies that $\text{Utility}^i(\mathbf{t})$ is either $\hbar - t_i^{\oplus}$ if i is not selected in $A(\mathbf{t})$, or $\hbar - t_i$ if i is selected in $A(\mathbf{t})$. Fact 2 says that $t_i^{\oplus} \leq \ell$ and, if i is selected in $A(\mathbf{t})$, then $t_i \leq t_i^{\oplus}$. Hence, $\text{Utility}^i(\mathbf{t}) \geq \hbar - \ell$. From this and from our choice of $\hbar$, we obtain

$$\sum_{i \in C} \text{Utility}^i(\mathbf{t}) \geq c(\hbar - \ell) = c\hbar - c\ell = c\hbar - \hbar.$$

The two inequalities above clearly imply (4).

If verification does not catch $\mathbf{t}$ misreported to $\mathbf{b}$ then we can show that for any $i \in C$ it holds

$$\text{Utility}^i(\mathbf{t}) \geq \text{Utility}^i(\mathbf{b}),$$

which clearly implies (4). There are four possible cases:

Case 1 (i is selected in $A(\mathbf{t})$ and i is selected in $A(\mathbf{b})$). In this case nothing changes for i. Indeed, by the definition of $p^i()$, we have $\text{Utility}^i(\mathbf{t}) = \hbar - t_i = \text{Utility}^i(\mathbf{b})$.

Case 2 (i is not selected in $A(\mathbf{t})$ and i is selected in $A(\mathbf{b})$). Fact 2 implies that $t_i^{\oplus} \leq t_i$. This and the definition of $p^i()$ imply $\text{Utility}^i(\mathbf{t}) = \hbar - t_i^{\oplus} \geq \hbar - t_i = \text{Utility}^i(\mathbf{b})$.

Case 3 (i is not selected in $A(\mathbf{t})$ and i is not selected in $A(\mathbf{b})$). Since A is c-resistant, we have that $t_i^{\oplus} \leq b_i^{\oplus}$. This and the definition of $p^i()$ imply $\text{Utility}^i(\mathbf{t}) = \hbar - t_i^{\oplus} \geq \hbar - b_i^{\oplus} = \text{Utility}^i(\mathbf{b})$.

Case 4 (i is selected in $A(\mathbf{t})$ and i is not selected in $A(\mathbf{b})$). Since i is selected in $A(\mathbf{t})$, Fact 2 implies $t_i \leq t_i^{\oplus}$. Since i is not selected in $A(\mathbf{b})$ and as A is c-resistant, we have that $t_i^{\oplus} \leq b_i^{\oplus}$, thus implying $t_i \leq b_i^{\oplus}$. This and the definition of $p^i()$ imply $\text{Utility}^i(\mathbf{t}) = \hbar - t_i \geq \hbar - b_i^{\oplus} = \text{Utility}^i(\mathbf{b})$.

This concludes the proof.   □

We next "specialize" the above result for the class of exact algorithm with fixed tie breaking rule and obtain a more easy-to-handle *sufficient* condition for obtaining n-truthful mechanisms with verification.

Definition 5 (threshold-monotone). *A monotone algorithm A is threshold-monotone if, for every $\mathbf{t}$ and every $\mathbf{b}$ obtained by increasing one agent entry of $\mathbf{t}$, the inequality $t_i^{\oplus} \leq b_i^{\oplus}$ holds for all i, where $t_i^{\oplus}$ and $b_i^{\oplus}$ are the threshold values of Definition 3.*

By showing that every threshold-monotone exact algorithm with fixed tie breaking rule is n-resistant from Theorem 4 we obtain another sufficient condition for n-truthful mechanisms. We believe this result might be useful in that the threshold-monotone condition might be simpler to exhibit.

Theorem 5. *Every threshold-monotone exact algorithm with fixed tie breaking rule admits an n-truthful mechanism with verification for single-parameter bounded domains.*

4   Truthful Mechanisms for Arbitrary Bounded Domains

In this section we derive truthful mechanisms for any exact algorithm with fixed tie breaking rule over arbitrary bounded domains. The main idea is to regard each agent as a *coalition* of (virtual) single-parameter agents.

4.1   Arbitrary Domains as Coalitions of Single-Parameter Agents

We call every agent whose domain is an arbitrary bounded domain a *multidimensional* agent. Since there are a alternative outcomes, and n multidimensional agents, we simply consider n coalitions $C_1, \ldots, C_n$, where each coalition C_i consists of a (virtual) single-parameter agents that correspond to the multidimensional agent i. (These are actually "known" coalitions which we use only for the purpose of defining the payments and analyzing the resulting mechanism.) This "new game" has $N = n \cdot |\mathcal{O}|$ single-parameter agents and a alternative outcomes. For each outcome x, we have a unique single-parameter agent per coalition being selected: denoted by $1^{(i)}, \ldots, |\mathcal{O}|^{(i)}$

the agents in coalition C_i, we have agent $x^{(i)}$ being selected in x, and every other agent in C_i being not selected in x; this holds for all coalitions above. We choose the parameter of the (virtual) single-parameter agents in the coalition C_i so that the cost for an agent $x^{(i)}$ selected is equal to the cost of the multidimensional agent i when outcome x is selected. That is, for all i and all outcomes x, the parameter $t_{x^{(i)}}$ of agent $x^{(i)}$ is equal to $t^i(x)$.

Observe that any type b^i in the domain of the multidimensional agent i can be seen as a vector

$$\mathbf{b}^i := (b_1^i, \ldots, b_a^i),$$

with $b_x^i = b^i(x)$ for every alternative outcome x. In particular, $\mathbf{b}^i$ is the vector of the parameters of the a agents in C_i, that is, b_x^i is the parameter of agent $x^{(i)}$. Consider an exact algorithm with fixed tie breaking rule B over the multidimensional agents, and fix the bids $\mathbf{b}^{-i}$ of all agents but i. Then the resulting *single player function* $B(b^i, \mathbf{b}^{-i})$ can be seen as another exact algorithm with fixed tie breaking rule $A(\mathbf{b}^i)$ whose domain (input) is restricted to the domains of the $a = |\mathcal{O}|$ single-parameter agents in C_i.

4.2   The Mechanism and Its Analysis

It turns out that every single player function $B(b^i, \mathbf{b}^{-i})$ as above is a-resistant. Based on this fact, we can apply the techniques developed for single-parameter agents and define the following class of mechanisms:

Definition 6 (threshold-based mechanism). *For any exact algorithm with fixed tie breaking rule B we consider its* single player function, *depending on $\mathbf{b}^{-i}$, as $A(\mathbf{b}^i) := B(b^i, \mathbf{b}^{-i})$. In this case, the single player function A has C_i as the set of virtual single-parameter agents. We define payment functions $q^i(b^i, \mathbf{b}^{-i}) := \sum_{j \in C_i} p^j(\mathbf{b}^i)$ where each $p^i()$ is the payment function of Theorem 4 when applied to A above and to the single-parameter agents in C_i. The resulting mechanism with verification (B, q) is* called *threshold-based mechanism.*

In the sequel we prove that every threshold-based mechanism is truthful *for multidimensional agents*. In order to prove this result, we first observe that the threshold-based mechanism needs only be resistant to the "known" coalitions defined above (recall that we have one virtual single-parameter agent per solution and thus coalitions are of size at most $|\mathcal{O}|$):

Lemma 1. *If every single player function A of B is $|\mathcal{O}|$-resistant with respect to its virtual single-parameter agents, then the threshold-based mechanism is truthful for the multidimensional agents.*

PROOF SKETCH. We observe that the utility of a multidimensional agent i is the sum of the utilities of all single-parameter agents in the coalition C_i. Therefore, if (B, q) was not truthful, then the mechanism (A, p) would not be a-truthful, thus contradicting Theorem 5.   □

Theorem 6. *Every exact algorithm with fixed tie breaking rule admits a truthful mechanism with verification over any arbitrary bounded domain.*

PROOF SKETCH. It is possible to show that every single player function A of B is threshold-monotone. But then every single player function is a-resistant (see discussion above Theorem 5). The theorem thus follows from Lemma 1.   □

We next observe that one cannot extend the result of Theorem 6 by relaxing the definition of exact algorithm with fixed tie breaking rule. Indeed, the "non-decreasing cost function", the "fixed tie breaking rule" and the "optimality" assumptions are necessary in order to guarantee the existence of exact truthful mechanisms with verification without introducing other conditions. The optimality condition is necessary as we obtain exact mechanisms. As for the other two assumptions we can prove the next two theorems.

Theorem 7. *For any cost function that is* not *monotone nondecreasing there exists a bounded domain such that no algorithm that minimizes such a cost function admits a truthful mechanism with verification.*

We next remove the fixed tie breaking rule from our assumptions and show that there exists an exact algorithm not admitting truthful mechanisms with verification.

Theorem 8. *There exists a bounded domain and a monotone cost function such that the following holds. There exists an exact algorithm (not using a fixed tie breaking rule) which does not admit any truthful mechanism with verification.*

We conclude this section by observing that the mechanisms presented here have a further advantage of giving an explicit formula for the payments (see Equation 6 and Definition 6). In particular, this improves over the construction in [22] since it gives efficient mechanisms for the case of arbitrary finite domains. The idea is to perform a binary search to determine the threshold values of Definition 3. For threshold-based mechanisms the running time is polynomial in the size of the input $\mathbf{t}$, where each t^i is a vector of $|\mathcal{O}|$ values, one for each outcome. Such an "explicit" representation of the input is in general necessary, as implied by communication complexity lower bounds for certain instances of combinatorial auction [14] which fall into the class of finite domains.

Corollary 1. *Every polynomial-time exact algorithm with fixed tie breaking rule over an arbitrary finite domain admits a polynomial-time truthful mechanism with verification. For finite single-parameter domains, every polynomial-time c-resistant exact algorithm with fixed tie breaking rule admits a polynomial-time c-truthful mechanism with verification.*

Acknowledgements. We wish to thank Riccardo Silvestri for several useful comments on an earlier version of this work.

References

1. Archer, A., Tardos, E.: Truthful mechanisms for one-parameter agents. In: Proc. of FOCS, pp. 482–491 (2001)
2. Auletta, V., De Prisco, R., Penna, P., Persiano, G.: The power of verification for one-parameter agents. In: Díaz, J., Karhumäki, J., Lepistö, A., Sannella, D. (eds.) ICALP 2004. LNCS, vol. 3142, pp. 171–182. Springer, Heidelberg (2004)

3. Auletta, V., De Prisco, R., Penna, P., Persiano, G., Ventre, C.: New constructions of mechanisms with verification. In: Bugliesi, M., Preneel, B., Sassone, V., Wegener, I. (eds.) ICALP 2006. LNCS, vol. 4052, pp. 596–607. Springer, Heidelberg (2006)
4. Christodoulou, G., Koutsoupias, E., Vidali, A.: A lower bound for scheduling mechanisms. In: Proc. of SODA, pp. 1163–1170 (2007)
5. Clarke, E.H.: Multipart Pricing of Public Goods. Public Choice, 17–33 (1971)
6. Elkind, E., Sahai, A., Steiglitz, K.: Frugality in path auctions. In: Proc. of SODA, pp. 701–709 (2004)
7. Feigenbaum, J., Papadimitriou, C.H., Sami, R., Shenker, S.: A bgp-based mechanism for lowest-cost routing. Distributed Computing 18(1), 61–72 (2005)
8. Gamzu, I.: Improved lower bounds for non-utilitarian truthfulness. In: Kaklamanis, C., Skutella, M. (eds.) WAOA 2007. LNCS, vol. 4927, pp. 15–26. Springer, Heidelberg (2008)
9. Goldberg, A.V., Hartline, J.D.: Collusion-resistant mechanisms for single-parameter agents. In: Proc. of SODA, pp. 620–629 (2005)
10. Groves, T.: Incentive in Teams. Econometrica 41, 617–631 (1973)
11. Koutsoupias, E., Vidali, A.: A lower bound of $1 + \phi$ for truthful scheduling mechanisms. In: Kučera, L., Kučera, A. (eds.) MFCS 2007. LNCS, vol. 4708, pp. 454–464. Springer, Heidelberg (2007)
12. Mu'alem, A., Schapira, M.: Setting lower bounds on truthfulness. In: Proc. of SODA, pp. 1143–1152 (2007)
13. Nisan, N., Ronen, A.: Algorithmic Mechanism Design. Games and Economic Behavior 35, 166–196 (2001)
14. Nisan, N., Segal, I.: The communication requirements of efficient allocations and supporting prices. Journal of Economic Theory (2006)
15. Nisan, N., Ronen, A.: Computationally Feasible VCG Mechanisms. In: Proc. of EC, pp. 242–252 (2000)
16. Papadimitriou, C.H.: Algorithms, games, and the internet. In: Proc. of STOC (2001)
17. Penna, P., Ventre, C.: Collusion-resistant mechanisms with verification yielding optimal solutions. Technical report (2008),
    http://www.dia.unisa.it/~penna/papers/esa08full.pdf
18. Penna, P., Ventre, C.: Optimal collusion-resistant mechanisms with verification. Technical Report (2008)
19. Proietti, G., Widmayer, P.: A truthful mechanism for the non-utilitarian minimum radius spanning tree problem. In: Proc. of SPAA, pp. 195–202 (2005)
20. Roberts, K.: The characterization of implementable choice rules. Aggregation and Revelation of Preferences, 321–348 (1979)
21. Schummer, J.: Manipulation through bribes. Journal of Economic Theory 91(3), 180–198 (2000)
22. Ventre, C.: Mechanisms with verification for any finite domain. In: Spirakis, P.G., Mavronicolas, M., Kontogiannis, S.C. (eds.) WINE 2006. LNCS, vol. 4286, pp. 37–49. Springer, Heidelberg (2006)
23. Vickrey, W.: Counterspeculation, Auctions and Competitive Sealed Tenders. Journal of Finance, 8–37 (1961)

Improved BDD Algorithms for the Simulation of Quantum Circuits

Vasilis Samoladas

Technical University of Crete, Chania, Greece
vsam@softnet.tuc.gr

Abstract. In this paper we develop novel algorithms for the simulation of quantum circuits on classical computers. The most efficient techniques previously studied, represent both quantum state vectors and quantum operator matrices as Multi-Terminal Binary Decision Diagrams (MTB-DDS). This paper shows how to avoid representing quantum operators as matrices. Instead, we introduce a class of quantum operators that can be represented more compactly using a symbolic, BDD-based representation. We propose algorithms that apply operators on quantum states, using the symbolic representation. Our algorithms are shown to have superior performance over previous techniques, both asymptotically and experimentally.

1 Introduction

The study of quantum computing can be greatly aided by the ability to actually execute quantum algorithms. As quantum hardware is still unavailable, the only viable option is simulation by classical computer. The problem is generally intractable by currently known techniques. However, it is of great practical significance to simulate even small-scale systems. Most simulation algorithms reported in the literature represent quantum states in the so-called state-vector representation, i.e., use a complex vector of 2^n elements to store the state of an n-qubit memory. With current hardware, this approach is limited to $n \approx 30$. In order to break through this barrier, either (a) the state-vector representation must be abandoned, or (b) suitable compression techniques must be employed to reduce the space needed to represent the state vector.

The first option is an intriguing one, and in fact there exist at least two approaches that follow this path. Unfortunately, they are only applicable in limited cases. To our knowledge, every known *general* technique for quantum simulation is based on the state vector representation.

Compression of the state representation for classical computations has been extensively studied by the formal methods community over the past 20 years, particularly in the context of formal verification. In formal verification, one is interererested in verifying mechanically that all legal computations of a classical computer satisfy a given specification. A plethora of algorithmic breakthroughs in the past 20 years has enabled the verification of gradually larger classical systems. There is an interesting analogy with quantum simulation, where a qunatum

D. Halperin and K. Mehlhorn (Eds.): ESA 2008, LNCS 5193, pp. 720–731, 2008.

computation exploiting quantum parallelism is, in some sense, a simulation of all behaviours of an equivalent classical system.

A major breakthrough in formal verification was the introduction of Reduced Ordered Binary Decision Diagrams (ROBDDS) by Bryant [3]. ROBDDs can often compress an exponentially large structure down to a manageable size. It has been shown in previous works [12,10,11,6] that an extension of ROBDDs, called Multi-Terminal BDDs (MTBDDs) [4], can be employed effectively in compressing the state vector of a quantum system. By representing quantum operators as MTBDDs as well, linear-algebraic operations can be performed in time quadratic to the size of the operand MTBDDs. This approach premits us to simulate large quantum circuits. However, in most non-trivial cases, the compressed state vector representation still grows exponentially (albeit much more gradually) as larger circuits are simulated. Thus, MTBDD-based quantum simulation is still computationally expensive, and it is vital to improve the efficiency of the algorithms involved.

In this paper we propose novel MTBDD-based algorithms for quantum circuit simulation. Our algorithms are distinguished in that they operate with symbolic representations of quantum operators, instead of matrix-based ones (compressed or otherwise). This technique exhibits significant performance advantages over previous work. Our experimental evaluation demonstrates that our techniques outperform previous ones by roughly two orders of magnitude. We also prove our algorithms to be asymptotically faster that previous work.

2   Related Work

2.1   Binary Decision Diagrams

In its most general form, a Binary Decision Diagram is a directed acyclic labelled graph representing a function $f(x_0, \ldots, x_{n-1})$ on some domain D, where x_i are boolean variables. A sink vertex t is associated with a value $val(t) \in D$, while an internal node u is labeled by a boolean variable $var(u)$ and has exactly two neighbors, a 0-neighbor and a 1-neighbor, denoted by $next(u, 0)$ and $next(u, 1)$ respectively. There is a single source vertex s. To each assignment of values to x_i, corresponds a unique path through the graph, starting from s, and terminating to a sink t, yielding the associated value $val(t)$.

Bryant [3] developed efficient algorithms for the case $D = \{0, 1\}$ (i.e., BDDs of boolean functions), by introducing two conditions on the structure of the BDD, ordering and reduction. Ordering states that the variable indices along each path are strictly increasing, while reduction states that (a) the neighbors of each node are distinct and (b) there are no equivalent nodes (with equal labelling or associated value).

Of close relevance to this work are MTBDDs, introduced by Fujita et al. in [4]. An MTBDD is a reduced, ordered BDD where D is a numeric set, typically $\mathbb{R}$ or $\mathbb{C}$. In a series of papers, Viamontes et al. [12,10,11] explore the potential of QuIDDs, a slight adaptation of MTBDDs, for quantum simulation. QuIDDs of n boolean variables represent state vectors of n qubits, and QuIDDs of $2n$ boolean variables represent n-qubit quantum operators. Their experiments demonstrate that QuIDDs offer significant compression of quantum states and allow for efficient application of quantum operators, compared to various other techniques which represent state vectors more-or-less explicitly. Their experiments are mainly concerned with simulations of simple cases of Grover's algorithm. Koufogiannakis [6] applies their techniques to Shor's algorithm and also observes very good compression. Recently, other MTBDD variants have been introduced to facilitate synthesis and simulation of quantum circuits [1,7].

2.2   Quantum Simulation

Quantum circuit simulation is very useful in physical sciences, both in the context of quantum computation and because the Hamiltonians of many dynamic physical systems can be expressed as quantum circuits. A large number of simulation-related works appear in the literature, mostly by the physics community. In the majority of cases, these works use a more-or-less explicit state vector representation and are thus limited by exponential space requirements. For example, the Fraunhofer Quantum Computing Portal (`http://www.qc.fraunhofer.de/`) allows users to submit circuits of up to 31 qubits, which are subsequently executed on a 32-node cluster. Also, the simulator of [9] affords a limit of 30 qubits, and runs on a Sun Enterprise 4500. These techniques are inferior to MTBDD-based simulations reported previously, and in this work.

3   Symbolic Representation of Quantum Operators

In this section we introduce some definitions that will allow us to represent quantum operators by recursive matrix expressions. These expressions are subsequently used to derive and prove the correctness of our MTBDD algorithms.

3.1   Powermatrices and Powervectors

A powermatrix A (or PM for short) is a complex square matrix of dimensions $2^k \times 2^k$, where $k \geq 0$ is the *order* of A and is denoted by $\mathrm{ord}(A)$. PMs of order 0 are *scalars*. Two (or more) PMs of the same order are called *similar*. By I_k we denote the unit PM of order k.

Now we define operator $\square$, as

$$A \,\square\, B = \begin{bmatrix} A & \mathbf{0} \\ \mathbf{0} & B \end{bmatrix}$$

where $\mathbf{0}$ is the zero PM similar to A, B. Although $\square$ seems limited in that it is not possible to construct a PM from scalars, unless it is diagonal, it is actually a handy notation for quantum operator matrices, as will be seen subsequently.

A powervector a (or PV for short) of order k is a vector of dimension 2^k, where $k \geq 0$ is the *order* of PV a, denoted by $\mathrm{ord}(a)$. As for PMs, PVs of order 0 are *scalar* and PVs of equal order are *similar*.

For similar PVs a and b, $a \,\square\, b$ is the concatenation of a and b, a PV of order $\mathrm{ord}(a) + 1$.

Relationship to MTBDDs. In the literature, MTBDDs are usually treated as functions of boolean variables. Unfortunately, the functional notation is quite cumbersome in expressing linear algebraic operators, and equations (esp. recursive ones) involve unnecessarily long and error-prone index manipulations. This issue is addressed eloquently in [8], from which the $\square$ operator was inspired.

By contrast, $\square$ allows us to manipulate MTBDDs algebraically, avoiding indexing notation almost completely, resulting in much cleaner formulae. Any function $f(x_0, x_1, \ldots, x_{n-1}) : \{0,1\}^n \rightarrow D$, can be writen as a concatenation of its *cofactors* in x_0, $f = f_0 \square f_1$, where $f_c(x_1, \ldots, x_n) = f(c, x_1, \ldots, x_{n-1})$. Repeating this cofactor decomposition until we reach scalars, we obtain a $\square$-based expression for f, whose expression tree is isomorphic to an ordered (but unreduced) BDD.

Algebraic properties. The following properties of $\square$ are trivial. In these equations, uppercase letters denote PMs, lowercase latin letters denote PVs and greek letters denote scalars.

$$\lambda(A \square B) = (\lambda A) \square (\lambda B) \qquad (A_0 \square A_1) \otimes U = (A_0 \otimes U) \square (A_1 \otimes U)$$
$$(A \square B)^t = A^t \square B^t \qquad (A \square B)(C \square D) = (AC) \square (BD)$$
$$\lambda(a \square b) = (\lambda a) \square (\lambda b) \qquad (a_0 \square a_1) \otimes u = (a_0 \otimes u) \square (a_1 \otimes u)$$
$$(a \square b) + (c \square d) = (a + c) \square (b + d) \qquad (A \square B) + (C \square D) = (A + C) \square (B + D)$$

The most useful property for our purposes is *trading* with matrix-vector product:

$$(A \square B)(a \square b) = (Aa) \square (Bb) \tag{1}$$

3.2   Algebraic Construction of Quantum Operators

We now turn our attention to quantum operators. Every quantum operator (unitary or measurement) on n qubits can be represented as a PM of order n. In this section, we show that our $\square$ operator allows us to express controlled unitary operations elegantly.

Let U be an n-qubit unitary operator. A simple construction is to extend U to the $(n + 1)$-qubit operator $I \otimes U$, by adding a qubit above U on which $I \otimes U$ operates trivially. The linear algebra expression for the construction of the *controlled-U* operator (see Fig. 1) is not as elegant; usually, controlled operators are described using the "truth table" notation, i.e. the effect of the operator on the computational basis vectors.

The linear algebra and truth table notations of Fig. 1 are not as useful in revealing the structure of the operator matrix. By contrast, controlled operators have extremely simple $\square$-based expressions. If U, V are two n-qubit operators, then $U \square V$ is the $(n + 1)$-qubit operator which means: "if the top qubit is zero, apply operator U to the bottom n qubits, else apply V".

3.3   Controlling from Below

Viamontes [13] observed that, when a unitary operator can be constructed by a $\square$-expression from small (say, order 1) operands, then the recursive application

	extended U	1-controlled U	0-controlled U
circuit	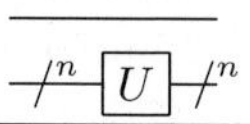	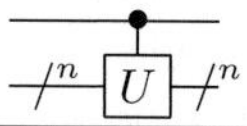	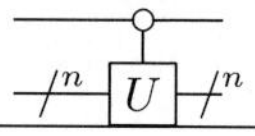
linear algebra	$I \otimes U$	$\lvert 0 \rangle \langle 0 \rvert \otimes I + \lvert 1 \rangle \langle 1 \rvert \otimes U$	$\lvert 1 \rangle \langle 1 \rvert \otimes I + \lvert 0 \rangle \langle 0 \rvert \otimes U$
truth table	$\lvert x \rangle \lvert y \rangle \to \lvert x \rangle U \lvert y \rangle$	$\lvert x \rangle \lvert y \rangle \to \lvert x \rangle U^{x} \lvert y \rangle$	$\lvert x \rangle \lvert y \rangle \to \lvert x \rangle U^{\bar{x}} \lvert y \rangle$
powermatrices	$U \,\Box\, U$	$I_{\mathrm{ord}(U)} \,\Box\, U$	$U \,\Box\, I_{\mathrm{ord}(U)}$

Fig. 1. Three constructions based on U and corresponding representations

of trading (Eq. 1) is much more efficient than representing the operator by an MTBDD.

Unfortunately, when the control qubit lies below the operator, the matrix of a controlled operator cannot be constructed from $\Box$ in this manner. For example, when $U = \begin{bmatrix} u_0 & u_1 \\ u_2 & u_3 \end{bmatrix}$, the matrix of the controlled-U operator with the control qubit below is $\begin{bmatrix} 1 & 0 & 0 & 0 \\ 0 & u_0 & 0 & u_1 \\ 0 & 0 & 1 & 0 \\ 0 & u_2 & 0 & u_3 \end{bmatrix}$. A possible solution proposed in [13] is the following: before an operator controlled from below is to be applied on a state vector, the vector is permuted appropriately to reflect a reordering of the qubits, so that the operator over the reordered qubits is now controlled only from above. This approach could substantially increase the cost of applying an operator, both because of the additional processing, and—more importantly—because by reordering the qubits, the resulting MTBDD of the state vector could potentially increase significantly in size. Therefore this approach is unappealing.

4   Algorithms for Quantum Simulation

4.1   Boolean Projectors

Quantum circuit simulation must handle efficiently both unitary and measurement operators. There is an intimate relationship between measurement operators and controlled unitary operators. This section treats this issue, and introduces a general class of unitary and measurement operations.

We overview some elementary facts regarding projectors in quantum mechanics. Let $\mathcal{M}$ be a set of *measurement outcomes*. In quantum physics, $\mathcal{M}$ is usually the set of eignevalues of some Hermitian operator (called an *observable*), but for our purposes it can be an arbitrary finite set. A projective measurement on $\mathcal{M}$ is defined by a family of orthogonal projectors $\mathbf{P} = \{P_m\}$, indexed by $\mathcal{M}$. Projectors are Hermitian operators (i.e., $P_m = P_m^{\dagger}$) with the following properties:

$$P_m P_{m'} = \delta_{m,m'} P_m \qquad \text{(orthogonality)} \qquad (2)$$

$$\sum_{m \in \mathcal{M}} P_m = I \qquad \text{(completeness)} \qquad (3)$$

The main reference to projectors in the quantum mechanics literature is as measurement operations. A measurement of $\mathcal{M}$ on quantum state $|\psi\rangle$ will return $m \in \mathcal{M}$ with probability $\langle\psi|P_m|\psi\rangle$, and will set the new state to $\dfrac{P_m|\psi\rangle}{\sqrt{\langle\psi|P_m|\psi\rangle}}$.

However, projectors can also be seen as quantum controls. Consider a family $\mathbf{U} = \{U_m\}$ of unitary operators, also indexed by $\mathcal{M}$, and a quantum state $|\psi\rangle\,|\phi\rangle$ of $\text{ord}(P_m) + \text{ord}(U_m)$ qubits. Then, operator

$$\mathbf{U_P} = \sum_{m \in \mathcal{M}} P_m \otimes U_m$$

is unitary, and its meaning is roughly: "if (for some m), $P_m|\psi\rangle = |\psi\rangle$ then apply U_m to $|\phi\rangle$". This operator is analogous to a `switch` statement in conventional programming languages. For example, the standard controlled-U gate can be derived by taking $\mathcal{M} = \{0, 1\}$, $P_0 = |0\rangle\langle0|$, $P_1 = |1\rangle\langle1|$, $U_0 = I$ and $U_1 = U$.

We now turn our attention to the class of *boolean projectors*, which are simply all projectors with diagonal matrix (consisting entirely of zeros and ones, since $P^2 = P$). Their significance derives from being isomorphic to boolean functions. Boolean projectors can be constructed from scalars (0 and 1) and $\square$. The diagonal of the matrix of boolean projector F of order m is the truth table of a corresponding boolean function of m variables, which we denote also by F. The decomposition of PM $F = F_0 \square F_1$ corresponds to the *Shannon expansion* of boolean function F, with F_0, F_1 corresponding F's cofactors.

In quantum algorithms one often encounters the so-called *quantum if-then* operator $\text{QIT}(F, U)$. $\text{QIT}(F, U)$ is defined by a boolean function $F(x_1, \ldots, x_n)$ and a unitary 1-qubit gate U, with the following mapping of basis states:

$$|x_1 \ldots x_n\rangle\,|y\rangle \to |x_1 \ldots x_n\rangle\, U^{F(x_1, \ldots, x_n)}\,|y\rangle$$

The QIT operator is a special case of the switch operator, where the measurable is the boolean set $\mathcal{M} = \{0, 1\}$, and $P_0 = I - F$, $P_1 = F$. Thus,

$$\text{QIT}(F, U) = F \otimes U + (I_{\text{ord}(F)} - F) \otimes I_{\text{ord}(U)}$$

In turn, QIT operators generalize controlled gates: a unitary operator constructed by a 1-qubit gate U, controlled by some other qubits, is simply a QIT, where the boolean projector corresponds to a simple conjunction. For example, the operators of Fig. 2 are $\text{QIT}(x_0 \wedge x_2, U)$ and $\text{QIT}(x_0 \wedge \overline{x_1}, H)$.

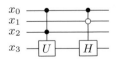

Fig. 2. Two controlled gates

4.2 Applying QIT Operators

A popular set of unitary operators for quantum algorithms consists of all 1-qubit gates, controlled by zero or more control qubits. This class of quantum circuit operators is the analog of unrestricted fan-in gates in logic circuits. Here, we consider a broader set of operators: 1-qubit gates, controlled by boolean projectors.

Consider a 1-qubit unitary gate U and boolean projector F of order m. Expression $[F : k : U]$, where $0 \leq k \leq m$, denotes a QIT operator on $m + 1$ qubits, with U applied to qubit k from the top (starting with 0), controlled by F on the remaining m qubits (ordered from top to bottom). This operator has the following truth table

$$|x_0 x_1 \ldots x_m\rangle \rightarrow |x_0 \ldots x_{k-1}\rangle \left(U^{F(x_0 \ldots x_{k-1}, x_{k+1}, \ldots, x_m)} |x_k\rangle \right) |x_{k+1} \ldots x_m\rangle \quad (4)$$

Recursive application of $[F : k : U]$ on quantum state ψ can done straightforwardly, when $k > 0$. Let $F = F_0 \,\square\, F_1$ and $\psi = \psi_0 \,\square\, \psi_1$. From Eq. 4, it is easy to see that

$$[F : k : U]\psi = \left([F_0 : k - 1 : U]\psi_0 \right) \square \left([F_1 : k - 1 : U]\psi_1 \right). \quad (5)$$

When $k = m = 0$, F is scalar (either 0 or 1) and $[F : 0 : U]\psi = U^F \psi$. The remaining case is $k = 0 < m$, where U is applied to the top qubit, controlled by F from below.

Applying $[F : 0 : U]$ on ψ recursively is treated as follows: first, permute the state vector ψ by swapping the top two qubits, then apply $[F : 1 : U]$ recursively, and finally swap the top two qubits again.

Swapping of the two top qubits of a state PV ψ can be performed quite easily in algebraic/MTBDD terms. Given PV $\psi = (\psi_0 \,\square\, \psi_1) \,\square\, (\psi_2 \,\square\, \psi_3)$ (of order at least 2), the reordered PV $S(\psi)$ is easily seen to be

$$S((\psi_0 \,\square\, \psi_1) \,\square\, (\psi_2 \,\square\, \psi_3)) = (\psi_0 \,\square\, \psi_2) \,\square\, (\psi_1 \,\square\, \psi_3).$$

Thus,

$$[F : 0 : U]\psi = S\big([F : 1 : U] S(\psi) \big) \quad (6)$$

Putting everything together, we have

$$[F : k : U]\psi = \begin{cases} U^F \psi & \text{if } \mathrm{ord}(F) = 0 \\ ([F_0 : k - 1 : U] \,\square\, [F_1 : k - 1 : U])\psi & \text{if } k > 0 \text{ and } F = F_0 \,\square\, F_1 \\ S\big(([F_0 : 0 : U] \,\square\, [F_1 : 0 : U]) S(\psi) \big) & \text{if } k = 0 \text{ and } F = F_0 \,\square\, F_1 \end{cases} \quad (7)$$

By careful implementation, function S in the above formula can be inlined, incurring zero overhead.

4.3 Implementation Issues for MTBDD Algorithms

We implemented an MTBDD library incorporating the above ideas. In our package, MTBDDs represent complex PVs. We have not implemented PMs as MTBDDs, although we could have done so along the lines of [10]. Besides all the common MTBDD algorithms that are described in [4], we also support functions to perform measurement with boolean projectors and application of QIT operators. The measurement algorithms are straightforward, since boolean projectors are diagonal, and thus can be multiplied with state vectors by pointwise multiplication.

We show an efficient implementation of QIT application, as described by Eq. 7. The most interesting feature of our implementation is the inlining of swap function S, so that it incurs no overhead.

Our implementation uses the standard MTBDD API functions:

TNode(z): Return a unique terminal node u with val$(u) = z$.

Node(a,b,i): If $a = b$ return a, else return a unique non-terminal node u with var$(u) = i$, next$(u, 0) = a$ and next$(u, 1) = b$.

Decompose(a,i): If $i < $ var(a), return node pair (a, a), else return node pair $($next$(a, 0),$ next$(a, 1))$.

Lookup(k), Cache(k,v): Implement a hash-based cache mapping keys k to values v.

The code for QIT application is shown in Alg. 1, as Python-like pseudocode. The implementation is split among two recursive functions. The first function, **Apply**(F, ψ) is the main function called. It only accepts two MTBDDs as arguments, the boolean projector F and the state vector ψ; k and $U = \begin{bmatrix} u_0 & u_1 \\ u_2 & u_3 \end{bmatrix}$ of QIT operator $[F : k : U]$ are passed as global variables. Function **Apply** is quite straightforward, and it calls itself recursively, until processing reaches nodes which belong to qubits below k, in which case processing passes to **ApplySwap**. The latter is distinguished in that it accepts a pair of state vectors and also returns a pair of state vectors. The idea is to avoid extra calls to function **Node** (as would be made by an explicit implementation of swap function S), since it is somewhat expensive (it requires memory allocation and hash table lookups). The actual inlining of function S happens in the **else** clause.

5   Empirical Study

In this section we report on the experimental evaluation of our algorithms. We compared our implementation, called PVLIB, against two different MTBDD-based quantum simulators. For each comparison we simulated exactly the same quantum circuit. In both cases, our algorithm outperformed the other implementation by at least an order of magnitude, and typically by around two orders of magnitude. All experiments were conducted on a machine with two twin core SMP Intel Xeon processors at 1.6 GHz, with 8 Gb of RAM (all experiments were run on a single CPU).

In the first experiment, we compared against the QuIDDPro software, created by Viamontes et al. We were provided with the latest version. For simulation, we created several stabilizer circuits, with number of qubits per circuit varying from 5 to 100 qubits. Each stabilizer circuit consisted of 1000 randomly generated quantum gates. The cirquits were generated using a utility provided by

---

Algorithm 1. MTBDD algorithm for application of a QIT operator.

Apply(F,ψ) {
    if $F = 0$ **or** $\psi = 0$: **return** ψ
    if Lookup(F,ψ) $\neq$ **nil**: **return Lookup**(F,ψ)
    $v := \min(\text{var}(F), \text{var}(\psi))$
    $\psi_0, \psi_1 := $ **Decompose**(ψ, v)
    if $k \leq v$:
        $\psi_a, \psi_b := $ **ApplySwap**(F, ψ_0, ψ_1)
        $\psi' := $ **Node**(ψ_a, ψ_b, v)
    else:
        $F_0, F_1 := $ **Decompose**(F, v)
        $\psi' := $ **Node**(**Apply**(F_0, ψ_0), **Apply**(F_1, ψ_1), v)
    Cache((F, ψ), ψ')
    return ψ'
}

ApplySwap(F, ψ_0, ψ_1) {
    if $F = 0$: **return** (ψ_0, ψ_1)
    if Lookup(F, ψ_0, ψ_1) $\neq$ **nil**: **return Lookup**(F, ψ_0, ψ_1)
    $v := \min(\text{var}(F), \text{var}(\psi_0), \text{var}(\psi_1))$
    if $v = \infty$:   # *terminals reached*
        $\psi_a, \psi_b := $ (**TNode**($u_0 \text{ val}(\psi_0) + u_1 \text{ val}(\psi_1)$), **TNode**($u_2 \text{ val}(\psi_0) + u_3 \text{ val}(\psi_1)$))
    else:
        $F_0, F_1 := $ **Decompose**(F, v)
        $y_0, y_1 := $ **Decompose**(ψ_0, v)
        $y_2, y_3 := $ **Decompose**(ψ_1, v)
        $q_0, q_1 := $ **ApplySwap**(F_0, y_0, y_2)
        $q_2, q_3 := $ **ApplySwap**(F_0, y_1, y_3)
        $\psi_a, \psi_b := $ (**Node**(q_0, q_2, v), **Node**(q_1, q_3, v))
    Cache((F, ψ_0, ψ_1), (ψ_a, ψ_b))
    return (ψ_a, ψ_b)
}

Aaronson as part of the CHP simulator. Results of this experiment are shown in Fig. 3(a). As can be seen, the runtimes of our implementation and QuID-DPro are proportional, with our implementation being about 100 times faster. The proportional behaviour is not unexpected, since both implementations use identical state representations, and operation times are proportional to the size of the state representation.

For the second experiment, we implemented Shor's quantum factoring algorithm, by simulating the quantum circuits proposed by [2]. We compared against ShorADD, a hand-tuned MTBDD-based simulation of Shor's algorithm developed by Koufogiannakis [6]. ShorADD uses the algorithms of QuIDD, but simulates a hand-tuned version of the quantum circuit of [2], and includes also some application specific optimizations. Fig. 3(b) depicts the runtimes of factoring several numbers, simulating circuits of up to 53 qubits. Note that this simulation is

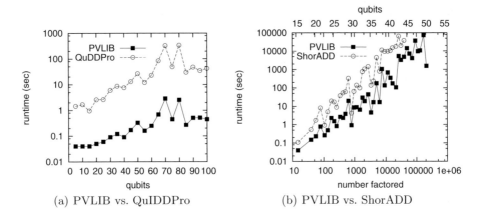

Fig. 3. Runtimes of quantum simulations for PVLIB and ShorADD for factoring various numbers using Shor's algorithm

expensive computationally, as the number of gates in the circuit grows roughly with n^3, where n is the number of qubits in the circuit. For the largest circuits we simulated, each run consisted of approximately 350,000 quantum gates. Again, our implementation outperformed the MTBDD-based implementation, typically by 2 orders of magnitude.

5.1 Discussion

The speedup obtained by our algorithm is, at first glance surprising. After all, it is not obvious that our technique should provide runtime advantages over previous techniques, since it uses the same state vector representation. However, our algorithms are actually provably more efficient than previous MTBDD-based algorithms (e.g., those used by the QuIDD software). In [10], it is shown that if a quantum operator is represented as an MTBDD of m nodes, and is applied on a state vector ψ of size $|\psi|$, then the runtime is bounded by $O(m^2|\psi|^2)$. The runtime of our Alg. 1 is at worst $O(|F| \cdot |\psi|^2)$. To see this, note that the runtime of our algorithm is proportional to the number of calls to procedure **Node**. By virtue of the caching performed by **Lookup** and **Cache**, there are at most $O(|F| \cdot |\psi|)$ such calls from inside **Apply** and $O(|F| \cdot |\psi|^2)$ calls from inside **ApplySwap**.

The size of the MTBDD for a controlled-U operator on n qubits is $\Theta(n)$. On the other hand, the size of the BDD for the projector matrix F is much smaller: it is equal to the number of control qubits. For example, the projector for the Toffoli gate is represented by a BDD of 2 (internal) nodes, regardless of the number of qubits. Thus, the QuIDD algorithms will apply a Toffoli gate in time $\Omega(n^2|\psi|^2)$ in the worst case, whereas our algorithm will only need time $O(|\psi|^2)$.

In practice, the $|\psi|^2$ factor is pessimistic, although there exist contrived state vectors ψ where even a simple CNOT gate application will cause a quadratic increase in the size of the resulting state vector (and thus the runtime). Yet, in our experiments with Shor's algorithm, we measured the runtime of **Apply**; for almost *every operator*, the runtime was $\lambda|\psi|$ with λ between 50 and 500 nanoseconds. In fact, the variance of λ seems to depend more on CPU cache misses, and less on the actual operator applied.

6   Conclusions

We have presented novel algorithms for quantum simulation, using MTBDD-based state vector representations. Our algorithms represent quantum operators symbolically rather than as compressed matrices and are able to handle a broad class of operators, namely QIT unitary operators and boolean projective measurements. By adopting a symbolic representation, we were able to improve performance by ≈ 2 orders of magnitude compared to the previously fastest simulation package. To develop and prove the correctness of our algorithms, we introduced a handy matrix operator, inspired by the powerlist data structure [8], which allowed us to present MTBDD-based algorithms in a concise manner.

Our work paves the way for a number of improvements in quantum simulation. By removing the need to represent quantum operators as matrices, we can concentrate future research on more efficient representations of the state vector. A number of BDD variants from the areas of model checking and circuit synthesis seem worth considering (e.g., zero-suppressed BDDs [5]). We are also interested in investigating the possibilities for hardware-accelerated, MTBDD-based quantum simulation. So far, BDD-based techniques have proved very hard to acelerate in hardware (or even on a parallel computer), because two complex graphs are involved in each operation. In our case, only one complex graph (the state vector MTBDD) is involved in each operation, whereas the other graph (the projector F) may be quite small and simple to "hard-code" on silicon, e.g., on an FPGA.

Acknowledgements

We thank George Viamontes for graciously providing the QuIDDPro simulator. Also, our thanks to Chris Koyfogiannakis for providing ShorADD, and for stimulating discussions.

References

1. Abdollahi, A., Pedram, M.: Analysis and synthesis of quantum circuits by using quantum decision diagrams. In: DATE 2006: Proc. of the Conf. on Design, Automation and Test in Europe, 3001 Leuven, Belgium, pp. 317–322. European Design and Automation Association (2006)
2. Beckman, D., Chari, A.N., Devabhaktuni, S., Preskill, J.: Efficient networks for quantum factoring. Phys. Rev. A 54(2), 1034–1063 (1996)

3. Bryant, R.E.: Graph-based algorithms for boolean function manipulation. IEEE Trans. Comput. 35(8), 677–691 (1986)
4. Fujita, M., McGeer, P.C., Yang, J.C.-Y.: Multi-terminal binary decision diagrams: An efficient data structure for matrix representation. Form. Methods Syst. Des. 10(2-3), 149–169 (1997)
5. Minato, S.i.: Zero-suppressed BDDs for set manipulation in combinatorial problems. In: DAC 1993: Proceedings of the 30th international conference on Design automation, pp. 272–277. ACM Press, New York (1993)
6. Koufogiannakis, C.: Techniques for simulating quantum computers. Master's thesis, Technical U. of Crete (2004)
7. Miller, D.M., Thornton, M.A., Goodman, D.: Qmdd: A decision diagram structure for reversible and quantum circuits. In: IEEE Int'l Symp. on Multiple-Valued Logic (ISMVL), pp. 30–30 (2006)
8. Misra, J.: Powerlist: a structure for parallel recursion. ACM Trans. Program. Lang. Syst. 16(6), 1737–1767 (1994)
9. Niwa, J., Matsumoto, K., Imai, H.: General-purpose parallel simulator for quantum computing. Phys. Rev. A 66(6), 062317 (2002)
10. Viamontes, G., Markov, I., Hayes, J.: Improving gate-level simulation of quantum circuits. Quantum Information Processing 2(5), 347–380 (2003)
11. Viamontes, G.F., Markov, I.L., Hayes, J.P.: Graph-based simulation of quantum computation in the density matrix representation. Quantum Information Processing 5(2), 113–130 (2005)
12. Viamontes, G.F.: Gate-level simulation of quantum circuits. In: Proc. of the 6th Intl. Conference on Quantum Communication, Measurement, and Computing, pp. 311–314 (2002)
13. Viamontes, G.F.: Efficient Quantum Circuit Simulation. PhD thesis, University of Michigan (2007)

Mobile Route Planning*

Peter Sanders, Dominik Schultes, and Christian Vetter

Universität Karlsruhe (TH), 76128 Karlsruhe, Germany
{sanders,schultes}@ira.uka.de, veaac@gmx.de

Abstract. We provide an implementation of an exact route planning
algorithm on a mobile device that answers shortest-path queries in a road
network of a whole continent instantaneously, i.e., with a delay of about
100 ms which is virtually not observable for a human user. Our main
algorithmic contribution of is a highly compressed blocked representation
of the underlying hierarchical graph and a new fast yet compact route
reconstruction data structure. Our representation exploits the locality
properties of the graph using a very simple algorithm that does not use
any a priori information.

1 Introduction

In recent years, there has been a lot of work on route planning algorithms, particularly for road networks, aiming for fast query times and accurate results.
The various real-world applications of such algorithms can be classified according to their respective platform into *server* applications (e.g., providing driving
directions via the internet, optimising logistic processes) and *mobile* applications
(in particular car navigation systems). On the one hand, many approaches have
been evaluated successfully with respect to the server scenario – the fastest variant of transit-node routing [1] computes shortest-path distances in the Western
European road network in less than two microseconds on average. On the other
hand, there have been only few results on efficient implementations of route
planning techniques on mobile devices like a PDA. In this paper, we want to
close this gap.

The main challenge is the memory hierarchy of typical PDAs, which consists
of a limited amount of fast main memory and a larger amount of comparatively
slow flash memory, which has similar properties as a hard disk regarding read
access. In order to obtain an efficient implementation, we have to arrange the
data into blocks, respecting the locality of the data. Then, reading at a single
blow a whole block that contains a high percentage of relevant data is much more
efficient than reading single data items at random. Furthermore, compression
techniques can be used to increase the amount of data that fits into a single
block and, consequently, decrease the number of required block accesses.

---

* Partially supported by DFG grant SA 933/5-1.

D. Halperin and K. Mehlhorn (Eds.): ESA 2008, LNCS 5193, pp. 732–743, 2008.

Our Contributions. We present an efficient and practically useful implementation of a fast and exact route planning algorithm for road networks on a *mobile device*. For this purpose, we select contraction hierarchies [2] as our method of choice – we review the most relevant concepts in Section 2. In Section 3, we design an external-memory graph representation that takes advantage of the locality inherent in the data to compress the graph and to reduce the number of required I/O operations – which are the bottleneck of our application. The graph is divided into several blocks, each containing a subset of the nodes and the corresponding edges. We put particular efforts in exploiting the fact that the edges in one block only lead to nodes in a small subset of all blocks; many edges even lead to nodes in the same block.

By this means, our 'mobile' implementation achieves a considerable improvement compared to the original implementation of contraction hierarchies (CH) [2], which, in turn, is already considerably better than the bidirectional variant of Dijkstra's algorithm, as summarised in the following table, which refers to experiments on an European road network with about 18 million nodes.[1]

	only length		complete path	
	time [ms]	space [MB]	time [ms]	space [MB]
bidir. Dijkstra	298 209	408	298 209	408
CH [2]	394.9	350	3 025.6	560
CH mobile	59.4	140	96.6	275

All details on our experimental setting can be found in Section 4. We conclude our paper in Section 5, where we also discuss related work, draw further comparisons, and outline possible future work.

2   Contraction Hierarchies

We decided to use contraction hierarchies [2] for our mobile implementation due to their simplicity, low memory requirements, and its hierarchical properties that can be exploited to improve the locality of the accessed data. We now review the most important concepts of contraction hierarchies.

Preprocessing. In a first step, the nodes of a given graph $G = (V, E)$ (with $n := |V|$) are ordered by 'importance' using heuristics that try to obtain hierarchies with few edges and important nodes uniformly distributed over the network. We obtain a bijection $\ell : V \rightarrow \{1, 2, 3, \ldots, n\}$, where n represents the highest importance.

In a second step, we first set $G' = (V', E') := G$ and then, while $V' \neq \emptyset$, we *contract* the node v with the lowest importance in V', i.e., we remove v from G

---

[1] Running times refer to the query type 'cold' (Section 4), where the cache is cleared after each random query. Since the priority queue of Dijkstra's algorithm would not fit in the main memory, we ran Dijkstra only on the Dutch subnetwork of Europe and linearly extrapolated the obtained query times.

in such a way that the shortest paths distances between the remaining nodes are preserved. To this end, whenever a shortest path contains a subpath of the form $\langle u, v, u' \rangle$, we add a so-called *shortcut* edge (u, u') whose weight corresponds to the length of the path $\langle u, v, u' \rangle$.

In a third step, we build the so-called *search graph* $G^* = (V, E^*)$. We define $\hat{E}$ to contain all edges from E and all shortcut edges that have been added at some point during the second step. Then, $E_\uparrow := \{(u, v) \in \hat{E} \mid \ell(u) < \ell(v)\}$, $E_\downarrow := \{(u, v) \in \hat{E} \mid \ell(u) > \ell(v)\}$, and $\overline{E_\downarrow} := \{(v, u) \mid (u, v) \in E_\downarrow\}$. Finally, $E^* := E_\uparrow \cup \overline{E_\downarrow}$. Furthermore, we introduce a forward and a backward flag such that for any edge $e \in E^*$, $f(e) = \text{true}$ iff $e \in E_\uparrow$ and $b(e) = \text{true}$ iff $e \in \overline{E_\downarrow}$. Note that G^* is a directed acyclic graph.

Query. We perform two normal Dijkstra searches in G^*, one from the source using only edges where the forward flag is set and one from the target using only edges where the backward flag is set. Forward and backward search are interleaved, we keep track of a tentative shortest-path length and abort the forward/backward search process when all keys in the respective priority queue are greater than the tentative shortest-path length. To further reduce the search space size, we employ the *stall-on-demand* technique [3,4,2] which stops the search at nodes that can be proven to be outside the shortest path tree.

In order to determine not only the shortest-path *length*, but also a full description, the shortcut edges have to be unpacked to obtain the represented subpaths in the original graph. A simple recursive unpacking routine can be used provided that we have stored the middle node v of each shortcut (u, u') that represents the path $\langle u, v, u' \rangle$.

3   External-Memory Graph Representation

Locality. Reading data from external memory is the bottleneck of our application. To get a good performance, we want to arrange the data into blocks and access them blockwise. Obviously, the arrangement should be done in such a way that accessing a single data item from one block typically implies that a lot of data items in the same block have to be accessed in the near future. In other words, we have to exploit locality properties of the data.

The node order of the real-world road networks that we have obtained already respects *spatial* locality, i.e., the nodes are ordered somehow by spatial proximity. However, we can do better. We consider the reverse search graph $\overline{G^*} = (V, \overline{E^*})$, where $\overline{E^*} := \{(v, u) \mid (u, v) \in E^*\}$, which is an acyclic graph (as G^*), and compute a topological order defined by the finishing times of a depth-first search (DFS). We demonstrate in the full paper that this order already greatly improves the locality and is almost as good as a more sophisticated order that can be obtained using a much more expensive technique. One reason for the success of this method is presumably the small depth of the search graph.

We can further stress the *hierarchical* locality: nodes of a similarly high importance should be close to each other since – due to the nature of the query algorithm – they are likely to be visited together. For a fixed *next-layer fraction* f, we divide the nodes into two groups: the first group contains the $(1 - f) \cdot |V|$ nodes of smaller importance, the second group the $f \cdot |V|$ nodes of higher importance. Within each group, we keep the topological order obtained by our modified DFS. We recurse in the second group until all nodes fit into a single block. This *hierarchical reordering* step is a slightly generalised version of a technique used in [5]. It is important to note that the resulting order is still a topological order.

Note that a good node order has not only the obvious advantage that a loaded block contains a lot of relevant data, but also can be exploited to compress the data effectively. In particular, we exploit that many target nodes belong to the same block.

Main Data Structure. The starting point for our compact graph data structure is an *adjacency array* representation: All edges (u, v) are kept in a single array, grouped by the source node u. Each edge stores only the target v and its weight. In addition, there is a node array that stores for each node u the index of the first edge (u, v) in the edge array. The end of the edge group of node u is implicitly given by the start of the edge group of u's successor in the node array. We want to divide this graph data structure into blocks. In order to decrease the number of required block accesses, we decided not to store node and edge data separately, but to put node and the associated edge data in a common block.

When encoding the target v of an edge (u, v), we want to exploit the existing locality, i.e., in many cases the difference of the IDs of u and v is quite small and, in particular, u and v often belong to the same block. Therefore, we distinguish between *internal* and *external* edges: internal edges lead to a node within the same block, external edges lead to a node in a different block. We use a flag to mark external edges. In case of an internal edge, it is sufficient to just store the node index within the same block, which requires only a few bits. In case of an external edge, we need the block ID of the target and the node index within the designated block. We introduce an additional indirection to reduce the number of bits needed to encode the ID of the adjacent block: It can be expected that the number of blocks adjacent to a given block B is rather small, i.e., there are only a few different blocks that contain all the nodes that are adjacent to nodes in B. Thus, it pays to explicitly store the IDs of all adjacent blocks in an array in B. Then, an external edge need not store the full block ID, but it is sufficient to just store the comparatively small block index within the adjacent-blocks array.

Building the Graph Representation. We pursue the following goals: the graph data structure should occupy as little memory as possible, and accessing the data should be fast. We make the following design choices: each block has the same constant size and contains a subset of consecutively numbered nodes together with all their incident edges; all three 'logical' arrays (adjacent blocks, nodes, edges) are stored in a single byte array one after the other, the starting index of each logical array is stored in the header of the block; within each block, we use the minimal number of bits to store the respective attributes. For example, if a block has 42 different adjacent blocks, then each external edge (u, v) in this block uses 6 bits to address the adjacent block that contains v.

In general, building the blocks is not trivial due to a cyclic dependency: On the one hand, the distribution of the nodes into blocks depends on the required memory for each edge – in particular, an internal edge typically occupies less memory than an external edge. In other words, a block can accommodate more internal than external edges. On the other hand, the distinction whether an edge is internal or external depends on the distribution of the nodes: if the target node of an edge fits into the same block, we have an internal edge; otherwise, we have an external edge.

Fortunately, we can exploit the fact that we sorted the nodes topologically. When we process the nodes from the most important one to the least important one, all edges (u, v) point to nodes v that have already been processed. This implies that we already know whether (u, v) is an internal or external edge and, in case of an external edge, we also know the number of nodes in the corresponding block B so that we can choose the minimal number of bits required to encode the index of node v within the block B. This way, we can easily calculate the memory requirements of the current edge. If all edges of the current node u fit into the current block, the node and its incident edges are added. Otherwise, a new block is started. Note that when we consider to add another node and its edges, we have to account not only for the memory directly used by these additional objects, but also for a potential memory increase of the other nodes and edges in the same block: for example, whenever the number of edges in the block exceeds the next power of two, all nodes in the block need an additional bit to store the index of the first outgoing edge.

Since most edge weights in our real-world road networks are rather small and only comparatively few edges (e.g., long shortcuts that leave important nodes) are long, we use one bit to distinguish between a long and a short edge; depending on the state of this bit, we use more or less bits to store the weight.

Storing the Graph Representation. The blocks representing the graph are stored in external memory. In main memory, we manage a cache that can hold a subset of the blocks. We employ a simple least-recently used (LRU) strategy. In the external-memory graph data structure, a node u is identified by its block ID $B(u)$ and the node index $i(u)$ within the block. We need a mapping from the node ID u used in the original graph to the tuple $(B(u), i(u))$. Such a mapping is realised in a simple array, stored in external memory.

We want to access the external memory *read-only* in order to improve the overall performance and in order to preserve the flash memory, which can get unusable after too many write operations. Therefore, we clearly separate the read-only graph data structures from some volatile data structures, in particular the forward and the backward priority queue. We use a hash map to manage pointers from reached nodes to the corresponding entries in the priority queues. Since the search spaces of contraction hierarchies are so small (a few hundred nodes out of several million nodes in the graph), it is no problem to keep these data structures in main memory. Note that in [6], a similar distinction between read-only and volatile data structures has been used.

Path Unpacking Data Structures. The above data structures are sufficient to determine the shortest-path *length*. In order to generate actual driving directions, it must also be possible to generate a description of the shortest path. First of all, since we have changed the node order, we need to store for each node its original ID so that we can perform the reverse mapping. Furthermore, we need the functionality to unpack shortcut edges. To support a simple recursive unpacking routine, we store the ID of the middle node of each shortcut (see Section 2). We distinguish between internal and external shortcuts (u, u'), where the middle node v belongs to the same block as u or not. For an internal shortcut, the middle node can be stored as an index within the block, for an external shortcut, we have to specify the block $B(v)$ and the index within $B(v)$.

To accelerate the path unpacking, we refine the approach from [7] to store explicit descriptions of the paths underlying some of the shortcuts. Looking up the edges (v, u) and (v, u') in case of an *external* shortcut (u, u') with middle node v might require an expensive additional block read. Therefore, it is reasonable to completely pre-unpack all external shortcuts and to store the corresponding node sequences in some additional data blocks. Instead of the middle node, we store the starting index within these additional data blocks. A new feature is that we exploit the fact that an external shortcut can contain other external shortcuts. We do not have to store these contained shortcuts explicitly, it is sufficient to just note the correct starting position and a direction flag since contained shortcuts might be filed in the reverse direction. We use a top-down approach. We consider external shortcuts in a descending order of importance. A shortcut is unpacked only if it is not contained in an already unpacked shortcut.

4   Experiments

Experiments have been done on a Nokia N800 Internet Tablet equipped with 128 MB of RAM and a Texas Instruments OMAP 2420 microprocessor, which features an ARM11 processor running at 330 MHz. We use a SanDisk Extreme III SD flash memory card with a capacity of 2 GB; the manufacturer states a sequential reading speed of 20 MB/s. The operating system is the Linux-based Maemo 3.2 in the form of Internet Tablet OS 2007. The program was compiled by the GNU C++ compiler 4.2.1 using optimisation level 3. Preprocessing has been done on one core of a single AMD Opteron Processor 270 clocked at 2.0 GHz with 8 GB main memory and 2×1 MB L2 cache, running SuSE Linux 10.3 (kernel 2.6.22). The program was compiled by the GNU C++ compiler 4.2.1 using optimisation level 3.

Most experiments have been done on a road network of Europe[2], which has been made available for scientific use by the company PTV AG. For each edge, its

---

[2] Austria, Belgium, Denmark, France, Germany, Italy, Luxembourg, the Netherlands, Norway, Portugal, Spain, Sweden, Switzerland, and the UK.

length and one out of 13 road categories (e.g., motorway, national road, regional road, urban street) is provided. In addition, we perform some experiments on a publicly available version of the US road network (without Alaska and Hawaii) that was obtained from the DIMACS Challenge homepage [8] and on a new version[3] of the European road network ("New Europe") that was provided for scientific use by the company ORTEC. In all cases, we use a travel time metric. Our starting point are precomputed contraction hierarchies [2]. Preprocessing takes 31 min, 32 min, and 58 min for Europe, USA, and New Europe, respectively. We distinguish between four different query types:

1. *'cold'*: Perform 1 000 random queries; after each query, clear the cache. This way, we can determine the time that is needed for the first query when the program is started since in this scenario the cache is empty.
2. *'warm'*: Perform 1 000 random queries to warm up the cache; then, perform a different set of 1 000 random queries without clearing the cache; determine the average time of the latter 1 000 queries. This way, we can determine the average query time when the device has been in use for a while.
3. *'recompute'*: Select 100 random target nodes $t_1, \ldots, t_{100}$ and for each target t_i, 101 random source nodes $s_{i,0}, \ldots, s_{i,100}$. For each target t_i and each $j, 1 \leq j \leq 100$, perform one query from $s_{i,0}$ to t_i without measuring the running time and one query from $s_{i,j}$ to t_i performing time measurements, and clear the cache. This way, we can determine the time needed to recompute the shortest path to the same target in case only the source node changes – which can happen if the driver does not follow the driving directions.
4. *'w/o I/O'*: Select 100 random source-target pairs. For each pair, repeat the same query 101 times; ignore the first iteration when measuring the running time. This way, we obtain a benchmark for the actual processing speed of the device when no I/O operations are performed.

For practical scenarios, the first and the third query type are most relevant; The second query time is closest to the situation reported in related work.

Unless otherwise stated, our experiments refer to the case that the path-unpacking data structures exist, but are not used. Note that the query times always include the time needed to map the original source and target IDs to the corresponding block IDs and node indices, while figures on the memory consumption do not include the space needed for the mapping.

In the following we use a block size of 4 KB, that was found using experiments with block sizes from 1 KB to 64 KB. This block size is optimal with respect to both space consumption and query time. We use a cache size of 64 MB. Additional experiments indicate that going to 32 MB has negligible effect on the performance of 'warm'-queries. Even only 256 KB of cache are sufficient to achieve the performance of our 'cold' queries. Finally, we use a value of 1/16 for the next-layer fraction from Sect. 3. This minimizes query time and has only a small detrimental effect on the space consumption for which even smaller values would be better.

---

[3] In addition to the old version, the Czech Republic, Finland, Hungary, Ireland, Poland, and Slovakia.

Table 1. Building the graph representation. We give the number of nodes, the number of edges in the original graph and in the search graph, the number of graph-data blocks (without counting the blocks that contain pre-unpacked paths), the average number of adjacent blocks per block, the numbers of internal edges, internal shortcuts and external shortcuts as percentage of the total number of edges, the time needed to pre-unpack the external shortcuts and to build the external-memory graph representation (provided that the search graph is already given), and the total memory consumption including pre-unpacked paths.

	$|V|$ [$\times 10^6$]	$|E|$ [$\times 10^6$]	$|E^*|$ [$\times 10^6$]	#blocks	#adj. blocks	int. edges	int. shcs.	ext. shcs.	time [s]	space [MB]
Europe	18.0	42.2	36.9	52 107	9.1	70.6%	32.2%	7.7%	123	275
USA	23.9	57.7	49.4	80 099	8.4	69.2%	33.7%	8.0%	186	400
New Europe	33.7	75.1	65.7	103 371	8.3	70.3%	32.7%	7.5%	210	548

Table 1 gives an overview of the external-memory graph representation. Building the blocks is very fast and can be done in about 2–4 minutes. Although the given memory consumption already covers everything that is needed to obtain very fast query times (including path unpacking), we need 30% *less* space than the original graph would occupy in a standard adjacency-array representation in case of Europe. Most of the savings come from using less bits than the naive representation. As already observed in [2] we also save space because contraction hierarchies need to store bidirectional edges only at one of their end points.

The results for the four query types are represented in Tab. 2. On average, a random query has to access 39 blocks in case of the European road network. When the cache has been warmed-up, most blocks (in particular the ones that contain very important nodes) reside in the cache so that on average less than four blocks have to be fetched from external memory. This yields a very good query time of 23 ms. Recomputing the optimal path using the same target, but a different source node can be done in 34 ms. As expected, the bottleneck of our application are the accesses to the external memory: if all blocks had been preloaded, a shortest-path computation would take only about 8 ms instead of the 72 ms that include the I/O operations. For comparison, on a PC (2 GHz Opteron), the same code runs about 13 times faster (0.64 ms) – this is basically the speed difference between the CPUs. The code from [2] is another four times faster (0.16 ms) – this is the overhead due to the compressed data structure.

Path Unpacking. In Tab. 3, we compare five different variants of path (not-)unpacking, using the first query type ('cold') in each case. First (a), we store no path data at all. This makes the query very fast since more nodes fit into a single block. However, with this variant, we can only compute the shortest-path length. For all other variants, we also store the middle nodes of the shortcuts in the data blocks. This slows down the query even if we do not use the additional data (b). After having computed the shortest-path length, getting the very first edge of the path (which is useful to generate the very first driving direction) is almost for free (c). Computing the complete path takes considerably longer if we do not use pre-unpacked path data (d). Pre-unpacked paths (e) somewhat

Table 2. Query performance for four different query types

	settled nodes	cold blocks read	cold time [ms]	warm blocks read	warm time [ms]	recompute blocks read	recompute time [ms]	w/o I/O time [ms]
Europe	280	39.2	72.4	3.6	22.9	7.9	34.1	8.4
USA	223	30.1	56.5	4.4	17.1	6.1	28.0	6.1
New Europe	351	44.5	84.2	4.6	24.0	8.5	39.9	12.3

Table 3. Comparison between different variants of path unpacking

	Europe time [ms]	Europe space [MB]	USA time [ms]	USA space [MB]	New Europe time [ms]	New Europe space [MB]
(a) no path data	59.4	140	47.2	213	66.8	257
(b) only length	72.4	203	56.5	312	84.2	403
(c) first edge	72.5	203	56.7	312	84.4	403
(d) complete path	458.3	203	932.8	312	698.9	403
(e) compl. path (fast)	96.6	275	90.6	400	117.8	548

increase the memory requirements, but greatly improve the running times. Note that almost half of the pre-unpacked paths are contained in other pre-unpacked paths so that they require no additional space.

5 Discussion

As far as we know, we provide the first implementation of an *exact* route planning algorithm on a *mobile device* that answers queries in a road network of a whole continent *instantaneously*, i.e., with a delay that is virtually not observable for a human user. Furthermore, our graph representation is comparatively *small* (only a few hundred megabytes) and the employed query algorithm is quite *simple*, which suggests an application of our implementation in car navigation systems.

It is algorithmically interesting that a DFS based topological ordering of the contraction hierarchy yields a numbering of the graph with locality comparable to much more complicated schemes. Another generally interesting observation is that compressed storage of DAGs is easier than for general graphs since all encoding lengths are known when building the graph in topologically sorted order.

5.1 Related Work

There is an abundance of shortest-path speedup techniques, in particular for road networks. For a broad overview, we refer to [9,4]. In general, we can distinguish between goal-directed and hierarchical approaches.

Goal-Directed Approaches. (e.g., [10,11,12,13,6]) direct the search towards the target t by preferring edges that shorten the distance to t and by excluding edges that cannot possibly belong to a shortest path to t – such decisions are usually made by relying on preprocessed data. For a purely goal-directed approach, it is difficult to get an efficient external-memory implementation since no hierarchical locality (see Section 3) can be exploited. In spite of the large memory require-ments, Goldberg and Werneck [6] successfully implemented the ALT algorithm on a Pocket PC. Their largest road network (North America, 29 883 886 nodes) occupies 3 735 MB and a random query takes 329 s. Using similar hardware[4], a slightly larger graph ("New Europe"), and a slightly smaller cache size (8 MB instead of 10 MB), our graph representation requires only 548 MB (about 1/7 of the space needed by [6]) and our random queries (including path unpacking) take 42 ms (more than 7 500 times faster) when our cache has been warmed up and 118 ms (more than 2 500 times faster) when our cache is initially empty.

Hierarchical Approaches. (e.g., [14,5,15,16,3,4]) exploit the hierarchical structure of the given network. In a preprocessing step, a hierarchical representation is extracted, which can be used to accelerate all subsequent queries. Although hierarchical approaches usually can take advantage of the hierarchical locality, not all of them are equally suitable for an external-memory implementation, in particular due to sometimes large memory requirements. The RE algorithm [14,5] has been implemented on a mobile device, yielding query times of "a few seconds including path computation and search animation" and requiring "2–3 GB for USA/Europe" [17].

Commercial Systems. We made a few experiments with a commercial car nav-igation system, a recent TomTom One XL[5], computing routes from Karlsruhe to 13 different European capital cities. We observe an average query time of 59 s to compute the route, not including the time needed to compose the driving di-rections. Obviously, this is far from being a system that provides instantaneous responses.[6] Furthermore, to the best of our knowledge, current commercial sys-tems do *not* compute exact routes.

More Related Work. Compact graph representations have been studied earlier. In [18], the nodes of the graph are rearranged according to the in-order of a separator tree that results from recursively removing edges to separate the graph

---

[4] We use a more recent version of the ARM architecture, but with a slightly slower clock rate (330 MHz instead of 400 MHz); in [6], random reads of 512-byte blocks from flash memory can be done with a speed of 366 KB/s, compared to 326 KB/s on our device.

[5] AK9SQ CSBUS, ARM9 processor clocked at 266 MHz, application version 6.593, OS version 1731, 29 MB RAM, road network of Western Europe version 675.1409.

[6] Note that such a commercial product is slowed down due to various reasons (e.g., some time is spent to refresh the display in order to update a progress bar), which are neglected in our test environment. Therefore, a direct quantitative comparison is not possible.

into components. By this means, the difference between the IDs of adjacent nodes gets small so that applying suitable encoding schemes yields a better compression rate than we achieve. However, the study in [18] does not take into account additional edge attributes like the edge weight and, more importantly, it does not refer to the external-memory model, which is crucial for our application.

There has been considerable theoretical work on external-memory graph representations and external-memory shortest paths (e.g. [19,20,21,22]). Indeed, although road networks (let alone our hierarchical networks) are not planar, the basic ideas in [20] lead to a similar approach to blocking as we use it. Also, the redundant representation proposed in [20], which adds a neighbourhood of all nodes to a block, might be an interesting approach to further refinements. However, the worst case bounds obtained are usually quite pessimistic and there are only few implementations: the closest one we are aware of [23] only works for undirected graphs with unit edge weights and does not exploit the kind of locality properties we are dealing with.

5.2   Future Work

Increasing the compression rate seems possible, in particular by using more sophisticated techniques, e.g. from [18]. However, we have to bear the decoding speed in mind: it might be counterproductive to use techniques that are very complicated.

One particularly relevant scenario is the case that the driver deviates from the computed route (query type 'recompute'). The recomputation could be accelerated by explicitly storing and reusing the backward search space.

Acknowledgements. We would like to thank Robert Geisberger for providing precomputed contraction hierarchies [2] for various networks.

References

1. Bauer, R., Delling, D., Sanders, P., Schieferdecker, D., Schultes, D., Wagner, D.: Combining hierarchical and goal-directed speed-up techniques for Dijkstra's algorithm. In: McGeoch, C.C. (ed.) WEA 2008. LNCS, vol. 5038, pp. 319–333. Springer, Heidelberg (2008)
2. Geisberger, R., Sanders, P., Schultes, D., Delling, D.: Contraction hierarchies: Faster and simpler hierarchical routing in road networks. In: McGeoch, C.C. (ed.) WEA 2008. LNCS, vol. 5038, pp. 303–318. Springer, Heidelberg (2008)
3. Schultes, D., Sanders, P.: Dynamic highway-node routing. In: Demetrescu, C. (ed.) WEA 2007. LNCS, vol. 4525, pp. 66–79. Springer, Heidelberg (2007)
4. Schultes, D.: Route Planning in Road Networks. PhD thesis, Universität Karlsruhe (TH) (2008)
5. Goldberg, A.V., Kaplan, H., Werneck, R.F.: Better landmarks within reach. In: Demetrescu, C. (ed.) WEA 2007. LNCS, vol. 4525, pp. 38–51. Springer, Heidelberg (2007)
6. Goldberg, A.V., Werneck, R.F.: Computing point-to-point shortest paths from external memory. In: Workshop on Algorithm Engineering and Experiments (ALENEX), pp. 26–40 (2005)

7. Delling, D., Sanders, P., Schultes, D., Wagner, D.: Highway hierarchies star. In: 9th DIMACS Implementation Challenge [8] (2006)
8. 9th DIMACS Implementation Challenge: Shortest Paths (2006), http://www.dis.uniroma1.it/~challenge9/
9. Sanders, P., Schultes, D.: Engineering fast route planning algorithms. In: Demetrescu, C. (ed.) WEA 2007. LNCS, vol. 4525, pp. 23–36. Springer, Heidelberg (2007)
10. Lauther, U.: An extremely fast, exact algorithm for finding shortest paths in static networks with geographical background. In: Geoinformation und Mobilität – von der Forschung zur praktischen Anwendung, IfGI prints, Institut für Geoinformatik, Münster, vol. 22, pp. 219–230 (2004)
11. Köhler, E., Möhring, R.H., Schilling, H.: Fast point-to-point shortest path computations with arc-flags. In: 9th DIMACS Implementation Challenge [8] (2006)
12. Hilger, M.: Accelerating point-to-point shortest path computations in large scale networks. Diploma Thesis, Technische Universität Berlin (2007)
13. Goldberg, A.V., Harrelson, C.: Computing the shortest path: A^* meets graph theory. In: 16th ACM-SIAM Symposium on Discrete Algorithms, pp. 156–165 (2005)
14. Gutman, R.: Reach-based routing: A new approach to shortest path algorithms optimized for road networks. In: Workshop on Algorithm Engineering and Experiments (ALENEX), pp. 100–111 (2004)
15. Sanders, P., Schultes, D.: Engineering highway hierarchies. In: Azar, Y., Erlebach, T. (eds.) ESA 2006. LNCS, vol. 4168, pp. 804–816. Springer, Heidelberg (2006)
16. Bast, H., Funke, S., Sanders, P., Schultes, D.: Fast routing in road networks with transit nodes. Science 316, 566 (2007)
17. Goldberg, A.: personal communication (2008)
18. Blandford, D.K., Blelloch, G.E., Kash, I.A.: An experimental analysis of a compact graph representation. In: Workshop on Algorithm Engineering and Experiments (ALENEX) (2004)
19. Nodine, M.H., Goodrich, M.T., Vitter, J.S.: Blocking for external graph searching. Algorithmica 16, 181–214 (1996)
20. Agarwal, P.K., Arge, L.A., Murali, T.M., Varadarajan, K., Vitter, J.: I/O-efficient algorithms for contour-line extraction and planar graph blocking. In: 9th ACM-SIAM Symposium on Discrete Algorithms, pp. 117–126 (1998)
21. Hutchinson, D., Maheshwari, A., Zeh, N.: An external memory data structure for shortest path queries. In: Asano, T., Imai, H., Lee, D.T., Nakano, S.-i., Tokuyama, T. (eds.) COCOON 1999. LNCS, vol. 1627, pp. 51–60. Springer, Heidelberg (1999)
22. Meyer, U., Zeh, N.: I/O-efficient undirected shortest paths with unbounded edge lengths. In: Azar, Y., Erlebach, T. (eds.) ESA 2006. LNCS, vol. 4168, pp. 540–551. Springer, Heidelberg (2006)
23. Ajwani, D., Dementiev, R., Meyer, U.: A computational study of external-memory BFS algorithms. In: ACM-SIAM Symposium on Discrete Algorithms, pp. 601–610 (2007)
24. Ajwani, D., Malinger, I., Meyer, U., Toledo, S.: Characterizing the performance of flash memory storage devices and its impact on algorithm design. In: McGeoch, C.C. (ed.) WEA 2008. LNCS, vol. 5038, pp. 208–219. Springer, Heidelberg (2008)
25. Karypis Lab: METIS - Family of Multilevel Partitioning Algorithms (2008)
26. R Development Core Team: R: A Language and Environment for Statistical Computing (2004), http://www.r-project.org

How Reliable Are Practical
Point-in-Polygon Strategies?*

Stefan Schirra

Otto von Guericke University, Department of Computer Science,
Magdeburg, Germany
stschirr@ovgu.de

Abstract. We experimentally study the reliability of geometric software
for point location in simple polygons. As expected, the code we tested
works very well for random query points. However, our experiments reveal that the tested code often fails for more challenging degenerate and
also nearly degenerate queries.

1 Introduction

Assume you would like to test points for inclusion in a simple polygon. Most likely,
you will end up using one of the so-called practical point-in-polygon strategies instead of implementing one of the more sophisticated theoretically optimal point
location data structures developed in computational geometry. Code for such practical point-in-polygon strategies is available on the WWW. Or you might decide to
use components from CGAL [3], LEDA [10] or some other software library providing
code for point-in-polygon testing or more general point location queries. Most of
the available floating-point based code is very efficient and works well for query
points chosen uniformly at random inside the bounding box of the polygon.

As we shall see in Section 4 most of the existent code produces wrong results
for query points near or on the polygon edges, however, see also Fig. 1 where
queries answered correctly are marked by a grey box ▪, false positives by a red
disk ●, and false negatives by a green disk ●. If you know that the coordinates of
query points and polygon vertices are inaccurate anyway, you might be willing to
accept this. Unfortunately, sometimes there are errors not only for such problem-
specific degenerate queries, but also for algorithm-specific degeneracies, cf. Fig. 7
in more or less rare cases. Are you willing to accept this for your applications?
And what if your data is not subject to uncertainty at all? This is the case we
are most interested in. In this paper, we consider simple closed polygons and the
corresponding binary point-inclusion predicate only. This is the most important
case and can be used for point location in polygons with holes, too. Furthermore,
point-in-polygon testing is a subtask in landmarks algorithms for point location
in arrangements of straight lines [8].

After a very brief look at related work in the next section, we report on experimental studies regarding the reliability of practical point-in-polygon testing
software. The studies include code from [7], code available on the WWW, and

---

* Partially supported by DFG grant SCHI 858/1-1.

D. Halperin and K. Mehlhorn (Eds.): ESA 2008, LNCS 5193, pp. 744–755, 2008.

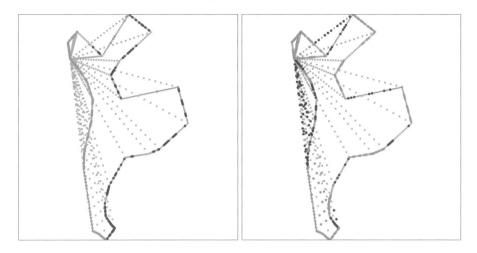

Fig. 1. Results for query points near or on the edges and the diagonals of a real-world polygon with 30 edges for strategies *crossings* (left) and *halfplane* (right)

code provided by computational geometry software libraries. Furthermore, we briefly discuss how to achieve full reliability without paying too much for this benefit in Section 5 .

2   Related Work

Testing a query point for inclusion in a polygon is a fundamental problem in computational geometry with many applications, e.g. in computer graphics and geographic information systems, and has been the subject of many research papers in computer science and related application disciplines. For an overview we refer to Snoeyink's survey paper [15]. Probably the most common algorithm for point-in-polygon testing without preprocessing is the crossing number algorithm. Interestingly, already the first description of the algorithm by Shimrat [14] contained a flaw fixed later by Hacker [6]. It is well known that handling degenerate cases in a crossing number algorithm is not obvious. Forrest [4] nicely illustrates the problems involved.

While previous case studies on practical point-in-polygon testing, e.g. [7,16], focus on query time and sometimes on memory usage, here we are concerned with the correctness or at least the numerical stability of practical point-in-polygon algorithms.

3   Experimental Setup

We concentrate on practical point-in-polygon algorithms with no or little preprocessing without sophisticated data structures. Our selection of existent code includes the fastest algorithms from the beautiful graphic gems collection of Haines [7], namely *crossings*, a "macmartinized" crossing number algorithm, see also [1], the triangle-fan algorithms *halfplane*, *barycentric*, and *spackman*, and finally *grid*. Crossing number algorithms compute the parity of the number of intersections of an (horizontal) ray with the polygon boundary. Triangle-fan algorithms consider the collection of triangles formed by an initial vertex v and each polygon edge that is not incident to v. Then they check how many triangles contain the query point. Again, the parity tells us about the relative position of the query point with respect to the polygon. *Halfplane* precomputes line equations for faster triangle testing, *barycentric* and *spackman* compute barycentric coordinates in addition to point location. This might be useful for some applications. *Grid* imposes a 20×20 grid on the bounding box of the polygon and uses a crossing number like strategy to resolve those cases where the grid cell containing the query point is not completely contained in the interior or exterior of the polygon. For the sake of completeness, we also tested Weiler's code [17] which computes the winding number using quadrant movements. Furthermore, we consider Franklin's PNPOLY code [5], which is another crossing number based algorithm available on the WWW. Walker and Snoeyink [16] use CSG representations of polygons for point location. We include their code[1], *csg*, in our case study because of the reported efficiency, although the code is not publicly available. Finally, we also consider point location code for polygons from CGAL using the obvious inexact geometry kernel with double precision floating-point coordinates. Of course, with an exact kernel, CGAL's point location code for polygons is fully reliable. The same holds for LEDA's rat_polygon code (floating-point filtered rational kernel).

Regarding polygon data, we use both artificial "random" polygons and real world data. The random polygons are generated from a random set of vertices using the 2-opt heuristic [2]. The vertices are generated uniformly at random inside the unit square. The real world polygons we use are city and village boundaries from south-west of Germany, scaled to the unit square.

We use different methods to generate query points, cf. Fig. 2. For points generated uniformly at random inside the unit square using a generator from CGAL, all tested code usually works without any problems. Thus we challenge the code with problem-dependent (near) degeneracies. We use CGAL's point generator for generating points "on" a line segment. Given endpoints v and w of a segment and a number $n > 2$, this generator creates a sequence of equally spaced points on the segment $\overline{vw}$, more precisely, it creates points $v + \frac{i}{n-1}(w-v)$ for $i = 0, \ldots, n-1$ and hence the generated set of points includes the segment endpoints. Because we use double precision coordinates, usually not all points are exactly on the segment, but only very close to it. Next we consider potentially algorithm-dependent degeneracies. We create points on the vertical and horizontal lines through the polygon vertices. These are potentially degenerate cases for the crossing number algorithms. Furthermore we generate query points "on" the diagonals bounding the triangles considered by the triangle-fan algorithms, again using a generator from CGAL. These are potentially degenerate cases for such algorithms. Besides this we generate points "on" the lines supporting the polygon edges in order to challenge the code based on CSG representations. Finally we use the polygon vertices as query points.

---

[1] Thanks to Robert Walker for making the code available to us.

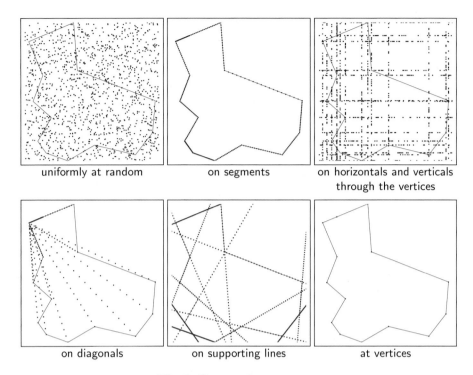

uniformly at random	on segments	on horizontals and verticals through the vertices
on diagonals	on supporting lines	at vertices

Fig. 2. Query point generators

A strong point of this case study is its independence: we test only code not written by the author! For the sake of reproducibility, testbed code and data are available online [12].

4   Experimental Results

The reported results hold on any machine compliant to the IEEE 754 double precision floating-point standard. As stated above, all tested code works very well for random query points. Thus we turn to more interesting query points. Points (almost) on the polygon edges are challenging for all strategies. Fig. 3 and Fig. 4 show typical results for a real-world and a random polygon, respectively.

All tested code produces some false results. Table 1 shows the percentage of false positives and false negatives for query points near the polygon edges for the polygons from Figs. 3 and 4. For all but the CGAL code the percentage of false results is significant. However, the CGAL code is about an order of magnitude slower than the fastest algorithms from [7], but it is also much more reliable for (nearly) degenerate query points. Especially, polygon vertices cause problems for all but the CGAL code, see also Table 4.

Unfortunately, it is not obvious how to measure sensitivity to errors as a function of closeness to degeneracy, because, as illustrated by Kettner et al. [9]

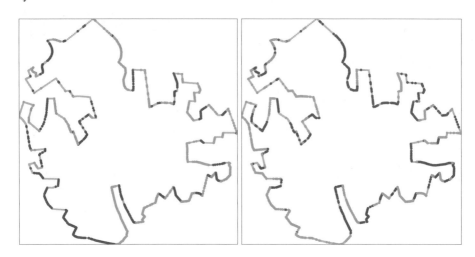

Fig. 3. Results for query points near or on the edges of a a real-world polygon with 304 vertices for strategies PNPOLY (left) and *grid* (right)

Table 1. Results for points "on" polygon edges

	real-world polygon 304 vertices		random polygon 64 vertices	
	false positives	false negatives	false positives	false negatives
crossings	12.5 %	17.8 %	18.4 %	18.8 %
weiler	11.9 %	18.0 %	13.4 %	23.0 %
halfplane	15.2 %	24.0 %	16.3 %	24.8 %
barycentric	20.2 %	17.5 %	17.9 %	14.1 %
spackman	20.2 %	18.5 %	19.6 %	15.2 %
grid	16.7 %	15.9 %	17.0 %	19.7 %
PNPOLY	11.9 %	18.0 %	13.5 %	23.4 %
csg	23.9 %	23.7 %	26.0 %	18.0 %
CGAL	0.4 %	0.0 %	3.4 %	0.6 %

for the orientation test, the set of floating-point points near an edge where a floating-point implementation of a geometric predicate fails does not necessarily form a homogeneous sleeve around the edge.

Interestingly, Shimrat [14] already states that his crossing number algorithm does not apply to query points on the boundary of the polygon. Haines [7] writes

> "When dealing with floating-point operations on these polygons we do not care if a test point exactly on an edge is classified as being inside or outside, since these cases are extremely rare.

However, our experiments show that we get false results not only for points *exactly* on the boundary. Second, for polygons with axis-parallel edges like the

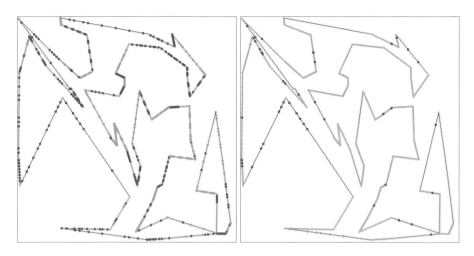

Fig. 4. Results for query points near or on the edges of a random polygon with 64 vertices for strategies *csg* (left) and CGAL (right)

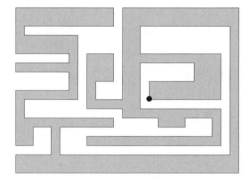

Fig. 5. For polygons with axis-parallel edges query points exactly on an edge are not unlikely

polygon in Fig. 5, points exactly on the edges are not unlikely to arise in real-world applications.

Next we turn to algorithm-dependent degeneracies. We create points on the vertical and horizontal lines through the polygon vertices. These are potentially degenerate cases for the crossing number algorithms. Because of a conceptual perturbation, namely considering vertices on the ray as being infinitesimally above the ray, both crossing number algorithms work very well for random query points on the horizontals and verticals through vertices, unless we have axis-parallel edges, see Fig. 6.

Next we generate query points (almost) on the diagonals that bound the triangles considered in the triangle-fan algorithms. Fig. 7 illustrates some results. Table 2 shows the percentage of false positives and false negatives for query

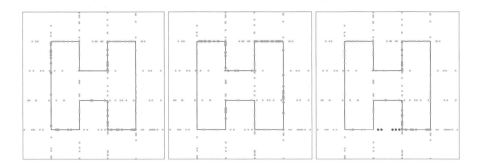

Fig. 6. Results for query points on verticals and horizontals through the vertices of a polygon with axis-parallel edges for *crossings* (left), PNPOLY (middle), and *barycentric* (right)

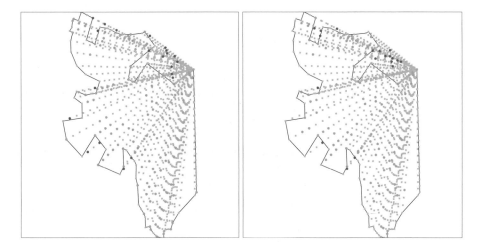

Fig. 7. Results for query points on diagonals of a real-world polygon with 78 vertices for *spackman* (left) and *barycentric* (right)

points generated as described above for the real world polygon from Fig. 7 and for the random polygon from Fig. 4. As we have suspected the triangle-fan algorithms err for many points near or on the edges of the triangles considered by the algorithms. We have many false results, both false positives as well as false negatives. The percentage is higher for the triangle-fan algorithms compared to their competitors. Haines [7] admits that the triangle-fan based code *"does not fully address this problem"*. Again, the problems occur not only for points exactly on triangle edges.

There are usually more false-negative results, because the total part of diagonal edges inside a polygon is usually larger. The false results of the remaining methods are mainly caused by query points on the first diagonal which coincides with the first edge of the polygon and by the endpoints of the diagonals, i.e.,

Table 2. Results for points "on" diagonal edges

	real-world polygon 78 vertices		random polygon 64 vertices	
	false positives	false negatives	false positives	false negatives
crossings	0.6 %	7.8 %	0.8 %	3.3 %
weiler	0.2 %	6.8 %	0.7 %	3.4 %
halfplane	5.5 %	25.5 %	16.1 %	25.6 %
barycentric	1.2 %	11.9 %	6.4 %	12.8 %
spackman	1.4 %	13.5 %	6.7 %	14.0 %
grid	0.6 %	7.7 %	0.4 %	2.9 %
PNPOLY	0.3 %	6.8 %	0.7 %	3.4 %
csg	0.0 %	7.7 %	0.0 %	8.3 %
CGAL	0.0 %	0.0 %	0.0 %	0.0 %

polygon vertices. Since vertices are false negative if misclassified, this explains the larger percentage of false negatives for the remaining non triangle-fan based methods.

We move on to query points on the lines supporting the polygon edges. The corresponding generator was added to the test set in order to challenge the *csg* method. Fig. 8 shows results for *csg* for the real-world and the random polygon discussed in Table 3. For the real-world polygon from Fig. 8, the percentage of both false negatives and false positives is below 1% for all competitors. Indeed, *csg* reliability is slightly worse than the reliability of the crossing number algorithms. In some examples, however, the triangle-fan algorithms are worse. As

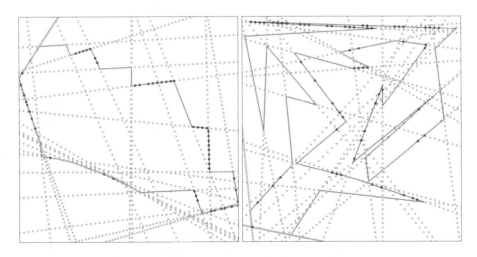

Fig. 8. Results for query points on supporting lines of polygon edges for a real-world polygon with 34 vertices (left) and a random polygon with 32 vertices (right) for *csg*

Table 3. Results for points "on" supporting lines of polygon edges

	real-world polygon 34 vertices		random polygon 32 vertices	
	false positives	false negatives	false positives	false negatives
crossings	1.1 %	0.6 %	1.7 %	1.4 %
weiler	0.4 %	0.9 %	0.8 %	1.4 %
halfplane	0.8 %	1.9 %	3.6 %	7.2 %
barycentric	2.2 %	0.7 %	5.1 %	2.2 %
spackman	2.1 %	0.8 %	5.4 %	2.7 %
grid	1.2 %	1.0 %	2.8 %	1.8 %
PNPOLY	0.4 %	0.9 %	0.8 %	1.2 %
csg	3.1 %	0.9 %	4.2 %	1.4 %
CGAL	0.3 %	0.0 %	0.6 %	0.0 %

Table 4. Results for polygon vertices as query points

	real-world polygon 304 vertices	random polygon 256 vertices
	false negatives	false negatives
crossings	52.3 %	51.6 %
weiler	48.4 %	49.6 %
halfplane	53.3 %	54.7 %
barycentric	41.4 %	45.3 %
spackman	48.0 %	48.0 %
grid	45.4 %	50.4 %
PNPOLY	48.4 %	48.0 %
csg	42.8 %	49.2 %
CGAL	0.0 %	0.0 %

can be seen in Fig. 8, *csg* errs only for query points near the actual polygon edges, not elsewhere. The same behavior shows up in all our other experiments with query points on supporting lines. In all examples we study, CGAL produces the largest number of correct results.

Finally, we take a closer look at polygon vertices as query points. Since we consider our polygons as topologically closed, there can be false negatives only. Unfortunately, most algorithms produce many wrong results, as shown in Table 4. Besides CGAL, all err for about half the query points! If we would consider polygons to be open, the other "half" of the vertices would be misclassified. Besides CGAL, all produce inconsistent results for polygon vertices as query points. If you are not willing to accept this, you have to add a separate routine for checking whether a query point coincides with a polygon vertex.

5   Reliability and Numerical Stability

For all tested programs there are query points where they produce incorrect results. Besides the triangle-fan algorithms, all algorithms are apparently numerically stable, i.e., whenever they err there is a point close to the current query point for which the computed result is the correct one. The triangle-fan based programs, however, also compute incorrect results far away from the boundary edges, cf. Fig. 1 (right) and Fig. 7. Hence, they are not numerically stable. Although the remaining programs are numerically stable, they show fairly different behavior for challenging queries.

Wesselink's CGAL code is by far the most reliable, but is also much slower, although it is an implementation of the crossing number algorithm as well. The code does a lot of reasoning based on comparison of coordinates. In terms of efficiency this is not a good idea as the branching breaks the pipelining in the processor. In terms of reliability, in IEEE 754 compliant architectures, it is a great approach, because coordinate comparisons are always exact thanks to denormalized floating-point numbers. CGAL competitors prefer to perform numerical computations instead of coordinate comparisons. These computations are fast, but error-prone. The crossing number algorithms test whether a horizontal leftward ray r starting at query point $q = (q_x, q_y)$ intersects a polygon edge s. This is often implemented by computing the intersection point p of the supporting line of r and the supporting line of s and then testing whether p lies on both r and s. MacMartin et al. [11] observe that s cannot intersect r if the y-coordinates of both endpoints of s are smaller or larger than q_y. CGAL uses comparison of x-coordinates to save further calculations as well, assuming that we already did the comparison of y-coordinates. Then, if the x-coordinates of both endpoints of s are smaller than q_x, there is no intersection, and if both are larger, there is one. If these comparisons do not suffice to decide the test, CGAL uses an orientation test to check whether q is to the left of s.

The straightforward approach to implement geometric algorithms reliably is to use exact rational arithmetic instead of inherently imprecise floating-point arithmetic. Unfortunately, this slows down the code by orders of magnitude. As suggested by the exact geometric computation paradigm [18] a better approach is to combine exact rational arithmetic with floating-point filters, e.g. interval arithmetic, in order to save most of the efficiency of floating-point arithmetic for nondegenerate cases. This approach is implemented in the exact geometry kernels of CGAL [3] and LEDA [10]. The use of adaptive predicates à la Shewchuck [13] is highly recommended. Interestingly, exact rational arithmetic does not suffice to let the tested crossing number code always produce correct results. Due to the conceptual perturbation of the vertices, vertices as query points still cause incorrect results many times.

We briefly describe an alternative reliable implementation of the crossing number algorithm. We suggest to add some preprocessing to compensate for more expensive arithmetic. Use an interval skip list (or interval tree) to store the y-ranges of all nonhorizontal polygon edges. In order to handle degeneracies correctly, store half-open intervals: Only the y-coordinate of the first endpoint is included, the y-coordinate of the second endpoint is not. Here we assume that polygon edges are consistently oriented along the polygon boundary. Use another interval skip list (or a dictionary data structure) to store the y-coordinates of all vertices and all horizontal edges. The CGAL library provides a flexible and adaptable implementation of interval skip list. Note that all operations on the interval skip lists are exact, because we need only comparisons of floats besides arithmetic on small integers.

To answer a query for $q = (q_x, q_y)$, we use the second interval skip list (or a dictionary data structure) to check exactly whether q lies on a horizontal ray or coincides with a polygon vertex. If not, we use the first skip list to get candidate edges for intersection with the leftward horizontal ray starting at q and use the comparison-based strategy described above for testing for intersection. Thanks to the half-openness of the intervals, we count intersections at vertices only once. In pathological cases we still have to consider a linear number of edges and vertices, in practice, however, we get only a few, leading to good performance for most random and real-world polygons.

6   Conclusions

Our experiments show that the tested practical point-in-polygon code often produces wrong results for challenging queries, where we find inconsistent handling of vertices as query points most annoying. The experiments also show that the triangle-fan based code is not even numerically stable. Furthermore, the experiments show that the slower CGAL code is much more reliable.

References

1. Akenine-Möller, T., Haines, E.: Real-Time Rendering, 2nd edn. AK Peters, Ltd. (2002)
2. Auer, T., Held, M.: Heuristics for the generation of random polygons. In: Proc. of CCCG 1996, pp. 38–44 (1996)
3. CGAL, Computational Geometry Algorithms Library, http://www.cgal.org
4. Forrest, A.R.: Computational geometry in practice. In: Earnshaw, R.A. (ed.) Fundamental Algorithms for Computer Graphics. NATO ASI, vol. F17, pp. 707–724. Springer, Heidelberg (1985)
5. Franklin, W.R.: PNPOLY–point inclusion in polygon test, http://www.ecse.rpi.edu/Homepages/wrf/Research/Short_Notes/pnpoly.html
6. Hacker, R.: Certification of algorithm 112: position of point relative to polygon. Commun. ACM 5, 606 (1962)
7. Haines, E.: Point in polygon strategies. In: Heckbert, P. (ed.) Graphics Gems IV, pp. 24–46. Academic Press, Boston (1994), http://tog.acm.org/editors/erich/ptinpoly/
8. Haran, I., Halperin, D.: An experimental study of point location in general planar arrangements. In: Proc. of ALENEX 2006, pp. 16–25 (2006)
9. Kettner, L., Mehlhorn, K., Pion, S., Schirra, S., Yap, C.: Classroom examples of robustness problems in geometric computations. Comput. Geom. Theory Appl. 40(1), 61–78 (2008)

10. Mehlhorn, K., Näher, S.: LEDA: A Platform for Combinatorial and Geometric Computing. Cambridge University Press, Cambridge (2000)
11. Nassar, A., Walden, P., Haines, E., Dickens, T., Capelli, R., Narasimhan, S., Jam, C., MacMartin, S.: Fastest point in polygon test. Ray Tracing News 5(3) (1992)
12. Schirra, S.: Companion pages to How reliable are practical point in polygon strategies? http://wwwisg.cs.uni-magdeburg.de/ag/pointInPolygonReliability/
13. Shewchuk, J.R.: Adaptive precision floating-point arithmetic and fast robust geometric predicates. Discrete & Computational Geometry 18(3), 305–368 (1997)
14. Shimrat, M.: Algorithm 112: position of point relative to polygon. Commun. ACM 5, 434 (1962)
15. Snoeyink, J.: Point location. In: Goodman, J.E., O'Rourke, J. (eds.) Handbook of Discrete and Computational Geometry, ch. 34, 2nd edn., pp. 767–786. CRC Press LLC, Boca Raton (2004)
16. Walker, R., Snoeyink, J.: Practical point-in-polygon tests using CSG representations of polygons. In: Goodrich, M.T., McGeoch, C.C. (eds.) ALENEX 1999. LNCS, vol. 1619, pp. 114–123. Springer, Heidelberg (1999)
17. Weiler, K.: An incremental angle point in polygon test. In: Heckbert, P. (ed.) Graphics Gems IV, pp. 16–23. Academic Press, Boston (1994)
18. Yap, C.-K.: Towards exact geometric computation. Comput. Geom.–Theory and Appl. 7, 3–23 (1997)

Fast Divide-and-Conquer Algorithms for Preemptive Scheduling Problems with Controllable Processing Times – A Polymatroid Optimization Approach

Natalia V. Shakhlevich[1], Akiyoshi Shioura[2], and Vitaly A. Strusevich[3]

[1] School of Computing, University of Leeds, Leeds LS2 9JT, U.K.
ns@comp.leeds.ac.uk
[2] Graduate School of Information Sciences, Tohoku University,
Sendai 980-8579, Japan
shioura@dais.is.tohoku.ac.jp
[3] Department of Mathematical Sciences, University of Greenwich, Old Royal Naval
College, Park Row, London SE10 9LS, U.K.
V.Strusevich@greenwich.ac.uk

Abstract. We consider a variety of preemptive scheduling problems with controllable processing times on a single machine and on identical/uniform parallel machines, where the objective is to minimize the total compression cost. In this paper, we propose fast divide-and-conquer algorithms for these scheduling problems. Our approach is based on the observation that each scheduling problem we discuss can be formulated as a polymatroid optimization problem. We develop a novel divide-and-conquer technique for the polymatroid optimization problem and then apply it to each scheduling problem. We show that each scheduling problem can be solved in $O(T_{feas}(n) \times \log n)$ time by using our divide-and-conquer technique, where n is the number of jobs and $T_{feas}(n)$ denotes the time complexity of the corresponding feasible scheduling problem with n jobs. This approach yields faster algorithms for most of the scheduling problems discussed in this paper.

1 Introduction

We consider a variety of preemptive scheduling problems with controllable processing times on a single machine and on identical/uniform parallel machines. In this paper, we propose fast divide-and-conquer algorithms for these scheduling problems.

Our Problems. *Preemptive scheduling problems with controllable processing times* discussed in this paper are described as follows. We have n jobs, which are to be processed on m machines. The sets of jobs and machines are denoted by $N = \{1, 2, \ldots, n\}$ and by $M = \{1, 2, \ldots, m\}$, respectively. Each job j has *processing requirement* $\bar{p}(j)$. If $m = 1$, we have a *single* machine; otherwise we have m (≥ 2) *parallel* machines. The parallel machines are called *identical* if

D. Halperin and K. Mehlhorn (Eds.): ESA 2008, LNCS 5193, pp. 756–767, 2008.

their speeds are equal; otherwise, the machines are called *uniform* and machine i has a speed s_i, so that processing a job j on machine i for τ time units reduces its overall processing requirement by $s_i\tau$.

In the processing of each job *preemption* is allowed, so that the processing of any job can be interrupted at any time and resumed later, possibly on another machine. No job is allowed to be processed on several machines at a time, and each machine processes at most one job at a time. Job j also has *release date* $r(j)$ and *due date* $d(j)$, and any piece of job j should be scheduled between the time interval $[r(j), d(j)]$.

Suppose that the processing requirement $\overline{p}(j)$ $(j \in N)$ cannot be feasibly scheduled on the machines. Then, we can reduce the processing requirement $\overline{p}(j)$ to $p(j)$ $(\leq \overline{p}(j))$ by paying the cost $w(j)(\overline{p}(j) - p(j))$ so that jobs can be feasibly scheduled. We here assume that the lower bound $\underline{p}(j)$ of the processing requirement $p(j)$ is given and $p(j) \geq \underline{p}(j)$ should be satisfied. The objective is to minimize the total cost $\sum_{j=1}^{n} w(j)(\overline{p}(j) - p(j))$ subject to the constraints that (i) processing requirement $p(j)$ $(j \in N)$ can be feasibly scheduled on m machines, and (ii) $\underline{p}(j) \leq p(j) \leq \overline{p}(j)$ $(j \in N)$. In this paper, we mainly consider an equivalent problem of maximizing $\sum_{j=1}^{n} w(j)p(j)$ under the same constraints (i) and (ii). We refer to [10] for comprehensive treatment of this problem.

Preemptive scheduling problem with controllable processing times is also known by different names with different interpretations. *Scheduling of imprecise computation tasks* (see, e.g., [2,10,19,20,21]; see also [17]) is an equivalent problem, where the portion $\overline{p}(j) - p(j)$ of job j is interpreted as the error of computation and $\sum_{j=1}^{n} w(j)(\overline{p}(j) - p(j))$ is regarded as the total weighted error. *The scheduling minimizing the weighted number of tardy task units* (see, e.g., [7,11]) is equivalent to the special case with $\underline{p}(j) = 0$ for all job j, where the value $\overline{p}(j) - p(j)$ is regarded as the portion of the processing requirement which cannot be processed before the due date $d(j)$.

There are many kinds of preemptive scheduling problems with controllable processing times, depending on the setting of the underlying scheduling problems. In this paper, we consider three types of machines: a single machine, identical parallel machines, and uniform parallel machines. We also consider the cases where release/due dates of jobs are the same or arbitrary. We assume $r(j) = 0$ (resp., $d(j) = d \, (> 0)$) for all $j \in N$ if all jobs have the same release dates (resp., due dates).

We denote each problem as {Single, Ide, Uni}-{SameR, ArbR}-{SameD, ArbD}. For example, Ide-SameR-ArbD denotes the the identical parallel machine scheduling problem with the same $r(j)$ and arbitrary $d(j)$. We note that the problem {Single, Ide, Uni}-SameR-ArbD is equivalent to {Single, Ide, Uni}-ArbR-SameD (see, e.g, [8,15,16]), and therefore need not be considered. Hence, we deal with nine problems in this paper.

Previous Results. We review the current fastest algorithms for nine scheduling problems discussed in this paper. The summary is given in Table 1.

Single-SameR-SameD can be easily solved in $O(n)$ time. Janiak and Kovalyov [9] formulate Single-SameR-ArbD as a linear program and show that the

Table 1. Summary of Our Results and Previous Results

Single	Feasibility Problem	Optimization Problem	
		Previous Results	**This Paper**
same $r(j)$ same $d(j)$	$\Theta(n)$ (trivial)	$\Theta(n)$ (trivial)	—
same $r(j)$ arb. $d(j)$	$O(n \log n)$ [13]	$\Theta(n \log n)$ [9]	—
arb. $r(j)$ arb. $d(j)$	$O(n \log n)$ [8] $(O(n)$ w/o sorting$)$	$O(n \log n + \kappa n)$ [11] $\Theta(n \log n)$ (for $\mathbb{Z}$) [19]	$\Theta(n \log n)$
Identical			
same $r(j)$ same $d(j)$	$\Theta(n)$ [13]	$\Theta(n)$ [17]	—
same $r(j)$ arb. $d(j)$	$O(n \log n)$ [15] $(O(n \log m)$ w/o sorting$)$	$O(n^2 (\log n)^2)$ [12]	$O(n \log m \log n)$
arb. $r(j)$ arb. $d(j)$	$O(n^2 (\log n)^2)$ (cf. [2,21])	$O(n^2 (\log n)^2)$ [12]	—
Uniform			
same $r(j)$ same $d(j)$	$O(m \log m + n)$ [6]	$O(mn + n \log n)$ [14]	$O(\min\{n \log n, n+m \log m \log n\})$
same $r(j)$ arb. $d(j)$	$O(mn + n \log n)$ [16] $(O(mn)$ w/o sorting$)$	$O(mn^3)$ [12]	$O(mn \log n)$
arb. $r(j)$ arb. $d(j)$	$O(mn^3)$ [3]	$O(mn^3)$ [12]	—

The time complexity with "w/o sorting" means the time complexity except for the time required for sorting input numbers of size $O(n)$ such as $w(j), r(j), d(j)$.

linear program can be solved in $O(n \log n)$ time. For Single-ArbR-ArbD, Leung et al. [11] slightly improve the analysis of the $O(n^2)$-time greedy algorithm in [20] and obtain a better bound $O(n \log n + \kappa n)$, where κ is the number of distinct $w(j)$. Shih et al. [19] propose an $O(n \log n)$-time divide-and-conquer algorithm for Single-ArbR-ArbD, which works only for instances with the numbers $\overline{p}(j), \underline{p}(j), r(j), d(j)$ given by integers.

Ide-SameR-SameD can be formulated as the continuous knapsack problem by using the result of McNaughton [13], and therefore can be solved in $O(n)$ time (see [17]). McCormick [12] shows that Ide-ArbR-ArbD (and also Ide-SameR-ArbD) can be formulated as a parametric max flow problem, and applies the algorithm of Gallo et al. [5] to achieve the time complexity $O(n^3 \log n)$, which can be reduced to $O(n^2 (\log n)^2)$ by using the balanced binary tree representation of time intervals as in Chung et al. [2,21].

Uni-SameR-SameD can be solved by a greedy algorithm in $O(mn + n \log n)$ time [14]. McCormick [12] shows that Uni-ArbR-ArbD (and also Uni-SameR-ArbD) can be formulated as a parametric max flow problem on a bipartite network, and applies the algorithm of Ahuja et al. [1] to achieve the time complexity $O(mn^3)$.

Our Approach and Results. The summary of our results is given in Table 1. Our approach is based on the observation that each of nine scheduling problems discussed in this paper can be formulated as a polymatroid optimization problem of the following form:

(LP) Maximize $\displaystyle\sum_{j=1}^{n} w(j)p(j)$

subject to $p(Y) \leq \varphi(Y)$ $(Y \in 2^N)$, $\underline{p}(j) \leq p(j) \leq \bar{p}(j)$ $(j \in N)$,

where $p(Y) = \sum_{j \in Y} p(j)$ and $\varphi : 2^N \rightarrow \mathbb{R}_+$ is a polymatroid rank function, i.e., a nondecreasing submodular function with $\varphi(\emptyset) = 0$. This observation is already made in [12,17,18] and used to show the validity of greedy algorithms for the scheduling problems. On the other hand, we use this observation in a different way; we develop a novel divide-and-conquer technique for the problem (LP), and apply it to the scheduling problems to obtain faster algorithms.

We define a function $\widetilde{\varphi} : 2^N \rightarrow \mathbb{R}$ by

$$\widetilde{\varphi}(X) = \min_{Y \in 2^N} \{\varphi(Y) + \bar{p}(X \setminus Y) - \underline{p}(Y \setminus X)\} \quad (X \in 2^N).$$

Then, $\widetilde{\varphi}$ is also a polymatroid rank function, and the set of maximal feasible solutions of (LP) is given as $\{p \in \mathbb{R}^n \mid p(Y) \leq \widetilde{\varphi}(Y)$ $(Y \in 2^N)$, $p(N) = \widetilde{\varphi}(N)\}$ (cf. [4, Sect. 3.1(b)]). Our divide-and-conquer technique is based on the following property, where the proof is given in Sect. 2:

Theorem 1. *Let $k \in N$ and $N_k = \{j \in N \mid w(j) \geq w(k)\}$. Suppose that $X_* \in 2^N$ satisfies*

$$\widetilde{\varphi}(N_k) = \varphi(X_*) + \bar{p}(N_k \setminus X_*) - \underline{p}(X_* \setminus N_k). \tag{1}$$

Then, there exists an optimal solution $q \in \mathbb{R}^n$ of the problem (LP) satisfying $q(X_*) = \varphi(X_*)$, $q(j) = \bar{p}(j)$ $(j \in N_k \setminus X_*)$, and $q(j) = \underline{p}(j)$ $(j \in X_* \setminus N_k)$.

By Theorem 1, the problem (LP) can be decomposed into two subproblems of similar structure, where the one is with respect to the variables $\{p(j) \mid j \in X_*\}$ and the other with respect to $\{p(j) \mid j \in N \setminus X_*\}$. Moreover, Theorem 1 shows that some of the variables can be fixed, which implies that each of the two subproblems contains at most $n/2$ non-fixed variables if we choose $k = n/2$. Hence, we can show that the depth of recursion is $O(\log n)$ when this decomposition technique is applied recursively to (LP).

We also show that a subset $X_* \in 2^N$ satisfying (1) can be computed in $O(\mathrm{T_{feas}}(n))$ time for each of the scheduling problem, where $\mathrm{T_{feas}}(n)$ denotes the time complexity for computing a feasible schedule with n jobs, except for the time required for sorting the input numbers (see Table 1 for the actual time complexity for computing a feasible schedule). This implies that each scheduling problem can be solved in $O(\mathrm{T_{feas}}(n) \times \log n)$ time by using our divide-and-conquer technique. By applying this approach, we can obtain faster algorithms for four of the nine scheduling problems discussed in this paper (see Table 1).

Organization of This Paper. In Sect. 2 we explain our divide-and-conquer algorithm for (LP). We then apply the divide-and-conquer technique to each scheduling problem in the following sections. We first give an $O(n \log n)$-time algorithm for Single-ArbR-ArbD in Sect. 3. We show in Sect. 4 that Ide-SameR-ArbD and Uni-SameR-ArbD can be solved in $O(n \log m \log n)$ time and $O(mn \log n)$ time, respectively, in Sect. 4. Finally, two algorithms for Uni-SameR-SameD, which run in $O(n \log n)$ time and $O(n+m \log m \log n)$ time, respectively, are presented in Sect. 5. Some proofs are omitted due to the page limitation.

2   Divide-and-Conquer Technique for Polymatroid Optimization

We explain our divide-and-conquer technique for the problem (LP). The discussion in this section is based on basic properties of polymatroids and submodular polyhedra (see, e.g., [4]).

We, without loss of generality, assume that the weights $w(j)$ $(j \in N)$ are all distinct; this assumption can be easily fulfilled, e.g., by using perturbation. In addition, we suppose that a subset $F \subseteq N$ such that $p(j) = \bar{p}(j)$ $(j \in F)$ is given, i.e, the variable $p(j)$ for each job $j \in F$ is already fixed. The set F is called a *fixed-job set*, and will be used in the divide-and-conquer algorithm. We denote by $\hat{n}$ the number of non-fixed variables in (LP), i.e., $\hat{n} = n - |F|$.

We first show how to decompose the problem (LP) into subproblems. Let $k \in N$ be an integer with $|N_k \setminus F| = \lfloor \hat{n}/2 \rfloor$, where $N_k = \{j \in N \mid w(j) \geq w(k)\}$. Suppose that (1) holds for some $X_* \in 2^N$. By Theorem 1, the problem (LP) can be decomposed into the following two subproblems of smaller size:

(SLP1) Maximize $\sum_{j \in X_*} w(j)p(j)$
         subject to $p(Y) \leq \varphi_1(Y)$ $(Y \in 2^{X_*})$,
                  $\underline{p}(j) \leq p(j) \leq \bar{p}(j)$ $(j \in X_* \cap N_k)$,
                  $p(j) = \underline{p}(j)$ $(j \in X_* \setminus N_k)$,
(SLP2) Maximize $\sum_{j \in N \setminus X_*} w(j)p(j)$
         subject to $p(Y) \leq \varphi_2(Y)$ $(Y \in 2^{N \setminus X_*})$,
                  $\underline{p}(j) \leq p(j) \leq \bar{p}(j)$ $(j \in (N \setminus N_k) \setminus X_*)$,
                  $p(j) = \bar{p}(j)$ $(j \in N_k \setminus X_*)$,

where $\varphi_1 : 2^{X_*} \to \mathbb{R}$ and $\varphi_2 : 2^{N \setminus X_*} \to \mathbb{R}$ are defined as

$$\varphi_1(Y) = \varphi(Y) \quad (Y \in 2^{X_*}), \qquad \varphi_2(Y) = \varphi(Y \cup X_*) - \varphi(X_*) \quad (Y \in 2^{N \setminus X_*}).$$

Note that the subproblems (SLP1) and (SLP2) (and their corresponding scheduling problems) have a structure similar to that of the original problem (LP).

Lemma 1. *Suppose that $p_1 \in \mathbb{R}^{X_*}$ (resp., $p_2 \in \mathbb{R}^{N \setminus X_*}$) is an optimal solution of (SLP1) with $p_1(X_*) = \varphi_1(X_*)$ (resp., (SLP2) with $p_2(N \setminus X_*) = \varphi_2(N \setminus X_*)$). Then, the direct sum $p = p_1 \oplus p_2 \in \mathbb{R}^n$ of p_1 and p_2 defined by*

$$(p_1 \oplus p_2)(j) = \begin{cases} p_1(j) & (j \in X_*), \\ p_2(j) & (j \in N \setminus X_*) \end{cases}$$

is an optimal solution of (LP) with $p(N) = \varphi(N)$.

The fixed-job sets for (SLP1) and (SLP2) are given by $F_1 = (F \cap X_*) \cup (X_* \setminus N_k)$ and $F_2 = (F \setminus X_*) \cup (N_k \setminus X_*)$, respectively. Since

$$|X_* \setminus F_1| \le |N_k \setminus F| = \lfloor \hat{n}/2 \rfloor, \quad |(N \setminus X_*) \setminus F_2| \le |(N \setminus N_k) \setminus F| = \lceil \hat{n}/2 \rceil, \quad (2)$$

the numbers of non-fixed variables in (SLP1) and in (SLP2) are at most half of that in (LP). This implies that the depth of recursion is $O(\log n)$ when this decomposition is applied recursively.

We then explain how to compute $X_* \in 2^N$ satisfying (1). We have

$$\tilde{\varphi}(N_k) = -\underline{p}(N \setminus N_k) + \min_{X \in 2^N} \{\varphi(X) + \overline{p}(N_k \setminus X) + \underline{p}((N \setminus N_k) \setminus X)\}, \quad (3)$$

and the second term in the right-hand side of (3) is equal to the optimal value of the following problem (cf. [4, Sect. 3.1 (b)]):

$$\text{(ULP)} \quad \text{Maximize} \quad \sum_{j=1}^{n} p(j)$$
$$\text{subject to} \quad p(X) \le \varphi(X) \quad (X \in 2^N),$$
$$0 \le p(j) \le u(j) \quad (j \in N),$$

where

$$u(j) = \begin{cases} \overline{p}(j) \ (j \in N_k), \\ \underline{p}(j) \ (j \in N \setminus N_k). \end{cases} \quad (4)$$

The problem (ULP) is a special case of (LP) where the objective function is unweighted, i.e., $w(j) = 1$ $(j \in N)$, and the lower bound of the variable $p(j)$ $(j \in N)$ is equal to zero, and therefore easier to solve. The scheduling problem corresponding to (ULP) is to maximize the sum of processing requirements under the upper bound constraint and the feasibility constraint that the processing requirements can be feasibly scheduled on machines, and can be solved in $O(T_{\text{feas}}(n))$ time, in a similar way as computing a feasible schedule.

Let $q \in \mathbb{R}^n$ be an optimal solution of (ULP), and $X_* \in 2^N$ the unique maximal set with $q(X_*) = \varphi(X_*)$. It is shown in the following sections that such X_* can be computed in $O(T_{\text{feas}}(n))$ time. By the optimality of q and submodularity of φ, we have $q(j) = \overline{p}(j)$ $(j \in N_k \setminus X_*)$ and $q(j) = \underline{p}(j)$ $(j \in (N \setminus N_k) \setminus X_*))$, implying that X_* satisfies (1) since

$$\tilde{\varphi}(N_k) = -\underline{p}(N \setminus N_k) + q(N)$$
$$= -\underline{p}(N \setminus N_k) + \{\varphi(X_*) + \overline{p}(N_k \setminus X_*) + \underline{p}((N \setminus N_k) \setminus X_*)\}$$
$$= \varphi(X_*) + \overline{p}(N_k \setminus X_*) - \underline{p}(X_* \setminus N_k).$$

Finally, we analyze the time complexity of our divide-and-conquer algorithm. Let $T(n, \hat{n})$ be the time complexity for solving the problem (LP) with n variables and $\hat{n}$ non-fixed variables, except for the time required for sorting input numbers. Then, we have

$$T(n, \hat{n}) = O(T_{\text{feas}}(n)) + T(n_1, n_1') + T(n_2, n_2'),$$

where $n_1 + n_2 = n$, $n_1' \le \min\{n_1, \lfloor \hat{n}/2 \rfloor\}$, and $n_2' \le \min\{n_2, \lceil \hat{n}/2 \rceil\}$. By solving the recursive equation, we have $T(n, \hat{n}) = O(T_{\text{feas}}(n) \times \log n)$.

Theorem 2. *Suppose that a subset $X_* \in 2^N$ satisfying (1) can be computed in $O(T_{\text{feas}}(n))$ time. Then, problem (LP) can be solved in $O(T_{\text{feas}}(n) \times \log n)$ time.*

Finally, we give a proof of Theorem 1.

Proof (Proof of Theorem 1). Since the set of maximal feasible solutions of (LP) is given as $\{p \in \mathbb{R}^n \mid p(Y) \leq \widetilde{\varphi}(Y) \ (Y \in 2^N), \ p(N) = \widetilde{\varphi}(N)\}$, the vector $p^* \in \mathbb{R}^n$ given by $p^*(j) = \widetilde{\varphi}(N_j) - \widetilde{\varphi}(N_{j-1}) \ (j = 1, 2, \ldots, n)$ is an optimal solution of (LP) (cf. [4, Sect. 3.1]). We show that the vector $q = p^*$ satisfies the conditions

$$q(X_*) = \varphi(X_*), \quad q(j) = \overline{p}(j) \ (j \in N_k \setminus X_*), \quad q(j) = \underline{p}(j) \ (j \in X_* \setminus N_k). \quad (5)$$

Since p^* is a feasible solution of the problem (LP), we have

$$p^*(X_*) \leq \varphi(X_*), \ p^*(j) \leq \overline{p}(j) \ (j \in N_k \setminus X_*), \ -p^*(j) \leq -\underline{p}(j) \ (j \in X_* \setminus N_k). \quad (6)$$

By the definition of p^*, we have $p^*(N_k) = \widetilde{\varphi}(N_k) = \varphi(X_*) + \overline{p}(N_k \setminus X_*) - \underline{p}(X_* \setminus N_k)$, which, together with (6), implies that all the inequalities in (6) hold with equality. Hence, (5) follows.

3   Single Machine with Arbitrary Release/Due Dates

We apply the divide-and-conquer technique in Sect. 2 to the problem Single-ArbR-ArbD. To describe the algorithm, we consider a restriction on the availability of the machine. Let $\tilde{I} = \{[g_k, g_{k+1}] \mid k = 1, 2, \ldots, 2n-1\}$ be a set of time intervals, where g_k is the k-th largest number in $\{r(j), d(j) \mid j \in N\}$. We are given a set of time intervals $I = \{[e_1, f_1], [e_2, f_2], \ldots, [e_\ell, f_\ell]\} \subseteq \tilde{I}$ such that the machine is available only in these time intervals, where $e_1 \leq f_1 \leq \cdots \leq e_\ell \leq f_\ell$. In addition, we are given a subset F of jobs (*fixed-job set*) such that $\underline{p}(j) = \overline{p}(j)$ for $j \in F$. We denote this variant of the problem Single-ArbR-ArbD by $P(I, N, F)$. Any subproblem which appears during the recursive decomposition of the problem Single-ArbR-ArbD is of the form $P(I, N, F)$; in particular, the original problem Single-ArbR-ArbD coincides with $P(\tilde{I}, N, \emptyset)$.

The problem $P(I, N, F)$ can be formulated as the problem (LP) with the polymatroid rank function $\varphi : 2^N \to \mathbb{R}$ given by

$$\varphi(X) = \sum \{f_k - e_k \mid 1 \leq k \leq \ell, \ [e_k, f_k] \subseteq [r(j), d(j)] \text{ for some } j \in X\}.$$

Let $k \in N$ be an integer with $|N_k \setminus F| = \lfloor \hat{n}/2 \rfloor$, where $\hat{n} = n - |F|$, and suppose that $X_* \in 2^N$ satisfies (1). Then, $P(I, N, F)$ is decomposed into the subproblems $P(I_1, N_1, F_1)$ and $P(I_2, N_2, F_2)$, where

$$\begin{cases} I_1 = \{[e_k, f_k] \mid 1 \leq k \leq \ell, \ [e_k, f_k] \subseteq [r(j), d(j)] \text{ for some } j \in X_*\}, \\ N_1 = X_*, \ F_1 = (F \cap X_*) \cup (X_* \setminus N_k), \\ I_2 = I \setminus I_1, \ N_2 = N \setminus X_*, \ F_2 = (F \setminus X_*) \cup (N_k \setminus X_*). \end{cases}$$

In addition, we update $\underline{p}$ and $\overline{p}$ by

$$\overline{p}(j) := \underline{p}(j) \ (j \in X_* \setminus N_k), \qquad \underline{p}(j) := \overline{p}(j) \ (j \in N_k \setminus X_*). \quad (7)$$

We decompose the problem $P(I, N, F)$ recursively in this way and compute an optimal solution.

We now explain how to compute $X_* \in 2^N$ satisfying (1) in $O(n)$ time. It is assumed that the numbers $r(j), d(j)$ $(j \in N)$ and e_k, f_k $(k = 1, 2, \ldots, \ell)$ are already sorted. We firstly compute an optimal solution $q \in \mathbb{R}^n$ of the problem (ULP) corresponding to $P(I, N, F)$, which can be done in $O(T_{\text{feas}}(n)) = O(n)$ time by using either of the algorithms in [7,20]. Then, we compute a partition $\{N_0, N_1, \ldots, N_v\}$ of N such that $q(N_h) = \max_{j \in N_h} d(j) - \min_{j \in N_h} r(j)$ $(h = 1, 2, \ldots, v)$ and that $N \setminus N_0$ is maximal under this condition, which can be done in $O(n)$ time. Since $\max_{j \in N_h} d(j) - \min_{j \in N_h} r(j) = \varphi(N_h)$ $(h = 1, \ldots, v)$, the set $X_* = N \setminus N_0$ is the unique maximal set with $q(X_*) = \varphi(X_*)$. Hence, Theorem 2 implies the following result.

Theorem 3. *The problem* $P(I, N, F)$ *can be solved in* $O(n \log n)$ *time. In particular, the problem* Single-ArbR-ArbD *can be solved in* $O(n \log n)$ *time.*

It should be mentioned that our algorithm for Single-ArbR-ArbD is similar to the divide-and-conquer algorithm by Shih et al. [19], but the two algorithms are based on different ideas. Indeed, the algorithm in [19] works only for instances with the numbers $\overline{p}(j), \underline{p}(j), r(j), d(j)$ given by integers, while ours can be applied to any problem with real numbers.

4   Identical Parallel Machines with the Same Release Dates and Different Due Dates

We apply the divide-and-conquer technique in Sect. 2 to the problem Ide-SameR-ArbD. To describe the algorithm, we consider a restriction on the availability of the machines. Suppose that we are given numbers b_i $(i \in M)$ and c such that machine i is available in the time interval $[b_i, c]$. In addition, we are given a subset F of jobs (*fixed-job set*) such that $p(j) = \overline{p}(j)$ for $j \in F$. We denote this variant of the problem Ide-SameR-ArbD by $P(m, B, c, N, F)$, where $B = \{b_i \mid i \in M\}$. Any subproblem which appears during the recursive decomposition of the problem Ide-SameR-ArbD is of the form $P(m, B, c, N, F)$; in particular, the original problem Ide-SameR-ArbD is the case where $b_1 = \cdots = b_m = 0$, $c = \max_{j \in N} d(j)$, and $F = \emptyset$.

The problem $P(m, B, c, N, F)$ can be formulated as the problem (LP) with the polymatroid rank function $\varphi : 2^N \to \mathbb{R}$ given by

$$\varphi(X) = \sum_{i=1}^{m} \max\{\min\{d(i), c\} - b_i, 0\},$$

where we assume that $b_1 \leq b_2 \leq \cdots \leq b_m$ and that $d(i)$ is the i-th largest number in $\{d(j) \mid j \in N\}$ for $i = 1, \ldots, m$. Let $k \in N$ be an integer with $|N_k \setminus F| = \lfloor \hat{n}/2 \rfloor$, where $\hat{n} = n - |F|$, and suppose that $X_* \in 2^N$ satisfies (1). Then, the problem $P(m, B, c, N, F)$ is decomposed into subproblems $P(m_1, B_1, c_1, N_1, F_1)$ and $P(m_2, B_2, c_2, N_2, F_2)$, where

$$
\begin{cases}
m_1 = \min\{m, |X_*|\}, \ B_1 = \{b_1, b_2, \ldots, b_{m_1}\}, \ c_1 = \min\{c, d(j_{m_1})\}, \\
N_1 = X_*, \ F_1 = (F \cap X_*) \cup (X_* \setminus N_k), \\
m_2 = m, \ B_2 = \{d(j_1), \ldots, d(j_{m_1}), b_{m_1+1}, \ldots, b_m\}, \ c_2 = c, \\
N_2 = N \setminus X_*, \ F_2 = (F \setminus X_*) \cup (N_k \setminus X_*),
\end{cases}
$$

where we assume that $\{j_1, j_2, \ldots, j_{m_1}\} \subseteq X_*$ and $d(j_i)$ is the i-th largest number in $\{d(j) \mid j \in X_*\}$ for $i = 1, \ldots, m_1$. In addition, we update p and $\bar{p}$ by (7). Finally, we put $\underline{p}(j) := \underline{p}(j) - \max\{0, d(j) - d(j_{m_1})\}$ and $\bar{p}(j) := \bar{p}(j) - \max\{0, d(j) - d(j_{m_1})\}$ for $j \in X_*$.

Suppose that $p_1 \in \mathbb{R}^{X_*}$ (resp., $p_2 \in \mathbb{R}^{N \setminus X_*}$) is an optimal solution of $P(m_1, B_1, c_1, N_1, F_1)$ (resp., $P(m_2, B_2, c_2, N_2, F_2)$). Then, the vector $p_* \in \mathbb{R}^n$ defined by

$$
p_*(j) = \begin{cases}
p_1(j) + \max\{0, d(j) - d(j_{m_1})\} & (j \in X_*), \\
p_2(j) & (j \in N \setminus X_*)
\end{cases}
$$

is an optimal solution of $P(m, B, c, N, F)$.

We now explain how to compute $X_* \in 2^N$ satisfying (1) in $O(n \log m)$ time. It is assumed that the numbers $d(j)$ ($j \in N$) are already sorted. By using a slight modification of the algorithm by Sahni [15], we can compute an optimal solution $q \in \mathbb{R}^n$ of the problem (ULP) corresponding to $P(m, B, c, N, F)$ in $O(T_{\text{feas}}(n)) = O(n \log m)$ time. Then, we compute the unique maximal set $X_* \in 2^N$ with $q(X_*) = \varphi(X_*)$. Using the following simple observations, we can find such X_* in $O(n \log m)$ time.

Lemma 2. We have $\{j \in N \mid p(j) < u(j)\} \subseteq X_*$. Moreover, any $j' \in N$ is contained in X_* if there exist $j \in X_* \setminus \{j'\}$ and a time interval $[e, f]$ satisfying the following conditions: $[e, f] \subseteq [r(j), d(j)]$, any portion of job j is not processed on $[e, f]$, and some portion of job j' is processed on $[e, f]$.

Theorem 4. The problem $P(m, B, c, N, F)$ can be solved in $O(n \log m \log n)$ time. In particular, Ide-SameR-ArbD can be solved in $O(n \log m \log n)$ time.

We can solve the problem Uni-SameR-ArbD in a similar way as Ide-SameR-ArbD by using the algorithm of Sahni and Cho [16]. The details are omitted.

Theorem 5. The problem Ide-SameR-ArbD can be solved in $O(mn \log n)$ time.

5   Uniform Parallel Machines with the Same Release/Due Dates

We apply the divide-and-conquer technique in Sect. 2 to the problem Uni-SameR-SameD. For the description of the algorithm, we consider the problem Uni-SameR-SameD with a subset F ob jobs (*fixed-job set*) such that $\underline{p}(j) = \bar{p}(j)$ for $j \in F$. We denote this problem by $P(M, N, F)$, where M and N denote the sets of machines and jobs, respectively. Note that $P(M, N, \emptyset)$ coincides with the original problem Uni-SameR-SameD. It is assumed that the speed of machines are already sorted and satisfy $s_1 \geq s_2 \geq \cdots \geq s_m$.

5.1   The First Algorithm

The problem $P(M, N, F)$ can be formulated as (LP) with the polymatroid rank function $\varphi : 2^N \to \mathbb{R}$ given by $\varphi(X) = dS_{\min\{m, |X|\}}$ $(X \in 2^N)$, where $S_h = \sum_{i=1}^h s_i$ $(h = 1, \ldots, m)$. It can be decomposed (or reduced) into subproblems of smaller size, as follows. We assume that the numbers $\{\overline{p}(j) \mid j \in N\} \cup \{\underline{p}(j) \mid j \in N\}$ is already sorted.

The next property is a direct application of Theorem 1 to the problem $P(M, N, F)$.

Lemma 3. *Let $k \in N$, and suppose that $X_* \in 2^N$ satisfies (1). Then, there exists an optimal solution $q \in \mathbb{R}^n$ of the problem $P(M, N, F)$ satisfying the following properties, where $h = |X_*|$:*
(i) if $h < m$, then $q(X_*) = dS_h$, $q(j) = \overline{p}(j)$ $(j \in N_k \setminus X_*)$, $q(j) = \underline{p}(j)$ $(j \in X_* \setminus N_k)$.
(ii) If $h \geq m$, then $q(N) = dS_m$ and $q(j) = \underline{p}(j)$ $(j \in N \setminus N_k)$.

Let $k \in N$ be an integer with $|N_k \setminus F| = \lfloor \hat{n}/2 \rfloor$, where $\hat{n} = n - |F|$, and suppose that $X_* \in 2^N$ satisfies (1). Such X_* can be computed in $O(n)$ time by Lemma 4 given below.

Lemma 4. *Suppose that the sorted list of the numbers $\mathcal{P} \equiv \{\overline{p}(j) \mid j \in N\} \cup \{\underline{p}(j) \mid j \in N\}$ is given. For any $X \in 2^N$, we can compute the value of $\widetilde{\varphi}(X)$ and a set $Y_* \in 2^N$ with $\widetilde{\varphi}(X) = \varphi(Y_*) + \overline{p}(X \setminus Y_*) - \underline{p}(Y_* \setminus X)$ in $O(n)$ time.*

Let $h = |X_*|$. If $h < m$, then the problem $P(M, N, F)$ can be decomposed into the following two subproblems $P(M_1, N_1, F_1)$ and $P(M_2, N_2, F_2)$, where

$$\begin{cases} M_1 = \{1, 2, \ldots, h\}, & N_1 = X_*, & F_1 = (F \cap X_*) \cup (X_* \setminus N_k), \\ M_2 = M \setminus M_1, & N_2 = N \setminus X_*, & F_2 = (F \setminus X_*) \cup (N_k \setminus X_*). \end{cases}$$

In addition, we update $\underline{p}$ and $\overline{p}$ by (7). Before solving the subproblems, we sort the numbers $\mathcal{P}_1 \equiv \{\overline{p}(j) \mid j \in N_1\} \cup \{\underline{p}(j) \mid j \in N_1\}$ and $\mathcal{P}_2 \equiv \{\overline{p}(j) \mid j \in N_2\} \cup \{\underline{p}(j) \mid j \in N_2\}$, which can be done in $O(n)$ time. Hence, the decomposition can be done in $O(n)$ time.

If $h \geq m$, then $P(M, N, F)$ can be reduced to the subproblem $P(M_1, N_1, F_1)$, where $M_1 = M$, $N_1 = N$, and $F_1 = F \cup (N \setminus N_k)$. In addition, we update $\underline{p}$ by $\overline{p}(j) := \underline{p}(j)$ $(j \in N \setminus N_k)$. Hence, the reduction can be done in $O(n)$ time as well.

The following result follows from Theorem 2 and the discussion above.

Theorem 6. *The first algorithm solves the problem $P(M, N, F)$ in $O(n \log n)$ time. In particular, Uni-SameR-SameD can be solved in $O(n \log n)$ time.*

5.2   The Second Algorithm

The running time of the first algorithm is dominated by the time for sorting the numbers in $\mathcal{P}$. To reduce the time complexity, we modify the first algorithm by using the information of the fixed-job set, so that it does not require the sorted list. We assume that the $\min\{m, |F|\}$ largest numbers in $\{\overline{p}(j) \mid j \in F\}$ and the number $\overline{p}(F)$ are given in advance. Recall that $\hat{n} = n - |F|$.

Lemma 5. *Suppose that the* $\min\{m, |F|\}$ *largest numbers in* $\{\overline{p}(j) \mid j \in F\}$ *and the number* $\overline{p}(F) = \sum_{j \in F} \overline{p}(j)$ *are given. For any* $X \in 2^N$, *we can compute the value of* $\widetilde{\varphi}(X)$ *and a set* $Y_* \in 2^N$ *with* $\widetilde{\varphi}(X) = \varphi(Y_*) + \overline{p}(X \setminus Y_*) - \underline{p}(Y_* \setminus X)$ *in* $O(\hat{n} + m \log m)$ *time.*

Hence, we can compute $X_* \in 2^N$ satisfying (1) in $O(\hat{n} + m \log m)$ time. Using the set X_* we decompose (or reduce) the problem $P(M, N, F)$ into subproblems in the same way as the first algorithm.

If $|X_*| < m$, then the problem $P(M, N, F)$ can be decomposed into the two subproblems $P(M_1, N_1, F_1)$ and $P(M_2, N_2, F_2)$. The second subproblem $P(M_2, N_2, F_2)$ is solved recursively by the second algorithm, while the first subproblem $P(M_1, N_1, F_1)$ is solved by the first algorithm in $O(|M_1| \log |M_1|) = O(m \log m)$ time. Before solving $P(M_2, N_2, F_2)$, we compute the $\min\{|M_2|, |F_2|\}$ largest numbers in $\{\overline{p}(j) \mid j \in F_2\}$ and the number $\overline{p}(F_2)$, which can be done in $O(\hat{n} + m \log m)$ time.

If $|X_*| \geq m$, the problem $P(M, N, F)$ is reduced to the subproblem $P(M_1, N_1, F_1)$, which is recursively solved by the second algorithm. Before solving the subproblem, we compute the $\min\{m, |F_1|\}$ largest numbers in $\{\overline{p}(j) \mid j \in F_1\}$ and the number $\overline{p}(F_1)$, which can be done in $O(\hat{n} + m \log m)$ time as well.

Let $T_2(m, n, \hat{n})$ denote the running time of the second algorithm for $P(M, N, F)$. Then, the following recursive formula holds:

$$T_2(m, n, \hat{n}) = \begin{cases} O(m \log m) & (\text{if } \hat{n} \leq 1), \\ O(\hat{n} + m \log m) + T_2(|M_2|, |N_2|, |N_2| - |F_2|) & (\text{if } \hat{n} \geq 2, |X_*| < m), \\ O(\hat{n} + m \log m) + T_2(|M_1|, |N_1|, |N_1| - |F_1|) & (\text{if } \hat{n} \geq 2, |X_*| \geq m). \end{cases}$$

Note that $|N_2| - |F_2| \leq \lceil \hat{n}/2 \rceil$ and $|N_1| - |F_1| \leq \lfloor \hat{n}/2 \rfloor$ by (2). Hence, we have $T_2(m, n, \hat{n}) = O(\hat{n} + m \log m \log \hat{n})$. As a preprocessing, we need to compute the $\min\{m, |F|\}$ largest numbers in $\{\overline{p}(j) \mid j \in F\}$ and the number $\overline{p}(F)$, which requires $O(n + m \log m)$ time. Hence, the following result holds.

Theorem 7. *The problem* $P(M, N, F)$ *can be solved in* $O(n + m \log m \log n)$ *time by the second algorithm. In particular,* Uni-SameR-SameD *can be solved in* $O(n + m \log m \log n)$ *time.*

Acknowledgements. The authors thank Satoru Iwata for discussions and valuable comments.

References

1. Ahuja, R.K., Orlin, J.B., Stein, C., Tarjan, R.E.: Improved algorithms for bipartite network flow. SIAM J. Comput. 23, 906–933 (1994)
2. Chung, J.Y., Shih, W.-K., Liu, J.W.S., Gillies, D.W.: Scheduling imprecise computations to minimize total error. Microprocessing and Microprogramming 27, 767–774 (1989)
3. Federgruen, A., Groenevelt, H.: Preemptive scheduling of uniform machines by ordinary network flow techniques. Management Sci. 32, 341–349 (1986)

4. Fujishige, S.: Submodular Functions and Optimization, 2nd edn. Elsevier, Amsterdam (2005)
5. Gallo, G., Grigoriadis, M.D., Tarjan, R.E.: A fast parametric maximum flow algorithm and applications. SIAM J. Comput. 18, 30–55 (1989)
6. Gonzales, T.F., Sahni, S.: Preemptive scheduling of uniform processor systems. J. ACM 25, 92–101 (1978)
7. Hochbaum, D.S., Shamir, R.: Minimizing the number of tardy job unit under release time constraints. Discrete Appl. Math. 28, 45–57 (1990)
8. Horn, W.: Some simple scheduling algorithms. Naval Res. Logist. Quat. 21, 177–185 (1974)
9. Janiak, A., Kovalyov, M.Y.: Single machine scheduling with deadlines and resource dependent processing times. European J. Oper. Res. 94, 284–291 (1996)
10. Leung, J.Y.-T.: Minimizing total weighted error for imprecise computation tasks and related problems. In: Leung, J.Y.-T. (ed.) Handbook of Scheduling, ch. 34. Chapman & Hall, Boca Raton (2004)
11. Leung, J.Y.-T., Yu, V.K.M., Wei, W.-D.: Minimizing the weighted number of tardy task units. Discrete Appl. Math. 51, 307–316 (1994)
12. McCormick, S.T.: Fast algorithms for parametric scheduling come from extensions to parametric maximum flow. Oper. Res. 47, 744–756 (1999)
13. McNaughton, R.: Scheduling with deadlines and loss functions. Management Sci. 12, 1–12 (1959)
14. Nowicki, E., Zdrzałka, S.: A bicriterion approach to preemptive scheduling of parallel machines with controllable job processing times. Discrete Appl. Math. 63, 237–256 (1995)
15. Sahni, S.: Preemptive scheduling with due dates. Oper. Res. 27, 925–934 (1979)
16. Sahni, S., Cho, Y.: Scheduling independent tasks with due times on a uniform processor system. J. ACM 27, 550–563 (1980)
17. Shakhlevich, N.V., Strusevich, V.A.: Preemptive scheduling problems with controllable processing times. J. Sched. 8, 233–253 (2005)
18. Shakhlevich, N.V., Strusevich, V.A.: Preemptive scheduling on uniform parallel machines with controllable job processing times. Algorithmica 51, 451–473 (2008)
19. Shih, W.-K., Lee, C.-R., Tang, C.-H.: A fast algorithm for scheduling imprecise computations with timing constraints to minimize weighted error. In: 21th IEEE Real-Time Syst. Symp., pp. 305–310. IEEE Computer Society, Los Alamitos (2000)
20. Shih, W.-K., Liu, J.W.S., Chung, J.-Y.: Algorithms for scheduling imprecise computations with timing constraints. SIAM J. Comput. 20, 537–552 (1991)
21. Shih, W.-K., Liu, J.W.S., Chung, J.-Y., Gillies, D.W.: Scheduling tasks with ready times and deadlines to minimize average error. ACM SIGOPS Oper. Syst., Rev. 23, 14–28 (1989)

Approximability of Average Completion Time Scheduling on Unrelated Machines

René A. Sitters*

Technische Universiteit Eindhoven
r.sitters@tue.nl

Abstract. We show that minimizing the sum of completion times on unrelated machines is APX-hard if preemption of jobs is allowed. Additionally, we show that randomized rounding of a convex quadratic program gives a non-preemptive schedule for which the sum of weighted completion times is less than 1.81 times the optimal preemptive sum. This factor is 2.78 if release dates are involved. We sketch how the ratios can be reduced further.

1 Introduction

In the last decade extensive research has been done on approximation algorithms for machine scheduling problems with minsum objective. The most difficult problems are the ones with precedence constraints. The area is still wide open here. (See [9] for a recent overview.) The approximability of classical machine scheduling problems without precedence constraints is much better understood. Almost all problems have shown to be either polynomial time solvable, or approximable within a factor $1 + \epsilon$ for arbitrary small constant ϵ. A few have shown to be APX-hard. A recent paper by Afrati and Milis [2] gives an extensive overview. Among the classical machine scheduling problems there is one problem that has not been classified so far: the problem of minimizing total completion time on unrelated machines in the preemptive setting: $R|pmtn|\sum C_j$. This holds also in the presence of release dates and job weights. All techniques for designing polynomial time approximation schemes have failed for these problems. In this paper we prove that even the simplest of these problems is APX-hard. Hence, none of these problems can be approximated in polynomial to within an arbitrary small constant, unless P=NP.

This result is interesting for two reasons: First, this provides one of the last missing pieces in the overall picture of machine scheduling with weighted sum of completion times objective. Second, the problem $R|pmtn|\sum C_j$ has the peculiar property that the preemptive problem is much harder to solve than the non-preemptive problem which was shown to be solvable by weighted matching thirtyfive years ago [3,6]. Intuitively, preemption should make problems easier, just as LP's are in general easier than ILP's. Indeed, for almost all scheduling

---

* Supported by a research grant from the Netherlands Organization for Scientific Research (NWO-veni grant).

D. Halperin and K. Mehlhorn (Eds.): ESA 2008, LNCS 5193, pp. 768–779, 2008.

problems the non-preemptive version is at least as hard to solve as the problem in the preemptive setting. In fact, $R|pmtn|\sum C_j$ is the only classical scheduling problem for which the preemptive version is APX-hard and the non-preemptive version is solvable in polynomial time.

The second contribution of this paper is an improvement of the best known approximation ratio for $R|pmtn|\sum w_j C_j$ (and $R|pmtn|\sum_j C_j$). Skutella [13] gave a 2-approximation algorithm for this problem. In this paper he showed the first application of convex quadratic programs to machine scheduling problems. Schulz and Skutella [10] and Queyranne and Sviridenko [8] published a $(2 + \epsilon)$-approximation using an interval-indexed linear program. One difficulty of improving on the constant 2 is finding good lower bounds on the optimal solution. Here, we give a new lower bound and show how a modification of the convex program used in [13] reduces the approximation ratio to 1.81

In [10], Schulz and Skutella raised the question whether a stronger LP-formulation could improve on the factor 2. We sketch how a similar modification leads to the same improved ratio. We also sketch how a combination of [8] and our algorithm leads to an even smaller approximation ratio. The analysis of this improvement is quite complicated and not included here.

The remaining of the paper is divided in two sections: approximability and non-approximability.

Table 1. Approximability of some classical parallel machine problems. The new results are written in <red>. A larger table is given in the recent paper by Afrati and Milis [2].

Problem	Lower bound	Upper bound
$Q\|r_j\|\sum_j w_j C_j$	NP-hard	PTAS [4]
$Q\|r_j, pmtn\|\sum_j w_j C_j$	NP-hard	PTAS [4]
$Rm\|r_j\|\sum_j w_j C_j$	NP-hard	PTAS [1]
$Rm\|r_j, pmtn\|\sum_j w_j C_j$	NP-hard	PTAS [1]
$R\|\|\sum_j C_j$	$-$	$\in$ P [3,6]
$R\|pmtn\|\sum_j C_j$	< APX-hard >, NP-hard [11]	< 1.81 >, 2 [13]
$R\|\|\sum_j w_j C_j$	APX-hard [5]	3/2 [13], $3/2 + \epsilon$ [10]
$R\|pmtn\|\sum_j w_j C_j$	< APX-hard >, NP-hard [11]	< 1.81 >, 2 [13]
$R\|r_j\|\sum_j C_j$ and $R\|r_j\|\sum_j w_j C_j$	APX-hard [5]	2 [13], $2 + \epsilon$ [10]
$R\|r_j, pmtn\|\sum_j w_j C_j$	< APX-hard >, NP-hard [11]	$2 + \epsilon$ [8], < 2.78 >

2   Approximability

In this section we present an algorithm that gives a non-preemptive schedule for which the sum of weighted completion times is less than 1.81 times the optimal preemptive sum. The algorithm builds on the convex program relaxations by Skutella [13]. In the end of this section we discuss how to get the same ratio using an LP-formulation given by Schulz and Skutella [10] and how we can get even smaller ratios if we combine any of these two algorithms with the algorithm by Quayranne and Sviridenko [8].

An instance of our problem $R|pmtn|\sum_j w_j C_j$ is given by numbers m and n and numbers $w_j, p_{ij} \in \mathbb{Q}^+$ for all $i \in \{1, 2 \ldots, m\}$ and $j \in \{1, 2 \ldots, n\}$. The time it takes to process job j completely on machine i is p_{ij}. Given the process time p_{ij}, we say that job j is processed with a *speed* $s_{ij} = 1/p_{ij}$ if it is processed on machine i. If job j is processed for a time t on machine i then the processed *fraction* will be $t \cdot s_{ij} = t/p_{ij}$. A schedule is an assignment of jobs to machines over time such that all jobs are completely processed. We do not allow a machine to work on more than one job at the time or two machines to work on the same job simultaneously. For a given schedule we denote the completion time of job j by C_j and the objective value is the sum of the weighted completion times, i.e., $\sum_{j=1}^{n} w_j C_j$.

Given a preemptive schedule σ we define $f_j^\sigma(x)$ as the speed at which job j is processed at time x and call f_j^σ the *density function* of job j in σ. The *mean busy time* M_j^σ of job j is defined as the average time at which it is processed. More precisely,

$$M_j^\sigma := \int_0^T f_j^\sigma(x)x\, dx,$$

where T is any upper bound on the completion time of j. Additionally, we define for given σ the *process time* P_j^σ as the total time that job j is processed.

Minimizing a linear function of mean busy times and processing times is in general easier than minimizing a linear function of completion times. For example, preemptively minimizing the total weighted mean busy time on a single machine with job release times is simply done by always processing the job with largest ratio w_j/p_j. However, minimizing the total weighted completion time is NP-hard.

One difficulty of improving on the approximation ratio of 2 is to find new lower bounds. If all machines are identical then $M_j^\sigma + P_j^\sigma/2$ is a lower bound on the completion time C_j^σ of a job j. This bound no longer holds in the unrelated machine model. The ratio's in [8,10,13] are based on the weaker bound $M_j^\sigma \leq C_j^\sigma$ and the bound $P_j^\sigma \leq C_j^\sigma$. The next theorem gives a new relation between the three concepts: completion time, mean busy time and process time. The proof is given in Section 2.1

Theorem 1. *For any instance I of $R|pmtn|\sum w_j C_j$ and feasible preemptive schedule σ for I there exists a feasible preemptive schedule σ' for I such that $M_j^{\sigma'} + P_j^{\sigma'} < 1.81\, C_j^\sigma$ for any job j.*

Corollary 1 (Lower bound). *For any instance I of $R|pmtn|\sum w_j C_j$ we have*

$$\min_\sigma \left(\sum_j w_j P_j^\sigma + w_j M_j^\sigma \right) < 1.81 \min_\sigma \left(\sum_j w_j C_j^\sigma \right). \tag{1}$$

We use this corollary in the following way. First, we give a convex quadratic program for which the optimal value Z^* is a lower bound on the left side of (1).

Second, we show how we can round any solution of the program with value Z to obtain a feasible non-preemptive schedule for which the expected sum of weighted completion times is at most Z. These two observation combined with Corollary 1 give us our approximation algorithm.

We introduce variables x_{ij} ($i \in \{1, 2, \ldots, m\}$ and $j \in \{1, 2, \ldots, n\}$) to denote the fraction of job j processed on machine i. To simplify notation we introduce for each machine i a total order $\prec_i$ on the set of jobs by setting $j \prec_i k$ if $w_j/p_{ij} > w_k/p_{ik}$ or $w_j/p_{ij} = w_k/p_{ik}$ and $j < k$.

Consider the following quadratic program (QP).

$$\text{minimize} \quad \sum_{j=1}^{n} w_j \left(P_j^{\text{QP}} + M_j^{\text{QP}} \right)$$

$$\text{subject to } P_j^{QP} = \sum_{i=1}^{m} x_{ij} p_{ij} \qquad \text{for all } j \quad (2)$$

$$M_j^{QP} = \sum_{i=1}^{m} x_{ij} \Big(\sum_{k \prec_i j} x_{ik} p_{ik} + x_{ij} p_{ij}/2 \Big) \qquad \text{for all } j \quad (3)$$

$$\sum_{i=1}^{m} x_{ij} = 1 \qquad \text{for all } j,$$

$$x_{ij} \geq 0 \qquad \text{for all } i, j$$

If the values x_{ij} are taken from a feasible preemptive schedule σ then (2) is exactly the process time of a job j. For given values x_{ij} the sum of weighted mean busy times is minimized if, on each machine, the jobs are ordered by Smith's ratio rule [14], i.e., in non-increasing order of w_j/p_{ij}. Hence, the mean busy time for a job j in the feasible schedule σ is at least

$$\sum_{i=1}^{m} x_{ij} \Big(\sum_{k \prec_i j} x_{ik} p_{ik} + x_{ij} p_{ij}/2, \Big)$$

which equals (3).

We rewrite (QP) in matrix notation and adopt the notation from [13]. Define $c_{ij} = w_j p_{ij}$ and, for any $i \in \{1, 2, \ldots, m\}$, let $i_1, i_2, \ldots, i_n$ be the indices of the jobs according to $\prec_i$. Let $c, x \in \mathbb{R}^{mn}$ be, respectively, the vector of all c_{ij}'s and x_{ij}'s ordered by increasing i and then, for each i, in the order $\prec_i$. The $mn \times mn$ matrix A is given by

$$A = \begin{pmatrix} A_1 & 0 & 0 & 0 \\ 0 & A_2 & 0 & 0 \\ \vdots & \vdots & \ddots & \vdots \\ 0 & 0 & \cdots & A_m \end{pmatrix} , \text{ where } A_i = \begin{pmatrix} w_{i_1} p_{i_1} & w_{i_2} p_{i_1} & \cdots & w_{i_n} p_{i_1} \\ w_{i_2} p_{i_1} & w_{i_2} p_{i_2} & \cdots & w_{i_n} p_{i_2} \\ \vdots & \vdots & \ddots & \vdots \\ w_{i_n} p_{i_1} & w_{i_n} p_{i_2} & \cdots & w_{i_n} p_{i_n} \end{pmatrix}.$$

Precisely, the entry (j, k) of submatrix A_i is $w_{i_{\max\{j,k\}}} p_{i_{\min\{j,k\}}}$. Now we can rewrite (QP) as

$$\text{minimize}\quad c^T x + \frac{1}{2} x^T A x \tag{4}$$

$$\text{subject to}\quad \sum_{i=1}^{m} x_{ij} = 1 \qquad\qquad \text{for all } j$$

$$x \geq 0$$

Convexity of this program now follows from the following lemma.

Lemma 1 (Skutella [13]). *Matrix A is positive semidefinite.*

The main difference with [13] is that our convex program (QP) is not a proper relaxation of $R|pmtn|\sum_j w_j C_j$. The objective value may be strictly larger than the minimum sum of weighted completion times. However, Theorem 1 makes up for this.

Randomized rounding. Given a solution with values x_{ij}, $(i \in \{1, 2, \ldots, m\}, j \in \{1, 2, \ldots, n\})$, we assign each job j independently from the others to one of the machines, where job j is assigned to machine i with probability x_{ij}. Then, on any every machine i we place the assigned jobs in the order $\prec_i$. For the given values x_{ij} let P_j^{QP} and M_j^{QP} be defined by (2) and (3) respectively. The new schedule is non-preemptive and expected completion time $E[C_j]$ of job j is easily expressed in the values x_{ij} as follows.

$$E[C_j] = \sum_{i=1}^{m} x_{ij} \Big(\sum_{k \prec_i j} x_{ik} p_{ik} + p_{ij} \Big)$$

$$= \sum_{i=1}^{m} x_{ij} p_{ij} + \sum_{i=1}^{m} x_{ij} \sum_{k \prec_i j} x_{ik} p_{ik}$$

$$< P_j^{QP} + M_j^{QP}.$$

Corollary 2. *Solving (QP) up to a sufficiently small additive constant ϵ and applying randomized rounding as above gives a randomized 1.81-approximation for $R|pmtn|\sum w_j C_j$.*

Corollary 3. *For any instance of $R|pmtn|\sum w_j C_j$, the value of the optimal non-preemptive schedule is no more than 1.81 times the value of the optimal preemptive schedule.*

In particular, the last corollary implies that we immediately get a deterministic 1.81-approximation for the unweighted problem $R|pmtn|\sum C_j$ by computing the optimal non-preemptive schedule. This problem can be formulated as a weighted matching problem ([3,6]) which solvable in polynomial time. We can easily de-randomize the algorithm using the method of conditional probabilities. We need to show that we can bound expected completion times on the condition that some jobs are already assigned to machines. In the related program, the matrix A in (4) is adjusted by removing the rows and columns of the assigned jobs and therefore remains positive semidefinite. The changes in the vector c are slightly more involved but have no effect on the convexity of the adjusted program.

2.1 Proof of Theorem 1

The theorem states that for any instance I of $R|pmtn|\sum w_j C_j$ and feasible preemptive schedule σ for I there exists a feasible preemptive schedule σ' for I such that $M_j^{\sigma'} + P_j^{\sigma'} < 1.81\, C_j^{\sigma}$ for any job j. Our proof is constructive.

For any $\beta \geq 1$ we can change schedule σ into a feasible schedule σ' by removing a $1 - 1/\beta$ fraction of every job and stretching the remaining schedule by a factor β. The fraction of a job processed in the new schedule will be exactly $1/\beta \cdot \beta = 1$. For a given $\beta \geq 1$ we may decide for each job *independently* what part to remove. We will compute a function $F(\beta)$ for which any job j can be rescheduled in this way such that its sum of mean busy time and processing time in the new schedule is at most $F(\beta)$ times its original completion time. Then, we minimize over β.

We now describe exactly how the schedule of an arbitrary j is modified for a given $\beta \geq 1$. Basically, we keep the $1/\beta$ fraction of j that has minimum processing time. To simplify notation assume w.l.o.g. that the machines are ordered in increasing processing time for job j, i.e., $p_{1j} \leq p_{2j} \leq \cdots \leq p_{mj}$. Let t_{ij} be the total time that machine i processes job j and let α_{ij} be the fraction of job j that is processed on machine i, i.e., $\alpha_{ij} = t_{ij}/p_{ij}$. Let $k_j \in \{1, \ldots, m\}$ and $q_j \in\,]0, 1]$ satisfy

$$1/\beta = \alpha_{1j} + \alpha_{2j} + \cdots + \alpha_{k_j-1,j} + q_j \cdot \alpha_{k_j,j}.$$

If we define $\gamma_j = t_1 + \cdots + t_{k-1} + q_j t_k$, then γ_j is the minimum amount of time in which a fraction $1/\beta$ of job j is processed in σ. Consequently, $\gamma_j \leq C_j/\beta$.

From job j we keep all its fractions processed on on machines $1, 2, \ldots, k_j - 1$ and an arbitrary $q_j \alpha_{k_j}$ fraction on machine k_j. Let $I_j \subseteq [0, C_j]$ be that part of the time in which these fractions are processed. Consequently, $|I_j| = \gamma_j$. We may assume that I_j is the union of a finite number of intervals. Since the whole schedule σ is stretched by a factor β, the set I_j is mapped onto a set I'_j of size $|I'_j| = \beta \gamma_j$. In the new schedule we process job j completely during I'_j.

Let p'_j and M'_j be, respectively, the total processing time and mean busy time of job j in σ'.

Lemma 2. $M'_j + p'_j \leq \max_{\tau \in]0, 1/\beta]} (\mathcal{M}(\beta, \tau) + \mathcal{P}(\beta, \tau)) \cdot C_j$, where

$$\mathcal{M}(\beta, \tau) := \frac{(\beta - \beta^2)\tau^2}{2(1 - \tau)} + \beta \quad and \quad \mathcal{P}(\beta, \tau) = \beta\tau. \tag{5}$$

Proof. Define $\tau = \gamma_j/C_j$. Then $\tau \in\,]0, 1/\beta]$. The part of job j that we keep has length γ_j and its new length becomes $p'_j = \beta\gamma_j = \beta\tau C_j = \mathcal{P}(\beta, \tau)C_j$.

The analysis for M'_j is more involved. Let $f_j(x)$ and $f'_j(x)$ be the density functions of job j in σ and σ', respectively. Then $f'_j(\beta x) = f_j(x)$ for any $x \in I_j$.

Now let $M_j^{(I)}$ be the part of M_j contributed by the fraction $1/\beta$ that is processed in I_j, i.e.,

$$M_j^{(I)} = \int_{x \in I_j} f_j(x)x\,dx.$$

The mean busy time of j in the new schedule is β^2 times $M_j^{(I)}$ since the schedule is stretched by a factor β and the processed fraction increases from $1/\beta$ to 1. More precisely,

$$M_j' = \int_{y \in I_j'} f_j'(y)y\,dy = \int_{x \in I_j} f_j'(\beta x)\beta x\,d(\beta x) = \beta^2 \int_{x \in I_j} f_j(x)x\,dx = \beta^2 M_j^{(I)}.$$

Next, we give a lower bound on the density $f_j(x)$ for $x \in I_j$. Since we assumed that the machines are ordered according to their processing time for j, we have $p_{k_j j} = t_{k_j j}/\alpha_{k_j j} \le t_{k_j+1,j}/\alpha_{k_j+1,j} \le \cdots \le t_{mj}/\alpha_{mj}$, where k_j is defined as before. This implies

$$p_{k_j j} = \frac{t_{k_j j}}{\alpha_{k_j j}} = \frac{(1-q_j)t_{k_j j}}{(1-q_j)\alpha_{k_j j}} \le \frac{(1-q_j)t_{k_j j} + t_{k_j+1,j} + \cdots + t_{mj}}{(1-q_j)\alpha_{k_j j} + \alpha_{k_j+1,j} + \cdots + \alpha_{mj}} \le \frac{C_j - \gamma_j}{1 - 1/\beta}.$$

Thus, the speed at which job j is processed in σ at time $x \in I_j$ is

$$f_j(x) \ge 1/p_{k_j j} \ge \delta_j, \quad \text{where } \delta_j := (1 - 1/\beta)/(C_j - \gamma_j). \tag{6}$$

An upper bound on $M_j^{(I)}$ now follows from the following optimization problem. We compute the maximum of

$$\int_{x \in I_j} f_j(x)x\,dx,$$

where the maximum is taken over all density functions f_j that satisfy

$$\text{(i)} \ \ f_j(x) \ge \delta_j \text{ for all } x \in I_j, \text{ and (ii)} \int_{x \in I_j} f_j(x)\,dx = 1/\beta.$$

Constraint (i) is given by (6) and (ii) is by definition of I_j. Clearly, the maximum is attained in the limit situation where the density is δ_j everywhere except for an infinitesimal region before time C_j, where a fraction $1/\beta - \gamma_j\delta_j$ is processed. Hence,

$$M_j^{(I)} \le \int_{x \in I_j} \delta_j x\,dx + (1/\beta - \gamma_j\delta_j)C_j. \tag{7}$$

An upper bound for the first term follows from

$$\int_{x \in I_j} x\,dx \le \int_{C_j - \gamma_j}^{C_j} x\,dx = \frac{1}{2}C_j^2 - \frac{1}{2}(C_j - \gamma_j)^2 = \gamma_j C_j - \frac{\gamma_j^2}{2}.$$

Substituting this in (7) we get

$$M_j^{(I)} \le \delta_j(\gamma_j C_j - \frac{\gamma_j^2}{2}) + (\frac{1}{\beta} - \gamma_j \delta_j)C_j = -\delta_j \frac{\gamma_j^2}{2} + \frac{1}{\beta}C_j$$

Next we substitute the values $\gamma_j = \tau C_j$ and $\delta_j = (1 - 1/\beta)/(C_j - \gamma_j)$.

$$M_j' = \beta^2 M_j^{(I)} \le -\delta_j \frac{\tau^2}{2}\beta^2 C_j^2 + \beta C_j$$

$$= -\frac{1 - 1/\beta}{(1 - \tau)C_j}\frac{\tau^2}{2}\beta^2 C_j^2 + \beta C_j$$

$$= \left(\frac{(\beta - \beta^2)\tau^2}{2(1 - \tau)} + \beta\right) C_j.$$

This completes the proof of Lemma 2. □

For fixed β, the expression $\mathcal{M}(\beta, \tau) + \mathcal{P}(\beta, \tau)$ is maximized for value $\tau^* = 1 - \sqrt{(\beta - 1)/(\beta + 1)}$. (This can easily be computed by hand but is omitted in this abstract. It is also easily verified that $\tau^* \in]0, 1/\beta]$.) Now define

$$F(\beta) := \mathcal{M}(\beta, \tau^*) + \mathcal{P}(\beta, \tau^*).$$

Lemma 2 says that for any $\beta \ge 1$, schedule σ can be transformed in a feasible schedule σ' such that

$$M_j^{\sigma'} + p_j^{\sigma'} \le F(\beta)C_j^{\sigma},$$

for any job j. With a mathematical solver we find that the minimum of F is attained for $\beta^* = \frac{1}{24}u^2 + (\frac{1}{56}\sqrt{78} - \frac{1}{42})u - \frac{1}{12}$ with $u = (8 + 6\sqrt{78})^{1/3}$, implying $\beta^* \approx 1.089$. Note however that for our proof it is not necessary to know this exact value and it suffices to verify that $F(1.089) < 1.81$, which completes the proof of Theorem 1.

2.2 Release Dates

We sketch how to adjust the algorithm if jobs have arbitrary release dates r_j. We only comment on the part that differs from [13] and refer the reader to that paper for more details.

We denote the new convex quadratic program by QP2. The n release dates partition the time into at most n timeslots. Instead of using variables x_{ij} we use variables x_{ijk} to model the fraction of job j processed on machine i in the k'th timeslot. Again we formulate expressions P_j^{QP2} and M_j^{QP2} that are lower bounds on, respectively, the processing time and mean busy time of job j in the following sense. If the values x_{ijk} are taken from a feasible schedule σ, then $P_j^{QP2} = P_j^{\sigma}$ and $M_j^{QP2} \le M_j^{\sigma}$ for any job j. The exact formulation is quite extensive and is found in a slightly different form in [13]. The next theorem is similar to Theorem 1 and is given here without proof.

Theorem 2. *For any instance I of $R|r_j, pmtn| \sum w_j C_j$ and feasible preemptive schedule σ for I there exists a feasible preemptive schedule ρ for I such that $2M_j^\rho + P_j^\rho < 2.78\, C_j^\sigma$ for any job j.*

The objective function we use in QP2 is essentially different however:

$$\text{minimize } \sum_{j=1}^{n} w_j \left(2M_j^{QP2} + P_j^{QP2} \right).$$

Randomized rounding of the program is similar to the case without release dates. The only difference is that no job can start before its release date.

Lemma 3

$$E[C_j] \leq 2M_j^{QP2} + P_j^{QP2}.$$

Corollary 4. *Solving (QP2) up to a sufficiently small additive constant ϵ and applying randomized rounding as above gives a randomized 2.78-approximation for $R|r_j, pmtn| \sum w_j C_j$.*

The approximation factor that was originally obtained by Skutella is 3 and Quayranne and Sviridenko [8] give a randomized $(2+\epsilon)$ approximation using an LP-relaxation. Hence, we do not improve on the best approximation ratio here. However, unlike [8], the schedule that we compute here is non-preemptive which yields the following corollary.

Corollary 5. *For any instance of $R|r_j, pmtn| \sum w_j C_j$, the value of the optimal non-preemptive schedule is less than 2.78 times the value of the optimal preemptive schedule.*

2.3   Improving the Approximation Ratio

Before showing how we can improve the constant 1.81, we will sketch how the interval-indexed LP-formulation and randomized rounding technique given by Schulz and Skutella [10] leads to the same approximation ratios 1.81 and 2.78. Queyranne and Sviridenko [8] use a different random assignment to get a $2 + \epsilon$-approximation but that technique does not lead to an improved ratio here. The interval indexed LP uses variables y_{ijt} indicating the fraction of interval t on machine i used by job j. Given an LP-solution, a job is assigned to interval t on machine i with probability $y_{ijt}\Delta_t/p_{ij}$, which is the fraction of j processed in this slot t of length Δ_t. Given the assignment, we get a feasible schedule by processing on each machine the jobs as early as possible in the order of the timeslots assigned to the jobs. See [10] for a precise formulation. That papers shows that any solution to the LP can be rounded such that the expected completion time of any job is at most $P_j^{LP} + M_j^{LP}$, where P^{LP} and M_j^{LP} are the process time and mean busy time of the pseudo-schedule defined by the LP-solution. Hence, all we need to do is to change the objective function to $P_j^{LP} + M_j^{LP}$. Theorem 1 now guarantees a 1.81-approximation. In case of release dates we use $P_j^{LP} + 2M_j^{LP}$.

Now we sketch how the $(2 + \epsilon)$-approximation algorithm by Queyranne and Sviridenko [8] can be used to improve on the constant 1.81. The main idea in that paper is the following. Given a feasible schedule σ for $R|(r_j), pmtn| \sum C_j$, we stretch the schedule by a factor $\beta \geq 1$ and then process each job within its new intervals as early as possible. If $1/\beta$ is chosen at random from $]0, 1]$ with density function $f(x) = 2x$, then the expected sum of weighted completion times is at most $2 \sum_j w_j M_j^\sigma$. Finding a schedule that minimizes $\sum_j w_j M_j^\sigma$ can be done up to a factor $(1+\epsilon)$ by an interval-indexed linear programming. Placing this algorithm next to the machinery of Theorem 1, we observe that the worst case scenario for this algorithm is precisely the best scenario for Theorem 1. To illustrate this consider an instance I with

$$\min_\sigma \sum_j w_j M_j^\sigma = \alpha \min_\sigma \sum_j w_j C_j^\sigma, \quad (\alpha \leq 1). \tag{8}$$

The approximation guarantee obtained from the algorithm of Queyranne and Sviridenko is $2\alpha(1 + \epsilon)$. Hence, the worst situation occurs when $\alpha \approx 1$. From the proof of Theorem 1 we see that in that case

$$\min_\sigma \sum_j w_j (M_j^\sigma + P_j^\sigma) \approx \min_\sigma \sum_j w_j C_j^\sigma.$$

The approximation factor of our algorithm is approximately 1 in this case. We can actually prove that applying both algorithms and taking the best of the two gives a ratio strictly smaller than 1.81. This optimization still has to be done but we do not expect the ratio to be smaller than 1.5.

3   Inapproximability

The problem $R|pmtn| \sum C_j$ is known to be NP-hard [11]. Surprisingly, the non-preemptive version can be solved in polynomial time. Here, we give a reduction which shows that the problem is even APX-hard. The reduction itself is simpler than the one used in [11]. This simplification is essential to obtain an approximation preserving reduction. However, the proof that this reduction is correct is much more difficult and it is omitted here. (See technical report [12] for the full proof).

We reduce from the maximum bounded 3-dimensional matching problem which was proven to be APX-hard by Kann [7].

Maximum bounded 3-Dimensional Matching (Max-3DM-B)

An instance is given by sets $A = \{a_1, \ldots, a_m\}$, $B = \{b_1, \ldots, b_m\}$, and $C = \{c_1, \ldots, c_m\}$ and a set $T \subseteq A \times B \times C$ of cardinality n, such that $n \leq \delta m$ for some constant $\delta > 1$. The goal is to find a subset $S \subseteq T$ of maximum cardinality such that no two triples of S agree in any coordinate.

In fact, for any $\delta > 1$ there is a constant $\gamma < 1$ such that is an NP-complete problem to decide wether there is a matching of size m or wether the largest matching has size at most γm.

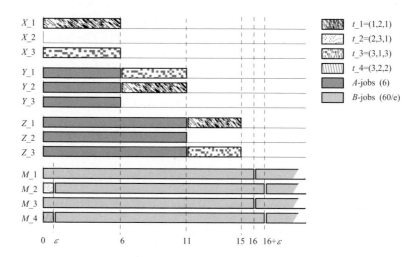

Fig. 1. An optimal schedule σ^* for the given instance in which $m = 3$ and $n = 4$. The maximum matching has cardinality $k = 2$.

Theorem 3. *The problem $R|pmtn|\sum C_j$ is APX-hard.*

Proof. We reduce from the maximum bounded 3-dimensional matching problem and take $\delta = 2$, i.e. $n = 2m$. Given an instance I_M of MAX-3DM-B we write $T = \{t_1, \ldots, t_n\}$ and simplify notation by writing $t_j = (x_j, y_j, z_j) \in \{1, \ldots, n\}^3$ in stead of $t_j = (a_{x_j}, b_{y_j}, c_{z_j})$. We define an instance I_R of the scheduling problem with $3m + n$ machines and $(15/\epsilon + 1)n + 2m$ jobs, where $1/\epsilon$ is a large integer which value we choose appropriately later. (We will show that $1/\epsilon = 15$ suffices, giving a total of $226n + 2m = 454m$ jobs.)

Machines: For each of the three coordinates we define m machines: $X_1, \cdots, X_m, Y_1, \cdots, Y_m$ and $Z_1, \cdots, Z_m$. Further, we define for each triple $t_j \in T$ one machine M_j.

Next we define 3 types of jobs: *A-jobs, B-jobs,* and *triple jobs.*

A-jobs: For each machine Y_i we define one job with processing requirement 6 on this machine and with an infinite processing requirement on any of the other $3m + n - 1$ machines. Similarly, for each machine Z_i we define one job with processing requirement 11 on that machine and with an infinite processing requirement on any other machine. These $2m$ jobs form the set of A-jobs.

B-jobs: The B-jobs are defined in a similar way: for each machine M_i we define $15/\epsilon$ jobs with processing requirement 16 on that specific machine and an infinite processing requirement on any of the other machines. The total number of B-jobs is $15n/\epsilon$.

Triple jobs: For each triple $t_j = (x_j, y_j, z_j)$ we define one triple job j with processing requirements $18, 15,$ and 12 on, respectively, machine $X_{x_j}, Y_{y_j},$ and

Z_{z_j}. The processing requirement on machine M_j is ϵ and is infinite on any of the other $3m + n - 4$ machines.

This completes the reduction. The proof of correctness is omitted in this abstract and can be found in [12].

References

1. Afrati, F., Bampis, E., Chekuri, C., Karger, D., Kenyon, C., Khanna, S., Milis, I., Queyranne, M., Skutella, M., Stein, C., Sviridenko, M.: Approximation schemes for minimizing average weighted completion time with release dates. In: FOCS 1999, pp. 32–44 (1999)
2. Afrati, F., Milis, I.: Designing ptass for min-sum scheduling problems. Discrete Appl. Math. 154(4), 622–639 (2006)
3. Bruno Jr., J., Coffman, E.G., Sethi, R.: Scheduling independent tasks to reduce mean finishing time. Communications of the ACM 17, 382–387 (1974)
4. Chekuri, C., Khanna, S.: A PTAS for minimizing weighted completion time on uniformly related machines. In: Orejas, F., Spirakis, P.G., van Leeuwen, J. (eds.) ICALP 2001. LNCS, vol. 2076, pp. 848–861. Springer, Heidelberg (2001)
5. Hoogeveen, J.A., Schuurman, P., Woeginger, G.J.: Non-approximability results for scheduling problems with minsum criteria. INFORMS Journal on Computing 13, 157–168 (2001)
6. Horn, W.A.: Minimizing average flow time with parallel machines. Operations Research 21, 846–847 (1973)
7. Kann, V.: Maximum bounded 3-dimensional matching is MAX SNP-complete. Information Processing Letters 37, 27–35 (1991)
8. Queyranne, M., Sviridenko, M.: A (2+epsilon)-approximation algorithm for the generalized preemptive open shop problem with minsum objective. J. Algorithms 45(2), 202–212 (2002)
9. Queyranne, M., Schulz, A.S.: Approximation bounds for a general class of precedence constrained parallel machine scheduling problems. SIAM J. Comput. 35(5), 1241–1253 (2006)
10. Schulz, A.S., Skutella, M.: Scheduling unrelated machines by randomized rounding. SIAM Journal on Discrete Mathematics 15, 450–469 (2002)
11. Sitters, R.A.: Complexity of preemptive minsum scheduling on unrelated parallel machines. J. Algorithms 57(1), 37–48 (2005)
12. Sitters, R.A.: Inapproximability of average completion time scheduling, SPOR-report, Technische Universiteit Eindhoven (2008)
13. Skutella, M.: Convex quadratic and semidefinite programming relaxations in scheduling. J. ACM 48(2), 206–242 (2001)
14. Smith, W.E.: Various optimizers for single-stage production. Naval Research Logistics Quarterly 3, 59–66 (1956)

Relative Convex Hulls
in Semi-dynamic Subdivisions

Mashhood Ishaque[1,*] and Csaba D. Tóth[2,**]

[1] Dept. of Comp. Sci., Tufts University, Medford, MA
`mishaq01@cs.tufts.edu`
[2] Dept. of Mathematics, University of Calgary, AB
`cdtoth@ucalgary.ca`

Abstract. We present data structures for maintaining the relative convex hull of a set of points (*sites*) in the presence of pairwise non-crossing line segments (*barriers*) that subdivide a bounding box into simply connected faces. Our data structures have $O((n + m) \log n)$ size for n sites and m barriers. They support $O(m)$ barrier insertions and $O(n)$ site deletions in $O((m + n) \operatorname{polylog}(mn))$ total time, and can answer analogues of standard convex hull queries in $O(\operatorname{polylog}(mn))$ time.

Our data structures support a generalization of the sweep line technique, in which the sweep *wavefront* may have arbitrary polygonal shape, possibly bending around obstacles. We reduce the total time of m online updates of a polygonal sweep wavefront from $O(m\sqrt{n}\operatorname{polylog} n)$ to $O((m + n) \operatorname{polylog}(mn))$.

1 Introduction

Relative convex hull of a set of sites in a simply connected polygonal domain.
The *convex hull*, ch(S), of a set S of points (*sites*) in the plane is the shortest polygon that circumscribes S (see Fig. 1(a)). If the configuration space is restricted to a polygonal domain, then the Euclidean distance is typically replaced by the Euclidean *shortest path* (or *geodesic*) distance. There is a *unique* shortest path between any two sites iff the domain is *simply connected*. We consider two interpretations of the *relative convex hull*. For a finite set S of point sites and a simply connected open polygonal domain P,

- the *geodesic hull* gh$_P(S)$ is the shortest weakly simple polygon contained in P and circumscribing $S \cap P$;
- the *bubble hull* bh$_P(S)$ is a collection of *simple* polygons such that they jointly circumscribes all sites of $S \cap P$, each polygon is gh$_P(S')$ for some subset $S' \subseteq S$, and the number of polygons is minimal.

See Fig. 1(b-c). If D is a set of pairwise interior-disjoint polygons, then we denote by gh$_D(S)$ (resp. bh$_D(S)$) the collection of geodesic (resp., bubble) hulls of S w.r.t. the polygons in D. The set of all points circumscribed by the polygons in

---

* Partially supported by NSF grant CCF-0431027.
** Partially supported by NSERC grant RGPIN-328155.

D. Halperin and K. Mehlhorn (Eds.): ESA 2008, LNCS 5193, pp. 780–792, 2008.

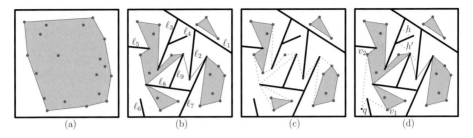

Fig. 1. (a) A convex hull of 20 points; (b) the geodesic hulls of the points in two simply connected domains formed by 9 barriers; (c) the bubble hull of the same point set in the same subdivision; (d) a tangent query q and an extreme point query h

$\text{gh}_D(S)$ (resp. $\text{bh}_D(S)$) is denoted by $\overline{\text{gh}}_D(S)$ (resp. $\overline{\text{bh}}_D(S)$). Clearly, we have $\overline{\text{bh}}_D(S) \subseteq \overline{\text{gh}}_D(S)$. Intuitively, the bubble hull is the kernel of the geodesic hull, it can be obtained from the geodesic hull by successively splitting it at singularities (i.e., reflex vertices of P visited twice by the geodesic hull). Obviously, if P is convex, then $\text{gh}_P(S) = \text{bh}_P(S) = \text{ch}(S \cap P)$.

The *geodesic hull* was introduced by Sklansky *et al.* [20] in the digital imaging community and later rediscovered in computational geometry (c.f. [21]).

Results. We present data structures to maintain the bubble hull and the geodesic hull. For n sites and m barriers they both have size $O((n + m) \log n)$, and can be built in $O((n + m) \operatorname{polylog}(mn))$ preprocessing time. They both support a mixed sequence of $O(m)$ barrier insertions and $O(n)$ site deletions in $O((n + m) \operatorname{polylog}(mn))$ total time. The worst case time of a single update operation is $O(m \operatorname{polylog}(nm))$ for a site deletion, and $O((m+n^{1/2+\delta}) \operatorname{polylog}(mn))$ for a barrier insertion for any $\delta > 0$.

Queries. We would like our data structures to answer certain elementary queries, similar to classical convex hull queries. Here $\text{rch}_P(S)$ may refer to either one of the two relative convex hulls $\text{gh}_P(S)$ and $\text{bh}_P(S)$); queries (iv) and (v) are defined for $\text{gh}_P(S)$ only, since $\text{bh}_P(S)$ may consists of several components:

(i)   find the adjacent vertices of $\text{rch}_P(S)$ for a given vertex (*gift-wrapping*);
(ii) decide whether a given point in P lies in $\overline{\text{rch}}_P(S)$ (*point inclusion*);
(iii) find the intersection $\ell \cap \text{rch}_P(S)$ for a given line segment $\ell \subset P$ (*line stabbing*).
(iv) for a given point q in P but outside of $\overline{\text{gh}}_P(S)$, find all vertices $v \in \text{gh}_P(S)$ such that the segment of the geodesics between q and v is tangent to $\text{gh}_P(S)$ at vertex v (the analogue of the *tangent* query, Fig. 1.(d)).
(v)   For a given chord h of P disjoint from $\text{gh}_P(S)$, find a parallel chord h', if possible, which is tangent to $\text{gh}_P(S)$ and separates h from $\text{gh}_P(S)$ (the analogue of the *extreme point* query, Fig. 1.(d)).

Our bubble hull data structure answers query (i), defined below, in $O(1)$ time, since the bubble hull is maintained explicitly; it also answers queries (ii)–(iii) in $O(\operatorname{polylog}(mn))$ time. Our geodesic hull data structure answers queries (i)–(v) in $O(\text{polylog}\,(mn))$ time. Our geodesic hull data structure relies on the bubble hull structure, and hence the updates and the queries are slightly more expensive than for the bubble hull.

1.1   Applications

Adversarial polyline sweep. In a classical sweep line algorithm, a vertical line scans the plane from left to right. The sweep line meets any set of sites in the order determined by their x-coordinates. It is not so easy to determine the order in which sites are scanned if the plane is swept by a polyline wavefront, driven by obstacles that has to be avoided and paths that has to be followed, although polygonal wavefronts are used in many applications. We consider a model where we are given n sites, and an adversary sweeps the plane with a polyline wavefront in m *moves*. The wavefront is a simple polygon at all times: initially it is an empty triangle, and each move expands the interior of the polygon by a triangle with one side adjacent to the current wavefront, each move may be modeled as a continuous deformation of the wavefront. Determining the order in which n sites are swept with currently available data structures, would require either m distinct relative convex hull computations (in $O(m(n + m)\log n)$ total time) or m simplex range reporting queries (in $O(m\sqrt{n})$ total time).

The adversarial polyline sweep problem can be solved with our data structure in $O((m+n)\,\text{polylog}\,(mn))$ time, using site deletions and barrier insertions only. For each move of the adversary, we insert the two new edges of the wavefront boundary into our subdivision. These edges separate a triangle adjacent to the current wavefront. With respect to a triangle (or any convex polygon), the relative convex hull is just the (classical) convex hull. We can move continuously the wavefront from one edge of the triangle to the two other edges, and repeatedly delete the first site hit by the wavefront.

1.2   Related Results

Sweep-line algorithms. Graham's scan [13] computed the convex hull of n points in the plane in $O(n\log n)$ time by scanning the plane with a line rotating about an extremal point, it is considered the first sweep-line algorithm. A typical plane sweep, of Bentley and Ottmann [2], scans the plane with a vertical line from left to right. The topological sweep of Chazelle and Edelsbrunner [5,10] (originally developed for optimal segment intersection detection) scans the plane with a polyline *wavefront* which deforms in response to the data it encounters.

Dynamic convex hulls. Preparata [19] gave a semi-dynamic (insert-only) convex hull data structure, which supports point insertion in $O(\log n)$ time. Chazelle [4] and later Hershberger and Suri [14] gave a semi-dynamic (delete-only) data structure, which supports n point deletions in $O(n\log n)$ time. The classic data structure for fully dynamic convex hull in the plane is due to Overmars and van Leeuwen [18], supporting updates in $O(\log^2 n)$ worst-case time.

So far, Brodal and Jacob [3,15] gave the best data structure for dynamic convex hull in the plane. It supports updates in $O(\log n)$ amortized time, and basic convex hull queries in $O(\log n)$ time.

Geodesic paths. The theoretical study of geodesics in the interior of a simple polygon was pioneered by Toussaint [21,22]. He showed that the geodesic hull $\mathrm{gh}_P(S)$ of a set S of n points in a simple n-gon P can be computed in $O(n \log n)$ time, and any line segment in the interior of P crosses at most two edges of $\mathrm{gh}_P(S)$. Mitchell [17] and Ghosh [11] survey results on geometric shortest paths.

Dynamic subdivisions. Chiang *et al.* [9] dynamically maintained the trapezoidal subdivision of n noncrossing segment barriers in the plane with $O(\log^3 n)$ amortized update time. Goodrich and Tammasia [12] gave an improved method based on balanced geodesic triangulation for maintaining dynamic planar subdivisions. The data structure uses $O(n)$ space and $O(\log^2 n)$ update time.

Range reporting. A data structure for simplex reporting, which is based on Matoušek's technique of simplicial partitioning with low crossing number [16], uses $O(n \operatorname{polylog} n)$ space, and achieves a query time of $O(n^{1/2+\epsilon} + k)$. The best lower bound for simplex reporting queries in the plane is due to Chazelle and Rosenberg [7] who showed that, on a pointer machine, a query time of $O(n^\delta + k)$ requires $\Omega(n^{2(1-\delta)-\epsilon})$ space. Thus for any data structure for planar simplex reporting that uses $O(n \operatorname{polylog} n)$ space, there is a lower bound of $\Omega(n^{1/2-\epsilon} + k)$ on the query time.

2   Tools

Shortest paths, point location, and ray shooting in a dynamic subdivision. Chazelle *et al.* [6] showed that a balanced geodesic triangulation of a polygon with n vertices can be used for answering ray shooting queries in the polygon in $O(\log n)$ time. Goodrich and Tamassia [12] generalized this data structure to dynamic subdivisions defined by noncrossing line segments where each face is a simple polygon. They maintain a balanced geodesic triangulation of each face. For m segments, the data structure has $O(m)$ size. Each segment insertion and deletion, point location, and ray shooting query takes $O(\log^2 m)$ time. It reports a shortest (geodesic) path between two points in $O(\log^2 m + k)$ time, where k is the length of the path. However, it can report $O(1)$ information about the shortest paths in $O(\log^2 m)$ time.

Geometric partition trees. A *geometric partition tree* for n points in the plane is a rooted binary tree T where (1) every node $v \in T$ corresponds to a convex cell C_v in the plane; (2) the root at level 0 corresponds to the plane (or a bonding box); (3) for every nonleaf node $v \in T$ the cell C_v is tiled by the two convex cells corresponding to the children of v; and (4) every cell C_v, $v \in T$ at level k of T contains at most n/λ^k points, for some fixed λ, $1 < \lambda \le 2$. In particular, the convex cells C_v, for all leaf nodes $v \in T$ form a subdivision of the entire plane (or the bounding box).

Geometric partition trees with low stabbing numbers. The *stabbing number* of a geometric graph or a subdivision is the maximum number of edges crossed by a straight line. Chazelle *et al.* [8,1] showed that one can construct a geometric partition tree in $O(n \log n)$ time such that the stabbing number of the corresponding subdivision of the plane is $O(n^{\frac{1}{2}+\delta})$, for any fixed $\delta > 0$.

3   Barriers and Geometric Partition Trees

We present a few basic structural properties of the bubble hull (without proof).

Proposition 1.   *1. For a set S of sites and a simply connected domain P, the bubble hull $\mathrm{bh}_P(S)$ is unique.*
  2. A line segment $\ell \subset P$ intersects both $\mathrm{gh}_P(S)$ and $\mathrm{bh}_P(S)$ in at most two points.
  3. If $P_1 \subset P_2$, then $\overline{\mathrm{bh}}_{P_1}(S) \subseteq \overline{\mathrm{bh}}_{P_2}(S)$.

The motivation for introducing bubble hulls is the following feature of geodesic hulls: The insertion of m barriers may induce $\Omega(m(m+n))$ combinatorial changes in $\mathrm{gh}_P(S)$ (see Fig. 2). However, we show in Proposition 2 below that the insertion of m barriers induce only $O(m + n)$ combinatorial changes in $\mathrm{bh}_P(S)$.

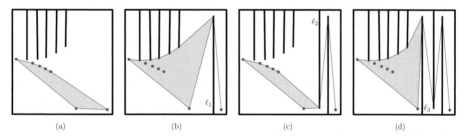

(a)   (b)   (c)   (d)

Fig. 2. The successive insertion of m barriers may induce $\Omega(m(m+n))$ combinatorial changes in $\mathrm{gh}_P(S)$

Representation of geodesic hulls. In each simply connected face f, the geodesic hull $\mathrm{gh}_f(S)$ is connected and its vertices are sites and barrier endpoints. If two consecutive vertices are sites, then they belong to the same component of $\mathrm{bh}_f(S)$. The portions of $\mathrm{gh}_f(S)$ between two consecutive sites is the geodesic path between those sites. We represent $\mathrm{gh}_f(S)$ as a cyclic alternating sequence of paths $(b_1, g_1, b_2, g_2, \ldots, g_k)$, where b_i is a portion of a component of $\mathrm{bh}_f(S)$ between two sites and g_i is a geodesic path between sites along distinct components of $\mathrm{bh}_f(S)$; only the first and last vertex of each portion will be stored.

   The backbone of our data structure is a geometric partition tree T for n point sites in a bounding box B, which is computed at preprocessing and remains fixed thereafter. Each node $v \in V(T)$ corresponds to a cell C_v. If D is a subdivision of the bounding box B into simply connected faces, let $D(v)$ denote the subdivision of cell C_v by the portion of the barriers clipped to C_v. Storing $D(v)$ for every node $v \in V(S)$ would be prohibitively expensive: if every barrier intersects $\Omega(\sqrt{n})$ cells then storing $D(v)$ for all leaf nodes would require $\Omega(m\sqrt{n})$ space. Therefore, we store only some carefully chosen portions of $D(v)$ (c.f. Section 4). The size of the relative convex hulls, however, for all $v \in V(T)$ is close to linear.

Lemma 1. *The union of all* $\mathrm{bh}_{D(v)}(S)$ *(resp.,* $\mathrm{gh}_{D(v)}(S)$*) for all nodes* $v \in V(T)$ *of a geometric partition tree* T *is a plane graph with* $O(n + m \log n)$ *edges.*

Proof. For the planarity, note that due to the hierarchy of the geometric partition tree T, we have $\overline{\mathrm{bh}}_{D(w)}(S) \subseteq \overline{\mathrm{bh}}_{D(v)}(S)$ and $\overline{\mathrm{gh}}_{D(w)}(S) \subseteq \overline{\mathrm{gh}}_{D(v)}(S)$ wherever w is a descendant of v. Hence, the edges of the bubble hulls (resp., geodesic hulls) of different levels cannot cross.

Assume w.l.o.g. that the $2m$ endpoints of the barriers are disjoint (using virtual coordinates, if necessary). We say that an endpoint of barrier ℓ is incident to a face f if the endpoint and an incident portion of ℓ lie on the boundary of f. At the leaf nodes of T, $S \cap C_v$ is a singleton, and its convex hull has no edges. Consider now a non-leaf node $v \in V(T)$ whose children are w_1 and w_2. The faces of $D(w_1)$ are separated from the faces of $D(w_2)$ by a line h_v. Each face $f \in D(v)$ is the union of some faces $F_1 \subseteq D(w_1)$ and $F_2 \subseteq D(w_2)$ of the two child subdivisions (Fig. 3, middle). Hence, $\mathrm{rch}_f(S)$ can be constructed by merging the relative convex hulls $\mathrm{rch}_{D(w_1)}(S)$ and $\mathrm{rch}_{D(w_2)}(S)$. The merge step creates new edges along geodesic paths between components of $\mathrm{rch}_{D(W_1)}(S)$ and $\mathrm{rch}_{D(w_2)}(S)$ (each may consists of several components). Each geodesic is either a single edge (common tangent) or passes through barrier endpoints lying in C_v. At most two geodesics pass through any barrier endpoint in $\mathrm{gh}_f(S)$, and at most one geodesic for $\mathrm{bh}_f(S)$. If the merge step reduces the number of components by γ_v and the new geodesics pass through m_v barrier endpoints, then $O(\gamma_v + m_v)$ new edges are created. Summing up the terms $O(\gamma_v)$ over all $v \in V(T)$, we obtain $O(n)$. Summing up the terms $O(m_v)$ over all $v \in V(T)$ at a level of T, we have $O(m)$, which gives $O(m \log n)$ over all $\log n$ levels of T. $\qquad\square$

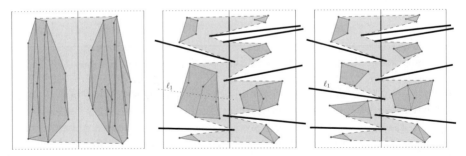

Fig. 3. Merging the relative convex hulls of two convex hulls (left). Merging the geodesic hulls of the subdivisions of two consecutive vertical slabs before (middle) and after (right) inserting a new barrier ℓ_i.

Combinatorial changes. If a new barrier ℓ partitions a face $f \in D(v)$ into two faces f_1 and f_2, we will replace $\mathrm{rch}_f(S)$ by $\mathrm{rch}_{f_1}(S)$ and $\mathrm{rch}_{f_2}(S)$. If ℓ has an endpoint in the interior of f (note that at most one endpoint of ℓ may lie in the interior of f since every face is simply connected), then f is deformed to a face f' and we will replace $\mathrm{rch}_f(S)$ by $\mathrm{rch}_{f'}(S)$. Of course, an update of a relative convex hull w.r.t. the subdivision $D(v)$ is necessary only if ℓ intersects $\mathrm{rch}_f(S)$. The following lemma counts the intersections between the edges of the relative convex hulls and successively inserted barriers.

Lemma 2. *We are given a set S of n sites in a bounding box B and a geometric partition tree T. If we update $\mathrm{rch}_{D(v)}(S)$ for all $v \in V(T)$ during an intermixed sequence of m barrier insertions and $O(n)$ site deletions, then there are altogether $O(m+n)$ intersections between new barriers and current edges of $\mathrm{rch}_{D(v)}(S)$ for all $v \in V(T)$ at each level of T.*

Proof. For every $i \in \mathbb{N}$, there are $O(2^i)$ nodes $v \in V(T)$ at level i such that C_v contains at least $n/2^{i+1}$ and less than $n/2^i$ sites. Distinguish two types of intersections between a new barrier ℓ and the current relative convex hull $\mathrm{rch}_{D(v)}(S)$ for $v \in V(T)$.

Type 1: ℓ partitions a current face $f \in D(v)$ into two faces, both of which contain sites of S. In this case, the number of connected components of $\mathrm{rch}_{D(v)}(S)$ increases by one. A set of k sites can recursively be partitioned into nontrivial subsets at most $k-1$ times. Hence, summing all type 1 events for all m barriers and all $v \in V(T)$ at level i, we obtain $O(n/2^i)O(2^i) = O(n)$.

Type 2: ℓ has an endpoint in the interior of a current face $f \in D(v)$, which contains sites of S. At each level of T, each barrier endpoint lies in a unique cell of $D(v)$ for a unique $v \in V(T)$. Hence there are $O(n)$ type 2 events.   □

In Section 4 below, we describe in detail how to maintain the relative convex hulls w.r.t. each subdivision $D(v)$, $v \in V(T)$.

Proposition 2. *Given n sites in a bounding box B, a mixed sequence of m barrier insertions and $O(n)$ site deletions induce $O(m+n)$ combinatorial changes in $\mathrm{bh}_D(S)$.*

Proof. $\mathrm{bh}_D(S)$ may split into several components due to a barrier insertion or a site deletion. A barrier insertion and a site deletion both decrease the region circumscribed by the bubble hull, that is, $\overline{\mathrm{bh}}_{D_1}(S_1) \subseteq \overline{\mathrm{bh}}_{D_2}(S_2)$ if $S_1 \subseteq S_2$ and $\mathrm{int}(D_1) \subseteq \mathrm{int}(D_2)$. Hence, if a point $p \in S$ is a vertex of $\mathrm{bh}_D(S)$ at one step, it remains a vertex of a polygon of $\mathrm{bh}_D(S)$ until p is deleted. If an endpoint q of a barrier ℓ is a vertex of $\mathrm{bh}_D(S)$ at one step, it remains a vertex of a polygon in $\mathrm{bh}_D(S)$ until all sites on one side of the line through ℓ are deleted, or a component of $\mathrm{bh}_D(S)$ visits q twice and it is split into two components. Every edge deletion or creation in $\mathrm{bh}_D(S)$ can be charged to an event involving an endpoint of that edge. There are four possible events: a site $s \in S$ becomes a vertex of $\mathrm{bh}_D(S)$; a vertex $s \in S$ of $\mathrm{bh}_D(S)$ is deleted; a barrier endpoint q becomes a vertex of $\mathrm{bh}_D(S)$; or a barrier endpoint q is no longer a vertex of

$\mathrm{bh}_D(S)$. There are $n + m$ possible events, each one is responsible for two edge changes in $\mathrm{bh}_D(S)$. □

Proposition 3. *Given n sites in a bounding box B, a mixed sequence of m barrier insertions and $O(n)$ site deletions induce $O(m+n)$ combinatorial changes in the our representation of $\mathrm{gh}_D(S)$ as a cyclic alternating sequences of portions of $\mathrm{bh}_D(S)$ and geodesic paths.*

Proof (sketch). A site deletion or barrier insertion may trigger the splitting of a component of $\mathrm{bh}_D(S)$ into several components $O(m)$ times (at most once for each barrier). If the corresponding portion of $\mathrm{bh}_S(D)$ lies in $\mathrm{gh}_D(S)$, then it is replaced by two portions of the resulting components of $\mathrm{bh}_D(S)$ and a geodesic path between them, that is, $O(1)$ combinatorial changes in the representation of $\mathrm{gh}_D(S)$. Besides the effects of splitting the bubble hull into several components, each site deletion or barrier insertion incurs only $O(1)$ change in the affected portion of $\mathrm{gh}_D(S)$ and in the two adjacent portions. □

4   Data Structure

Bubble hull data structure. We are given a set of n sites and a subdivision D formed by set of barriers in a bounding box B. Our data structure has three main components: (1) a geometric partition tree T for S, where every node $v \in V(T)$ will store numerous items; (2) plane graphs G_i, $i = 1, 2, \ldots, \log n$, one for each level of T. The vertices of G_i are the sites and the barrier endpoints, the edges are formed by the barriers, all bubble hulls $\mathrm{bh}_{D(v)}(S)$ for the subdivisions $D(v)$ at level i of the T, and an anchor edge between each convex component of $\mathrm{bh}_{D(v)}(S)$ and a nearby barrier endpoint, the faces are simply connected; (3) dynamic data structures of Goodrich and Tamassia [12] for each face of each G_i.

At each node $v \in V(T)$, we store C_v. We store some faces of the subdivision $D(v)$. Let the *parent* of a face $f \in D(v)$ be the face $f' \in D(v')$ such that $v' \in V(T)$ is the parent of v and $f \subseteq f'$. At node v, we store a face $f \in D(v)$ if f or its parent contains a site of S; we also store f if f or its parent is incident to a barrier endpoint. We store some edges of $\mathrm{bh}_{D(v)}(S)$. For a leaf $v \in V(T)$, we have $|S \cap C_v| \leq 1$, and so $\mathrm{bh}_{D(v)}$ has no edges. For a nonleaf node $v \in V(T)$, we store the line h_v that partitions C_v into two cells. We store each segment of h_v clipped in a stored face $f \in D(v)$. We store each component of $\mathrm{bh}_{D(v)}(S)$ in a doubly linked edge list and a binary search tree; and store also the cyclic list of sites along each component.

We store the plane graph G_i, $i = 1, 2, \ldots, \log n$, formed by the barriers and all edges of $\mathrm{bh}_{D(v)}(S)$ for all $v \in V(T)$ at level i of T (see Fig. 3). In addition, for every convex component of $\mathrm{bh}_{D(v)}(S)$, we store an *anchor* edge that connects it to a reflex vertex of D (recall that the components of $\mathrm{bh}_D(S)$ are mutually occluded from each other). The first edge where a component of $\mathrm{bh}_{D(v)}(S)$ diverge from $\mathrm{gh}_{D(v)}(S)$ is a good choice for an anchor. The anchors divide the region $f \backslash \overline{bh}_f(S)$ surrounding the bubble hull into a *simply connected* face (e.g., Fig. 3, right). Let $\Phi(G_i)$ denote the set of faces of G_i. We maintain the dynamic data structure of [12] for each face $\varphi \in \Phi(G_i)$. This completes our data structure for maintaining the bubble hull.

Geodesic hull data structure. In addition to all components of the bubble hull data structure, we store $\mathrm{gh}_{D(v)}(S)$ for every $v \in V(T)$. Here $\mathrm{gh}_{D(v)}(S)$ is represented as an cyclic alternating sequence of paths $(b_1, g_1, b_2, g_2, \ldots, g_k)$, where b_i is a portion of a component of $\mathrm{bh}_{D(v)}(S)$ (represented by the counter-clockwise first and last sites), and g_i is a geodesic path in a face of Φ between two sites of different components of $\mathrm{bh}_{D(v)}(S)$ (represented by the two sites).

Space requirement. The geometric partition tree T has size $O(n)$. Recall that the cells C_v for nodes $v \in V(T)$ at each level correspond to a partition of the bounding box B. If a face $f \in D(v)$ is incident to m_f barrier endpoints, then it has at most $4 + m_f$ edges. Each barrier endpoint is incident to two faces at each level of T. Hence storing faces of all subdivisions $D(v)$, which are either incident to a barrier endpoint or contain a site, requires $O((n+m)\log n)$ space. The bubble hulls $\mathrm{bh}_{D(v)}(S)$ for all nodes v at a single level of T jointly have $O(n+m)$ edges. Storing $\mathrm{bh}_{D(v)}(S)$ explicitly for all $v \in V(T)$ requires $O((n+m)\log n)$ space. The size of each G_i is $O(n+m)$, and so the dynamic data structure of Goodrich-Tamassia [12] for the all faces of G_i requires $O(n+m)$ space. All graphs G_i, $i = 1, 2, \ldots,, \log n$, jointly use $O((n+m)\log n)$ space. In our representation of geodesic hulls, with selected sites, $\mathrm{gh}_{D(v)}(S)$ for all nodes v at a level of T jointly have at most n edges. Storing $\mathrm{gh}_{D(v)}(S)$ for all $v \in V(T)$ requires $O(n\log n)$ space.

4.1   Updates and Queries

Primitives. In the Goodrich-Tamassia data structure [12], each barrier insertion and deletion, point location, or ray shooting query takes $O(\log^2 m)$ time. It reports the shortest path $\pi_f(p_1, p_2)$ between p_1 and p_2 in $O(\log^2 m + k)$ time where k is the size of $\pi_f(p_1, p_2)$. For two points, p_1 and p_2, it can report the first and the last segments, as well as the middle vertex of $\pi_f(p_1, p_2)$ in $O(\log^2 m)$ time. For two points p_1, p_2 and a chord h, it can report the intersection of $\pi_f(p_1, p_2)$ and h in $O(\log^2 m)$ time. Given three points p, q_1, q_2, the first segments where $\pi_f(p, q_1)$ and $\pi_f(p, q_2)$ differ can also be reported in $O(\log^2 m)$ time.

   With the queries of the data structure of [12], we can compute the *common tangent geodesics of two disjoint geodesic hulls*: Given two sets of sites, S_1 and S_2 in a face f such that $\mathrm{gh}_f(S_1)$ and $\mathrm{gh}_f(S_2)$ are disjoint, find the pairs of vertices $(v_1, v_2) \in S_1 \times S_2$ such that $\pi_f(v_1, v_2)$ is the shortest path in f tangent to $\mathrm{gh}_f(S_1)$ and $\mathrm{gh}_f(S_2)$ at the endpoints v_1 and v_2, respectively (Fig. 4(ab)). The common tangent geodesics can be used for merging the geodesic hulls into $\mathrm{gh}_f(S_1 \cup S_2)$. Searching for v_1 and v_2 is analogous to finding the common tangents between disjoint convex polygons [18]. With $O(\log n)$ shortest path queries, each in $O(\log^2 m)$ time, we can find pairs of *sites* $(s_1, s_2) \in S_1 \times S_2$ such that $\pi_f(s_1, s_2)$ is tangent to $\mathrm{gh}_f(S_1)$ and $\mathrm{gh}_f(S_2)$ at s_1 and s_2, respectively. If the endpoints s_1 and s_2 are the only common vertices of $\pi_f(s_1, s_2)$ with $\mathrm{gh}_f(S_1)$ and $\mathrm{gh}_f(S_2)$, then $v_1 = s_1$ and $v_2 = s_2$. Otherwise, v_1 and v_2 are the first vertices where

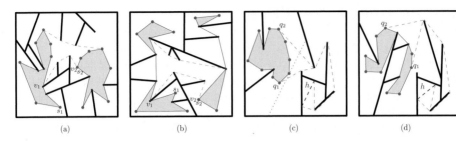

Fig. 4. The common tangent geodesics between two geodesic hulls (ab). The common geodesic hulls between a chord h and a geodesic hull (cd).

$\pi_f(s_1, s_2)$ diverges from $\mathrm{gh}_f(S_1)$ and $\mathrm{gh}_f(S_2)$, resp., and hence v_1 and v_2 can be computed with the above mentioned three-point query of [12] in $O(\log^2 m)$ time. The common tangent geodesics can be computed in $O(\log n \log^2 m)$ time.

The common tangent geodesics can be used to compute the bubble hull from the geodesic hull and the bubble hulls of the two subfaces. Let f be a face of a subdivision $D(v)$, where a line h_v partitions f into some faces $f_1, f_2, \ldots, f_\kappa$. Assume for a moment that we are given $\mathrm{gh}_f(S)$ explicitly and $\mathrm{bh}_{f_k}(S)$ for all $k = 1, 2, \ldots, \kappa$. Then we can compute $\mathrm{bh}_f(S)$ by successively pruning the singularities (i.e., vertices visited twice by $\mathrm{gh}_f(S)$). Refer to Fig. 1(c). If p is a singularity (which is necessarily a barrier endpoint), then find the two pairs of closest sites, (s_1, s_2) and (s_3, s_4) along $\mathrm{gh}_f(S)$ such that s_1, s_3 are on the same side of p. Here both $\pi_f(s_1, s_2)$ and $\pi_f(s_3, s_4)$ pases through p. Denote by R_j the component of a bubble hull $\mathrm{bh}_{f_k}(S)$ that contains s_j for $j = 1, 2, 3, 4$. Split the $\mathrm{gh}_f(S)$ into two geodesic hulls, by removing $\pi_f(s_1, s_2)$ and $\pi_f(s_3, s_4)$, and inserting instead the common tangent geodesic between R_1, R_3 and the common tangent geodesic between R_2, R_4. The pruning each singularity takes $O(\log n \log^2 m)$ time. If $\mathrm{bh}_f(S)$ has t components, then we can compute it in $O(t \log n \log^2 m)$ time.

Site deletion. Assume we delete site $s \in S$, where s corresponds to a leaf $v_0 \in V(T)$. Update the information at all $\log n$ nodes $v \in V(T)$ where $s \in C_v$. Delete every face $f \in D(v)$ whose parent face contained no other site but s. Update $\mathrm{bh}_{D(v)}(S)$ bottom up. No update is necessary if s is in the interior of $\mathrm{bh}_{D(v)}(S)$. Assume that s is on the vertex of a component $\mathrm{gh}_f(S')$ of $\mathrm{bh}_f(S)$ for some face $f \in D(v)$ and $S' \subseteq S$. If f contains no other site, then $\mathrm{bh}_f(S)$ is deleted. Otherwise assume that s has already been deleted from $\mathrm{bh}_{f_1}(S)$, where f_1 is the child face of f containing s.

Compute $\mathrm{gh}_f(S' \setminus \{s\})$ in $O(\log n \log^2 m)$ time as follows. Let a and b denote the two closest sites of s along $\mathrm{gh}_f(S')$. Let R_a and R_b be the components of the corresponding bubble hulls $\mathrm{bh}_{f_k}(S)$ containing a and b, resp. (which have already been updated). Compute the common geodesic tangent of R_a and R_b. If $\mathrm{gh}_f(S' \setminus \{s\})$ is a simple polygon, then $\mathrm{bh}_f(S' \setminus \{s\}) = \mathrm{gh}_f(S' \setminus \{s\})$ and we are done. However, if $\mathrm{gh}_f(S' \setminus \{s\})$ is not a simple polygon, we need to compute $\mathrm{bh}_f(S \setminus \{s\})$ by successively pruning the singularities as described above (Fig. 1(c)).

Barrier insertion. Let ℓ be a barrier inserted (refer to Fig. 3). Insert ℓ into the Goodrich-Tamassia data structures in $O(\log^2 m)$ time. Since ℓ does not cross other barriers, it intersects at most one face in each subdivision $D(v)$, $v \in V(T)$. In a top-down traversal of T, find all faces $f_v \in D(v)$ in our data structure that intersect ℓ. Update the faces f_v. Some of the faces may be split by ℓ into two faces. If a new face and its parent contain no site, the new face is deleted from our data structure.

Compute all intersection points with $\mathrm{bh}_{D(v)}(S)$ using a ray shooting data structure at $O(\log^2(m + n))$ cost per intersection. Locate all faces $f \in D(v)$ where ℓ intersects $\mathrm{bh}_f(S)$ in a top-down traversal of T. If ℓ is disjoint from $\mathrm{bh}_f(S)$, then it is disjoint from the bubble hull in all descendent faces. Update $\mathrm{bh}_f(S)$ in all faces bottom-up as follows.

Assume that ℓ intersects the component $\mathrm{gh}_f(S')$ of a bubble hull $\mathrm{bh}_f(S)$, for some $f \in D(v)$ and $S' \subseteq S \cap f$. Assume that all descendant faces have already been updated. Distinguish two cases:

Case 1: ℓ intersects $\mathrm{bh}_f(S)$ in exactly one point p. Find the pair of sites, say s_1 and s_2, along $\mathrm{gh}_{f(v)}(S')$ closest to p. Let R_1 and R_2 be the bubble hulls at the children faces of f containing s_1 and s_2, respectively. Compute $\mathrm{gh}_{f\setminus\ell}(S')$ by replacing $\pi_f(s_1, s_2)$ with the common tangent geodesics between R_1 and p, and between p and R_2. If $\mathrm{gh}_{f\setminus\ell}(S')$ is a simple polygon, then we are done; otherwise prune successively the singularities to obtain $\mathrm{bh}_{f\setminus\ell}(S')$.

Case 2: ℓ intersects $\mathrm{bh}_{f(v)}(S)$ in two points. Then ℓ partitions the point set S' into some point sets S_1' and S_2'. Find the pairs of sites, say (s_1, s_2) and (s_3, s_4), along $\mathrm{gh}_f(S')$ closest to the intersection points with ℓ, such that s_1 and s_3 are on the same side of ℓ. Let R_j be the bubble hulls at the children faces of f containing s_j for $j = 1, 2, 3, 4$. Compute $\mathrm{gh}_{f\setminus\ell}(S_1')$ and $\mathrm{gh}_{f\setminus\ell}(S_2')$ by replacing $\pi_f(s_1, s_2)$ and $\pi_f(s_3, s_4)$ with the common tangent geodesics between R_1, R_3 and R_2, R_4 in the face $f \setminus \ell$. If $\mathrm{gh}_{f\setminus\ell}(S_1')$ and $\mathrm{gh}_{f\setminus\ell}(S_2')$ are simple polygons, then we are done; otherwise prune successively the singularities to obtain $\mathrm{bh}_{f\setminus\ell}(S')$. The geodesic hull $\mathrm{gh}_{f\setminus\ell}(S)$ can be updated analogously in a bottom-up traversal.

A single barrier insertion takes $O(\kappa_\ell \text{ polylog}(mn))$ time, where κ_ℓ is the number of cells stabbed by ℓ. Here $\kappa_\ell = O(n \log n)$ is a trivial bound (which is tight, e.g., for a partition tree into vertical slabs [18]); and we have $\kappa_\ell = O(m + n^{1/2+\delta})$ for a $\delta > 0$ for a partition tree of low stabbing number [1,8].

Queries. Here, we discuss query (v) only for space limitations. Refer to the full paper for a detailed description of the remaining queries (i)–(iv).

Query (v) We can check whether the query chord $h = p_1 p_2$ is indeed disjoint from $\mathrm{gh}_D(S)$ in $O(\log n \log^2 m)$ time, using the line stabbing query (iii). Then locate the face f of the subdivision D containing h. Compute the common tangent geodesics between h and $\mathrm{gh}_f(S)$, which meet $\mathrm{gh}_f(S)$ at some vertices q_1 and q_2. The chord h, the two common tangent geodesics, and the porion of $\mathrm{gh}_f(S)$ between q_1 and q_2 forms a geodesic quadrilateral (Fig. 4(cd)). Every chord parallel to h that separates h from $\mathrm{gh}_f(S)$ must cross both common tangent geodesics, so the point of tangency along $\mathrm{gh}_f(S)$, if exists, must be between q_1 and q_2. The portion of $\mathrm{gh}_f(S)$ between q_1 and q_2 is a convex polygonal chain, hence it has at most one tangent parallel to h. Since $\mathrm{gh}_f(S)$ is not stored directly, we first find the portion of $\mathrm{gh}_f(S)$ (a geodesic path or a portion of $\mathrm{bh}_f(S)$) that possibly has a tangent parallel to h in a binary search in $O(\log n)$ time. If it is in a portion of a bubble hull, then we can find the tangency point in a binary search in $O(\log n)$ time. If it is in some geodesic path $\pi_f(v_1, v_2)$ along $\mathrm{gh}_f(S)$, then a binary search takes $O(\log m)$ queries with the [12] data structure, in $O(\log^3 m)$ total time. Altogether, query (v) can be answered in $O(\log(mn) \log^2 m)$ time.

References

1. Agarwal, P.K., Sharir, M.: Applications of a new space-partitioning technique. Discrete Comput. Geom. 9, 11–38 (1993)
2. Bentley, J.L., Ottmann, T.A.: Algorithms for reporting and counting geometric intersections. IEEE Trans. Comput. C-28(9), 643–647 (1979)
3. Brodal, G.S., Jacob, R.: Dynamic planar convex hull. In: Proc. FOCS, pp. 617–626. IEEE, Los Alamitos (2002)
4. Chazelle, B.: On the convex layers of a planar set. IEEE Trans. Inform. Theory IT-31(4), 509–517 (1985)
5. Chazelle, B., Edelsbrunner, H.: An optimal algorithm for intersecting line segments in the plane. J. ACM 39(1), 1–54 (1992)
6. Chazelle, B., Edelsbrunner, H., Grigni, M., Guibas, L.J., Hershberger, J., Sharir, M., Snoeyink, J.: Ray shooting in polygons using geodesic triangulations. Algorithmica 12, 54–68 (1994)
7. Chazelle, B., Rosenberg, B.: Simplex range reporting on a pointer machine. Comput. Geom. Theory Appl. 5(5), 237–247 (1996)
8. Chazelle, B., Sharir, M., Welzl, E.: Quasi-optimal upper bounds for simplex range searching and new zone theorems. Algorithmica 8, 407–429 (1992)
9. Chiang, Y.-J., Preparata, F.P., Tamassia, R.: A unified approach to dynamic point location, ray shooting, and shortest paths in planar maps. SIAM J. Comput. 25, 207–233 (1996)
10. Edelsbrunner, H.: Algorithms in Combinatorial Geometry. EATCS Monographs on Theoretical Computer Science, vol. 10. Springer, Heidelberg (1987)
11. Ghosh, S.: Visibility Algorithms in the Plane. Cambridge University Press, New York (2007)
12. Goodrich, M.T., Tamassia, R.: Dynamic ray shooting and shortest paths in planar subdivisions via balanced geodesic triangulations. J. Algorithms 23, 51–73 (1997)
13. Graham, R.L.: An efficient algorithm for determining the convex hull of a finite planar set. Inform. Process. Lett. 1, 132–133 (1972)
14. Hershberger, J., Suri, S.: Applications of a semi-dynamic convex hull algorithm. BIT 32, 249–267 (1992)
15. Jacob, R.: Dynamic Planar Convex Hull, PhD thesis, University of Aarhus, Aarhus, Denmark (2002)
16. Matousek, J.: Geometric range searching. ACM Comput. Surv. 26
17. Mitchell, J.S.B.: Geometric shortest paths and network optimization. Handbook of Computational Geometry. Elsevier, Amsterdam (2000)
18. Overmars, M.H., van Leeuwen, J.: Maintenance of configurations in the plane. J. Comput. Syst. Sci. 23, 166–204 (1981)

19. Preparata, F.P.: An optimal real-time algorithm for planar convex hulls. Commun. ACM 22, 402–405 (1979)
20. Sklansky, J., Chazin, R.L., Hansen, B.J.: Minimum perimeter polygons of digitized silhouettes. IEEE Trans. Comput. C-21, 260–268 (1972)
21. Toussaint, G.T.: Shortest path solves translation separability of polygons, Report SOCS-85.27, School Comput. Sci., McGill Univ., Montreal, PQ (1985)
22. Toussaint, G.T.: An optimal algorithm for computing the relative convex hull of a set of points in a polygon. In: Signal Processing III: Theories and Applications, pp. 853–856 (1986)

An Experimental Analysis of Robinson-Foulds Distance Matrix Algorithms

Seung-Jin Sul and Tiffani L. Williams

Department of Computer Science
Texas A&M University
College Station, TX 77843-3112
{sulsj,tlw}@cs.tamu.edu

Abstract. In this paper, we study two fast algorithms—HashRF and PGM-Hashed—for computing the Robinson-Foulds (RF) distance matrix between a collection of evolutionary trees. The RF distance matrix represents a tremendous data-mining opportunity for helping biologists understand the evolutionary relationships depicted among their trees. The novelty of our work results from using a variety of different architecture- and implementation-independent measures (i.e., percentage of bipartition sharing, number of bipartition comparisons, and memory usage) in addition to CPU time to explore practical algorithmic performance. Overall, our study concludes that HashRF performs better across the various performance measures than its competitor, PGM-Hashed. Thus, the HashRF algorithm provides scientists with a fast approach for understanding the evolutionary relationships among a set of trees.

Keywords: phylogenetic trees, RF distance, performance analysis.

1 Introduction

Given a collection of organisms (or taxa), the objective of a phylogenetic analysis is to produce an evolutionary tree describing the genealogical relationships between the taxa. Since the true evolutionary history for a set of taxa is unknown, many phylogenetic techniques use stochastic search algorithms to solve NP-hard optimization criteria such as maximum likelihood and maximum parsimony. During a phylogenetic search, thousands of candidate trees can be found, each representing a hypothesis of the true tree. The collection of candidate trees represent a tremendous data-mining for understanding the evolutionary relationships depicted among the trees. For example, trees could be clustered based on the topological distances between every pair of trees [1]. However, such clustering strategies require fast algorithms for computing the distance between every pair of trees in the collection of interest.

In this paper, we study two of the fastest algorithms—HashRF [2], [3] and PGM-Hashed [4]—to compute a $t \times t$ Robinson-Foulds (RF) distance [5] matrix in $O(nt^2)$ time. Figure 1 presents an overview of the RF matrix problem. Here, t is the number of trees in the collection and n is the number of taxa (or leaves) in

D. Halperin and K. Mehlhorn (Eds.): ESA 2008, LNCS 5193, pp. 793–804, 2008.
© Springer-Verlag Berlin Heidelberg 2008

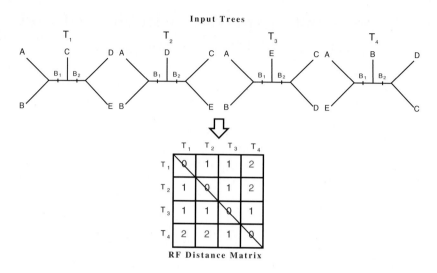

Fig. 1. Overview of computing the RF distance matrix. The tree collection consists of four phylogenies: T_1, T_2, T_3, and T_4. Bipartitions (or internal edges) in a tree are labeled B_i, where i ranges from 1 to 2. For example, according to the RF matrix, the number of bipartition that are different between trees T_1 and T_2 is 1.

each tree. Day [6] provided an optimal linear time algorithm for computing the RF distance between two trees by utilizing a special cluster representation of the trees. By using repeated applications of Day's algorithm, the RF distance matrix can be computed in $O(nt^2)$ time. Although the PGM-Hashed algorithm by Pattengale, Gottlieb, and Moret has the same theoretical complexity as repeated applications of Day's approach, PGM-Hashed is much faster in practice [4],[3]. We compare the PGM-Hashed approach to an algorithm we developed called HashRF, which also has the same theoretical complexity of $O(nt^2)$.

Given that the RF matrix algorithms under investigation have the same theoretical complexity, what is to be gained from studying their actual performance in practice? The *novelty* of our study is that we explore algorithmic performance by: (i) varying the amount of shared evolutionary relationships among the t trees, (ii) counting the actual number of bipartitions compared, and (iii) considering the memory usage of the algorithms. Theoretical complexity does not provide the algorithm designer with such insightful information as it relates to the above criteria.

In this study, we use artificial trees to assess the performance of the RF matrix approaches. Although biological tree collections are preferable, their availability for the parameters of interest in this study are limited (see Section 3.2). For our artificial tree collections, the number of taxa, n, and number of trees, t, ranged from 128 to 2,048. The experimental results show that HashRF's performance decreases as the number of shared relationships among the trees increases. PGM-Hashed, on the other hand, shows the opposite performance. That is, PGM-Hashed executes faster as the number of shared bipartitions increases. Overall, regardless of the number of evolutionary relationships shared among the trees, HashRF is about 1.2 to 13 times faster than PGM-Hashed depending on the level of bipartition sharing in the collection of trees. Our results also demonstrate that HashRF requires a smaller number of bipartition comparisons among the t trees than PGM-Hashed. Finally, we show that HashRF uses one-third of the memory required by its competitor.

Given that the grand challenge in phylogenetics is to infer *The Tree of Life*, which is estimated to contain 10 to 100 million taxa, significant reductions in the running time and storage requirements of RF matrix algorithms is necessary to handle the increasing size of evolutionary trees and the collections that contain them. Our experimental study shows that the HashRF algorithm provides scientists with a fast approach for computing the all-pairs RF distance between their collection of trees, which could lead scientists to understanding the evolutionary relationships among their collection of trees in new and exciting ways.

2   Computing the Robinson-Foulds Matrix

In a phylogenetic tree, modern organisms (or taxa) are placed at the leaves and ancestral organisms occupy internal nodes, with the edges of the tree denoting evolutionary relationships. Oftentimes, it is useful to represent phylogenies in terms of their *bipartitions*. Removing an internal edge e from a tree separates the taxa (or leaves) on one side from the taxa on the other. The division of the taxa into two subsets is the non-trivial bipartition B associated with internal edge e. (Note: all trees have trivial bipartitions denoted by external edges.) In Figure 1, T_2 has two bipartitions: $AB|CDE$ and $ABD|CE$. An evolutionary tree is uniquely and completely defined by its set of $O(n)$ bipartitions.

The Robinson-Foulds (RF) distance between two trees is the number of bipartitions that differ between them. Let $\Sigma(T)$ be the set of bipartitions defined by all edges in tree T. The RF distance between trees T_1 and T_2 is defined as:

$$d_{RF}(T_1, T_2) = \frac{|\Sigma(T_1) - \Sigma(T_2)| + |\Sigma(T_2) - \Sigma(T_1)|}{2} \tag{1}$$

Figure 1 depicts how the RF distance between two trees T_1 and T_2. The set of bipartitions defined for tree T_1 is $\Sigma(T_1) = \{AB|CDE, ABC|DE\}$. $\Sigma(T_2) = \{AB|CDE, ABD|CE\}$. The number of bipartitions appearing in T_1 and not T_2 (i.e., $|\Sigma(T_1) - \Sigma(T_2)|$) is 1, since $\{ABC|DE\}$ does not appear in T_2. Similarly, the number of bipartitions in T_2 but not in T_1 is 1. Hence, $d_{RF}(T_1, T_2) = 1$.

In this paper, we are interested in computing the *all-to-all RF distance* or *RF distance matrix*. Given a set of t input trees, the output is a $t \times t$ matrix of RF distances. Here, the matrix represents the topological distances between every pair of trees. Our work assumes that the input trees are binary. Hence, the largest possible RF distance between two binary trees is $n - 3$.

2.1   Bipartition Representations

For each tree in the collection of input trees, we find all of its bipartitions (internal edges) by performing a postorder traversal. In order to process the bipartitions, we need some way to store them in the computer's internal memory.

An intuitive bitstring representation requires n bits, one for each taxon. Consider Figure 1. The first bit is labeled by the first taxon name (e.g., taxon A), the second bit is represented by the second taxon (e.g., taxon B), etc. We can represent all of the taxa on one side of the tree with the bit '0' and the remaining taxa on the side of the tree with the bit '1'. Consider the bipartition $ABE|CD$ from tree T_4. This bipartition would be represented as 11001, which means that taxa A, B, and E are one side of the tree, and the remaining taxa are on the other side. Here, taxa on the same side of a bipartition as taxon A receive a '1'. For each tree in the collection of unrooted input trees, we arbitrarily root it. We find all of its bipartitions by performing a postorder traversal of each tree while performing an OR operation to the bitstrings of an internal node's (parent's) children.

The PGM-Hashed RF matrix algorithm [4] uses a compressed k-bitstring. Each input taxon is represented by a random k-bitstring, where $k < n$. Similarly to the n-bitstring case, all bipartitions are found by performing a depth-first search traversal of the tree. However, the bitstrings of an internal node's (parent's) children are *exclusive-OR*'ed together in this representation. One consequence of using a compressed bitstring is that there is a possibility that two different bipartitions may in fact be represented by the same compressed bitstring. If this happens, then the resulting RF matrix will be incorrect. Pattengale et al. show that the probability of colliding compressed bitstrings decreases exponentially with the number of bits chosen for representing the bitstrings [4].

2.2   HashRF

Figure 2(a) provides an overview of the HashRF algorithm, which runs in $O(nt^2)$ time. Each input tree, T_i, is traversed in post-order, and its bipartitions are fed through two hashing functions, h_1 and h_2. Hash function h_1 is used to generate the location needed for storing a bipartition in the hash table. h_2 is responsible for creating bipartition identifiers (BIDs). For each bipartition, its associated hash table record contains its BID along with the tree index (TID) where the bipartition originated.

Similarly to Amenta et al. [7], Our h_1 and h_2 universal hash functions are defined as follows.

$$h_1(B) = \sum b_i r_i \bmod m_1 \qquad (2)$$

$$h_2(B) = \sum b_i s_i \bmod m_2 \qquad (3)$$

m_1 represents the number of entries (or locations) in the hash table. m_2 represent the largest bipartition ID (BID) that we can be given to a bipartition. That is,

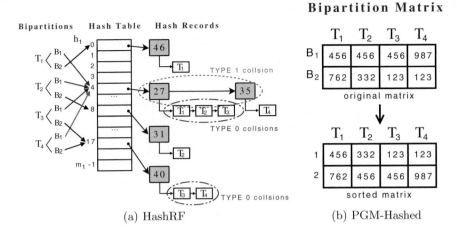

Fig. 2. Overview of the RF matrix algorithms under study. Bipartitions are from Figure 1. (a) The implicit representation of each bipartition, B_i, is fed to the hash functions h_1 and h_2. The shaded value in each hash record contains the bipartition ID (or h_2 value). Each bipartition ID has a linked list of tree indexes that share that particular bipartition. (b) Each unique bipartition in the tree is represented by a unique integer value. Both the original matrix and its sorted version, which is then used to compute the RF distance matrix, are shown.

instead of storing the n-bitstring, a shortened version of it (represented by the BID) will be stored in the hash table instead. $R = (r_1, ..., r_n)$ is a list of random integers in $(0, ..., m_1 - 1)$, $S = (s_1, ..., s_n)$ is a list of random integers in $(0, ..., m_2 - 1)$, and $B = (b_1, ..., b_n)$ is a bipartition represented by an n-bitstring. By using an implicit representation, we can avoid sending the n-bitstring representations to our hashing functions. An implicit bipartition is simply the integer value (instead of the n-bitstring) that provides the representation of the bipartition.

A consequence of using hash functions is that bipartitions may end up residing in the same location in the hash table. Such an event is considered a collision. There are three types of collisions that our hashing algorithms must resolve. *Type 0* collisions occur when the same bipartition (i.e. $B_i = B_j$), is shared across the input trees. Such collisions are not serious and are a function of the set of input trees. *Type 1* collisions result from two different bipartitions B_i and B_j (i.e., $B_i \neq B_j$) residing in the same location in the hash table. That is, $h_1(B_i) = h_1(B_j)$. *Type 2* collisions occur when B_i and B_j hash to the same location in the hash table with the same bipartition IDs (BIDs). In other words, $h_1(B_i) = h_1(B_j)$ and $h_2(B_i) = h_2(B_j)$. If a Type 2 occurs, the result output matrix will be incorrect. The probability of an incorrect answer is $O\left(\frac{1}{c}\right)$, where c can be made arbitrarily large. Since $c = 1,000$ in our experiments, there is a 0.001% chance that our HashRF algorithm will return an incorrect result.

Once all the bipartitions are organized in the hash table, then the RF distance matrix can be calculated. For each non-empty hash table location i, we have a list of tree index (TID) nodes for each unique bipartition index (BID) node. HashRF uses a $t \times t$ dissimilarity matrix, D, to track the number of bipartitions that are different between all tree pairs. In the case of binary trees, the $D_{i,j}$ entries are initialized to $n - 3$, the number of internal edges in a binary tree.

For each BID node at location l, every pair of TID nodes in the linked list are compared to each other. Then, the counts of $D_{i,j}$ and $D_{j,i}$ are decremented by one. That is, we have found a common bipartition between T_i and T_j and decrement the difference counter by one. For example, trees with BID 27 at location 4 in the hash table shows that the pairs (T_1, T_2), (T_1, T_3), and (T_2, T_3) share a bipartition ($ABC|DE$ from Figure 1). Thus, entries $D_{1,2}$, $D_{1,3}$, and $D_{2,3}$ are decremented by one. Once we have computed D, we can compute the RF matrix quite easily. Thus, $RF_{i,j} = \frac{D_{i,j} + D_{j,i}}{2}$, for every tree pair i and j.

2.3   PGM-Hashed

Pattengale, Gottlieb, and Moret [4] develop an $O(nt^2)$ algorithm that uses k-length bitstrings to represent each tree's bipartitions. In their paper, Pattengale et al. describe a number of exact and approximate algorithms to compute the RF distance matrix. Since we focus strictly on exact approaches, we study Pattengale et al.'s Hashed algorithm, which we call PGM-Hashed.

The algorithm starts by assigning a 64-bit integer random number to each taxon and using the XOR accumulator to combine the taxa numbers to represent the bipartition found during depth-first search traversal. Since each binary tree contains $n-3$ bipartitions, the entire set of bipartitions collected from the t trees are stored in a $(n-3) \times t$ two-dimensional array (or bipartition table). Entry (i, j) in the table represents the integer (converted from the 64-bitstring) representing bipartition i from tree j (see Figure 2(b)). Although the PGM-Hashed does not explicitly use a hash table, it is considered a hashing approach because different bipartitions may be represented with the same 64-bit integer.

Once the $(n-3) \times t$ bipartition table is constructed, the RF distance matrix is computed. Each of tree j's bipartitions (i.e., column j in the bipartition table) are sorted since they are stored as integer values. After the sort, the RF distance between the trees is computed. For each pair of trees T_i and T_j, two pointers p and q are used to compare the bipartitions of T_i and T_j, respectively. If the bipartition pointed to by p is equal to the one referred to by q, then both pointers are incremented which means they have the same bipartition. However, if the bipartitions are different, a difference counter is incremented, and either the p or q pointer is incremented appropriately. To get the RF distance, the value of the difference counter is subtracted from $n - 3$ since we are assuming binary input trees.

3   Our Collection of Evolutionary Trees

3.1   Overview

We test the performance of the HashRF and PGM-Hashed algorithms by using tree collections that share varying number of bipartitions between them. We

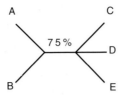

Fig. 3. Majority consensus tree for the input trees shown in Figure 1. The bipartition weight implies that 75% of the t trees must have the bipartition $AB|CDE$.

measure the amount of sharing among the t trees in a collection by the resolution rate, r, of the resulting majority consensus tree, which is one of the most popular consensus tree techniques used in a phylogenetic analysis. Majority trees contain bipartitions that appear in more than half of the t input trees. In Figure 3, the majority tree has a resolution rate of 50%. That is, for five taxa there are $n-3$ (or 2) possible bipartitions in the resulting phylogenetic tree. However, the majority tree only has 1 of the 2 possible bipartitions. A 0% resolved tree represents a star whereas a 100% resolution rate denotes a binary tree. Larger resolution rates denote more shared bipartitions among the input trees.

3.2   Motivation for Using Artificial Trees

Our objective is to assess the RF matrix algorithms on large tree collections as a function of the number of taxa, n, the number of trees, t, and the resolution rate, r. In this paper, we create artificial tree collections to provide the diverse input trees we require to evaluate the algorithms. (Although their tree generation approach differs from ours, we note that Pattengale et al. also use artificial trees in their work.) There are a few large biological tree collections available, but they are often limited in one or more of the input parameters of interest. For example, we evaluate the performance of RF matrix algorithms on several biological tree collections provided to us by life scientists, where we found that HashRF is the best overall algorithm followed by PGM-Hashed [3]. The biological tree collections used contained trees with less than 600 taxa and the trees were quite similar since majority tree resolution rates were above 85%. Unfortunately, the biological tree collections are too limited (e.g., we are interested in bigger collections with more diverse bipartition sharing among the trees) for the objectives of interest in this paper. Our experiments are designed to understand how the algorithms perform under very diverse conditions of $n, t,$ and r. These results will then allow us to predict how the algorithms will respond as more biological tree collections become available for post-processing analysis.

3.3   Creating Artificial Tree Collections

To create our artificial tree collections, we used `apTreeshape` [8]—a R package for the simulation and analysis of phylogenetic tree topologies—to create a random,

Yule model tree consisting of n taxa. Next, we transform this tree into a $r\%$ resolved multifurcating tree by randomly removing bipartitions. We take our $r\%$ resolved tree and use it to generate t input trees. The resolved tree represents the majority consensus tree, $T_{r\%}$, of interest. Each bipartition in tree $T_{r\%}$ is given a weight in the interval (50%, 100%], which represents the percentage of the t trees that have that bipartition (see Figure 3).

Once all of the bipartitions from the majority tree $T_{r\%}$ have been distributed, each of the t trees is constructed. For each tree T_i, where $1 \leq i \leq t$, we construct tree T_i with the bipartitions that have been distributed to it. After the construction, any remaining multifurcating nodes are randomly resolved into binary nodes. These randomly resolved bipartitions (non-majority bipartitions) are then distributed to $\lfloor p \rfloor$ trees, where $1 < p \leq 0.50t$ and $i < p \leq t$. We distribute the non-majority bipartitions to the remaining trees in order to increase the amount of sharing among them in the tree collection. The above process is repeated five times for each n, t, and r. Thus, our plots show the average performance on our artificial datasets.

4   Experimental Results

We ran a series of experiments to study the performance of HashRF and PGM-Hashed for computing the all-to-all RF distance problem across varying number of taxa (n), trees (t), and bipartition sharing (r). We obtained the source code for PGM-Hashed from the authors. For HashRF, we pick a a prime number to represent the size of our hash table, m_1, which is the smallest prime number bigger than $O(tn)$, the total number of bipartitions in the collection of trees. For m_2, we choose the smallest prime number larger than $c \cdot tn$, where c is chosen to be 1,000. Experimental results were compared across the competing algorithms for experimental validation. All experiments were run on an Intel Pentium platform with 3.0GHz dual-core processors and a total of 2GB of memory. HashRF and PGM-Hashed were written in C++ and compiled with gcc 4.1.0 with the -02 compiler option. Each plot shows the average performance over five runs.

Figure 4 shows the actual CPU time performance and bipartition comparison counts of the HashRF and PGM-Hashed algorithms on four of our artificial tree collection datasets as a function of the consensus tree resolution rate. CPU time includes the time to traverse the input trees, insert each tree's bipartitions into the hash table (HashRF) or bipartition table (PGM-Hashed), and compute the resulting RF distance matrix. Counting the number of bipartition comparisons to compute the RF distance matrix comes into play once all bipartitions have been collected and organized into the appropriate data structure used by the RF matrix algorithm.

HashRF and PGM-Hashed show contrasting results in how they perform under different levels of bipartition sharing. Interestingly, the plots show that counting the number of bipartition comparisons is an effective measure for obtaining insights about algorithmic behavior since the trends shown by CPU time and bipartition comparison counts match very well. HashRF is the best overall performer both in

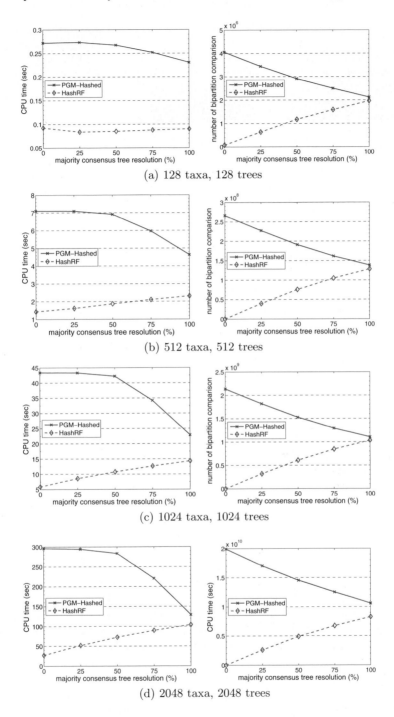

Fig. 4. RF matrix algorithms performance on four of our tree collections. The scale of the y-axis is different for all the plots.

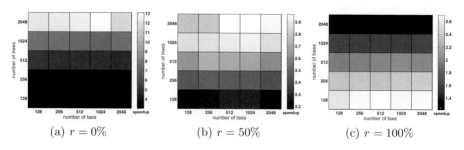

(a) $r = 0\%$ (b) $r = 50\%$ (c) $r = 100\%$

Fig. 5. Heatmaps depicting the speedup of HashRF over PGM-Hashed for various levels of bipartition sharing. The scale of the y-axis is different for all the plots. *For best results, please view electronically.*

terms of actual CPU time and number of bipartition comparisons performed. In Figure 4, the worst case for HashRF is when many bipartitions are shared, which is depicted with increasing consensus tree resolution rates. HashRF's performance gets worse with increased bipartition sharing as a result of processing longer linked lists of trees in the hash table to compute the RF distance matrix. PGM-Hashed, on the other hand, gets faster as the amount of bipartition sharing increases. In PGM-Hashed, for each pair of trees T_i and T_j, two pointers p and q are used to compare the bipartitions, which are in sorted order based on their integer values. Two trees with identical bipartitions result in $n - 3$ comparisons to compute the RF distance between them. Two trees that do not share any bipartitions require $2(n - 3) - 1$ (or $2n - 7$) bipartition comparisons. Thus, PGM-Hashed runs faster as the similarity among the trees increases.

In Figure 5, we use heatmaps to explore the speedup in terms of CPU time of HashRF over PGM-Hashed at specific majority resolution rates, r. In the heatmap representation, each speedup value (or cell) in the 5×5 matrix is represented as a color. Darker (lighter) colors represent smaller (higher) speedup values in terms of how much faster HashRF is compared to PGM-Hashed. The speedup of HashRF over PGM-Hashed ranges from about 1.2 to 13. The plots clearly show that with increasing r, HashRF's speedup over PGM-Hashed decreases significantly. Again, this is a result of HashRF having longer chains of linked lists to process. Another interesting observation from the plots is that with high resolution rates (e.g., $r = 100\%$), HashRF performs worse as the number of trees increases.

Finally, Figure 6 shows the memory usage of the RF matrix approaches. We used version 3.3.0 of the Valgrind software package (http://www.valgrind.org) to obtain our results. HashRF uses about three times less memory than PGM-Hashed. Interestingly, HashRF memory usage decreases as the number of shared bipartitions increases. When there are many unique bipartitions, a bipartition index (BID) and tree index (TID) have to be stored for each bipartition. However, for shared bipartitions, a single BID is stored for a linked list of TIDs. Thus, for HashRF this translates into less memory consumption. For PGM-Hashed, the memory usage is essentially constant.

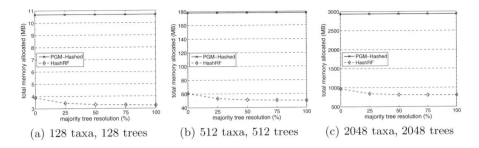

(a) 128 taxa, 128 trees   (b) 512 taxa, 512 trees   (c) 2048 taxa, 2048 trees

Fig. 6. Memory usage of the HashRF and PGM-Hashed algorithms. For the case of 2,048 taxa and 2,048 trees additional swap space beyond the 2 GB of physical memory on our platform was required. The scale of the y-axis is different for all the plots.

5 Conclusions and Future Work

Phylogenetic searches usually produce a large number of candidate trees, which present a huge data-mining challenge for understanding the evolutionary relationships between them. In our study, we empirically compare the performance of HashRF and PGM-Hashed—which are the two fastest RF matrix algorithms available—for computing the $t \times t$ RF distance matrix. Given that large collections of real biological trees are not readily available, we characterize the behavior of our algorithms on artificial tree instances. The *novelty* of our work concerns our methodology for assessing the practical performance of these $O(nt^2)$ RF matrix algorithms. Thus, algorithmic performance of HashRF and PGM-Hashed is evaluated based on (i) the number of shared bipartitions among the t trees, (ii) the number of bipartition comparisons, and (iii) the amount of memory used.

Our experiments show that although the performance of the algorithms are impacted significantly by the number of shared bipartitions, HashRF shows better performance in all cases. Hence, the constants involved in the running time analysis are smaller for HashRF than for PGM-Hashed. For high levels of bipartition sharing ($r \geq 50$), HashRF can execute from 1.2 to 3.9 times faster than PGM-Hashed. When there is very little sharing ($r = 0\%$), HashRF is over 13 times faster. By using the number of bipartition comparisons as an architecture- and implementation-independent substitute for CPU time, HashRF's good performance is not based on programmer skill or taking advantage of specific architectural features of the underlying platform. Furthermore, our experiments show that HashRF also requires less memory than its counterpart. Given HashRF's good performance on the wide-range of bipartition sharing provided by our artificial tree collections, it should perform quite well when confronted with diverse collections of biologically-based trees.

Our work can be extended in many different directions. In this paper, we assumed that the input trees are binary. We plan to extend our study by including datasets that include multifurcating evolutionary trees. Additional experiments will study much larger sets of trees since the goal of a phylogenetic is to reconstruct the *Tree of Life*, which is estimated to contain between 10 to 100 million taxa. Finally, we are currently obtaining large collections of biological trees from life scientists to compliment the results shown here.

Acknowledgements

Funding for this project was supported by the National Science Foundation under grants DEB-0629849 and IIS-0713618. The authors wish to thank Eric Gottlieb, Bernard Moret, and Nick Pattengale for providing the PGM-Hashed code.

References

1. Hillis, D.M., Heath, T.A., John, K.S.: Analysis and visualization of tree space. Syst. Biol. 54(3), 471–482 (2005)
2. Sul, S.J., Williams, T.L.: A randomized algorithm for comparing sets of phylogenetic trees. In: Proc. Fifth Asia Pacific Bioinformatics Conference (APBC 2007), pp. 121–130 (2007)
3. Sul, S.J., Williams, T.L.: HashRF: a fast algorithm for computing the Robinson-Foulds distance matrix. Technical Report TR-CS-2008-6-1, Department of Computer Science, Texas A& M University (2008),
   http://www.cs.tamu.edu/academics/tr/tamu-cs-tr-2008-6-1
4. Pattengale, N., Gottlieb, E., Moret, B.: Efficiently computing the Robinson-Foulds metric. Journal of Computational Biology 14(6), 724–735 (2007)
5. Robinson, D.F., Foulds, L.R.: Comparison of phylogenetic trees. Mathematical Biosciences 53, 131–147 (1981)
6. Day, W.H.E.: Optimal algorithms for comparing trees with labeled leaves. Journal Of Classification 2, 7–28 (1985)
7. Amenta, N., Clarke, F., John, K.S.: A linear-time majority tree algorithm. In: Workshop on Algorithms in Bioinformatics. LNCS, vol. 2168, pp. 216–227 (2003)
8. Bortolussi, N., Durand, E., Blum, M., Franois, O.: apTreeshape: statistical analysis of phylogenetic tree shape. Bioinformatics 22(3), 363–364 (2006)

On the Size of the 3D Visibility Skeleton: Experimental Results

Linqiao Zhang[1], Hazel Everett[2], Sylvain Lazard[2],
Christophe Weibel[3], and Sue Whitesides[1]

[1] McGill University, School of Computer Science, Montreal,
Quebec H3A 2A7, Canada
{lzhang15,sue}@cs.mcgill.ca
[2] INRIA Nancy Grand Est , Université Nancy 2, LORIA, Nancy, France
FirstName.LastName@loria.fr
[3] McGill University, Math Department, Montreal, Quebec H3A 2A7, Canada
weibel@math.mcgill.ca

Abstract. The 3D visibility skeleton is a data structure used to encode global visibility information about a set of objects. Previous theoretical results have shown that for k convex polytopes with n edges in total, the worst case size complexity of this data structure is $\Theta(n^2 k^2)$ [Brönnimann et al. 07]; whereas for k uniformly distributed unit spheres, the expected size is $\Theta(k)$ [Devillers et al. 03].

In this paper, we study the size of the visibility skeleton experimentally. Our results indicate that the size of the 3D visibility skeleton, in our setting, is $C\,k\sqrt{n\,k}$, where C varies with the scene density but remains small. This is the first experimentally determined asymptotic estimate of the size of the 3D visibility skeleton for reasonably large n and expressed in terms of both n and k. We suggest theoretical explanations for the experimental results we obtained. Our experiments also indicate that the running time of our implementation is $O(n^{3/2} k \log k)$, while its worst-case running time complexity is $O(n^2 k^2 \log k)$.

1 Introduction

Computing visibility information is crucial to many problems in computer graphics, vision and robotics, such as computing the view from a given point, determining whether two objects partially see each other, and computing the umbra and penumbra cast by a light source.

In a given scene, two points are visible if the segment joining them does not properly intersect any obstacle in the scene. The study of visibility is thus intimately related to the study of the set of free line segments in a scene. The visibility complex, which is, roughly speaking, a partition of the space of maximal free line segments into connected components of segments that touch the same objects, was proposed by Pocchiola and Vegter as a data structure encoding visibility information of a scene in 2D [21]. Durand et al. [8,10] initiated the study of the visibility complex in 3D, and furthermore, introduced the visibility skeleton,

D. Halperin and K. Mehlhorn (Eds.): ESA 2008, LNCS 5193, pp. 805–816, 2008.

which is essentially the zero and one-dimensional cells of the visibility complex, arguing that this smaller and simpler structure suffices for solving interesting visibility queries related to shadow computation [8,9]. Although smaller than the visibility complex, the visibility skeleton is, nevertheless, a potentially enormous structure; it has worst-case size complexity $O(n^4)$. Note that the visibility skeleton is related to the aspect graph [19] as the embedding of the visibility skeleton in $\mathbb{R}^3$ is almost the partition of $\mathbb{R}^3$ whose dual is the aspect graph.

Durand et al. implemented the visibility skeleton for polygonal scenes and demonstrated that use of the skeleton indeed results in higher quality light simulation in rendered images with improved computation time compared to previous algorithms [9]. Despite these positive results their pioneering approach suffers a major drawback. Their algorithm is not efficient because it is based on a systematic enumeration of all possibilities and thus has worst-case time complexity $\Theta(n^5)$ although the use of heuristics gives an observed complexity $\Theta(n^{2.4})$ [8]. Two other implementations, one by Glaves [14] for random triangles and another by Schröder [22] for polytopes, yielded similar results. Duguet et al. [7] report an implementation that computes elements of the visibility skeleton needed for light simulations in the restricted setting of point-light sources (possibly at infinity); their results can thus not be compared to those mentioned previously.

Worst-case examples are somewhat artificial and indeed Durand et al. [8] provide empirical evidence indicating that the $O(n^4)$ worst-case upper bound on the size of the visibility skeleton is largely pessimistic in practical situations; they observe a quadratic growth rate, albeit for the rather small scenes (at most 1,500 triangles) that they were able to test. Again, these results were experimentally confirmed by Glaves [14] and Schröder [22]. Some recent theoretical results also support the observation that the $O(n^4)$ is pessimistic. When the inputs are k polytopes with n edges in total, [17,2] show that the number of vertices of the visibility skeleton is $\Theta(n^2 k^2)$ in the worst case. If the polytopes are disjoint and their silhouettes have worst-case complexity $O(\sqrt{n/k})$, then the size of the visibility skeleton is $O(nk^2\sqrt{nk})$ [15]. Moreover, when the inputs are randomly distributed unit balls, the expected size is linear [6]. Nevertheless, the problem of estimating the size of the visibility skeleton in practice for reasonably large input scenes has remained open for years because of the absence of a sufficiently efficient implementation.

We address in this paper the problem of computing and estimating the size of the visibility skeleton of k disjoint polytopes of total complexity n in generic position. In fact, we measure the size of the skeleton as the number of its vertices (since vertices have constant degree under general position assumptions). A definition of the visibility skeleton is given in Section 2. We present a robust implementation based on a sweep-plane algorithm that was first presented in [17] for the case of pairwise disjoint polytopes and generalized to the case of possibly intersecting polytopes in [2]. We then present experiments on k disjoint polytopes of size n/k, with vertices on congruent spheres randomly distributed with fixed densities in a given (spherical) universe. These experiments show that the number of vertices of the visibility skeleton is roughly $C k \sqrt{nk}$ where the observed constant C varies with scene density but remains small (less than 5 in our setting). Our experiments also indicate that the average running time of our implementation is $O(n^{3/2}k \log k)$. By contrast, the theoretical worst-case running time of the algorithm in our setting is $O(n^2 k^2 \log k)$.

These results are significant for three reasons. First, this is the first experimentally determined asymptotic estimate of the number of vertices of the 3D visibility skeleton that takes into account not only the total number n of edges, but also the number k of polytopes in the scene. The results show that the size of the visibility skeleton may be sub-quadratic; in particular, they show a sub-linear growth in n and a sub-quadratic growth in k. Second, assuming that the size of the silhouette of a polytope on n/k vertices is $O(\sqrt{n/k})$, our results show that we may express the size of the visibility skeleton as a function that is linear in the size of the silhouette and quadratic in the number of polytopes; that is, the number of vertices in the scene impacts the size of the visibility skeleton only insofar as it increases the size of the silhouettes. Finally, our results indicate that there is no large constant hidden in the big-Oh notation.

In the next section, we give a definition of the visibility skeleton. In Section 3, we review the algorithm and discuss technical details of our implementation. We present our experimental results in Section 4 and conclude in Section 5.

2   The Visibility Skeleton of a Set of Polytopes

We start with some preliminary definitions. A *polytope* is the convex hull of a point set. Here, polytopes are assumed to have nonempty interior. A plane is *tangent* to a polytope if it intersects the polytope but not its interior. A line or segment is *tangent* to a polytope if it intersects the polytope and is contained in a tangent plane. A line or segment is *free* if it does not intersect the interior of any polytope. A free line segment is *maximal* if it is not properly contained in another free line segment.

A *support vertex* of a line is a polytope vertex that lies on the line. A *support edge* of a line is a polytope edge that intersects the line but has no endpoint on it (a support edge intersects the line at only one point of its relative interior). A *support* of a line is one of its support vertices or support edges. The supports of a segment are defined to be the supports of its relative interior; thus if a maximal free segment ends at a vertex of a polytope, this vertex is not a support.

The visibility complex of smooth disjoint objects is, roughly speaking, the partition of the space of maximal free line segments into connected components of segments that are tangent to the same objects [21]. For polytopes, each cell of the complex is further subdivided so that the corresponding maximal free line segments have the same set of supports. The visibility skeleton [8] is then defined as the one-skeleton (*i.e.* the vertices and arcs) of the visibility complex.

Here we study not the full one-skeleton but rather the skeleton containing only those arcs that correspond to local changes in the view, *i.e.*, arcs such that, when a viewpoint crosses the surface generated by the set of segments corresponding to the arc, a new polytope comes into view or a previously seen polytope disappears;

in particular, we do not consider the appearance or disappearance of a polytope feature as a change in the view. For pairwise disjoint convex smooth algebraic surfaces, it well known that these arcs consist of one-dimensional sets of maximal free line segments that are tangent to three objects or that are tangent to two objects in planes tangent to the two objects (tangent crossing events) [20]. This also holds for pairwise disjoint polytopes [5].[1]

With this in mind, we classify the arcs and vertices of the skeleton, in the spirit of Durand et al. [8], as follows. Unless stated otherwise, no two supports come from the same polytope. An arc is of type *EEE* if its set of supports consists of three edges; it is of type *EV* if its set of supports consists of an edge and a vertex that define a plane tangent to their respective polytopes. A vertex is of type *EEEE* if its set of supports consists of four edges; it is of type *VEE* if its set of supports consists of a vertex and two edges; it is of type *FEE* if its set of supports consists of two edges on one face, and two additional edges; it is of type *VV* if its set of supports consists of two vertices that lie on a plane that is tangent to their two respective polytopes.[2]

In this paper, we study the number of vertices of the visibility skeleton thus defined and refer to it, with abuse of notation, as the size of the visibility skeleton. Since, under our general position assumptions, the degree of each skeleton vertex is bounded by a constant, the actual size of the skeleton, including the arcs, will be a constant factor away from what we measure.

3   Algorithm and Implementation

Algorithm. We give here a brief overview of the $O(n^2k^2 \log k)$ algorithm for computing the vertices of the visibility skeleton of k convex disjoint polytopes with n edges in total and in general position. (Discussion about the general position assumption can be found below.) This algorithm was presented in [17] for the case of pairwise disjoint polytopes[3] and then generalized to possibly intersecting polytopes in [2].

Given k convex disjoint polytopes in general position, that have n edges in total, the algorithm sweeps a plane about each edge e of each polytope in turn.

---

[1] Note that the visibility skeleton for smooth objects does not contain the arcs that correspond to tangent crossing events. On the other hand, the one-skeleton of the visibility complex of polytopes contains all arcs corresponding to visual events (as they appear as sets of segments tangent to two objects); however, it also contains many arcs that do not correspond to a local changes in the view (but only to the the appearance or disappearance of a polytope feature).

[2] This catalog is a subset of the one in [8] because Durand et al. essentially consider the one-skeleton of the visibility complex. They consider, in particular, line segments supported by two vertices which do not lie on a plane tangent to the two polytopes. This has an impact on the asymptotic size of the structure since the number of such vertices is presumably linear in the total complexity of the polytopes (in our experimental setting).

[3] Efrat et al. [11] presented a similar algorithm for computing not necessarily free isolated transversals in the same setting.

The sweep plane is initially coplanar with one face incident to edge e and rotates about edge e until it becomes coplanar with the other face incident to e.

Initially, the sweep plane intersects the input polytopes in a set of polygons and the 2D visibility skeleton of these polygons is computed. This involves computing all the *bitangents* that are tangent to two polygons at two vertices. Each of these vertices lies on an edge of the input polytope; we call these edges the *support edges* of the bitangent. During the sweep, we maintain the 2D visibility skeleton of the polygons intersected by the sweep plane. An event occurs whenever a bitangent appears or disappears, or support edges of a bitangent change. The *EEEE, VEE,* and *FEE* skeleton vertices arise from some of these events. (See [23] for a video on the algorithm.)

The worst-case running time of this algorithm is $O(nk^2 \log k)$ per sweep, that is $O(n^2k^2 \log k)$ in total.[4] Notice that the $\Theta(nk^2 \log k)$ worst-case bound for one sweep can be quite pessimistic: the time complexity of each sweep is, modulo the logarithmic factor, proportional to the complexity of the 2D visibility skeleton over the whole sweep, that is, to the number of combinatorially distinct bitangents occurring during the sweep. In particular, the time complexity of one sweep can be sub-linear in n. Note that this differs from the algorithms presented in both [11] and [2] which maintain all line segments tangent to two polygons in the sweep plane, even if they are not free.

Implementation. While our ultimate objective is a robust implementation that correctly computes the visibility skeleton vertices on a set of polyhedra in arbitrary position in a reasonable amount of time, our current implementation takes as input any set of convex polyhedra and either outputs the skeleton vertices or reports that the polytopes are not in general position (see below). We implemented the algorithm in C++ using the *CGAL* library [3] with the 2D visibility skeleton package due to Angelier and Pocchiola [1].

Predicates. Several predicates are required by the algorithm including, for example, determining whether four segments admit a line transversal. As in all sweep algorithms, an essential predicate is one that compares two positions of the sweep plane. The algebraic degree of some of these predicates is quite high; in particular, comparing two positions of the sweep plane is implemented with a procedure of degree 168 in the Cartesian coordinates of the input vertices. See [12] for details.

Number type. Our implementation follows the paradigm of exact computation; we have implemented all predicates using the `Filtered_exact` number type of CGAL (3.2.1) templated with CGAL interval arithmetic (based on `double` number type) and the CORE library [4]. This means that the predicates are first evaluated using interval arithmetic, and only when this fails are they evaluated

---

[4] Note that both [17] and [2] report algorithms having time complexity $O(n^2k^2 \log n)$ instead of $O(n^2k^2 \log k)$; the reason for this is that, in [17], the skeleton is reconstructed which is not the case here and, in [2], the event queue may be of size $\Theta(n)$ because the polytopes may intersect.

using the CORE exact number type. Using filtered exact computation ensures that no predicate is ever incorrectly evaluated.

General position assumption. By polytopes in general position we mean that no predicate evaluates to zero.[5] In particular, this guarantees that each event corresponds to a unique position of the sweep plane.[6] It also implies more familiar assumptions such as that no two polytope faces are coplanar; see [2] for more details. To the best of our knowledge, there exists no implementation of the 3D visibility skeleton that handles degeneracies, including the implementation of Durand in which degeneracies were avoided by perturbing the input scenes by hand (Duguet [7] proposed a method for handling degeneracies but, as previously noted, only for computing a section of the visibility skeleton, that is a set of maximal free line segments that are supported by concurrent lines.) Our code represents an improvement in the sense that we systematically detect all degeneracies although the code to handle them remains unwritten.

Software validation. We verified the correctness of our implementation by comparing its output with that of an implementation of the brute force algorithm, the latter being straightforward, having only about a thousand lines of code. We ran tests on twenty input scenes of up to 100 polytopes with up to 1 000 edges and obtained the same results for both implementations, that is, the same list of vertices.

4   Experiments

The model. We generate the input scene by first generating k uniformly distributed disjoint unit spheres in a spherical universe with density μ. For each sphere, we then uniformly generate a set of vertices on its surface and compute their convex hull to generate our polytope scene. We note that the density of the polytopes is somewhat less than the density μ of the spheres. We emphasize that our objective is not to study uniformly distributed disjoint polytopes approximating spheres. We have chosen this scene model because it provides a simple way to generate large scenes containing disjoint polytopes. Furthermore, it allows us to compare our results with the theoretical results of [6].

The experiments. We consider scenes of polytopes, as defined above, depending on three parameters, the number k of polytopes, the total number n of polytope edges, and the scene density μ. We perform two suites of experiments in which we measure the number of visibility skeleton vertices.

---

[5] Note that filtered-exact arithmetic is still needed under this general position assumption since predicates could still be evaluated incorrectly with a fixed-precision floating-point arithmetic. It appears that, even in the random setting of our experiments, predicates are evaluated incorrectly about 0.1% of the times when using the `double` number type.

[6] Actually, this guarantees that no two *unrelated* events correspond to the same position of the sweep plane.

(a)   (b)   (c)

Fig. 1. Three sample scenes with scene density $\mu = 0.3$ and $k = 50$ polytopes whose number of edges, n/k, is approximately equal to (a) 6, (b) 42, and (c) 84

In Suite I, we fix the scene density μ and the number n/k of edges per polytope. For different values of k, we generate scenes of k polytopes each having n/k edges. We perform experiments for $\mu = 0.3, 0.05$ and 0.01 and for $n/k \approx 6, 42$ and 84.[7] (A sample scene with $k = 50$ is shown in Fig. 1.) For each value of n/k, we vary the number k of polytopes as follows: (a) when $n/k \approx 6$, we vary k from 10 to 190 (giving $n \in [75, 1\,425]$), (b) when $n/k \approx 42$, we vary k from 10 to 130 (giving $n \in [400, 5\,200]$), and (c) when $n/k \approx 84$, k varies from 10 to 110 (giving $n \in [850, 9\,400]$). As we will see, the number of visibility skeleton vertices appears to be roughly $C_\mu\, k\sqrt{nk}$ in these experiments where C_μ is a constant that depends on the density.

In Suite II of our experiments, we also fix the scene density μ to 0.3 and vary the number n/k of edges per polytope for fixed numbers of polytopes. Namely, we consider $k = 30, 60$, and 90 and vary n/k from 6 to 102. As we will see, these experiments confirm that when n/k varies (in the given range), the complexity observed in the first set of experiments holds.

Note that a scene with density $\mu = 0.3$ is very dense (see Fig. 1 and recall Kepler's Theorem that the density of any sphere packing in 3D space is at most $\pi/3\sqrt{2} \approx 0.74$). Density $\mu = 0.3$ is close to the highest density we can reach in a reasonable amount of time with our scene generation scheme.

Machine characteristics. All the experiments were done on an $i686$ machine with a *Pentium* 2.80 GHz CPU, 2 GB of main memory, running Linux. Running time was measured with the *getrusage()* command and the *ru_utime* attribute.

4.1   Experimental Results and Analysis

Number of skeleton vertices in terms of n and k. Fig. 2 shows the number of skeleton vertices in terms of $k\sqrt{nk} = k^2\sqrt{n/k}$. The number of these skeleton

---

[7] In fact, we generate polytopes whose numbers of vertices range in $[4, 6]$, $[15, 17]$ and $[30, 32]$, respectively. The number of edges per polytope is thus not actually fixed but varies slightly; the polytopes we generated have, on average, 7.5, 40, and 85 edges, respectively.

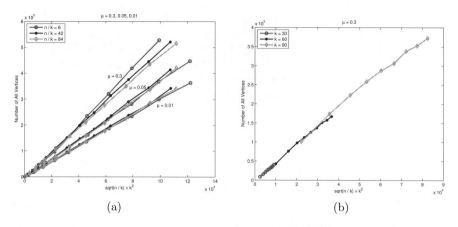

Fig. 2. Total number of skeleton vertices in terms of $k^2\sqrt{n/k}$ when (a) the polytopes have a constant (n/k) number of edges (Suite I) and (b) the number k of polytopes is constant (Suite II)

vertices appears to be linear in this parameter with a constant that depends on the scene density μ. For $\mu = 0.3, 0.05$, and 0.01, the constant is roughly 5, 4, and 3. The constant appears to decrease in terms of μ which is consistent with the intuition that the constant goes to zero as the scene density goes to zero (since the probability that there exists a line transversal to three polytopes goes to zero as the density goes to zero, and it can be argued that the number of vertices of type VV is asymptotically negligible).

Note that, for any fixed density μ and any given value of $k^2\sqrt{n/k}$, the number of these skeleton vertices varies very little in terms of the polytope complexity n/k (Fig. 2(a)) and in terms of the number of polytopes (Fig. 2(b)). This suggests that $C_\mu\, k^2\sqrt{n/k}$ is a good predictor of the number of these skeleton vertices regardless of the polytope complexity, at least for the scene density μ and the ranges of n/k used here.

Our experiments thus indicate that, in our setting, the number of skeleton vertices is roughly $C_\mu\, k^2\sqrt{n/k}$, where C_μ is a constant that depends on the density μ of the scene. The experiments hint that this constant is small and is a decreasing function of μ.

This observed complexity is, as expected, much smaller than worst-case bounds. Recall that, for k polytopes with n edges in total, the worst-case number of skeleton vertices is $\Theta(n^2k^2)$ [2]. Also, if the silhouettes of the polytopes have size $\sqrt{n/k}$ in the worst case, the worst-case number of skeleton vertices is $O(nk^3\sqrt{n/k})$ [15, §6.7]. These worst-case bounds are much larger than our observed size (by a factor $n\sqrt{nk}$ and nk).

We analyze below the observed complexity of $C_\mu\, k^2\sqrt{n/k}$ in terms of (i) k when the complexity of the polytopes is constant, and (ii) the silhouette size of the polytopes when the number k of polytopes is constant.

Analysis of the number of skeleton vertices in terms of k. If each polytope has constant complexity (*i.e.*, n/k in $\Theta(1)$), our experiments exhibit a quadratic growth (in terms of k) of the number of skeleton vertices. This is consistent with previous experiments [8,14] in which the scenes consist of polygons of constant complexity and is also consistent with the best known theoretical *expected* upper bound of $O(k^2)$ [6] corresponding to our setting. However, this contradicts the intuitive linear bound of $\Theta(k)$ when n/k is constant; indeed, recall that for k randomly distributed congruent spheres, the expected number of visibility events is linear and, for constant-size polytopes of bounded aspect ratio inside such spheres, the expected number of visibility events is linear for events that occur sufficiently inside the universe but it is only upper bounded by $O(k^2)$ for events near the boundary of the universe [6]. It is possible that the expected upper bound of $O(k^2)$ is tight but it is also possible that our experiments did not reach the asymptotic behavior. If this is the case, it is then reasonable to believe that our experimental estimate of the complexity is an overestimate.

Analysis of the number of skeleton vertices in terms of the silhouette size of the input polytopes. If we fix the number k of polytopes and vary the total number n of edges, our experiments show that the number of skeleton vertices depends linearly on $\sqrt{n/k}$. We argue below that this means that, in our setting, when k is fixed, the number of skeleton vertices depends linearly on the silhouette size of the input polytopes and explain why.

Recall that, for any polyhedron of size $\Theta(m)$, the size of its silhouette viewed from a random point is $O(\sqrt{m})$ under some reasonable hypotheses [16] (see also [18] for the special case of polyhedra that approximate spheres). Since the vertices of the polytopes we consider are randomly distributed on a sphere, it is reasonable to assume that the size of the silhouette does not depend much on the choice of the viewpoint. In other words, for any polytope with n/k edges we consider, it is reasonable to assume that its silhouette has size $O(\sqrt{n/k})$ from any viewpoint. Hence, when k is fixed, the number of skeleton vertices depends linearly on the silhouette size of the input polytopes.

We offer the following intuitive explanation of this observation. Consider the arcs of type *EEE* of the skeleton. The endpoints of these arcs are vertices of type *VEE*, *FEE* or *EEEE*. When the number k of polytopes is fixed and the number n of edges tends to infinity, the polytopes tend to spheres and the segments corresponding to vertices of type *EEEE* converge to segments that are tangent to four spheres; hence, in our setting, the number of *EEEE* vertices converges to a constant. Similarly, for those *VEE* vertices that correspond to intersections of two arcs of types *VE* and *EEE* (thus corresponding to segments tangent to three polytopes while lying in planes that are tangent to two of them). Moreover, in the successive refinements of polytopes as n increases, each *EEE* arc incident to an *EEEE* vertex or one of the above *VEE* vertices will become a sequence of *EEE* arcs joined at *VEE* vertices (that is, subdivision vertices such that the sets of supports are invariant along the subdivided arcs). For such a sequence of arcs, the number of these *VEE* vertices is the number of polytope vertices encountered by a maximal free line segment as it slides from the segment corresponding to one

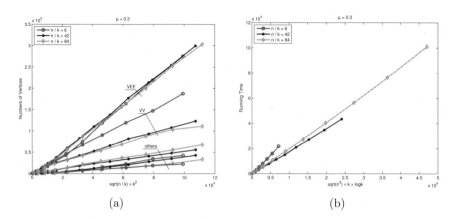

Fig. 3. Suite I (k polytopes having a constant, n/k, number of edges; $\mu = 0.3$): (a) proportion of number of vertices in terms of $k^2\sqrt{n/k}$ and (b) running time (in seconds) in terms of $n^{1.5}k\log k$

end of the sequence to the other, while remaining tangent to the three polytopes (nearly spheres) involved. The number of such polytope vertices is, intuitively, at most the worst-case size of the silhouette of each polytope, which we have assumed to be in $O(\sqrt{n/k})$. As a polytope gets more complex and tends to a sphere, the subset of lines in the line space that are tangent to the polytope on its vertices tends towards the subset of lines that are tangent to the sphere. This is also the case for lines tangent to the polytope on its faces. For this reason, the number of *FEE* vertices is asymptotically the same as that of *VEE* vertices. Thus, intuitively, we can expect that, for fixed k, (i) the number of vertices of type *EEEE* converges to a constant as n goes to infinity, (ii) the number of vertices of type *VEE* or *FEE* is in $O(\sqrt{n/k})$ times the number of *EEEE* vertices, and thus that (iii) the number of *VEE* and *FEE* vertices is in $O(\sqrt{n})$ (for k fixed). In experiments not reported here, we have observed (ii) and (iii), but not (i). In Figure 3(a), the number of *VEE* vertices is much larger than the number of *EEEE* vertices, which is consistant with the previous discussion, while the convergence of *EEEE* is not seen in our experimental range.

Finally, the number of *VV* vertices is, intuitively, bounded by the product of the number of pairs of polytopes that are mutually visible (which is asymptotically linear in k for any given density) and the size of the polytope silhouettes. Hence the number of *VV* vertices is presumably in $\Theta(k\sqrt{n/k})$. In our experiments (Fig. 3(a)) we observe a complexity of roughly $\Theta(k^2\sqrt{n/k})$ because the number of visible pairs of polytopes is quadratic in k in our experimental range.

Running time in terms of n and k. We study the running time of our implementation in terms of $n\sqrt{n}k\log k$ for experiments in Suite I, and show the results for scene density $\mu = 0.3$ in Fig. 3(b) (our results for other densities are omitted here). We observe that for a fixed polytope complexity n/k, the running time seems linear in $n\sqrt{n}k\log k$. More precisely, we observe a running time of $C'_\mu n\sqrt{n}k\log k$ seconds with C'_μ no more than $3\cdot 10^{-4}$ for the considered densities. Note, however, that for density 0.3, the data we obtained from groups $n/k \approx 42$ and 84 fit the estimated time complexity well, whereas the data from the group $n/k \approx 6$ is a constant factor away.

The observed running time can be intuitively explained as follows. Note first that $n \sqrt{n}\, k \log k$ is equal to $n \sqrt{n/k}\, k\sqrt{k} \log k$. We dissect this expression as follows. First, n is the number of sweeps performed by the algorithm. We observe that the factor $k\sqrt{k}$ is linearly related to the average over all sweeps of the maximal number of bitangents encountered in the sweep plane during a sweep (we omit here the presentation of these experiments). This is reasonable since the number of bitangents in the sweep plane varies from $\Theta(k^2)$, the trivial worst-case bound, to $\Theta(k)$, the expected bound in the right setting [13]. Furthermore, the factor $\sqrt{n/k}$ naturally relates to the number of updates caused by each bitangent during the sweep; indeed, following a bitangent during a sweep, the bitangent will encounter vertices on each of the two polytopes supporting it; the number of these vertices on each polytope is related and, intuitively, is less than the worst-case size of the silhouettes of the polytopes which, as we argued above, is in $O(\sqrt{n/k})$ in our setting. Finally, $\log k$ is the complexity of each update of the event list.

5 Conclusion

We have presented here an implementation of the sweep-plane algorithm to compute the visibility skeleton. Our experiments suggest that, in our setting, the number of vertices of the 3D visibility skeleton is $C_\mu\, k\sqrt{n\,k}$. The constant C_μ, which depends on the scene density, is no more than 5 for n and k in our experimental range, and for the various densities that we studied.

This is the first prediction of the actual size of the 3D visibility skeleton for reasonably large n, and expressed in terms of both n and k. Assuming that the size of the silhouette of a polytope with n/k edges is $O(\sqrt{n/k})$, our results show that the size of the visibility skeleton is linear in the size of the silhouette and quadratic in the number of polytopes. Surprisingly, the constant C_μ is rather small; this indicates that there is no large constant hidden in the big-Oh notation.

The experiments also suggest that the expected running time of our implementation of the sweep plane algorithm is $C'_\mu\, n \sqrt{n}\, k \log k$ seconds, where C'_μ depends on the scene density but is, on our machine, no more than $3 \cdot 10^{-4}$ for the considered densities.

Our results indicate that the visibility skeleton is of reasonable size and can be computed exactly in a reasonable length of time. Further work includes completing the implementation for degenerate situations. A major challenge is to extend the sweep algorithm to handle general polyhedra.

References

1. Angelier, P., Pocchiola, M.: CGAL-based implementation of visibility complexes. Technical Report ECG-TR-241207-01, Effective Computational Geometry for Curves and Surfaces (ECG) (2003)

2. Brönnimann, H., Devillers, O., Dujmovic, V., Everett, H., Glisse, M., Goaoc, X., Lazard, S., Na, H.-S., Whitesides, S.: Lines and free line segments tangent to arbitrary three-dimensional convex polyhedra. SIAM Journal on Computing 37(2), 522–551 (2007)
3. CGAL: Computational Geometry Algorithms Library, http://www.cgal.org
4. The CORE library, http://cs.nyu.edu/exact/
5. Demouth, J.: Événements visuels et limites d'ombres. PhD thesis, Université Nancy 2 (to appear, 2008)
6. Devillers, O., Dujmović, V., Everett, H., Goaoc, X., Lazard, S., Na, H.-S., Petitjean, S.: The expected number of 3D visibility events is linear. SIAM Journal on Computing 32(6), 1586–1620 (2003)
7. Duguet, F., Drettakis, G.: Robust epsilon visibility. In: Hughes, J. (ed.) Proceedings of ACM SIGGRAPH 2002, pp. 567–575. ACM Press / ACM SIGGRAPH (July 2002)
8. Durand, F., Drettakis, G., Puech, C.: The visibility skeleton: a powerful and efficient multi-purpose global visibility tool. Computer Graphics Proceedings, Annual Conference Series 31, 89–100 (1997); Proceedings of Siggraph 1997
9. Durand, F., Drettakis, G., Puech, C.: Fast and accurate hierarchical radiosity using global visibility. ACM Transactions on Graphics 18(2), 128–170 (1999)
10. Durand, F., Drettakis, G., Puech, C.: The 3D visibility complex. ACM Transactions on Graphics 21(2), 176–206 (2002)
11. Efrat, A., Guibas, L., Hall-Holt, O., Zhang, L.: On incremental rendering of silhouette maps of a polyhedral scene. Comput. Geom.: Theory and App. 38(3), 129–138 (2007)
12. Everett, H., Lazard, S., Lenhart, B., Zhang, L.: On the degree of standard geometric predicates for line transversals in 3D. Comput. Geom.: Theory and App. (to appear, 2008)
13. Everett, H., Lazard, S., Petitjean, S., Zhang, L.: On the expected size of the 2D visibility complex. Int. J. of Comput. Geom. and App. 17(4), 361–382 (2007)
14. Glaves, L.: An exploration of the 3D visibility complex. Master's thesis, Polytechnic University, Brooklyn, NY (2007)
15. Glisse, M.: Combinatoire des droites et segments pour la visibilité 3D. PhD thesis, Université Nancy 2 (October 2007)
16. Glisse, M., Lazard, S.: An upper bound on the average size of silhouettes. Discrete and Computational Geometry (to appear, 2008)
17. Goaoc, X.: Structures de visibilité globales: tailles, calculs et dégénérescences. PhD thesis, Université Nancy 2 (May 2004)
18. Kettner, L., Welzl, E.: Contour edge analysis for polyhedron projections. In: Strasser, W., Klein, R., Rau, R. (eds.) Geometric Modeling: Theory and Practice, pp. 379–394. Springer, Heidelberg (1997)
19. Plantinga, H., Dyer, C.: Visibility, occlusion, and the aspect graph. International Journal of Computer Vision 5(2), 137–160 (1990)
20. Platonova, O.A.: Singularities of relative position of a surface and a line. Uspekhi Mat. Nauk 36(1), 221–222 (1981); Russian Math. Surveys 36(1), 248–249 (1981)
21. Pocchiola, M., Vegter, G.: The visibility complex. Int. J. of Comput. Geom. and App. 6(3), 279–308 (1996)
22. Schröder, A.: Globale Sichtbarkeitsalgorithmend. PhD thesis, Philipps-Universität Marburg (June 2003)
23. Zhang, L., Everett, H., Lazard, S., Whitesides, S.: Towards an implementation of the 3D visibility skeleton. In: Proceedings of the 23rd ACM Annual Symposium on Computational Geometry (SoCG 2007), S. Korea, pp. 131–132 (2007); Video

An Almost Space-Optimal Streaming Algorithm for Coresets in Fixed Dimensions

Hamid Zarrabi-Zadeh

School of Computer Science, University of Waterloo
Waterloo, Ontario, Canada, N2L 3G1
hzarrabi@uwaterloo.ca

Abstract. We present a new streaming algorithm for maintaining an ε-kernel of a point set in $\mathbb{R}^d$ using $O((1/\varepsilon^{(d-1)/2}) \log(1/\varepsilon))$ space. The space used by our algorithm is optimal up to a small logarithmic factor. This substantially improves (for any fixed dimension $d \geqslant 3$) the best previous algorithm for this problem that uses $O(1/\varepsilon^{d-(3/2)})$ space, presented by Agarwal and Yu at SoCG'07. Our algorithm immediately improves the space complexity of the best previous streaming algorithms for a number of fundamental geometric optimization problems in fixed dimensions, including width, minimum enclosing cylinder, minimum-width enclosing annulus, minimum-width enclosing cylindrical shell, etc.

1 Introduction

The coreset framework has recently attracted considerable attention as a powerful tool for approximating various measures of a geometric data set. In this framework, a small subset of the input point set, called a *coreset*, is extracted in such a way that solving the optimization problem on the coreset yields an approximate solution to the entire set.

Agarwal *et al.* [2] developed a generic method for computing coresets for various optimization problems by introducing the notion of ε-kernel. Roughly speaking, a subset $Q \subseteq P$ is called an *ε-kernel* of P if for every slab S containing Q, the $(1+\varepsilon)$-expansion of S contains P. The technique of Agarwal *et al.* yields approximation algorithms for a wide range of shape-fitting problems.

The coreset framework also plays an essential role in designing approximation algorithms operating under the *data stream* model. In this model, the input is given to the algorithm as a stream over time, and the algorithm has to process the input elements as they arrive in only one pass. Furthermore, the algorithm has only a limited amount of working storage and cannot store the whole input in its memory. This one-pass streaming model is attractive both in theory and in practice due to emerging applications which involve massive data sets. The coreset framework is useful here as it allows streaming algorithms to maintain only a "sketch" of the input, which is typically small compared to the whole data set. For example, see [1,9,11,12] on the growing literature of streaming algorithms developed over the recent few years for various geometric problems using the notion of coresets.

D. Halperin and K. Mehlhorn (Eds.): ESA 2008, LNCS 5193, pp. 817–829, 2008.

Table 1. Space complexity of various streaming algorithms for maintaining ε-kernels in $\mathbb{R}^d$

ALGORITHM	SPACE BOUND	REF
Agarwal, Har-Peled, and Varadarajan '04	$O((1/\varepsilon^{\frac{d-1}{2}}) \log^d n)$	[2]
Chan '06	$O((1/\varepsilon^{d-(3/2)}) \log^d(1/\varepsilon))$	[9]
Agarwal and Yu '07	$O(1/\varepsilon^{d-(3/2)})$	[6]
This work	$O((1/\varepsilon^{\frac{d-1}{2}}) \log(1/\varepsilon))$	Here

In this paper, we are interested in space-efficient streaming algorithms for maintaining ε-kernels in $\mathbb{R}^d$. Using the general dynamization technique of Bentley and Saxe [8], Agarwal *et al.* [2] gave a streaming algorithm for maintaining an ε-kernel of a stream of points in $\mathbb{R}^d$ using $O((1/\varepsilon^{(d-1)/2}) \log^d n)$ space and $O(1/\varepsilon^{d-1})$ time per update, where n is the number of points in the stream. Chan [9] succeeded to remove the dependency of the space bound to n and gave the first constant-space streaming algorithm that uses only $O([(1/\varepsilon) \log(1/\varepsilon)]^{d-1})$ space and requires $O(1)$ amortized time for processing each new point. He also showed how the space bound can be improved to $O((1/\varepsilon^{d-(3/2)}) \log^d(1/\varepsilon))$ at the expense of increasing the update time to $O(1/\sqrt{\varepsilon})$. Later on, Agarwal and Yu [6] removed the extra logarithmic factors and slightly improved the space complexity to $O(1/\varepsilon^{d-(3/2)})$, with $O(\log(1/\varepsilon))$ update time per input point. Agarwal and Yu's algorithm is indeed space-optimal in two dimensions, but is still far from optimal in dimensions higher than two.

Our Results. Chan [9] left this question open whether the space bound for the problem of maintaining ε-kernels in $\mathbb{R}^d$ can be brought down to near $O(1/\varepsilon^{(d-1)/2})$. In this paper, we answer Chan's question in the affirmative by providing a streaming algorithm that uses a near optimal space. More precisely, our algorithm maintains an ε-kernel in $\mathbb{R}^d$ using only $O((1/\varepsilon^{(d-1)/2}) \log(1/\varepsilon))$ space and $(1/\varepsilon)^{O(d)}$ update time per insertion. The space bound of our algorithm is optimal up to a logarithmic factor, as one can easily verify that any ε-kernel for sufficiently many points uniformly distributed on the surface of a d-dimensional hypersphere has size $\Omega(1/\varepsilon^{(d-1)/2})$ [3]. Our algorithm differs from its predecessors [6,9] in that the high level structure of our algorithm is not dimensionality-reduction (which ultimately exploits efficient techniques in two dimensions), but rather a high-dimensional partition of the input stream into d-dimensional "fat substreams" for which ε-kernels can be maintained efficiently by a kind of bucketing scheme. Our algorithm can be viewed as a generalization of the algorithm proposed by Chan [9] in two dimensions, which also employs a version of the compression technique used in [6]. See Table 1 for a comparison between the space complexity of our algorithm and the previous ones.

Our algorithm immediately improves the space complexity of the best previous streaming algorithms for a wide range of geometric problems in fixed dimensions, including width, minimum enclosing cylinder, minimum-width enclosing annulus, minimum-width enclosing cylindrical shell, etc. The improvement obtained by our algorithm is substantial when the problem's dimension is large. However, the algorithm improves several previous results in lower dimensions as well. For example, for the two-dimensional minimum-width spherical shell problem, combined with the lifting technique of Agarwal *et al.* [2], our algorithm requires only $O((1/\varepsilon) \log(1/\varepsilon))$ space, while the best previous space bound for this problem was $O(1/\varepsilon^{3/2})$. As a byproduct of our algorithm, we also show how to maintain an ε-kernel of a stream of points in $\mathbb{R}^d$ in an optimal time of $O(1)$ using $O((1/\varepsilon^{d-(3/2)}) \log(1/\varepsilon))$ space, which improves the best previously known time-optimal algorithm by Chan [9] that requires $O([(1/\varepsilon) \log(1/\varepsilon)]^{d-1})$ space.

2   Preliminaries

We first introduce the notation used in this paper. For a point set $P \subseteq \mathbb{R}^d$ and a direction $u \in \mathbb{S}^{d-1}$, the *directional width* of P along u is defined by $w(P, u) = \max_{p,q \in P} \langle p - q, u \rangle$, where $\langle \cdot, \cdot \rangle$ denotes the inner product function. A subset $Q \subseteq P$ is called an ε-*kernel* of P, if for all $u \in \mathbb{S}^{d-1}$,

$$w(Q, u) \geqslant (1 - \varepsilon)w(P, u).$$

We use the following result from Chan throughout this paper:

Theorem 1 (Chan [9]). *Given a set P of n points in $\mathbb{R}^d$, an ε-kernel of P of size $O(1/\varepsilon^{(d-1)/2})$ can be computed in $O(n + 1/\varepsilon^{d-(3/2)})$ time for $d \geqslant 2$, or in $O((n + 1/\varepsilon^{d-2}) \log(1/\varepsilon))$ time for $d \geqslant 3$.*

Let $S = \{p_1, \ldots, p_k\}$ be a set of k points in $\mathbb{R}^d$ ($k \leqslant d+1$). We denote by $\mathcal{F}(S)$ the *flat* spanned by S, i.e., $\mathcal{F}(S) = \left\{ \sum_{i=1}^{k} a_i p_i \mid a_1, \ldots, a_k \in \mathbb{R} \text{ and } \sum_{i=1}^{k} a_i = 1 \right\}$. Given a point $p \in \mathbb{R}^d$ and a flat $\mathcal{F} \in \mathbb{R}^d$, the *orthogonal projection* of p onto $\mathcal{F}$ is defined as $\text{proj}(\mathcal{F}, p) = \arg\min_{p' \in \mathcal{F}} \|pp'\|$. The Euclidean distance between p and its projection onto $\mathcal{F}$ is denoted by $d_{\mathcal{F}}(p)$. Throughout this paper, we simply use $d_S(p)$ instead of $d_{\mathcal{F}(S)}(p)$ to refer to the distance of p to a flat defined by the point set S. If $S = \emptyset$, then $d_S(p) = 0$ by definition.

Let $X = \langle x_0, x_1, \ldots, x_k \rangle$ be a sequence of $k + 1$ points in $\mathbb{R}^d$ ($k \leqslant d$). We say that a point $p \in \mathbb{R}^d$ is X-*respecting*, if for every $0 \leqslant i < k$,

$$d_{X_i}(p) \leqslant 2 \cdot d_{X_i}(x_{i+1}),$$

where $X_i = \{x_0, x_1, \ldots, x_i\}$. If $|X| \leqslant 1$, then every point is X-respecting by definition. The sequence X is called *self-respecting*, if for every $1 \leqslant j \leqslant k$, x_j is $\langle x_0, \ldots, x_{j-1} \rangle$-respecting. Moreover, a point set P is called X-*respecting*, if for every point $p \in P$, p is X-respecting.

3   Algorithm for Fat Substreams

In this section, we present a simple efficient algorithm for maintaining ε-kernels of fat substreams to be used as a subroutine in Section 4. Let $\mathbb{B}$ be a hyperbox in $\mathbb{R}^d$. A point set $P \subseteq \mathbb{R}^d$ is called *fat with respect to* $\mathbb{B}$, if there exist a positive constant $\alpha \leqslant 1$ and two points v and v' so that $v + \alpha \mathbb{B} \subseteq \operatorname{conv}(P) \subseteq v' + \mathbb{B}$. If P is fat with respect to some hyperbox $\mathbb{B}$, then an ε-kernel of P of size $O(1/\varepsilon^{(d-1)/2})$ can be computed efficiently using a simple grid-rounding method proposed in [9,14] based on Dudley's construction [10]. Dudley's method actually works for the case where $\mathbb{B}$ is a hypercube. However, we can easily transform $\mathbb{B}$ to a hypercube by an affine transform τ, and then compute an ε-kernel Q of the set $\tau(P)$. The set $\tau^{-1}(Q)$ is then an ε-kernel of P, as proved in [2]. In the following, we show how this idea can be used for X-respecting substreams.

Let $X = \langle x_0, x_1, \dots, x_d \rangle$ be a sequence of $d+1$ points in $\mathbb{R}^d$. For each $1 \leqslant i \leqslant d$, we denote by $\hat{x}_i$ the projection of x_i onto $\mathcal{F}(X_{i-1})$, where $X_i = \{x_0, x_1, \dots, x_i\}$. Let $w_i = \|\hat{x}_i x_i\|$ and $u_i = (1/w_i)\overrightarrow{\hat{x}_i x_i}$. We denote by $\mathcal{B}_X$ the d-dimensional box centered at x_0, whose i-th side has length $4w_i$ in direction u_i $(1 \leqslant i \leqslant d)$. The following lemma (which is analogous to what is proved in [7] for three dimensions) provides a connection between X-respecting and fat sets.

Lemma 1. *Let* X *be a self-respecting sequence of* $d+1$ *points in* $\mathbb{R}^d$. *Given a point set* $P \in \mathbb{R}^d$, *if* P *is* X-*respecting, then* $P \cup X$ *is fat with respect to* $\mathcal{B}_X$.

Proof. Obviously, $\mathcal{B}_X$ contains all the points of $P \cup X$. In the following, we show that $\operatorname{conv}(X)$ (and therefore, $\operatorname{conv}(P \cup X)$) contains a translated copy of $(1/4)^d \mathcal{B}_X$. Suppose by induction that $\operatorname{conv}(X_{i-1})$ contains an $(i-1)$-dimensional box B_{i-1}, whose j-th side has length $w_j/4^{i-1}$ in direction u_j $(1 \leqslant j < i)$. Now, consider an i-dimensional pyramid $\mathcal{P}_i$ obtained by connecting x_i to all facets of B_{i-1}. Clearly, $\mathcal{P}_i \subseteq \operatorname{conv}(X_i)$. We only need to show that $\mathcal{P}_i$ contains an i-dimensional box B_i, whose j-th side has length at least $w_j/4^i$ in direction u_j $(1 \leqslant j \leqslant i)$.

Fix a k $(1 \leqslant k < i)$, and consider the plane $\mathcal{H}$ through $x_i \hat{x}_i$ parallel to u_k (see Fig. 1). The projection of B_{i-1} onto $\mathcal{H}$ is a line segment ab of length $w_k/4^{i-1}$. Let o be the orthogonal projection of x_0 onto $\mathcal{H}$. Then we have $\|oa\|, \|ob\| \leqslant w_k$ (because $B_{i-1} \subset \operatorname{conv}(X_{i-1})$), and $\|o\hat{x}_i\| \leqslant \|x_0 x_i\| \leqslant 2w_k$ (because X is self-respecting).

Let a' (respectively, b') be a point on $\overleftrightarrow{ab}$ whose vertical distance (in direction u_i) from $x_i a$ (respectively, from $x_i b$) is equal to $w_i/4^i$. We have $\|aa'\|, \|bb'\| \leqslant$

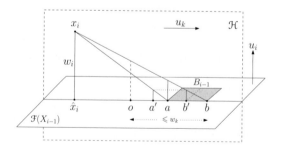

Fig. 1. Proof of Lemma 1

$3w_k/4^i$, due to similarity of triangles, and because $\|a\hat{x}_i\|, \|b\hat{x}_i\| \leqslant 3w_k$. Let $s_k = \overline{ab} - (\overline{aa'} \cup \overline{bb'})$. If one of the two angles $\angle abx_i$ and $\angle bax_i$ is obtuse, then one of the segments aa' and bb' falls completely outside ab, and therefore $\|s_k\| \geqslant w_k/4^i$. If both $\angle abx_i$ and $\angle bax_i$ are at most $\pi/2$, then $\|aa'\| + \|bb'\| = \|ab\|/4 = w_k/4^i$, and therefore, $\|s_k\| = 3w_k/4^i \geqslant w_k/4^i$. Now, we cut that portion of B_{i-1} whose projection onto $\mathcal{H}$ lies inside s_k, and repeat this procedure for every $1 \leqslant k < i$. The remaining box, B'_{i-1}, has length at least $w_k/4^i$ in each direction u_k. If we expand B'_{i-1} by $w_i/4^i$ units in direction u_i, we obtain the desired i-dimensional box B_i which completely remains inside $\mathcal{P}_i$. □

Algorithm for Fat Streams. Let P be a point set in $\mathbb{R}^d$ which is fat with respect to some hyperbox B. By a translation, we may assume that B is centered at origin. Moreover, we may assume that $B = [-1, 1]^d$ by an affine transform. According to Chan [9] and Yu *et al.* [14], one can easily compute an ε-kernel of P using a simple grid method as follows: Let $\mathcal{R}$ be the set of points of a $\sqrt{\varepsilon}$-grid over the boundary of the cube $[-2, 2]^d$, and let $\xi_S(r)$ denote the nearest neighbor of a point $r \in \mathcal{R}$ in the set S. Then the set $Q = \{\xi_P(r) \mid r \in \mathcal{R}\}$ is an ε-kernel of P (see Fig. 2). Obviously, $|Q| \leqslant |\mathcal{R}| = O(1/\varepsilon^{(d-1)/2})$. It just remains to show how we can efficiently maintain Q when new points are inserted into P, while P remains fat with respect to B.

Let $\text{KERNEL}(S) = \{\xi_S(r) \mid r \in \mathcal{R}\}$. The function INSERT-BOX described below inserts a point p into the fat stream P (enclosed by B) and returns an ε-kernel of P. The algorithm maintains two subsets Q_0 and Q_1 at each time, which are initially empty.

$B.\text{INSERT-BOX}(p)$:

1:   $Q_1 \leftarrow Q_1 \cup \{p\}$

2:   **if** $|Q_1| > 1/\varepsilon^{(d-1)/2}$ **then**

3:       $Q_0 \leftarrow \text{KERNEL}(Q_0 \cup Q_1)$

4:       $Q_1 \leftarrow \emptyset$

5:   return $Q_0 \cup Q_1$

The algorithm divides the stream P into substreams of size $\lfloor 1/\varepsilon^{(d-1)/2} \rfloor$. Whenever a substream is completely received, it is merged to the kernel maintained for the previous substreams in order to obtain a single kernel for the whole stream received so far. The correctness of the algorithm immediately follows from the following two facts: (i) $\text{KERNEL}(P \cup Q) \subseteq \text{KERNEL}(P) \cup \text{KERNEL}(Q)$, and (ii) $\text{KERNEL}(\text{KERNEL}(P)) = \text{KERNEL}(P)$. The kernel in line 4 can be computed using Theorem 1 in $O(n + 1/\varepsilon^{d-(3/2)})$ or $O((n + 1/\varepsilon^{d-2})\log(1/\varepsilon))$ time, where $n = |Q_0 \cup Q_1| = \Theta(1/\varepsilon^{(d-1)/2})$. Therefore, the amortized update time charged to each input point is $\max\{O(1), O((1/\varepsilon^{(d-3)/2})\log(1/\varepsilon))\}$. We conclude:

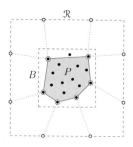

Fig. 2. Constructing an ε-kernel of a fat point set

Theorem 2. *Given a stream of points P in $\mathbb{R}^d$ which is fat with respect to a fixed hyperbox, an ε-kernel of P can be maintained using $O(1/\varepsilon^{(d-1)/2})$ space and $\max\{O(1), O((1/\varepsilon^{(d-3)/2})\log(1/\varepsilon))\}$ amortized time per input point.*

Remark. In two dimensions, Agarwal and Yu [6] used a balanced binary search tree to maintain an ε-kernel of a fat stream in $O(\log(1/\varepsilon))$ time. Theorem 2 immediately improves their method by providing an algorithm that requires only $O(1)$ amortized time. Meanwhile, our method is more direct and does not require any extra data structure.

Corollary 1. *Let X be a self-respecting sequence of $d+1$ points in $\mathbb{R}^d$. Given an X-respecting stream P in $\mathbb{R}^d$, an ε-kernel of $P \cup X$ can be maintained using $O(1/\varepsilon^{(d-1)/2})$ space and $\max\{O(1), O((1/\varepsilon^{(d-3)/2})\log(1/\varepsilon))\}$ amortized update time.*

4   The Main Algorithm

In this section, we describe the main algorithm for maintaining an ε-kernel of a data stream $P \subseteq \mathbb{R}^d$. The INSERT function in Fig. 3 inserts a point p into an X-respecting stream P and returns an ε-kernel Q of it. Each new point p is inserted into the stream by calling P.INSERT$(p, \langle\rangle)$, where $\langle\rangle$ denotes the empty sequence. In this algorithm, $b = \lceil\log(1/\varepsilon)\rceil$, and ϕ_i (used in line 15) is a function to be defined precisely at the end of this section.

The algorithm divides the input X-respecting stream P into substreams $P_1, \ldots, P_i$. Each substream P_i is $(X + \langle v_i\rangle)$-respecting, where v_1 is the first point of P, and each subsequent v_i is chosen by the algorithm as the first point for which $d_X(v_i) > 2 \cdot d_X(v_{i-1})$.

If the new input point p is $(X + \langle v_i\rangle)$-respecting, we add p to the current substream P_i by recursively calling the INSERT function in line 6. When the recursion in the size of X reaches $|X| = d+1$ (line 3), the stream P is fat with respect to $\mathcal{B}_X$, and therefore, we can use the INSERT-BOX function described in Section 3 (Corollary 1) to compute an ε-kernel of P of size $O(1/\varepsilon^{(d-1)/2})$.

P.INSERT(p, X):

1: **if** p is the first point of P **then**
2:      $i \leftarrow 1,\ v_1 \leftarrow p$
3: **if** $|X| = d + 1$ **then**
4:      return $Q = \mathcal{B}_X.$INSERT-BOX(p)
5: **if** $d_X(p) \leqslant 2 \cdot d_X(v_i)$ **then**
6:      $Q_i \leftarrow P_i.$INSERT$(p, X + \langle v_i \rangle)$
7: **else**
8:      **if** $|Q_i| > 1/\varepsilon^{(d-1)/2}$ **then**
9:          $Q_i \leftarrow \varepsilon\text{-}$KERNEL$(Q_i)$
10:      $P_i.$FREE$()$
11:      $i \leftarrow i + 1,\ v_i \leftarrow p$
12:      $Q_i \leftarrow P_i.$INSERT$(p, X + \langle v_i \rangle)$
13:      **if** $i - b > 0$ **then**
14:          **for** each $q \in Q_{i-b}$ **do**
15:              $q' \leftarrow \phi_1 \circ \cdots \circ \phi_i(q)$
16:              $Q' \leftarrow P'.$INSERT$(q', \langle \rangle)$
17:          $Q_0 \leftarrow \{q \mid q' \in Q'\}$
18:          $P_{i-b}.$FREE$(),\ Q_{i-b} \leftarrow \emptyset$
19: return $Q = \cup_{j=0}^{i} Q_j$

Fig. 3. The main algorithm

If the new point p is not $(X + \langle v_i \rangle)$-respecting, then we need to open a new substream P_{i+1} for p. But before that, we check the size of the ε-kernel Q_i currently maintained for P_i, and if $|Q_i| > 1/\varepsilon^{(d-1)/2}$, we reduce it to $O(1/\varepsilon^{(d-1)/2})$ (in line 9) using Theorem 1. After this compression step, all kernels previously maintained for P_i and its substreams are discarded by calling function FREE in line 10. Lines 11–12 increment i and create a new substream P_i initialized with $\{p\}$. (See Fig. 4.)

Lines 13–18 ensure that only b coresets $Q_{i-b+1}, \ldots, Q_i$ are active; earlier ones are mapped into a $(d-1)$-dimensional substream P' whose coreset is maintained in Q'. The mapping $\phi_1 \circ \cdots \circ \phi_i$ used in line 15 is defined as follows: let $\hat{v}_i = \text{proj}(\mathcal{F}(X), v_i)$, and let $u_i = \overrightarrow{\hat{v}_i v_i}$. We denote by $\mathcal{H}_0$ an arbitrary hyperplane through X, and for $1 \leqslant i \leqslant d$, denote by $\mathcal{H}_i$ the hyperplane through X perpendicular to u_i. The function ϕ_i denotes the projection to $\mathcal{H}_{i-1}$ parallel to the direction u_i (see Fig. 5). We keep the mapping function $\phi_1 \circ \cdots \circ \phi_i$ in a single matrix and update it only once whenever i is increased.

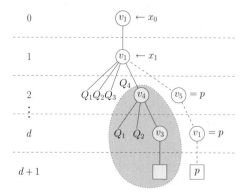

Fig. 4. An example of the execution of the algorithm. The new inserted point, p, is not $\langle x_0, x_1, v_4 \rangle$-respecting. As a result, the coreset maintained for the substream started at v_4 is compressed and stored in Q_4, the subtree rooted at v_4 is discarded, and a new substream is created with p as its first point.

5   Analysis

In this section we prove the correctness of our algorithm, and analyze its space and time complexity. The notation used here closely follows the one used in [9]. Let π_i denote the orthogonal projection onto $\mathcal{H}_i$. Note that π_i is a weak inverse of ϕ_i in the sense that $\pi_i \circ \cdots \circ \pi_1 \circ \phi_1 \circ \cdots \circ \phi_i = \pi_i$ (see Fig. 5). In the following, f denotes the final value of i, and $\psi = \pi_f \circ \cdots \circ \pi_1$. We first prove two technical lemmas.

Lemma 2. *For every $i \leqslant f$ and every direction $u \in \mathbb{S}^{d-1}$, $\langle v_i - \pi_i(v_i), u \rangle \leqslant 4^d w(P \cup X, u)$.*

Proof. Let $\mathcal{X}$ be a sequence of $d + 1$ points obtained as follows: starting from $\mathcal{X} = X$, we repeatedly add to $\mathcal{X}$ a point from P which is farthest from $\mathcal{F}(\mathcal{X})$, until $\mathcal{X}$ has $d + 1$ points. Obviously, P is $\mathcal{X}$-respecting and $P \cup \mathcal{X} = P \cup X$.

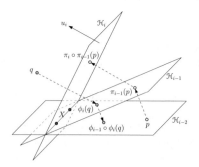

Fig. 5. Mapping functions π_i and ϕ_i

Thus, by Lemma 1, $\text{conv}(P \cup X)$ is sandwiched between $\mathcal{B}_X$ and a translated copy of $(1/4)^d \mathcal{B}_X$. Both v_i and $\pi_i(v_i)$ lie inside $\mathcal{B}_X$. Therefore, for each direction $u \in \mathbb{S}^{d-1}$,

$$\langle v_i - \pi_i(v_i), u \rangle \leqslant w(\mathcal{B}_X, u) = 4^d w((1/4)^d \mathcal{B}_X, u) \leqslant 4^d w(P \cup X, u). \qquad \square$$

Lemma 3. *Let $q \in Q_{j-b}$ for some $b < j \leqslant f$, and let $q' = \phi_1 \circ \cdots \circ \phi_j(q)$. Then for every direction $u \in \mathbb{S}^{d-1}$, $\langle q - \psi(q'), u \rangle \leqslant 4^{d+1} \varepsilon w(P \cup X, u)$.*

Proof. By the doubling property we have $d_X(q) \leqslant 2d_X(v_{j-b}) \leqslant 2^{1-b} d_X(v_j)$. Moreover, $\langle q - \pi_i(q), u \rangle / d(q, \mathcal{H}_i) = \langle v_i - \pi_i(v_i), u \rangle / d(v_i, \mathcal{H}_i)$. Since $d_X(v_i) = d(v_i, \mathcal{H}_i)$ and $d_X(q) \geqslant d(q, \mathcal{H}_i)$, we have

$$\langle q - \pi_i(q), u \rangle \leqslant \frac{d_X(q)}{d_X(v_i)} \langle v_i - \pi_i(v_i), u \rangle \leqslant \frac{d_X(q)}{d_X(v_i)} \cdot 4^d w(P \cup X, u), \qquad (1)$$

where the last inequality holds by Lemma 2. Now, define $q_j = q$, and $q_t = \pi_{t-1} \circ \cdots \circ \pi_j(q)$ for all $t > j$. It is clear that $\pi_i(q_i) = q_{i+1}$. Therefore, $\sum_{i=j}^{f} \langle q_i - \pi_i(q_i), u \rangle = \sum_{i=j}^{f} \langle q_i - q_{i+1}, u \rangle \geqslant \langle q_j - q_{f+1}, u \rangle$. We have $q_{f+1} = \pi_f \circ \cdots \circ \pi_j(q) = \psi(q')$, due to the weak-inverse relationship between π_i's and ϕ_i's. Furthermore,

$$\sum_{i=j}^{f} \frac{d_X(q_i)}{d_X(v_i)} \leqslant \sum_{i=j}^{f} \frac{1}{2^{(j-i)}} \cdot \frac{d_X(q_i)}{d_X(v_j)} \leqslant 2 \cdot \frac{d_X(q)}{d_X(v_j)} \leqslant 2(2^{1-b}) \leqslant 4\varepsilon.$$

Therefore, if we replace q by q_i in (1) and sum up the inequality over i from j to f, we get

$$\begin{aligned}
\langle q - \psi(q'), u \rangle = \langle q_j - q_{f+1}, u \rangle &\leqslant \sum_{i=j}^{f} \langle q_i - \pi_i(q_i), u \rangle \\
&\leqslant \sum_{i=j}^{f} \frac{d_X(q_i)}{d_X(v_i)} \cdot 4^d w(P \cup X, u) \\
&\leqslant 4^{d+1} \varepsilon w(P \cup X, u). \qquad \square
\end{aligned}$$

Theorem 3. *Given a stream of points P in $\mathbb{R}^d$, an ε-kernel of P can be maintained using $O((1/\varepsilon^{(d-1)/2}) \log(1/\varepsilon))$ space and $\max\{O(1), O((1/\varepsilon^{(d-3)/2})\} \log(1/\varepsilon))$ update time.*

Proof. We show that for every X-respecting stream P, the set Q returned by our algorithm is an ε-kernel of $P \cup X$. If $|X| = d + 1$, then the set Q computed in line 4 is an ε-kernel of $P \cup X$ by Corollary 1. Otherwise, $|X| \leqslant d$. Consider an arbitrary point $p \in P$. The algorithm inserts p into a substream P_i ($1 \leqslant i \leqslant f$) upon its arrival. If $i = f$, then the set Q_i is an ε-kernel of $P_i \cup X$ by induction. If $f - b < i < f$, then Q_i has passed the compression step in lines 8–9, but it is still active, i.e., is not merged into Q_0. Therefore, Q_i is a (2ε)-kernel of $P_i \cup X$ due to the fact that an ε-kernel of a ε'-kernel of a set, is an $(\varepsilon + \varepsilon')$-kernel of that set. The only remaining case is when $i \leqslant f - b$. In this case, Q_i is merged into Q_0 in lines 13–18. Since Q_i is a (2ε)-kernel of $P_i \cup X$ before merging, there exists a point $q \in Q_i$ such that for every direction $u \in \mathbb{S}^{d-1}$, $\langle q, u \rangle \geqslant \langle p, u \rangle - 2\varepsilon w(P_i \cup X, u)$.

The mapped point of q, q', is inserted into P' in line 16. Since Q' is an ε-kernel of P', $\psi(Q')$ is an ε-kernel of $\psi(P')$. Moreover, there exists a point $r \in Q_0$ with $r' \in Q'$, such that $\langle r', u \rangle \geqslant \langle q', u \rangle - \varepsilon w(P', u)$, and hence

$$\langle \psi(r'), u \rangle \geqslant \langle \psi(q'), u \rangle - \varepsilon w(\psi(P'), u). \tag{2}$$

Let $\rho = 4^{d+1}$. By Lemma 3, for every $q \in Q_1 \cup \cdots \cup Q_{f-b}$ and its corresponding $q' \in P'$,

$$\langle q, u \rangle - \rho \varepsilon w(P \cup X, u) \leqslant \langle \psi(q'), u \rangle \leqslant \langle q, u \rangle + \rho \varepsilon w(P \cup X, u),$$

which implies that $w(\psi(P'), u) \leqslant w(Q_1 \cup \cdots \cup Q_{f-b}, u) + 2\rho \varepsilon w(P \cup X, u) \leqslant (1 + 2\rho \varepsilon) w(P \cup X, u)$. Furthermore, by Lemma 3 we have $\langle \psi(r'), u \rangle \leqslant \langle r, u \rangle + \rho \varepsilon w(P \cup X, u)$ and $\langle \psi(q'), u \rangle \geqslant \langle q, u \rangle - \rho \varepsilon w(P \cup X, u)$. Replacing in (2), we get

$$\langle r, u \rangle + \rho \varepsilon w(P \cup X, u) \geqslant \langle q, u \rangle - \rho \varepsilon w(P \cup X, u) - \varepsilon[(1 + 2\rho \varepsilon) w(P \cup X, u)],$$

and hence, $\langle r, u \rangle \geqslant \langle q, u \rangle - O(\varepsilon) w(P \cup X, u)$. Since $\langle q, u \rangle \geqslant \langle p, u \rangle - 2\varepsilon w(P \cup X, u)$, we have $\langle r, u \rangle \geqslant \langle p, u \rangle - O(\varepsilon) w(P \cup X, u)$. Therefore, in any of the above cases, there exists a point in $\cup_{i=0}^{f} Q_i$ whose projected length along direction u differs from that of p by at most $O(\varepsilon) w(P \cup X, u)$, and hence, $Q = \cup_{i=0}^{f} Q_i$ is an $O(\varepsilon)$-kernel of $P \cup X$. (Note that in our proof, the algorithm returns an $O(\varepsilon)$-kernel rather than an ε-kernel; but this is not a problem as the depth of the recursion tree of our algorithm is $d + 1$, and therefore, we can adjust ε at the beginning by a constant, depending only on d.)

Space Complexity. Let $S(d, k)$ denote the space used by the algorithm to compute an ε-kernel of the d-dimensional X-respecting stream P, where $|X| = k$. Then, $|Q_0| = |Q'| = S(d - 1, 0)$, $|Q_1|, \ldots, |Q_{f-b}| = 0$ by the merging step, $|Q_{f-b+1}|, \ldots, |Q_{f-1}| = O(1/\varepsilon^{(d-1)/2})$ by the compression step, and $|Q_f| = S(d, k + 1)$. Therefore, $S(d, k)$ is upper-bounded by the following recurrence:

$$S(d, k) = \begin{cases} S(d, k+1) + S(d-1, 0) + \log(1/\varepsilon)O(1/\varepsilon^{(d-1)/2}) & 0 \leqslant k \leqslant d, \\ O(1/\varepsilon^{(d-1)/2}) & k = d + 1, \\ O(1) & d = 1, \end{cases}$$

which solves to $S(d, k) = O((1/\varepsilon^{(d-1)/2}) \log(1/\varepsilon))$, for every $0 \leqslant k \leqslant d$.

Update Time. The compression step in line 9 can be done using Theorem 1 in $O(|Q_i| + 1/\varepsilon^{d-(3/2)})$ or $O((|Q_i| + 1/\varepsilon^{d-2}) \log(1/\varepsilon))$ time. Since $|Q_i| = \Theta(1/\varepsilon^{(d-1)/2}))$, we can charge an amortized time of $\max \{O(1), O((1/\varepsilon^{(d-3)/2})\} \log(1/\varepsilon))$ to each point of Q_i. In lines 14–16, each point is inserted into P' at most once. Therefore, the cost of insertion into the $(d - 1)$-dimensional stream P' can be charged to each point upon its insertion to a P_i, which at most doubles its total insertion cost. The main cost incurred by each point is therefore the time needed to insert the point into a fat subset, which is $\max \{O(1), O((1/\varepsilon^{(d-3)/2}) \log(1/\varepsilon))\}$ by Corollary 1. $\qquad \square$

6   Reducing Update Time

While the main focus in designing streaming algorithms is to optimize the working storage, the time needed to process each element is also of particular interest, especially in applications where a huge amount of date arrives in a short period of time. For the problem of maintaining ε-kernels in $\mathbb{R}^d$, Chan [9] proposed a streaming algorithm that processes each input point in $O(1)$ time using a data structure of size $O([(1/\varepsilon)\log(1/\varepsilon)]^{d-1})$. Here, we show how to improve the space complexity of Chan's algorithm for all fixed dimensions, while the optimal update time, $O(1)$, is preserved.

We provide a general framework to trade-off between time and space complexity in our algorithm as follows: Let $\lambda(\varepsilon) = \Omega(1/\varepsilon^{(d-1)/2})$ be a function of ε. We replace $1/\varepsilon^{(d-1)/2}$ by $\lambda(\varepsilon)$ in line 2 of the INSERT-BOX function and in line 9 of the main INSERT function. It is easy to verify that the amortized update time of the new algorithm is $O([1/\varepsilon^{d-(3/2)}]/\lambda(\varepsilon))$ for $d \geqslant 2$, and $O(\log(1/\varepsilon) + [(1/\varepsilon^{d-2})\log(1/\varepsilon)]/\lambda(\varepsilon))$ for $d \geqslant 3$. Furthermore, the space complexity of the algorithm is upper-bounded by the recurrence $S(d, k) = S(d, k + 1) + S(d - 1, 0) + \log(1/\varepsilon)O(\lambda(\varepsilon))$, with the base cases $S(d, d+1) = O(\lambda(\varepsilon))$ and $S(1, k) = O(1)$. The recurrence solves to $S(d, k) = O(\lambda(\varepsilon)\log(1/\varepsilon))$. Setting $\lambda(\varepsilon) = 1/\varepsilon^{d-(3/2)}$, we immediately get the following result:

Theorem 4. *Given a stream of points P in $\mathbb{R}^d$, an ε-kernel of P can be maintained using $O((1/\varepsilon^{d-(3/2)})\log(1/\varepsilon))$ space and $O(1)$ amortized update time.*

7   Applications

In this section, we briefly review some of the implications of our result. Consider a measure μ so that for any point set $P \in \mathbb{R}^d$, an ε-kernel of P is an $O(\varepsilon)$-coreset for P with respect to μ. Examples of such measures include diameter, width, volume of the smallest enclosing box, and radius of the smallest enclosing cylinder. Theorem 3 provides space-efficient streaming algorithms to maintain ε-approximation to all these measures using near $O(1/\varepsilon^{(d-1)/2})$ space. Note that $O(1/\varepsilon^{(d-1)/2})$-space streaming algorithms were previously known for diameter [5], while the best space bound for other measures was $O(1/\varepsilon^{d-(3/2)})$ [6]. Using the general technique described in [2], our result implies improved streaming algorithms for various other shape-fitting problems like minimum-width spherical shell/annulus and minimum-width cylindrical shell. Improved results for kinetic versions of the above problems (where input is a stream of moving points) are implied as well.

Our streaming algorithm can be also used in noisy environments, using the "robust kernel" paradigm proposed in [4,13]. Roughly speaking, a subset $Q \subseteq P$ is called a (k, ε)-kernel of P, if Q ε-approximates the directional width of P, for any direction, when k outliers can be ignored in that direction. According to [4], one can simultaneously run $2k + 1$ instances of our streaming algorithm to obtain the following result:

Corollary 2. *Given a stream P of points in $\mathbb{R}^d$ and a parameter $k \geqslant 0$, a (k, ε)-kernel of P can be maintained using $O((k/\varepsilon^{(d-1)/2})\log(1/\varepsilon))$ space.*

The kernel size obtained by Corollary 2 substantially improves over the previous known upper bound $O(k/\varepsilon^{d-(3/2)})$ [6], and is very close to the lower bound which is proved to be $O(k/\varepsilon^{(d-1)/2})$ in the worst case [13].

8   Conclusions

In this paper, we presented a streaming algorithm for maintaining an ε-kernel of a stream of points in $\mathbb{R}^d$ using $O((1/\varepsilon^{(d-1)/2})\log(1/\varepsilon))$ space. The space complexity of our algorithm is optimal up to a $\log(1/\varepsilon)$ factor. In the special case of two dimensions, Agarwal and Yu [6] proposed a rather involved technique to remove this extra log factor at the expense of increasing update time from $O(1)$ to $O(\log(1/\varepsilon))$. It remains open whether this small log factor can be removed in any fixed dimension.

Acknowledgements. The author would like to thank Timothy M. Chan for his valuable comments and helpful discussions.

References

1. Agarwal, P.K., Har-Peled, S.: Maintaining approximate extent measures of moving points. In: Proc. 12th ACM-SIAM Sympos. Discrete Algorithms, pp. 148–157 (2001)
2. Agarwal, P.K., Har-Peled, S., Varadarajan, K.R.: Approximating extent measures of points. J. ACM 51(4), 606–635 (2004)
3. Agarwal, P.K., Har-Peled, S., Varadarajan, K.R.: Geometric approximation via coresets. In: Goodman, J.E., Pach, J., Welzl, E. (eds.) Combinatorial and Computational Geometry, Math. Sci. Research Inst. Pub., Cambridge (2005)
4. Agarwal, P.K., Har-Peled, S., Yu, H.: Robust shape fitting via peeling and grating coresets. In: Proc. 17th ACM-SIAM Sympos. Discrete Algorithms, pp. 182–191 (2006)
5. Agarwal, P.K., Matoušek, J., Suri, S.: Farthest neighbors, maximum spanning trees and related problems in higher dimensions. Comput. Geom. Theory Appl. 1(4), 189–201 (1992)
6. Agarwal, P.K., Yu, H.: A space-optimal data-stream algorithm for coresets in the plane. In: Proc. 23rd Annu. ACM Sympos. Comput. Geom., pp. 1–10 (2007)
7. Barequet, G., Har-Peled, S.: Efficiently approximating the minimum-volume bounding box of a point set in three dimensions. J. Algorithms 38(1), 91–109 (2001)
8. Bentley, J.L., Saxe, J.B.: Decomposable searching problems I: Static-to-dynamic transformations. J. Algorithms 1, 301–358 (1980)
9. Chan, T.M.: Faster core-set constructions and data stream algorithms in fixed dimensions. Comput. Geom. Theory Appl. 35(1–2), 20–35 (2006)
10. Dudley, R.M.: Metric entropy of some classes of sets with differentiable boundaries. J. Approx. Theory 10, 227–236 (1974)

11. Frahling, G., Sohler, C.: Coresets in dynamic geometric data streams. In: Proc. 37th Annu. ACM Sympos. Theory Comput., pp. 209–217 (2005)
12. Har-Peled, S., Mazumdar, S.: On coresets for k-means and k-median clustering. In: Proc. 36th Annu. ACM Sympos. Theory Comput., pp. 291–300 (2004)
13. Har-Peled, S., Wang, Y.: Shape fitting with outliers. SIAM J. Comput. 33(2), 269–285 (2004)
14. Yu, H., Agarwal, P.K., Poreddy, R., Varadarajan, K.R.: Practical methods for shape fitting and kinetic data structures using core sets. In: Proc. 20th Annu. ACM Sympos. Comput. Geom., pp. 263–272 (2004)

Deterministic Sampling Algorithms for Network Design

Anke van Zuylen[*]

School of Operations Research and Information Engineering,
Cornell University, Ithaca, NY 14853
Fax: (607) 255-9129
avz2@cornell.edu

Abstract. For several NP-hard network design problems, the best known approximation algorithms are remarkably simple randomized algorithms called Sample-Augment algorithms in [11]. The algorithms draw a random sample from the input, solve a certain subproblem on the random sample, and augment the solution for the subproblem to a solution for the original problem. We give a general framework that allows us to derandomize most Sample-Augment algorithms, i.e. to specify a specific sample for which the cost of the solution created by the Sample-Augment algorithm is at most a constant factor away from optimal. Our approach allows us to give deterministic versions of the Sample-Augment algorithms for the connected facility location problem, in which the open facilities need to be connected by either a tree or a tour, the virtual private network design problem, 2-stage rooted stochastic Steiner tree problem with independent decisions, the *a priori* traveling salesman problem and the single sink buy-at-bulk problem. This partially answers an open question posed in Gupta et al. [11].

1   Introduction

For several NP-hard network design problems, the best known approximation algorithms are remarkably simple randomized algorithms. The algorithms draw a random sample from the input, solve a certain subproblem on the random sample, and augment the solution for the subproblem to a solution for the original problem. Following [11], we will refer to this type of algorithm as a Sample-Augment algorithm. We give a general framework that allows us to derandomize most Sample-Augment algorithms, i.e. to specify a specific sample for which the cost of the solution created by the Sample-Augment algorithm is at most a constant factor away from optimal. The derandomization of the Sample-Augment algorithm for the single source rent-or-buy problem in Williamson and Van Zuylen [21] is a special case of our approach, but our approach also extends to the Sample-Augment algorithms for the connected facility location problem, in which the open facilities need to be connected by either a tree or a tour [3],

---

[*] Supported by NSF grant CCF-0514628.

D. Halperin and K. Mehlhorn (Eds.): ESA 2008, LNCS 5193, pp. 830–841, 2008.
© Springer-Verlag Berlin Heidelberg 2008

the virtual private network design problem [12,11,1,2], 2-stage stochastic Steiner tree problem with independent decisions [13], the *a priori* traveling salesman problem [18], and even the single sink buy-at-bulk problem [12,11,9], although for this we need to further extend our framework.

Generally speaking, the problems we consider are network design problems: they feature an underlying undirected graph $G = (V, E)$ with edge costs $c_e \geq 0$ that satisfy the triangle inequality, and the algorithm needs to make decisions such as on which edges to install how much capacity or at which vertices to open facilities. The Sample-Augment algorithm proceeds by randomly marking a subset of the vertices, solving some subproblem that is defined on the set of marked vertices, and then augmenting the solution for the subproblem to a solution for the original problem. We refer the reader to the paper by Gupta, Kumar, Pál and Ravi [11], which is the journal version of the papers which first introduced Sample-Augment algorithms [12,10], for further discussions of Sample-Augment algorithms for the problems we consider.

As an example, in the single source rent-or-buy problem, we are given a source $s \in V$, a set of sinks $t_1, \ldots, t_k \in V$ and a parameter $M > 1$. An edge e can either be *rented* for sink t_j in which case we pay c_e, or it can be bought and used by any sink, in which case we pay Mc_e. The goal is to find a minimum cost set of edges to buy and rent so that for each sink t_j the bought edges plus the edges rented for t_j contain a path from t_j to s. In the Sampling Step of the Sample-Augment algorithm in Gupta et al. [12,11] we mark each sink independently with probability $\frac{1}{M}$. Given the set of marked sinks D, the Subproblem Step finds a Steiner tree on $D \cup \{s\}$ and buys the edges of this tree. In the Augmentation Step, the subproblem's solution is augmented to a feasible solution for the single source rent-or-buy problem by renting edges for each unmarked sink t_j to the closest vertex in $D \cup \{s\}$.

To give a deterministic version of the Sample-Augment algorithm, we want to find a set D such that for this set D the cost of the Subproblem Step plus the Augmentation Step is at most the expected cost of the Sample-Augment problem. A natural approach is to try and use the method of conditional expectation [4] to achieve this. However, in order to do this we would need to be able to compute the conditional expectation of the cost of the Sample-Augment problem, conditioned on including / not including $t_j \in D$. Unfortunately, we do not know how to do this for any of the problems for which good Sample-Augment algorithms exist.

What we show is that we *can* find an upper bound on the cost of the Subproblem plus Augmentation Steps that can be efficiently computed. Suppose we can show that the expectation of the upper bound under the sampling strategy of the randomized Sample-Augment algorithm is at most βOPT, where OPT is the optimal value and $\beta > 1$ is some constant. Then we can use this upper bound and the method of conditional expectation to find a set D such that the upper bound on the cost of the Subproblem Step plus the Augmentation Step is not more than the expected upper bound for the randomized Sample-Augment algorithm, and hence at most βOPT as well.

Our upper bound on the cost of the Subproblem Step will be obtained from a particular feasible solution to a linear programming (LP) relaxation of the subproblem. We then use well-known approximation algorithms to obtain a solution to the subproblem that comes within a constant factor of the subproblem LP. We do not need to solve the LP relaxation of the subproblem: instead we show that the optimal solution to an LP relaxation *of the original problem* defines a set of feasible solutions to the *subproblem*'s LP relaxation. We note that for some of the problems we consider, for example the virtual private network design problem, this requires us to "discover" a new LP relaxation of the original problem.

Using this technique, we derive the best known deterministic approximation algorithms for the 2-stage rooted stochastic Steiner tree problem with independent decisions (2-stage Steiner), the *a priori* traveling salesman problem (a priori TSP), the connected facility location problem in which the open facilities need to be connected by a traveling salesman tour (CFL-tour), the virtual private network design problem (VPND) and the single sink buy-at-bulk problem (SSBaB). We thus partially answer an open question in Gupta et al. [11] (the only problem in [11] that we do not give a deterministic algorithm for is the multicommodity rent-or-buy problem). In addition, our analysis implies that the integrality gap of an (even more) natural LP relaxation than the one considered in [7,20] for the single-sink buy-at-bulk problem has integrality gap at most 27.72. We also match the best known bounds by deterministic algorithms for the single source rent-or-buy problem (SSRoB) and the connected facility location problem in which open facilities need to be connected by a tree (CFL-tree), which were obtained by applying the techniques from Williamson and Van Zuylen [21], which is a special case of our approach. We summarize our results in Table 1.

We remark that our method is related to the method of pessimistic estimators of Raghavan [17]: Raghavan also uses an efficiently computable upper bound in combination with the method of conditional expectation to derandomize a randomized algorithm, where he first proves that the expected "cost" of the randomized algorithm is small. (We note that in the problem he considers, the cost of the algorithm is either 0 (the solution is "good") or 1 (the solution is "bad")).

Table 1. The first column contains the best known approximation guarantees for the problems, which are obtained by randomized Sample-Augment algorithms. The second column gives the previous best known approximation guarantee by a deterministic algorithm. Entries marked with * are obtained by using the method in Williamson and Van Zuylen [21], which is a special case of our approach. The third column shows the approximation guarantees in this paper.

Problem	randomized	prev. best deterministic	our result
SSRoB	2.92 [3]	4.2 [14], 3.28* [21,3]	3.28
2-stage Steiner	3.55 [13]	$\log n$ [16]	8
a priori TSP	4 [18], $O(1)$ [6]	8* [18]	6.5
CFL-tree	4 [3]	8.29 [15], 4.23* [3]	4.23
k-CFL-tree	6.85 [3]	6.98* [3]	6.98
CFL-tour	4.12 [3]	-	4.12
VPND	3.55 [2]	$\log n$ [5]	8.02
SSBaB	24.92 [9]	216 [20]	27.72

However, in Raghavan's work the probabilities in the randomized algorithm depend on a solution to a linear program, but the upper bounds are obtained by a Chernoff-type bound. In our work, the probabilities in the randomized algorithm are already known from previous works, but we demonstrate *upper bounds* on the conditional expectations that depend on linear programming relaxations.

In the next section, we will give a general description of a Sample-Augment algorithm, and give a set of conditions under which we can give a deterministic variant of a Sample-Augment algorithm. In Section 3 we illustrate our method using the single source rent-or-buy problem as an example. In Section 4 we demonstrate how to obtain a deterministic version of the Sample-Augment type algorithm for the *a priori* traveling salesman problem proposed by Shmoys and Talwar [18], since this example illustrates some of the additional ideas we need to apply our method to the other problems we consider. Due to space constraints, we refer the reader to `http://people.orie.cornell.edu/~anke/ESA08.pdf` for a discussion of our results for the 2-stage rooted stochastic Steiner tree problem with independent decisions, connected facility location problems, the virtual private network design problem and the single sink buy-at-bulk problem. We conclude with a brief discussion of some future directions in Section 5.

2   Derandomization of Sample-Augment Algorithms

We give a high-level description of a class of algorithms first introduced by Gupta, Kumar and Roughgarden [12], which were called Sample-Augment algorithms in [11]. Given a (minimization) problem $\mathcal{P}$, the Sample-Augment algorithm is defined by

(i) a set of elements $\mathcal{D} = \{1, \ldots, n\}$ and sampling probabilities $p = (p_1, \ldots, p_n)$,
(ii) a subproblem $\mathcal{P}_{sub}(D)$ defined for any $D \subset \mathcal{D}$, and
(ii) an augmentation problem $\mathcal{P}_{aug}(D, \mathtt{Sol}_{Sub}(D))$ defined for any $D \subset \mathcal{D}$ and solution $\mathtt{Sol}_{sub}(D)$ to $\mathcal{P}_{sub}(D)$.

The Sample-Augment algorithm samples from $\mathcal{D}$ independently according to the sampling probabilities p, solves the subproblem and augmentation problem for the random subset, and returns the union of the solutions given by the subproblem and augmentation problem. We give a general statement of the Sample-Augment algorithm.

$\mathcal{P}$-Sample-Augment$(\mathcal{D}, p, \mathcal{P}_{Sub}, \mathcal{P}_{aug})$

1. *(Sampling Step)* Mark each element $j \in \mathcal{D}$ independently with probability p_j. Let D be the set of marked elements.
2. *(Subproblem Step)* Solve $\mathcal{P}_{sub}$ on D. Let $\mathtt{Sol}_{sub}(D)$ be the solution found.
3. *(Augmentation Step)* Solve $\mathcal{P}_{aug}$ on $D, \mathtt{Sol}_{sub}(D)$. Let $\mathtt{Sol}_{aug}(D, \mathtt{Sol}_{sub}(D))$ be the solution found.
4. Return $\mathtt{Sol}_{sub}(D)$ and $\mathtt{Sol}_{aug}(D, \mathtt{Sol}_{sub}(D))$.

We remark that we will consider Sample-Augment algorithms, in which the Augmentation Step only depends on D, and not on $\text{Sol}_{sub}(D)$.

In the following, we let OPT denote the optimal value of the problem we are considering. Let $C_{sub}(D)$ be the cost of $\text{Sol}_{sub}(D)$, and let $C_{aug}(D)$ be the cost of $\text{Sol}_{aug}(D, \text{Sol}_{sub}(D))$. Let $C_{SA}(D) = C_{sub}(D) + C_{aug}(D)$. We will use blackboard bold characters to denote random sets. For a function $C(D)$, let $\mathbb{E}_p\big[C(\mathbb{D})\big]$ be the expectation of $C(\mathbb{D})$ if $\mathbb{D}$ is obtained by including each $j \in \mathcal{D}$ in $\mathbb{D}$ independently with probability p_j.

Note that, since the elements are included in $\mathbb{D}$ independently, the conditional expectation of $\mathbb{E}_p\big[C_{SA}(\mathbb{D})\big]$ given that j is included in $\mathbb{D}$ is $\mathbb{E}_{p, p_j \leftarrow 1}\big[C_{SA}(\mathbb{D})\big]$, and the conditional expectation, given that j is not included in $\mathbb{D}$ is $\mathbb{E}_{p, p_j \leftarrow 0}\big[C_{SA}(\mathbb{D})\big]$. By the method of conditional expectation [4], one of these conditional expectations has value at most $\mathbb{E}_p\big[C_{SA}(\mathbb{D})\big]$. Hence if we could compute the expectations for different vectors of sampling probabilities, we could iterate through the elements and transform p into a binary vector (corresponding to a deterministic set D) without increasing $\mathbb{E}_p\big[C_{SA}(\mathbb{D})\big]$.

Unfortunately, this is not very useful to us yet, since it is generally not the case that we can compute $\mathbb{E}_p\big[C_{SA}(\mathbb{D})\big]$. However, as we will show, for many problems and corresponding Sample-Augment algorithms, it is the case that $\mathbb{E}_p\big[C_{aug}(\mathbb{D})\big]$ can be efficiently computed for any vector of probabilities p, and does not depend on the solution $\text{Sol}_{sub}(\mathbb{D})$ for the subproblem, but only on the set $\mathbb{D}$. The expected cost of the subproblem's solution is more difficult to compute. What we therefore do instead is replace the cost of the subproblem by an upper bound on its cost: Suppose there exists a function $U_{sub} : 2^{\mathcal{D}} \rightarrow R$ such that $C_{sub}(D) \leq U_{sub}(D)$ for any $D \subset \mathcal{D}$, and suppose we can efficiently compute $\mathbb{E}_p\big[U_{sub}(\mathbb{D})\big]$ and $\mathbb{E}_p\big[C_{aug}(\mathbb{D})\big]$ for any vector p. If there exists some vector $\hat{p}$ such that

$$\mathbb{E}_{\hat{p}}\big[U_{sub}(\mathbb{D})\big] + \mathbb{E}_{\hat{p}}\big[C_{aug}(\mathbb{D})\big] \leq \beta OPT \tag{1}$$

then we can use the method of conditional expectation to find a set D such that $U_{sub}(D) + C_{aug}(D) \leq \beta OPT$, and hence also $C_{sub}(D) + C_{aug}(D) \leq \beta OPT$.

Theorem 1. *Given a minimization problem $\mathcal{P}$ and an algorithm $\mathcal{P}$-Sample-Augment, suppose the following four conditions hold:*

(i) *$\mathbb{E}_p\big[C_{aug}(\mathbb{D})\big]$ depends only on $\mathbb{D}$, not on $\text{Sol}_{sub}(\mathbb{D})$, and can be efficiently computed for any p.*

(ii) *There exists an LP relaxation Sub-LP(D) of $\mathcal{P}_{sub}(D)$ and an algorithm for $\mathcal{P}_{sub}(D)$ that is guaranteed to output a solution to $\mathcal{P}_{sub}(D)$ that costs at most a factor α times the cost of any feasible solution to Sub-LP(D).*

(iii) *There exist known vectors b and $r(j)$ for $j = 1, \ldots, n$ such that $y(D) = b + \sum_{j \in D} r(j)$ is a feasible solution to Sub-LP(D) for any $D \subset \mathcal{D}$.*

(iv) *There exists a vector $\hat{p}$ such that*

$$\mathbb{E}_{\hat{p}}\big[C_{aug}(\mathbb{D})\big] + \alpha \mathbb{E}_{\hat{p}}\big[C_{LP}(y(\mathbb{D}))\big] \leq \beta OPT,$$

where $C_{LP}(y(D))$ is the objective value of $y(D)$ for Sub-LP(D).

Then there exists a deterministic β-approximation algorithm for $\mathcal{P}$.

Proof. Let $U_{sub}(D) = \alpha C_{LP}(y(D))$. If we use the algorithm from (ii) in the Subproblem Step of $\mathcal{P}$-Sample-Augment, then by (ii), $C_{sub}(D) \leq U_{sub}(D)$. By (iii) $\mathbb{E}_p[U_{sub}(\mathbb{D})]$ can be efficiently computed for any p, and by (iv) Equation (1) is satisfied. Hence we can use the method of conditional expectation to find a set D such that $C_{sub}(D) + C_{aug}(D) \leq U_{sub}(D) + C_{aug}(D) \leq \beta OPT$. □

In many cases, (i) is easily verified. In the problems we are considering here, the subproblem looks for a Steiner tree or a traveling salesman tour, so that there are well-known LP relaxations and algorithms such that $\alpha = 2$ if the subproblem is a Steiner tree problem [8], and $\alpha = 1.5$ if the subproblem is a traveling salesman tour problem [22,19]. The solution $y(D) = b + \sum_{j \in D} r(j)$ will be defined by using the optimal solution to an LP relaxation *of the original problem*, so that for appropriately chosen probabilities $\mathbb{E}_{\hat{p}}[C_{LP}(y(\mathbb{D}))]$ is bounded by a constant factor times OPT. Using the analysis for the randomized algorithm to bound $\mathbb{E}_{\hat{p}}[C_{aug}(\mathbb{D})]$, we can then show that (iv) holds.

Remark. In some cases, $\mathcal{P}_{sub}$ and $\mathcal{P}_{aug}$ are only defined for $D \neq \emptyset$. In such cases, we require that condition (i) holds for all p such that $p_j = 1$ for some j, and that condition (ii) holds for non-empty subsets D. Condition (iv) then asks for $\hat{p}$ such that $\hat{p}_j = 1$ for some j. The derandomization procedure will not change this element, so that the Sample-Augment algorithm is always well defined for the vectors p that we consider.

3   Single Source Rent-or-Buy

We illustrate Theorem 1 by showing how it can be used to give a deterministic algorithm for the single source rent-or-buy problem. We note that this was already done in [21]; however, we repeat this here because this is arguably the simplest application of Theorem 1 and hence provides a nice illustration of the more general approach.

In the single source rent-or-buy problem, we are given an undirected graph $G = (V, E)$, edge costs $c_e \geq 0$ for $e \in E$, a source $s \in V$ and a set of sinks $t_1, \ldots, t_k \in V$, and a parameter $M > 1$. A solution is a set of edges B to *buy*, and for each sink t_j a set of edges R_j to *rent*, so that $B \cup R_j$ contains a path from t to t_j. The cost of renting an edge e is c_e and the cost of buying e is Mc_e. For a set $T \subseteq E$, we denote by $c(T) = \sum_{e \in T} c_e$, hence the cost of solution $(B, R_1, \ldots, R_k)$ is $Mc(B) + \sum_{j=1}^{k} c(R_j)$. For $u, v \in V$, we denote by $\ell(u, v)$ the lenght of the shortest path from u to v with respect to costs c, and we let $\ell(u, F) = \min_{v \in F} \ell(u, v)$.

Gupta, Kumar, and Roughgarden [12] propose the random sampling algorithm given below, where they set $p_j = \frac{1}{M}$ for all $j = 1, \ldots, k$.

SSRoB-Sample-Augment$(G = (V, E), c, s, \{t_1, \ldots, t_k\}, p)$

---

1. *(Sampling Step)* Mark each sink t_j with probability p_j. Let D be the set of marked sinks.
2. *(Subproblem Step)* Construct a Steiner tree on $D \cup \{s\}$ and *buy* the edges of the tree.
3. *(Augmentation Step)* Rent the shortest path from each unmarked sink to the closest terminal in $D \cup \{s\}$.

Note that the expected cost of the Augmentation Step of SSRoB-Sample-Augment does not depend on the tree bought in the Subproblem Step. Gupta et al. [12] show that if each sink is marked independently with probability $\frac{1}{M}$ then the expected cost of the Augmentation Step can be bounded by $2OPT$.

Lemma 2 ([12]). *If* $p_j = \frac{1}{M}$ *for* $j = 1, \ldots, k$, *then* $\mathbb{E}\big[C_{aug}(\mathbb{D})\big] \leq 2OPT$.

Lemma 3 ([21]). *There exists a deterministic 4-approximation algorithm for SSRoB.*

Proof. We verify that the four conditions of Theorem 1 hold. It is straightforward to show that $\mathbb{E}_p\big[C_{aug}(\mathbb{D})\big]$, the expected cost incurred in the Augmentation Step, can be computed for any vector of sampling probabilities p. Now consider the subproblem on a given subset D of $\{t_1, \ldots, t_k\}$. From Goemans and Bertsimas [8] we know that we can efficiently find a Steiner tree on $D \cup \{s\}$ of cost at most twice the optimal value (and hence the objective value of any feasible solution) of the following Sub-LP:

$$\min \sum_{e \in E} Mc_e y_e$$

(Sub-LP(D)) s.t. $\sum_{e \in \delta(S)} y_e \geq 1 \quad \forall S \subset V : s \notin S, D \cap S \neq \emptyset$

$$y_e \geq 0 \quad \forall e \in E.$$

We now want to define a feasible solution $y(D)$ to Sub-LP(D) for any $D \subset \mathcal{D}$, such that $y(D)$ can be written as $b + \sum_{t_j \in D} r(j)$, since this form will allow us to efficiently compute $\mathbb{E}_p\big[C_{LP}(y(\mathbb{D}))\big]$. To do this, we use an LP relaxation of the single source rent-or-buy problem. Let b_e be a variable that indicates whether we buy edge e, and let r_e^j indicate whether we rent edge e for sink t_j.

$$\min \sum_{e \in E} Mc_e b_e + \sum_{e \in E} \sum_{j=1}^{k} c_e r_e^j$$

(SSRoB-LP) s.t. $\sum_{e \in \delta(S)} (b_e + r_e^j) \geq 1 \quad \forall S \subset V : t_j \in S, s \notin S$

$$b_e, r_e^j \geq 0 \quad \forall e \in E, j = 1, \ldots, k.$$

SSRoB-LP is a relaxation of the single source rent-or-buy problem, since the optimal solution to the single source rent-or-buy problem is feasible for SSRoB-LP and has objective value OPT. Let $\hat{b}, \hat{r}$ be an optimal solution to SSRoB-LP. For a given set $D \subset \mathcal{D}$ and edge $e \in E$ we let

$$y_e(D) = \hat{b}_e + \sum_{t_j \in D} \hat{r}_e^j.$$

Clearly, $y(D)$ is a feasible solution to Sub-LP(D) for any D.

Finally, we need to show the existence of a vector $\hat{p}$ such that $\mathbb{E}_{\hat{p}}\left[C_{aug}(\mathbb{D})\right] + 2\mathbb{E}_{\hat{p}}\left[C_{LP}(y(\mathbb{D}))\right] \leq 4OPT$. Let $\hat{p}_j = \frac{1}{M}$ for every $t_j \in \mathcal{D}$. Then by Lemma 2, the expected cost of the Augmentation Step is at most $2OPT$, and $2\mathbb{E}_{\hat{p}}\left[C_{LP}(y(\mathbb{D}))\right]$ is

$$2 \sum_{e \in E} M c_e \left(\hat{b}_e + \sum_{j=1}^{k} \frac{1}{M} \hat{r}_e^j\right) \leq 2OPT.$$

Hence, applying Theorem 1, we get that there exists a 4-approximation algorithm for SSRoB. $\qquad\square$

We note that it was shown in [21] that a better deterministic approximation algorithm exists, by using the improved analysis of the randomized algorithm given by Eisenbrand et al. [3], which allows us to more carefully balance the charge against the optimal renting and the optimal buying costs. We refer the reader to [21] for the details.

Lemma 4 ([21,3]). *There exists a deterministic 3.28-approximation algorithm for the single source rent-or-buy problem.*

4   A *Priori* Traveling Salesman Problem with Independent Decisions

In the *a priori* traveling salesman problem with independent decisions, we are given a graph $G = (V, E)$ with edge costs $c_e \geq 0$ and a set of terminals $t_1, \ldots, t_k$, where terminal t_j is active independently of the other terminals with probability q_j. The goal is to find a so-called *master tour* on the set of all terminals, such that the expected cost of shortcutting the master tour to the set of active terminals is minimized.

Shmoys and Talwar [18] recently showed that a Sample-Augment type algorithm for this problem is a 4-approximation algorithm. In the Sampling Step, they randomly mark the terminals, where each terminal t_j is marked independently with probability $p_j = q_j$. (If there is no t_j such that $q_j = 1$, then they need a revised Sampling Step to ensure at least one terminal is marked. We omit the details here.) In the Subproblem Step they find a tour on the marked terminals and finally, in the Augmentation Step they add two copies of the shortest path from each unmarked terminal to the closest marked terminal.

It is not hard to see that if at least one terminal is marked, then the Sample-Augment algorithm finds an Euler tour on the terminals, and we can shortcut the Euler tour to give the traveling salesman tour that will be the master tour.

To evaluate the expected cost of the shortcut tour on a set of active terminals A, Shmoys and Talwar upper bound the cost of shortcutting the master tour on A by assuming that for any A of size at least 2 we *always* traverse the edges found in the Subproblem Step, and we traverse the edges found in the Augmentation Step only for the active terminals. If $|A| < 2$, then the cost of the shortcut master tour is 0.

Since we are interested in upper bounding the expected cost of the shortcut tour, we can just consider the expectation of this upper bound. Let Q be the probability that at least 2 terminals are active, and let $\tilde{q}_j$ be the probability that t_j is active conditioned on the fact that at least 2 terminals are active, i.e. $\tilde{q}_j = \frac{q_j(1 - \prod_{i \neq j}(1 - q_i))}{Q}$. The expected cost for an edge e in the tour constructed by the Subproblem Step is Qc_e and the expected cost for an edge e that is added for terminal j in the Augmentation Step is $\tilde{q}_j c_e$.

Hence we can instead analyze the algorithm APTSP-Sample-Augment given below. We note that the vector of sampling probabilities must have at least one element set to 1, otherwise the Augmentation Step is not well defined. We will therefore make sure that the vector $\hat{p}$ with which we start the derandomization of APTSP-Sample-Augment has at least one element equal to 1 (in fact, it will have two elements set to 1).

APTSP-Sample-Augment$(G = (V, E), c, Q, \tilde{q}, s, \{t_1, \ldots, t_k\}, p)$

1. *(Sampling Step)* Mark each terminal t_j with probability p_j. Let D be the set of marked terminals.
2. *(Subproblem Step)* Construct a traveling salesman tour on D, and incur cost Qc_e for each edge on the tour.
3. *(Augmentation Step)* Add two copies of the shortest path from each unmarked terminal t_j to the closest terminal in D and incur cost $\tilde{q}_j c_e$ for each edge.

Shmoys and Talwar [18] show that if $\tilde{p}_j = q_j$ for every terminal, and if we were able to find a *minimum cost* solution to the subproblem, then $\mathbb{E}_{\tilde{p}}\big[C_{sub}(\mathbb{D}) \big| |\mathbb{D}| \geq 2\big] \leq OPT$, and $\mathbb{E}_{\tilde{p}}\big[C_{aug}(\mathbb{D}) \big| |\mathbb{D}| \geq 2\big] \leq 2OPT$.

This implies that there is some non-empty set D^* such that $C_{sub}(D^*) + C_{aug}(D^*) \leq 3OPT$. Let t^* be one of the terminals in D^*, and set $b_e = 1$ for each of the edges in the (minimum cost) subproblem's solution on D^*, and let $r_e^j = 1$ for the edges added for terminal j in the Augmentation Step. Then b, r defines a feasible solution to the following LP with objective value at most OPT and hence APTSP-LP is an LP relaxation of the *a priori* Traveling Salesman Problem.

$$\min \frac{1}{3} \sum_{e \in E} \left(Qc_e b_e + \sum_{j=1}^{k} \tilde{q}_j c_e r_e^j \right)$$

$$\text{(APTSP-LP) s.t.} \sum_{e \in \delta(S)} (b_e + r_e^j) \geq 2 \quad \forall S \subset V : t^* \notin S, t_j \in S$$

$$b_e, r_e^j \geq 0 \quad \forall e \in E, j = 1, \ldots, k.$$

Note that we do not know t^*, but we can solve APTSP-LP for any $t^* \in \{t_1, \ldots, t_k\}$ and use the LP with the smallest objective value. Let $\hat{b}, \hat{r}$ be an optimal solution to that LP. We let the Sub-LP on D be

$$\min \sum_{e \in E} Q c_e y_e$$

$$\text{(Sub-LP}(D)) \quad \text{s.t.} \sum_{e \in \delta(S)} y_e \geq 2 \quad \forall S \subset V : D \backslash S \neq \emptyset, D \cap S \neq \emptyset$$

$$y_e \geq 0 \quad \forall e \in E.$$

Note that this satisfies condition (ii) in Theorem 1 with $\alpha = 1.5$ by [22,19]. To define solutions $y(D)$ to Sub-LP(D), we let $y_e(D) = \hat{b}_e + \sum_{t_j \in D} \hat{r}_e^j$.

We now let $\tilde{p}_j = q_j$ and consider the expectation of $\mathbb{E}_{\tilde{p}}[C_{LP}(y(\mathbb{D}))||\mathbb{D}| \geq 2]$ and $\mathbb{E}_{\tilde{p}}[C_{aug}(\mathbb{D})||\mathbb{D}| \geq 2]$. From Shmoys and Talwar we know that the second term is at most $2OPT$. Also, since the probability that t_j is in $\mathbb{D}$ conditioned on $\mathbb{D}$ having at least 2 elements is $\tilde{q}_j$, we get

$$1.5\mathbb{E}_{\tilde{p}}[C_{LP}(y(\mathbb{D}))||\mathbb{D}| \geq 2] = 1.5 \left(\sum_{e \in E} Q c_e \hat{b}_e + \sum_{j=1}^{k} Q \tilde{q}_j c_e \hat{r}_e^j \right)$$

$$= 1.5 \sum_{e \in E} \left(Q c_e \hat{b}_e + \sum_{j=1}^{k} q_j (1 - \prod_{i \neq j}(1 - q_i)) c_e \hat{r}_e^j \right)$$

$$\leq 1.5 \sum_{e \in E} \left(Q c_e \hat{b}_e + \sum_{j=1}^{k} q_j c_e \hat{r}_e^j \right) \leq 4.5 OPT \qquad (2)$$

where the last inequality holds since we showed that APTSP-LP is a relaxation of the *a priori* Traveling Salesman Problem.

Finally, we want to get rid of the conditioning on $|\mathbb{D}| \geq 2$. By conditioning on the two smallest indices in $\mathbb{D}$ and then using basic properties of conditional expectation, one can show that there must exist two elements, say $j_1 < j_2$ such that if we let $\hat{p}_{j_1} = \hat{p}_{j_2} = 1$, $\hat{p}_j = 0$ for all other $j < j_2$ and $\hat{p}_j = q_j$ for all $j > j_2$, then

$$1.5\mathbb{E}_{\hat{p}}[C_{LP}(y(\mathbb{D}))] + \mathbb{E}_{\hat{p}}[C_{aug}(\mathbb{D})] \leq 1.5\mathbb{E}_{\tilde{p}}[C_{LP}(y(\mathbb{D}))||\mathbb{D}| \geq 2] + \mathbb{E}_{\tilde{p}}[C_{aug}(\mathbb{D})||\mathbb{D}| \geq 2].$$

Hence we can try all possible choices of j_1, j_2, and we will find $\hat{p}$ with at least two elements equal to 1, so that condition (iv) of Theorem 1 holds with $\beta = 6.5$. Hence we get the following result.

Lemma 5. *There exists a deterministic 6.5-approximation algorithm for a priori Traveling Salesman Problem.*

Remark. Shmoys and Talwar [18] use the Steiner tree LP as the Sub-LP. Since we can get a traveling salesman tour of cost at most twice the cost of a Steiner tree, $\alpha = 4$. They show that $\alpha \mathbb{E}_{\tilde{p}}\left[C_{LP}(y(\mathbb{D}))\,\middle|\,|\mathbb{D}| \geq 2\right] \leq 6OPT$, instead of what we find in (2), and thus get an 8-approximation algorithm.

5   Conclusion

We propose a specific method for derandomizing Sample-Augment algorithms, and we successfully apply this method to all but one of the Sample-Augment algorithms in Gupta et al. [11], and to the *a priori* traveling salesman problem and the 2-stage rooted stochastic Steiner tree problem with independent decisions. The question whether the Sample-Augment algorithm for multicommodity rent-or-buy problem can be derandomized remains open. If we want to use Theorem 1, we would need to be able to compute $\mathbb{E}_p\left[C_{aug}(\mathbb{D})\right]$ (or a good upper bound for it) efficiently and it is unclear how to do this for the multicommodity rent-or-buy algorithm, because unlike in the algorithms we discussed, $\mathbb{E}_p\left[C_{aug}(\mathbb{D})\right]$ does depend on the subproblem solution, and not just on $\mathbb{D}$. It may also be possible to extend our approach to the Boosted Sampling algorithms for stochastic optimization problems [13], but here again it is not obvious how to determine $\mathbb{E}_p\left[C_{aug}(\mathbb{D})\right]$.

Acknowledgements. The author would like to thank David P. Williamson and Frans Schalekamp for helpful comments on earlier drafts of this paper.

References

1. Eisenbrand, F., Grandoni, F.: An improved approximation algorithm for virtual private network design. In: SODA, pp. 928–932 (2005)
2. Eisenbrand, F., Grandoni, F., Oriolo, G., Skutella, M.: New approaches for virtual private network design. SIAM J. Comput. 37(3), 706–721 (2007)
3. Eisenbrand, F., Grandoni, F., Rothvoß, T., Schäfer, G.: Approximating connected facility location problems via random facility sampling and core detouring. In: SODA, pp. 1174–1183 (2008)
4. Erdős, P., Spencer, J.: Probabilistic methods in combinatorics. Academic Press, London (1974)
5. Fakcharoenphol, J., Rao, S., Talwar, K.: A tight bound on approximating arbitrary metrics by tree metrics. J. Comput. System Sci. 69(3), 485–497 (2004)
6. Garg, N., Gupta, A., Leonardi, S., Sankowski, P.: Stochastic analyses for online combinatorial optimization problems. In: SODA, pp. 942–951 (2008)
7. Garg, N., Khandekar, R., Konjevod, G., Ravi, R., Salman, F.S., Sinha, A.: On the integrality gap of a natural formulation of the single-sink buy-at-bulk network design problem. In: Aardal, K., Gerards, B. (eds.) IPCO 2001. LNCS, vol. 2081, pp. 170–184. Springer, Heidelberg (2001)
8. Goemans, M.X., Bertsimas, D.J.: Survivable networks, linear programming relaxations and the parsimonious property. Math. Program. 60(2, Ser. A), 145–166 (1993)

9. Grandoni, F., Italiano, G.F.: Improved approximation for single-sink buy-at-bulk. In: Asano, T. (ed.) ISAAC 2006. LNCS, vol. 4288, pp. 111–120. Springer, Heidelberg (2006)

10. Gupta, A., Kumar, A., Pál, M., Roughgarden, T.: Approximation via cost-sharing: A simple approximation algorithm for the multicommodity rent-or-buy problem. In: FOCS, pp. 606–615 (2003)

11. Gupta, A., Kumar, A., Pál, M., Roughgarden, T.: Approximation via cost sharing: simpler and better approximation algorithms for network design. J. ACM 54(3), 11 (2007)

12. Gupta, A., Kumar, A., Roughgarden, T.: Simpler and better approximation algorithms for network design. In: STOC, pp. 365–372 (2003)

13. Gupta, A., Pál, M., Ravi, R., Sinha, A.: Boosted sampling: approximation algorithms for stochastic optimization. In: STOC, pp. 417–426 (2004)

14. Gupta, A., Srinivasan, A., Tardos, É.: Cost-sharing mechanisms for network design. Algorithmica 50(1), 98–119 (2008)

15. Hasan, M.K., Jung, H., Chwa, K.-Y.: Approximation algorithms for connected facility location problems. J. Comb. Optim. (to appear, 2008)

16. Immorlica, N., Karger, D., Minkoff, M., Mirrokni, V.S.: On the costs and benefits of procrastination: approximation algorithms for stochastic combinatorial optimization problems. In: SODA, pp. 691–700 (2004)

17. Raghavan, P.: Probabilistic construction of deterministic algorithms: approximating packing integer programs. J. Comput. System Sci. 37(2), 130–143 (1988)

18. Shmoys, D., Talwar, K.: A constant approximation algorithm for the a priori traveling salesman problem. In: IPCO (2008)

19. Shmoys, D.B., Williamson, D.P.: Analyzing the Held-Karp TSP bound: A monotonicity property with application. Inf. Process. Lett. 35, 281–285 (1990)

20. Talwar, K.: The single-sink buy-at-bulk LP has constant integrality gap. In: Cook, W.J., Schulz, A.S. (eds.) IPCO 2002. LNCS, vol. 2337, pp. 475–486. Springer, Heidelberg (2002)

21. Williamson, D.P., van Zuylen, A.: A simpler and better derandomization of an approximation algorithm for single source rent-or-buy. Oper. Res. Lett. 35(6), 707–712 (2007)

22. Wolsey, L.A.: Heuristic analysis, linear programming and branch and bound. Math. Prog. Study 13, 121–134 (1980)

Author Index

Printing: Mercedes-Druck, Berlin
Binding: Stein+Lehmann, Berlin

Lecture Notes in Computer Science

Sublibrary 1: Theoretical Computer Science and General Issues

For information about Vols. 1– 4974
please contact your bookseller or Springer

Vol. 5126: L. Aceto, I. Damgård, L.A. Goldberg, M.M. Halldórsson, A. Ingólfsdóttir, I. Walukiewicz (Eds.), Automata, Languages and Programming, Part II. XXII, 730 pages. 2008.

Vol. 5125: L. Aceto, I. Damgård, L.A. Goldberg, M.M. Halldórsson, A. Ingólfsdóttir, I. Walukiewicz (Eds.), Automata, Languages and Programming, Part I. XXIII, 896 pages. 2008.

Vol. 5124: J. Gudmundsson (Ed.), Algorithm Theory – SWAT 2008. XIII, 438 pages. 2008.

Vol. 5123: A. Gupta, S. Malik (Eds.), Computer Aided Verification. XVII, 558 pages. 2008.

Vol. 5117: A. Voronkov (Ed.), Rewriting Techniques and Applications. XIII, 457 pages. 2008.

Vol. 5114: M. Bereković, N. Dimopoulos, S. Wong (Eds.), Embedded Computer Systems: Architectures, Modeling, and Simulation. XVI, 300 pages. 2008.

Vol. 5104: F. Bello, E. Edwards (Eds.), Biomedical Simulation. XI, 228 pages. 2008.

Vol. 5103: M. Bubak, G.D. van Albada, J. Dongarra, P.M.A. Sloot (Eds.), Computational Science – ICCS 2008, Part III. XXVIII, 758 pages. 2008.

Vol. 5102: M. Bubak, G.D. van Albada, J. Dongarra, P.M.A. Sloot (Eds.), Computational Science – ICCS 2008, Part II. XXVIII, 752 pages. 2008.

Vol. 5101: M. Bubak, G.D. van Albada, J. Dongarra, P.M.A. Sloot (Eds.), Computational Science – ICCS 2008, Part I. XLVI, 1058 pages. 2008.

Vol. 5092: X. Hu, J. Wang (Eds.), Computing and Combinatorics. XIV, 680 pages. 2008.

Vol. 5090: R.T. Mittermeir, M.M. Sysło (Eds.), Informatics Education - Supporting Computational Thinking. XV, 357 pages. 2008.

Vol. 5084: J.F. Peters, A. Skowron (Eds.), Transactions on Rough Sets VIII. X, 521 pages. 2008.

Vol. 5083: O. Chitil, Z. Horváth, V. Zsók (Eds.), Implementation and Application of Functional Languages. XI, 272 pages. 2008.

Vol. 5073: O. Gervasi, B. Murgante, A. Laganà, D. Taniar, Y. Mun, M.L. Gavrilova (Eds.), Computational Science and Its Applications – ICCSA 2008, Part II. XXIX, 1280 pages. 2008.

Vol. 5072: O. Gervasi, B. Murgante, A. Laganà, D. Taniar, Y. Mun, M.L. Gavrilova (Eds.), Computational Science and Its Applications – ICCSA 2008, Part I. XXIX, 1266 pages. 2008.

Vol. 5065: P. Degano, R. De Nicola, J. Meseguer (Eds.), Concurrency, Graphs and Models. XV, 810 pages. 2008.

Vol. 5062: K.M. van Hee, R. Valk (Eds.), Applications and Theory of Petri Nets. XIII, 429 pages. 2008.

Vol. 5059: F.P. Preparata, X. Wu, J. Yin (Eds.), Frontiers in Algorithmics. XI, 350 pages. 2008.

Vol. 5058: A.A. Shvartsman, P. Felber (Eds.), Structural Information and Communication Complexity. X, 307 pages. 2008.

Vol. 5050: J.M. Zurada, G.G. Yen, J. Wang (Eds.), Computational Intelligence: Research Frontiers. XVI, 389 pages. 2008.

Vol. 5045: P. Hertling, C.M. Hoffmann, W. Luther, N. Revol (Eds.), Reliable Implementation of Real Number Algorithms: Theory and Practice. XI, 239 pages. 2008.

Vol. 5038: C.C. McGeoch (Ed.), Experimental Algorithms. X, 363 pages. 2008.

Vol. 5036: S. Wu, L.T. Yang, T.L. Xu (Eds.), Advances in Grid and Pervasive Computing. XV, 518 pages. 2008.

Vol. 5035: A. Lodi, A. Panconesi, G. Rinaldi (Eds.), Integer Programming and Combinatorial Optimization. XI, 477 pages. 2008.

Vol. 5029: P. Ferragina, G.M. Landau (Eds.), Combinatorial Pattern Matching. XIII, 317 pages. 2008.

Vol. 5028: A. Beckmann, C. Dimitracopoulos, B. Löwe (Eds.), Logic and Theory of Algorithms. XIX, 596 pages. 2008.

Vol. 5022: A.G. Bourgeois, S.Q. Zheng (Eds.), Algorithms and Architectures for Parallel Processing. XIII, 336 pages. 2008.

Vol. 5018: M. Grohe, R. Niedermeier (Eds.), Parameterized and Exact Computation. X, 227 pages. 2008.

Vol. 5015: L. Perron, M.A. Trick (Eds.), Integration of AI and OR Techniques in Constraint Programming for Combinatorial Optimization Problems. XII, 394 pages. 2008.

Vol. 5011: A.J. van der Poorten, A. Stein (Eds.), Algorithmic Number Theory. IX, 455 pages. 2008.

Vol. 5010: E.A. Hirsch, A.A. Razborov, A. Semenov, A. Slissenko (Eds.), Computer Science – Theory and Applications. XIII, 411 pages. 2008.

Vol. 5008: A. Gasteratos, M. Vincze, J.K. Tsotsos (Eds.), Computer Vision Systems. XV, 560 pages. 2008.

Vol. 5004: R. Eigenmann, B.R. de Supinski (Eds.), OpenMP in a New Era of Parallelism. X, 191 pages. 2008.

Vol. 5000: O. Grumberg, H. Veith (Eds.), 25 Years of Model Checking. VII, 231 pages. 2008.

Vol. 4996: H. Kleine Büning, X. Zhao (Eds.), Theory and Applications of Satisfiability Testing – SAT 2008. X, 305 pages. 2008.

Vol. 4988: R. Berghammer, B. Möller, G. Struth (Eds.), Relations and Kleene Algebra in Computer Science. X, 397 pages. 2008.

Vol. 4985: M. Ishikawa, K. Doya, H. Miyamoto, T. Yamakawa (Eds.), Neural Information Processing, Part II. XXX, 1091 pages. 2008.

Vol. 4984: M. Ishikawa, K. Doya, H. Miyamoto, T. Yamakawa (Eds.), Neural Information Processing, Part I. XXX, 1147 pages. 2008.

Vol. 4981: M. Egerstedt, B. Mishra (Eds.), Hybrid Systems: Computation and Control. XV, 680 pages. 2008.

Vol. 4978: M. Agrawal, D.-Z. Du, Z. Duan, A. Li (Eds.), Theory and Applications of Models of Computation. XII, 598 pages. 2008.

Vol. 4975: F. Chen, B. Jüttler (Eds.), Advances in Geometric Modeling and Processing. XV, 606 pages. 2008.